Textbook of Physiology

BDS

Textbook of Physiology
BDS

Edited by

Donald Emslie-Smith
MD (Aberd) FRCP FRCP (Edin)
Reader in Medicine in the University of Dundee; Honorary
Consultant Physician, the Royal Infirmary and Ninewells
Hospital, Dundee

Colin R. Paterson
MA MSc (Oxon) DM MRCP (Edin) FRCPath
Senior Lecturer in Biochemical Medicine in the University
of Dundee; Honorary Consultant to the Tayside Area Health
Board

Thomas Scratcherd
MD (Newcastle) FRCP (Edin)
Professor of Physiology in the University of Sheffield

Nicholas W. Read
MA MD (Cantab) FRCP
Reader in Physiology in the University of Sheffield;
Honorary Consultant Physician, Royal Hallamshire Hospital,
Sheffield

ELEVENTH EDITION

CHURCHILL LIVINGSTONE
EDINBURGH LONDON MELBOURNE AND NEW YORK 1988

CHURCHILL LIVINGSTONE
Medical Division of Longman Group UK Limited

Distributed in the United States of America by Churchill
Livingstone Inc., 1560 Broadway, New York, N.Y. 10036,
and by associated companies, branches and representatives
throughout the world.

First Edition (Textbook of Physiology and Biochemistry)
1950
Second Edition 1953
Third Edition 1956
Fourth Edition 1959
Fifth Edition 1961
Sixth Edition 1965
Seventh Edition 1968
Eighth Edition 1972
Ninth Edition 1976
Tenth Edition (Textbook of Physiology) 1980
Eleventh Edition 1988

Previous editions translated into Spanish and Italian

ISBN 0-443-03412-5

British Library Cataloguing in Publication Data
Textbook of physiology.—11th ed.
　1. Human physiology
　I. Emslie-Smith, Donald
　612　QP34.5

Library of Congress Cataloging in Publication Data
Textbook of physiology (BDS).
　Rev. ed. of: Textbook of physiology (BDS) / George H.
Bell, Donald Emslie-Smith, Colin R. Paterson. 10th ed.
1980.
　Includes bibliographies and index.
　1. Human physiology.　I. Emslie-Smith, Donald.
II. Bell, George Howard.　Textbook of physiology (BDS).
[DNLM: 1. Physiology.　QT 104 T3552]
QP34.5.T47　1988　612　87-8002

Produced by Longman Singapore Publishers (Pte) Ltd.
Printed in Singapore

Preface to the Eleventh Edition

Gratefully we remember George Bell who died in the Spring of 1986. He had edited with us the Tenth Edition of his book and had told us he did not want to edit another. He was, however, delighted that there was to be an Eleventh Edition, and was always interested to hear about its progress. He would not have wanted an obituary notice here but, of course, we miss him greatly, both as a senior colleague and as a friend. His monument is his textbook published in ten editions over thirty years.

Some years ago he told one of us how the late Mr Charles Macmillan of Messrs E. & S. Livingstone approached him originally with the idea of preparing a new Textbook of Physiology and Biochemistry that would be relevant to medical practice. George Bell was then a Senior Lecturer in the University of Glasgow, before he moved to the Chair of Physiology in Dundee. He was fortunate in enlisting the help of two valuable colleagues: the late Professor Norman Davidson, FRS, then a Senior Lecturer in the University of Aberdeen, was a distinguished biochemist; and Professor Harold Scarborough, then a Clinical Tutor in the University of Edinburgh, who later occupied with distinction Chairs of Medicine in Wales and in Africa. The initials of their surnames, B, D and S, soon gave their textbook the affectionate nickname by which it became widely known, and with which we are proud to be associated.

We could not replace George Bell with any single person, so we now welcome Tim Scratcherd and Nick Read. Both are medically qualified physiologists with interests in clinical medicine, as befit editors of a textbook of physiology that still aims primarily to satisfy the needs of medical students, both undergraduate and postgraduate. This edition of BDS has been completely rearranged. Most of the chapters are new, and almost all the rest have been radically re-written. As previously, the editors are also the authors of many chapters.

Dundee
1987

D.E-S.
C.R.P.

Acknowledgments

We owe a great debt to our contributors in this as in previous editions of this book. Some were responsible for whole chapters; others made smaller contributions to the chapters associated with their names. We are grateful to them also for their tolerance of our editorial efforts to ensure a uniform style throughout the book.

We thank several colleagues who reviewed and criticised chapters or parts of chapters in draft; these included Dr E. Brookes, Professor P. Howie, Dr T. E. Isles, Dr R. T. Jung and Dr A. S. Todd.

This edition owes much to Miss Mary Benstead who prepared many new and beautiful line drawings, to Mrs M. Lawson and Mrs M. Alexander for their lettering and to Ms Maureen Hughes, Mrs Judith Murant and Mrs Mina Geekie for their skilled secretarial work.

Dundee and Sheffield   D.E-S.
1987   C.R.P.
                                       T.S.
                               N.W.R.

Contributors

Professor A. Angel,
Department of Physiology, University of Sheffield (Chapters 32, 35 and 36)

Mr K. Baxby,
Department of Surgery, University of Dundee (Chapter 27)

Miss M. C. K. Browning,
Department of Biochemical Medicine, University of Dundee (Chapters 24–27)

Dr J. Chapman,
Department of Physiology, Sheffield Polytechnic (Chapter 11)

Professor P. Cohen
Department of Biochemistry, University of Dundee (Chapter 23)

Professor M. de Burgh Daly,
Department of Physiology, St Bartholomew's Hospital Medical College (Chapter 10)

Dr P. W. R. Elliott,
Department of Physiology, University of Sheffield (Chapter 11)

Dr C. C. Forsyth,
Department of Child Health, University of Dundee (Chapter 30)

Professor R. Green,
Department of Physiology, University of Manchester (Chapters 12 and 13)

Professor G. R. Hervey,
Department of Physiology, University of Leeds (Chapter 41)

Dr P. Kohn,
Department of Physiology, University of Sheffield (Chapter 2)

Dr D. M. Lewis,
Department of Physiology, University of Bristol (Chapter 40)

Dr D. A. S. G. Mary,
Department of Cardiovascular Studies, University of Leeds (Chapter 7)

Dr J. A. Mills,
Department of Obstetrics and Gynaecology, University of Dundee (Chapters 27 and 28)

Dr R. O'Neil,
Department of Pathology, University of Dundee (Chapter 4)

Professor L. H. Opie,
Department of Medicine, University of Cape Town (Chapter 7)

Dr D. Parratt,
Department of Microbiology, University of Dundee (Chapter 5)

Dr N. Patel,
Department of Obstetrics and Gynaecology, University of Dundee (Chapter 28)

Professor I. C. Roddie,
Department of Physiology, University of Belfast (Chapter 8)

Professor L. B. Strang,
Department of Paediatrics, University College London School of Medicine (Chapter 28)

Dr A. J. Suggett,
Department of Medicine, University of Sheffield (Chapters 9 and 10)

Contents

1

Introduction

Human physiology is concerned with the way the human body works. It is the study of the functions of tissues and organs, and of the way these functions are integrated.

THE CELL

The basic unit of each tissue of the body is the cell. Each organ or tissue consists of many types of cell, held together by supporting structures. A schematic diagram of a 'typical' animal cell is shown in Figure 1.1. The cell consists of a nucleus and other organelles floating in a fluid cytosol or cell sap that is separated from the extracellular fluid by a selectively permeable lipid membrane.

Membranes

The plasma membrane and also the bounding membranes of the nucleus and other organelles have

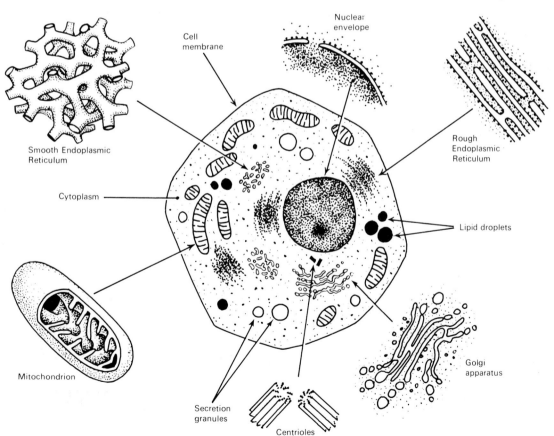

Smooth Endoplasmic Reticulum

Cytoplasm

Mitochondrion

Cell membrane

Nuclear envelope

Rough Endoplasmic Reticulum

Lipid droplets

Golgi apparatus

Secretion granules

Centrioles

Fig. 1.1 The composition of a typical cell. The organelles, as seen by electron microscopy, are shown in greater detail around the outside.

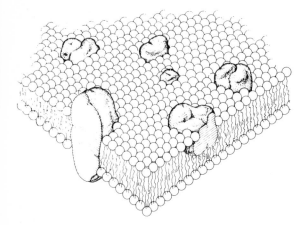

Fig. 1.2 A model to show current views of membrane structure. Irregularly shaped proteins float randomly in a lipid 'sea'. The proportion of protein varies greatly between membranes in different sites.

many features in common. All contain phospholipids and proteins; the lipids exist in a double layer with their hydrophilic 'heads' outermost and their hydrophobic fatty acid chains in the interior of the membrane (Fig. 1.2). The proteins are embedded in the membrane and serve as carriers for the transport of water-soluble substances and as markers to express immunological identity. They may also enclose aqueous channels for the passage of fluid and electrolytes into and out of the cell.

The ease with which a molecule can cross a membrane depends partly on its size but to a greater extent on its solubility in lipids. Thus membranes are usually impermeable to large charged molecules such as proteins but permeable to water and small uncharged molecules like urea. Water-soluble substances such as sugars and amino acids can only cross the cell membrane by combining with specific carrier proteins, bound to the membrane, or by diffusing through aqueous channels bounded by protein.

Because lipids are electrical insulators there may be considerable differences in electrical potential across a membrane; these differences may provide an electrical force for transport of charged particles through aqueous channels.

The organelles

Nucleus
The nucleus contains a mesh-work of densely staining DNA, the *chromatin* of the histologist. Before a cell divides, the chromatin condenses to form the chromosomes, which contain almost all the DNA of the cell. The nucleus is surrounded by a double membrane

pierced at intervals by pores. It contains one or more dense, spherical bodies termed nucleoli, which are rich in RNA. The nucleoli are the sites of synthesis of the ribosomal RNA responsible for protein synthesis.

Mitochondria
Surrounding the nucleus is the cytoplasm in which are found various organelles such as secretion granules, lysosomes and mitochondria. Each mitochondrion is bounded by two membranes, each consisting of a lipid bilayer containing proteins. The inner membrane is folded to produce the cristae, which divide the interior into compartments. The mitochondria contain the enzymes responsible for oxidative phosphorylation, and are the sites of production of adenosine triphosphate, ATP. They have been termed the 'power houses of the cell'. The mitochondria also regulate the intracellular calcium concentration by the uptake and release of calcium ions. This property is of considerable importance since calcium serves as an intracellular regulator of many of the metabolic, secretory, and contractile functions of the cell.

Endoplasmic reticulum
The cytoplasm also contains a complex meshwork of canals and vesicles, known as the endoplasmic reticulum (Fig. 1.1), that lead from the exterior of the cell to the nucleus. Two kinds of endoplasmic reticulum can be distinguished under the electron microscope, rough endoplasmic reticulum (RER) and smooth endoplasmic reticulum (SER). The SER contains enzymes responsible for detoxication of foreign substances and for the synthesis of hormones and glycoproteins. The surfaces of RER are studded with small round electron-dense particles (diameter 10–20 nm) known as *ribosomes*. These consist of protein and RNA and are responsible for protein synthesis.

Lysosomes
The cytoplasm of most cells also contains small organelles known as lysosomes, which are essentially little sacks of hydrolytic enzymes that can break down large molecules. These enzymes are discharged into vacuoles containing large molecules, such as proteins and nucleic acids. In white blood cells, lysosomal enzymes play an important part in the digestion of foreign substances such as bacteria (Chap. 5).

Golgi apparatus
Some cells contain a Golgi apparatus, which is concerned with the packaging of proteins produced by the RER before their extrusion from the cell. The Golgi apparatus is particularly important in cells that secrete enzymes.

Microfilaments

Contractile microfilaments and microtubules are concerned with movements of the cell and the movements of organelles within the cell; they form the spindle of the mitotic apparatus, which draws apart the chromosomes during cell division.

INTEGRATION OF ORGAN FUNCTION

The cells are continuously bathed in extracellular fluid which is in constant motion throughout the body, carrying nutrients and oxygen to the cells and taking waste products away. The constancy of this internal

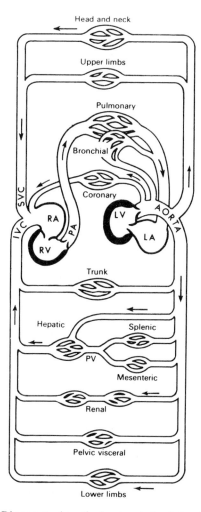

Fig. 1.3 Diagram to show the heart and circulation displayed as two (left and right) hearts and two circulations (systemic and pulmonary) arranged in series. Various important divisions of the systemic circulation are also indicated. Blood flows from arteries through capillary beds to veins. The renal circulation has two capillary beds, glomerular and tubular. PV = portal vein.

environment is essential for cell survival and function, and the ability of the body to maintain this constant internal environment is called *homeostasis*. Cells are only capable of living and performing their special functions if they are well supplied with nutrients and oxygen, and if the concentrations of ions, the pH and the temperature of the fluid in which they are bathed remain constant.

Cardiovascular system

Extracellular fluid is circulated around the body by the cardiovascular system, which consists of two circulations (Fig. 1.3). Oxygenated blood returning from the lungs is pumped by the heart to the other organs and tissues where it gives up its oxygen. It then returns to the heart and is pumped to the lungs. Although only about 3 litres of fluid are present in the cardiovascular system, this fluid circulates round the body at least once every minute (up to six times per minute during exercise) and is in equilibrium with the remaining 20 litres of extracellular fluid. The capillaries of most tissues are so permeable that large amounts of water, ions and small molecules can move rapidly between the blood

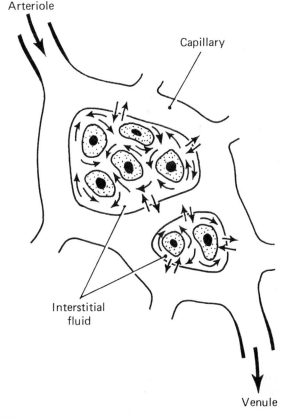

Fig. 1.4 A diagram showing how blood flowing through porous capillaries can mix the extracellular fluid.

and extravascular or interstitial fluid. Thus, circulation of only a proportion of the extracellular fluid by the cardiovascular system is sufficient to maintain the homogeneity of the extracellular fluid (Fig. 1.4).

The cardiovascular system conveys oxygen, which has entered the blood from the lungs, and nutrients, which have entered the blood from the intestine or liver, to the cells. It also transports waste products of metabolism to the lungs and kidneys where they are excreted. Since most cells are located within 50 μm of a capillary, transport between cells and blood is rapid.

The cardiovascular system has the flexibility to adjust flow and increase blood supply to certain organs when their demand for energy is greatest: to the muscles during exercise, to the gut after a meal and to the skin in order to lose heat, while at the same time maintaining the nutrition of other organs.

Respiratory system

Oxygen enters the body through the lungs. During respiration, contraction of the diaphragm and the muscles of the chest wall draws air into the lungs. Oxygen diffuses across the thin walls of the capillaries and combines with the haemoglobin in the red cells. The presence of haemoglobin ensures that the blood can carry sufficient oxygen for the energy requirements of all the cells of the body. Oxygen dissociates from haemoglobin in the tissues and is taken up by the cells. At the same time, carbon dioxide, the principal product of cellular oxidation, is released from the tissues and transported in the blood to the lungs, where it diffuses into the pulmonary air sacs or alveoli and is exhaled.

Gastrointestinal system

Most food consists of complex large molecules derived from plants and animals. After food has been eaten it passes slowly down the gastrointestinal tract where it is serially dismantled by enzymes, first in an acid and then in an alkaline medium, into smaller subunits, ultimately forming products that can be absorbed across the intestinal epithelium and reach the blood. Most nutrients are absorbed in the small intestine, but some of the remainder may undergo bacterial degradation and subsequent absorption in the colon. Any residue that cannot be absorbed is passed out of the anus as faeces.

Liver

Blood from the intestine drains through the liver before reaching the systemic circulation. The liver controls the supply, utilisation and ultimate degradation and excretion of nutrient material. It stores carbohydrate, iron and vitamins, releasing them according to the body's requirements. It possesses the enzymes responsible for the interconversion of protein, fat and carbohydrate in response to the body's requirements and for the synthesis of fats, glycogen, plasma proteins, bile acids and blood clotting factors. The liver breaks down and excretes certain hormones and drugs.

Excretory system

Waste products of cellular metabolism, particularly urea, are excreted in the kidney. Renal excretion involves the filtering of plasma through the glomerulus, followed by the selective reabsorption of certain important substances such as glucose, sodium and amino acids in the tubules, while waste products of metabolism pass out in the urine. This process allows the whole extracellular fluid volume to be 'cleaned' and its composition adjusted at least seven times a day, and provides the means by which the pH, ionic composition and osmolality of body fluids are regulated. The balance between filtration and reabsorption also regulates the normal extracellular fluid volume and plasma volume, and is therefore responsible for maintaining adequate perfusion of all the organs of the body.

Control of visceral functions

The maintenance of an adequate flow of blood to each organ and the regulation of the composition of the extracellular fluid requires a control system sensitive enough to detect and respond to minor changes in the composition of extracellular fluid or in the supply of nutrients or oxygen to an organ. Visceral function is largely controlled by the autonomic nervous system and the endocrine glands. The autonomic nervous system regulates the flow of blood to different organs and maintains a constant body temperature, whereas the endocrine system regulates intermediary metabolism and the composition of the extracellular fluid.

Although both systems of control use chemical transmitters to co-ordinate the function of different organs, they operate in different ways. In the autonomic nervous system, the transmitter is released from nerve endings adjacent to the site of action, interacts with a protein receptor on the cell membrane to alter cell function and is destroyed by nearby enzymes. This ensures a rapidly responsive control system; responses occur as soon as the stimulus commences and end soon after the stimulus ends and can involve different organs according to the site of release of the transmitter.

In the endocrine system transmitters called *hormones* are released into the blood. They circulate in the plasma and affect only those cells that have a specific protein receptor for the hormone. Hormones are not necessarily degraded locally; many are degraded in the liver and excreted in the bile and urine. Thus, in contrast with autonomic control, the control of visceral function exerted by hormones is often slow in response and long in duration.

Regulation of visceral function usually operates on the

principle of *negative feedback*, whereby the response corrects the abnormality providing the stimulus. For example, a rise in arterial pressure stimulates baroreceptors in major arteries and increases the rate of firing in vagal afferent nerve fibres. The increased afferent discharge inhibits the vasomotor centre so that the arterial pressure is reduced.

Control of movement

A person must be able to move purposefully in his environment in order to obtain food, to protect himself and to shelter from adverse environmental conditions. Survival may be severely limited when mobility is impaired.

The contraction of striated muscles alters the position of the bones, and allows respiration and speech. The complex movements of the limbs in walking, and of the tongue, lips and larynx and diaphragm in speech are co-ordinated by the central nervous system, consisting of the brain and spinal cord. Nerves called efferent or motor nerves leave this system and mediate muscular movement.

Central control is valueless unless the brain has information about events in the body and around it. This information is conveyed to the central nervous system by the sensory or afferent nerves. The special sense organs, such as the eyes, ears and nose receive and transmit information about the environment and allow the body to plan purposeful movements. Sensation from the muscles and joints provide information about the position of the body in space and enable the brain to monitor and adjust the movement according to what is needed.

Although many of the activities occurring in the central nervous system are exceedingly complex, few rise to consciousness. We are quite unaware, for example, of the muscular adjustments needed to maintain balance or to move our eyes so that images are kept fixed on the retinae. These adjustments are called *reflex* and the pathways involved, namely sensory nerves, central nervous system and motor nerves, are called *reflex arcs*.

Reproduction

Reproduction is the process by which new organisms can be generated to replace those that die. Most higher animals reproduce sexually. Sexual reproduction allows infinite combinations of genetic material, creating the adaptability of the species for survival in different or changing environments. Cells, called spermatozoa, carrying the genetic material of the male are produced in the testes. During sexual intercourse they are deposited in the female genital tract, where one of them may combine with and fertilise an ovum, which carries the genetic material of the female. The fertilised ovum divides and implants itself in the uterus, where it grows into an embryo. After implantation, a series of complex changes takes place to ensure provision of nutrients and oxygen to the fetus from the mother via the placenta. At the end of pregnancy the muscular wall of the uterus contracts rhythmically to expel the fetus, which then acquires oxygen directly from its lungs and obtains nutrients by suckling milk produced by the mother's breasts.

2

Biological membranes

The current view of the structure of the cell membrane was indicated in Chapter 1. Membranes are composed mainly of lipids and proteins together with much smaller amounts of carbohydrate.

The lipids of the cell membrane comprise a mixture of polar lipids, mostly phospholipids and cholesterol. All these molecules are amphipathic, that is, they possess one or more charged (polar) groups at one end of the molecule whilst the rest of the molecule is composed of fatty acyl side chains, or the uncharged sterol residue in the case of cholesterol. The polar group exerts an electrostatic attraction for water molecules and is described as *hydrophilic*, whilst the side chains are attracted to one another but exert no attractive forces on the water molecules and are described as *hydrophobic*. The membrane lipids therefore arrange themselves with their polar head groups pointing towards the aqueous regions at the surfaces of the membrane and their hydrophobic side-chains pointing to the middle of the membrane. This bilayer arrangement of the membrane lipids is inherently stable.

The membrane lipids are of three main types. The largest component in most membranes is the phospholipids. These molecules are based on the three-carbon glycerol molecule, which has three hydroxyl groups. At least one, and usually two of these groups are esterified to fatty acids; the third is esterified via a phosphate group to another alcohol, which is most commonly choline, serine, ethanolamine, inositol or a second glycerol molecule (Fig. 2.1). The phosphate group and its associated alcohol comprise the polar head group. The fatty acyl chains constitute the hydrophobic part of the phospholipid. The fatty acyl chains are unbranched, but may contain one or more double bonds (that is, the parent fatty acid is unsaturated).

A second group of membrane lipids is the sphingolipids. These molecules are based on the alcohol sphingosine. One fatty acyl chain is part of the sphingosine molecule and a second is attached via an amino residue (Fig. 2.2). As with a phospholipid, the phosphate–alcohol combination constitutes the polar head group. Together with the phospholipids and sphingolipids, cell membranes also contain various amounts of cholesterol.

Because most membrane lipids contain two fatty acyl chains, the polar head groups are relatively far apart and the stability of the bilayer depends mainly on the side chains. In particular, hydrophobic interactions between the fatty acyl side chains provide the main stabilising force for the membrane and these are reinforced by van der Waal's forces. The polar head groups contribute to the stability of the bilayer, mainly because of electrostatic and hydrogen-bonding interactions with the adjacent water molecules.

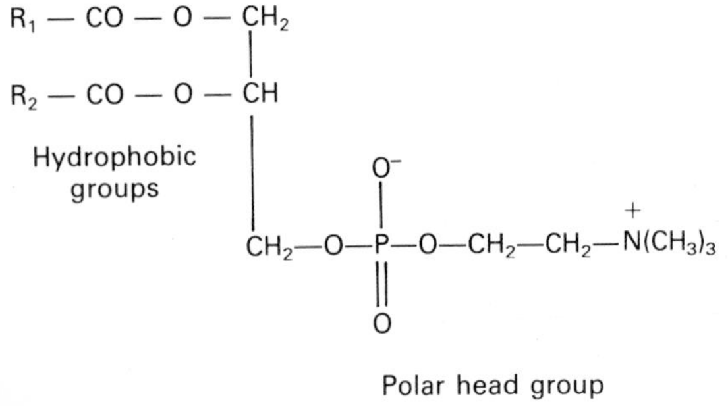

$$R_1 - CO - O - CH_2$$
$$R_2 - CO - O - CH$$

Hydrophobic groups

$$CH_2 - O - P - O - CH_2 - CH_2 - N(CH_3)_3^+$$

Polar head group

Fig. 2.1 Structures of phosphatidyl choline (lecithin), a typical phospholipid. R_1 and R_2 represent fatty acyl chains.

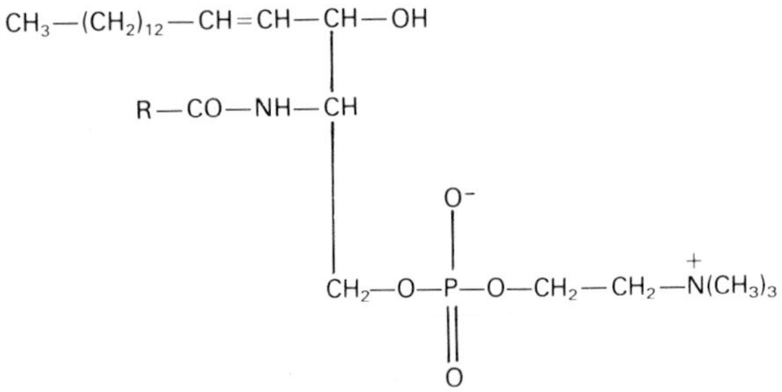

$$CH_3 - (CH_2)_{12} - CH = CH - CH - OH$$
$$R - CO - NH - CH$$

$$CH_2 - O - P - O - CH_2 - CH_2 - N(CH_3)_3^+$$

Fig. 2.2 Structure of sphingomyelin, the sphingolipid found in biological membranes in animals. R represents a fatty acyl chain.

Associated with the lipid bilayer are the membrane proteins. Many of these are so firmly attached to the membrane that they can only be removed by complete disruption of its structure. Such proteins are described as *integral*, or *intrinsic*. Other proteins, all of which seem to be associated with the inner face of the membrane, can be removed by changes in the pH or ionic strength of the adjacent aqueous medium, or by the use of chelating agents. These more easily removed proteins are termed *peripheral*, or *extrinsic*.

An examination of the amino acid composition of the membrane proteins shows that whilst peripheral proteins have a similar composition to cytoplasmic proteins, integral proteins contain long sequences of amino acids with hydrophobic side chains. Thus the hydrophobic parts of the integral proteins are associated with the hydrophobic core of the bilayer, whilst the hydrophilic parts are at the membrane surface.

In addition to lipids and proteins, membranes also contain carbohydrate. The amount is quite small, generally less than 10 per cent of the membrane by weight, and all of it is covalently linked to either lipid or protein. The glycolipids and glycoproteins are associated with the outer face of the membrane. They are thought to play a major part in molecular recognition processes; hormone receptors and the sites that confer immunological characteristics on cells include glycoproteins. It is likely that recognition between cells and their organisation into tissues also depends on the carbohydrate components.

The current view of the arrangement of the membrane components is known as the fluid-mosaic model, to emphasise the fluidity of the lipid and the heterogeneity of the structure as a whole (Fig. 2.3).

The main features of the model are the continuous bilayer which is regarded as being fluid in a number of ways. The lipid molecules may move laterally within the membrane by exchange of one molecule with another. At the same time the fatty acyl chains behave almost like a true fluid. Each C–C bond within the fatty acyl chain is a site about which the chain may rotate or vibrate. In addition, the whole chain may rotate or swing about its polar head group. The degree of fluidity increases towards the centre of the bilayer. Peripheral proteins are confined to the surface of the bilayer but integral proteins dip into one leaflet of the bilayer or in some cases span the entire membrane.

Recent studies have emphasised the asymmetry of the membrane in terms of the two leaflets of the bilayer. We have already seen that carbohydrate moieties are confined to the outer leaflet while most peripheral proteins are associated with the inner leaflet. Where it has been possible to separate the two leaflets of the bilayer, it has also been shown that the lipids themselves are distributed asymmetrically.

Similar constraints apply to the proteins. Many integral proteins are firmly anchored to peripheral proteins at the inner surface of the membrane. In the erythrocyte, such peripheral proteins help to define the shape of the cell (p. 24) and constitute what is termed the *cytoskeleton*. Similar cytoskeletons exist in other cells, although less is known about the molecules of which they are formed.

Even those proteins that are not anchored and can diffuse laterally in the plane of the membrane are unable to diffuse from one leaflet of the bilayer to the other. It requires a great deal of energy to move a hydrophilic molecule, or region of a molecule, through a hydro-

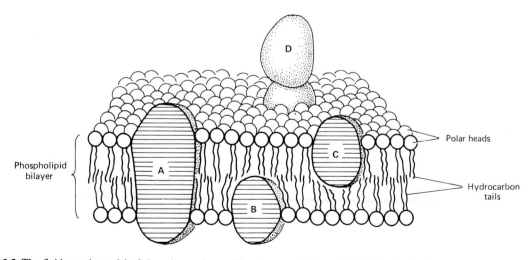

Fig. 2.3 The fluid-mosaic model of the cell membrane. Proteins may be integral (intrinsic; A, B, C), or peripheral (extrinsic; D). The integral proteins have hydrophobic regions that are associated with the hydrophobic parts of the lipid bilayer. (From C R Paterson 1983. Essentials of human biochemistry. Pitman, London).

Phospholipid bilayer

Polar heads

Hydrocarbon tails

phobic region of the membrane. Therefore, both lipids and proteins are confined to a single leaflet of the bilayer. Movements from one bilayer to the other are rare, perhaps impossible, for most membrane components.

The discussion so far has emphasised the many features common to all cell membranes. The diversity of membrane function reflects a diversity of composition and structure. At one extreme is nerve myelin, which has a largely structural role and contains around 80 per cent lipid by weight. The erythrocyte membrane contains slightly more protein than lipid, but most of the protein is associated with the inner leaflet of the bilayer. Membranes with a major metabolic role, such as the inner membrane of the mitochondrion, may contain more than 75 per cent protein.

MOVEMENT OF MOLECULES ACROSS THE CELL MEMBRANE

If a lipid bilayer is indeed the basis of plasma membranes, then only those molecules that can readily dissolve in the bilayer would be expected to cross the membrane. In most membranes, lipid-soluble molecules (those that dissolve readily in hydrocarbons) permeate easily. Perhaps surprisingly, such molecules include water itself. This is partly because water is present in extremely high concentrations on each side of the membrane (nearly 56 mol/l) and partly because of the small physical size of the water molecule.

Real biological membranes, however, are much more permeable to a whole range of ions and molecules to which a lipid bilayer might be expected to be relatively impermeable. This suggests that other membrane components, presumably proteins, are able to confer specific permeability properties on the membranes. Since most of these components form only a tiny fraction of the total composition of the membrane, isolating, purifying and studying such components has proved difficult and it has been easier to study their properties *in situ*.

Diffusion
By diffusion is meant the net movement of molecules from regions of higher concentration to regions of lower concentration as a result of the random molecular motion that results from thermal energy. Any molecule that can dissolve in the membrane matrix is able to cross the membrane by diffusion. The rate of diffusion across the membrane is proportional to the concentration of the substrate. It also depends on the partition coefficient of the substance between the aqueous medium and the membrane lipid (that is the relative solubilities in the two media), and on the diffusion coefficient for the substrate within the membrane. Thus the flow of solute across the membrane is linearly dependent on the concentration gradient. This relation is known as Fick's Law. Substances that cross membranes largely or entirely by diffusion include water, oxygen, carbon dioxide, cholesterol and steroid hormones, many lipid-soluble drugs and ethyl alcohol.

Hydrophilic substances, particularly ions, would be expected to have a low permeability through the lipid bilayer and this can be demonstrated with artificial lipid membranes prepared, for example, from pure phospholipids. However, in biological membranes ionic permeability is much higher and often seems to be related to the size of the ion. The highly polar ions exert electrostatic attractions on water molecules, which are also polar, and ions in aqueous solutions move with a more or less tightly associated set of water molecules described as a 'solvation shell'. Small ions, such as Na^+ are more polar and carry a larger solvation shell than larger ions such as K^+. The passive permeability of ions in biological membranes is more related to the 'hydrated ion radius' (the radius of the ion together with its solvation shell) than to the radius of the naked ion.

The permeability to some ions and to other small polar molecules suggests that membranes possess narrow, water-filled channels that provide an alternative route for diffusion through the membrane. The estimated pore diameter of such channels is somewhere between 0.4 and 0.8 nm; it is assumed they are associated with the integral proteins that span the membrane. The postulated dimensions of these channels is at the limit of resolution of the electron microscope and there is no unequivocal evidence for the presence of these pores.

Facilitated diffusion
Although many molecules cross the membrane by diffusion and at a predictable rate, many biologically important molecules cross the membrane much more readily than would be expected from their molecular size or their lipid solubility. Specific mechanisms seem to exist to allow their passage across the membrane and indeed such mechanisms appear to be necessary to allow the entry of very polar molecules such as D-glucose and many of the amino acids that are essential for the metabolism of the cell. Two types of mechanism are known. In one, *facilitated diffusion*, molecules move down their concentration gradients in a manner akin to simple diffusion, but at a greater rate than expected. In the second mechanism, movement is coupled to the movement of sodium ions and is not limited by the concentration gradient.

Facilitated diffusion has a number of characteristic features, many of which are shared by other specialised mechanisms of membrane permeation. First, such mechanisms show specificity. Thus, the facilitated diffusion system that assists the entry of D-glucose into the erythrocyte also facilitates the entry of D-galactose, D-mannose and a number of other hexoses and pentoses, but it is not equally effective for all of them. Other sugars such as D-fructose are not helped and neither are the L-isomers. The system has very little affinity for L-glucose, for example. This suggests that the permeation mechanism involves the combination of the transported molecule with a specific site in the cell membrane that can distinguish small differences in the structure of potential substrates.

Since any particular transport mechanism may be used by more than one substrate, the movement of one substrate is affected by the concentrations of each of the others. This phenomenon is known as *competition* and is similar to that which occurs between the substrates of an enzyme. The amount of each substrate transported depends in part on its concentration relative to each of the others and in part on the affinity of the binding site for each substrate. The number of sites is finite, so that when even a single substrate is present the rate of transport does not increase in proportion to the concentration of substrate but reaches a maximum when all the sites are occupied. This is termed *saturation*. The properties of saturation and competition can be formally analysed, as with enzymes, by using Michaelis–Menten kinetics.

Although passive and facilitated diffusion show very different relations to substrate concentration (Fig. 2.4), they are similar in that neither requires any input of metabolic energy. For both, movement is passive and net movement can only occur down a concentration gradient. Metabolic inhibitors would not be expected to affect either process, although this does not rule out indirect effects on membrane composition or structure. On the other hand, it may be possible to affect facilitated diffusion in a number of ways. It may be inhibited by specific poisons. For example, sugar transport in the erythrocyte can be specifically blocked by a number of substances, many of which are known to interact with many types of protein, whereas passive diffusion is generally unaffected by these compounds.

Most processes show some temperature dependence. This is most easily expressed by the Q_{10}, the ratio of the rate of the process at two temperatures that differ by 10°C. In general, most processes occur more rapidly at higher temperatures. This is certainly true for diffusion within the membrane and is also likely to be true for the penetration of the water–membrane interface. Permeation of a membrane by passive diffusion is therefore enhanced by a rise in temperature. In general, facilitated diffusion is more sensitive to temperature than is passive diffusion and has a higher Q_{10}. For both processes, temperature dependence varies with the temperature range. If facilitated diffusion is mediated by membrane proteins, exceeding physiological temperatures by more than a few degrees may lead to their denaturation and the slowing down of the facilitated diffusion.

Temperature changes also affect the lipid component of the membrane. Lowering the temperature reduces the fluidity of the lipid bilayer and it ultimately 'freezes'. The change in state of the bilayer is said to be from liquid–crystalline to crystal–crystalline. The latter state is much more ordered and diffusion more difficult. Because the lipid composition of most

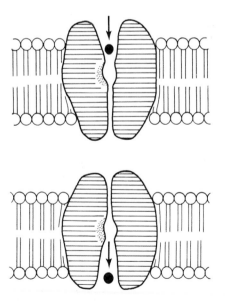

Fig. 2.5 Possible role of a protein carrier in the facilitated diffusion through a 'pore' in a transmembrane protein. The binding of a substrate leads to conformational changes that pass the substrate to the other side of the membrane. (After S J Singer 1975. In: G Weissmann, R Claiborne (eds) Cell membranes: Biochemistry, cell biology and pathology. Freeman, San Francisco).

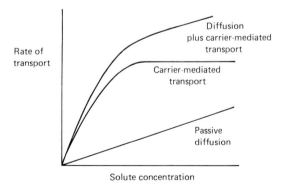

Fig. 2.4 Rates of transport with passive diffusion, facilitated (carrier-mediated) diffusion and with a combination of both processes.

membranes is very complex, the change of state is gradual and spread over a wide range of temperatures. The fluidity of the bilayer may also affect the functioning of the intrinsic proteins.

At a molecular level, we still do not know how facilitated diffusion functions but the most acceptable model depends on the known ability of protein molecules to undergo conformational changes. The carrier is envisaged as an intrinsic protein or a group of such proteins, which span the membrane and which present a specific site to one side of the membrane. Combination of the substrate allows the carrier to modify its conformation and present the site to the other side of the membrane (Fig. 2.5).

Facilitated diffusion enables glucose to enter most types of cell. It also allows the possibility of *control*. In both skeletal muscle and adipose tissue, the rate of entry of glucose is greatly enhanced by insulin: this hormone plays a major part in the control mechanism by which plasma glucose concentration is regulated (Chap. 23). Once glucose has entered a cell, it is immediately phosphorylated prior to further metabolism, and the intracellular concentration of glucose is usually extremely low. Thus there is a favourable concentration gradient for glucose entry and facilitated diffusion is a particularly appropriate system.

Active transport

For movement to occur against a concentration gradient, metabolic energy is required. When the energy is derived directly from metabolism, the process is known as *primary active transport*. In the cell membrane, energy is provided in the form of ATP. For many substrates, however, the energy is derived indirectly using the concentration gradient built up as a result of the primary active transport of sodium ions. This process is termed *secondary active transport*.

Transport coupled to sodium movement

In almost all cells the intracellular composition is very different from the composition of the extracellular medium, whether it be interstitial fluid, or the luminal content of the small intestine or the renal tubule. In general, extracellular Na⁺ concentration is high, typically around 140 mmol/l in mammals, whereas the intracellular Na⁺ concentration is kept about ten times lower by the continual outward pumping of Na⁺ ions. There is thus a very strong tendency for sodium ions to enter the cell, providing a source of potential energy that is used to drive other molecules into or out of the cell.

It is thought, for example, that the active transport of glucose in the intestinal mucosa and in the renal tubule is powered in this way. It is suggested that the carrier is similar to that involved in facilitated diffusion but possesses two specific binding sites, one for sodium and the second for the other transported substance. The binding of sodium leads to conformational changes that encourage the binding of the co-substrate. This in turn leads to further conformational changes that allow the sodium and the co-substrate to pass into the interior of the cell (Fig. 2.6). Coupled transport of this sort is very similar to facilitated diffusion in showing specificity, saturation and the potential for competition. The sodium dependence means that any factor that diminishes the sodium gradient also inhibits the transport process. Since the sodium gradient depends on a transport system, described below, that requires metabolic

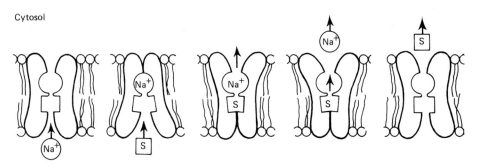

Cytosol

Extracellular fluid

Fig. 2.6 Possible mechanism by which the movement of sodium down its electrochemical gradient could be used to supply energy for the movement of another substance, the co-substrate, up its concentration gradient. A: at the extracellular face of the membrane with its high Na⁺ concentration, Na⁺ is more likely to be bound. B: Binding of Na⁺ leads to conformational changes that increase the carrier's affinity for the co-substrate. C: Binding of the co-substrate in turn leads to exposure of the bound Na⁺ to the cytosolic face of the membrane with its low Na⁺ concentration. D: Release of the Na⁺ leads to changes in the carrier's affinity for the co-substrate, which is then released and (E) the carrier returns to its original state. All the stages are reversible and the direction of transport depends on the concentrations of sodium and of the co-substrate on each side.

energy, the gradient is reduced by metabolic poisons and also by specific inhibitors of the sodium transport mechanism.

Confirmation of the correctness of the model can be obtained in various ways. For example, not only does sodium enhance the rate of entry of the co-substrate, but the co-substrate enhances the rate of entry of sodium. In the small intestine and kidney, the co-transport mechanism is present in the brush border, the membrane facing the lumen. It is possible to prepare vesicles composed of brush border membrane and to show that these vesicles can accumulate sugars and amino acids against a concentration gradient so long as a sodium ion gradient is maintained. The coupling of amino acid transport to sodium movement is also observed in a wide variety of other cells.

Since such transport systems depend on a specific membrane protein, they are under genetic control. A particular transport system is occasionally absent. Among the recognised disorders is one in which glucose and galactose are not absorbed in the gut and others in which various amino acids are not absorbed in the gut or in the renal tubule (Chap. 12).

Use of the sodium gradient to power transport is not confined to sugars and amino acids. For example, the re-uptake of noradrenaline into nerve endings is the most important mechanism for terminating the action of this neurotransmitter. Very large concentration gradients can be created and the system is strongly stereo-specific for L-noradrenaline. The system is totally dependent on the sodium gradient. Uptake of several other neurotransmitters also appears to be sodium-dependent, as is the transport of such substrates as lactate, citrate, choline and para-amino hippuric acid in the kidney, and the uptake of the iodide ion by the thyroid gland.

The sodium–potassium exchange pump

This is the most widely distributed and energetically demanding active transport mechanism. It is commonly known as the *sodium pump*. The energy provided by the hydrolysis of ATP is responsible for the exchange of sodium and potassium ions across the cell membrane. There is now extensive evidence linking this process to Na^+, K^+–ATPase. This enzyme is present in largest amounts in active tissues such as nerve and kidney, and in epithelia the enzyme is localised to the face of the cell in which sodium–potassium exchange is believed to occur, usually the basolateral membrane.

The enzyme requires magnesium ions for its function and it is thought that a Mg^{2+}–ATP complex is the true substrate for the enzyme. Typically the hydrolysis of a single ATP molecule leads to the expulsion of three Na^+ ions and the uptake of two K^+ ions, a process that is very efficient in energy terms.

At a molecular level, the sodium pump consists of four subunits, two of which are proteins that comprise the catalytic subunit and two of which are associated glycoproteins. Many details of the function are still unclear but it is known that the catalytic subunit also contains a binding site for ouabain. ATP hydrolysis and ouabain binding occur at opposite faces of the membrane, and this fact suggests that the catalytic subunit spans the membrane. This view is supported by the finding that antibodies to the enzyme are only effective on the outer face of the membrane. Although a number of models have been suggested, the detailed mechanism of the pump remains speculative.

The sodium pump regulates the intracellular Na^+ concentration. At normal intracellular Na^+ concentrations, hydrolysis of ATP and the transport of ions is less than maximal; a rise in intracellular Na^+ stimulates the pump and restores the Na^+ concentration to normal. The pump is also subject to hormonal control; for example, insulin stimulates it, particularly in skeletal muscle. Low levels of insulin in some forms of diabetes (Chap. 23) lead to loss of potassium from cells. Conversely, rises in plasma insulin levels stimulate the sodium–potassium exchange and lower plasma potassium concentrations. Catecholamine hormones (Chap. 16) also stimulate sodium–potassium exchange.

Calcium pump

A number of other active transport systems have been described, and it is probable that others remain to be discovered. Another ion for which intracellular concentration is much lower than would be predicted under equilibrium conditions is the calcium ion. It seems that there may be a number of mechanisms that can lead to the low intracellular calcium concentration including a 'calcium pump' associated with a membrane-bound ATPase.

The calcium pump is of particular importance in the sarcoplasmic reticulum of skeletal muscle. Changes in intracellular calcium concentration regulate the contractile process, and active transport of Ca^{2+} from the cytoplasm into the lumen of the sarcoplasmic reticulum is necessary for the termination of contraction. The calcium pump is a major constituent of the sarcoplasmic reticulum membrane and constitutes some 80 per cent of its integral protein.

Identification of active transport: the Nernst equation

The identification of the existence of active transport is greatly helped by the demonstration that a molecule is being maintained at a concentration away from equilibrium. For a charged particle, however, 'equilibrium' is not synonymous with equal concentration on the two sides of the membrane. Since the cell interior of almost all cells is electrically negative, positively charged particles equilibrate with an intracellular concentration higher than the extracellular, whilst negatively charged particles have a lower concentration. The negative cell interior attracts positive charges and repels negatively charged particles. Equilibrium occurs when the electrical forces exactly balance the forces associated with the concentration gradient across the membrane. This situation is most conveniently described by the *Nernst equation*.

The Nernst equation can be derived by considering the total energy associated with the ion on each side of the membrane. This energy includes chemical energy associated with the amount of the ion present. It is described by the chemical potential ($\bar{\mu}$), which can be shown to be given by the equation.

$$\bar{\mu} = RT \log_e C$$

where R is the gas constant, T the absolute temperature and C is the concentration. (Strictly one should use not concentration but 'activity', that is, the thermodynamically effective concentration. This can be important for intracellular ions in particular, since many of the ions are bound to protein molecules or other polyelectrolytes and the activity may be much lower than the apparent concentration.)

Energy is also associated with the electrical potential difference across the cell membrane. The *total electrochemical potential* ($\bar{\mu}$) of an ion in a compartment combines the chemical potential and the electrical potential and is given by

$$\bar{\mu} = RT \log_e C + zF\psi$$

where z is the algebraic charge associated with the ion (for example, $z = +1$ for Na^+, $z = -1$ for Cl^-, $z = +2$ for Ca^{2+}), F is the Faraday, and ψ is the electrical potential of the compartment (relative to an arbitrarily chosen zero of potential).

If an ion is in equilibrium between two compartments (such as the extracellular fluid and the cell interior), then the potential energy in the two compartments is equal. There is no tendency for *net* movement of ions from one compartment to another, but *individual* ions are continually exchanging.

At equilibrium the electrochemical potential of an ion in the two compartments is exactly equal:

$$\bar{\mu}_1 = \bar{\mu}_2$$

or

$$RT \log_e C_1 + zF\psi_1 = RT \log_e C_2 + zF\psi_2$$

This equation can be rearranged into a more useful form by collecting together all the electrical terms on one side

and all the concentration terms on the other side of the equation.

$$zF\psi_1 - zF\psi_2 = RT \log_e C_2 - RT \log_e C_1$$

that is

$$zF(\psi_1 - \psi_2) = RT \log_e \frac{C_2}{C_1}$$

or

$$\psi_1 - \psi_2 = \frac{RT}{zF} \log_e \frac{C_2}{C_1}$$

where ($\psi_1 - \psi_2$) is the electrical potential difference between the two compartments, usually denoted E. This is the Nernst equation. It should be noted that it is derived from the assumption that the ion is in equilibrium. It is obeyed by those ions that are passively distributed across the membrane but does not apply to ions that are actively transported.

Ionophores: ion channels

Although ions are strongly hydrophilic and would not be expected to permeate the phospholipid bilayer, observed membrane permeabilities are quite high for a number of ions, suggesting the existence of specific transport systems presumed to be associated with the membrane proteins. A system that increases the permeability of the membrane to an ion is described as an *ionophore*. A number of naturally occurring ionophores have been isolated and identified, and synthetic ionophores have also been produced. Such molecules give insights into the functioning of the cell membrane with respect to ions.

One group of synthetic ionophores behave as mobile carriers. These molecules are ring structures with nonpolar groups on the outside that make them readily soluble in lipid. The interior of the ring provides a polar environment for the ion and the whole molecule makes the ion soluble in the membrane. Ionophores that function in this way and that are normal membrane components have not yet been identified.

The second major group of ionophores are those that make a channel across the membrane. Channels are apparently formed by two ring-shaped molecules, one in each leaflet of the bilayer, coming together to make a continuous channel through the membrane. Such a channel is transient but can allow a rapid flow of ions. This suggests an important principle about membrane function: that two independent integral proteins in the two leaflets of the bilayer may be able to combine transiently and interact with one another.

Other channel-formers can make permanent channels across the membrane. Molecules of this type span the complete bilayer and resemble the Na^+–K^+ pump in being composed of several subunits. It seems likely that such channels form the basis of much of the electrical behaviour of the cell. In some instances, the ability of such channels to allow the passage of ions can be modified, and these changes can occur in one of three main ways. The permeability of some channels is altered by changes in the electrical potential difference across the cell membrane. These channels are described as *voltage-dependent* or *voltage-gated*, and form the basis of the action potential by which electrical signals are transmitted along nerve and muscle cells. A second group of channels can be activated by a specific chemical signal. Channels of this type are involved in the transmission of electrical signals between cells and in the initiation of electrical responses by chemical signals in general. These channels are termed *chemically dependent* or *chemically gated*. A third group of channels are mechanically activated. These channels are involved in the transduction of mechanical signals in a number of types of sensory receptor, including those concerned with hearing, balance, pressure on the skin and stretch in the walls of blood vessels. Finally, it should be noted that in some channels permeability changes spontaneously with time. These changes are the basis of the rhythmicity of cardiac muscle and of certain types of smooth muscle cells.

MEMBRANE POTENTIALS

The existence of an electric potential difference across the cell membrane has already been assumed in earlier sections without attempting to explain how such a potential might arise. Any process that leads to the separation of electrical charge gives rise to an electrical potential difference.

One mechanism by which a membrane potential could be generated is through the presence of charged molecules that are unable to cross the membrane. Such 'fixed charges' modify the distribution of ions that can cross the membrane. Charge may also be directly separated by the action of active transport processes if unequal numbers of ions are transported across the membrane. In addition to separating charge directly, active transport processes move ions away from equilibrium. Such ions tend to move down the electrochemical gradients created by the pump and the fixed charges, the rate of movement depending both on the magnitude of the gradient and on the permeability of the membrane. These 'downhill' movements of ions are the basis for the resting and action potentials in most cells.

The Gibbs–Donnan equilibrium

Any localised concentration of 'fixed charges' influences the distribution of other charged particles that are able to move. The cell membrane constitutes an almost impenetrable barrier to many charged molecules such as ATP and many metabolic intermediates. Many proteins are even more firmly 'fixed', being attached to intracellular membranes or constituting a cytoskeleton that persists after the removal of the plasma membrane. When the intracellular pH is normal most cellular proteins carry a net negative charge, as do ATP and the metabolic intermediates. These fixed negative charges play a part in regulating the distribution of mobile ions across the cell membrane but this distribution is greatly modified by the operation of metabolically powered ion pumps and the differential permeability of the membrane to the pumped ions. Where such pumps are not operating, for example across the wall of the capillary, the fixed charges (mainly those associated with the plasma proteins) are the main determinants of the distribution of those ions that can cross the capillary wall. The mobile ions are then able to achieve equilibrium and must obey the Nernst equation. In addition, very large amounts of work are necessary to achieve very small separations of positive and negative charges. Therefore, to within a very close approximation, the total amount of charge carried by anions must equal the total amount of charge carried by cations in each compartment. From these two constraints, equations can be developed to determine the ionic composition of each compartment. The system is referred to as the Gibbs–Donnan equilibrium.

The resting membrane potential

As a result of the activity of the sodium pump, both potassium and sodium ions are prevented from coming to equilibrium across the cell membrane. Application of the Nernst equation to cells suggests that sodium ions are far from equilibrium, even though their movement across the membrane can be clearly demonstrated by radio-isotope tracers. Morever, precise measurements of the membrane potential and the concentrations of potassium inside and outside the cell suggest that potassium is not precisely in equilibrium either. The cell interior is slightly less negative than would be predicted by the Nernst equation if potassium ions were in equilibrium. This finding can be explained by another equation, the *Goldman equation*, which takes account of the contributions of more than one ion not at equilibrium.

If sodium and potassium alone are considered, the equation is:

$$E = \frac{RT}{F} \log_e \frac{P_K[K^+]_o + P_{Na}[Na^+]_o}{P_K[K^+]_i + P_{Na}[Na^+]_i}$$

This equation resembles the Nernst equation, but also includes the terms P_K and P_{Na}, the permeabilities of the membrane to K^+ and Na^+ ions.

The membrane potential thus depends on two fundamental properties of the cell membrane: the differential permeability to K^+ and Na^+ and the maintenance of the concentration gradients for Na^+ and K^+ by the sodium pump. It has been estimated that up to one-third of the resting energy requirement of the body is needed for the sodium pump. In the resting state, the permeability to potassium is much greater than that to sodium and the potential largely depends on the distribution of potassium ions.

Not only does the Goldman equation help to explain the resting potential, but it also allows an understanding of the changes during electrical excitation in nerve and various types of muscle cells (Chap. 32). These changes depend on the changes in ionic permeability of the membrane that result from the activation of ion channels described earlier.

WATER MOVEMENT ACROSS CELL MEMBRANES

Although membranes are based on a phospholipid bilayer through which hydrophilic molecules penetrate with difficulty, water itself crosses most membranes with ease. There are, however, exceptions to this generalisation, notably in the kidney, where the generation of an osmotic gradient in the medullary interstititium depends on the impermeability to water of the ascending limb of the loop of Henle. Equally, the final regulation of the osmolality of the urine depends on a low membrane permeability to water in the distal parts of the nephron, which can be increased under the control of vasopressin.

Net water movement across biological membranes depends on osmotic gradients generated by the presence of non-equilibrating charged particles (the Gibbs–Donnan effect) and the operation of active ion-transport mechanisms. Water movement down on osmotic gradient resembles the movement of any other molecule: water moves from regions of higher to regions of lower concentration. A reduction in water concentration occurs in regions of high solute concentration (high osmotic pressure).

Osmotic pressure
The size of the driving force for water movement can be predicted from the osmotic pressures of the fluids on either side of the membrane. This cannot be determined directly from the total concentration of solutes. The osmolality of plasma calculated from its known constituents would be about 325 mmol/kg but the actual plasma osmolality measured by an osmometer is only around 291 mmol/kg. This difference results from the incomplete dissociation of the ionic components of plasma and the fact that some substances are partially bound to plasma proteins.

Clinically, it is convenient to compare the osmolality of a solution with that of interstitial fluid. A solution that is osmotically equivalent to interstitial fluid will not induce movement of fluid into or out of cells and tissues. Such a solution is said to be *isotonic*. More dilute solutions, which cause cells to swell, are said to be *hypotonic*, and more concentrated solutions are *hypertonic*. The simplest isotonic solution is 0.92 per cent NaCl (0.92 g/100 ml or 150 mmol Cl^- and 150 mmol Na^+ per litre). This solution is commonly used for fluid replacement intravenously and is often described as 'normal saline' or 'isotonic saline'.

MEMBRANE TURNOVER

It has already been emphasised that the cell membrane is regarded as a fluid and dynamic structure. Not only are the individual components able to move in relation to one another, but there is also a continual removal and replacement ('turnover') of individual molecules. This can be conveniently demonstrated by the use of radio-labelled membrane components.

The ability of the membrane constituents to turn over allows the possibility that the composition may alter in response to changing demands. Changes in the lipid composition of the membrane make it possible for the properties of the membrane to be modified. For example, the nature of the fatty acyl side-chains of the membrane lipids governs the fluidity of the core of the bilayer. In general, increased chain length makes it easier for the fatty acyl chains to pack together and produces a more ordered and rigid structure at any given temperature. On the other hand, a cis-double-bond produces a bend in the fatty acyl chain that makes packing of the side-chains more difficult and increases membrane fluidity. It seems likely that an appropriate fluidity of membrane lipids is necessary for the optimum functioning of the membrane proteins.

This concept can be illustrated by the differences between the inner and outer leaflets of the erythrocyte membrane. The inner leaflet of the bilayer contains far more proteins than the outer bilayer, and these include a number of enzymes. It can also be shown that the phospholipids of the inner leaflet contain a higher proportion of short-chain and unsaturated fatty acyl chains. Thus the inner leaflet is a more fluid environment which, it is suggested, is needed for the functioning of the membrane-bound enzymes.

Membrane proteins are also removed and replaced,

creating the possibility for adaptation of function. It seems that the numbers of at least some membrane proteins involved in transport or as receptors can be altered in response to changing needs. Moreover, at least some receptor proteins are known to be taken into the cytoplasm after combination with specific molecules that bind to them ('ligands'). In this way, some hormones with a low lipid permeability, such as insulin, may nevertheless enter the cell. This process is associated with specialised regions of the cell membrane known as 'coated pits'. These are associated with cytoskeletal elements within the cell and these regions of the membrane are become invaginated to form 'coated vesicles', which then migrate to specific targets within the cell (Fig. 2.7). The importance of this process is not fully understood but appears to be more concerned with degradation of the hormone rather than expression of its action, although long-term hormonal effects may depend on the movement of the hormone–receptor complex.

Most hormones and neurotransmitters, with the exceptions of the steroid and thyroid hormones, have low lipid solubility and act by combination with receptors in the plasma membrane. This binding may by itself lead to changes in membrane function. For example, many receptors for neurotransmitters are coupled to, or are part of, chemically gated ionophores and modify membrane ionic permeability. Other receptors, especially those for hormones, activate membrane-bound enzymes and lead to intracellular chemical changes. In particular, activation of membrane receptors leads to changes in the concentration of an intra-

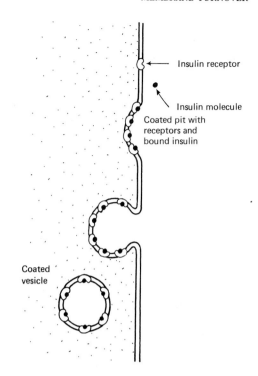

Fig. 2.7 The process whereby insulin is taken up by cells of target organs (From C R Paterson 1983. Essentials of human biochemistry. Pitman, London).

cellular *second messenger*, such as adenosine-3′, 5′-cyclic monophosphate (cyclic AMP), inositol trisphosphate or calcium ions (Chap. 23).

FURTHER READING

Bretscher M S 1985 The molecules of the cell membrane. Scientific American 253(4): 86

Dautry-Varsat A, Lodish H F 1984 How receptors bring proteins and particles into cells. Scientific American 250(5): 52

Finean J B, Coleman R, Michell R H 1984 Membranes and their cellular functions. 3rd edn. Blackwell Scientific, Oxford

Katz B 1966 Nerve, muscle and synapse. McGraw-Hill, New York

Keynes R D 1979 Ion transport in the nerve cell membrane. Scientific American 240(3): 126

Keynes R D, Aidley D J 1981 Nerve and muscle. Cambridge University Press

Unwin N, Henderson R 1984 The structure of proteins in biological membranes. Scientific American 250(2): 78

West I C 1983 The biochemistry of membrane transport. Chapman & Hall, London

The body fluids

Water accounts for about two-thirds of the weight of an adult's body, so that an individual of average weight (say 70 kg) holds about 40 litres. Apart from weight, the total body water (TBW) depends on a number of factors, particularly age, sex and obesity. In the newborn the TBW may be as high as 75 per cent of the body weight. The proportion decreases progressively with age, particularly during the first ten years of life. Females have a smaller proportion of water than males of the same weight, in part because of the greater proportion of fat making up the body weight. Adipose tissue has a low water content, so that the proportion of water in a tissue, or in the body as a whole, depends largely on the proportion of fat (Table 3.1).

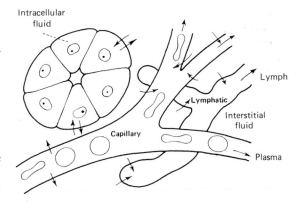

Fig. 3.2 The main subdivisions of the body fluid. The term extracellular fluid includes interstitial fluid, lymph and the protein-free fraction of plasma.

Table 3.1 Example of the relationship between body water and fat content at different body weights (kg)

Parameter	Wasted	Average	Obese
Body weight	33	60	90
Fat	3.5	18.5	40.5
Fat-free mass	29.5	41.5	49.5
Total body water	23	31	36
Body water as a percentage of body weight	70	52	40
Body water as a percentage of fat free mass	80	75	73

Table 3.3 Distribution of body water in a man of average build

Compartment	Volume (litres)	Percentage of body weight
Plasma	3.5	5
Interstitial fluid	12	17
Total extracellular fluid (ECF)	15.5	22
Intracellular fluid (ICF)	26.5	38
Total body water (TBW)	42	60

The distribution of water in the body

Figure 3.2 shows the principal 'compartments' into which the body water is divided. Table 3.3 shows the amount in a typical adult. Some 25 litres is within the cell membranes and although this is often regarded as one 'compartment' it is in fact the sum of the intracellular water in all cells.

The extracellular fluid (ECF) is the water in all the spaces outside cell membranes. The total amount in a man of average build (70 kg) is about 15 litres, or some 20 per cent of the body weight. The ECF can be divided into a number of subsidiary compartments, the *inter-stitial fluid*, the blood plasma and the transcellular fluid, for example the cerebrospinal fluid, the intra-ocular fluids and the fluids within the gastro-intestinal tract.

The measurement of the volume of the body fluid compartments

The volume of a compartment is measured by using the dilution principle. If a known quantity of a substance is added to a compartment it distributes evenly throughout the compartment. The extent to which the added substance is diluted allows the volume of the compartment to be measured. If Q = quantity of substance added, C = the concentration of the substance when evenly distributed and V = volume of the compartment then

$$V = \frac{Q}{C}$$

The following conditions, however, apply to the measurement of the volume of a compartment. The marker must be freely diffusible and must be confined to the compartment to be measured. If it is excreted it should be at a constant and measurable rate. The marker must be non-toxic and neither synthesised nor metabolised. Accurate measurement of the concentration of the marker must be possible. A representative sample must be easily obtained from the compartment.

Total body water

The measurement of total body water needs a marker that not only diffuses freely in the water outside the cells but also crosses cell membranes. Three such substances have been used, tritiated water, heavy water (D_2O), or a chemical called *antipyrine*. A known quantity of labelled water is injected intravenously as an isotonic solution of NaCl. It mixes freely with the water of the body in a few hours. At the end of this period a blood sample is taken and the concentration of the 'labelled' water measured. Some marker is lost in the urine so this loss must be allowed for.

TBW (volume) =

$$\frac{\text{amount injected} - \text{amount lost in urine}}{\text{concentration in plasma}}$$

Example: 100 ml of D_2O was infused into a 70 kg man. After 2 hours, when equilibrium had occurred, a sample of blood was taken and the concentration of D_2O was found to be 0.0025 ml/ml of plasma. At the time of the plasma sample, urine was voided and was found to contain 0.5 ml D_2O.

$$\begin{aligned} \text{TBW} &= \frac{100 \text{ ml} - 0.5 \text{ ml}}{0.0025 \text{ ml/ml}} \\ &= 39.8 \text{ l or } 57\% \text{ of the body weight} \end{aligned}$$

The extracellular fluid volume

The marker for ECF must be a substance that diffuses readily through the ECF space but does not enter the cells. A number of substances have been used, but all cross the cell membrane to some extent. It is usual to use radioactive isotopes of sodium, chloride, bromide, thiosulphate, thiocyanate, sucrose and inulin. Sucrose and inulin penetrate cell membranes to a smaller extent

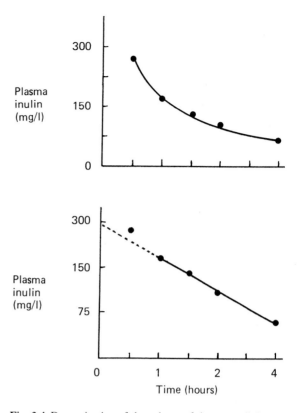

Fig. 3.4 Determination of the volume of the extracellular space using inulin. The concentration of marker is plotted as a function of time (above) and as a function of the log of time (below). The dotted line in the lower graph is extrapolated to cut the ordinate and this point gives the concentration that would have been found had the marker been distributed instantaneously.

than the others and probably give a more accurate estimate of ECF. Since all markers give slightly different values because of their varying ability to penetrate cell membranes, the results are often quoted as the 'sodium space', the 'thiocyanate space', the 'inulin space', etc.

In the determination of the inulin space, a known quantity of the polysaccharide inulin is injected intravenously. Plasma inulin concentrations are measured at intervals over 30 minutes. It can be seen that the plasma concentration falls off exponentially with time (Fig. 3.4a). This is due to two processes: the diffusion throughout the ECF space and excretion in the urine. This curve can be converted to a straight line by plotting concentration against the logarithm of time (Fig. 3.4b). After a period of mixing, the concentration of inulin falls off in a predictable manner because of loss in the urine. If the straight part of the curve is extrapolated back to cut the concentration axis, the value of the intercept is the concentration of inulin that would have been achieved had it been distributed instantaneously. This method allows for losses through the urine.

Example: 4 g of inulin are injected intravenously, extrapolation of the concentration time graph cuts the concentration axis at zero time (that is, the time of the injection) at 0.275 g/l.

$$\text{Volume distribution} = \frac{4g}{0.275 \text{ g/l}}$$
$$= 14.5 \text{ l for a 70 kg person}$$

Plasma volume

The markers used to measure the plasma volume are either a vital dye, called Evans blue (T1824), or iodinated albumin. When T1824 is used it is injected into the blood, where it binds to plasma proteins and is therefore largely confined to the plasma. However, as a small loss occurs through the capillary walls, the calculation is carried out as for the measurement of the ECF space to allow for this loss. The plasma volume is about 3 litres or 4.5 per cent of the body weight in a 70 kg man. It is about 2.4 litres in a woman.

Intracellular volume

This cannot be measured directly and must be determined by subtracting the extracellular volume from the total body water.

Interstitial fluid volume

There is no method to measure the interstitial fluid volume, which has to be calculated by substracting the plasma volume from the ECF volume. In a 70 kg adult it is about 12 litres.

COMPOSITION OF THE BODY FLUIDS

Sodium is the principal cation of the ECF, whereas potassium predominates in the cell (ICF). While chloride is an important anion in the ECF, phosphate and sulphate predominate within the cells. Protein also contributes significantly to the anion content of the ICF, but in the ECF it is largely confined to the plasma (Table 3.5).

It is not yet easy to measure the concentration of intracellular electrolytes but the composition of the ECF may be studied by using plasma to provide a guide to the composition of the ECF. In practice the concentrations of all the cations and anions are seldom measured. There is a discrepancy between the sums of the measured cations (Na and K) and the sum of the measured anions (Cl and HCO_3). This difference is known as the *anion gap* and is usually between 10 and 15 mmol/l. In some diseases alterations in the anion gap

Table 3.5 Typical concentrations of the principal anions and cations in plasma, interstitial fluid and intracellular fluid (mmol/l)

Ions	Plasma	Interstitial fluid	Intracellular fluid
Cations			
Sodium	142	145	10
Potassium	4	4	160
Calcium	2	1	1
Magnesium	1	1	13
Anions			
Chloride	101	114	3
Bicarbonate	27	31	10
Phosphate (HPO_4^{2-})	1	1	50
Sulphate	0.5	0.5	10
Organic anions	6	7	
Protein	2	1<0.1	8

By expressing the concentrations in milli-equivalents per litre it can be shown that the total anions are equivalent to the total cations.

may indicate biochemical abnormalities. For example, in patients with excessive quantities of lactate the anion gap is larger than normal.

The differences in ionic composition between ICF and ECF depend on two main mechanisms: the inability of large molecules to pass freely through cell membranes and the active transport of substances across cell membranes (Chap. 1). These transport mechanisms, for example the sodium pump, require the expenditure of energy. The differences in composition therefore depend on the integrity of cell membranes and a sufficient supply of energy. In disease these conditions may not be fulfilled and ions may leak out of cells. In stored blood, potassium leaks out of erythrocytes into the plasma.

Measurement of sodium and potassium

The total amounts of sodium and potassium in the body may be estimated by clinical analysis of the cadaver or by dilution techniques with radioactive isotopes ^{22}Na and ^{40}K. Since the latter isotope occurs naturally as a constant proportion of the total potassium, the body potassium may be also estimated by total body scanning.

Body sodium and exchangeable sodium

A known quantity of ^{22}Na is injected intravenously and all the urine passed is collected, with a final emptying of the bladder after 24 hours. During the last 12 hours the intake of sodium in the diet is restricted. At 24 hours a blood sample is taken and the concentration in serum is measured by flame photometry and the radioactivity is also measured. The exchangeable sodium is calculated as follows:

$$\text{Exchangeable Na} = \frac{^{22}\text{Na injected} - {}^{22}\text{Na excreted}}{^{22}\text{Na per mmol serum Na}}$$

In an average 70 kg man, the total sodium amounts to about 5000 mmol, whereas the exchangeable sodium is only about 3000 mmol. Thus 2000 mmol are non-exchangeable, most of which is fixed in bone. The body pools of sodium are illustrated in Figure 3.6.

Total body potassium and exchangeable potassium
By using the same method but injecting ^{42}K, or by total body scanning, the exchangeable potassium can also be measured. In this case the total body potassium is about 3200 mmol but only about 130 mmol is non-exchangeable. Thus most of the potassium is freely exchangeable. The body pools of potassium are illustrated in Figure 3.7.

Movements of fluid between extracellular and intracellular compartments
In the seriously ill patient, the physician will be confronted with the problem of maintaining fluid balance, ensuring that there are no large differences between input and output (see Chap. 13), and that there is a proper balance between extracellular and intracellular fluid volumes.

Water moves across membranes in part under the influence of any difference in the osmotic pressure of the solutions on either side. The osmotic pressure or *osmolality* of a solution can be measured by an *osmometer*, which measures the depression of the freezing point of the solution. In normal subjects the osmolality of plasma measured in this way is between 281 and 297 mmol/kg. Calculating the osmolality of plasma from its known constituents would give a figure of about 325 mmol/kg water. The difference between this value and the figure found in practice is explained by the facts that the electrolytes are not completely dissociated in solution and some substances are partly bound to proteins.

The osmotic relationships between extracellular and intracellular fluids
If the osmotic equilibrium between ECF and ICF is disturbed by a change in one compartment, a compensatory flow of water occurs so that equilibrium is regained within a few minutes. For example, on drinking a litre of water, absorption of the water occurs, diluting the ECF; this causes osmosis of water into the cells until a new equilibrium is reached. In this example, equilibrium is regained within a minute of the absorption of the water.

Dehydration of the subject has the reverse effect, water passing from the cells into the ECF.

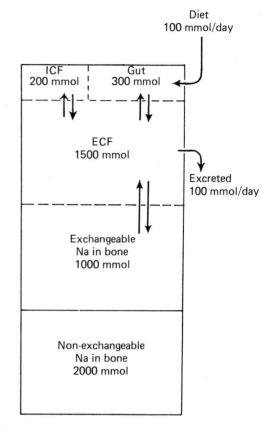

Fig. 3.6 The approximate distribution of ^{22}Na in the total body sodium of man 24 hours after intravenous injection. After Monro D S 1959 In E J Ross (ed) Clinical effects of electrolyte disturbances. Pitman, London.

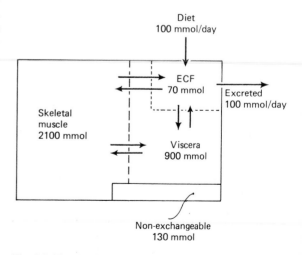

Fig. 3.7 The distribution of radiopotassium in man 24 hours after injection. Note the small proportion of body potassium that does not exchange in this period is chiefly in brain and red blood cells. After Monro D S 1959 In E J Ross (ed) Clinical effects of electrolyte disturbances. Pitman, London.

The formation of interstitial fluid

The exchange of water and dissolved substances through a capillary wall depends upon the type of capillary. In general three types have been described. Type 1 capillaries have uninterrupted membranes with pores of 4–5 nm in diameter. Such capillaries occur in muscle, in the pulmonary circulation and in adipose tissue. Type 2 capillaries have fenestrated membranes, the fenestrations being of the order of 0.1 μm. Typical sites are the glomeruli of the kidney and the intestinal epithelium. Type 3 capillaries have discontinuous membranes. They are interrupted by large intercellular spaces through which not only fluids but cells can pass. These capillaries are found in bone marrow, spleen and liver.

Two processes are involved in the transfer of fluid, nutrients and waste products across the capillary membrane: diffusion and filtration/reabsorption. Diffusion over short distances is a very fast process. Most cells are within 5–10 μm of a capillary and the diffusion distance between adjacent cells may be less than 0.1 μm, so that diffusion over the former distance to reach 90 per cent of equilibrium takes about 4.5 ms and over the latter distance about 0.45 ms. Diffusion is more effective the greater the capillary density in a tissue because the surface area is greater. An increase in capillary density and surface area occurs when a tissue becomes active during vasodilation (see Chap. 8).

The nature of the capillary membrane

The capillary membrane is very leaky; its permeability is high but its selectivity is low. The typical capillary behaves as if diffusion occurs through pores of 8–9 nm in diameter occupying about 0.1 per cent of the total area. Substances of molecular weight of less than about 70 000 cross freely down their concentration gradients to reach equal concentrations on both sides of the capillary and consequently do not contribute to an osmotic pressure difference across the wall. Plasma proteins are largely retained and create an osmotic pressure gradient, the *colloid osmotic pressure* or *oncotic pressure*, which is of the order of 25 mmHg (3.3 kPa). The rapid exchange of water and small water-soluble molecules between the plasma and interstitial fluid can be illustrated by the rate of diffusion of water through the capillary surface throughout the body, which is estimated to be about 60 l/min or 85 000 l/day.

Filtration/reabsorption across the capillary wall

Starling proposed that fluid exchange across the capillary wall between plasma and interstitial fluid was achieved by a balance between two forces. The hydrostatic pressure in the capillary, caused by the action of the heart, directs fluid movement outwards (*filtration*),

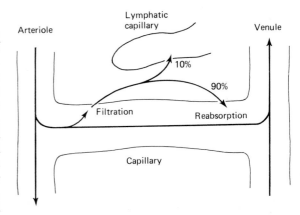

Fig. 3.8 A simplified scheme to illustrate the formation and fate of tissue fluid according to Starling's hypothesis. At the arterial end of a capillary, the hydrostatic pressure of the blood overcomes the colloid osmotic pressure of the plasma protein. At the venous end, the hydrostatic pressure has fallen to below the colloid osmotic pressure and reabsorption occurs by osmosis. One-tenth of the filtered fluid enters the lymphatics.

an effect that is opposed by the colloid osmotic pressure of the plasma proteins, a force that is directed inwards (reabsorption).

Thus, at the arterial end of a capillary, the hydrostatic pressure exceeds the colloid osmotic pressure and net filtration takes place; at the venous end the hydrostatic pressure falls below the colloid osmotic pressure and reabsorption occurs (Fig. 3.8). Two other factors affect the transcapillary movement of fluid. There is a small negative hydrostatic pressure in the tissues outside the capillary; this increases the outward force. Also the capillary is not entirely impermeable to protein and some escapes into the interstitial fluid, where it opposes the inwardly directed force of the colloid osmotic pressure.

The hydrostatic pressure at the arterial end of a capillary depends upon the type of tissue, the activity of the tissue and the vasomotor supply. In the resting state, the pressure in the glomerular capillaries of the kidney is 70 mmHg (9.3 kPa) and ultrafiltration only occurs; in the lungs and liver it is 8 mmHg (1.1 kPa) and absorption only occurs. In the human finger the pressure at the arterial end of the capillary is about 32 mmHg (4.3 kPa) and both filtration and reabsorption occur. It is important that filtration does not occur in the lung for otherwise respiratory exchange would be impeded.

Role of the lymphatics

The distal lymphatics form a closed system of tubes (Fig. 3.2) consisting of an endothelial lining supported by fibrous tissue. It is difficult to measure the near-atmospheric pressure in the tissue fluid or in the terminal lymphatics. There is still no satisfactory explanation of the movement of fluid into the terminal lymphatics. However, the lymphatics are much more permeable to protein than the capillaries. The capillary wall is not totally impermeable to protein and some leakage occurs from the plasma into the interstitial space. It cannot return to the capillary because of the adverse concentration gradient. Accumulation in the interstitial space would upset the Starling equilibrium and protein diffuses into the very permeable lymphatic capillary together with other large molecules produced by cells such as hormones, enzymes and lipoproteins including chylomicrons. The larger lymphatic vessels have muscle fibres in their walls. The lymphatic vessels possess numerous valves and the flow of lymph from the periphery to the thoracic duct is brought about by muscular and respiratory movements in the same way as the flow of blood in the veins. The lymphatics of the intestine (*lacteals*) show rhythmic contractions, which, because of the many valves, propel the lymph on to the thoracic duct. This contractile activity is an intrinsic property of the lymphatics and is not co-ordinated by the nervous system.

Lymph has the same concentrations of salts as interstitial fluids and plasma, a lower concentration of protein than plasma and a slightly higher concentration of protein than interstitial fluid (Table 3.9). Complete obstruction of the lymphatic vessels draining a part of the body leads to oedema of the area (*lymphoedema*). This oedema fluid has a protein concentration similar to that of plasma. Some indication of the daily volume of lymph is given by the fact that if the thoracic duct is severed, fat-laden lymph initially accumulates in the thorax (*chylothorax*) at a rate of about 3 litres per day.

Before reaching the blood, lymph passes through at least one or, more usually, 8–10 lymph nodes, the structure and function of which are described in Chapter 5. During its passage through a lymph node the lymph is altered in composition. Small molecules pass into the blood while large molecules are retained and newly formed antibodies (immunoglobulins) are added.

Table 3.9 Chemical composition of lymph compared with that of plasma and interstitial fluid

Component	Lymph	Interstitial fluid	Plasma
Protein (g/l)	26	1	71
Chloride (mmol/l)	116	104	101
Calcium (mmol/l)	1.7	1.3	2.4
Urea (mmol/l)	5.0	5.0	5.0

Oedema

The Starling hypothesis is helpful in explaining the occurrence of oedema, that is the accumulation of excessive amounts of salt and water in the interstitial space. In this condition the tissues, usually in dependent parts of the body, become swollen with fluid that resembles plasma but has a low protein content. Oedema may accumulate when the hydrostatic pressure in the veins is increased, as in congestive heart failure (p. 98), or when the colloid osmotic pressure of the plasma is reduced because the albumin level is low. Oedema from hypoalbuminaemia arises in malnutrition ('famine oedema'), in chronic liver disease (cirrhosis), when albumin synthesis is diminished, and in the nephrotic syndrome, in which excessive amounts of albumin are lost in the urine. Whatever the cause of the oedema, the kidney retains sodium. The cause of this sodium retention is not always clear but in some cases the output of aldosterone is excessive.

Tissue fluid balance

It is estimated that in an adult man some 20 litres of water are ultrafiltered from the capillaries. Of this some 16–18 litres return to the capillaries at the venular end by reabsorption; 2–4 litres return to the circulation through the lymph.

Table 3.10 indicates the amounts of some substances carried across the capillary wall by diffusion and by filtration. Transport by filtration or reabsorption is a slow process and is not important in the exchange of solutes. Diffusion is a very rapid process over the distances between capillaries and cells and between adjacent cells. It is the major mechanism for the transport of water, solutes, oxygen and carbon dioxide.

The Starling equilibrium described earlier is the mechanism that keeps fluid in the vessels by counteracting the 'leakiness' of the capillaries. In this way the volume of the circulating plasma is maintained.

Table 3.10 Typical figures for the amounts of some substances carried across capillary walls by diffusion or by filtration/reabsorption

Component	Amount carried by diffusion	Amount carried by filtration/ reabsorption	Comments
Water	84 000 l/day	20 l/day	—
Glucose	20 000 g/day	20 g/day	400 g/day used
Oxygen	360 l/day	60 ml/day	250 ml/min used

From Landis E M, Pappenheimer J R 1963 Handbook of physiology: Circulation, Vol 11. American Physiological Society, Washington

REFERENCES

Barcroft H 1976 Lymph formation by secretion or filtration? Journal of Physiology 260: 1–20

Cohen R D 1984 The body fluids. In Campbell E J M, Dickinson C J, Slater J D H, Edwards C R W, Sikora E K (eds) Clinical physiology, 5th edn. Blackwell Scientific, Oxford, pp 1–40

House C R 1974 Water transport in cells and tissues. Physiological Society Monograph 24. Arnold, London

Landis E M, Pappenheimer J R 1963 Exchange of substances through the capillary walls. Handbook of Physiology: Circulation, vol. 11, p 961. American Physiological Society, Washington

Maxwell M H, Kleeman C R 1980 Clinical disorders of fluid and electrolyte metabolism, 3rd edn. McGraw Hill, New York

Morgan D B 1984 Body water, sodium, potassium and hydrogen ions: some basic facts and concepts. Clinics in Endocrinology and Metabolism 13: 233–247

Robinson J R 1975 A prelude to physiology. Blackwell Scientific, Oxford

4

The blood

Blood is a fluid consisting of various types of cell suspended in plasma. Its function is the carriage of nutrients to and removal of waste products from the cells of the body, and the transport of hormones, antibodies and cells involved in homeostasis and in defences against infection or injury.

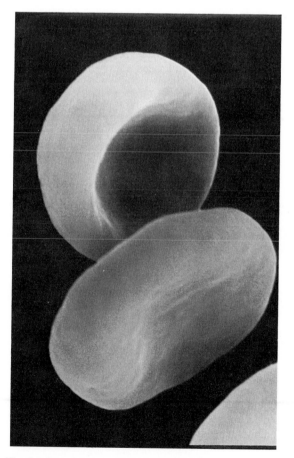

Fig. 4.1 Scanning electron micrograph of human erythrocytes, × 7200. (Courtesy of D G Newell)

THE ERYTHROCYTES

Normal red cells are biconcave discs (Fig. 4.1) about 7 μm in diameter with a volume of 80 to 95 fl. The cell membrane is flexible but not elastic, and allows considerable deformation of the cell within the circulation. The shape of the cell, with its large surface-to-volume ratio, also gives it flexibility. The mature red cell has homogeneous contents with no organelles, but is nevertheless metabolically very active. The main constituent of erythrocyte cytoplasm, *haemoglobin*, transports oxygen. The red cell also contains the enzymes of anaerobic glycolysis to provide energy, and mechanisms for protecting the haemoglobin against damage by oxidants.

Life span
Normal red cells circulate in the blood for about 120 days. Mature red cells lack ribosomes, mitochondria and nuclei and are unable to synthesise proteins or lipids; they cannot therefore make up any losses of enzymes or cell membrane constituents that occur as they age. Such senescent red cells are removed by the macrophages mainly in the spleen (p. 50); the haemoglobin and other components are degraded and the iron returns to the marrow for re-use.

A measure of red cell survival time can be obtained by labelling a sample of red cells with radioactive chromium (^{51}Cr). The labelled cells are reinjected and the half-life of the radioactive cells in the circulation can be measured.

The red cell membrane
The lipids of the red cell membrane are not uniformly distributed: the outer leaflet of the bilayer contains mainly phosphatidyl choline and sphingomyelin, while phosphatidyl ethanolamine and phosphatidyl serine predominate in the inner leaflet. Cholesterol is found in both.

The *membrane proteins* are also asymmetrically distributed. On the outer surface glycoproteins are exposed;

these carry blood group antigens and surface receptors. Other proteins span the lipid bilayer and are involved in transport across the membrane (Chap. 2). Peripheral membrane proteins are attached to the inner leaflet and make up the membrane skeleton (Fig. 4.2). This structure is a meshwork made up of *actin, spectrin* and a protein known as *band 4.1*; the meshwork is bound to the lipid bilayer by another protein, *ankyrin*, which links spectrin to the major integral membrane protein, *band 3*. Band 3 and band 4.1 are named from their band number in a gel electrophoresis preparation.

The membrane skeleton helps to determine red cell shape and deformability. Red cell deformability requires a flexible cytoskeleton and the high surface-to-volume ratio of the biconcave disc shape. It also depends on the internal viscosity of the cell, which is a function of the haemoglobin concentration. In turn this depends partly on the water content, which is controlled primarily by the ATP-dependent cation pumps such as Na^+-K^+-ATPase (p. 11). This enzyme promotes extrusion of Na^+ and inward transport of K^+. The red cell membrane also contains Ca^{2+}-ATPase, which pumps calcium out of the cell. The major membrane protein, band 3, is also a channel for *anion exchange* and is thus important in chloride exchange as well as bicarbonate and carbon dioxide transport.

Spherocytes and target cells

Alterations in the surface area of red cells, or of their volume, lead inevitably to changes in shape. As a red cell ages, lipid from its membrane is lost and the surface area decreases. The cell therefore tends to assume a spheroidal shape. Other causes of membrane loss besides ageing, such as antibody-induced damage, have the same effect. The spherical red cell is called a *spherocyte*. A red cell that gains in volume also tends to assume a spherical shape before eventually bursting. A decrease in cell volume, or an increase in surface area, has the opposite effect; a cell with redundant membrane, known as a *target cell* because of its appearance in blood smears, is formed. Spherocytes are much less deformable than normal red cells and therefore are less able to survive the mechanical stresses imposed by their passage through the capillaries.

Red cell metabolism

Red cell metabolism changes as the cell matures. In nucleated forms and reticulocytes, the major metabolic activity is globin synthesis, but with maturation the nucleus, the mitochondria and the ribosomes are progressively lost. In the mature erythrocyte, metabolic activity has two main aims; *energy production*, primarily to fuel the membrane pumps that maintain the ionic

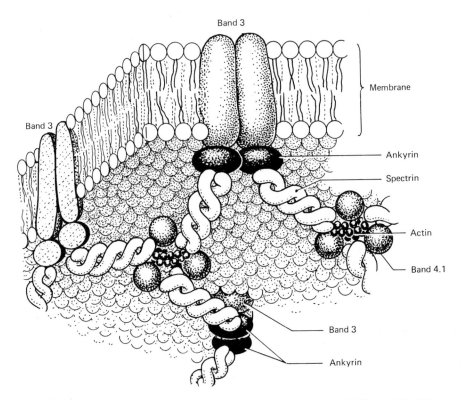

Fig. 4.2 Proteins of the membrane and cytoskeleton of an erythrocyte. (After S Lux 1979 Nature 281:426)

gradients across the membrane, and *antioxidant mechanisms*, which protect red cell structures and contents against damage by oxygen and its by-products.

Energy production

The main metabolic pathway for the supply of energy in the form of ATP in red cells is glycolysis with lactate production. Activity of the tricarboxylic acid cycle is present in young red cells containing mitochondria but these make up only about 2 per cent of circulating red cells. The glycolytic pathway also generates 2,3-bisphosphoglycerate (2,3-BPG), which regulates the oxygen affinity of haemoglobin (p. 148). Another important product of this pathway is reduced nicotinamide adenine dinucleotide (NADH), which participates in the reduction of methaemoglobin to haemoglobin (see below).

About 85 per cent of glucose metabolism in mature red cells is by the glycolytic pathway. The other 15 per cent is by the pentose phosphate pathway, the purpose of which is not to produce energy but to generate the reduced nicotinamide adenine dinucleotide phosphate (NADPH). This takes part in antioxidant mechanisms.

Antioxidant mechanisms

The usual interaction between haem and oxygen is *oxygenation*, which results in the reversible binding of O_2 to Fe^{2+} and the formation of oxyhaemoglobin. Occasionally, however, *oxidation* occurs, in which the Fe^{2+} loses an electron to the oxygen to produce the *superoxide* anion (O_2^-) and *methaemoglobin*, in which the haem ion is in the oxidised (Fe^{3+}) form (p. 26). Superoxide is a highly reactive free radical, which causes oxidation of lipids and proteins and can lead to the premature destruction of the cell.

A central role in the inactivation of superoxide is played by *reduced glutathione* (GSH) a sulphydryl-containing tripeptide molecule found in high concentration in red cells (Fig. 4.3). Superoxide is converted to hydrogen peroxide by the enzyme superoxide dismutase. Hydrogen peroxide is converted to water and oxygen by glutathione peroxidase by a reaction in which GSH is oxidised to glutathione (GSSG). GSSG is a hexapeptide formed by two GSH molecules combining, with the sulphydryl groups oxidised to form a disulphide bond. Reduction of this compound to regenerate GSH is catalysed by glutathione reductase. This reaction requires NADPH supplied by the pentose phosphate pathway, and specifically by the glucose-6-phosphate dehydrogenase (G6PD) step. A deficiency of this enzyme is common in certain populations, and leads to increased susceptibility of red cells to oxidant-induced destruction. Individuals with G6PD deficiency may develop acute haemolysis after exposure to various oxidant drugs, infections and even certain foods. The haem-containing enzyme *catalase* also converts hydrogen peroxide to water and oxygen but this action is much less important in red cells than glutathione peroxidation.

The reduction of methaemoglobin (with its ferric iron) to haemoglobin (with ferrous iron) is achieved by the enzyme *methaemoglobin reductase*, which requires NADH. There is also an NADPH-dependent system that requires an exogenous electron carrier such as methylene blue; this dye promotes methaemoglobin reduction in patients with high levels due, for example, to poisoning with oxidative substances or to methaemoglobin reductase deficiency. Ascorbic acid (vitamin C) is also used in these patients. Vitamin E (α-tocopherol) is lipid-soluble and protects membrane lipids against peroxidation especially in premature

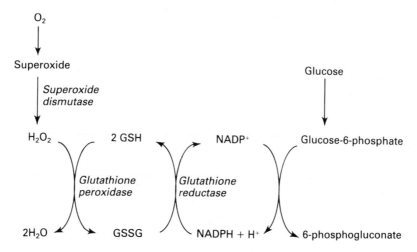

Fig. 4.3 Role of glutathione (G) in the disposal of oxidative groups in erythrocytes

infants, whose glutathione metabolism may be under-developed. Vitamins C and E are reducing agents that act independently of enzyme mechanisms.

HAEMOGLOBIN

Haemoglobin (Hb) is the red oxygen-carrying pigment found in all red cells. Each molecule consists of four subunits each containing one polypeptide chain (*globin*) and one iron-porphyrin complex (*haem*) (Fig 4.4). The iron is in the ferrous (Fe^{2+}) form. The main haemo-globin of normal adults, haemoglobin A (HbA), consists of two α-chains and two β-chains ($\alpha_2\beta_2$). This makes up some 98 per cent of normal adult haemoglobin. Much of the remaining 2 per cent is haemoglobin A_2 (HbA$_2$), which has the formula ($\alpha_2\delta_2$). Fetal haemo-globin (HbF) consists of two α-chains and two γ-chains ($\alpha_2\gamma_2$). It is the predominant haemoglobin in the fetus from about the middle of the first trimester until birth. It has a higher oxygen affinity than HbA, since it inter-acts only weakly with 2, 3-BPG (p. 148). It facilitates oxygen transfer across the placenta (p. 340). The conformation of two like and two unlike globin chains is essential for the oxygen-carrying property of haemo-globin, since the sigmoid shape of the oxygen dis-sociation curve (p. 148) depends on an alteration in the shape of the haemoglobin tetramer as it is oxygenated. This *haem–haem interaction* does not occur in single-chain molecules such as myoglobin, nor in haemoglo-bins containing four like chains such as β_4. (HbH) or γ_4 (Hb Barts). Finally, the maintenance of the iron in the ferrous state is of critical importance; if the iron is oxidised to the ferric (Fe^{3+}) state, the haemoglobin

Table 4.5 Principal normal and abnormal forms of haemoglobin

Name	Description
Oxyhaemoglobin	Oxygenated normal haemoglobin
Deoxyhaemoglobin	Deoxygenated normal haemoglobin
Methaemoglobin	Haemoglobin with ferrous ion is oxidised to ferric ($Fe^{2+} \rightarrow Fe^{3+}$). No oxygen-carrying capacity
Carboxyhaemoglobin	Carbon monoxide bound at O_2 binding site. No oxygen-carrying capacity
Sulphaemoglobin	Sulphur-containing haemoglobin usually resulting from drug ingestion

High levels in the blood of deoxyhaemoglobin, methaemoglobin and sulphaemoglobin cause cyanosis (p. 158). Carboxyhaemoglobin is bright red but unable to carry oxygen.

formed (*methaemoglobin*) is unstable and cannot carry oxygen (Table 4.5).

Globin

Each of the different globin chains (α, β, γ, δ, etc.) has a characteristic amino acid sequence (primary structure)

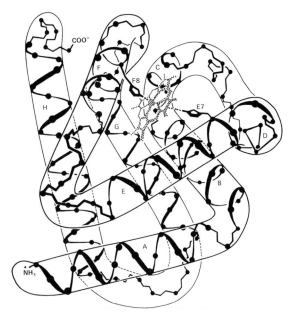

Fig. 4.6 Detail of structure of a globin–haem complex to show the lengths of α-helix within the globin chain. Two histidine residues (at E7 and F8) are linked to the haem component (dotted). (After R W Carrell and H Lehmann 1979. In: SS Brown et al (eds) The chemical diagnosis of disease. Elsevier, Amsterdam).

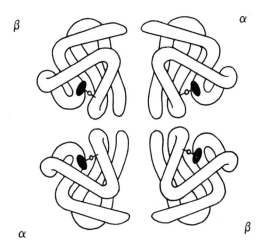

Fig. 4.4 Structure of a haemoglobin molecule to show the outline of the globin chains each with a haem molecule and one site for the binding of oxygen

and is coded by the corresponding globin gene. For example, β-chains are coded by β-genes on chromosome 11 and α-genes are duplicated, two being found on each chromosome 16.

Chains are helical and the helices are folded upon one another to give the molecule a globular tertiary structure, with a deep pocket into which the haem moiety is tucked (Fig. 4.6). The amino acid sequences of globin chains are known, and certain individual residues are essential for haemoglobin function. Many inherited *haemoglobin variants*, in which an alteration in the amino acid sequence has occurred, have been described; in some, substitution of an important residue leads to

Table 4.7 Haemoglobins distinguished by their different globin chain composition

Name	Chain composition	Comment
HbA	$\alpha_2 \beta_2$	Major adult haemoglobin (98%)
HbA$_2$	$\alpha_2 \delta_2$	Minor adult haemoglobin (2%)
HbF	$\alpha_2 \gamma_2$	Fetal haemoglobin — major haemoglobin during 2nd and 3rd trimesters of fetal life. Declines after birth. Normal adult level ~0.1%
Hb Gower I	$\zeta_2 \epsilon_2$ or ϵ_4	Embryonic haemoglobins — found during yolk sac haemopoiesis (p. 39)
Hb Gower II	$\alpha_2 \epsilon_2$	
Hb Portland	$\zeta_2 \gamma_2$	
Hb Barts	γ_4	Abnormal haemoglobins, formed when α-chain synthesis is reduced relative to β or γ (as in α-thalassaemia)
Hb H	β_4	
Hb S	$\alpha_2 \beta_2$	Sickle haemoglobin. Amino acid 6 in β-chains (normally glutamic acid) replaced by valine. One of many inherited globin chain abnormalities
Hb A1c	$\alpha_2 (\beta\text{-NH-glc})_2$	Glycosylated HbA. Glucose (glc) added to amino end of β-chains. Normally less than 8% of total, increased in diabetes

Most haemoglobins with different globin chain compositions are separable by electrophoresis or by chromatography. All of them are genetically determined, apart from HbA1c. Glycosylation is non-enzymatic, depending primarily on blood sugar levels.

impairment of haemoglobin function (*haemoglobinopathy*; Table 4.7). The best known haemoglobinopathy is sickle-cell disease, caused by a single amino acid substitution on the β-chains. The resulting haemoglobin, HbS, has abnormal physical properties and when deoxygenated polymerises into long fibres that aggregate and distort the red cells into a 'sickle' shape. These block small blood vessels and are destroyed; the results are chronic anaemia and repeated painful episodes of vascular occlusion. Heterozygotes for the condition, who have one normal and one abnormal β-chain gene, have red cells containing HbA and HbS. They have a much smaller liability to sickling. Many other haemoglobinopathies are known, as well as variants that do not cause disease.

Thalassaemias are conditions in which one or more of the globin genes are absent or not functioning normally. The result is a reduction in the rate of synthesis of the affected globin chain. For example, in β-thalassaemia, β-chain synthesis is impaired. As with the sickle genes, either one or two β-thalassaemia genes can be inherited; the severity of the disease depends on the number of genes and the degree of impairment of their function.

Haem

Haem is a ring structure formed of four pyrrole molecules with ferrous iron chelated at the centre of the ring (Fig. 4.8). It is essential for oxygen carriage. Haem is a constituent not only of haemoglobin but also of myoglobin, the cytochromes and enzymes such as catalase and peroxidase.

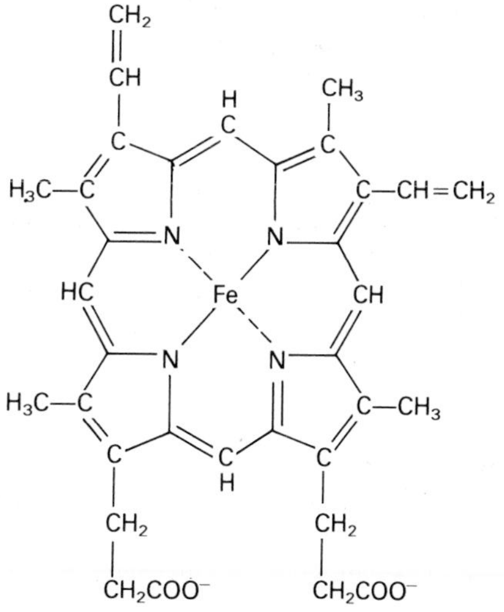

Fig. 4.8 Structure of haem

Synthesis

The initial step in synthesis of haem is the formation in the mitochondrion of δ-aminolaevulinic acid (ALA)

| Cytosol | Mitochondrial matrix |

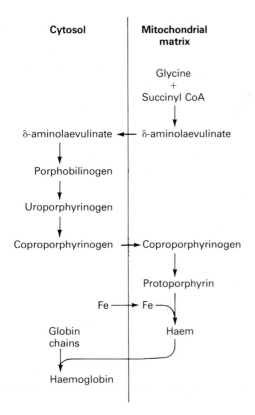

Fig. 4.9 Pathway for the synthesis of haem

from glycine and succinyl CoA (Fig. 4.9). This reaction is the major rate-limiting step in the process; the enzyme involved, ALA synthase, is inhibited both by haem and by haemoglobin. The whole pathway is thus regulated by end-product inhibition. The next step in the pathway is the formation of *porphobilinogen* (PBG) from two ALA molecules in the cytosol. Four molecules of PBG combine to give uroporphyrinogen. This in turn is converted to coproporphyrinogen III, which re-enters the mitochondrion. There it is converted to protoporphyrinogen IX and then protoporphyrin IX.

Finally, an iron atom is inserted into the ring to give haem. This step takes place in the mitochondria of the maturing red cell and is catalysed by the enzyme *ferrochelatase*. Ferric iron is reduced to the ferrous state, and four of its six available binding positions bind to the four central N atoms on the tetrapyrrole ring. The haem passes into the cytoplasm and the other two binding positions attach it to its globin chain. One of these attachments provides the binding site for oxygen (Fig. 4.6). Four haem–globin complexes join to give a haemoglobin molecule with a binding capacity for four oxygen atoms.

Iron

Iron is present in the body in association with a number of proteins. These include haemoglobin and myoglobin, the transport and storage proteins transferrin and ferritin, the microsomal and mitochondrial cytochromes, which contain haem, and various enzymes. The fact that iron has so many roles may explain the tissue effects of iron deficiency that are unrelated to anaemia, such as abnormalities of the finger nails.

The iron in the body of a normal adult amounts to 3–4 g and consists of haemoglobin (about 60 per cent), storage iron (about 30 per cent), transport iron (less than 1 per cent) and tissue iron, including myoglobin and cytochromes (5–10 per cent). In a normal individual the amount of iron absorbed and lost is small: most of the iron released from damaged or senescent cells is re-used.

There is no physiological means of regulating iron loss. Non-menstruating adults lose about 1 mg per day, in red blood cells lost from the gastrointestinal tract, in biliary excretion and in desquamating epithelial cells from the skin and mucous membranes. In menstruating women, however, iron loss may be up to 100 mg monthly; the iron balance is often precarious and storage iron may be depleted. There is an increased demand for iron during growth and in pregnancy (Table 4.10). Iron requirements in childhood and adolescence are related to growth rate. The highest physiological demand, and therefore the greatest risk of deficiency, occurs in the first year of life and during adolescence. The most important pathological cause of increased iron demand is blood loss, particularly from the gastrointestinal tract.

Table 4.10 Estimated physiological iron requirements

	Requirement (mg/day)
Minimal obligatory loss	0.5–1.0
Growth	
0–1 year	0.7–0.8
1–11 years	0.3
Adolescence	0.5
Normal menstruation	0.5–1.6
Lactation	0.5
Pregnancy*	
Obligatory loss	180 mg
Fetus	250 mg
Placenta	70 mg
Increase in maternal red cells	400 mg
Total	900 mg

* Average total iron requirement. This is accumulated mainly in the second half of pregnancy when the average daily iron requirements could be as high as 6 mg.

Iron absorption

Whatever the cause of increased iron demand, the body responds by increasing the absorption of iron from the food. Most dietary iron is either in the form of haem or in a complexed ferric ion form. The latter is relatively poorly absorbed; food components such as phytates and phosphates bind to it and impair its absorption further. In addition gastric acidity is necessary for absorption of non-haem iron: patients with absent gastric acid (achlorhydria) absorb non-haem iron poorly. Haem iron, on the other hand, is well absorbed, mainly in the duodenum and upper jejunum.

Absorption of iron occurs by active uptake into the intestinal epithelial cells. Haem is taken into the cells intact and its iron released. Free iron thus absorbed binds to the intracellular iron-storing protein *ferritin*. Some iron subsequently leaves the cell and is carried to other parts of the body in the circulating plasma, but much of it remains as ferritin in the cell and is lost when the cell is sloughed off. This mechanism may regulate iron absorption since, when iron is deficient, less ferritin is synthesised and therefore less iron is lost in this way. Conversely in iron overload the large amount of ferritin in the mucosal cells acts to limit iron absorption.

Iron storage

The intracellular protein *ferritin* is a water-soluble molecule that consists of a shell (apoferritin) made up of 24 subunits (Fig. 4.11) surrounding a core containing the iron atoms. These are in the ferric form, as a phosphate–oxide complex. Up to 4500 atoms of iron can be bound to each ferritin molecule. The other storage form of iron in the body is *haemosiderin*, which probably consists of aggregated ferritin molecules. Ferritin is synthesised in response to the availability of iron. It

takes up iron as it enters the cell, stores it in a harmless form and releases it when required; it therefore acts as a safe intracellular store for a necessary but potentially toxic metal ion. Ferritin is also found in very small amounts in the plasma. Its level is related to the amount of storage iron in the body.

Virtually all red cell precursors contain ferritin granules; when these aggregate to produce a particle large enough to be seen by the light microscope, the cells are called *sideroblasts*. Abnormal accumulation of iron in cells also occurs, for example in ring sideroblasts, in which iron accumulates in the mitochondria, forming a ring round the nucleus. The absence of iron particles in marrow red cell precursors is a feature of iron deficiency.

Iron transport

Iron in the plasma is bound to *transferrin*, a β-globulin of molecular weight 77 000. A normal adult has about 3–4 mg of iron in this form and the plasma transferrin is about 30 per cent saturated. Most of the iron entering the plasma comes from the normal breakdown of aged red cells, about 25 mg per day compared with only about 1 mg absorbed daily from the gut. The iron is taken up by the marrow from transferrin at a rate necessary to maintain red cell production. Red cell precursors (p. 40), like other cells requiring iron, have transferrin receptors on their surface. The transferrin binds, delivers its iron into the cell and is then released for use again in iron transport.

Iron kinetics

If radioactive ^{59}Fe is injected into the plasma, the rate of its clearance from the plasma can be measured. This depends largely on the rate at which the erythroid cells are taking it up in erythropoiesis. ^{59}Fe can be used to measure erythropoietic activity since effective erythropoiesis results in the appearance of red cells containing labelled haem in the circulation. In certain disorders, sites of erythropoiesis outside the bone marrow, such as the liver or spleen, are important; these can be identified by their uptake of ^{59}Fe.

BLOOD VOLUME AND RED CELL MASS

The fraction of the volume of a blood sample that is occupied by the red cells is easily measured by centrifuging the sample in a capillary tube and measuring the relative depth of the red cell layer (Fig. 4.12). The measurement obtained is referred to as the *packed cell volume* (PCV) or *haematocrit*.

The plasma volume of an individual can be estimated by injecting a sample of albumin labelled with radioactive iodine into a vein. The plasma level of radioac-

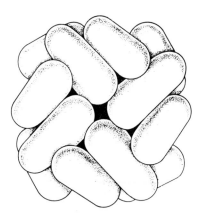

Fig. 4.11 Arrangement of subunits to make up a molecule of apoferritin (From P M Harrison et al 1980 In: Jacobs A & Worwood M (eds) Iron in biochemistry and medicine II Academic Press, London, by courtesy of author and publisher)

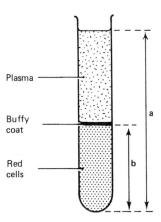

Plasma

Buffy
coat

Red
cells

a

b

Fig. 4.12 Measurement of the haematocrit (packed cell
volume; b/a). Normal figures for men are 0.40–0.54 and for
women 0.35–0.47

tivity after equilibration measures the volume in which
the dose is diluted. Assuming that there are no losses
from the circulation and that none of the label enters
the cells this volume is equal to the plasma volume
(Table 4.13).

A person's total red cell volume can similarly be
measured by injecting a sample of his red cells
previously labelled with an isotope such as ^{51}Cr. The
red cell volume is estimated from the extent of the
dilution of the isotope. The accuracy of this measurement is affected by the amount of ^{51}Cr lost from red
cells and by the loss of cells from the circulation.

From such measurements of plasma and red cell
volume the 'whole-body haematocrit' can be calculated.
If this is compared with the venous haematocrit measured by centrifugation, the whole body haematocrit is
lower than the venous haematocrit by about 10 per cent.
In capillaries, the haematocrit is lower than that in
venous blood; in splenic and bone marrow sinusoids it
is higher. Thus the red cell mass is unevenly distributed
within the blood.

Table 4.13 Typical figures for blood volume, plasma volume
and total red cell volume in adults

	Amount (ml/kg body weight)
Total blood volume	60–80
Plasma volume	40–50
Total red cell volume	
Men	26–32
Women	22–29

Plasma volume measured with ^{131}I-labelled albumin dilution.
Red cell volume measured with ^{51}Cr-labelled red cell
dilution.

Changes in red cell mass
Anaemia is usually defined as a lower than normal
concentration of haemoglobin in the blood. However,
the concentration of haemoglobin does not necessarily
reflect the red cell mass. For example, acute loss of
blood does not cause a fall in haemoglobin concentration
until the volume deficit has been made up by an
increase in plasma volume (haemodilution). Similarly,
a reduction in plasma volume (for example due to extensive burns with leakage of plasma) causes a rise in the
concentration of haemoglobin without a change in the
red cell mass. In pregnancy, both the plasma volume
and the red cell mass rise, but the result is a *fall* in
haemoglobin concentration because the plasma volume
rises disproportionately. In patients with chronic
anaemia the red cell mass and haemoglobin concentration may be very low, the volume being made up by
an expanded plasma volume, while the low concentration of haemoglobin is partly compensated by an
increased cardiac output. Finally, a large increase in red
cell mass (*polycythaemia*) is usually accompanied by a
reduction in plasma volume and a high concentration
of haemoglobin in the blood.

The concentration of haemoglobin in the peripheral
blood, therefore, like the haematocrit, reflects the relative proportions of plasma and red cells, and cannot be
accepted uncritically as a measure of the body's red cell
mass.

Modern automatic blood cell counters measure cell
numbers, cell volumes and haemoglobin concentration.
Derived indices include *mean cell haemoglobin concentration* (MCHC), the *mean cell haemoglobin* (MCH) and
the *mean red cell volume* (MCV). The use of these indices
can be illustrated by the changes seen in iron deficiency
in which the MCV is low (*microcytosis*) and the MCH
is also low (*hypochromia*). A high MCV (*macrocytosis*) is
seen in megaloblastic anaemia (p. 41).

Tissue blood flow and the haematocrit
Delivery of oxygen to tissues is determined by tissue
blood flow and arterial oxygen saturation. Oxygen saturation is determined by ventilation of the lungs, tissue
oxygen demand, cardiac output and by the concentration and physico-chemical state of the haemoglobin
in the blood. All of these can be altered physiologically
in response to a reduction in tissue oxygen availability
(*hypoxia*). For example, the oxygen-delivering capacity
of the haemoglobin is influenced by pH, $P\text{co}_2$ and the
concentration of 2, 3-bisphosphoglycerate in the red
cell (p. 148). The kidney responds to hypoxia by
increasing its output of erythropoietin, which increases
the number of red cells produced. The adaptation of the
body to high altitude, where inspired oxygen pressure
is reduced, is a physiological example of this process.

Tissue blood flow depends on the cardiac output,

local vascular tone, the volume of the circulating blood relative to the capacity of the intravascular compartment, and the viscosity of the blood. Blood viscosity varies with the haematocrit because it is determined largely by red cell deformability (p. 118).

Thus the haematocrit may have opposite effects on tissue blood flow and on arterial oxygen saturation. Paradoxically, a rise in haematocrit, while it may compensate for hypoxia by increasing oxygen carriage, can reduce tissue oxygenation by increasing blood viscosity and so reducing tissue blood flow. Optimal tissue oxygenation occurs at haematocrit values between 30 and 50 per cent.

Plasma viscosity

In normal individuals, the plasma viscosity is remarkably constant and the range of normal values is quite narrow. It depends mainly on the concentration of fibrinogen and globulins. These concentrations change in a wide variety of diseases, and the plasma viscosity is used in clinical laboratories as an index of the activity of such diseases.

The *erythrocyte sedimentation rate* (ESR), which depends partly on similar protein changes in the plasma, is also used for this purpose. In this test, red cells are allowed to sediment in a vertical column of blood and the amount of sedimentation in one hour is measured. High levels of fibrinogen or globulin promote the aggregation of red cells into formations resembling piles of coins (*rouleaux*). The resulting fall in the surface area of the cells exposed to the plasma decreases the stability of the red cell suspension by reducing the 'frictional' interaction between cells and plasma. These tests are non-specific but useful in detecting and assessing the activity of certain diseases.

THE LEUCOCYTES

Blood cells were first classified by the use of polychromatic stains introduced by Paul Ehrlich and modified by Romanowsky. Romanowsky stains contain eosin and methylene blue. At an appropriate pH the former binds to basic materials such as haemoglobin and some cytoplasmic granules, while the latter combines with acidic material such as nucleic acids. Thus, basic substances, often called acidophilic or eosinophilic, stain a red colour, and acidic components stain blue and are called basophilic. Cells whose cytoplasm stains with both are called polychromatic.

Leucocytes are classified into three categories: *granulocytes*, *monocytes* and *lymphocytes* (Table 4.14). The functions of monocytes and lymphocytes are described in Chapter 5.

Table 4.14 Normal leucocyte counts in peripheral blood

	Number
Total white blood cell count	$4-8 \times 10^9/l$
Granulocytes	
Neutrophil	$3.0-7.0 \times 10^9/l$
Eosinophil	$0.1-0.45 \times 10^9/l$
Basophil	$0-0.1 \times 10^9/l$
Monocytes	$0.3-0.7 \times 10^9/l$
Lymphocytes	$1.5-4.0 \times 10^9/l$

These figures are those found in healthy white adults. Racial variations do occur. For example, Africans and Yemeni Jews have lower neurophil counts. At birth the mean neutrophil count is about $12 \times 10^9/l$. Adult levels are reached within a few weeks and no further changes occur throughout life.

Granulocytes

A granulocyte (polymorphonuclear leucocyte, 'polymorph') has a segmented nucleus and abundant cytoplasmic granules. Granulocytes are divided into three groups — neutrophils, eosinophils and basophils — according to the staining behaviour of their granules.

Neutrophils

These are the predominant leucocytes in normal adult blood. In most the nucleus is segmented, that is, divided into between two and four distinct lobes separated by fine strands of chromatin (Fig. 4.15). A lesser degree of segmentation, for example, simply a flattened band-like nucleus, or rudimentary lobes separated by a thick chromatin bridge, is often known as a '*shift to the left*', and implies that the cells are less mature than normal. This may be seen during infections, and suggests to the haematologist that neutrophil turnover is increased because of increased consumption. Increased segmentation of the nucleus, with five or

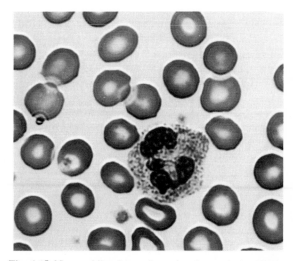

Fig. 4.15 Neutrophil polymorphonuclear leucocyte (× 1340). (Courtesy of R O'Neil)

more separate lobes, is called *hypersegmentation*, and is seen in conditions where cell growth is disturbed, particularly in megaloblastic anaemias (p. 41).

Eosinophils

These distinctive cells have large granules that stain bright pink with the basic dye eosin (Fig. 4.16). The granules are refractile and on electron microscopy are seen to have a core with a crystalline structure. This core contains the *major basic protein*, which is important in the killing of parasites. They also release substances that dampen down mast cell mediated reactions, for example anaphylaxis (p. 52). The nucleus of an eosinophil typically has only two lobes.

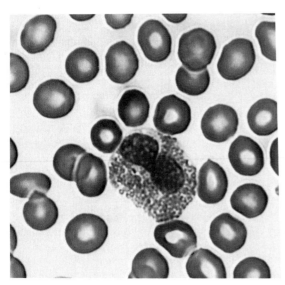

Fig. 4.16 Eosinophil polymorphonuclear leucocyte (× 1340). (Courtesy of R O'Neil)

Basophils

These cells have large, often rather scanty granules that stain a dark blue colour with standard stains. The granules contain histamine, 5-hydroxytryptamine and heparin. These substances have powerful inflammatory, haemostatic and vasomotor effects, and are released in allergic reactions of the atopic or anaphylactic type (p. 52). Immunoglobulin E (p. 46) is important in triggering the release of the basophil granules.

Granulocyte kinetics

The production of granulocytes in the bone marrow is described later. Mature neutrophil polymorphs are present in the body in a number of 'pools'. The first of these is the *marrow reserve*. This pool can rapidly discharge cells into the blood in response to a stimulus such as bacterial endotoxin, and includes metamyelo-

cytes (p. 41) as well as mature cells. Mobilisation of this pool therefore leads to a 'shift to the left' in the appearance of the peripheral blood granulocytes. The *circulating pool* consists of the granulocytes in the circulating blood. The *marginal pool* consists of granulocytes that are 'marginated', or parked, along the walls of capillaries and venules. There are thus two intravascular pools of granulocytes, of roughly equal size, which continuously exchange cells. All of these pools can rapidly provide competent granulocytes to a site of infection when required. Additional granulocytes are obtained through increased production by the marrow but this is a slower response.

HAEMOSTASIS

This is the process by which blood is kept within the blood vessels and also maintained in a fluid state. Haemostasis is activated by damage to the vascular endothelium. Exposed subendothelial tissue attracts platelets, which adhere to the damaged surface. These platelets release substances that attract more platelets and trigger off the plasma coagulation mechanisms to produce a *thrombus* or plug. Such a plug consists of platelets and fibrin, which together give it stability and adhesiveness so that an endothelial defect can be rapidly sealed. Various processes (p. 38) act to confine the process to the injury site, and when the endothelium is repaired the plug is removed by fibrinolytic mechanisms.

The blood vessel wall

The most obvious vascular response to injury is contraction, often transient, of the smooth muscle in the walls of arterioles and venules; this reduces the blood pressure 'downstream' and so is important in the initial haemostatic response to injury. A reduction in the blood flow reduces blood loss and ensures that platelets remain longer at the site of injury. Capillary walls contain no smooth muscle and in these vessels it is the properties of the endothelial cells and subendothelial structures that are important.

Endothelial cells

Endothelial cells have two major roles in haemostasis. The first is to provide an inert surface that does not activate coagulation of circulating blood. The second is to promote haemostatic processes when vascular surfaces are damaged.

The haemostatically 'inert' suface appears to depend on a negative electrical charge on the surface of the cells. This is provided by the glycosaminoglycans of the cell coat or *glycocalyx*. In addition, endothelial cells can release substances such as the platelet-inhibiting prostaglandin *prostacyclin* (p. 39), the fibrinolysis initiator *plasminogen activator* (p. 37) and the coagulation inhibitor *anti-thrombin III* (p. 38). The anticoagulant activity of *protein C* is also greatly enhanced by the endothelial cell surface protein *thrombomodulin* (p. 39). These mechanisms together help to regulate haemostasis and to prevent the undue spread of a localised reaction.

The second role of endothelial cells, the promotion of coagulation mechanisms, is triggered by damage to the endothelium. Loss of endothelial cells exposes sub-endothelial structures, which activate coagulation and promote platelet aggregation. Also, rather like platelets, endothelial cells can release coagulation factors like factor VIII (p. 35) and tissue factor, which participate in haemostatic mechanisms.

Platelets

Platelets are metabolically active anucleate cells formed by fragmentation of the cytoplasm of the megakaryocytes of the bone marrow. Circulating platelets are biconvex discs 2–5 μm in diameter (Fig. 4.17). They have a smooth outer coat called the glycocalyx, which consists of glycosaminoglycans and glycoproteins; these probably play a role in the interaction of platelets with other cells and surfaces. Beneath this coat the platelet is bounded by its plasma membrane. The protein portion of the membrane contains the contractile proteins actin and myosin and also, on the outer surface, the platelet glycoproteins. These are important as specific receptors for the mediation of platelet adhesion, aggregation and release. The lipid component of the membrane includes a number of unsaturated fatty acids derived from the diet. Of these, the most important is *arachidonic acid*, which, on activation of the platelet, is released from its esterified state to participate in the pathways for the synthesis of prostaglandin and thromboxane (p. 34).

The principal structural features of a platelet are shown in Figure 4.18. The plasma membrane invaginates extensively into the interior of the platelet to form the open *canalicular system*. The *microtubule cytoskeleton* is a circumferential band of microtubules that probably acts as a flexible support to maintain the discoid shape of the platelet. Platelets contain a *contractile apparatus* consisting mainly of actin and myosin. They also have a *dense tubular system*, which, like the sarcoplasmic reticulum of muscle cells, provides calcium ions to initiate contraction. Platelets contain a number of organelles, including mitochondria, glycogen granules and lysosomes. Peculiar to platelets are the *alpha granules* and the electron-dense *dense granules*. Alpha granules contain coagulation factors such as fibrinogen and factors V and VIII, and also specific proteins such as β-thromboglobulin, platelet-derived growth factors and platelet factor 4. The dense granules contain adenine nucleotides, mainly ADP, and 5-hydroxytryptamine. All of these substances are released by the activated platelet and play a part in haemostasis.

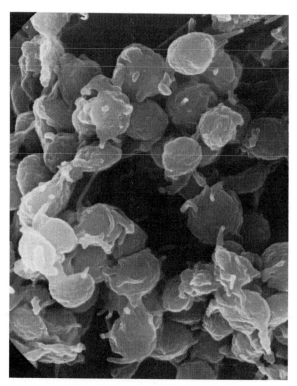

Fig. 4.17 Platelets from normal human blood (scanning electron micrograph × 9200). (Courtesy of D G Newell).

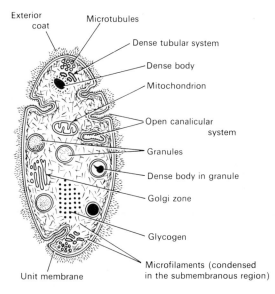

Fig. 4.18 Fine structure of a platelet

Platelet function

The peripheral blood normally contains $140 \times 10^9 - 400 \times 10^9$ platelets per litre. When the number is reduced below $80 \times 10^9/l$, haemostasis may be impaired. With a platelet count below $20 \times 10^9/l$, spontaneous bleeding, that is bleeding not caused by even minor trauma, may occur. A physiological rise in the platelet count (thrombocytosis) occurs in response to acute or chronic bleeding; it results from an increase in platelet production but the mechanism is not understood. It is possible that a humoral factor, *thrombopoietin*, plays a part in this response, but its nature and physiological role are not clear.

Platelet activation

The initiating event in platelet activation is *adhesion*. This occurs when the subendothelium of a blood vessel, and particularly its collagen, is exposed by endothelial cell damage. The interaction with collagen requires the presence of a glycoprotein receptor in the platelet surface and also the *von Willebrand factor* (factor VIII vWF), a plasma protein that acts as a bridge between the collagen and the receptor. The binding of this factor to the receptor leads to local changes in the platelet membrane. In the first of these the membrane phospholipids are rearranged so that negatively charged lipids are exposed on the outside of the cells; these phospholipids are then able to take part in the coagulation system. The second change is the release of small amounts of calcium from the membrane. This leads to alterations in the microtubule structure and to the polymerisation of actin and myosin. The microfilaments contract and the platelet changes shape, becoming a sphere with long finger-like processes (pseudopodia) on its surface. This contraction leads to the *release reaction*, in which the dense and alpha granules release their contents after fusing with the surface membrane or the canalicular system.

The secretion derived from the dense granules includes ADP and 5HT, which themselves promote *platelet aggregation*. This in turn helps to recruit more platelets to the forming clot. The contents of alpha granules include the coagulation factors fibrinogen, factor V and factor VIII. These factors, together with platelet membrane phospholipid, contribute to the formation of a fibrin network within the platelet plug.

Platelet prostaglandins

Arachidonic acid, an essential polyunsaturated fatty acid, is the precursor for prostaglandin synthesis (p. 233). In 'resting' platelets this is present in an esterified form as part of the membrane lipid. Activation of platelets, and in particular the release of calcium into the cytoplasm, leads to the activation of *phospholipases*, which cleave off the arachidonic acid so that it can enter

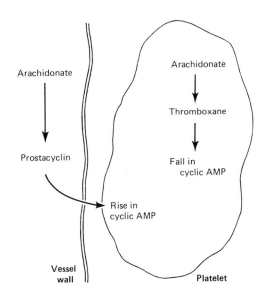

Fig. 4.19 Opposing roles of prostacyclin (PGI_2) and thromboxane (TXA_2) in altering cyclic AMP levels within a platelet and so in the control of platelet aggregation. (After S Moncada and J R Vane 1978 British Medical Bulletin 34:129)

the prostaglandin synthetic pathways. Another substance released is *platelet activating factor* (PAF), a phospholipid causing platelet aggregation. A platelet enzyme, cyclo-oxygenase, converts arachidonic acid to cyclic endoperoxidases; from these, various prostaglandins and degradation products are formed. The most important product in platelets is *thromboxane A2*. This is a potent platelet-aggregating and vasoconstricting agent, which thus opposes the action of the prostacyclin derived from the endothelial cells (Fig. 4.19).

Aggregation

Platelet aggregation is assessed in the laboratory by observing changes in the light-scattering behaviour of stirred platelet-rich plasma when substances such as ADP, adrenaline, 5HT, thrombin and collagen are added. All of these act by binding to specific membrane receptors. The adrenaline receptor is of the α-adrenergic type (p. 230); binding leads to the inhibition of platelet adenyl cyclase. The reduction in cyclic AMP levels leads to a rise in the calcium level within the platelet and so promotes the calcium-mediated activities described earlier. Thrombin and collagen also act through adenyl cyclase inhibition.

All of these agonists are important in vivo. ADP is released from damaged endothelial cells, platelets and red cells. Thromboxane A_2 and PAF are also important. Fibrinogen is essential for aggregation in every case; it binds to specific surface receptors, linking the platelets together.

Coagulation

Coagulation is the process by which insoluble fibrin is generated from soluble fibrinogen in the plasma. The system of coagulation factors involved is often referred to as a 'cascade'; many of the factors are protease enzymes that occur as inactive proenzymes until activated, when they catalyse the activation of the next factor in the series.

This succession of steps has two important features. The first is the 'amplification' of a small initial stimulus to give a large amount of the final product. The second is that control of individual reactions in the series allows 'fine tuning' of the process as a whole. Cascades of proteolytic enzymes are found in other extracellular processes, including the complement system (p. 48), the kinins and the fibrinolytic system.

The coagulation factors

Table 4.20 lists the factors. In each case the activated factor is designated by *a*; for example thrombin (activated prothrombin) is also known as factor IIa.

The coagulation factors are traditionally classified into three groups: the vitamin K-dependent group, the contact factors and the 'fibrinogen group'. The vitamin K-dependent group — factors II, VII, IX and X — are synthesised in the liver. They have in common their content of the amino acid residue, γ-carboxy-

Table 4.20 International nomenclature of blood coagulation factors with synonyms. The Roman numerals reflect the order in which the factors where discovered.

Factor	Synonyms
I	Fibrinogen
II*	Prothrombin
III	Thromboplastin (platelet membrane phospholipid)
IV	Calcium
V	Labile factor, proaccelerin
VII*	Stable factor, proconvertin
VIII	Antihaemophilic globulin (AHG), antihaemophilic factor A
XI*	Christmas factor, plasma thromboplastin component (PTC), antihaemophilic factor B
X*	Stuart–Prower factor
XI	Plasma thromboplastin antecedent (PTA)
XII	Hageman factor
XIII	Fibrin stabilising factor, fibrinoligase
HMWK	High-molecular-weight kininogen, Fitzgerald factor
Prekallikrein	Fletcher factor

* These factors are vitamin K dependent and are affected by the anticoagulant drugs (coumarins and indanediones) used in the treatment of thrombotic diseases.

glutamic acid. The γ-carboxy groups are needed for the calcium-dependent binding of the factors to a phospholipid surface. The essential step of γ-carboxylation of glutamic acid residues requires vitamin K and lack of this vitamin causes spontaneous bleeding. Vitamin K is fat-soluble and is acquired mainly from the diet and from synthesis by intestinal bacteria. Deficiency can result from malabsorption or from the suppression of intestinal bacteria by antibiotics. Apart from prothrombin, the vitamin K-dependent factors are not consumed during coagulation and are therefore present in serum.

The fibrinogen group — factors I, V, VIII and XIII — are consumed during coagulation and are therefore not present in serum. Apart from factor V, they also have the property of precipitating from frozen plasma as it is thawed. This is called *cryoprecipitation* and is used for concentrating factors VIII, XIII and fibrinogen for use in treatment.

The contact group comprises factors XI and XII, together with *high-molecular-weight kininogen* (Fitzgerald factor) and *prekallikrein* (Fletcher factor). They are involved in the initiation of coagulation by contact with a foreign surface. They are not consumed during coagulation.

Calcium

For many years, substances that bind calcium ions have been known to prevent coagulation in stored blood or plasma. Citrate is used in blood banks for this purpose, and oxalate and ethylenediamine tetracetic acid (EDTA) are often used as anticoagulants in laboratory specimens. In the coagulation cascade the main role of calcium appears to be in binding factors of the vitamin K-dependent group to a phospholipid surface to ensure the apposition of each factor to its substrate. The calcium seems to act as a bridge between the phospholipid and the γ-carboxyglutamyl groups on the factor molecule.

Coagulation cascade

This is divided for convenience into three parts: the *intrinsic pathway* and the *extrinsic pathway*, which are alternative routes to the production of factor Xa, and the *common pathway*, the process initiated by factor Xa leading to the production of fibrin (Fig. 4.21).

The intrinsic pathway begins with the contact activation of factor XII by exposure to certain negatively charged surfaces. Such surfaces include collagen, platelet membranes and, in the test tube, glass or kaolin. Binding of factor XII results in cleavages of its peptide chain, producing an active enzyme that can then activate more factor XII and also convert prekallikrein to kallikrein. The latter also rapidly converts further factor XII to XIIa. This is an example of 'positive feedback'. High-molecular-weight kininogen is required in

Intrinsic pathway   Extrinsic pathway

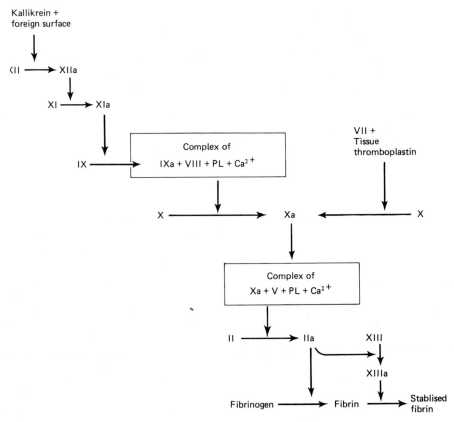

Fig. 4.21 The coagulation 'cascade'. 'Intrinsic' means intrinsic to plasma since all the factors can be generated from plasma. The extrinsic pathway requires tissue factors from outside the plasma. Extrinsic coagulation is more rapid and less inhibited than the intrinsic process, fewer steps being involved. PL = platelet phospholipid (Factor III)

these reactions. The cleavage of factor XI by factor XIIa produces factor XIa, which itself cleaves factor IX to produce factor IXa.

Factor IXa then forms a complex with factor VIII; the binding of this complex to a phospholipid surface involves its γ-carboxyglutamic acid residues and calcium ions. Factor X is also bound to the complex and the resulting interaction of IXa and X leads to the activation of X to Xa.

Factor VIII circulates as a complex of two separate proteins, factor VIII coagulant (factor VIII:C) and the von Willebrand factor (VIII:vWF). The von Willebrand factor is a large multimeric molecule that promotes platelet adhesion to the subendothelium (p. 38). Factor VIIIC is a smaller molecule that is a cofactor in the activation of factor X. Activation by thrombin enhances its cofactor function. The site of VIIIC synthesis is not known; the von Willebrand factor is synthesised by megakaryocytes and endothelial cells.

The extrinsic pathway is initiated by an interaction

between a *tissue factor* and factor VII, resulting in the activation of factor VII. The tissue factor is a phospholipid protein found in all tissues and is presumably released by tissue damage. Factor VII is cleaved on activation, to produce the active protease factor VIIa. This activation requires tissue factor, but is also promoted by other activated proteases including thrombin, factor XIIa, factor IXa and factor Xa itself. There is thus extensive interaction between the intrinsic and extrinsic systems. Activated factor VIIa cleaves factor X to produce factor Xa; this reaction also requires the presence of tissue factor.

In the common pathway, factor Xa, generated by either pathway, binds via its γ-carboxyglutamic acid residues to a phospholipid surface, much as factor IXa does. The phospholipid is provided by activated platelets (p. 34). Prothrombin also binds to the platelet membrane, and binding of factor V as cofactor permits the factor Xa to cleave the prothrombin in such a way as to produce *thrombin*.

Fibrinogen

This is a dimeric molecule, each half consisting of three parallel polypeptide chains (α, β and γ) linked by disulphide bridges. The two halves are joined by disulphide bonds. Each dimer therefore consists of six polypeptide chains and has a molecular weight of 340 000. The action of *thrombin* is to cleave off small fragments from the amino-terminal ends of the α and β chains: these fragments are known as fibrinopeptides A and B. Their presence in the plasma is an indicator of thrombin activity. These cleavages appear to expose sites on the fibrinogen molecule at which inter-chain hydrogen bonds can occur, allowing the molecules to polymerise together to form *fibrin*.

The fibrin so formed is unstable and the clot is easily disrupted. In the next step, stabilisation of the fibrin, covalent bonds form between adjacent monomers in the fibrin molecule. *Fibrin stabilising factor* (factor XIII) mediates this process. Factor XIII is a proenzyme that is activated by thrombin to form *fibrinoligase*. This enzyme is adsorbed on the fibrin, where it promotes covalent bonding between adjacent chains. The *cross-linked fibrin* that results is mechanically and chemically stable.

The fibrinolytic system

The haemostatic system prevents loss of blood from damaged vessels. For this process to lead to the restoration of the continuity of the endothelium and the resumption of normal blood flow through the vessel, a means of dismantling a thrombus, when appropriate, is clearly needed. This function is served by the fibrinolytic system (Fig. 4.22).

Fibrinolysis involves the splitting of peptide bonds within the chains making up the fibrin. Various fragments are produced and these, *fibrin degradation prod-* *ucts*, can be measured as an index of fibrinolytic activity. The enzyme that promotes these cleavages is the trypsin-like protease *plasmin*. This circulates as an inactive precursor, *plasminogen*, a glycoprotein synthesised mainly in the liver.

During the formation of a fibrin clot, plasminogen is bound to the fibrin and this adsorbed plasminogen is important for the subsequent lysis of the clot. Circulating plasmin is normally inactivated by binding to *antiplasmin* and other protease inhibitors. Plasminogen bound to fibrin is, however, protected from this inhibitory activity; if plasminogen activator from the endothelial cell is present, plasmin is produced, which leads to lysis of the fibrin (Fig. 4.23).

Plasminogen activation

This involves the cleavage of a specific peptide bond to produce a two-chain molecule. Other cleavages and conformational changes occur, leading to both increased proteolytic activity and increased affinity for fibrin. A variety of *plasminogen activators* are recognised in blood, tissues and secretions. *Tissue activator* is a tissue-bound protein with protease activity; it is found in particularly high concentrations in heart muscle and uterus, and also in certain tumour cells. *Vascular activator* is found in vascular endothelial cells, especially in the veins and venules. It may enter the circulation in response to such stimuli as exercise and the injection of adrenaline, and also venous occlusion.

In unstressed individuals, a low level of plasminogen activator activity is detectable in plasma. This plasma activator is probably identical to tissue activator and vascular activator. As well as being released from vascular endothelium, the plasminogen activator can be generated by the action of the contact factors in the coagulation pathway. Kallikrein, factor XIIa and factor

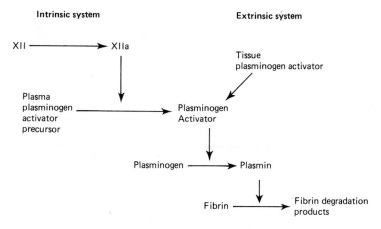

Fig. 4.22 The fibrinolytic system

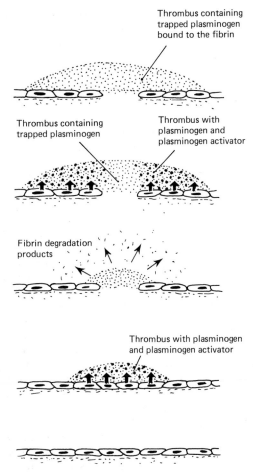

Thrombus containing trapped plasminogen bound to the fibrin

Thrombus containing trapped plasminogen

Thrombus with plasminogen and plasminogen activator

Fibrin degradation products

Thrombus with plasminogen and plasminogen activator

Fig. 4.23 The role of endothelial factors in limiting the size of a thrombus. Plasminogen activator, released from intact endothelial cells, activates plasminogen bound to fibrin in the overlying thrombus. The plasmin formed here cleaves the fibrin to form fibrin degradation products. Where the thrombus overlies damaged endothelial cells, plasminogen activator is not available until the endothelium is repaired. Other endothelial factors, such as prostacyclin, surface glycosaminoglycans and thrombomodulin, can also act locally to limit the spread of a thrombus. For simplicity, platelets are not shown in the thrombus

XIa are all able to generate plasminogen activator from a plasma precursor. This is the 'intrinsic' pathway of fibrinolysis (Fig. 4.22).

Plasminogen activators are found in secretions where they may play a role in maintaining the patency of small ducts. Urokinase, a plasminogen activator in urine, has been intensively studied and used clinically as a fibrinolysis-promoting agent.

Inhibitors and regulators of haemostasis

It is in the nature of a cascade system that a small stimulus leads to an explosive response, unless control is exerted at several points in the system. Various processes regulate the coagulation system but the endothelial cell is particularly important.

Blood flow

The movement of blood past a site of active haemostasis dilutes and carries away activated products that are generated locally. This limits the spread of a thrombus beyond the damaged site. Obstruction of a vessel causing stasis of the blood predisposes to extension of a thrombus. Stasis without endothelial damage does not, however, initiate thrombus formation.

Physical localisation

Vascular damage leads to aggregation, adhesion and activation of platelets. These, then, provide a phospholipid surface that is fixed and therefore localises the coagulation process. Endothelial cell products also act locally, either inhibiting or promoting haemostasis (Fig. 4.23).

Role of the liver

The liver is the site of synthesis of factors I, II, V, VII, IX, X, XI, XII and XIII, as well as of the various plasma antiproteases such as antithrombin III, α_2 macroglobulin and α_2 antiplasmin. It also produces plasminogen and protein C. In addition it clears activated factors from the circulation, and thereby plays an important role in regulation of haemostasis. Liver disease can, therefore, produce a variety of abnormalities of haemostasis depending upon which functions are most impaired. For example, a severe bleeding tendency can result from decreased coagulation factor synthesis, but a thrombotic tendency may also be present due to reduced synthesis of protease inhibitors and reduced hepatic clearance of activated factors. Excessive fibrinolysis may occur by the same mechanisms.

Plasma protease inhibitors

Several of these are important in haemostasis. They are *antithrombin III, antiplasmin, α_1-macroglobulin, α_1-antitrypsin*, and *C1 activator*. Antithrombin III is the most important natural inhibitor of coagulation. It forms a stable complex with activated factors, especially thrombin and factors Xa, IXa and XIa. Formation of the complex leads to inactivation of the factor, and the complex itself is removed by the macrophages, particularly in the liver.

Heparin

This is a glycosaminoglycan found in mast cells. It binds to antithrombin III and greatly increases its inhibitory activity. Heparin is useful clinically as an anticoagulant. Its physiological role is uncertain since little, if any, heparin circulates in the plasma. However several glycosaminoglycans in the glycocalyx of endo-thelial cells can interact with antithrombin III in a heparin-like manner to inactivate nearby proteases. They are not consumed in the process, but behave catalytically and remain on the surface as long as it is intact, providing protection against proteases and discouraging fibrin deposition.

Protein C

This is a plasma proenzyme with several features in common with prothrombin and factors VII, IX and X. In particular it is vitamin K dependent and on acti-vation has trypsin-like protease activity. It specifically cleaves and inactivates factors V and VIII. It is activated by a complex formed between the endothelial surface protein *thrombomodulin* and thrombin; the latter is simultaneously inactivated. Protein C also stimulates fibrinolysis by causing the release of plasminogen acti-vator into the plasma.

Prostacyclin

This is the major physiological inhibitor of platelet aggregation. It is synthesised and released by intact endothelial cells in response to thrombin. It is very unstable and acts only locally to confine platelet aggre-gation to the site of endothelial injury.

Feedback loops

Finally, the enzymes generated by the coagulation system are themselves able to inhibit further activation by feedback loops. Examples include the inhibition of factors VIII and V by thrombin and protein C. In addition, fibrin helps to inactivate thrombin by binding it.

Drugs affecting haemostasis

Heparin is used clinically and, given by injection, has an immediate anticoagulant effect. Coumarin drugs such as *warfarin* are vitamin K analogues and interfere with carboxylation of glutamic acid residues in the synthesis of the vitamin K–dependent factors, so that inactive forms of prothrombin and factors VII, IX and X are produced.

Aspirin causes acetylation of cyclo-oxygenase in plate-lets and therefore inhibits the production of throm-boxane A_2 and so inhibits platelet aggregation.

Disorders of coagulation

The inherited coagulation disorders are rare, but their study has provided much information about the various coagulation factors. The commonest disorder is *haemo-philia A*, in which factor VIIIC is deficient. Its preva-lence is about 1 in 20 000 in the UK. Factor IX deficiency (*Christmas disease, haemophilia B*) is about one-fifth as common. Both conditions cause severe

bleeding problems if the level of the deficient factor is less than 1 per cent of the normal. Von Willebrand's disease, in which vWF is deficient, has a similar preva-lence but severe disease is much rarer.

HAEMOPOIESIS

The earliest site of blood cell formation (haemopoiesis) in the embryo is in mesenchymal cell clusters in the yolk sac, in the third week of gestation. In these clusters or *blood islands*, the peripheral cells join other clusters to form a rudimentary vascular system, while the central cells differentiate into haemoglobin-producing cells. These primitive erythroblasts do not, however, lose their nuclei during maturation, as adult erythrocytes do.

Yolk-sac stem cells migrate into the liver, which, by the middle of the third month, is the major site of haemopoiesis. The spleen, lymph nodes and thymus also contribute to fetal blood cell formation. Hepatic erythropoiesis declines in importance after the sixth

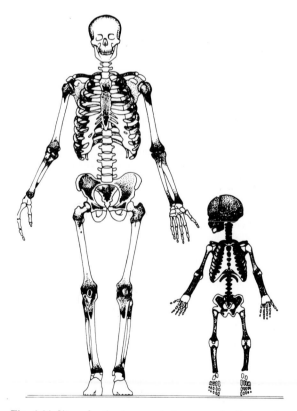

Fig. 4.24 Sites of active haemopoietic marrow (red marrow) in children and adults. There is a similar amount of red marrow (1000–1500 g) in each, despite the differences in body weight. (From H R Bierman 1961 In: MacFarlane R G & Robb-Smith A H T (eds) Functions of the blood Blackwell Scientific, Oxford, p. 357)

month of gestation, but persists until around the time of birth.

Blood cell production begins in the bone marrow at the fourth month of intrauterine life, and in the third trimester the marrow is the major site of haemopoiesis. At birth almost every bone in the body contains active (red) marrow. During growth the volume of this red marrow does not increase and in adults active haemopoiesis is confined to the central skeleton (vertebrae, ribs, upper femora and pelvis) and to the ends of the long bones (Fig. 4.24). The rest of the skeleton contains inactive (fatty or yellow) marrow. The red marrow can expand if necessary, for example when there is excessive destruction of red cells (*haemolysis*): In adults with haemolysis red marrow is found in the shafts of long bones. In children with severe chronic haemolysis expansion of the bone marrow can lead to disturbances of bone growth, producing deformities. Since the bones are fully occupied by red marrow, the resumption of hepatic and splenic haemopoiesis may occur in such children.

Bone marrow structure and function

The red bone marrow is soft and vascular, filling the intertrabecular spaces of the bone. The nutrient arteries of the bone give off branches, the arterioles of which enter the marrow sinusoids. The sinusoids drain into the central vein draining the bone. Sinusoids are lined by endothelium upon a basement membrane, and are supported externally by adventitial cells. The spaces between the sinusoids contain the haemopoietic cells. The walls of the sinusoids have gaps that allow mature cells from the marrow to enter the blood. In some way not yet understood, immature cells are normally prevented from entering the circulation by a marrow-blood barrier.

Before they enter the circulation, the blood cells mature within the marrow. At an early stage they enter the maturation sequence of a specific 'cell line' and remain committed to that sequence. The earliest committed progenitor cells in one cell line are not morphologically distinguishable from cells committed to other cell lines; as they develop they acquire recognisable attributes of a particular cell line, for example haemoglobin in the erythroid cell line.

The marrow contains a self-renewing population of stem cells, from which committed progenitor cells are derived. A number of *growth factors* have been identified; these promote the growth of cells committed to individual cell lines, for example erythropoietin in the case of the red cell line or colony stimulating factors for granulocytic or monocyte cell lines. These are identified by their activity in promoting colony growth in agar.

As well as growth factors, an important determinant for haemopoietic cell growth is the marrow micro-environment. This is the microstructural arrangement of cells and stroma that is necessary for haemopoiesis. There is evidence that interaction between haemopoietic cells, fibroblasts, fat cells, endothelial cells and the other cells in the marrow together produce the essential conditions for haemopoiesis, although the exact nature of such interactions is not yet fully understood.

Haemopoiesis and maturation

Erythropoiesis

The earliest morphologically recognisable red cell precursor is the *proerythroblast*. It is equipped for haemoglobin production with a large amount of cytoplasmic RNA. During maturation, the amount of RNA decreases and the amount of haemoglobin increases. Thus, on Romanowsky staining, the colour of the cytoplasm changes progressively from deep blue (basophilic) through purple (polychromatic) to the red colour of the mature erythrocyte.

At the same time the nucleus is also changing. The proerythroblast is initially able to synthesise DNA and about four cell divisions occur in these cells. As the concentration of haemoglobin in the cell rises (the *early polychromatic erythroblast*), the capacity for division is lost, and the metabolic resources of the cell are devoted largely to haemoglobin synthesis. At the same time the cell nucleus becomes denser and smaller (*pyknotic*), with clumping together of the chromatin strands. The DNA loses its function and the capacity for RNA synthesis is therefore lost. The nucleus is finally extruded, leaving a *reticulocyte*, which enters the blood.

Reticulocytes are so called because, on staining with a vital dye such as brilliant cresyl blue, the ribosomes clump together to form a visible network or reticulum. They are therefore RNA-containing non-nucleated erythrocytes. Reticulocytes undergo further maturation for 1 or 2 days in the bone marrow and for another day or two in the peripheral blood. During this time mitochondria and ribosomes disappear, leaving mature erythrocytes. The percentage of reticulocytes in the blood provides an index of the activity of erythropoiesis; a normal figure is between 1 and 2 per cent, reflecting the erythropoiesis needed to replace the senescent red cells lost from the circulation. A few cells normally die during erythropoiesis (*ineffective erythropoiesis* or *intramedullary haemolysis*). The numbers lost in this way are greatly increased in megaloblastic anaemia (p. 41) and in other blood disorders.

Granulopoiesis

During maturation granulocytes undergo nuclear and cytoplasmic changes comparable to those described for erythrocytes. The earliest morphologically recognisable cell is the myeloblast; the subsequent sequence is promyelocyte — myelocyte — metamyelocyte — juvenile form — segmented granulocyte. The myelocyte is the most mature form capable of division. The myeloblast is a relatively large cell, and the cell becomes smaller as it matures. The promyelocyte has very prominent *primary granules*, which normally disappear during maturation: in infections, however, they may persist as 'toxic granulation' in mature neutrophils. The *specific granules* (neutrophil, eosinophil or basophil) are present in the myelocyte and remain prominent in the mature segmented forms (Fig. 4.15 and 4.16).

Nuclear maturation consists of a progressive condensation of chromatin, and the nucleus shrinks and darkens. It then becomes indented and elongated, and is finally segmented with fine strands joining the segments together.

Megakaryopoiesis

Maturation of the recognisable precursors of megakaryocytes involves the replication of DNA without division of the nucleus or cytoplasm (*endomitosis*). The earliest recognisable form, the *megakaryoblast*, already contains twice the normal amount of DNA but is no longer able to divide. The next stage, the *basophilic megakaryocyte*, has a very basophilic cytoplasm, reflecting the many ribosomes actively engaged in protein synthesis, particularly of granules and membranes. DNA synthesis falls off at this stage, when most of the cells contain eight times the normal diploid amount of DNA. The final stage is the *granular megakaryocyte*, which has lost much of its RNA. Its cytoplasm contains many granules and the *demarcation membrane system*, branching throughout the cell and communicating with the outside. This cell develops pseudopodia, which enter sinusoids, finally breaking up to release individual platelets into the circulation. Megakaryocytes also enter the circulation, lodging in the lungs where they may well be capable of platelet generation.

Megaloblastic haemopoiesis

The vitamins folic acid and vitamin B_{12} (cobalamin) are needed for the synthesis of DNA. When either vitamin is deficient, impaired DNA synthesis causes morphological abnormalities in the nuclei of dividing cells. The cells are also abnormally large (*megaloblasts*). Nuclear maturation is delayed and the normal clumping of chromatin fails, but cytoplasmic maturation and haemoglobin production are unimpaired. Many of the abnormal cells are unable to enter the circulation and are destroyed by the marrow macrophages.

Vitamin B_{12}

This is synthesised only by certain micro-organisms. The dietary sources for man are foods of animal origin. Absorption of vitamin B_{12} occurs in the terminal ileum. To be absorbed, the vitamin must first be bound to a glycoprotein called *intrinsic factor*, which is secreted by the parietal cells of the stomach. Damage to these cells is the underlying cause of *pernicious anaemia*, the commonest cause of vitamin B_{12} deficiency.

The normal daily requirement of vitamin B_{12} is about 2 μg. The body stores are normally 1–5 mg, so that deficiency may take several years to develop. Deficiency due to dietary lack occurs in individuals who eat no animal products (*vegans*).

Folic acid

This is synthesised by plant leaves and by many bacteria. Dietary sources include vegetables, but also animal products, such as liver and kidney, which are sites of storage. Folic acid is absorbed mainly in the jejunum and duodenum. Deficiency may be due to malabsorption or to dietary lack; it also occurs when demand is increased, especially in pregnancy. The normal daily requirement is 100–200 mg and normal stores are between 10 and 20 mg. Therefore deficiency appears within a few months of stopping the intake or absorption of folic acid.

FURTHER READING

Born G V R, Begent N A, Cusack N J 1984 Functional physiology of platelets. In: Biggs R, Rizza C R (eds) Human blood coagulation, haemostasis and thrombosis, 3rd edn. Blackwell Scientific, Oxford, pp 319–348

Chanarin I, Brozovic M, Tidmarsh E, Waters D A W 1984 Blood and its diseases, 3rd edn. Churchill Livingstone, Edinburgh

Gordon M Y, Barrett A J 1985 Normal haemopoiesis. In: Bone marrow disorders. Blackwell Scientific, Oxford, pp 1–136

Ogston D, Bennett B 1985 The blood coagulation cascade. In: Poller L (ed) Recent advances in blood coagulation. Churchill Livingstone, Edinburgh, pp 1–10

Ogston D 1983 The fibrinolytic enzyme system, chapter 4. In: The physiology of haemostasis. Croom Helm, London

Williams W J, Beutler E, Ersler A J, Lichtman M A (eds) 1983 Hematology, 3rd edn. McGraw Hill, New York

5

Immunity and the defence mechanisms against foreign substances

This chapter is concerned with the body's defences against foreign materials such as bacteria, viruses and also proteins from other animals. Some of the mechanisms are innate (or non-specific) and not dependent on previous exposure of a person to the foreign substance. Other defence mechanisms, particularly the specific immune response, operate only when a person has been previously exposed to a particular substance.

Innate defence mechanisms
Innate defence mechanisms exist in various parts of the body. For example, skin has an outer horny layer that acts as a barrier to the entry of bacteria; desquamation of this layer assists the removal of micro-organisms. Sweat and sebaceous secretions contain bacteriostatic substances, and the normal harmless flora of staphylococci and diphtheroids provides nutritional competition for invading micro-organisms. This combination of a barrier effect with inhibitory substances, a harmless commensal flora, and movement that reduces the accumulation of organisms, is a regular feature of innate immunity in other parts of the body.

The respiratory tract, the nose, mouth and pharynx always have commensal micro-organisms. In the trachea and bronchi, the cilia of the mucosal membranes propel mucus, which contains trapped organisms, into the larynx, from which it is coughed into the pharynx and either swallowed or expectorated. In the intestinal tract, gastric juice is inhibitory to most micro-organisms, and the movement of contents down the small intestine prevents stagnation and growth of large populations of micro-organisms. The contents of the large intestine, however, are relatively stagnant and include vast numbers of bacteria, which play a part in the nutrition of the host (p. 217) and also prevent colonisation by more harmful organisms. Competition by the faecal flora of the colon has an inhibitory effect.

Some mechanisms of innate immunity, such as the presence of, *lysozyme* are more specific. This enzyme, found in various tissues but particularly in the tears that bathe the eyes, acts by destroying the cross-linkages of the cell walls of some bacteria, an action similar to that

of the antibiotic penicillin. Destruction of the cell wall leads to swelling and disintegration of the organism because it can no longer resist the osmotic tension of the surrounding fluids.

Effector immunity
In the tissues and blood, phagocytic cells ingest and destroy foreign particles. These include the polymor-

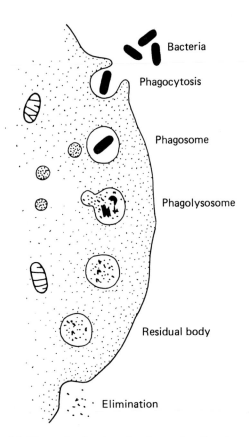

Bacteria

Phagocytosis

Phagosome

Phagolysosome

Residual body

Elimination

Fig. 5.1 The mode of action of a phagocytic cell such as a polymorphonuclear leucocyte or a macrophage. A bacterium is ingested by pinocytosis and lysosomal enzymes are poured into the resulting vacuole

42

phonuclear leucocytes of the blood and the larger cells of the *macrophage system*, namely the monocytes in the blood and the histiocytes in the tissues. These cellular actions are together known as *effector immunity*. The process of phagocytosis is shown in Figure 5.1.

The polymorphonuclear leucocytes (p. 32) provide an important early defence against bacterial invasion by migrating from the blood to the sites where bacteria are multiplying. These cells are capable of engulfing and digesting many of the bacteria that cause acute infections; some bacteria are engulfed but not digested. The ingestion of foreign particles, such as bacteria, or of some endogenous material such as damaged erythrocytes, is enhanced when they are coated by specific antibodies. This process is known as *opsonisation* (p. 47) and complement (p. 48) is also involved. Bacteria are destroyed, not only by lysosomal enzymes but also by hydrogen peroxide produced within the cell in glucose metabolism. This mechanism is initiated by phagocytosis.

Many bacterial infections are controlled at an early stage by the local action of polymorphonuclear leucocytes; pus contains the remains of these cells. If an infection is too severe to be controlled in this way, bacteria escape into the blood vessels and lymphatics and are carried to the lymph nodes and spleen. There they are trapped by the macrophages (p. 49), which play a part in stimulating the immune response.

Specific immunity
Substances capable of stimulating immune responses are known as *antigens* and generally have a molecular weight greater than 5000. Examples include proteins, polysaccharides (such as those of bacterial cell walls) and complex lipids. There are two kinds of specific immune mechanism: *humoral immunity*, which involves the production of antibodies, and *cell-mediated immunity*, in which special T-lymphocytes react directly with foreign material. Both mechanisms involve lymphocytes.

The lymphocytes
Lymphocytes are formed in the bone marrow in adults; in the fetus, the yolk sac, the liver and possibly the thymus are additional sources. Lymphocytes are found in all tissues except the central nervous system. The lymphatic tissue contains 100 g of lymphocytes, the bone marrow 70 g and the blood 3 g; the total amount in the body is about 1300 g. Stress or the administration of adrenal corticoids inhibits the production of lymphocytes.

Lymphocytes are continually circulating from the blood into the tissues and then into lymphatic vessels and back to the blood (Fig. 5.2). This circulation of lymphocytes is of great importance in ensuring that all parts of the body are surveyed for foreign material. In addition, when lymphocytes pass through the lymph

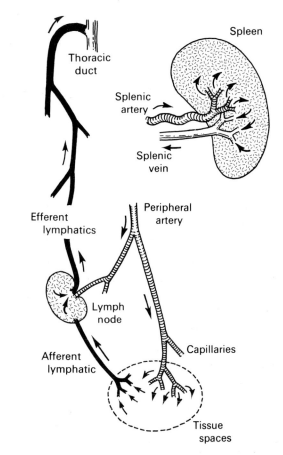

Fig. 5.2 The main pathways of lymphocyte circulation

nodes and spleen they are brought into close proximity to macrophages containing foreign antigens.

There are two classes of lymphocytes, T-lymphocytes and B-lymphocytes. Their different functions are described below. T- and B-lymphocytes cannot be distinguished by light microscopy but can be identified by complicated *in vitro* tests. About 75 per cent of circulating lymphocytes are T-cells.

The thymus
The thymus consists of a peripheral cortex densely packed with lymphocytes and a central medulla in which the lymphocytes are less numerous. The medulla also contains epithelial cells and 'Hassall's corpuscles', spherical structures composed of keratin and concentric layers of spindle-shaped cells that may be macrophages.

In mammals the thymus arises from the endoderm of the third and fourth branchial clefts and usually consists of two or more lobes on each side of the midline. In the evolutionary development of the immune response, the thymus appears at the same time as immunological activity. In the fetus, the thymus is the first tissue in which lymphocytes can be recognised. In the young child the thymus is large and very active. It contains many dividing lymphocytes and the thymus appears to be the organ responsible for the production of 'competent' T-lymphocytes (see below).

After adolescence the thymus becomes much smaller. As a result the lymphoid tissues dependent on it, the spleen and lymph nodes, are less active and the effectiveness of cell-mediated immunity declines.

CELLULAR IMMUNITY

The T-lymphocytes (thymus-dependent lymphocytes) are concerned with cellular immunity and once stimulated they migrate to sites of foreign antigens like tuberculous lesions or grafts such as transplanted kidneys or skin grafts taken from another person (allografts). T-lymphocytes also regard as 'foreign' some antigens found in malignant neoplasms.

The T-lymphocyte is derived from a stem cell in the bone marrow, which migrates to the thymus and is

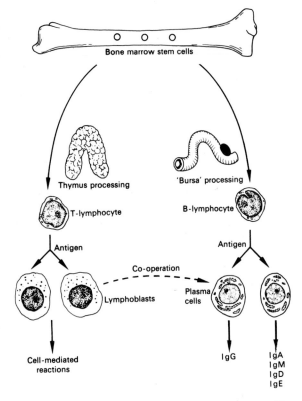

Fig. 5.3 Processing of bone marrow cells by the thymus and by the lymphoid tissue of the alimentary tract to become immunocompetent T- and B-lymphocytes, respectively. On antigenic stimulation, lymphocytes proliferate and transform themselves into lymphoblasts and plasma cells. (From Roitt I M 1971 Essential immunology. Blackwell Scientific, Oxford

there processed to become effective or *immunologically competent* (Fig. 5.3). This process is marked by the acquisition of new surface antigens of which the best known (in the mouse) is designated theta (θ). This maturation in the thymus is under the influence of a local polypeptide hormone known as *thymosin*.

The immunologically competent T-lymphocyte then circulates until it meets a foreign antigen, generally in a lymph node or another lymphoid tissue such as the spleen or the aggregated lymph follicles (Peyer's patches) in the intestine. There, after contact with antigens, the T-lymphocyte undergoes *blast-transformation*, giving rise to numerous progeny that have specific receptors for that antigen on their surface. When an activated T-lymphocyte encounters its antigen it releases a number of humoral factors of low molecular weight (*lymphokines*), which include factors responsible for the attraction (chemotaxis) of macrophage cells and also *lymphotoxin* (which kills foreign cells) and *interferon*, which inactivates viruses. Recent evidence suggests that there are several subgroups of T-lymphocytes; two important groups are *suppressor cells*, whose role is to modify the immunological response by other lymphocytes, and *helper cells*, which co-operate with B-lymphocytes in the production of antibodies.

Cellular immunity plays an important role in the body's defence against viral, bacterial and fungal infections, in transplant rejection and in the defence against neoplastic growths. The presence of T-cell immunity to tuberculosis can be demonstrated with the *Mantoux reaction* (tuberculin reaction); when products of *Mycobacterium tuberculosis* are injected into the skin of a person who has had a previous infection with the same organism, a red indurated area appears at the injection site in two or three days.

Overactivity of T-cell immunity causes one form of hypersensitivity reaction (p. 52). T-lymphocyte function may be suppressed by steroid hormones or by the drug azathioprine. Such drugs are used to prevent rejections of a grafted tissue or organ. Congenital lack of the thymus in childhood causes a severe deficiency of T-lymphocytes and an increased susceptibility to certain infections.

HUMORAL IMMUNITY

B-lymphocytes are concerned with humoral immunity. When exposed to foreign antigens they synthesise RNA and differentiate into the historically distinctive *plasma cells* (Fig. 5.4), which produce immunoglobulins (antibodies). A group of plasma cells that produces an antibody against a single antigen is known as a *clone*. B-lymphocytes are so called because in the chicken they disappear, and antibody production ceases, after

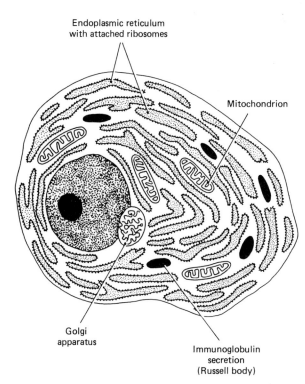

Fig. 5.4 A diagram of a plasma cell showing the abundant endoplasmic reticulum with attached ribosomal (RNA) granules. (After Weir D M 1973 Immunology for undergraduates. Churchill Livingstone, Edinburgh)

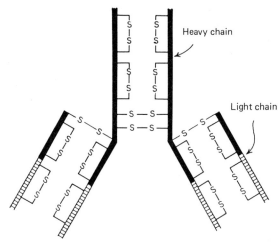

Fig. 5.6 Structure of immunoglobulin G (IgG), showing the two heavy chains and the two light chains linked by disulphide bonds. The amino acid composition of the black parts of each chain is constant whereas that at the amino-terminal end, which is the antigen-binding site, is variable (striped). A number of IgG classes with differences in the numbers and position of the disulphide bonds are recognised

excision of the bursa of Fabricius, a mass of lymphoid tissue near the cloaca. Mammals do not possess a bursa, but the corresponding tissue may be the lymphoid tissue of the tonsils, intestine and appendix.

When an antigen is introduced into the body, antibodies that react specifically with it are produced after a few days. The specificity of this reaction is a fundamental characteristic of the immune response.

The immunoglobulins

Five classes of immunoglobulin are known, namely IgM, IgG, IgA, IgD and IgE (Table 5.5). A typical immunoglobulin molecule, such as IgG, consists of four polypeptide chains, two identical heavy chains each having a molecular weight of about 50 000 and two identical light chains each with a molecular weight of about 25 000. The chains are held together by disulphide bonds (Fig. 5.6).

There are two binding sites for antigen at the amino-terminal ends of the chains and each binding site is made up of the amino-terminal segment of one heavy and one light chain. Two types of light chain are recognised, κ (kappa) and λ (lambda); both occur in all classes of immunoglobulin. The heavy chains, on the other hand, are specific for each class of immunoglobulin: γ (gamma) for IgG, μ (mu) for IgM, α (alpha) for IgA, δ (delta) for IgD and ε (epsilon) for IgE.

The immunoglobulins are secreted by B-lymphocytes that have been stimulated either by an antigen directly or by an antigen that has been processed by macrophages. The active B-lymphocyte appears as a plasma cell on microscopy. IgM, IgA and IgE are produced by

Table 5.5 Human immunoglobulins

	IgG	IgA	IgM	IgD	IgE
Heavy chains	γ	α	μ	δ	ε
Light chains	κ & λ	κ & λ	κ & λ	κ & λ	κ & λ
Molecular weight	150 000	170 000	960 000	184 000	188 100
Normal serum concentration	8.0–16.0 g/l	1.4–4.0 g/l	0.5–2.0 g/l	0–0.4 g/l	0.1–1.3 mg/l
Complement activation	Yes	No	Yes	No	No
Ability to cross placenta	Yes	No	No	No	No

B-lymphocytes that have the corresponding immuno-globulin determinants on their surfaces. Most IgG is produced by co-operation between B-lymphocytes and T-lymphocytes in the presence of macrophages.

IgG

IgG is the most abundant immunoglobulin in man. IgG antibodies are found throughout the tissue spaces and are directed against a wide variety of antigens. Most antitoxins and virus antibodies belong to this class of immunoglobulins, which is the only one that crosses the placenta.

IgM

The structure of IgM is unique in that it consists of five units linked together by a small polypeptide known as a J-chain (Fig. 5.7). IgM antibodies are found in the circulation and, because they have at least five sites for attachment to antigens, are very efficient in reacting with bacteria and foreign cells. The isoagglutinins of blood groups A and B belong to this class (p. 53), as do antibodies against the bacterial body of typhoid and paratyphoid bacilli.

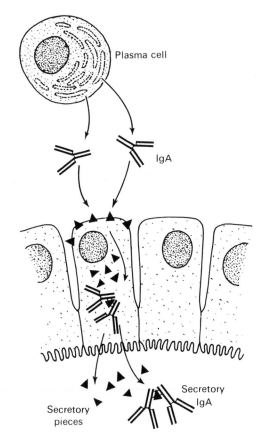

Fig. 5.8 The formation of secretory IgA in the gut. IgA is synthesised by plasma cells in the submucosa. The secretory pieces are synthesised within the mucosal cell and migrate to the cell membrane where each is linked by J-chains to two IgA molecules. This complex is then transported across the cell and released into the lumen of the gut together with some free secretory pieces

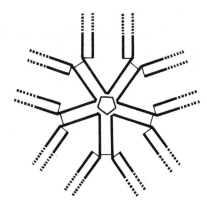

Fig. 5.7 Structure of immunoglobulin M. The J-chain is represented by the pentagon at the centre of the molecule. The dotted areas indicate the parts of the molecule the amino acid content of which varies according to the antigen that recognises, as in Figure 5.6

IgA

IgA circulates in the plasma as a monomer, like IgG: it is secreted on to a mucosal surface as a dimer held together by a small glycoprotein known as the secretory piece (Fig. 5.8). The function of IgA in the plasma is unknown; the principal role of IgA appears to be the protection of mucous membranes. The IgA is specific and, in the gut for example, is formed in response to bacteria and other foreign substances within the lumen of the gut. Immunisation against certain diseases such

as poliomyelitis, which gains access to the body via the gut, can be achieved with an oral vaccine that stimulates the production of IgA in the gut. Similarly, in the respiratory tract the major humoral defence is IgA, which is particularly important in combating viral infections of the respiratory tract such as influenza. IgA is produced in plasma cells in the submucosa of the trachea and passes through the epithelial cells in the same way as in the gut.

IgD and IgE

IgD has little or no antibody activity but may be important in early life as an antigen-trapping determinant on the surface of some B-lymphocytes. IgE is involved in hypersensitivity reactions (p. 52) such as asthma and hay fever. Its physiological function is not certain but it may have a role in the defence against intestinal parasites such as roundworms and tapeworms.

Immune responses

When an antigen such as bovine serum albumin is injected into a rabbit, antibodies appear in the rabbit's serum after a few days (the latent period). The amount of antibody increases rapidly to a peak and then declines. The first antibodies to be produced are IgM; later IgG antibodies appear and the IgM antibodies disappear. These features constitute the *primary response* to the bovine serum albumin.

If the same rabbit is again injected with bovine serum albumin, the response occurs sooner and the amount of antibody is greater. Most of the antibody produced on this occasion is IgG. This is the *secondary response* to the bovine serum albumin. The more rapid appearance of antibody and the greater production are due to the persistence of long-lived B-lymphocytes, sometimes called *memory cells*, which divide and produce large amounts of antibody when exposed to their specific antigen. In the secondary response not only is the antibody concentration higher, but it also remains high for much longer than in the primary response (Fig. 5.9).

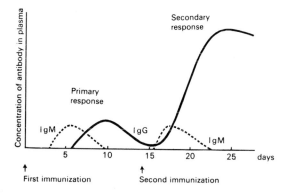

Fig. 5.9 The primary and secondary responses to immunisation with an antigen

Passive immunity

Passive immunity may be given to a patient by injection of gamma globulin (containing the immunoglobulins) from the plasma of another person or of an animal that has already been actively immunised against a particular disease. Human gamma globulin is used in the treatment of tetanus and in the prevention of infectious hepatitis.

Some newborn animals acquire passive immunity by absorbing antibodies from the colostrum, the protein-rich fluid initially produced in lactation (p. 348), but the human baby obtains antibodies almost entirely via the placenta. These antibodies are all IgG; none of the other immunoglobulins can cross the placenta.

Antigen–antibody reactions

Antigens and antibodies react with each other in a number of different ways. The most important are as follows.

Precipitation

Antibody reacts with soluble antigens to form immune complexes. Depending on the relative amounts of antibody and antigen, complexes form that are either soluble or insoluble. The latter precipitate and are easily removed by phagocytic cells in the tissues or in the spleen or liver. Soluble complexes are more difficult to deal with but complement (p. 48) assists their removal. Sone types of antibody are more efficient than others in precipitation, the most effective being IgG antibodies.

Precipitation by antibody is particularly useful for removing toxins, which are classically produced by pathogenic micro-organisms. The effectiveness of antibody as a precipitant of such harmful substances is illustrated by antitetanus antibody used in the treatment of tetanus to neutralise tetanus toxin.

Agglutination

Agglutination is the clumping together of cells including bacteria and endogenous cells such as erythrocytes. Agglutinated cells can be easily destroyed by fixed macrophages (histiocytes) in the liver and spleen (p. 50). IgM antibodies are very efficient in agglutination reactions, probably because each molecule has numerous binding sites. IgG often agglutinates but the activity is weaker than that of IgM. Other types of immunoglobulin are not good agglutinators.

Opsonisation

In this process the phagocytosis of foreign particles is assisted and made more efficient. Phagocytic cells such as polymorphonuclear leucocytes and macrophages are relatively inefficient unless they are given signals that indicate what they should ingest. IgG antibody provides such a signal, by virtue of a receptor sited on heavy chains distant from the antigen-binding site. Thus bacteria coated with IgG antibody provide a strong signal and are efficiently engulfed and destroyed. The other immunoglobulin types do not have this opsonising activity, but some components of complement (p. 48) act in a similar way.

Neutralisation

The activity of antibody in the precipitation and neutralisation of toxins was mentioned earlier. Another important activity of antibodies is to neutralise the attachment of micro-organisms to tissues. Viruses, for example, have receptors that aid their attachment to tissue cells, thus increasing their *infectivity*. Antibody to these receptors effectively neutralises the infectivity and this type of antibody is therefore protective. Other antibodies combine with the cilia of bacteria, so immobilising them and reducing their infectivity.

Complement

It has been known for many years that a heat-labile substance in serum can cause the lysis of red blood cells and the destruction of certain bacteria when the appropriate antibody is also present. This substance was called complement, and the actions ascribed to complement are known to result from the interaction of at least nine proteins (designated C1 to C9). The activation of this series of components can occur in two sequences, the classical and alternative pathways (Fig. 5.10).

The classical pathway

The classical pathway is triggered by immune complexes (formed from antigen and antibody), DNA, aggregated IgG and some enzymes such as plasmin and trypsin. The nine components react in the sequence C1–C4–C2–C3–C5–C6–C7–C8–C9. The *recognition unit* is C1, which consists of three subunits, C1q, C1r and C1s. C1q specifically recognises IgG and IgM

molecules when these are combined with antigen and, undergoing a conformational change, activates C1r; this in turn activates C1s, which becomes *C1 esterase*. The *activation unit* is formed from the interaction of C4, C2 and C3. C1 esterase cleaves C4 and C2, producing two major fragments, which combine to form the complex, $\overline{C42}$ (the bar indicates an active fragment). $\overline{C42}$ then cleaves C3 into C3a and C3b; C3a is liberated and has important biological activities (described below), whereas C3b binds to the original fragment to produce $\overline{C423}$. The *membrane attack unit* is initiated by $\overline{C423}$, which is bound to plasma membranes and cleaves C5 into two fragments, C5a and C5b. The former has activities similar to C3a and the latter binds into the $\overline{C423}$. C6, C7, C8 and C9 are then added and the C8 component brings about the lysis of red cells.

The alternative pathway

The alternative pathway is activated by bacterial endotoxins, aggregated immunoglobulins, cobra venom and some tissue proteins. This pathway provides a separate activation system for the complement components at C3 in the chain of reactions. The *recognition unit* is a plasma protein called initiating factor (IF), which is activated

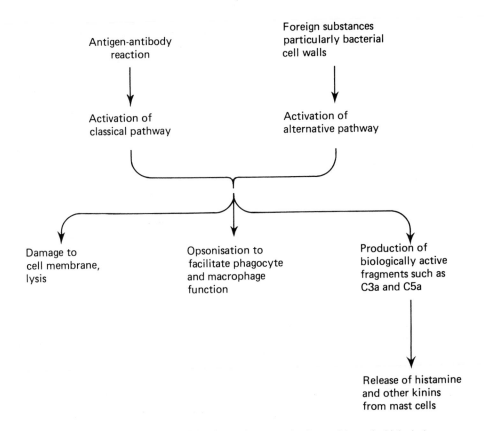

Fig. 5.10 Summary of the principal methods of complement activation and its main biological consequences

by the substances listed. The *activation unit* is formed when IF interacts with another plasma protein, *factor B*, and native C3 to form a complex that can convert further C3 molecules to subunits C3a and C3b; these are then deposited on cell membranes. Another plasma factor, properdin, is then added to the complex to produce an enzyme that cleaves C3 and C5. Cleavage of C5 leads to the formation of a membrane attack unit with C5, C6, C7, C8 and C9, as described earlier.

Complement fragments

At various points in both pathways biologically active fragments are released. C3a and C5a, for example, are called *anaphylotoxins* and cause the release of histamine from mast cells and platelets. Histamine causes contraction of smooth muscle and an increase in capillary permeability, allowing leucocytes to penetrate more easily into the tissues. C3a and C5a are also powerful chemotactic factors for polymorphonuclear leucocytes, eosinophils and macrophages. These factors, generated at a site of infection in the tissues, guide the leucocytes to the place where they are needed.

C3b adheres to cells, stimulating phagocytosis by polymorphonuclear leucocytes and macrophages, which have receptors for this fragment. Thus cells or bacteria coated with C3b are more easily removed.

Complement inhibitors

Since the complement system may mediate cell destruction, it is not surprising that the plasma also contains regulating substances; most stages of the activation sequence have inhibitors that prevent over-activation of the system. one of the most important of these is *C1 esterase inhibitor*, which is congenitally absent in people with a rare inherited disorder, *hereditary angio-neurotic oedema*. In these patients excessive activation of the early components of the classical pathway leads to the release of kinins, which in turn increase vascular permeability and so produce swelling of the face, larynx and intestinal tract. If the laryngeal swelling is severe the patient may die.

THE MACROPHAGE SYSTEM

Certain cells found in all parts of the body are able to engulf particulate material including macro-organisms, effete erythrocytes, disintegrating fibrin, tissue debris and any finely divided or colloidal substance that may be introduced parenterally into the body. Thus, if an animal is killed some days after the intravenous or intraperitoneal injection of Indian ink or the dye trypan blue, the particles of carbon or dyestuff are not distributed generally throughout the body but are concentrated in cells in certain organs in amounts depending on their content of phagocytic cells. These cells comprise the macrophage system, formerly called the reticulo-endothelial system.

Tissue histiocytes

Cells of the macrophage type occur in most connective tissues; many appear to be long-term residents. In most sites they are scanty but they are relatively abundant in the omentum of the fetus and the newborn, where they appear beneath the peritoneum as pale milky aggregates. In the adult they are found in the liver, spleen and lymph nodes. When the need arises for histiocytes in greater number, as in some forms of inflammations, these 'fixed' histiocytes are rapidly supplemented by others, the 'wandering' histiocytes, that appear to be constantly 'on patrol' in most tissues. These in turn are supplemented by yet other cells, formerly circulating blood monocytes.

Monocytes

Monocytes arise mostly in bone marrow and spleen. Many of those in the circulating blood are destined to become wandering tissue histiocytes.

Lymph nodes

At the lymph nodes, lymphocytes are brought into close contact with particulate matter that has been collected by the lymph and fixed by macrophages.

Figure 5.11 shows the ways in which lymphocytes pass through a lymph node. The lymph enters the node in afferent lymphatics, which penetrate the capsule; it leaves through the efferent lymphatic at the hilum. From there the lymph is collected into larger and larger lymphatics. The lymph from most parts of the body passes into the thoracic duct and so into the great veins of the neck. During the passage of lymph through a lymph node, small molecules are transferred to the blood and proteins, including antibodies, are added to it. In the fasting state the lymph from the thoracic duct is pale yellow and transparent. After a fatty meal it becomes milky because the lymph from the intestine then contains chylomicrons (p. 270). Lymph also contains large numbers of lymphocytes, mainly T-lymphocytes.

Within a lymph node a meshwork of reticular cells gives it its fibrous structure. Large numbers of lymphocytes are embedded in the cortical area. The endothelial lining of the sinuses consists of macrophages.

Spleen

The spleen has an unusual circulation (Fig. 5.12). The splenic artery enters at the hilum and breaks up into numerous branches with few anastomoses. Near their terminations the arterioles are surrounded by sleeves of lymphoid tissue (Malpighian bodies). It is difficult to

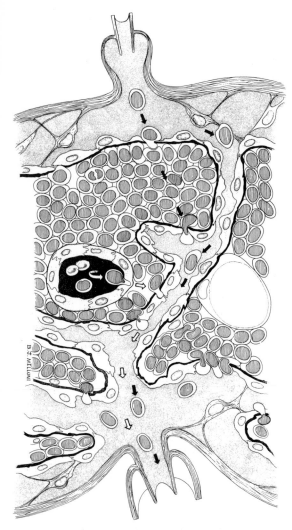

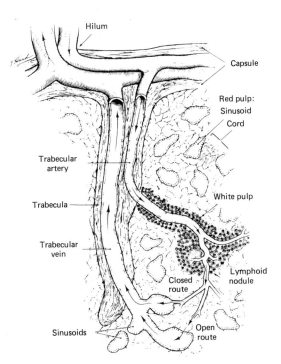

Fig. 5.12 Structure of the spleen to show the lymphoid tissue adjacent to the terminal arterioles and the possible routes from arteriole to sinuses. (From Bellanti J A 1971 Immunology. Saunders Philadelphia)

Fig. 5.11 The circulation of lymphocytes within a lymph node. The sinuses are lined by macrophages. Note that lymphocytes come both from afferent lymphatics (black arrows) and from post-capillary venules (white arrows). (From Bellanti J A 1971 Immunology. Saunders Philadelphia)

trace the pathway of the blood through the spleen from this point, but probably the arterioles, after a terminal dilatation, link up in a loose way with sinuses; the flow by this direct route is fairly rapid. The incomplete walls of these sinuses are made up of rod-like cells with narrow gaps between them lying parallel with the long axis of the sinus. Blood seems to pass from the sinus through the gaps in the wall into the pulp and back again into the sinus, but circulation by this indirect route must be slow. Most of the plasma and some of the red cells go by the direct path to the sinuses, where they are joined by red cells that have taken the indirect

path. The sinuses either link up with one another or join a venule. The veins unite in the hilum to form the splenic vein. The slow element of the circulation through the spleen leads, in effect, to a sequestration of red cells and affords an opportunity for the phagocytosis of aged red cells or of foreign substances such as bacteria.

The Malpighian bodies make up the white pulp of the spleen and consist principally of lymphocytes and macrophages surrounding the arterioles. Thus, the spleen, like the lymph nodes, has an architecture that allows the lymphocytes to come into contact with foreign particles. The significance of the spleen is shown by the fact that after splenectomy patients have an increased liability to serious infections.

Liver

If an animal is injected intraperitoneally or intravenously with colloidal carbon, sections of liver obtained only minutes later show that much carbon has entered the *Kupffer cells*, fixed macrophages that form part of the endothelial lining of the sinusoids. Some of these cells, when laden with particles, become detached and pass in the hepatic veins or the lymphatics to the lungs and regional lymph nodes; replacement is achieved by division of adjacent sinusoidal endothelial cells.

Bone marrow

The experimental intravenous injection of appropriate suspensions has shown that the disposition of phagocytes in the bone marrow is similar to that in the spleen. The endothelium of the marrow is discontinuous, so that particulate material and ageing erythrocytes have ready access to the extravascular compartment.

Microglia

Histological methods involving metallic impregnation reveal cells within the central nervous system, especially round small arteries and arterioles, that are neither astrocytes nor oligodendrocytes. Such cells change their appearance in areas of brain damage and become clearly recognisable as macrophages. They are known as the microglia. Their origin is not yet clear, but the use of labelled blood monocytes has shown that in areas of injury cells of apparently microglial type are rapidly formed from monocytes. In health microglial cells do not engulf material from dyestuffs or colloidal suspensions injected intravenously, presumably because such material does not cross the blood–brain barrier (Chap. 31).

Respiratory tract

In the lung there are large numbers of wandering histiocytes. Macrophages cannot be seen unless particulate matter enters the lung but as a result of atmospheric pollution macrophages with engulfed carbon or other material are almost always present in the alveoli and airways and can be seen in bronchial secretion or sputum. Larger particles are trapped directly in the mucus of the respiratory tract and then coughed up or swallowed. Smaller particles are engulfed by macrophages, which are then likewise removed in the mucus (Fig. 5.13); some are carried by the macrophages into the lymphatics, from which they eventually become deposited in the small foci of lymphoid tissue in the lung or in the regional lymph nodes.

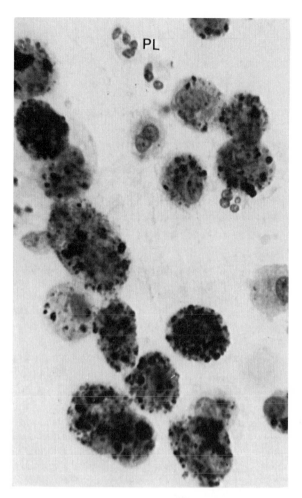

Fig. 5.13 Macrophages of bronchial origin in sputum. The cells are relatively large and contain different amounts of particulate material (mostly soot and dust). The amount is so great in some cells as to obscure the nucleus completely. At the top may be seen the multilobed nuclei of two polymorphonuclear leucocytes (PL); their cytoplasm is devoid of particles. Papanicolaou stain × 900. (By courtesy of W W Park.)

Function of macrophages

Macrophages differ from polymorphonuclear leucocytes in their much greater avidity for, or ability to engulf, inorganic particulate material such as carbon. Macrophages also have the unusual capacity, when confronted by particularly insoluble material, to fuse together, with the formation of multinucleated giant cells. Most forms of organic foreign material such as a thorn, a spicule of fish bone or surgical catgut can be destroyed by enzyme action and lysis. Most forms of inorganic material cannot be destroyed by lysis; some of it is transported to lymph nodes by the macrophages but the rest remains undisturbed throughout life. Bile pigment, haemosiderin, melanin, lipid substances and carbon may be seen in different circumstances within macrophages. In damaged tissues macrophages may also contain dead and dying micro-organisms and polymorphonuclear leucocytes, tissue debris, sterol crystals and fibrin. Cells of the macrophage system are also responsible for the phagocytosis and breakdown of erythrocytes and for the catabolism of haemoglobin.

Relationship to immune mechanisms

Macrophages can ingest and store antigens but cannot manufacture antibodies; the recognition of antigen and the manufacture of antibody are functions of lymphocytes. The macrophages present antigen, or antigen modified in some way, to the T- and B-lymphocytes so that the lymphocytes can develop cellular immunity or a humoral response. The macrophages, by retaining antigens, prevent the exposure of lymphocytes to excess antigenic material, with a resulting loss of their activity.

DISORDERS OF THE IMMUNE MECHANISMS

Although the immune mechanisms are essential for survival, their action may at times be damaging, as in hypersensitivity reactions and autoimmune disease. Other defects are caused by failure of the immune responses. Tumours of the B-lymphocytes (*myeloma*) lead to the excessive production of immunoglobulins.

Hypersensitivity

While the ideal immune response to an incoming antigen consists of disposal of the antigen without any damage to the host's cells, an overreaction (hypersensitivity reaction) leads to 'self-inflicted' damage to the tissues. Four main types of hypersensitivity reaction are recognised.

Type 1 hypersensitivity (anaphylaxis)

For reasons that are poorly understood, IgE antibodies are overproduced in response to certain common environmental antigens such as pollens, animal dandruff, house dust mites and some drugs. On a second or subsequent exposure, the IgE stimulates mast cells to release histamine and other amines. In turn, these cause vasoconstriction and, later, vasodilatation of small blood vessels and constriction of the bronchioles.

A massive release of histamine produces two main clinical effects: shock (p. 126), because of a fall in blood pressure caused by pooling of blood in the dilated peripheral blood vessels, and difficulty of breathing, because of bronchoconstriction (asthma). Collapse and death may be rapid in this extreme form (generalised anaphylaxis). Lesser degrees of hypersensitivity in particular tissues are responsible for urticarial rashes ('nettle rash'), bronchial asthma and hay fever.

Type 2 hypersensitivity

While it is generally accepted that the immune system does not ordinarily attack the cells of the host, some *autoimmune diseases* are now recognised in which antibody production leads to destruction of particular cells in the host. Examples include *autoimmune haemolytic anaemia*, with premature lysis of red cells, *pernicious anaemia* (p. 41), caused by autoimmune damage to the parietal cells of the stomach and consequent deficiency of vitamin B_{12} (p. 255) and *autoimmune thyroiditis*, caused by antibodies to thyroid cells. In each of

these conditions the detection of antibodies in the plasma may be helpful in diagnosis.

The reason for the lack of the normal self-tolerance in these disorders is poorly understood. Genetic factors may be important and in some cases infection or drugs may alter the cell surfaces so that either they appear to have new antigens, or antigenic material sequestered within the cell is exposed to antibodies.

Type 3 hypersensitivity

This form of hypersensitivity results from damage to the tissues by *immune complexes*, combinations of antibodies and antigens. Soluble immune complexes activate complement and the released chemotactic factors attract polymorphonuclear leucocytes. In turn these discharge enzymes that lead to tissue damage. While all antigen–antibody reactions yield immune complexes, clinical problems arise only when the interaction continues for a long time.

Local type 3 hypersensitivity reactions are known as *Arthus reactions*, and occur typically in the skin or the lungs. A generalised reaction is known as *serum sickness*. One well-known example is that caused by the administration of an antiserum (for example against tetanus or diphtheria) derived from horses. Some 20 per cent of patients so treated develop skin rashes, joint pains and renal damage 10 to 14 days later. These effects result from immune complexes formed by reactions between antibodies to the proteins and residual horse proteins.

Type 4 hypersensitivity

This hypersensitivity results from over-activity of cell-mediated (T-lymphocyte) immunity. Tuberculosis provides the best known example. A tuberculous infection early in life sensitises the T-lymphocytes so that the patient is immune to a second exposure. Occasionally the T-lymphocyte response is so great that re-exposure provokes a hypersensitivity reaction that damages the lungs.

The degree of T-lymphocyte responsiveness can often be assessed by skin tests. For example in the Mantoux test (p. 44) an inflamed, slightly swollen lesion 5–10 mm in diameter indicates immunity to tuberculosis. Hypersensitivity is shown by a much larger lesion, intensely inflamed and swollen and often 20–40 mm in diameter, which sometimes becomes necrotic in the centre.

Immunodeficiency

A number of diseases, some of which are inherited, are due to impaired immune responses. There may be a failure of antibody response or a failure of cellular immunity or a combination of both. The diseases reveal themselves by recurring bacterial or fungal infections.

Myeloma

In myeloma a clone of plasma cells undergoes malignant change and immunoglobulin production is increased. Such a clone produces a single class of immunoglobulin. In some patients with this disorder light chains appear in the urine and are known as *Bence-Jones protein*. Production of this abnormal immunoglobulin may impair the production of normal antibodies and serious infections may result.

BLOOD GROUPS AND TISSUE ANTIGENS

If samples of blood from two individuals are mixed together, for example on a microscope slide, the red cells may clump together (*agglutinate*). Haemolysis may occur at the same time. In these circumstances the two blood samples are described as incompatible with each other. If incompatible blood is transfused, the recipient becomes seriously ill as a result of the blockage of capillaries by agglutinated red cells and damage to the tubules of the kidney by precipitated haemoglobin (p. 200). Such a reaction can be fatal.

The cause of these events is an antibody–antigen reaction. The antigen consists of specific complex carbohydrates that are part of the glycolipids of the plasma membrane. These antigens exist in a number of distinct groups or systems, of which there are at least fourteen. The best known are ABO, Rhesus, MNS, Lutheran, Kell, Lewis, Duffy, and Kidd. All the blood group antigens are controlled by autosomal genes, except Xg, which is controlled by a gene on the X-chromosome.

Two groups of antibodies are involved in transfusion reactions. Some occur naturally in the plasma of an individual who has never been exposed to the appropriate antigen. Examples include the antibodies to ABO antigens, anti-A and anti-B. These naturally occurring antigens are usually IgM and do not cross the placenta. Other antibodies arise only as a result of a previous exposure to an antigen lacking in the patient. The best-known examples are the antibodies to the Rhesus antigens, particularly the Rhesus antigen designated D. These antibodies are usually IgG and readily cross the placenta.

ABO system

The ABO group of a person depends on whether his red cells contain one, both or neither of the antigens A and B. There are therefore four main ABO groups, AB, A, B and O. If the A antigen is not present on a person's cells (that is he is either Group B or Group O), his plasma contains the naturally occurring antibody, *anti-A*. Similarly, if the cells lack a B antigen (that is he is Group A or Group O), the plasma contains *anti-B*. The plasma of a Group AB person contains neither of these

Table 5.14 ABO blood groups

Group	Possible genotypes	Antigens on red cells	Antibodies in plasma
AB	AB	A and B	None
A	AO, AA	A	Anti-B
B	BO, BB	B	Anti-A
O	OO	Neither	Anti-A Anti-B

antibodies (Table 5.14). No clear evidence has yet been obtained of an 'O' antigen or of an anti-O antibody.

Rhesus system

In 1940 it was demonstrated that rabbits injected with blood from Rhesus monkeys developed an antibody that agglutinated not only the red cells of the monkey but also the cells of some 85 per cent of a large series of blood samples from Europeans. The antibody was called anti-Rhesus (anti-Rh) and the cells agglutinated by it were called Rhesus positive (Rh-positive). Soon afterwards anti-Rh antibodies were demonstrated in the plasma of some Rh-negative patients who had previously been transfused with Rh-positive blood or the plasma of some Rh-negative women who had borne Rh-positive children. It is now clear that the Rhesus system consists of at least five different antigen, C, D, E, c and e. Of these D is the most important, and in clinical practice persons with the D antigen are regarded as Rhesus positive and those lacking this antigen as Rhesus negative.

It is important to recognise that the Rhesus and ABO systems differ in that the antibodies to antigens A and B are naturally present while the antibodies to Rhesus antigens, particularly D, develop only after a patient has been exposed to the antigen. This exposure (sensitisation) can result from the transfusion of unmatched blood or during pregnancy. Towards the end of pregnancy, or during an abortion, small numbers of red cells may pass from the blood of the fetus to that of the mother. If the fetus is D-positive and the mother D-negative, the mother may then be sensitised and develop anti-D antibodies. These are not harmful during the first such pregnancy but in a subsequent pregnancy with a D-positive fetus, the anti-D antibody may cross from the mother to the fetus and cause destruction of the fetal red cells. The severity of this condition varies greatly. In the severest cases destruction of the red cells of the fetus is so rapid and widespread that the fetus dies. In milder cases the child is born alive but may develop jaundice because of the excessive haemolysis.

The development of antibodies in a Rhesus negative mother can be prevented by the administration of anti-D immunoglobulin immediately after delivery. This procedure destroys any Rhesus-positive erythrocytes that have entered her circulation and prevents the production of antibodies.

Blood transfusions

Before a transfusion, donor blood is selected that is compatible in terms of the ABO grouping and the D antigen with that of the recipient. In addition, blood from the prospective donor and from the recipient are *cross-matched* to minimise the possibility of error in the choice of donor or incompatibility due to blood groups systems other than ABO or Rhesus. In cross-matching the erythrocytes of the donor are mixed with plasma from the recipient in one test and, in a second test, the donor's plasma is mixed with red cells from the recipient. If agglutination does not occur in either test transfusion can safely be carried out.

Table 5.15 Some typical figures to show racial differences in the percentages of different ABO blood groups and of rhesus-negatlve (D-) blood. (Data of Mourant A E, Kopek A C, Domaniewska-Sobczak 1976 The distribution of human blood groups. University Press, Oxford)

Racial group	Blood group				Rhesus (D) negative
	O	A	B	AB	
Most Europeans	43	44	9	4	17
English (south)	44	45	8	3	17
Scots	52	34	11	3	20
Basques	52	45	2	1	29
Lapps	20	59	16	5	2
Africans (Nigeria)	52	24	21	3	5
Indians (Punjab)	31	21	40	8	7
Vietnamese	42	22	30	6	0
Indonesians	40	27	26	7	0
Chinese (Canton)	44	24	26	6	1
Japanese	32	36	23	9	0
Australian aborigines	70	20	9	1	0
Native Americans	77	16	6	1	0
Eskimos	36	55	5	4	0

It is usually not difficult to find donor blood that is compatible with a recipient of the same race. There are major differences between races in the proportions of various blood groups (Table 5.15); travellers and immigrants may be difficult to match with appropriate donors. For example, a Rhesus-negative European travelling in Africa or China may not be able to obtain Rhesus-negative blood. Similarly, African immigrants to Europe may have antigens that make cross-matching difficult.

Tissue antigens

Just as erythrocytes have antigens on their surface, so do nucleated cells. These *tissue antigens* or *histocompatibility antigens* stimulate an immune response whenever a person receives nucleated cells with antigens different from those of his own cells, for example in a graft from another person. This immune response consists of both antibody production and lymphocyte sensitisation and leads to the rejection of grafted tissue in 7 to 10 days. Only between identical twins is it possible to graft tissues successfully without the need for drugs that suppress the immune responses; the likelihood of rejection is greatly reduced by the best possible matching of donor and recipient cells by *tissue typing*.

Histocompatibility antigens are found on nucleated tissue cells and also on leucocytes and platelets. In practice lymphocytes and platelets in the peripheral blood are used in tests for these antigens. The most important system of tissue antigens is known as the *HLA system* (human leucocyte-A system), which is determined by a number of genes situated on chromosome 6. The determination of HLA compatibility as well as ABO compatibility is usually made before renal transplants, skin grafts and bone marrow transfers are undertaken.

One further histocompatibility antigen, the H-Y antigen, is specific to the Y-chromosome and may play a part in the normal differentiation of gonadal tissues according to the composition of their sex-chromosome.

FURTHER READING

Amos W M G 1981 Basic immunology. Butterworth, London
Davis B D, Dulbecco R, Eisen H N, Ginsberg H S 1980 Microbiology, 3rd edn. Harper & Row, Hagerstown, Md.
Holborow E J, Reeves W G (eds) 1983 Immunology in medicine, 2nd edn. Grune & Stratton, London
Kirkwood E, Lewis C 1983 Understanding medical immunology. Wiley, Chichester
Lachmann P J, Peters D K 1982 Clinical aspects of immunology, 4th edn. Blackwell Scientific, Oxford
Mims C A (ed) Virus immunity and pathogenesis. British Medical Bulletin 41: 1–102
Mollison P L 1982 Blood transfusion in clinical medicine, 7th edn. Blackwell Scientific, Oxford

Powell R J 1984 Serum complement levels. British Journal of Hospital Medicine 32: 104–110
Rosen F S, Cooper M D, Wedgwood R J P 1984 The primary immunodeficiencies. New England Journal of Medicine 311: 235–242, 300–310
Thompson R A (ed) 1983 Recent advances in clinical immunology 3. Churchill Livingstone, Edinburgh
Twomey J J 1982 The pathophysiology of human immunologic disorders. Urban & Schwartzenberg, Baltimore

6

The electrical activity of the heart

Myocardial cells

Heart muscle is not a syncytium but consists of discrete, electrically excitable cells of different types. The two main varieties are 'working' myocardial cells and specialised 'conducting' cells. Within each of these two groups there are differences: for example, working cells in the atrium are anatomically and physiologically different from working cells in the ventricle, and there are similar differences between the cells of different parts of the specialised conducting tissue (p. 58). Each cell is enclosed by its membrane, or sarcolemma, the structure through which the cardiac electrical activity exerts its important function (Fig. 6.1).

The sarcolemma

The myocardial cell membrane resembles other cell membranes (Fig. 6.2) but adjacent cells are held together by a complicated system of interdigitating projections, which appear on light microscopy as the 'intercalated discs' (Fig. 6.2). These consist of the two surface membranes of adjacent cells within the same column and the intercellular space between them. They are similar in structure to the rest of the cell membrane and continuous with them. The thin actin myofilaments seem to be attached to the inner surfaces of these areas. Here and there desmosomes are present.

As in skeletal muscle, invaginations of the sarcolemma extend into the substance of the cell to form the 'transverse tubules' of the sarcoplasmic reticulum lying in relation to the Z-lines of the sarcomeres as shown in Figure 6.1. The *longitudinal sarcoplasmic reticulum*, a true intracellular organelle, is finer and scantier in cardiac muscle than in skeletal muscle but in the neighbourhood of the Z-lines it forms flattened *terminal cisternae*, which are separate from, but closely apposed to, the transverse tubules. The terminal cisternae and transverse tubules appear in electron microscope sections as 'triads' or 'diads' (Fig. 6.1).

Another important modification of the sarcolemma is found especially in areas along the longitudinal surface of the cells where the contact between two adjacent cells is closer than elsewhere and the surface membranes seem to be fused, with obliteration of the intercellular space. These regions are called '*nexuses*' or '*gap junctions*' and seem to contain a system of intercellular pores (Fig. 6.2). The intercalated discs and the nexuses probably account for the relatively low electrical resistance between adjacent cardiac muscle cells.

The physiological differences between cardiac and skeletal muscle are probably related to three ways in which the membranes of the two kinds of striated muscle cells differ. First, unlike skeletal muscle, which contracts in response to a stimulus conveyed by a motoneurone (Chap. 40), cardiac muscle of all kinds has, at least in certain circumstances, the fundamental property of contracting with *innate rhythmicity*. This property is particularly well developed in the modified myocardial cells forming the *specialised conducting tissue*, and especially in cells in certain regions, called *pacemakers*, that generate electrical current, spontaneously and fairly regularly, at inherent rates characteristic of different sites in the system. Secondly, the myocardium is very sensitive to the *direct action of neurohumoral transmitters* such as adrenaline and acetylcholine. Thirdly, the *duration of the action potential* of myocardial cells is very much greater than that of skeletal muscle: the upstroke is no slower, but the return to the resting potential takes much longer, especially in ventricular muscle (Fig. 6.3).

These three features have an important bearing on the functioning of the heart. The innate rhythmicity of a hierarchy of potential pacemakers ensures the continued beating of the heart; the direct action of neurohumoral transmitters powerfully affects the contractility of the muscle (p. 78); the plateau of the action potential prolongs the *refractory period* of the cell (Fig. 6.5), making it incapable in ordinary physiological conditions of producing summated contractions. Tetanic contraction of the myocardium would prevent the co-ordinated rhythmic contraction and relaxation that constitute the normal beating of the heart (p. 79).

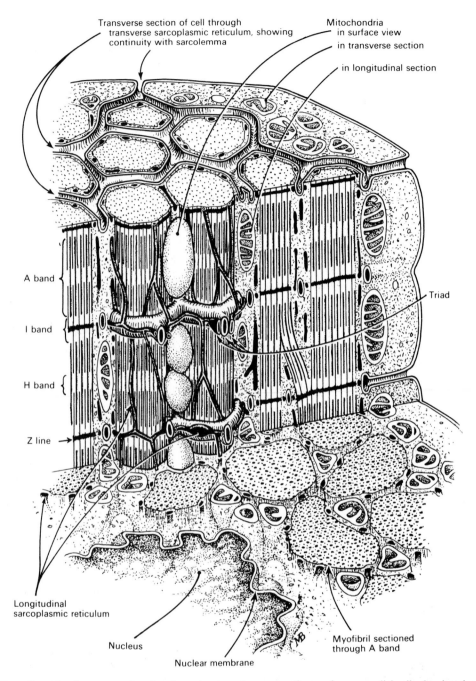

Fig. 6.1 Three-dimensional reconstruction, based on electron microscopy, of part of a myocardial cell, showing the relationship between the transverse tubular system of the sarcoplasmic reticulum, the terminal cisternae of the longitudinal sarcoplasmic reticulum (triads) and the Z lines of sarcomeres. The transverse system has some horizontal branches (not shown) and cisternae are also in apposition to them and to the sarcolemma.

CARDIAC EXCITATION

Transmembrane resting and action potentials can be determined for myocardial cells by the same techniques that are applied to nerve and are the result of differences of ionic concentrations and ionic fluxes across cell membranes. There are, however, important differences between the transmembrane potentials and ion fluxes of

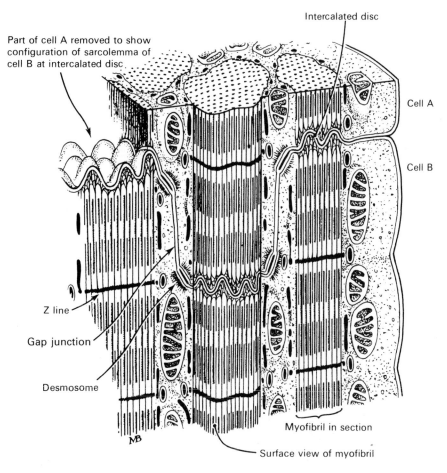

Fig. 6.2 Three-dimensional reconstruction of adjacent parts of two myocardial cells (A and B) separated by part of the intercalated disc, showing the gap junctions (nexuses) where the surface membranes of the two cells seem, on electron microscopy, to be fused.

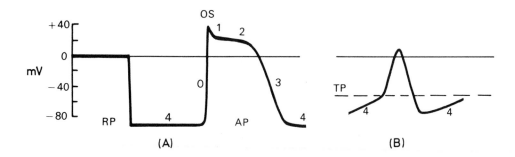

Fig. 6.3 The thick line shows the potential recorded by a microelectrode (against time in ms) at first just outside the resting myocardial cell (O mV), then inserted into the cell to give the transmembrane resting potential. The diagram on the left (A) shows the transmembrane potential in a working ventricular muscle cell; the diagram on the right (B) that of a nodal pace-maker cell. RP, resting potential. AP, action potential. TP, threshold potential. OS, overshoot. Phase O of the action potential represents the depolarisation of the cell. Phases 1, 2 and 3 represent stages of repolarisation. Phase 4 = RP in A, the pace-maker potential in B.

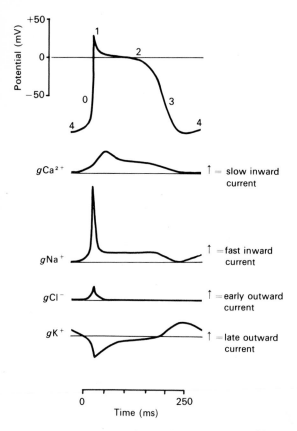

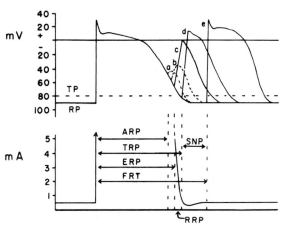

Fig. 6.5 Diagram to show the effect of the refractory states of a myocardial cell on attempts to elicit an action potential. Above is a normal membrane action potential (MAP). a-e, MAPs evoked by stimuli applied at times as indicated. The diagram below shows the excitability of the cell to cathodal stimulation. ARP, absolute refractory period. ERP, effective refractory period. TRP, total refractory period. RRP, relative refractory period. FRT, full recovery time. TRP-ERP = RRP. FRT-TRP = supranormal phase (SNP). The first potential to be *propagated* at all (c) arises at the end of ERP. The response, d, is not propagated normally. The first normal response (e) occurs at the end of FRT. (Hoffmann B F, Singer D 1964 Progress in cardiovascular disease 7: 226)

Fig. 6.4 Idealised model of a membrane action potential (MAP) and pacemaker activity of a Purkinje cell. The conductances (*g*) of the sarcolemma for various ions are shown non-quantitatively. In pacemaking cells of the SA, and possibly AV, nodes the important inward channel may be that related to Ca^{2+} influx. In ventricular working muscle Cl^- flux is not important. (Adapted from Katz A M 1977 Physiology of the heart, Raven Press, New York p. 237, and Noble D 1979 The initiation of the heartbeat, Clarendon Press, Oxford, p. 165).

myocardium and those of nerve: in myocardium there is a slow inward calcium current not found in nerve and the potassium gating mechanisms are more complicated (Fig. 6.4).

The transmembrane *resting potential* is about -90 mV, the inside negatively charged with respect to the outside ('polarised'). After excitation the polarity of charge on the membrane is reversed, and the transmembrane potential changes very rapidly to perhaps $+30$ mV ('depolarisation'). The subsequent voltage-time curve of the membrane *action potential* is much longer than that of nerve (Fig. 6.3). The prolonged depolarisation, which lasts 400 to 500 ms in Purkinje cells and ventricular working cells, is mainly the result of the slow inward calcium current. For the greater part of this time the cardiac cell is refractory to further

stimuli (Fig. 6.5). In working muscle cells and non-pacemaking special conducting tissue, phase 4 is the resting potential of the cell and remains constant until the cell membrane is excited again. The cell is then rapidly depolarised with a sudden and explosive increase in the membrane permeability to sodium; sodium ions move rapidly into the cell down their electro-chemical gradient and a new action potential begins.

The special conducting system
The innate rhythmicity of cardiac muscle contraction is normally controlled by the electrical activity of the heart initiated by *pacemaking cells* in the specialised myocardial cells of the *conducting system*. Although experimentally, in unphysiological conditions, working myocardial cells are capable of spontaneous depolarisation, they are normally excited by an electrical current passing along the surface of the cell membrane and from cell to cell through the intercalated discs and gap junctions.

Cells of the special conducting tissue vary greatly in size and character, some being smaller and some larger than working myocardial cells. They have a higher glycogen content and appear paler on staining than working cells; the electron microscope shows that they contain fewer myofibrils and mitochondria and poorly

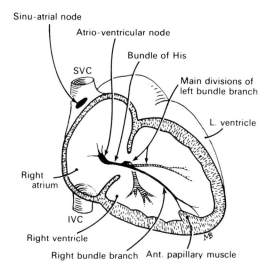

Fig. 6.6 Diagram to show the main parts of the cardiac specialised conducting tissue. The heart is viewed from the front and right, into the right atrium and ventricle, and has been cut in a plane parallel with the septa, which, in this display, are assumed to be transparent. The AV nodal tissue lies in the right atrium, the bundle of His runs below the membranous part of the interventricular septum, the two main divisions of the left bundle-branch lie beyond the septum. The Purkinje network, which ramifies in the subendocardium of both ventricles, is not shown.

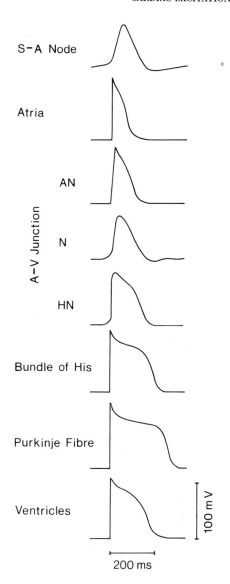

Fig. 6.7 Characteristic shapes of the action potential from various types of myocardial cell. The duration is prolonged progressively from the atria to the peripheral Purkinje fibre. N denotes cells in the central part of the AV node; AN, cells nearer the atrium; HN, cells nearer the bundle of His. (Watanabe Y, Dreifus L S 1968 American Heart Journal 76: 114)

developed sarcoplasmic reticulum. With the exception of a group of cells at the centre of the atrioventricular node, which seem to exert only a delaying effect on conduction, it is likely that all the cells in the special conducting tissue are potential pacemaker cells, and together they act like a series of electrical oscillators the rates of which are locked to that with the fastest inherent frequency.

The specialised conducting system (Fig. 6.6) consists of the *sinu-atrial node* near the junction of the superior vena cava and the right atrium; a diffuse area of cells, known as the *atrioventricular (AV) node*, lying above the right annulus fibrosus and near the mouth of the coronary sinus and the opening of the inferior vena cava; the *bundle of His*, with its main left and right branches and the terminal ramifications of the *Purkinje network* in the subendocardial muscle.

The duration of the action potential in cells of the special conducting tissue increases progressively from the atrioventricular node to the Purkinje fibres (Fig. 6.7). Thus, as the electrical impulse is conducted down the system, the distal fibres with their longer effective refractory period may fail to respond to the higher rate of stimulation of proximal fibres. The abnormal condition 'heart block' (p. 70) may result.

Another important feature of the special conducting tissue is that the inherent rate of discharge of the pace-maker cells declines progressively from the sinu-atrial node to the cells of the Purkinje network. Thus under ordinary conditions the sinu-atrial node, which has the fastest intrinsic rate, controls the rate of excitation of the whole heart because of the very rapid conduction of the excitatory current along the special conducting tissue. Table 6.8 shows conduction velocities through various parts of the conduction system and the working myocardium.

Table 6.8 Speeds of conduction in the mammalian heart

Tissue	Approx cell diameter (μm)	Velocity (m/s)
Atrial fibres	10	0.3–0.5
AV node	5	0.05
Purkinje fibres	30	2.0–5
Ventricular cells	9–16	0.4–1

The action potential of pace-making cells differs from that of working myocardium: for example the rate of rise of the upstroke is less, the peak is more rounded and there is no great overshoot. There is considerable evidence to suggest that these features are the result of the action of the slow calcium current, with little or no contribution from a sodium flux. The most important physiological difference, however, lies in phase 4 (Fig. 6.3). In active pacemaking cells the resting potential steadily lessens ('pacemaker potential'), probably because of increasing permeability to K$^+$ and Na$^+$.

Transmembrane potentials from the sinu-atrial node (Fig. 6.9) have all the characteristics of pace-making cells and the rate of automatic discharge can be varied in three ways. The threshold can be altered, as with changes in external Ca^{2+} concentration; the slope of the diastolic depolarisation (Phase 4) can change, as under the influence of catecholamines; the level of the initial membrane resting potential can change, as with an altered K$^+$ concentration or under the influence of acetylcholine or drugs such as digoxin. The action of the sympathetic (noradrenergic) and the vagus (cholinergic) nerves on the rate of the heart beat is described in chapter 7 (p. 91).

Normally electrical current spreads from the pacemaker cells in the sinu-atrial node to excite the neighbouring atrial cells and then spreads from cell to cell along the working myocardial fibres of the atrium, depolarising them. The excitation leads to contraction of the sarcomeres.

The excitatory local membrane currents run from cell to cell through the atrial muscle towards the atrioventricular (AV) ring (annulus fibrosus). This structure would act as a complete barrier to the spread of electrical activity from the atria to the ventricles were it not for the gap through which the specialised *atrio-ventricular junctional system* runs in the form of the bundle of His (Fig. 6.6).

The AV node lies subendocardially on the atrial side of the right annulus fibrosus and consists of successive layers of cells. Those near the atrial working muscle (AN in Fig. 6.7) propagate the impulse increasingly slowly, a property that seems to be associated with the slow upstroke and blunter peak of the action potential. Propagation through the middle zone of the node (N in Fig. 6.7) is remarkably slow and accounts for about 30 ms of the total delay in atrio-ventricular conduction. After the impulse crosses this central zone of the AV node its conduction velocity increases progressively to the main branches of the bundle of His. The first fibres to leave the bundle of His are those that form the posteroinferior division of the left bundle-branch. The next to leave are those that form the anterosuperior division of the left bundle-branch. Finally the remaining fibres become the right bundle-branch. The two main divisions of the left bundle-branch fan out under the endocardium of the left side of the interventricular septum and adjacent ventricle and end in the Purkinje network in the septum and near the two left-ventricular papillary muscles. The right bundle-branch runs to the Purkinje network near the anterior papillary muscle of the right ventricle.

Ventricular excitation
The first parts of the ventricles to be excited are small subendocardial areas on the left side of the interventricular septum. A few milliseconds later the subendocardial muscle of the right ventricle is excited near the anterior papillary muscle. During the next 60 ms or so the electrical activity spreads through the ventricular muscle from endocardium to epicardium as shown in Figure 6.10. The epicardium is first depolarised near the apex of the right ventricle about 20 ms after ventricular excitation begins. Excitation of both ventricles is complete in about 70 to 80 ms. This intrinsic cardiac electrical activity is to the heart what the impulse in the motoneurone is to skeletal muscle, an essential prerequisite for normal contraction.

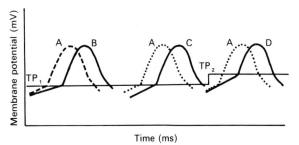

Fig. 6.9 Diagram to show how the rate of firing of transmembrane action potentials recorded from a cell in the SA node may be slowed by three different mechanisms. When the pacemaker potential (Phase 4, Fig. 6.3) reaches the normal threshold potential (TP$_1$) the cell fires (A). If the rate of depolarisation is slower (slope of Phase 4 less) it fires as B. If the resting potential is increased it fires as C. If the threshold potential is raised to TP$_2$ the cell fires as D. The shape and height of the action potentials are purely diagrammatic.

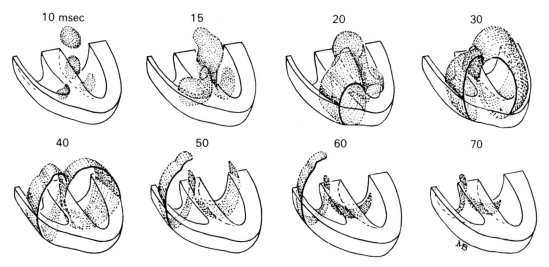

Fig. 6.10 Diagram to show the wavefronts of electrical excitation spreading through the human ventricles at successive instants after the start of ventricular depolarisation. When a wavefront reaches the epicardium it is no longer moving and is therefore not represented in this diagram. The first part of the epicardium to be excited is the apical part of the right ventricle at about 20 ms. The septum is excited from both sides, and excitation in both ventricles moves from endocardium to epicardium, in the left fairly concentrically, in the right more tangentially.

Excitation-contraction coupling

The electrical excitation of a myocardial cell membrane is the result of the generation of a local circuit current by the membrane action potential, similar to that in unmyelinated nerve. This current, by positive feedback (Fig. 6.14), is responsible for the propagation of the explosively self-perpetuating action potential. In addition, the gap junctions and intercalated discs provide a low electrical resistance between cells, probably because of their high permeability to current-carrying K^+. The membrane current is transmitted toward the interior of the cell along the surfaces of the transverse tubular system. In the region of the 'triads' the electrical impulse in some way allows Ca^{2+}, sequestered in the nearby cisternae of the longitudinal system, to move out into the myofibrils. There is evidence to suggest the activity of a Ca^{2+}–ATPase pump. Ca^{2+} is bound to troponin C; the tropomyosin molecules then shift, removing their inhibiting action on contraction. ATP is split by the myosin ATPase in the presence of Mg^{2+} and the filaments are propelled past each other to successive new sites for reaction with making and breaking of actin-myosin bonds. The sarcomere shortens and the myofibril contracts (Fig. 6.11).

The relaxation of the sarcomere is probably associated with the active transfer of Ca^+ from the vicinity of the myofibrils back into the cisternae, and the resumption of the inhibiting actions of troponin and tropomyosin.

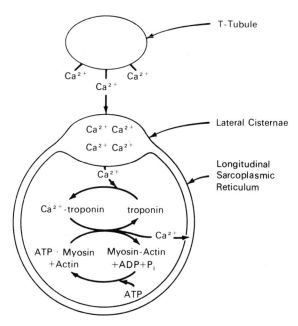

Fig. 6.11 Mechanism of excitation-contraction coupling (Morkin B, LaRaia P J 1974 New England Journal of Medicine 290:445)

THE ELECTROCARDIOGRAM

The electrical excitation leading to mechanical contraction (p. 73) can be recorded as a potential difference

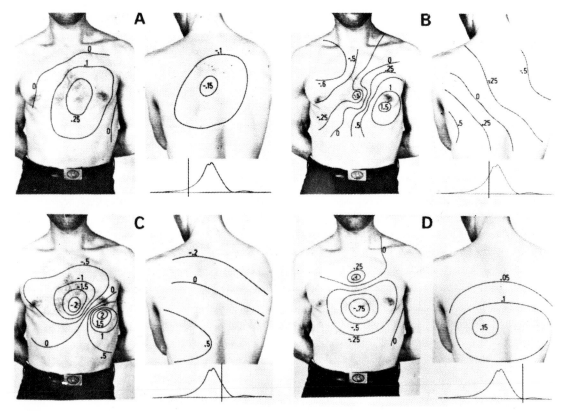

Fig. 6.12 Distribution on the chest surface of a normal subject of electrical potentials arising from cardiac excitation at four instants of time during ventricular activation ('isopotential field map'). The vertical lines intersecting the QRS complex of the electrocardiograms (p. 67) at the bottom of the figures indicate the instants of time to which the maps are related. (Taccardi B 1963 Circulation Research, 12:341)

(voltage) on the surface of the body by electrodes applied to the skin and linked to an *electrocardiograph*. The distribution of these potentials on the skin of the thorax can be mapped by computerised techniques. The *isopotential map* thus recorded varies at different moments during ventricular excitation (Fig. 6.12). Accordingly an electrode at any one site on the body records potential differences that vary as a function of time. The electrocardiograph usually records these voltage-time curves on moving paper throughout each cardiac cycle and from beat to beat: such a record is called an *electrocardiogram* (ECG) (Figs. 6.13 and 6.21).

The electrocardiogram is useful to the physiologist because its various 'deflections' or 'waves' allow the timing of various events in the cardiac cycle. In clinical medicine it is even more valuable, for it provides information about the rate and rhythm of the heart, about conduction abnormalities, about the mass of the active myocardium and, together with pulse records, allows timing of the various phases of the cardiac cycle.

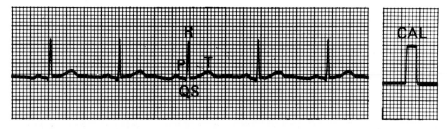

Fig. 6.13 Normal electrocardiogram (ECG) recorded by 'standard lead II' (p. 66). Time intervals (horizontal), 40 and 200 ms. Voltage scale (vertical), 0.1 and 0.5 mV. CAL, calibration signal (1 mV).

Wavefronts of depolarisation

The electrical excitation of a cardiac muscle cell spreads from the point of stimulation, accompanied by the regenerating membrane action potential set up by the

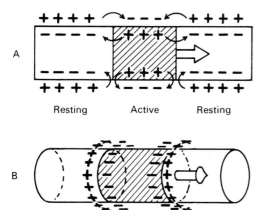

Resting   Active   Resting

Fig. 6.14 Diagram of a myocardial fibre during the passage of excitation (depolarisation) and recovery (repolarisation). In the resting state the outside of the cell membrane is positively charged with respect to the inside; in the active state the polarity is reversed. Local membrane currents flow as indicated by the small arrows in (A) at the junctions of active and resting parts of the cell. These junctions form charged wavefronts of excitation and recovery (depolarisation and repolarisation). These wavefronts have direction, polarity and magnitude and so each can be represented as a vector: the solid arrow in (B) represents the advancing wavefront of excitation.

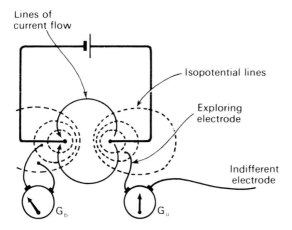

Fig. 6.15 Diagram to show the lines of current flow and the lines of equal potential (isopotential field) between two terminals immersed in a large volume of electrolyte solution ('volume conductor'). G_b represents the galvanometer of a 'bipolar' lead system recording the potential difference between two points of relatively high potential that are close together. G_u represents the galvanometer of a 'unipolar' lead system where the electrodes are at points far apart, and one ('indifferent electrode') is at a point of relatively very low potential.

ion fluxes through the sarcolemma and membrane currents (Fig. 6.14A) that are transmitted from cell to cell through the low-resistance pathways of the intercalated discs and the gap junctions. As the excitation advances along a cell, the distribution of charges at the junction between the resting and active regions is as shown in Fig. 6.14B. The excitation is conducted so rapidly from cell to cell that this distribution of charges may be regarded as an advancing 'wavefront' of excitation through the myocardium. Such a wavefront

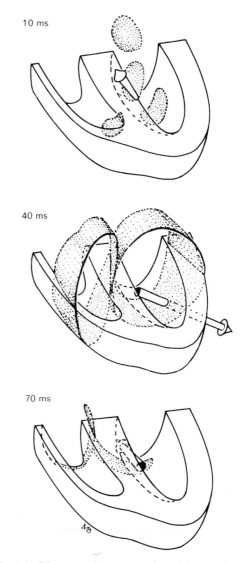

Fig. 6.16 Diagrammatic representation of the wavefronts of excitation of the ventricles at 10, 40 and 70 ms after the onset of ventricular depolarisation (see Fig. 6.10). The solid arrows indicate vectors representing the total unbalanced electrical activity at each instant.

carries opposite electrical charges on its two surfaces and therefore produces appropriate fields of potential and current.

Electrical current seems to flow in the heart much as it does between two terminals immersed in a *volume conductor*, such as a large volume of electrolyte solution, through which the current can flow in three dimensions. The lines of current-flow in a volume conductor are accompanied in the usual manner by appropriate isopotential lines, also distributed in three dimensions (Fig. 6.15). Although the thorax contains organs with electrical resistances different from those of the heart, for example the lungs, it is probable that the intrathoracic contents act as a volume conductor, extending that of the heart and providing a more or less homogeneous conducting medium for the three-dimensional fields of current and potential. The potentials are greatest near the positive and negative terminals of the 'cardiac electrical generator' and diminish as the square of the distance from them.

During the excitation of the heart charged wavefronts move through the muscle of the atria and the ventricles (Fig. 6.10). At any instant the apparent cardiac generator is the vectorial resultant of several complex and differently directed wavefronts. Figure 6.16 shows the *resultant vectors* at 10, 40, and 70 ms after the onset of ventricular excitation. The resultant vectors at successive instants determine the form of the voltage-time curve (ECG) recorded by an electrode at any site on the trunk, or from the extremities of the limbs if they are regarded as forming part of the electrode attached to the trunk. The vector-electrocardiographic principles involved are illustrated in Figures 6.17 and 6.18. The magnitude and sign of each deflection in the QRS complex (Fig. 6.17) of the scalar (surface) ECG are determined by the relation between, on the one hand, the size and the position in space of the responsible vector and, on the other, a plane passing through the origin of the vector and at right angles to the 'lead axis' (p. 66). Figure 6.18 shows how these early, middle and late

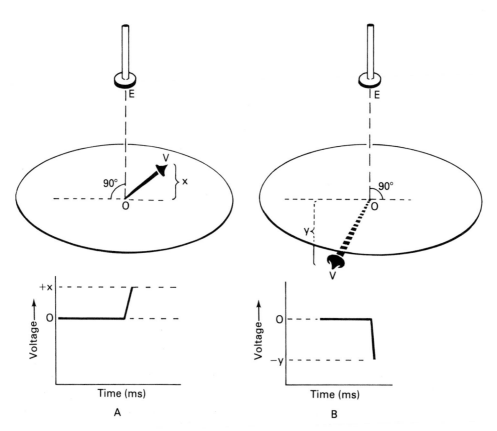

Fig. 6.17 Diagrams to show the relation between two vectors representing the unbalanced electrical activity of the heart at different moments, the 'lead axis' of a unipolar electrode, and the size and sign of the electrocardiographic deflection recorded from the electrode. In A the vector (V) is comparatively small and points *towards* the electrode (E); its tip is at a distance, *x*, *above* the plane that passes through the origin (O) of the vector and at right angles to the lead axis (EO) of the electrode (E). The resulting deflection is *positive* (+*x*). In B the vector is longer, and points *away from* the electrode with its tip at a distance, *y*, *below* the plane: the deflection is therefore larger and *negative* (−*y*)

vectorial forces of Figure 6.16 contribute to the formation of characteristic deflections in the electrocardiogram recorded from conventional electrode sites on the surface of the body during ventricular depolarisation. Similar principles can be applied to the consideration of atrial depolarisation.

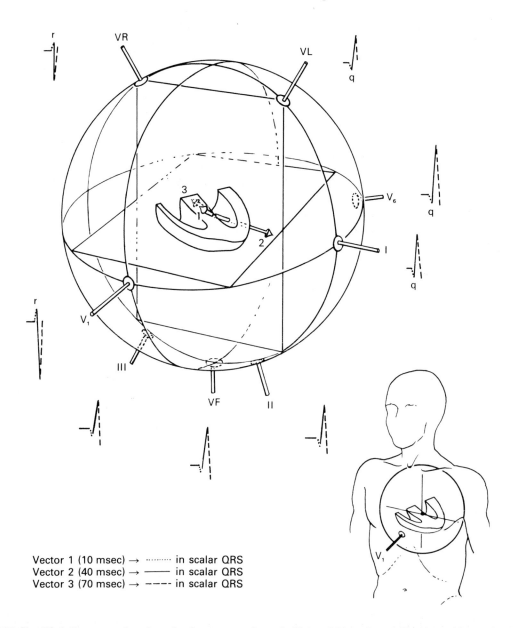

Vector 1 (10 msec) → ········ in scalar QRS
Vector 2 (40 msec) → ——— in scalar QRS
Vector 3 (70 msec) → ---- in scalar QRS

Fig. 6.18 Simplified diagram to show how the three vectors shown in Figure 6.16 can be considered as arising at the centre of a spherical volume conductor in the thorax, and indicating the positions on the surface of this sphere of some conventional electrode positions used in electrocardiography. Beside each electrode is an indication of the contribution made by each of the three vectors to the surface (scalar) QRS complex recorded at each site. In this diagram the lead axes are not shown but each runs from the site of a surface electrode to the origin of the vectors. Thus, the 10 ms vector, being short and directed upward and to the right toward the electrode sites for scalar leads VR and V_1 gives a small positive (upward) deflection (r) in these leads; it is, however, directed away from the electrode sites of other leads and so gives negative (downward) deflections (q) in them. The unipolar exploring electrodes VR, VL and VF are actually applied to the right and left arms and the left leg, respectively. As shown in the smaller diagram, V_1 is sited on the precordium, V_6 is sited in the left axillary region. The standard bipolar leads (roman numerals) record complexes similar to those recorded by unipolar exploring electrodes sited as shown, though the actual lead arrangements are more complex (Fig. 6.20).

Repolarisation

The same general principles also apply to the repolarisation of both the atria and the ventricles. Since the polarity of the charged wavefront that accompanies the restoration of the resting state is opposite to that of the depolarising wavefront (Fig. 6.14), one might expect that the deflections in the ECG representing repolarisation would always be opposite in direction to those that represent depolarisation. However, repolarisation does not proceed through the intact heart in the same order as depolarisation: excitation lasts longer at the base of the heart than at the apex.

During the first rapid phase (O) of the membrane action potential (Fig. 6.3) the depolarisation of the 'working' cell is associated with the sudden increase in the permeability of the sarcolemma that allows the passive inward Na^+ flux. Repolarisation, on the other hand, involves the active extrusion of Na^+ by the much slower mechanism of the Na^+–K^+ pump, which involves metabolic work and the action of ATPase, and is much more readily disturbed by changes such as altered electrolyte concentrations and oxygen tension in the myocardium. There is no direct experimental evidence about the course of repolarisation through the heart under normal conditions, but it is certainly true that the segment of the ECG that reflects repolarisation (ST-T, Fig. 6.21) is much more readily altered by comparatively small changes in the state of the myocardium than that which reflects depolarisation (QRS; Fig. 6.19).

Atrial repolarisation is not usually recognised in the normal ECG because it occurs during the inscription of the QRS deflections that accompany ventricular depolarisation. When AV conduction is delayed atrial repolarisation can sometimes be recognised as a low-voltage negative deflection following that of atrial depolarisation (P wave).

'Lead systems' and terminology

The electrocardiograph detects potential differences between the sites of two electrodes. In a volume conductor the potential far away from the source of the current is negligible, so an electrode sited far from the source provides a reference point of virtually zero potential and is known as an 'indifferent' electrode. The

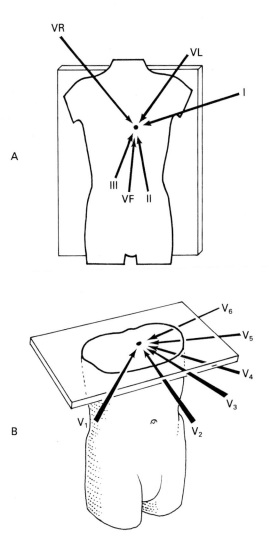

Fig. 6.20 Lead axes of the '12-lead electrocardiogram' used in clinical practice. The axes of the limb leads lie in the frontal plane (A). Leads I, II and III are bipolar leads with paired electrodes on right and left arm (I), right arm and left leg (II) and left arm and left leg (III). Leads VR, VL, and VF are unipolar leads from right shoulder, left shoulder and left groin respectively (p. 67). The precordial ('chest') leads lie around the horizontal plane (B). The axes are shown as arrows, to indicate that a lead axis can be regarded as pointing from the electrode position towards the origin of the changing vector that represents the unbalanced electrical activity of the heart at successive moments in the course of excitation.

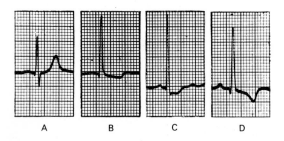

Fig. 6.19 A, single PQRST complex from a normal electrocardiogram (see Fig. 6.21) B, C and D are abnormal complexes, with characteristic changes in the ST segment and T wave (ventricular repolarisation) while QRS (ventricular depolarisation) is hardly altered. B, patient receiving digoxin; C, low serum K^+ level (1.3 mmol/l); D, left ventricular hypertrophy.

other, 'exploring' electrode can then be used to measure potentials in any part of the volume conductor or on its surface (Fig. 6.15). These leads are known as *unipolar leads* or *V-leads* because they record values that represent meaningful voltages.

When both electrodes are near the source of current, the ECG records the difference between two potentials of comparable size, each of which is constantly changing through the cardiac cycle. Such *bipolar* leads were those originally used, for example, by Einthoven, and, though harder to understand than unipolar lead systems, they are still used (as the 'standard leads', I, II and III) in clinical practice, together with unipolar leads (Fig. 6.20).

The axes of the various unipolar and bipolar leads used in clinical electrocardiography are shown in Figure 6.20. The lead axes of unipolar and bipolar limb leads lie on the frontal plane, those of the unipolar chest leads lie more or less on a horizontal plane, through the thorax. An electrode may be considered as 'looking down' its lead axis to the origin of the resultant vector that represents the unbalanced electrical activity of the heart at any instant.

The normal EGG

A normal electrocardiogram (lead 1) is represented diagrammatically in Figure 6.21, which is enlarged for ease in labelling.

The P wave begins as the excitatory process passes from the SA node to the atria, its duration indicating the time taken for excitation to spread throughout the atrial muscle. The QRS complex indicates the depolarisation of the ventricles. The T wave signals the last part

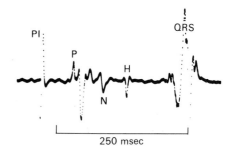

Fig. 6.22 Direct recording made by an electrode catheter of the electrical impulse in the special conducting system in the human heart. PI, artificial pacing impulse in the right atrium. Between the excitation of the atrium (P) and that of the ventricles (QRS) the electrode records the activity of the AV node (N) and the bundle of His (H) as smaller polyphasic deflections. (Damato A N et al. 1969 Circulation 39: 435)

of repolarisation in the ventricles; the U wave, not always seen, is probably related to after-potentials (p. 386). The PR interval gives the time taken by the excitatory process to travel over the atria and through the AV junctional tissue to the ventricular muscle. During the ST segment all parts of the ventricles have been depolarised; the record is, however, not quite isoelectric (horizontal) but inclined slightly in the same direction as the T wave, because repolarisation begins very slowly during this period. Ventricular repolarisation is completed during the T wave. In the TP or UP interval, that is between two cycles of cardiac activity, the whole heart is in the resting polarised state and the record is isoelectric.

The P wave lasts from 60 to 110 ms. The PR interval usually lasts from 120 to 200 ms and, like QT, varies inversely with the heart rate. The QRS complex varies considerably in form, lasting from 60 to 110 ms. Values greater than this indicate either that the electrical events are prolonged in one ventricle or that the ventricles are not being excited simultaneously. The amplitude of the QRS complex is usually from 0.5 to 1.5 mV in leads I, II and II, but is considerably higher in unipolar leads from electrode sites on the precordium ('chest leads').

Special exploring 'leads' may be used: for example, cardiac catheters (p. 81) with electrodes at the tip can record local intra-cardiac electrocardiograms and direct recordings are made of the electrical impulse travelling through the AV nodal tissue, the bundle of His and the right and left bundle-branches of the special conducting system (Fig. 6.22).

The appearance of the ECG gives no information at all about the force of cardiac contraction; indeed, evidence of electrical activity can be present in the ECG when the heart has stopped contracting.

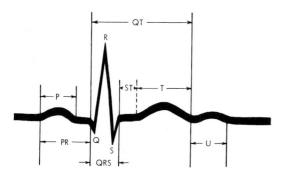

Fig. 6.21 A diagram showing the various parts of the electrocardiogram, namely the P wave, QRS complex, T and U waves, the PR and QT intervals, and the PQ and ST segments. The TP segment from the end of T to the beginning of P is not labelled. By convention an upward deflection in the record indicates electrical negativity of right arm in leads I and II and of left arm in lead III. The standard record is made with the apparatus adjusted so that a vertical movement of 1 cm is produced by a potential change of 1 mV.

DISORDERED CARDIAC RHYTHMS

The clinical aspects of cardiac arrhythmias lie outside the scope of this book but their mechanisms are of interest to students of physiology because they illustrate some important principles.

Ectopic pace-makers

The premature discharge of a pacemaker cell lower than the sinus node (ectopic focus) produces premature excitation and contraction of the chamber where it is sited (*extrasystole*). When the ectopic focus lies above the AV node there is a premature excitation of the whole heart (*supraventricular ectopic beat;* Fig. 6.23). Because the spread of atrial excitation is abnormal it may cause an abnormal P wave, but ventricular excitation occurs normally through the AV node and bundles; the QRST complex is therefore normal.

When the ectopic focus lies below the division of the bundle of His into its main right and left bundles, or in the cells of the Purkinje network in the ventricles, there is a premature and abnormal spread of excitation in the ventricles (*ventricular ectopic beat*). An abnormal QRST occurs with no preceding P wave (Fig. 6.24). If the excitation spreads backward up the AV conducting

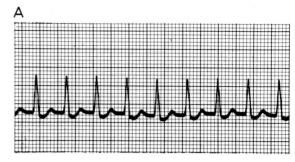

A

B

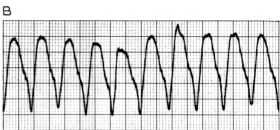

Fig. 6.25 Paroxysms of tachycardia. A, *Supraventricular (atrial) tachycardia;* because the ectopic pacemaker discharges above the division of the AV conducting system (p. 59), the QRST complexes have a normal shapes. B. *Ventricular tachycardia;* the ectopic pacemaker lies below the division of the AV conducting tissue, so the complexes are bizarre, like ventricular extrasystoles.

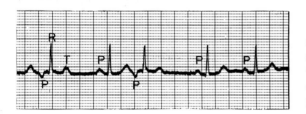

Fig. 6.23 Electrocardiogram, lead II, showing two *supraventricular extrasystoles*. The ectopic focus is low in the atrium or in the AV junctional tissue. Atrial excitation occurs in a direction the reverse of normal. The first and third P waves are therefore inverted. Ventricular conduction is normal so the abnormal premature P waves are followed by normal premature QRST complexes.

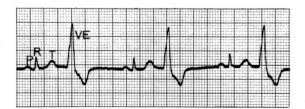

Fig. 6.24 ECG, lead II, showing *ventricular extrasystoles* (VE) following each normal complex. The abnormal spread of excitation from the ectopic pace-maker below the divisions of the conducting tissue (p. 59) causes wide and abnormally shaped QRST complexes.

system there will be retrograde excitation of the atria and a P wave may follow the QRS complex. During ventricular ectopic beats the abnormal ventricular contraction is inefficient, and the intraventricular pressure and stroke volume are low. The distension of the aortic root is therefore small and a pulse wave may not be propagated to the wrist.

The premature excitation of the myocardium after the discharge of an ectopic focus may leave the muscle refractory to the next pacemaking stimulus arising in the sinu-atrial node. Sometimes retrograde atrial excitation prematurely discharges the SA node. Ectopic beats are then followed by a longer diastole than usual ('compensatory pause'). The patient may feel that his heart has 'missed a beat'. A series of ectopic beats arising from a focus in the atria or ventricles can produce a paroxysm of tachycardia (atrial or ventricular) that may impede filling of the heart and so lower the cardiac output (Fig. 6.25A and B).

Atrial fibrillation and flutter

During atrial systole in a normally functioning heart all the atrial muscle fibres contract practically simultaneously and, in the ventricular systole that follows, all the ventricular muscle fibres contract in an orderly sequence. In certain diseases of the heart, or after elec-

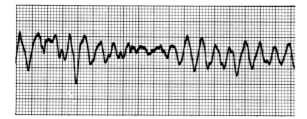

Fig. 6.26 *Ventricular fibrillation.* There are no recognisable P waves or QRS complexes. The chaotic cardiac electrical activity gives rise to random oscillations only.

trical or chemical stimulation, this orderly contraction may be replaced by very irregular activity, in which the individual muscle fibres contract in a disorderly sequence all out of step with one another so a fine rapid tremulous movement (*fibrillation*) is seen over the surface of either the atria or the ventricles. The affected chambers of the heart do not contract as a whole and their pumping action is lost. If the ventricles fibrillate (Fig. 6.26) the blood is not pumped out into the systemic or pulmonary circulations and death rapidly results from anoxia of the brain. If, however, fibrillation is confined to the atria, the ventricles still force the blood round the circulation and a patient with atrial fibrillation may have a reasonably efficient circulation (Chap. 7).

If an atrium of the exposed heart of the dog is subjected to a brief period of rapid electrical stimulation (300 to 600 per minute) the atria may change their rhythm and beat about 300 times per minute (*atrial flutter*). This abnormal rhythm also occurs in diseased or even normal human hearts (Fig. 6.27).

The mechanism of atrial flutter and fibrillation was studied by Prinzmetal and his colleagues with high-speed cinephotography (2000 frames per second) and a cathode-ray oscillograph. In atrial fibrillation minute irregular contractions occur continuously throughout the atrial muscle, each one involving an area from 0.03 or 3 mm in diameter. Superimposed on these are larger contractions that sweep across the atrium fairly regularly at rates of 400 to 600 per minute, giving an appearance of fibrillation to the unaided eye. Prinzmetal claimed that all the atrial arrhythmias arose from the discharge of a single ectopic focus. At rates of impulse formation in the ectopic focus below the normal sinus rate premature atrial systoles are produced; when the rate of impulse formation is in the range 100 to 250 per minute, atrial tachycardia is the result. Flutter and fibrillation are found at rates of impulse formation of approximately 300 to 400 per minute, respectively. Not all workers agree with Prinzmetal. For example Rytand marshalled much evidence in support of the earlier idea that atrial flutter, when it occurs in patients and is not induced experimentally, is caused by 'circus movement'; that is to say the wave of excitation is trapped in a circular pathway in the atria because of the refractory period and so becomes perpetuated.

In both atrial flutter and fibrillation the rate of stimulation is so rapid that the AV node is incapable of responding to every impulse reaching it from the atria. When flutter is present the ventricles usually respond in a regular manner to every third or fourth atrial contraction (Fig. 6.27), while in atrial fibrillation the response of the ventricles is irregular (Fig. 6.28) and often rapid, giving an irregular rapid pulse and a systolic blood pressure that varies from beat to beat because of the varying length of diastole.

Any disorder of cardiac rhythm that causes very rapid ventricular contractions tends to reduce the cardiac output and may lead to heart failure (p. 98). Many fast abnormal rhythms, however, can be converted to normal sinus rhythm by a single direct-current electric shock applied across the patient's thorax. The high-voltage shock, which lasts only a few milliseconds, is usually triggered by the R wave of the ECG and has an energy value of between 50 and 400 joules.

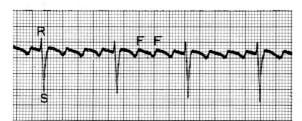

Fig. 6.27 ECG, lead II, showing *atrial flutter*. A regular succession of characteristically abnormal P waves (F or flutter waves) indicates the abnormal excitation of the atria but the ventricles respond only to every fourth beat. There is therefore '4:1 AV block'.

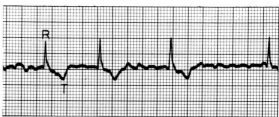

Fig. 6.28 ECG, lead II, showing *atrial fibrillation*. Low voltage irregular oscillations of the base line represent the atrial arrhythmia. The QRS complexes occur irregularly because the AV node can only transmit some of the impulses it receives. In this record the T wave is inverted because of an abnormality of repolarisation (see Fig. 6.19).

Heart block

Since the conduction of excitation in the AV junctional tissues does not normally occupy more than 210 ms, a PR interval above this value denotes impaired AV conduction (*incomplete heart block*; Fig. 6.29 A and B). In *complete heart block* (Fig. 6.30) the contractions of the atria and ventricles are completely dissociated from one another, the atria being activated from the SA node and the ventricles from a pace-maker with a slower rate of impulse formation in the bundles. In such a case the ECG shows regularly recurring P waves of normal form and, superimposed upon this, a regular succession of

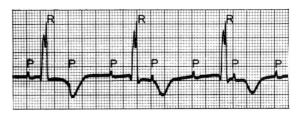

Fig. 6.30 *Complete heart block.* The P waves occur regularly at a rate at 100 per minute and represent atrial systole at this rate. The wide and abnormal QRS complexes also occur regularly, but at a much slower rate (45 per minute) and represent the discharge of an independent ventricular pace-maker. Atrial and ventricular activities are entirely dissociated.

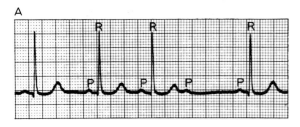

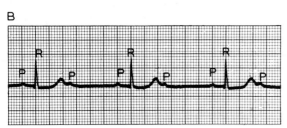

Fig. 6.29 Two forms of *incomplete heart block*. A. The PR interval increases from complex to complex because the impulse takes an increasingly long time to traverse the AV node; eventually the impulse is not conducted to the ventricles and no QRS complex follows the P wave. The cycle then begins again ('Wenckebach periods') B. There is no QRS complex after every second P wave because of failure of AV conduction ('fixed' 2:1 AV block, 'dropped beats').

ventricular complexes at a slower rate (*idioventricular rhythm*).

Continuous ECG Monitoring

The ECG of healthy subjects of all ages can easily be recorded continuously on tape throughout 24 hours while they pursue their usual activities ('Holter monitoring'). In all age groups thus studied, ranging from the newborn to early middle age, when covert heart disease might confuse the findings, a surprising number of arrhythmias have been detected. They are transient and symptomless, but include both disorders of conduction and ectopic activity. In the infant, disorders of sinu-atrial conduction seem commonest. As the child becomes older, supraventricular and ventricular ectopic activity appears and AV conduction defects, especially short Wenckebach periods, are seen. These ectopic beats, short paroxysms of supraventricular and even ventricular tachycardia and incomplete heart block become commoner in older school children and students. Thus, 'normal sinus rhythm' is often not maintained without interruption throughout 24 hours in normal subjects.

REFERENCES

Berne R M, Levy M N 1977 Cardiovascular physiology. Mosby, St Louis

Burch G E, De Pasquale N P 1964 A history of electrocardiography. Year Book Publishers, Chicago

Durrer D, Van Dam R T, Freud G E, Janse M J, Meijler F L, Arzbaecher R C 1970 Total excitation of the isolated human heart. Circulation 41: 899–912

Noble D 1979 The initiation of the heartbeat. Clarendon Press, Oxford

Opie L H 1984 The heart: physiology, metabolism, pharmacology and therapy. Grune & Stratton, London

Reuter H 1979 Properties of two inward membrane currents in the heart. Annual Review of Physiology 41: 413–424

Sperelakis N 1979 Propagation mechanisms in the heart. Annual Review of Physiology 41: 441–457

Vasalle M 1979 Electrogenesis of the plateau and pacemaker potential. Annual Review of Physiology 41: 425–440

Wellens H J J, Lie K I, Janse M J (eds) 1978 The conduction system of the heart. Nijhoff, The Hague

7

Cardiac contraction

The walls of the human atria are thin, appropriate to the small amount of work required to force their contents into the *inflow tracts* of the ventricles. The thick-walled ventricles do most of the work of the heart, expelling the blood through the *outflow tracts* into the system of branching arteries that offer a high impedance to the flow of the blood. The wall of the left ventricle is three or four times thicker than the wall of the right ventricle at the corresponding position, for the left ventricle functions as a pressure pump against a high aortic impedance, while the right ventricle acts as a volume pump against the lower impedance of the pulmonary artery.

The cavities may contain roughly 400 ml of blood (*end-diastolic volume*), an amount that is much greater than the quantity expelled by both ventricles each time they contract (about 140 ml). In other words the cavities are not completely empty even at the end of systole. The left ventricular residual volume at the end of systole in untrained persons is estimated to be about 50 ml and in endurance athletes about 120 ml.

Each ventricle has the same capacity and each expels the same amount of blood during systole (*stroke volume*). If this were not so the circulation would eventually cease. If the left ventricle were to expel 60 ml per beat and the right ventricle 60.1 ml per beat, then in one hour, if the heart beats 80 times a minute, the left would expel 288 000 ml and the right 288 480 ml. The difference, 480 ml, would have to be accommodated in the pulmonary vessels and the lungs, with grave effects on the pulmonary circulation and respiration. This does not mean, however, that for *short* periods the amounts of blood expelled by the two ventricles is always identical; at certain phases of the respiratory cycle, for example, there are small, temporary differences between the stroke volumes of the right and left ventricles. In health, though, the average outputs must be equal. In heart failure a discrepancy between the two outputs has serious consequences. In some types of congenital heart deformities in which blood is shunted from one side of the circulation to the other there may be quite large differences between the ventricular outputs.

The atria and the ventricles are completely separated by the fibrotendinous ring, which gives attachment to most of the muscular fibres and to the atrioventricular valves. The only muscular connection between atria and ventricles is the atrioventricular (junctional) bundle of His composed of specialised conducting tissue.

Heart valves

The heart valves (Fig. 7.1) are formed so that they permit the blood to flow only from the atria to the ventricles and onward into the arteries. The points of entry of the veins into the atria have no functional valves.

The cusps of the *atrioventricular valves* are large, sail-like structures that arise from the atrioventricular rings and pass down into the cavity of the ventricles (Fig. 7.1). Their margins are connected by thin cords (*chordae tendineae*) to the papillary muscles that form part of the muscular mass of the ventricles. As the ventricles contract the papillary muscles pull on the chordae tendineae so that the cusps cannot prolapse into the atria. On the left side, between the left atrium and left ventricle, two cusps form the mitral valve. Closure of the tricuspid valve is brought about mainly by the more mobile anterior cusp. Functionally the cusps, chordae and papillary muscles act as a single atrioventricular valve mechanism, and damage to any one component may make the valve incompetent.

The aortic and pulmonary valves each have three semilunar cusps of very thin fibrous tissue covered by endocardium. In the intact heart the three pockets meet along three lines and prevent blood from flowing back into the ventricle.

Working myocardial cells

The main bulk of the atria and ventricles consists of working myocardial cells arranged in columns. Each cell contains one central nucleus, many myofibrils aligned along the cell's axis and an exceptionally large number of mitochondria lying close to the myofibrils. The myofibrils, as in skeletal muscle (Chap. 40), are the fundamental contractile units of the myocardium. The

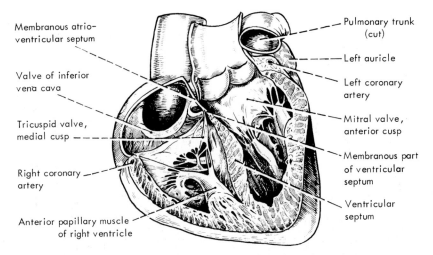

Fig. 7.1 Section through the human heart to show the valves. On the right side the atrioventricular orifice has been cut across. On the left side the section passes through the aortic valve and in front of the mitral valve. The AV valve system includes cusps, chordae and papillary muscles. The cusps make the open valves funnel-shaped

microstructure of the cardiac sarcomere resembles that of skeletal muscle (Fig. 40.3, p. 492), with sets of actin and myosin myofilaments hexagonally arranged. The modulating proteins tropomyosin and troponin are also present in the thin filaments of cardiac muscle, though there is some evidence that all four proteins may not be identical with those in skeletal muscle. It is probable, however, that they act in essentially the same way as described for skeletal muscle (Chap. 40).

Myocardial metabolism

Myocardial cells resemble skeletal muscle cells in containing glycogen, ATP and phosphocreatine, but their metabolic behaviour is somewhat different.

The metabolism of the heart is normally almost entirely aerobic and accounts for about 7 per cent of the body's oxygen consumption. At rest, the heart consumes about 10 ml/100 g tissue per minute and extracts 65 to 75 per cent of the oxygen in the coronary

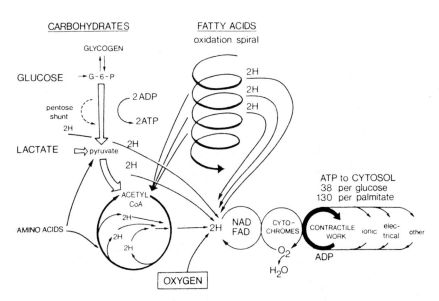

Fig. 7.2 Principal metabolic pathways for the conversion of carbohydrate and fatty acid fuels to the energy used in the cytosol for contractile work. After Opie L H 1984 The heart: Its metabolism and physiology, Academic Press, London

arterial blood. The main metabolic substrate of the heart is free fatty acids, which supply about two-thirds of its energy when the body is in the fasting state. Important amounts of glucose and lactate are also consumed, accounting together for about 30 per cent of the total oxygen extracted. Glucose is used particularly after meals, and the lactate normally comes from the metabolism of skeletal muscle; when free fatty acids are available glucose utilisation is suppressed. Pyruvate and ketone bodies are also used to a small extent by the myocardium. Most of the very small amounts of amino acids taken up are used for protein synthesis; there is an active turnover of proteins in the myocardium with constant synthesis and destruction.

Cardiac energy metabolism consists of (i) the conversion of fatty acids, glucose and lactate to acetyl CoA, which produces reduced cofactors, such as NADH, in the citrate cycle; (ii) the oxidation of such cofactors with the passage of electrons through the cytochrome chain to produce ATP in the mitochondria; and (iii) the release of ATP into the cytosol, where most is used for contractile work (Fig. 7.2).

If the heart becomes hypoxic or mildly ischaemic, there is a steep increase in anaerobic glycolysis so that the lactate content of the coronary sinus blood rises. In severe ischaemia, glycolysis is inhibited by accumulated protons and lactate.

When ventricular contraction is increased to overcome a raised arterial impedance (pressure load, afterload) the oxygen consumption is greater than that involved in a corresponding contraction to expel an increased end-diastolic volume of blood (volume load, preload).

MYOCARDIAL CONTRACTION

The excitation-contraction coupling of the myocardium has already been described (p. 61).

If the function of the heart and lungs is taken over by a pump and oxygenator it is possible to open the ventricles of the dog and study the mechanical movements of the myocardium by high-speed cinephotography. The order of contraction agrees with the order of electrical excitation already described (p. 60). In the left ventricle contractions are seen first in the papillary muscles and in the adjacent septum and reach their maximum in 40 ms. The contraction waves spread from this area in such a way that the maximal contraction of the inflow tract occurs in 60 ms, of the outflow tract in 100 ms and of the aortic infundibulum in 120 ms. Relaxation occurs in the same order. The sequence of events in the right side is the same but the time course is shorter because of the shorter conduction time through the thinner walls. The early contraction

of the papillary muscles tightens the chordae and so prevents the cusps of the AV valves from bulging much into the atrium during systole.

The length–tension relation

Spiral and transverse muscle bundles have been described in the myocardium but since they were only seen after very crude methods of preparation they were likely to be artifacts. In a papillary muscle all the fibres are aligned in much the same direction, so these thin cardiac muscles provide simpler samples than the more complex ventricular wall. The behaviour of isolated papillary muscles subjected to a *preload* and *afterload* has been much studied with a myograph (Fig. 7.3). With such a preparation, the unstimulated muscle is progressively stretched and the 'resting (passive) tension' rises.

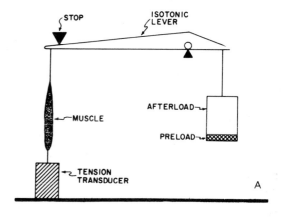

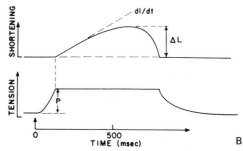

Fig. 7.3 Diagram showing (A) the experimental arrangement for studying the loaded contraction of a papillary muscle with a myograph. The initial length is set by a 'preload' and held constant by the stop. When the muscle shortens it lifts the 'afterload'. B illustrates tension and shortening of a typical after-loaded contraction. Starting at O the isometric tension increases until, when it reaches P, the muscle begins to shorten and the afterload is lifted. The initial velocity of shortening of the subsequent isotonic contraction is given by dl/dt. ΔL indicates the maximum shortening during the contraction. Sonnenblick E H 1966 The mechanics of myocardial contraction. In: Briller S A, Conn J J (eds) University of Pennsylvania Press, The myocardial cell, Philadelphia, p. 173

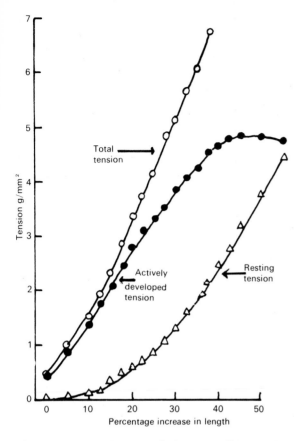

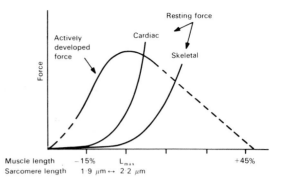

Fig. 7.5 The relationship between tension (force) and initial muscle length for cat papillary muscle and for the sartorius muscle of the frog. Muscle length has been normalised relative to that length where the actively developed tension is maximum (L_{max}). Active tension is normalised relative to the tension developed at L_{max}. Resting tension is the tension produced by the passively stretched muscle. Active tension is the tension the striated muscle generates when stimulated. (Leyton R A, Sonnenblick E H 1971 The sarcomere as the basis of Starling's law of the heart in the left and right ventricles. In: Bajusz E, Jasmin G (eds) Functional morphology of the heart: Methods and achievements in experimental pathology, Vol. 5, Karger, Basel, p. 22)

Fig. 7.4 Length-tension curves for human papillary muscle removed at a cardiac operation (Sonnenblick E H, Braunwald E, Marrow A G 1965 Journal of Clinical Investigation 44:966). Similar curves are obtained from human ventricular myocardium *in situ* at operation.

When the muscle is then held at a fixed length and electrically stimulated, an isometric force can be measured at one end. If, at various lengths, the muscle is stimulated, active contraction is superimposed on the resting *length-tension relationship* for each length, giving a curve of 'total tension' (Fig. 7.4). The 'actively developed' tension can be derived from the total tension by subtracting the resting tension. Figure 7.5 shows a '*length-tension curve*' for papillary muscle. The range of muscle lengths at which the active tension is almost maximum (L_{max}) is relatively wide, and corresponds to the rounded peak of the active tension curve. As the muscle is shortened the actively developed tension and the resting tension both fall.

The length–tension curves of cardiac and skeletal muscle are similar in shape. Figure 7.5 also shows the curve for the sartorius muscle of the frog, corrected for the different cross-sectional areas and for the pro-

portions of the contractile material in the two types of striated muscle cell. The peak active tension at L_{max} is generally the same for cardiac and skeletal muscle. By contrast the resting tension at L_{max} is considerable in cardiac muscle and exists during the major part of the ascending limb of the length–active-tension curve, while in skeletal muscle resting tension is minimal at L_{max}, rising only appreciably during the descending limb of the length–active-tension curve. Cardiac muscle therefore operates along the ascending limb of the length–active-tension curve while skeletal muscle operates mainly near the apex. It is not known why cardiac muscle has this high resting tension.

The length–tension curves in Figure 7.5 are related to sarcomere lengths that correlate closely with the theoretical limits to the shortening of sarcomeres in the ventricles. These relationships, and the fact that the length of the sarcomere is directly proportional to muscle length along the ascending limb of the length–active-tension curve, form the ultra-structural basis of Starling's 'Law of the Heart', which is considered later.

Length–tension curves of this general form have been derived experimentally from mammalian and human papillary muscle, and from the human heart *in situ* (Fig. 7.4). The concepts of preload and afterload (Fig. 7.6) of the whole heart are used in clinical medicine.

The force-velocity relation

A. V. Hill's model to explain the mechanical activity of skeletal muscle (Fig. 7.6 and Chap. 40) has proved useful in considering cardiac muscle as well, although the series elastic (SE) component of myocardium seeems to be more compliant than that of skeletal muscle, and the parallel elastic component (PE), to be stiffer. Hill studied the relation between the load on a muscle and the velocity of its shortening, the *'force–velocity relation'*, which is a fundamental property of the contractile element (CE), that is the actin–myosin mechanism (Fig. 7.7). When the force, or load, (P) approaches zero the velocity of initial shortening (V) is maximal and is termed V_{max}. As the load is increased the amount and the velocity of contraction both decrease progressively until no shortening can occur and the maximum isometric force (P_O) is reached.

The 'active state' of myocardium is a measure of the processes that generate force and shortening at contractile sites. It is characterised by instantaneous relations between muscle length, force and velocity of contraction, during the whole course of a contraction. The activation of heart muscle is relatively slow, so early in the contraction the slow increase in the active state gives low values for the shortening velocity of the lightly loaded muscle. Late in the contraction the load is heavy and this fact and the sensitivity of the CE to displacement give low velocities of shortening. During most of the contraction, however, when the muscle acts most intensely, it operates on this *force–velocity curve*. The 'intensity of the active state' is thus an expression of the capacity of the contractile mechanism of muscle at any

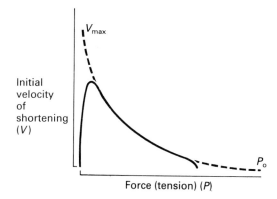

Fig. 7.7 A force-velocity curve for muscle. Theoretically a hyperbolic relationship exists between the initial contraction velocity (V) and the muscle tension (P). V_{max}, maximum velocity of initial shortening at zero load: P_0, maximum tension at zero shortening (isometric). Experimentally, the force–velocity relations of a muscle are not expressed by this curve either early, or late, in contraction, but are as indicated by the solid lines.

moment after stimulation to produce tension, force and motion.

If the ends of the muscle are fixed and the isometric tension developed is maximal, all the active sites that generate tension to bring about shortening would tend to be in a 'combined', rather than a 'free', state: thus the maximum tension (P_O) should be determined by the total number of actin–myosin sites that are combined, which in turn may be related to the amount of Ca^{2+} present, to the action of troponin and to the sarcomere length (Chap. 40). With progressively lighter loads fewer and fewer actin–myosin sites would be combined, and more would be free, until eventually both the rate of release of energy and the speed of shortening of the muscle are maximal, and the muscle shortens freely with no load. Because almost all active sites are now free, V_{max} would be determined by the maximal intrinsic rate at which energy can be released to allow an actin–myosin interaction to produce the cyclic changes in position that lead to shortening. This is related to myosin ATPase, and the rate of activity of this enzyme has been found to provide an excellent index to the V_{max} of muscle. Force-velocity curves for cardiac muscle have been obtained experimentally from animal and human papillary muscle, canine left ventricle and intact human ventricle (Fig. 7.8). The value for V_{max} must be obtained by extrapolation.

Changes in force–velocity relations characterise the two most important general properties of cardiac muscle: the change in *initial muscle length*, the basis of the 'Starling mechanism' to be considered later, and changes in the *contractile state* of the myocardium. An increase in the initial length of the muscle produces a

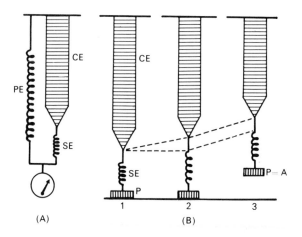

Fig. 7.6 A. V. Hill's model of muscle contraction. (A) CE, contractile element (actin-myosin mechanism); SE, series elastic component; PE, parallel elastic component. (B) during contraction — 1, initial resting state; 2, the CE shortens, the SE is stretched but the preload, P, is not moved (isometric contraction); 3, further shortening of CE lifts the preload, which now becomes an afterload, A (isotonic contraction).

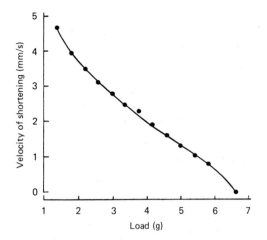

Fig. 7.8 Force–velocity curve for human papillary muscle removed at a cardiac operation. Initial velocity of isotonic shortening on ordinate, afterload on abscissa. (Sonnenblick E H, Braunwald E, Morrow A G 1965 Journal of Clinical Investigation 44:966.) Similar curves have been obtained during isovolumetric contraction of intact ventricle.

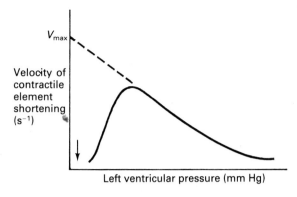

Fig. 7.9 Force–velocity curve for intact human left ventricle (LV) in a semi-log plot to show how the resultant straight-line extrapolation to LV end-diastolic pressure (zero developed pressure) may be used to give an index of V_{max}. The velocity of the contractile element (V_{CE}) is $(dP/dt)/KP$. The arrow indicates LV end-diastolic pressure. See text. After Swanton R H 1984 Cardiology, Blackwell Scientific, Oxford, p. 416

rise in P_O without a change in V_{max}. A change in the contractile state of the myocardium alters V_{max} with or without a change in P_O.

This behaviour of the myocardium contrasts with that of skeletal muscle. Under physiological conditions the force–velocity curve of a skeletal muscle does not alter; its force is altered mainly by its innervation, which controls the number of contracting fibres, each of which contracts almost maximally, though at varying rates. The nerve supply of the heart, however, cannot change the total number of contracting fibres; the contractile force of myocardium depends on the point on the ascending part of the length–tension curve at which cardiac muscle cells are operating.

Length, force and velocity
Both the force–velocity and the length–tension relations apply to a papillary muscle preparation at a given contractile state: that is to say, the greater the load, the slower is the contraction, and, within limits, the longer the fibre the greater is the force developed. It has been shown that during myocardial contraction the velocity of shortening at any instant is a function of the length of the muscle and also of its afterload at that moment. Three variables are concerned: the force or 'load', the velocity of contraction and the fibre length. A three-dimensional plot is therefore needed to demonstrate adequately the course of events during a single contraction. Such plots, however, are hard to understand and several 'indices of ventricular contractility' have been used in experimental and clinical cardiology. None is free from objection (p. 79).

The maximum velocity of shortening of the contractile element at zero load (V_{max}, Fig. 7.7) is often used clinically. The left ventricular (LV) pressure is recorded by a high-fidelity manometer in the tip of a cardiac catheter. This pressure is differentiated to give the rate of rise of LV pressure in mm Hg/s (dP/dt) and that is divided by the instantaneous LV pressure (P) multiplied by the coefficient of series elasticity (Fig. 7.6), K, which has been calculated as 28 in dogs but is unknown in man. The assumption is made that $(dP/dt)/KP =$ VCE, the velocity of the contractile element or V_{max}. If the graph, which resembles that in Figure 7.7, is plotted with the vertical axis on a log scale the extrapolation to the vertical axis is a straight line (Fig. 7.9).

Starling's law of the heart
In E. H. Starling's famous experiments with the isolated and denervated *heart-lung preparation* the venous return to the heart or the arterial resistance could each be increased independently. As a result of either change the heart responded by an increase in both the end-diastolic volume and the contractile activity. As a result of his experiments Starling stated his 'Law of the Heart': *'that the energy of contraction, however measured, is a function of the length of the muscle fibre'.*

Starling believed at first that his law described the way in which the cardiac output of the healthy heart was automatically adjusted to the varying needs of the body. It is now recognised that in the intact heart the regulation of cardiac output is principally due to nervous and hormonal factors, but there is also experimental evidence that the end-diastolic volume is a major determinant of the strength of contraction (Fig. 7.10).

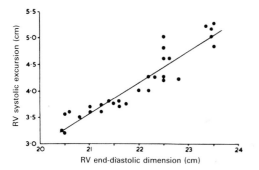

Fig. 7.10 Beat-to-beat relations between the end-diastolic length of a right ventricular (RV) segment and its systolic shortening during the next beat in a patient with sinus rhythm and after the release of a Valsalva manoeuvre. Both variables are changes in distance measured from cineradiographs of patients whose ventricular epicardium had been previously marked by radio-opaque clips at the time of a cardiac operation. (After Braunwald E 1965 British Heart Journal 27:1)

Non-contractile components in heart muscle

Consideration of the force of contraction of cardiac muscle is complicated by the fact that some of the resting tension is maintained by non-contracting elastic structures, Hill's SE and PE (Fig. 7.6). Anatomically they cannot yet be identified and, indeed, need not even be structurally separate. Further, during a cardiac contraction more and more of the force exerted in the resting state may be transferred from the elastic elements to the myofilaments, and during ventricular systole a significant amount of the tension may be borne by the PE, though the SE probably plays no part in alterations to the contractile state of the myocardium. The PE, moreover, determines the resting (diastolic) pressure-volume relationship of the ventricle.

VENTRICULAR PERFORMANCE

Starling showed that the stroke volume of a heart that was not failing is a function of the diastolic fibre length, or ventricular diastolic volume, which in turn is related to the diastolic filling pressure. This last relationship is, however, complicated by the law developed by Laplace for arteries, modified to apply to a ventricle: it implies that the tangential force in the myocardial wall needed to produce a given intraventricular pressure is a direct function of the ventricular radius ($T = (P \times R)\ 2h$, where T = tangential intramyocardial tension, P = intraventricular pressure, R = internal radius of ventricular cavity, h = thickness of ventricular wall). If the diastolic volume of the ventricle is increased a greater intramyocardial tension is needed to keep the intraventricular pressure constant.

Ventricular function curves

Ventricular function can be described in a family of curves (Fig. 7.11) in which ventricular stroke volume or work is related to the atrial or ventricular end-diastolic pressures as measures of the diastolic volume. The simple Starling relationship applies to the modifications needed to allow for changes in posture or for sinus arrhythmia. Other changes, however, such as exercise, apparently lead to changes in cardiac contractility that over-ride the simple relationship.

Despite these difficulties it is still useful to think of cardiac performance in terms of ventricular function curves, if we remember that many factors play a part in both main variables — the ventricular end-diastolic volume and the myocardial contractility. Factors that affect the ventricular end-diastolic volume are shown in Figure 7.12, those that affect the contractile state of the myocardium in Figure 7.13.

When the blood volume is drastically reduced by a sudden severe haemorrhage ventricular performance is impaired. On standing, the blood tends to pool in the lower parts of the body so the intra-thoracic volume and ventricular end-diastolic blood volume are reduced; lying with the legs raised, however, tends to raise the cardiac output unless the heart is failing. The normal negative intra-thoracic pressure is an important factor in maintaining the diastolic filling of the heart. Artificial positive-pressure ventilation can interfere with this mechanism and, by impairing the venous return to the heart, may reduce the cardiac output. During exercise

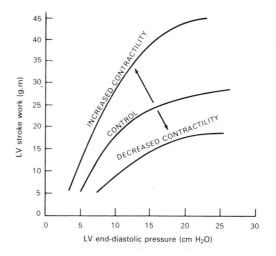

Fig. 7.11 Diagrammatic representation of ventricular function curves obtained under control conditions, during the administration of a positive inotropic agent (increased contractility) and during a negative inotropic state (decreased contractility). LV, left ventricle. (Braunwald E, Ross J, Sonnenblick E H 1967 Mechanisms of contractions of the normal and failing heart. Churchill, Edinburgh)

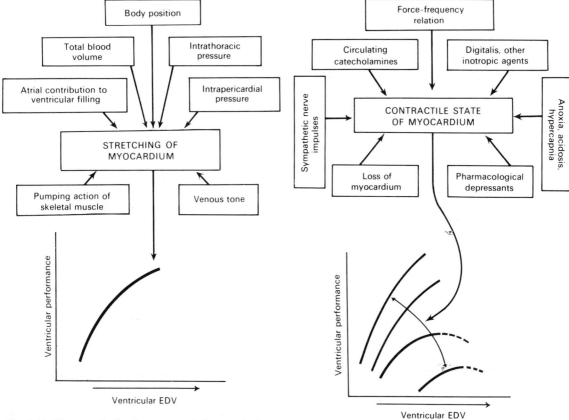

Fig. 7.12 Diagram of a Starling curve, relating ventricular end-diastolic volume (EDV) to ventricular performance and the major influences that determine the degree of stretching of the myocardium, that is, the magnitude of the EDV. (After Braunwald E, Ross J, Sonnenblick E H 1967 Mechanisms of contraction of the normal and failing heart. Churchill, Edinburgh)

Fig. 7.13 Diagram showing the major influences that elevate or depress the contractile state of the myocardium, and the manner in which alterations in the contractile state of the myocardium affect the level of ventricular performance at any given level of ventricular end-diastolic volume. (After Braunwald E, Ross J, Sonnenblick E H 1967 Mechanisms of contraction of the normal and failing heart. Churchill, Edinburgh)

the smooth muscle in the walls of the veins is constricted, probably by sympathetic stimulation, and tends to increase the filling of the heart, as does the pumping action of skeletal muscles on the veins (p. 89). The *atrial transport function* can increase the ventricular end-diastolic volume (p. 79) by acting like a 'booster-pump'.

The contractile state, or 'inotropy', of the myocardium can be increased ('positive inotropy') or decreased ('negative inotropy') by physiological, pharmacological or pathological causes. In physiological conditions the main positive inotropic factor is the noradrenaline released by the sympathetic nerve endings in the heart and acting upon the β-adrenergic receptors in the myocardium. The amount of this noradrenaline depends on the frequency of sympathetic nervous impulses arriving at the heart, but circulating catecholamines also have a direct effect on the myocardium and increase its

contractility. Many drugs have a positive or negative inotropic action: for example, digoxin is frequently used to increase the power of ventricular contraction in heart failure, and drugs that block the β-adrenergic receptors in the myocardium may impair ventricular contractility. In pathological conditions, hypoxia, hypercapnia and acidosis, and damage to the muscle itself, all reduce the contractile power of the ventricle.

The inotropic state of the heart, independent of changes in afterload and preload, has so far proved difficult to assess; it is likely that V_{max} in isolated myocardium can be altered by several inotropic stimuli, though there is some doubt about its validity as an index of contractility independent of fibre length. If the ventricular end-diastolic pressure (preload) and the aortic pressure (afterload) are held constant in the intact heart, positive and negative inotropic stimuli increase and diminish the stroke volume, and the ejection velocity and maximum rate of rise of pressure (dP/dt) of the left ventricle (Fig. 7.16). However, these measurements can also be altered by changes in loading.

The left ventricular stroke volume expressed as a percentage of the end-diastolic volume is known as the 'ejection fraction' and may be estimated by various methods, including biplane cine-angiocardiography. The left ventricular ejection fraction in man is about 50 to 65 per cent. Positive inotropic agents increase the ejection fraction at any given end-diastolic volume.

THE CARDIAC CYCLE

In considering the *cardiac cycle* we are concerned with the working of the pump, not simply in terms of the contraction of one ventricle, but with the cyclical contraction (*systole*) and relaxation (*diastole*) of the two atria and the two ventricles (Fig. 7.14). During diastole each chamber fills with blood; during systole the blood is expelled. Although the blood moves through the two cardiac pumps in series, the right and left hearts are arranged anatomically in parallel and both atria and both ventricles contract almost simultaneously (Fig. 7.19).

Atrial function

Although the thin-walled atria act as central venous reservoirs, their contraction produces comparatively small, but important, increases in atrial blood pressure. Atrial systole begins at about the peak of the P wave of the ECG, contraction of the right atrium usually slightly preceding that of the left. The muscular contraction forces blood from the atria through the AV valves into the ventricles during the last phase of passive ventricular filling; it causes small increases in the pressures in both the atria (atrial '*a wave*', Fig. 7.22) and ventricles, because at this stage the AV valves are still open. Since there are no valves between the right atrium

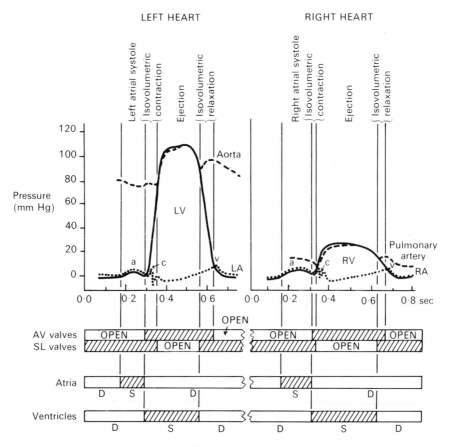

Fig. 7.14 The main haemodynamic events associated with the cardiac cycle on the left and right sides of the heart in man. LV, left ventricle; RV, right ventricle. LA, left atrium; RA, right atrium. AV, atrioventricular; SL, semilunar. D, diastole; S, systole. See also Figures 7.15, 7.16, 7.19, 7.21, 7.22 (pressure pulses), 7.17 (angiocardiogram), 7.22, 7.23 and 7.24 (phonocardiogram), 8.30 (jugular phlebogram) and Table 7.20.

and the venae cavae, some blood is expelled backwards during atrial systole into the superior vena cava, where it causes a rise in the pressure and the volume. These changes are transmitted upward to the internal jugular vein and cause a wave in the jugular phlebogram (Fig. 7.15 and Fig. 8.30 p. 122).

In normal hearts, beating with a normal rhythm, the volume of blood transported by the atria into the ventricles by atrial systole varies with the heart rate. When the heart is beating slowly diastole is long and passive ventricular filling is almost complete; atrial transport is small. When the heart rate is faster ventricular filling may never be complete and the atria may contract soon after the end of the rapid-filling phase of the ventricles (Fig. 7.19), when there is a relatively high pressure gradient between the atria and the ventricles; the atrial transport function is then considerable. At even faster rates, when the atria contract during the phase of rapid ventricular filling, it may be the transport function of the atria that maintains the adequate filling of the ventricle and so prevents a fall in cardiac output. In the common dysrhythmia called *atrial fibrillation* (p. 68), atrial contraction is not co-ordinated and there is therefore no transport function. The patient is rarely handicapped while the ventricular rate remains low, but when it is fast the patient's cardiac output may be reduced and can only be restored to normal when the ventricular rate is reduced by a drug, such as digitalis, that slows the discharge rate of the AV nodal pacemakers. Clinical studies of patients with atrial fibrillation and complete heart block (p. 70) indicate that the atrial transport function can be responsible for increases in the cardiac output varying from about 10 to about 40 per cent.

Atrial function may also normally play a part in closing the AV valves. At the end of atrial systole the blood continues to move through the valve because of its inertia, causing a momentary reduction in atrial pressure that tends to 'suck' the valve cusps towards each other.

When the electrical excitation of the atria is complete the excitation of the ventricles begins after a delay caused mainly by the slow conduction velocity through the central part of the AV node. This delay is responsible for most of the PR interval in the ECG.

Ventricular function
Ventricular contraction (Figs 7.14 to 7.20) begins soon after the start of ventricular excitation denoted by the beginning of the QRS complex of the ECG. The pressure of blood in the ventricles begins to rise while that in the relaxing atria is falling. About 50 ms after the atrial and ventricular pressure curves cross, the cusps of the atrioventricular valves close and then bulge momentarily backward into the atria. In ordinary

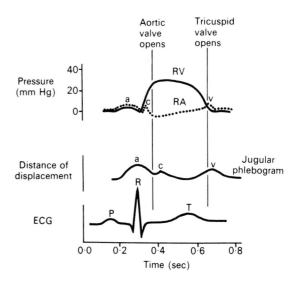

Fig. 7.15 Above downwards: pressure pulses (see Table 7.20) in right atrium (RA) and right ventricle (RV) during one cardiac cycle; jugular phlebogram (Fig. 8.30 and p. 122); electrocardiogram.

circumstances the valves do not leak, the surfaces of their cusps being held in apposition by the pull of the papillary muscles on the chordae tendineae attached to the cusp edges. This momentary backward bulging of the AV valve cusps produces slight transient increases of pressure in the atria (*c wave*; Figs 7.15 and 7.22). These intra-atrial *c* waves are not the same as the *c* waves in the jugular phlebogram, which are caused by the transmitted pulsation of the underlying carotid artery (Figs 7.15 and 8.30).

After the closure of the AV valves, the blood pressure rises in both ventricles but because both the AV and the semilunar valves are closed the volume of intraventricular blood remains constant. During this *isovolumetric* (isometric) phase of ventricular contraction the ventricles alter their shape, becoming plumper, and the apex and AV ring move nearer to one another. This 'descent of the base' stretches the right atrium and the consequent reduction in intra-atrial pressure contributes to the descending limb of the atrial *a* wave. When the rising ventricular pressures exceed the pressures in the aorta and pulmonary artery the semilunar valves open, the isometric phase ends and the *ejection* (isotonic) phase of contraction begins.

The ejection phase of ventricular contraction is strongly influenced by changing impedances in the great arteries. In the early, short, rapid ejection phase the ventricle contracts against an increasing afterload (auxotonic contraction) and the maximum velocity of blood flow is in fact attained earlier than the peak of the ventricular pressure curve (Fig. 7.16). The volume of

periphery exceeds that from the ventricle to the aorta, the shortened muscle fibres generating progressively less tension. At the end of this phase the ventricular muscle relaxes, and when the ventricular pressures fall below those in the aorta and pulmonary artery the semilunar valves shut. The closure of the aortic valve may be assisted by the effects of vortices in the blood in the aortic sinuses.

Throughout ventricular systole the ventricular volume, as measured by a bell cardiometer (Fig. 7.18) falls steeply (Fig. 7.19). At the same time blood has been returning to the atria, assisted by the negative intra-thoracic pressure; because the AV valves are closed the intra-atrial pressure gradually rises to form the ascending limb of the intra-atrial *v wave* (Fig. 7.22).

After the closure of the semilunar valves isovolumetric ventricular relaxation continues rapidly, the pressures in the ventricles soon falling below those in the atria. At this point, the summit of the *v* wave in the atrial pressure curve, the atrioventricular valves open and the blood flows passively from the atria to the ventricles, at first very fast, later more slowly. Immediately after the end of systole an elastic recoil of muscle rapidly lowers the ventricular pressure, causing an increased flow of blood from the atria. Negative pressures of up to 11 cm H_2O have been recorded in the left ventricle of dogs with the mitral valve temporarily clamped.

In diastole, during the first rapid phase of ventricular filling, the pressures in both atria and ventricles continue to fall but the ventricular volume increases sharply. At normal heart rates the first rapid phase of ventricular filling is succeeded by a slower phase in which the slope of the curve of the ventricular volume is flatter. If the ventricular rate is slow enough the volume curve may eventually become almost level because the ventricles are full (*ventricular diastasis*).

Cardiac catheterisation

In 1929 Forssmann passed a thin, flexible ureteric catheter from an arm vein into his own heart, watching its progress by the help of an X-ray screen and a mirror held by a nurse. This brave experiment opened a new era in human cardiovascular physiology based on the technique of cardiac catheterisation, which is now used routinely by clinical cardiologists.

Cardiac catheters intended to explore the great veins, the right side of the heart, the coronary sinus and the pulmonary artery are usually introduced through the antecubital or femoral vein. The left atrium and left ventricle can be catheterised from the right atrium by the use of a special catheter with a tip sharp enough to penetrate the interatrial septum. The aorta and left ventricle are usually catheterised from the femoral artery.

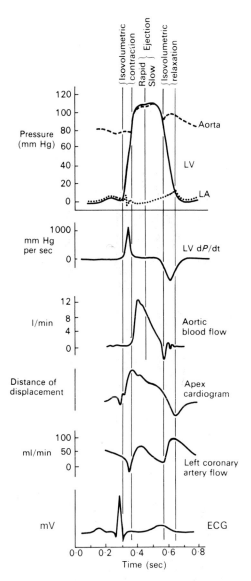

Fig. 7.16 The main haemodynamic events associated with the left atrium (LA) and left ventricle (LV) and the aorta throughout one cardiac cycle. Above downwards: pressure pulses (see Table 7.20); maximum rate of rise of LV pressure, dP/dt; aortic blood flow; apex cardiogram (p. 87); left coronary artery blood flow (p. 97); ECG.

blood ejected (*stroke volume*) from each ventricle is partly accommodated in the root of the great vessels by a transient expansion, which is the origin of the arterial pulse wave. It also displaces the blood expelled by the previous systole (p. 101). The later, longer phase ('reduced ejection') characterised by a fall in both the ventricular and the aortic and pulmonary arterial pressures takes place during the T wave of the ECG. During this time the flow of blood from the aorta to the

POSTERO-ANTERIOR

LEFT LATERAL

1

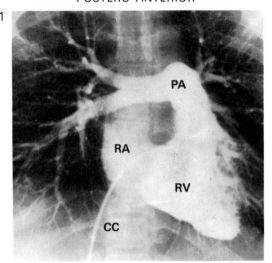

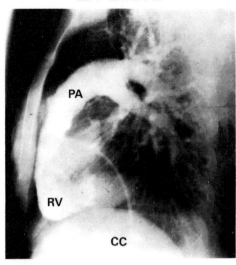

2

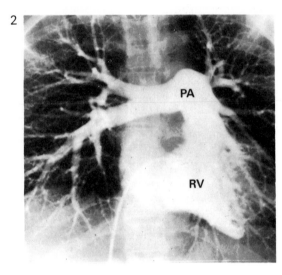

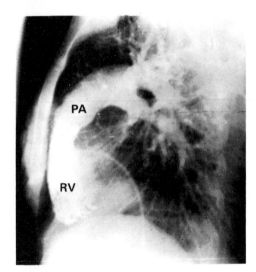

3

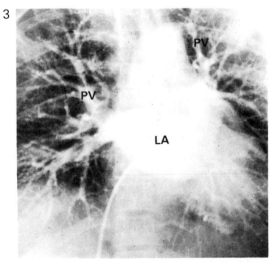

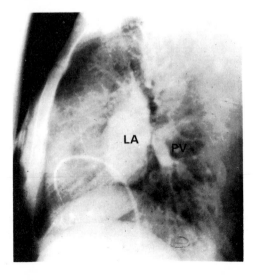

POSTERO-ANTERIOR

LEFT LATERAL

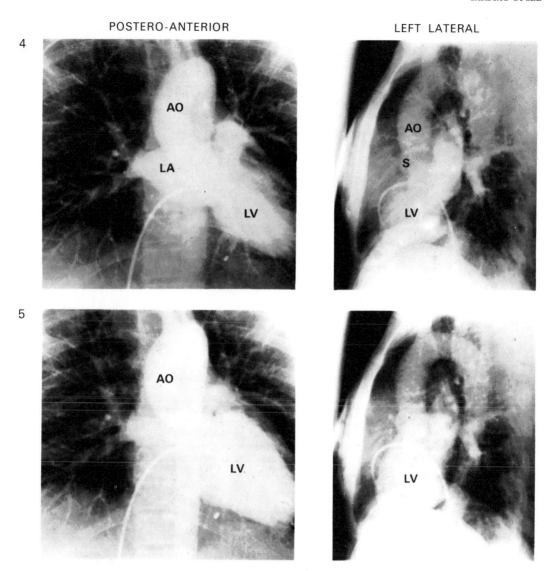

Fig. 7.17 Frames from simultaneous postero-anterior and left lateral rapid still radiographs during angiocardiography of a normal human heart. The contrast medium was injected through a cardiac catheter (CC) sited in the right ventricle (RV) during a previous cardiac cycle, and fills various cardiac chambers and vessels at subsequent stages of the cardiac cycle: (1) right ventricular diastole, with slight filling of the right atrium (RA) because of tricuspid incompetence caused by the catheter; (2) RV systole expels contrast into the pulmonary arteries (PA); (3) the contrast has passed through the pulmonary capillaries and is returning through the pulmonary veins (PV) to fill the left atrium (LA); (4) systole expels blood from the left ventricle (LV) into the aorta (AO) and in the lateral view an aortic sinus (S) is evident; (5) by the time the LV has relaxed in diastole the contrast has moved farther down the descending aorta. (*By courtesy of the Royal Postgraduate Medical School, London.*)

Special catheters can be used to obtain samples of blood from the great veins, any of the four chambers of the heart, the coronary sinus, the aorta or the pulmonary artery. Analysis of the oxygen content of mixed venous blood from the pulmonary artery can be used to calculate the cardiac output by the Fick principle (p. 87). The catheters can be attached to manometers or have manometers at the tip to record intravascular pressures and to demonstrate pressure gradients by withdrawal of the catheter tip across valves. Table 7.20 shows normal intracardiac pressures in man and Figures 7.21 and 7.22 show records of intracardiac pressure curves obtained by cardiac catheterisation. Electrode catheters have already been

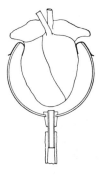

Fig. 7.18 The bell cardiometer for measuring changes in biventricular volume of the exposed heart of an animal.

Table 7.20 Normal average values of intracardiac pressures in man (from various authors). LV peak systolic pressure is approximately the level of the systolic blood pressure recorded in the brachial artery, that is about 110 mmHg. (See also Figs 7.21 and 7.22).

Site	Mean (mmHg)	Range (mmHg)
RA	3	1–5
RV (peak-systolic)	26	19–31
(end-diastolic)	4	2–6
PA (mean)	14	10–18
(peak-systolic)	23	16–29
(end-diastolic)	9	5–13
LA (mean)	8	2–12
LV (end-diastolic)	9	5–12

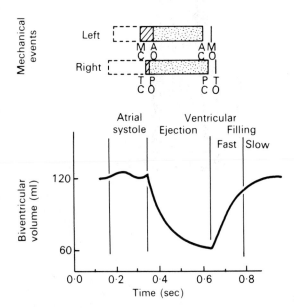

Fig. 7.19 The relationship between the main mechanical events in the right and left sides of the heart and the biventricular volume. Above, systolic events in the right and left atrium and ventricle are asynchronous: open areas enclosed by dashed lines indicate atrial systole; hatched areas indicate ventricular isovolumetric contraction; dotted areas indicate ventricular systole. MC, mitral valve closure; TC, tricuspid valve closure. AO, aortic valve opening; PO, pulmonary valve opening. AC, aortic valve closure; PC, pulmonary valve closure. MO, mitral valve opening; TO, tricuspid valve opening.

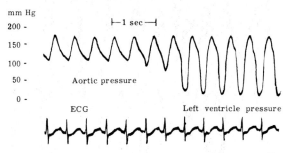

Fig. 7.21 Pressure records from the aorta and left ventricle in a female patient aged 39 with a normal aortic valve. As the catheter is gradually withdrawn from the aorta into the ventricle there is a fairly sudden change (diastolic pressure gradient) in the record, which is normal in this patient. (Fleming H A, Hancock E W, Milstein B B, Ross D N 1958 Thorax 13: 97–102)

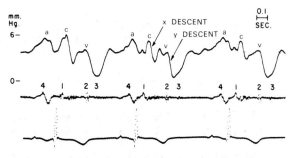

Fig. 7.22 Normal pressures and heart sounds simultaneously recorded from inside the right atrium. Above down: right atrial pressure pulse, intra-atrial phonocardiogram, surface ECG for reference. (Moscovitz H L, Donoso E, Gelb I J, Wilder R J 1963 An atlas of haemodynamics of the cardiovascular system. Grune & Stratton, New York, p. 31)

mentioned (Chap. 6, p. 67). Tiny microphones at the tips of cardiac catheters have been used to identify the sources of normal and abnormal cardiac sounds (p. 85; Fig. 7.22). Some cardiac catheters have at the tip a special platinum electrode capable of producing an electric potential in the presence of hydrogen: with such a 'hydrogen electrode' sited in a cardiac chamber a lung-to-electrode circulation time can easily be determined by making the subject inhale a breath of pure hydrogen gas. Other catheters end in an electrode capable of delivering a stimulating electrical impulse ('pacing').

Light-weight plastic catheters (Swan–Ganz catheters) may be 'floated' in the venous blood and thus carried from, say, the antecubital vein via the right atrium and ventricle to the pulmonary artery, even in very ill patients, to determine the cardiac output (p. 88).

A radio-opaque fluid ('contrast medium') can be injected into any chamber of the heart or into the great vessels (*selective angiocardiography*). The passage of this opaque medium through the heart can be recorded by rapid still or cine X-ray photography and gives useful information about the anatomy of the chambers and the flow of blood between them (Fig. 7.17, pp. 82, 83). The right and left coronary arteries can be selectively catheterised, and the *coronary arteriograms* thus obtained demonstrate the coronary arterial circulation (Fig. 7.43).

Not only has cardiac catherisation yielded a great deal of knowledge about the physiology of the normal heart but it is an invaluable part of the investigation of many patients with heart disease, providing information obtainable by no other means. Cardiac pacing is used to treat cases of heart block (p. 70).

Heart sounds

During the cardiac cycle the blood flows through the heart with sharply varying velocities and both accelerations and decelerations of flow produce vibrations of the cardiac muscle and valves, the walls of the great vessels and the blood they contain. The vibrations have a low frequency and are rapidly damped, but some of their components lie above the threshold of human hearing (see Chap. 38) and can therefore be appreciated as *heart sounds*.

The two main groups of normal heart sounds can usually be heard if the listener presses his ear firmly against the skin of the precordium. They are more easily heard by the use of a stethoscope that amplifies the sounds and reduces other distracting noises. A graphical recording of heart sounds, a *phonocardiogram* (PCG), can be made by using microphones, amplifiers and filters to overcome some of the limitations imposed by the human ear. The PCG usually shows four main groups of vibrations in every cardiac cycle (Figs. 7.22, 7.23 and 7.24, pp. 84 and 86).

Studies by intracardiac phonocardiography indicate that changes of velocity and turbulence in the blood produce vibrations that are most intense 'downstream' from their site of production. This technique, combined with that of echocardiography (p. 87), has thrown some fresh light on the origin of these four normal heart sounds.

The two sounds heard by the unaided ear are called the 'first' and 'second' heart sounds. The *first heart sound* is the longest and loudest of the normal heart sounds. The PCG shows a group of vibrations of mixed

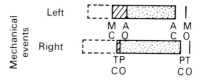

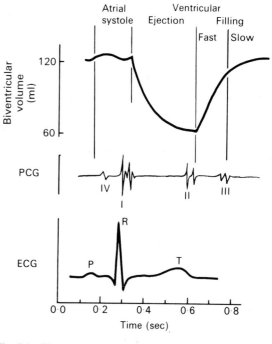

Fig. 7.23 The relationships between the heart sounds (phonocardiogram) and mechanical events in the heart. Above downwards: mechanical events and biventricular volume (labelled as in Fig. 7.19); phonocardiogram (PCG); electrocardiogram (ECG).

frequency occurring at the end of the QRS complex. It is associated with the beginning of ventricular systole and is mainly caused by vibrations set up by the closure of the AV valves. Often there are two main groups of vibrations and on auscultation with the stethoscope the first sound is heard to be 'split'. This splitting is the result of the closure of, first, the mitral, and then the tricuspid, valve. Because the vibrations are most intense 'downstream' from the AV valves, the first heart sound is best heard at an area of the chest wall near the apex beat (p. 87). Because of its length and the comparatively low frequency of its components it is traditionally represented by the syllable, *lub*.

The *second heart sound* shows on the PCG as two shorter groups of vibrations of higher frequency occurring about the end of the T wave in the ECG. These sounds are caused by the sudden closure of, first, the aortic, and then the pulmonary, valve. They are best heard 'downstream' from these valves in an area on the

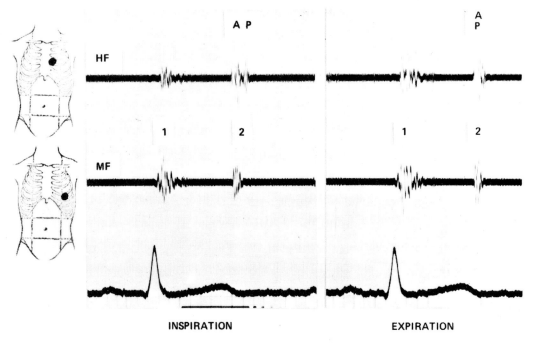

Fig. 7.24 Phonocardiogram of a normal young adult. One microphone at the left sternal edge provides a high-frequency (HF) record, the other, at the region of the cardiac apex provides a medium frequency (MF) record. 1 and 2, first and second heart sounds. A and P, vibrations associated with closure of the aortic and pulmonary valves. The lowest trace is ECG, lead II. On inspiration the increased negative intrathoracic pressure increases the filling of the right ventricle in diastole. The increased right ventricular volume delays closure of the pulmonary valve: the pulmonary valve closure sound (P) is delayed, causing audible splitting of the second heart sound (0.04 s in this record). On expiration, pulmonary valve closure occurs so soon after aortic valve closure that the second heart sound seems single on auscultation.

chest wall about the second intercostal space just to the right and left of the sternum. The untrained ear may not appreciate the split between the aortic and pulmonary components. The second heart sound, being shorter and of higher pitch than the first heart sound, is traditionally represented by the syllable 'dupp'. Careful ausculation, however, during slow continued respiration, or phonocardiography, confirms that the second heart sound is usually only single during the phase of full expiration. During the inspiratory phase the increase in the negative intra-thoracic pressure increases the volume of blood in the right ventricle, which delays the closure of the pulmonary valve, and hence the pulmonary component of the second heart sound. The second heart sound then sounds more like 'trupp'. At the height of inspiration the delay in the closure of the pulmonary valve is maximal, the split between the aortic and pulmonary components is widest and the sound may be represented as 'tu-rupp'. During expiration the split narrows again. This 'movement' of the splitting of the second heart sound is most easily heard in young people in the erect position (Fig. 7.24).

The *third heart sound* is heard in children and young adults. In the PCG it is shown as a short group of vibrations of very low frequency in early diastole, occurring towards the end of the phase of rapid ventricular filling. These vibrations are probably set up in the blood at a time when the left ventricular wall is changing from a state of active relaxation to one of passive distension and when the whole mitral valve system reaches a certain tension (Fig. 7.23, p. 84).

The fourth heart sound, or *atrial sound* is inaudible in normal people and can usually only be demonstrated by phonocardiography. It consists of a few low-frequency vibrations during the PR interval of the ECG and is caused by the contraction of the atria and the flow of blood through the AV valves. In abnormal conditions, such as delayed AV conduction when the PR interval is long, the atrial sound may be heard on auscultation as a faint low thud.

In abnormal hearts altered cardiac haemodynamics may give rise to abnormal vibrations or turbulence. These may be heard on auscultation as extra sounds, such as the 'opening snap' of a pliant cusp in a narrowed mitral valve (mitral stenosis), or as cardiac 'murmurs', such as the sound that occupies the whole of systole caused by the turbulence of the blood regurgitated into the left atrium through an incompetent mitral valve.

Movements of the heart

The heart is quite soft in diastole, its shape being determined mainly by the amount of blood within it and by the position of the body. When the ventricles contract the heart becomes hard and there is an increase in the antero-posterior, and a decrease in the transverse, diameter. The movement of the heart within the chest, as a diffuse *cardiac impulse*, can often be felt by a hand laid on the precordium. A localised pulsation (*apex beat*) is often felt in the fifth left intercostal space about the midclavicular line. X-rays show that the actual apex is about 2 cm lower down.

The pulsations of the apex beat can be more critically analyzed if they are recorded by appropriate techniques in the form of the *apex cardiogram*. The main outward pulsation is caused by ventricular systole, but this is preceded by the smaller pulsation associated with atrial contraction and followed by an inward pulsation marking the opening of the AV valves (Fig. 7.16, p. 81).

In patients with abnormal hearts some of these features may be pronounced enough to be seen or felt by the hand: hypertrophy of one or other ventricle produces a prolonged and more powerful pulsation of appropriate parts of the precordium, while hypertrophy of the atria may be associated with a palpable atrial component of the apex beat, associated with an audible atrial sound.

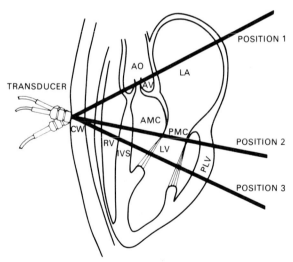

Fig. 7.25 Sagittal section of the heart showing normal anatomical relationships of the cardiac chambers and aortic and mitral valves. The ultrasound beam of the echocardiograph is directed along positions 1, 2 and 3 to explore areas of interest. CW, chest wall; AO, aorta; AV, aortic valve; LA, left atrium; LV, left ventricle; RV, right ventricle; IVS, interventricular septum; AMC, anterior mitral valve cusp; PMC, posterior mitral valve cusp; PLV, posterior left ventricular wall. (Vérel D, Grainger R G 1978 Cardiac catheterization and angiocardiography. Churchill Livingstone, Edinburgh)

Echocardiography

Appropriately directed beams of ultra-sound can be reflected as echoes from moving structures in the heart. The echoes are detected and displayed by the *echocardiograph*. Figure 7.25 shows the general principles involved, and Figure 7.26 indicates how the movement of various cardiac structures can be shown. Echocardiography gives information about the opening and closing of aortic and mitral valves and the movement and thickness of ventricular walls and the interventricular septum.

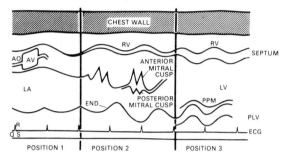

Fig. 7.26 Diagram of echocardiogram obtained as the direction of the ultrasonic beam is gradually changed from position 1 to position 3 in Fig. 7.25. Position 1 demonstrates opening and closing of the aortic valve. Position 2 shows movements of anterior and posterior cusps of the mitral valve and the size of the ventricles in systole and diastole. Position 3 shows the movements of the interventricular septum and posterior papillary muscle of the left ventricle. END, endocardium posterior wall LV; PPM, posterior papillary muscle; other abbreviations as in Fig. 7.25 (Vérel D, Grainger R G 1978 Cardiac catheterization and angiocardiography. Churchill Livingstone, Edinburgh)

CARDIAC OUTPUT

The Fick principle

For the determination of the cardiac output in man only indirect methods are applicable. Fick pointed out in 1870 that in a given time the total amount of any gas gained or lost in the lungs must be equal to the difference between the amounts of the gas brought to the lungs in the arterial blood and the amount leaving the lungs in the venous blood. Thus if we can measure (a) the amount of oxygen passing from the lungs into the blood per unit of time, (b) the oxygen content of the arterial blood, and (c) the oxygen content of mixed venous blood, then the output of the heart is easily calculated. An average value for (a) is 250 ml per minute, for (b) is 19 ml per 100 ml blood, and for (c) is 14 ml per 100 ml blood. Each 100 ml of blood in passing through the lungs gains 5 ml of oxygen, that is, the arteriovenous difference. Since 250 ml of oxygen actually passes into the blood per minute (Fig. 7.27)

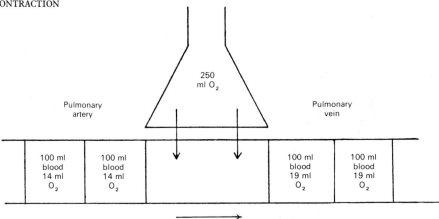

Fig. 7.27 Scheme to illustrate the determination of cardiac output by the Fick principle. Each rectangle represents 100 ml of blood, which gains 5 ml of oxygen in passing through the lungs. 250 ml of oxygen disappears from the lungs per minute. This volume would be accounted for by 250/5 or 50 rectangles. The flow is therefore 250/5 × 100 ml, or 5 litres per minute.

$$\frac{250}{5} \times 100 \text{ ml} = 5000 \text{ ml or 5 litres}$$

of blood are needed to carry that amount of oxygen, and this is the cardiac output per minute (*minute volume*). If the heart contracts 71 times per minute then the *stroke volume* of each ventricle is 5000 ÷ 71 = 70 ml.

The oxygen consumption can be determined by a spirometer or by the Douglas bag technique (p. 163). The oxygen content of arterial blood can be measured directly in a specimen obtained by arterial puncture. A specimen of mixed venous blood can be obtained only by catheterising the pulmonary artery since there are large regional differences in the oxygen content of blood from superficial veins, and even between streams within the right ventricle.

The results obtained in this way represent the effective output of each ventricle but do not allow for any run-back of blood into the ventricles such as may occur with valvular disease. If all the oxygen taken up from the inspired air is carried in the blood and none is used up in the lungs the results should be correct for normal persons. The range of cardiac output in normal adults under basal conditions is from 4 to 7 litres per minute, with a mean of 5.3 litres. This corresponds to a stroke volume from each ventricle of 70 to 80 ml.

The cardiac output in exercise may be increased to as much as 40 litres per minute, partly by an augmented stroke volume and partly by an increase in heart rate. The rise in cardiac output with exercise is, however, not accompanied by a parallel rise in venous pressure (see also Chap. 11). Apprehension and anxiety may be accompanied by an increase of some 10 to 20 per cent

over the basal value. The output is some 10 per cent lower during sleep. In healthy persons there is an increase in cardiac output up to about 25 per cent on lying down, presumably the result of an increased venous return. It seems reasonable to expect that the cardiac output would be closely correlated with body size and for many years it has been customary to express the *cardiac index* as the minute volume per m² of body surface (about 3.8 litres).

Indicator dilution

The cardiac output in man may also be measured by the indicator dilution method. A known amount (X mg) of a non-diffusible dye is injected into the pulmonary artery or a central vein and the rapid rise and fall of its concentration in arterial blood is followed by sampling from, say, the brachial artery. The falling concentration, before recirculation of the dye begins, can be plotted as a graph, which, if extrapolated to zero concentration or 0.1 mg/l in Figure 7.28, gives the time after injection at which all the dye must have been ejected from the heart if there had been no recirculation (Y seconds). Since the concentration falls off exponentially it can be plotted as a straight line on semilog paper (Fig. 7.28). If the average concentration of the dye in the blood is calculated for this period (Z mg/litre) then X/Z litres is the amount of blood required for the ejection of X mg of dye. Since this took place in Y seconds the cardiac output in litres per min must have been $X/Z \times 60/Y$. The indicator does not enter the red cells but is carried in the plasma so this formula gives the plasma flow from which the blood flow can be calculated. Brachial artery puncture can be avoided by measuring the rise and fall of the concentration of the dye by

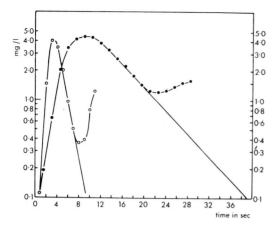

Fig. 7.28 Dye concentration curves (Evan's blue) plotted on semilogarithmic paper. ●——● Rest experiment. Cardiac output 4·73 litres per minute. ○——○ Work experiment. 1260 kg m per minute. Cardiac output 21.9 litres per minute. The second upward trend of the curves is due to recirculation of dye. (Asmussen E, Neilsen M 1952–1953 Acta Physiologica Scandinavica 27:217)

RETURN OF BLOOD TO THE HEART

The most important cause of the venous return is the action of the heart in pumping blood round the circulation. The pressure within the chest, but outside the lung, that is the *intrathoracic pressure*, is normally negative, that is a little below atmospheric pressure. Accordingly blood flows from the abdomen and other parts where the pressure is above atmospheric into the thoracic veins where the pressure is lower. The effective filling pressure of the right side of the heart is therefore the difference between the extra-thoracic venous pressure and the diastolic pressure in the right atrium, the pressure in the relaxed atrium being the same as the intrathoracic pressure. The intrathoracic pressure becomes more negative during inspiration and the filling pressure therefore higher. During inspiration the descent of the diaphragm causes an increase of intra-abdominal pressure that aids the return of blood to the thorax.

shining a light through the vasodilated lobe of the ear on to a photocell (*oximetry*).

Serum albumin labelled with a radio-isotope may be used instead of a dye; the quantity in the blood is estimated by an appropriate isotope-counting technique. With the thermo-dilution technique cold fluid is injected into the right atrium and 'detected' in the pulmonary artery by a special catheter that carries thermistors. A computer calculates the cardiac output. The indicator-dilution method of estimating the cardiac output is unreliable for giving a single 'absolute' value, but useful to compare short-term changes in one subject, as shown in Figure 7.28.

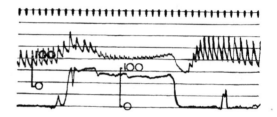

Fig. 7.29 Professional trumpet player blowing Concert A against a pressure of about 80 mmHg for 17 seconds, effectively performing Valsalva's manoeuvre (forced expiration against a closed glottis). Upper curve, arterial pressure. Lower curve, mouth pressure. Calibration in mmHg and time marker in seconds. (Faulkner M, Sharpey-Schafer E P 1959 British Medical Journal 1: 685–686)

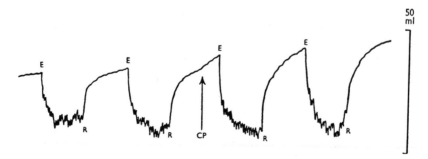

Fig. 7.30 A record in the changes in volume of the calf of the leg measured with a plethysmograph (p. 107) to show the effects of the 'muscle pump'. A fall in volume is indicated by a downward movement of the trace. At E a pedal was pressed down once per second for 10 s; R indicates the beginning of a rest period of 10 s. At CP a cuff just above the knee was inflated to 90 mmHg until the end of the trace. During each period of exercise blood was forced out of the calf and its volume diminished. Even when the venous pressure was raised to 99 mmHg blood was forced out of the calf by the exercise. (Barcroft H, Dornhorst A C 1949 Journal of Physiology 109:402.)

The importance of this *respiratory pump* is shown in the performance of static effort, such as pulling on a tug-of-war rope or blowing a trumpet. Both require considerably expiratory effort so the pressure in the thorax becomes positive (*Valsalva manoeuvre*, Fig. 7.29). The return of blood to the heart is much reduced or ceases entirely, the superficial veins of the head and neck become engorged and the mean arterial blood pressure falls. The blood flow through the brain may be so much reduced that the subject feels giddy and may lose consciousness (*syncope*, p. 125).

The return of the blood to the heart is also assisted by the contraction of muscles all over the body, especially in the legs. When the muscles contract blood is squeezed out of the capillaries and smaller veins within the muscles into the larger veins between the muscles. The alternate contractions and relaxations of the leg muscles that occur in walking serve to drive the blood back through the venous valves to the heart. The intramuscular pressure in the calf muscles in man can be measured by passing a fine catheter into them; at rest it is about 10 mm Hg, on standing 30 mm Hg, while a maximal contraction may raise the pressure to 200 mm Hg. Thus the *muscle pump*, as Figure 7.30 shows, is quite powerful. A person standing rigidly at attention for a prolonged period may eventually faint because the reduced venous return to the heart caused by inactivity of the muscle pump results in a diminished cardiac output and a decreased blood supply to the brain.

The distensibility of the pericardial sac sets a limit to the filling of the heart in diastole. If the sac contains fluid neither atria nor ventricles can dilate fully, and so the cardiac filling falls. The output per beat is therefore diminished (cardiac tamponade). If the pericardial pressure rises above the venous pressure, as may happen after perforation of a ventricle, blood cannot enter the heart and the circulation ceases.

Cardiac output and venous return

The *right atrial pressure* plays a central role in controlling both the venous return and the cardiac output. At first its action may seem paradoxical, for a rise in right atrial pressure both increases the cardiac output and reduces the venous return. The cardiac output is increased, by the Starling mechanism, in response to the increased filling of the ventricle caused by the raised right atrial pressure. The venous return falls because the raised right atrial pressure slows down the inflow of blood from the periphery. Except for periods of time lasting not more than a few seconds, the cardiac output is equal to the venous return, equilibrium being maintained by the overall velocity of blood flow through the circulation.

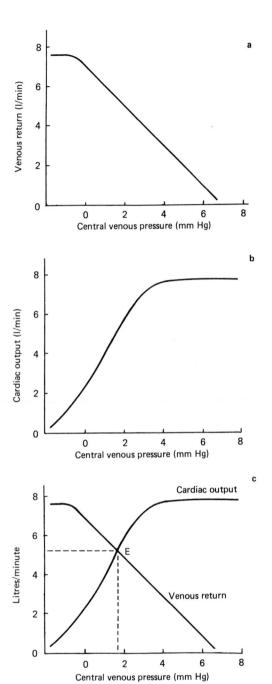

Fig. 7.31 Diagrams to show the relationship between cardiac output and venous return to the heart. (a) Shows the relation between venous return and right atrial (central venous) pressure. Contrary to the usual convention the central venous pressure is plotted on the abscissa. (b) Shows the relation between cardiac output and right atrial pressure. (c) Shows the curves in (a) and (b) superimposed. The axes remain the same. E, equilibrium point, where cardiac output equals venous return. (*After* Guyton A C 1963 Circulatory physiology: cardiac output and its regulation. Saunders, London)

The relationships between the venous return, the cardiac output and the right atrial pressure are shown in Figure 7.31. The venous return decreases when the right atrial pressure increases (Fig. 7.31a), the cardiac output increases with the right atrial pressure (Fig. 7.31b). Because the right atrial pressure or *central venous pressure* is plotted along the abscissa in each graph and the units are the same (mm Hg for pressure and litres per minute for blood flow) the venous pressure curve may be superimposed on the cardiac output curve as in Figure 7.31c. The point at which the curves intersect represents the 'equilibrium point' of the system where the cardiac output equals the venous return. The regulation of the circulatory system, when considered in this way, involves the recovery of the equilibrium point after transient disturbances of the system, or the establishment of new equilibrium points when homeostatic mechanisms are ineffective: for example, in Figure 7.32 if the central venous pressure rises from the equilibrium point to point A, the total blood volume remaining constant, the cardiac output of the next ventricular contraction would be increased to B because of the Starling mechanism. This increased stroke volume would reduce the venous pressure to point C, and so the adjustment would go on during the next few beats until the original equilibrium point is reached again. If we consider again the family of ventricular function curves shown in Figure 7.11 we can see that a change in the contractile state of the muscle will alter the cardiac output in Figures 7.31 and 7.32 and the equilibrium point will be a different one.

NERVOUS REGULATION OF THE HEART

The nervous regulation of the heart involves reflexes, the afferent pathways of which include receptors in the heart itself, in blood vessels, in viscera and in skin. The efferent pathways of these reflexes comprise vagal and sympathetic nerve fibres the activity of which is also influenced by higher centres. These fibres directly innervate the heart and the sympathetic nerves affect it also through the adrenal medulla and circulating catecholamine levels. The primary effects of the efferent cardiac nerves are on the heart rate, conduction tissue and the muscle of the heart; these effects can be demonstrated in experimental animals by electrical stimulation of the efferent nerves.

The vagal nerves

The cell bodies of the cardiac vagal neurones lie mainly in the region of the nucleus ambiguus in the medulla. The axons of these neurones run as preganglionic fibres in the vagal nerves and synapse in local ganglia near the heart. Short postganglionic nerve fibres supply the sinu-atrial (SA) node, the atrioventricular (AV) node and the muscles of the heart.

Stimulation of the efferent cardiac vagal nerves liberates acetylcholine at their ends and primarily causes a decrease in the heart rate ('negative chronotropic' effect) and a slowing of conduction through the AV node. There is no good evidence of a consistent inotropic effect of the vagal nerves on the ventricular muscle. In contrast, vagal stimulation has a striking negative inotropic effect on the atrial muscle. In studies of the transmembrane potentials of conduction tissues in the heart, vagal stimulation or the application of acetylcholine causes hyperpolarization of the resting membrane potentials, suppression of pacemaker-potentials and a

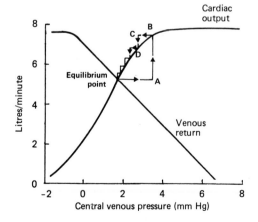

Fig. 7.32 Diagram to show how the equilibrium point is regained after a sudden shift to A (increased venous pressure) by subsequent beat-to-beat changes in cardiac output and central venous pressure. (Berne R M, Levy M N 1967 Cardiovascular physiology. Mosby, St Louis)

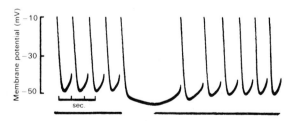

Fig. 7.33 The effect of vagal stimulation on the membrane potential in a spontaneously beating frog sinus venosus. The record is taken at an amplification that shows only the lower part of the action potential. During the fifth cycle, stimulation of the vagus at 20 stimuli/s started and continued for about 3 s, as indicated by a break in the reference line. This caused a suppression of pacemaker potentials and a gradual increase in the membrane potentials (downward deflection) to a value of 9 mV greater than that usually reached during diastole. (Hutter O F, Trautwein W T 1956 Journal of General Physiology 39: 715–733)

reduction in the duration of the action potential (Fig. 7.33). Vagal stimulation can even block the transmission of atrial excitation through the AV node to the ventricle.

The negative inotropic effect on the atrial muscle secondarily reduces the contribution of the atria to ventricular filling; through the Starling mechanism this effect leads to a reduction in the stroke volume, which in conjunction with the fall in heart rate leads to a reduction in the cardiac output and arterial blood pressure. In addition, the decrease in the heart rate and blood pressure leads to a secondary negative inotropic effect on the ventricular muscle.

The sympathetic nerves

The preganglionic sympathetic neurones lie in the intermediolateral horn of the upper thoracic segments of the spinal cord. Their preganglionic axons leave the spinal cord and synapse in ganglia of the sympathetic chain with postganglionic neurones, the axons of which run in the cardiac sympathetic nerves to supply the SA node, AV node and the muscle of the heart.

Stimulation of the efferent cardiac sympathetic nerves primarily causes an increase in the heart rate, a shortening of the conduction time through the AV node and a positive inotropic effect on the atria and the ventricles. The inotropic effect of the sympathetic nerves on the *ventricular* muscle is illustrated in Figure 7.34. In pacemaker tissues sympathetic stimulation causes an increase in the slope of the pacemaker potentials and an

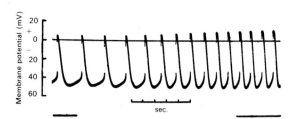

Fig. 7.35 The effect of sympathetic stimulation on the action potentials in frog sinus venosus. The vagosympathetic trunk was stimulated at 20 stimuli/second, as indicated by the break in reference line, and the preparation treated with atropine sulphate, 1 in 10⁶, to block the effect of acetylcholine liberated at the vagal nerve terminals. Note the increase in the slope of the pacemaker potentials and in the amplitude of the action potentials, attributed to sympathetic stimulation. (Hutter O F, Trautwein W T 1956 Journal of General Physiology 39:715)

increase in the amplitude of the action potential (Fig. 7.35).

The combination of a positive inotropic effect on the ventricular muscle and a rise in heart rate leads to an increase in the cardiac output and blood pressure. In addition the increase in the heart rate and blood pressure contribute to the positive inotropic effect on the ventricular muscle.

Reflex effects

In general, a reflex increase in the activity of efferent cardiac sympathetic or vagal nerve fibres leads to effects

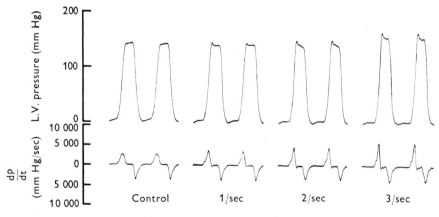

Paced H.R. 168 beats/min

Fig. 7.34 The effect of stimulation of efferent cardiac sympathetic nerves on the inotropic state of the left ventricle in an anaesthetised dog. From above downwards are recordings of the pressure in the left ventricle (L.V. pressure) and the rate of change in left ventricular pressure (dP/dt). The panel on the left shows recordings during the control period and the other three panels show recordings during sympathetic stimulation at 1, 2 and 3 stimuli per second. The mean aortic pressure and the heart rate (heart paced at 168 beats/min) were kept constant. With an unpaced heart sympathetic stimulation at a frequency of 3 stimuli per second increased the heart rate from a control value of 114 beats/min to 136 beats/min. An increase in the frequency of stimulation caused a progressive increase in dP/dt max from 2622 (control) to 6348 mmHg/s (at 3 stimuli per second), indicating a positive inotropic effect on the left ventricular muscle. (By courtesy of R. J. Linden).

on the heart similar to those obtained by electrical stimulation of these nerves. The reflexes that have been shown to regulate the activities of the heart have their afferent pathways in autonomic or somatic nerve fibres that transmit impulses from receptor organs to the central nervous system; complex connections are then made with the efferent neurones and efferent nerve fibres to the heart and blood vessels.

Systemic arterial baroreceptors

The baroreceptors are specialised nerve endings situated in the adventitia of the carotid sinus, the aortic arch, subclavian artery and branches of the common carotid artery (Fig. 7.36). Though known as baroreceptors, these nerve endings are mechanoreceptors, that is, they are sensitive to mechanical deformation such as stretch, which is usually caused by a rise in intraluminal blood pressure expanding the arterial wall (Fig. 7.37) or by external pressure on the carotid sinus (Fig. 7.38). The receptors in the carotid sinus discharge into afferent nerve fibres contained in the sinus nerve, which is a branch of the glossopharyngeal nerve. The receptors in the aortic arch discharge into afferent nerve fibres

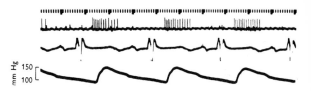

Fig. 7.37 Examples of discharge of action potentials from baroreceptors in the carotid sinus region in an anaesthetised cat. The recordings from above downwards are the time signals in 1/10 and 1/100 s, activity in a single baroreceptor unit from the right carotid sinus nerve with an intact circulation through the sinus, the electrocardiogram and arterial blood pressure. Note the association, between the activity of the unit and the increase in blood pressure. (Robertson J D, Swan A A B, Whitteridge D 1956 Journal of Physiology 131: 463–472)

contained in the aortic nerve and the vagal nerves. These afferent fibres synapse with neurones in the region of the nucleus of the tractus solitarius that have complex neuronal connections with efferent preganglionic neurones in the regions of the nucleus ambiguus and spinal intermediolateral horn.

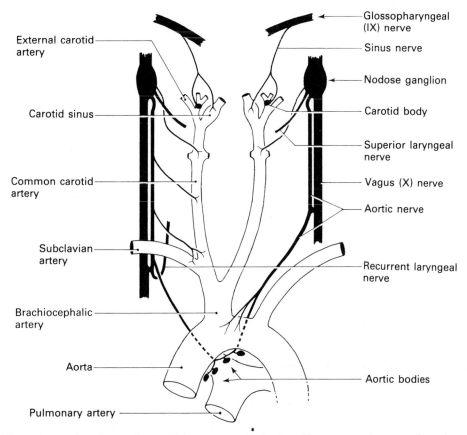

Fig. 7.36 Afferent innervation of systemic arterial baroreceptors in the dog. The neurones shown are those that connect the baroreceptors with neurones in the medulla oblongata

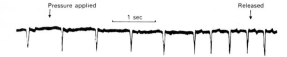

Pressure applied   Released

|← 1 sec →|

Fig. 7.38 Effect of left carotid pressure on heart rate as shown on the ECG of a human subject. The rate is slowed. The nerve endings in the adventitia of the carotid sinus normally discharge when the pressure in the sinus rises but these baroceptor endings also discharge if the sinus is distorted by traction on the carotid artery or, as in this case, by direct pressure.

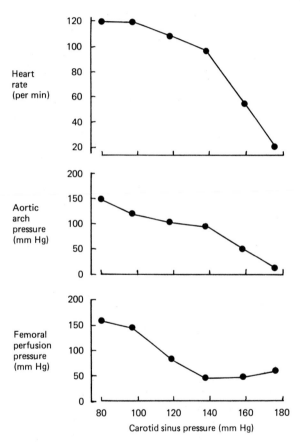

Fig. 7.39 The effect of stimulation of carotid sinus baroreceptors on the heart rate, systemic blood pressure and peripheral vascular resistance in the hind limb of an anaesthetised dog. The regions of both common carotid bifurcations, the aortic arch and the left hind limb were each isolated from the remainder of the arterial tree and each perfused with arterial blood at a constant rate of flow. The pressure within the aortic pouch was kept constant and the pressure within the carotid sinuses was increased stepwise from about 80 mmHg to 180 mmHg. This increase leads to a progressive decrease in heart rate, in the systemic arterial pressure and in the hind limb vascular resistance (indicated by a decrease in femoral perfusion pressure). (By courtesy of R. Hainsworth)

The normal function of the baroreceptor reflexes can be illustrated by experiments in which the carotid sinus is isolated and the pressure within it adjusted. In one typical experiment (Fig. 7.39) a rise in the pressure within the carotid sinus leads to a fall in the heart rate and a fall in the arterial pressure, which is caused in part by a negative inotropic effect on the ventricular muscle and in part on the decrease in systemic vascular resistance. A mean blood pressure of about 65 mmHg is required to stimulate receptors in the carotid sinus. The corresponding figure for the aortic arch is about 90 mmHg.

Systemic arterial chemoreceptors

These chemoreceptors mainly lie in the carotid bodies, found near the bifurcation of the common carotid artery and in the aortic 'bodies' scattered around the aortic arch (Fig. 7.36) The receptors are nerve endings that lie close to the blood in sinusoidal capillaries. These receptors are sensitive to a reduction in Po_2, (Fig. 8.17, p. 112), to a rise in Pco_2 or to a fall in pH; since a decrease in the blood flow through the bodies leads to a fall in the local Po_2, this too stimulates the receptors. The afferent discharge from these receptors is carried to neurones in the nucleus of the tractus solitarius through the carotid sinus nerve, a branch of the glosso-pharyngeal nerve, which innervates the carotid sinus, and through vagal nerves, which innervate the aortic 'bodies'.

In studies of the chemoreceptor reflex the carotid or aortic bodies are separately perfused, and the receptors are stimulated by reducing the oxygen tension or raising carbon dioxide tension, substituting the perfusing arterial blood with venous blood. Care is taken not to deform the adjoining mechanoreceptors. Stimulation of the carotid chemoreceptors primarily results in an increase in activity in efferent vagal fibres and an inhibition of activity in efferent sympathetic nerve fibres. These changes result in a decrease in heart rate, a negative inotropic effect on the ventricular muscle and an increase in systemic vascular resistance. In contrast, the reflex response to stimulation of the aortic chemoreceptors consists of an increase in heart rate, a positive inotropic effect on the ventricular muscle and an increase in systemic vascular resistance.

Atrial receptors

These receptors are complex unencapsulated nerve endings found in the subendocardium mainly at the junctions of the pulmonary veins or the venae cavae with the atria. They are mechanoreceptors; normally, those in the veno-atrial junctions discharge when deformed by atrial systole and those around the junctions discharge when wall tension is increased during atrial filling (Fig. 7.40). The atrial receptors discharge

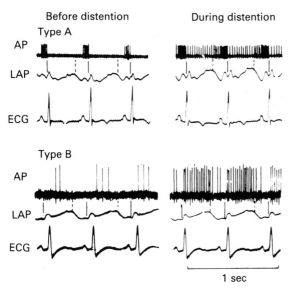

Before distention   During distention

Type A

AP

LAP

ECG

Type B

AP

LAP

ECG

1 sec

Fig. 7.40 Examples of the effect of stretching the atrial walls on the discharge of two types of atrial receptors in anaesthetised dogs. In each case, small balloons at the end of a cannula were inflated to distend the atria. With type A receptors the discharge is greatest during atrial contraction, when the balloons were not distended. The type B receptors discharged maximally during atrial filling. Intermediate receptors discharging both during filling and during contractions are also recognised. Distension of the atria with the balloon led to an increase in the frequency of the action potentials in afferent fibres in the left cervical vagus. (Courtesy of R. J. Linden) AP, action potential; LAP, left atrial pressure; ECG, electrocardiograph.

into afferent myelinated vagal nerve fibres that connect with the nucleus of the tractus solitarius and the central reticular formation in the medulla. Stimulation of these receptors results in a reflex increase in heart rate without a direct inotropic effect on the ventricular muscle or an effect on vascular resistance. The response of an increase in heart rate is caused solely by a reflex increase in the activity in efferent cardiac sympathetic nerve fibres; stimulation of the atrial receptors does not affect the efferent cardiac vagal nerve fibres. The efferent sympathetic nerve fibres that mediate the reflex increase in heart rate to stimulation of the atrial receptors are different from those that mediate the baroreceptor and chemoreceptor reflex of an increase in heart rate and inotropic effect.

Other receptors
Painful stimuli to the skin or electrical stimulation of afferent somatic cutaneous nerves cause an increase in heart rate, which is mediated by efferent sympathetic and vagal nerve fibres, and an increase in blood pressure. Distension of the stomach or the urinary

bladder results in an increase in the heart rate and arterial blood pressure.

Integration of nervous regulation
In general the opposing effects of the vagal and sympathetic nerves on the heart represent the final common pathways of many reflex mechanisms the effects of which are not necessarily additive and which are subject to modification by higher centres. The negative inotropic response in the ventricular muscles to stimulation of the carotid chemoreceptors, mediated by an inhibition of efferent cardiac sympathetic nerves, is abolished by the simultaneous stimulation of the carotid sinus mechanoreceptors, which reflexly inhibits the same efferent sympathetic nerves and causes a negative inotropic response. During stimulation of the carotid chemoreceptors the reflex slowing of the heart rate is abolished by the concomitant reflex response of overbreathing.

In the resting state the heart rate is maintained through an inhibitory vagal activity, called the *vagal tone*, brought about mainly by the operation of the baroreceptor reflex. The reflex slowing of the heart after an increase in blood pressure is mainly caused by activation of the efferent vagal nerves. Activation of central inspiratory neurones can inhibit the effects of the carotid baroreceptor and chemoreceptor reflex on the efferent cardiac vagal neurones. The heart rate quickens with inspiration and slows during expiration; this fluctuation is called *sinus arrhythmia* (p. 102) and is attributed to central neuronal effects as well as to peripheral effects related to respiration. During exercise the sympathetic nerves are responsible for the increase in the inotropic state of the ventricular muscle that operates in conjunction with the Starling mechanism to increase the stroke volume of the heart; these nerves are also involved during exercise in the increase in heart rate. During episodes of emotion or in biological emergencies, for example in preparation for exercise, the heart rate and blood pressure increase; the reverse occurs during fainting due to a sudden shock. These cardio-circulatory changes have been attributed to inhibition or excitation of the efferent preganglionic sympathetic and vagal nerves, through complex neural pathways descending from higher centres in the sensory cortex, and involving the cerebellum, hypothalamus and medulla.

The Rate of the Heart
The heart rate in healthy young men under basal conditions lies between 60 and 65 beats per minute, the figures for women being somewhat higher. However, under ordinary conditions the heart rates of men average about 78, and of women 84 beats per min, and the American Heart Association accepts between 50 and

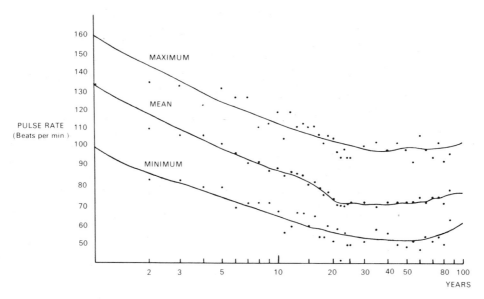

Fig. 7.41 Diagram to show variation of resting pulse rate with age constructed from data of Tigerstedt in Lehrbuch der Physiologie des Kreislaufes.

100 heart beats per min as the normal range. The heart rate of children is faster but tends to fall as childhood advances. (Fig. 7.41). The heart rate increases progressively with increasing exercise up to some 200 beats per minute but the rate of increase is less in trained subjects.

The heart rate is increased by all kinds of emotional disturbances (Fig. 7.42), but it falls progressively during sleep. The heart rate is also affected by body temperature, increasing on the average by 20 beats per min per °C rise in temperature.

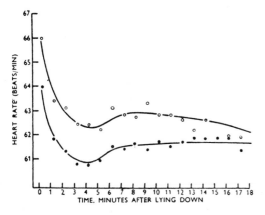

Fig. 7.42 Mean heart rate of 46 healthy young men for 18 min after lying down. ○———○, on first visit to laboratory; ●———●, on second visit, approximately 8 days later. (Tanner J M 1951 Journal of Physiology 115: 391–409)

THE CORONARY CIRCULATION

Coronary vessels

Three bulges of the aortic wall just above the aortic valve are termed the aortic sinuses and from two of them the two main coronary arteries arise. It is thought that eddies in the blood in these sinuses prevent the cusps of the aortic valve from obstructing the orifices of the coronary arteries, and may play a part in closure of the valve. The right coronary artery usually supplies the right atrium, right ventricle, diaphragmatic surface of the left ventricle and SA and AV nodes; the left coronary artery supplies the greater part of the left heart (Fig. 7.43). The coronary arteries and their larger branches lie in the sub-epicardium but from them smaller vessels pass into the substance of the myocardium where their branches form rich plexuses of arterioles, capillaries and venules. From these vessels arise luminal vessels that may open into any of the four chambers of the heart. From 30 to 60 per cent of the coronary artery blood flow is returned to the heart by these luminal vessels rather than by the veins leading to the coronary sinus. The luminal vessels may either drain or nourish the myocardium, according to the difference between the pressure in them and the pressure in the chambers of the heart. Numerous arterial anastomoses occur in all areas of the heart, especially in the deeper layers of the left ventricle and interventricular septum. The capillary supply of heart muscle is about six times as rich as that of skeletal muscle, and greater in the inner than in the superficial parts of the myocardium.

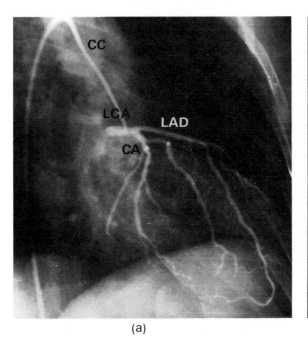
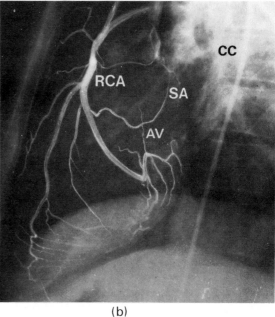

(a)   (b)

Fig. 7.43 Radiographs of the human coronary arterial system. In (a) and (b) contrast medium has been injected into the left (a) and right (b) coronary arteries of a beating heart through a cardiac catheter (CC) sited accurately in the ostium (*selective coronary arteriography*). In (a) the 'trunk' of the tree is the left coronary artery (LCA), the uppermost main branch is the left anterior descending artery (LAD) and its smaller branches, the lower main branch is the circumflex artery (CA) and its branches. In (b) the right coronary artery (RCA) is shown with its branches including those to the sinu-atrial node (SA) and AV node (AV). (By courtesy of the Cardiac Department, Victoria Infirmary, Glasgow)

Coronary blood flow

About 4 per cent of the output of the left ventricle passes into the coronary vessels (Fig. 7.43) so the blood flow in the aorta is not the total cardiac output; that can only be found by measuring the flow in the pulmonary artery.

The peculiarities of the venous drainage (p. 96) make it difficult to estimate human coronary blood flow accurately. Samples of blood can be obtained from the coronary sinus through a cardiac catheter (p. 81) introduced into the mouth of the sinus through the right atrium. If a sample of arterial blood is obtained while the patient is breathing nitrous oxide or radioactive krypton, the arteriovenous gas difference can be obtained. This method measures only the blood flow through the left ventricle but it is unlikely that the flow through the right ventricle is substantially different. The coronary blood flow in an adult at rest is about 200 ml per min. About 70 per cent of the total coronary blood flow occurs during diastole.

During systole the coronary vessels lying within the heart muscle are compressed. This compression increases the total resistance of the coronary vascular bed and actually momentarily reverses the flow in early systole (Fig. 7.16). Since the blood pressure in the left

ventricle during systole is slightly higher than it is in the aorta the tissue pressure in the inner half of the ventricular wall is greater than the arterial blood pressure, and the total blood flow, systolic and diastolic, in subendocardial muscle is about half that in the superficial part of the myocardium. This flow gradient is partly offset by the greater density of capillaries in the deeper myocardium. Nevertheless cells in the sub-endocardial myocardium tend to be most severely damaged by hypoxia (ischaemic necrosis).

The pressure in the right ventricle is, of course, at all times much lower than in the aorta so perfusion of the coronary vessels in the right ventricle is much more efficient. It is probably for these reasons that ischaemic necrosis (myocardial infarction) affects mainly parts of the left ventricle rather than the right.

When the heart beats faster and more strongly its oxygen consumption is increased: during exercise, therefore, the myocardial blood flow is increased, like the blood flow to the skeletal muscle and the skin. The coronary blood flow during severe exercise with a cardiac output of 25 litres per minute could amount to 1 litre per minute (but see Table 7.44). The coronary vessels are dilated or constricted by an autoregulatory system in which the myocardial oxygen tension (Po_2)

Table 7.44 Distribution of the cardiac output at rest and during the steady state of supine leg exercise in a normal subject and a patient with a narrowed mitral valve and cardiac failure (oxygen uptake during exeicse 500 ml/min per m²)

Blood flow (ml/min)	Normal subject		Patient with mitral stenosis	
	Rest	Exercise	Rest	Exercise
Splanchnic	1400	1300	800	400
Renal	1100	900	650	300
Cerebral	750	750	600	600
Coronary*	250	450	300	500
Resting skeletal muscle	700	700	700	350
Leg				
muscle	500⎫	5000	500⎫	3400
skin	250⎭		50⎭	
Skin (other than leg)	250	1000	100	50
Other organs	600	400	300	200
Cardiac output	5800	10 500	4000	5800

* It is likely that when the rise in cardiac output due to exercise reaches high levels the proportion passing through the coronary circulation falls below 4 per cent. Wade O L, Bishop J M 1962 Cardiac output and regional blood flow. Blackwell Scientific, Oxford

determines the blood flow by altering the coronary vascular resistance.

Hypoxia can cause vasodilatation and an increase of flow of as much as 500 per cent. Since neither carbon dioxide nor lactic acid can increase the flow by more than 50 per cent it is assumed that the hypoxic muscle fibres liberate a vasodilator substance. A vasodilator metabolite has not been identified but adenosine is a likely candidate. If the coronary circulation is occluded the Po_2 of the myocardium falls and when the occlusion is released the blood flow increases (reactive hyperaemia, p. 108) and the Po_2 rises above normal. This suggests that the capillaries, not arteriovenous shunts, carry the increased flow. Large changes of pressure in the aorta can also influence coronary perfusion. When the arterial pressure falls the consequent release of adrenergic substances from the adrenal medulla produces coronary vasodilatation and increased coronary blood flow while the flow through the skin, kidneys and splanchnic vessels is severely restricted. The circulation through the heart, like that through the brain, is therefore maintained.

The coronary blood vessels are supplied with both sympathetic and parasympathetic nerves. In animals, sympathetic stimulation and noradrenaline and adrenaline produce an increase in blood flow but whether this is due to vasodilatation, to alteration in heart rate and aortic pressures, or to metabolic effects is not yet clear. Drugs that block either the α- or β-adrenergic receptors have been used to study the effect of sympathetic stimulation on the coronary vascular bed of the dog. Sympathetic vasoconstriction in cardiac muscle is only slight, in contrast to that in skeletal muscle, and is largely overcome by local chemical vasodilatation. Unlike skeletal muscle vessels, the coronary vascular bed is not supplied by sympathetic vasodilator fibres. During exercise, although diastole is shortened because of tachycardia, a normal heart does not suffer from a reduced blood supply. If the coronary arteries are diseased, however, the myocardium can become hypoxic during exercise: this is the cause of cardiac ischaemic pain on exertion (angina pectoris).

CARDIAC FAILURE

Cardiac failure has been defined as 'a state in which the heart fails to maintain an adequate circulation for the needs of the body despite a satisfactory venous filling pressure'.

Whatever the actual cardiac output at the time, failure involves a reduction of output from previous levels and an increase in the venous pressure, apparent at first only during exercise, but later also at rest. The fall in output is accompanied by a redistribution of blood throughout the body (Table 7.44) and an alteration in the function of many organs and tissues. Retention of sodium and water occurs early in cardiac failure and leads to an increased blood volume that further overloads the heart. In some patients the secretion of aldosterone (Chap. 26) is increased and in many there is an increased release of vasopressin (Chaps 13 and 24). Both may contribute to the fluid retention, the mechanism of which is not yet fully understood. The increase of systemic venous pressure must also be a factor in producing oedema and may interfere with hepatic function. Increased pulmonary venous pressure and volume is associated with pulmonary oedema, which reduces the compliance of the lungs and may cause the breathlessness that is such a prominent feature of heart failure.

FURTHER READING

Berne R M, Levy M N 1977 Cardiovascular physiology. Mosby, St Louis

Hainsworth R, Kidd C, Linden R J 1979 Cardiac receptors. University Press, Cambridge

Hurst J W (ed) 1978 The heart, arteries and veins. McGraw-Hill, New York

Jackson J R 1972 The mechanism of ventricular ejection, British Medical Journal 4: 166–169

Katz A M 1977 The physiology of the heart. Raven Press, New York

Kelman G R 1977 Applied vascular physiology. Butterworth, London

Linden R J, Snow H M 1974 The inotropic state of the heart. Recent Advances in Physiology 9: 148–190

Opie L H 1984 The heart: physiology, metabolism, pharmacology and therapy. Grune & Stratton, New York

Randall W C (ed) 1984 Nervous control of cardiovascular function. University Press, Oxford

Rushmer R F 1976 Structure and function of the cardiovascular system. Saunders, London

Wikman-Coffelt J, Mason D T 1985 Mechanisms of cardiac contraction: Structural, biochemical and functional relations. In: Sodeman W A, Sodeman T M (eds) Pathologic physiology. Saunders, Philadelphia, pp. 261–291

8

The circulation

The object of the circulation is to provide the cells of the body with a local environment appropriate for their function. This is achieved by the exchange of nutrients and waste products across the walls of the capillary blood vessels and the rest of the circulatory apparatus is designed to keep these vessels perfused adequately with blood.

It is helpful to think of the circulation in functional rather than in anatomical terms. Figure 1.3 (p. 3) shows that the circulation can be regarded as a number of circuits in parallel. There is one circuit for the renal circulation, one for the skin circulation, one for the muscle circulation and so on. Each circuit consists of a number of sections arranged in series. The chief function of the first section is to damp the huge pressure fluctuations generated by the heart to give a fairly steady driving pressure. Anatomically, these *damping* vessels correspond fairly closely to the arteries. The second section is composed of vessels that offer a high and variable resistance to the flow of blood around the circuit. They act as taps that regulate the flow in any particular circuit. They may be referred to as *resistance vessels* and correspond to the arterioles. The third section in each circuit is composed of the vessels that permit exchange of material across their walls. These may be referred to as the *exchange vessels* and correspond to the capillaries and some of the thin-walled venules. The final section in each circuit consists of the vessels that contain about 75 per cent of the blood volume. These are referred to as the *capacity vessels* and correspond anatomically to the veins and venules. By altering their dimensions, they adjust the capacity of the circulation to meet variations in the volume and distribution of blood in the circulation.

Although it is useful to think about each section of the circulation in terms of its chief feature, that is damping, resistance, exchange or capacity, it should be stressed that all vessels have all these features to some extent. For example, all vessels offer some resistance to flow but the greater part of the resistance lies in the arterioles. Similarly, all vessels have the capacity to hold blood but a large fraction of the blood volume is contained in the venules and veins. Each functional variety of blood vessel will now be considered.

THE ARTERIAL OR DAMPING VESSELS

These vessels have three main features. They convert the intermittent pressure generated by the heart into a fairly steady pressure head. They distribute blood to the tissues at low energy cost and the pressure head within them is maintained at a fairly constant value by a number of complex control systems.

Structure of arteries

All the blood vessels of whatever size have a smooth inner lining of flattened *endothelial cells* joined edge to edge. This inner lining is continuous from the arteries through the capillaries to the veins and to the internal lining of the heart (the *endocardium*).

The arteries have three main coats and the following description refers mainly to a medium-sized artery (Fig. 8.1). The endothelial layer is surrounded by an elastic layer, the two together forming the *tunica intima*, or inner coat. After death, when the internal pressure falls, the elastic tissue contracts and forms the wavy inner border of an artery seen in histological preparations. The tunica intima is surrounded by smooth muscle fibres that pass circularly round the vessel, forming the *tunica media*, or middle coat. Finally there is an external coat, or *tunica adventitia*, of collagen-rich connective tissue that blends with the general tissue of the body. In the larger arteries the elastic layer takes the form of a fenestrated membrane and there is also a certain amount of subendothelial fibrous tissue. The muscle fibres of the middle coat are reinforced by a network of elastic fibres and the outer coat contains elastic fibres in addition to collagen fibres. The large arteries, and particularly the aorta, thus contain a greater proportion of elastic tissue in their walls than do the smaller arteries. The walls of the arterioles are almost entirely muscular. At the point where an artery divides, the combined cross-sectional area of the two

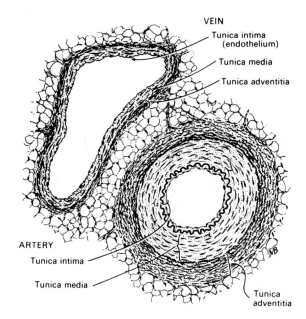

VEIN
Tunica intima
(endothelium)
Tunica media
Tunica adventitia

ARTERY
Tunica intima
Tunica media
Tunica adventitia

Fig. 8.1 Cross-section of a medium sized artery and its accompanying vein (× 80). The cross-sectional area of a major vein is more than twice that of the corresponding artery; small veins draining a tissue may have six or seven times the cross-section of the little arteries supplying it. (Wiedman M P 1963 Circulation Research 12: 375–378)

divisions is greater than that of the original artery. The total cross-sectional area of the vascular system, therefore, gradually increases as the vessels themselves become smaller (see Fig. 8.9) so that at the capillaries it may be one thousand times that at the aorta.

The walls of the veins are very much thinner than those of the corresponding arteries and their internal diameter is generally greater (Fig. 8.1). The elastic tissue is usually quite inconspicuous and some veins, for example those of the bones and placenta, are said to have little or no muscular tissue.

The veins are easily distended by a small rise of pressure; the arteries, on the other hand, withstand a considerable increase of internal pressure with a relatively small increase in volume. The elasticity of the aorta gradually diminishes with age. The veins, unlike the arteries, can accommodate relatively large volumes of added (transfused) fluid with only small changes in pressure.

Role of the elastic tissue
When the left ventricle contracts, all the energy imparted to the blood does not appear immediately as kinetic energy. Some is used to stretch the elastic fibres in the arterial walls and is stored there as potential energy. During systole this 'give' in the arterial wall limits the rise in the systolic arterial pressure. If the

walls were rigid, the systolic pressure would be higher. With increasing age the elastic tissue degenerates and the arterial walls become stiffer. As this happens the systolic pressure tends to rise. During diastole the recoil of the elastic tissue returns the energy stored in the wall to the blood and this limits the fall in arterial pressure. If the walls were rigid, diastolic pressure would be lower. Thus the elastic tissue tends to damp pressure fluctuations in the arterial system to provide a fairly constant pressure head.

Role of the arterial smooth muscle
The media in the major arteries is predominantly elastic in character, but it also contains a considerable amount of smooth muscle. Contraction and relaxation of this smooth muscle is not of great importance in the regulation of blood flow. The resistance offered by the larger arterial vessels is so low that changes in their calibre do not have much effect on the total resistance offered by the circuit. In the smaller muscular arteries the smooth muscle may be important in determining local vascular resistance.

The smooth muscle can be excited by mechanical irritation, for example puncturing the arterial wall with a needle to take an arterial blood sample. It may be that the muscle has a protective function so that in a severe injury when an artery is severed the irritation of the vessel wall may induce spasm, which reduces blood loss.

Smooth muscle in blood vessels, like smooth muscle elsewhere, responds to stretch by contracting. When a person stands up the arterial pressure in his feet rises by about 100 mm Hg, the hydrostatic equivalent of the column of blood from the heart to the feet. This would tend to distend the arteries and the smooth muscle contraction induced by stretch helps to limit the distension.

The arterial pulse
The rapid rise of pressure following the ejection of some 60 ml of blood from the left ventricle at each systole expands the aorta and a pressure wave or pulse passes along its wall. The pulse is *not* due to the passage of blood along the arteries — the blood travels at about 50 cm/second — but to a pressure wave travelling at

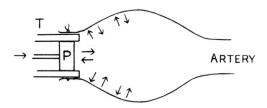

Fig. 8.2 Diagram to illustrate the initiation of a pulse wave in the aorta.

about 700 cm/second. If the piston P in Figure 8.2 is driven towards the right in the tube T tied into an artery, the vessel is distended locally because the blood is incompressible. This produces a local increase of pressure that has little effect on the advancing piston, which is in fact a mass of incompressible blood; instead the next section of the artery is stretched so that a wave of pressure travels along the vessel wall without involving actual transmission of blood.

The record (Fig. 8.3) of the pulse wave in the brachial artery shows a steeply ascending limb, due to ventricular systole, followed by a more gradual fall in diastole. However, the curve in diastole is not smooth as would be expected if it were merely the result of a slow decline of pressure, but contains several minor oscillations. The most constant of these is the *dicrotic wave*, the largest wave on the descending line of the trace. It has been ascribed to rebound from the closed aortic valves but it is more likely that this wave, together with other smaller subsidiary waves often observed, represents oscillations of the aorta at its own natural frequency. The difference between the systolic and diastolic pressures is about 40 mm Hg in normal people and is called the *pulse pressure*.

The form of the pulse wave is changed as it passes to the periphery by the frictional resistance of the arterial walls and by reflected waves, so that interpretation of the wave form is difficult. For clinical purposes, however, useful information about the shape of the pulse wave can be obtained by feeling the carotid artery. A wave that rises slowly and dies away slowly (plateau pulse) is a good indication that the aortic valve is narrowed (stenosed); on the other hand, a pulse wave that rises and falls quickly (collapsing pulse) may mean that the aortic valve is incompetent, allowing a proportion of the systolic discharge to run back (regurgitate) into the left ventricle.

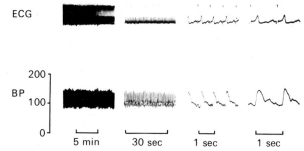

Fig. 8.3 Records of arterial blood pressure recorded directly by an indwelling catheter from the brachial artery of a normal ambulant subject who wore the miniature tape-recording apparatus, perfusing pump and transducer in a harness. The records were made at different speeds; the first two provide information such as is shown in Figure 8.7, the last shows the shape of the brachial arterial pressure pulse. (Courtesy of P. Sleight)

Pulse wave velocity

If the pulse is recorded simultaneously from the carotid and the radial arteries, the velocity of the pulse wave is found to be about 5 m/s at 5 years and 8 m/s at 60 years; the difference in the velocities is due to the fact that arteries become stiffer with increasing age.

It is useful to know that the pulse wave normally arrives at almost the same moment at the beginning of the femoral artery and at the radial artery at the wrist. If the femoral pulse is later than the radial it is probable that the wave is reaching the femoral artery along collateral channels developed as the result of a congenital narrowing of the aorta (coarctation).

The pulse rate

The pulse rate varies considerably from individual to individual and in the same subject at different times,

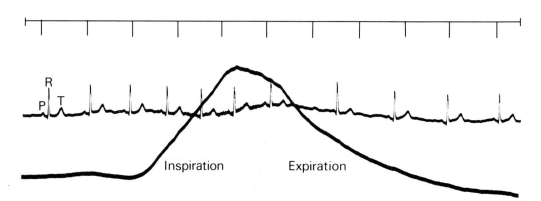

Fig. 8.4 Sinus arrhythmia. ECG (lead II) from a healthy male aged 24 showing cardiac acceleration during inspiration and slowing during expiration. Timing marks, 1.0 second apart.

depending on a large number of factors, which are considered in Chapter 7. The resting pulse rate tends to fall as a child grows up, as shown in Figure 7.41.

The pulse is not quite regular. Accurate records show that there is a slight acceleration during inspiration and a slight deceleration during expiration (Fig. 8.4) provided that the respiratory rate is low. This is termed *sinus arrhythmia*. In children this fluctuation in rhythm is much more marked than in adults. During inspiration the thoracic pressure falls while the abdominal pressure rises and, therefore, blood flows more readily into the thoracic veins, producing a rise of atrial and central venous pressure and an acceleration of the heart. This is only a partial explanation of sinus arrhythmia, since alterations of heart rate related to respiratory activity also occur independently of any alteration in venous pressure.

In heart disease when the cardiac rhythm is irregular (atrial fibrillation, premature beats, p. 68) the rate of the heart may exceed the pulse rate because the volume of some of the systolic discharges is insufficient to promote a pulse wave in the arterial walls great enough to reach the wrist. This is called a *pulse deficit*.

Arterial pressure

Measurement

It is well known that blood escapes from a cut artery under considerable pressure, and the first attempt to measure the pressure was made by Stephen Hales in 1732. After occluding the femoral artery of a mare with a temporary ligature he tied a brass pipe into it and connected to it a glass tube 9 ft (2.7 m) long. When he loosened the ligature on the artery the blood rose 8 ft 3 in (about 2.5 m) above the level of the heart. He noted that alterations in pressure occurred with each beat of the heart and with the movements of respiration. These results are of great historical interest but the method is not very useful because the blood clots in the manometer in a few minutes.

Nowadays accurate and continuous records of arterial blood pressure in man can be obtained with strain-gauge or condenser manometers communicating directly with an artery through a needle or catheter (Fig. 8.3). Such records show oscillations between the maximum or *systolic pressure* (SBP) and the minimum or *diastolic pressure* (DBP). A point half-way between the maximum and minimum pressures does not represent the *mean arterial pressure*, which is, in fact, closer to the diastolic than to the systolic pressure. For convenience it may be taken as the diastolic pressure plus one-third of the pulse-pressure but more strictly it is the level of the line halving the area between the pulse wave contour and the diastolic pressure level. This value can be calculated and recorded electronically.

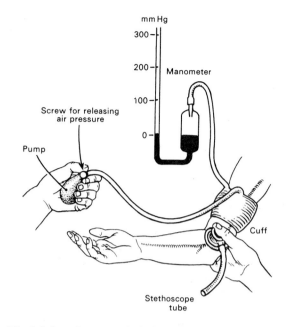

Fig. 8.5 Auscultatory method of measuring blood pressure in man. The cuff should be at heart level.

The direct method just described is obviously unsuitable for routine clinical use but the blood pressure can be estimated in man indirectly, although less accurately, by a *sphygmomanometer*, a mercury manometer with one wide and one narrow limb (Fig. 8.5). A rubber bag of standard size (18 cm × 12 cm for adults) covered with cloth is wrapped round the upper arm, leaving the cubital fossa exposed, and connected to the manometer and pump with which it is rapidly inflated to a point above the systolic blood pressure. The pressure in the bag is allowed to fall gradually while the operator listens through a stethoscope, the diaphragm or bell of which is placed over the brachial artery. The pressure in the cuff is raised rapidly until the radial pulse disappears; at this point the pressure in the cuff is greater than the SBP and the artery is occluded throughout the pulse cycle. When the pressure falls a little below SBP (line A, Fig. 8.6) the artery opens momentarily when the internal pressure is greater than the external (cuff) pressure and a soft thudding sound is heard at each pulse. As the pressure is further reduced these sounds are gradually succeeded by a distinct tapping, which becomes louder as the pressure is reduced. As the pressure in the cuff is allowed to fall, the character of the sound suddenly changes from a sharp, loud tapping to a softer thudding or muffled noise ('fourth phase'; Fig. 8.6, line C). This is taken as the DBP. Finally the sounds disappear, usually quite suddenly ('fifth phase'), when the pressure in the bag falls below a certain pressure (line D) because below this pressure the

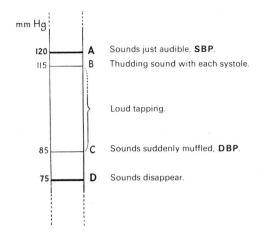

Fig. 8.6 The auscultatory method of measuring arterial blood pressure.

internal pressure in the brachial artery is always greater than the pressure applied externally by the bag; the flow of blood along the artery is not interrupted and usually no sound is heard.

Several investigators have compared the pressure readings obtained from a cannula inserted into the brachial artery in one arm with the readings obtained in the other by the auscultatory method. Considerable discrepancies have been observed. The indirect method usually gives readings of SBP about 25 mm Hg lower than the 'true' SBP given by the direct method. The DBP reading by the indirect method is on average 8 mm Hg higher at line C but about 2 mm Hg higher at line D. Although indirect sphygmomanometry does

not give an accurate (absolute) measurement of either SBP or DBP, yet, since the direct and indirect readings are highly correlated, the indirect method is of great practical value in medicine.

Normal values

When the subject is supine the mean arterial pressure in the brachial and femoral arteries are approximately the same, that is, about 100 mm Hg. When the subject is standing, however, the femoral pressure is higher than that in the brachial artery, the difference being the pressure of a column of blood equal in height to the vertical distance between one artery and the other.

In any individual, arterial pressure is not constant but subject to appreciable variations over short intervals of time (Fig. 8.7). It also varies with each respiratory cycle. During sleep the SBP may fall below 80 mm Hg. The pressure recorded at some moment in ordinary conditions of life is referred to as the *casual* blood pressure. The figure is higher, sometimes much higher, than the *basal* blood pressure, that is the pressure recorded when the subject is at complete physical and mental rest.

Many attempts have been made to define normal values for blood pressure but all have been unsatisfactory. The pressure obtained by the sphygmomanometer is affected by the thickness of the arm, the thicker the arm the higher the value obtained. Arterial pressure increases with age (Fig. 8.8), more in some subjects than in others, and no dividing line can be set at any age below which the pressure is normal and above which it is abnormal. Indeed, it is considered by some that arterial pressure is inherited as a graded characteristic like height and that the range of variation includes

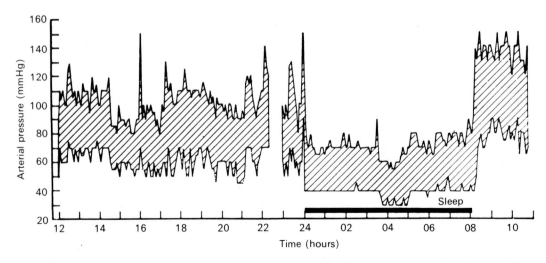

Fig. 8.7 Continuous record of arterial blood pressure of a healthy man during 24 hours made by means of an indwelling arterial cannula. Note the fall of SBP and DBP during sleep. The high pressure shown at 16.00 is due to a painful stimulus, that at 24.00 to coitus. (Bevan A T et al. 1969 Clinical Science 36: 329–344)

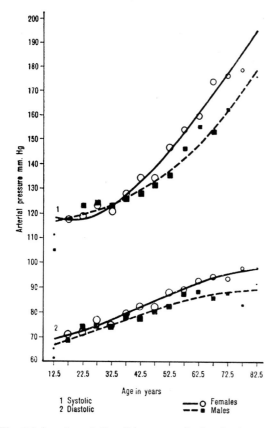

1 Systolic   ——○ Females
2 Diastolic   – – –■ Males

Fig. 8.8 Systolic and diastolic pressures for females (open circles) and males (black squares) for each five-year age group of the population sample, together with the fitted curves. The area of each circle or square is proportional to the number of subjects in that age group. (Hamilton M et al. 1954 Clinical Science 13: 11–35)

values hitherto regarded as abnormal. It seems likely that at least three factors are concerned in the production of high blood pressure, namely age, heredity and environment.

Factors determining arterial pressure
Blood enters the arterial system from the left ventricle and leaves through the arterioles. The amount entering is determined by the cardiac output and the amount leaving is determined by the resistance offered by the arterioles (*peripheral resistance*). If more blood enters, that is if the cardiac output increases or if less blood leaves, that is if the peripheral resistance rises, the pressure in the arterial system rises. Conversely if cardiac output or peripheral resistance falls, the arterial pressure decreases. Blood pressure (BP) is therefore a function of cardiac output (CO) and peripheral resistance (PR). This relationship can be expressed as BP = CO × PR. Changes in the elasticity of the arteries

affect pulse pressure more than mean pressure in the arterial system.

Factors regulating arterial pressure
Control systems within the body tend to maintain mean arterial pressure within fairly strict limits. In this way the head of pressure in the arteries perfusing a tissue is maintained relatively constant despite the changes that frequently occur in both cardiac output and peripheral resistance. Stretch receptors are found in the wall of the proximal arterial tree, especially in the region of the aortic arch and carotid sinuses (Chap. 7, p. 93; Fig. 7.36). When the arterial pressure rises there is increased stimulation of these nerve endings. The increased traffic of impulses up the vagus and glossopharyngeal nerves leads to reflex vagal slowing of the heart and reflex release of vasoconstrictor tone in the peripheral blood vessels. The resulting fall in cardiac output and the reduction of peripheral resistance tend to restore the blood pressure to normal. Similarly a fall in arterial pressure decreases the stimulation of the arterial stretch receptors. The reflex tachycardia and vasoconstriction that ensue tend to raise the blood pressure towards its normal value.

Even when the arterial baroreceptors are denervated, blood pressure can still be regulated to some extent by the renin-angiotensin system. It is known that a fall in renal blood flow, such as would occur if arterial pressure fell, results in the release of the hormone renin from the kidney. Renin converts the plasma protein angiotensinogen to the angiotensin polypeptides, which constrict blood vessels and cause the release of aldosterone from the adrenal cortex. The salt and water retention brought about by aldosterone together with the vasoconstriction produced by angiotensin tend to raise arterial pressure to the set value.

THE ARTERIOLES OR RESISTANCE VESSELS

The changes in intravascular pressure, cross-sectional area and velocity of blood flow at various points of the vascular system are shown in Figure 8.9. The greatest fall in arterial pressure occurs in the arterioles which offer the greatest resistance to flow. Regional blood flow is regulated by variations in the resistance they offer.

Peripheral resistance
Peripheral resistance is caused by the frictional resistance offered by the circulatory system to the flow of blood around it. From the wall to the centre of a blood vessel the blood flows along the vessel in a series of concentric laminae with increasing velocity. The laminae move at different speeds relative to one another and it is the lack of slipperiness or the cohesive forces

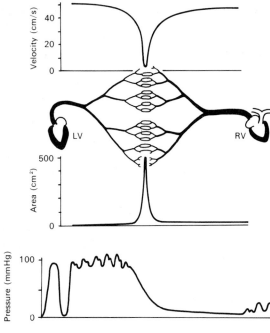

Fig. 8.9 Diagram showing the relations between blood pressure, blood velocity and the total cross-sectional area in arteries, capillaries and veins (After Rushmer R F 1976 Structure and function of the cardiovascular system, 2nd edn. Saunders, Philadelphia).

between adjacent layers that is responsible for the friction. All the energy imparted to the blood by the heart is used up in overcoming this frictional resistance in one transit round the circulatory system.

Peripheral resistance (R) can be measured using the hydraulic equivalent of Ohm's law, that is $R = \Delta P/F$ where ΔP is the pressure drop across and F the flow around the circulation. For the calculation it is necessary to measure mean arterial pressure, mean venous pressure and the cardiac output.

From Poiseuille's law, which describes the factors governing the laminar flow of fluid through capillary tubes with rigid walls, it can be derived that peripheral resistance (R) is directly proportional to the length of the tube (l), the viscosity of the fluid (η), and inversely proportional to the fourth power of the radius (r), that is $R \propto l\eta/r^4$.

Since the length of the vessels and the viscosity of the blood are relatively constant, changes in peripheral resistance are usually induced by changes in the radius of the vessels. Because of the fourth power relationship small changes in radius cause large changes in resistance; for example, a doubling of the radius of a vessel would cause a sixteenfold decrease in the resistance offered.

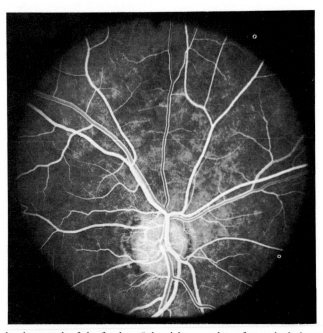

Fig. 8.10 A retinal fluorescein photograph of the fundus of the right eye taken after a single intracarotid injection of 4 ml of 5 per cent fluorescein in a healthy man aged 30 years. Fluorescein appears white in the photograph taken 12 seconds after the injection of fluorescein. The arteriolar system is filled with fluorescent blood. The main veins are seen filling from the smaller branches and the fluorescein maintains its position at the edge of the vein, demonstrating laminar flow. Just inferior to the optic disc, two veins showing laminar flow unite. A thin central stream has formed in the main vein from the merging of the streams at the walls of the tributary veins. (By courtesy of D F J Archer)

Blood flow in the circulation is normally *laminar*, as shown in Figure 8.10. If it becomes *turbulent* peripheral resistance is increased. As the rate of flow of a fluid in a tube is gradually increased there comes a point at which laminar flow is replaced by turbulence and the conditions mentioned above no longer apply. By injecting a stream of dye into a stream of water flowing in a long straight tube Reynolds (1883) found that turbulence developed if the expression rVd/η, in which r is the radius of the tube, V the mean velocity of flow, d the density and η the viscosity, exceeded a certain value. Reynolds' number is about 1000 for water and slightly less for blood. It is obvious that *turbulent flow* occurs more readily when the fluid is of low viscosity and the velocity relatively great so that it tends to develop first in large vessels. These conditions are found in the heart and aorta of severely anaemic patients and turbulence may account for the cardiac murmurs readily audible with the stethoscope over the heart and large arteries in such people. The high velocity of the flow of blood through narrowed valves in the heart may be sufficient itself to cause turbulence and the development of audible murmurs.

The experiments of Poiseuille and Reynolds were carried out with homogeneous fluids, steady flow and rigid tubes. Blood, with its cellular content, is certainly not homogeneous, its flow is pulsatile and the arteries are elastic. However, although the various laws suggested by these workers may not be exactly applicable to the circulation they are probably a good approximation.

Regulation of peripheral resistance
Since most of the resistance offered by the circulation lies in the arterioles, changes in the calibre of these vessels cause much greater changes in peripheral resistance than comparable changes in other vessels. If perfusion pressure is held constant, flow is inversely proportional to peripheral resistance. Thus changes in the calibre of arterioles largely determine the amount of blood flowing around the circulation. Through regulation of the calibre of arterioles, local peripheral resistance and hence local blood flow is controlled. It should be noted that arterioles control blood flow not blood velocity. Flow depends on resistance whereas velocity depends on the total cross-sectional area of the vascular bed.

Measurement of blood flow
The simplest method of determining the blood flow through an organ is to collect and measure over a given period of time all the blood emerging from its veins. Various methods of measuring blood flow without loss of blood have been invented. In Rein's flow meter heat is applied to an artery in the living animal by a coil

situated midway between two thermocouples placed upstream and downstream on the artery. If the flow is fast the temperature difference between the two couples is small, if slow the difference is large. The apparatus is calibrated by noting the thermocouple readings at various known rates of flow through an excised artery of the same size. The electromagnetic flow meter depends on the fact that an electromotive force (EMF) is induced in a conductor (in this case the blood) moving through a magnetic field. The EMF is picked up by two electrodes placed on opposite sides of the unopened artery at right angles to the direction of flow and to the magnetic field.

The changes of volume of a limb or part of a limb can be recorded by means of a *plethysmograph* (Fig. 8.11). This is a rigid box that can be slipped over the part to make a closed system in which small changes of volume can be recorded. If the veins are obstructed for a *short* time (without obstructing the arterial inflow) the record shows an increase in volume, which indicates the flow of blood into the part during the period of obstruction. The rigid plethysmograph has now largely been replaced by the strain gauge plethysmograph. It consists of a thin plastic tube with a narrow lumen filled with mercury, which is fastened around the arm to measure its circumference and hence the volume of the part of the limb. If the venous return is prevented, the swelling of the limb increases the length of the column of mercury and increases its resistance which can be recorded electronically.

Since the heat loss from a part is directly related to its blood flow it is possible to assess the flow in a hand

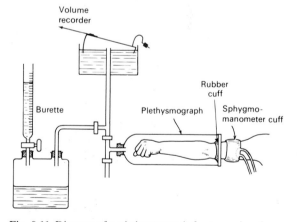

Fig. 8.11 Diagram of a plethysmograph for measuring the rate of blood flow through the arm. A thin rubber cuff makes an air-tight junction just above the elbow. The sphygmomanometer cuff is connected to a pump and manometer as in Figure 8.5; it is inflated to obstruct the venous return but not the arterial inflow. The forearm swells and expels air into the volume recorder. The excursion of the volume recorder is calibrated by running water from the burette into the Wolff's bottle.

or a finger in which the heat loss is high by measuring the heat gained by a water-calorimeter in which the part is immersed. Since the temperature of the skin is related to the rate of blood flow through it, measurements of surface temperature may be used as an index of blood flow in superficial tissues. The Fick principle (p. 87) can be applied to the determination of the blood flow through an organ, for example the heart (cardiac output), the kidney (pp. 178–180) or the brain.

CONTROL OF BLOOD FLOW

Although all blood vessels offer some resistance to the flow of blood, the main resistance lies in the small arteries and arterioles. These vessels are controlled by the local action of chemical or physical factors, hormones circulating in the blood or by the autonomic nerves that supply them. Although changes in the calibre of resistance vessels tend to change the pressure levels and gradients in the circulation, the main effect is on blood flow. Blood flow to any tissue is normally regulated by local factors to serve the needs of that tissue but it may be subordinated to supply the needs of the entire body by hormonal or nervous factors.

Local control

Effect of metabolites
Figure 8.12 shows schematically the effect of temporary occlusion of the circulation on blood flow in a limb. On release of the occlusion, the blood flow is raised well above the resting level and then gradually returns towards the resting level. The increase in blood flow after occlusion is known as *reactive hyperaemia*. The excess blood flow after release is sometimes referred to as the *blood flow repayment* for the *blood flow debt* incurred during occlusion. Though there is not a precise relationship, increasing the period of occlusion tends to increase both the intensity and duration of the reactive hyperaemia. Reactive hyperaemia is caused by a local mechanism since it is confined to those tissues whose circulation has been reduced. It is not mediated by vasomotor nerves since it is unaffected by severance of the autonomic nerves to the limb.

A similar increase in blood flow is seen after a period of exercise in a limb. When the exercise stops the blood flow is increased greatly above the resting level and then falls in an exponential fashion towards the resting level. This phenomenon is called *exercise hyperaemia*. Like reactive hyperaemia it is confined to the exercising tissues and still occurs after section of the autonomic nerves to the tissue. The intensity of the exercise hyperaemia is related to the severity and duration of the exercise.

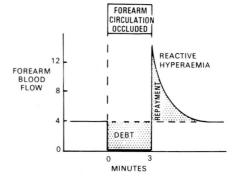

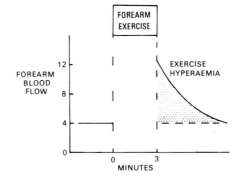

Fig. 8.12 Change in forearm blood flow (ml/100 ml per min) after occlusion of the circulation (above) and exercise of the forearm muscles (below) (By courtesy of I C Roddie)

In both exercise and reactive hyperaemia, the increase in blood flow is thought to be due to an increased concentration of metabolites in the tissues, which can cause blood vessels to dilate. In the case of circulatory arrest, metabolism continues to produce metabolites even when the blood flow is stopped. So the concentration of metabolites, and hence the vasodilatation in the tissue, increases in the period of circulatory arrest. When the circulation is re-established, the increased blood flow through the dilated vessels washes away the metabolites in an exponential manner until their concentration in the tissues, and thus the blood flow, has returned to normal. The increase in blood flow that occurs in muscles during exercise is not adequate to supply the needs of the increased metabolism. Metabolites therefore accumulate in the tissues and the resulting vasodilatation is responsible for the hyperaemia that follows exercise. When the raised blood flow has cleared the excess of metabolites the blood flow returns to normal.

It is the local control of resistance blood vessels by metabolites that ensures that the blood supply to tissues is precisely regulated to meet their metabolic needs. If heart muscle has to do more work, the increased local metabolism that this entails increases the local production of metabolites and hence local coronary blood flow. The parts of the heart muscle that undergo the greatest increases in work get the greatest increases in blood flow. The occurrence of metabolic hyperaemia is most evident in tissues such as muscle and liver where blood flow is mainly determined by metabolic needs. In tissues such as skin and kidney, where blood flow is related to functions other than metabolism, metabolic hyperaemia is less evident.

There has been much argument on the relative importance of the metabolic factors responsible for dilating the blood vessels; these include carbon dioxide and hydrogen ion excess, oxygen lack, potassium excess, an increase in the osmolality of the local tissue fluids, adenosine triphosphate, adenosine, phosphate and bradykinin. All can dilate blood vessels; some, such as adenosine triphosphate and bradykinin, do so strongly and others, such as potassium and phosphate, weakly. It is likely that most of the above substances contribute to metabolic hyperaemia, the contribution of any particular substance varying in different tissues and under different conditions.

Effect of local temperature
If the hand or foot is put into water at 45°C the blood flow through the part increases several fold. The increase is restricted to the part that is immersed. It is independent of the autonomic nerve supply since it can occur even if the part is denervated. This vasodilatation serves to protect the extremity from the damaging effect of heat. If the extremity is immersed in water at 45°C with the circulation occluded, it becomes painful as the tissue temperature rises. The vasodilatation that normally occurs tends to keep the tissues relatively cool by increasing their perfusion with blood at central body temperature. Since heat causes vasodilatation in denervated tissues it is likely that its effect is a direct local one on the smooth muscle in the walls of the arterioles. In intact tissues the stimulating effect of heat on local tissue metabolism may contribute to the dilatation.

The immersion of an extremity in moderately cold water normally causes vasoconstriction, which reduces the loss of heat from the blood to the environment. In people whose limbs are exposed to cold water for prolonged periods, say after shipwreck, the prolonged decrease in blood flow may lead to local tissue death (necrosis) in the toes and feet (immersion foot syndrome).

An extremity exposed to near-freezing temperatures, for example 0 to 4°C, shows a characteristic pattern of events (Fig. 8.13). The local blood flow falls to about zero initially and the part becomes painful. Blood flow then starts to rise rapidly to a value well above the resting level. At this time pain disappears. After another short interval flow falls again and pain reappears. This cyclic pattern of blood flow persists while the immersion in ice continues. It is referred to as *cold-induced vasodilatation* (CIVD).

This vasodilatation may be elicited locally in the fingers, toes, ears and the tip of the nose, parts that are particularly rich in arterio-venous (AV) anastomoses. It does not depend on an intact nerve supply but the exact mechanism underlying it is not fully understood. Its effect is clearly protective since it tends to prevent tissue damage due to freezing of the extremities.

Effect of transmural pressure
The pressure difference across the wall of a blood vessel is measured by subtracting the external tissue pressure from the intravascular pressure. It is referred to as the *transmural pressure*. Changes in transmural pressure cause local changes in the arterioles.

As the transmural pressure in the vessels rises, one would expect the arterioles to dilate due to distension and the blood flow to increase. However, as Figure 8.14 shows, this expectation is not fulfilled. If the arterial pressure is raised above the normal value of about 100 mm Hg, blood flow rises only very slowly until, at a high critical pressure, it rises sharply. The fact that flow does not change very much when the pressure is raised suggests that the increase in transmural pressure elicits an increase in vascular resistance. The large increase in flow at very high pressures is thought to be

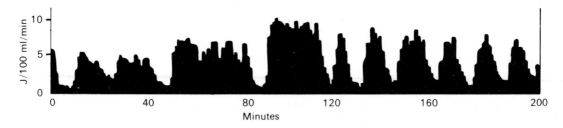

Fig. 8.13 The heat loss in J/100 ml tissue per min from the right index finger to water at 0 to 6°C. The black area represents the heat loss from the circulating blood. Pain was felt when heat loss was at a minimum (After Greenfield A D M et al. 1951 Irish Journal of Medical Science 309:415)

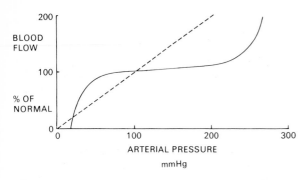

Fig. 8.14 The effect of arterial pressure on blood flow. The broken line shows the relation that would be expected if the blood vessels behaved as rigid tubes. (By courtesy of I C Roddie)

due to the distending forces overcoming the vasoconstrictor response.

If the pressure is lowered below normal, the blood flow at first does not fall proportionately; this indicates that a fall in transmural pressure decreases the vascular resistance. However, at very low perfusion pressures the flow stops even while there is still a positive perfusion pressure head. This closure of the vessels below a certain critical transmural pressure is known as *critical closure*.

Figure 8.14 also shows that over a very wide range of perfusion pressures the blood flow is relatively independent of the pressure head. This phenomenon, referred to as *autoregulation*, is seen to some extent in most vascular beds but is an obvious feature in kidney, brain and muscle. It is a useful phenomenon since it tends to keep blood flow to an organ fairly constant despite fluctuations in blood pressure provided its metabolic requirements do not change.

A number of mechanisms have been suggested to account for autoregulation. According to the *myogenic theory* a rise in transmural pressure tends to stretch the walls of the resistance vessels. Smooth muscle is excited by stretching and responds by contracting. The resulting vasoconstriction increases vascular resistance and limits the tendency for flow to increase. The converse reaction would explain the decrease in resistance when transmural pressure is lowered. A second possible mechanism is contained in the *tissue pressure theory*. In an encapsulated organ such as the kidney a rise in transmural pressure would result in a rise in tissue fluid formation. The accumulation of tissue fluid would increase tissue pressure and result in a mechanical compression of the resistance vessels. This would also tend to limit the increase in blood flow when transmural pressure rises. A third possibility is contained in the *tissue metabolite theory*. The increase in blood flow resulting from a rise in transmural pressure would tend

to wash away local metabolites and reduce the metabolite concentration in the tissues. This in turn would cause vasoconstriction and so limit the increase in blood flow.

It is likely that all these mechanisms contribute in different degrees to the autoregulation seen in different tissues.

Effect of oxygen partial pressure in pulmonary alveoli
As mentioned earlier, oxygen lack is thought to be one of the factors responsible for vasodilation in active tissues. However, when the pressure of oxygen in the alveoli of one part of the lungs falls, vasoconstriction occurs in the blood vessels perfusing that part. In this situation hypoxia acts as a vasoconstrictor agent. This response ensures that blood is not sent to poorly ventilated alveoli and so helps to maintain the normal ventilation-to-perfusion ratio in the lungs. It may also contribute to pulmonary arterial hypertension in people with chronic lung disease.

Nervous control

Vasoconstrictor nerves
These are nerves which, when stimulated, cause blood vessels to contract. Impulses reaching their nerve terminals release noradrenaline, which excites the smooth muscle in the walls of the blood vessel.

The central origin of the vasoconstrictor nerve impulses can be traced in animals by making sections through the brain stem at various levels. A large number of cells and fibres in the medulla are concerned with the transmission of impulses to blood vessels and this area is, therefore, called the *vasomotor centre*. Afferent impulses are constantly reaching the vasomotor centre from all parts of the body, especially from the pressor receptors in the carotid sinus and aortic arch and from the cardiac and respiratory centres in the medulla itself; efferent impulses are thus initiated or modified and appropriate adjustments made in the circulatory system via the sympathetic nervous system. In disease of the afferent nervous system, as for example in the neuropathy of diabetes mellitus, reflex alterations of vascular tone may disturbed.

The vasoconstrictor impulses pass down from the medulla into the cord and leave by the anterior spinal roots of the thoracic and upper lumbar part of the cord. The fibres pass by way of the white rami communicantes to the sympathetic ganglia (*preganglionic fibres*; Fig. 16.3). Here new fibres (*postganglionic fibres*) arise, some going straight to the main blood vessels, others returning to the mixed spinal nerves, to be carried in them to the blood vessels in the periphery.

If the sympathetic nerves to the extremities of man are cut, the blood flow through the extremities increases. This increase is greatest in the skin of the hands and feet, but is also transiently seen in the skeletal muscles of the forearm and calf. It can be concluded that the blood vessels of these parts are normally subjected to considerable vasoconstrictor tone and that blood flow may be increased by release of vasoconstrictor tone.

The frequency of impulses in vasoconstrictor nerve is usually quite low compared with that in somatic motor fibres. It has been shown that almost complete vasoconstriction is produced when vasoconstrictor nerves are stimulated at rates of about 8 impulses per second. The resting level of vasoconstrictor tone could be mimicked by about 1 impulse per second. In somatic fibres, maximum contractions of skeletal muscle are achieved with impulse frequencies of about 50 per second.

Vasodilator nerves

These are nerves which, when stimulated, cause dilatation of the blood vessels they innervate. They are thought to do this by releasing a vasodilatator substance such as acetylcholine at their nerve endings. Vasodilator nerve fibres occur in both sympathetic and parasympathetic systems.

Stimulation of the following parasympathetic nerves produces vasodilatation in the part supplied: chorda tympani to the submandibular gland, small petrosal nerve to the parotid gland, lingual nerve to the tongue and the pelvic splanchnic nerves to the external genitalia.

After a muscle has been treated with atropine to make its blood vessels insensitive to acetylcholine, stimulation of the vasodilatator nerves to that muscle is without effect. However, atropinisation of the muscles in a limb of an intact animal does not reduce the limb blood flow. This shows that vasodilator fibres, unlike vasoconstrictor fibres, are not tonically active under normal circumstances. They appear to be brought into action whenever the need for them arises.

Vasomotor reflexes

These permit the general circulatory requirements of the body to override the local requirements of the tissues. In most cases their effects are seen throughout the body. Vasomotor reflexes are most evident in tissues such as skin, muscle and gut where the blood supply can be restricted without an immediate threat to the tissue. The flow through some tissues, such as the heart and the brain, that cannot tolerate prolonged restriction of flow, is only partly controlled by vasomotor nerves (see p. 97 and Chap. 31). Many vasomotor reflexes have been described but only some of the more important ones that can be elicited in man are described below.

Thermoregulatory reflexes

When a subject is heated by immersing his legs in warm water, the blood flow to his hands increases. This is reflexly mediated by release of sympathetic vasoconstrictor tone since it does not occur if the sympathetic nerves to the hand are cut or if the vasoconstrictor fibres are selectively blocked (Fig. 8.15). A similar release of vasoconstrictor tone occurs in the other extremities, such as the ears, nose and lips. Vasodilatation also occurs in the skin of other parts of the body but this is the result of activity in the sympathetic cholinergic nerves. The dilatation may be secondary to the release of bradykinin-forming enzyme by active sweat glands, which have a sympathetic cholinergic innervation. Reflex vasodilatation in response to body heating is not seen in vascular beds such as muscle, which lie deep to the skin. Skin vasodilatation, by raising skin temperature, normally leads to increased heat loss from the body. If the body is cooled, a reflex increase in vasoconstrictor tone occurs in most of the skin areas of the body. The vasoconstriction, by decreasing skin temperature and therefore the temperature gradient between the body and the environment, helps the body conserve heat.

The co-ordinating centres for these reflexes are thought to lie in the hypothalamus (Chap. 41). The centres are controlled not only by changes in the

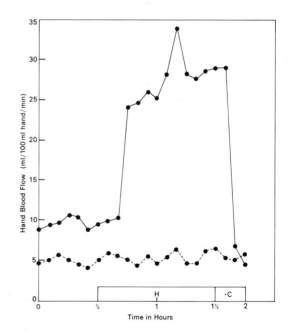

Fig. 8.15 Blood flow in a normal and a sympathectomised hand during body heating. H represents time during which feet were in hot water (45°C); C represents time during which feet were in cold water (12 to 16°C). (Hamilton G T C 1947 Ulster Medical Journal 16:18)

temperature of the blood impinging upon them but also by afferent impulses travelling from thermoreceptors in the heated parts.

Blood shift reflexes

Many stimuli, which have in common the effect of shifting blood towards or away from the chest, can produce reflex alterations in vasoconstrictor tone. These reflex changes are most evident in the blood vessels of the muscles but can also be observed in skin. Tilting a person into the foot-down position, the application of negative pressure to the lower part of the body, breathing at positive pressure (Fig. 8.16) and forced expiration against a closed glottis (Valsalva manoeuvre) all tend to shift blood away from the chest towards the feet. These stimuli are associated with a reflex increase in vasoconstrictor tone in muscle blood vessels. Tilting a person into the foot-up position, the application of positive pressure to the lower limbs and squatting, all tend to move blood towards the chest and result in reflex vasodilatation. The efferent limb of these reflexes is composed of sympathetic vasoconstrictor fibres. The reflex changes are not seen in sympathectomised tissues. Neither the location nor the nature of the receptors concerned in the afferent limb of the reflexes is known. The receptors may be one of the large number of stretch receptors that have been identified in the walls of the low-pressure vessels in the thorax. The baroreceptors in the arterial system do not have much effect on vaso-constrictor tone in man. When the blood pressure at the carotid sinus is altered in man the changes in blood flow in the limbs are small and can be explained by the changes that occur in arterial pressure.

Chemoreceptor reflexes

As mentioned earlier, the direct effect of carbon dioxide on the blood vessels is to dilate them. However, when carbon dioxide is breathed by man in high concentration a reflex increase in peripheral vascular resistance occurs in the muscles. This is mediated by way of sympathetic vasoconstrictor fibres. If these fibres are blocked, peripheral vasodilatation occurs when high concentrations of carbon dioxide are breathed. Carbon dioxide is thought to act directly on the vasomotor centre in the medulla but it probably acts on the peripheral chemo-receptors also. Severe oxygen lack also produces some reflex increase in peripheral resistance (Fig. 8.17) but its effect is small relative to that of carbon dioxide.

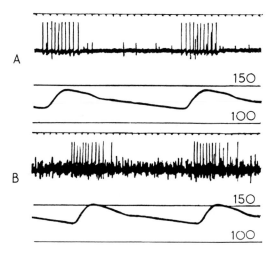

Fig. 8.17 Cat. Thiopentone anaesthesia. Right carotid sinus nerve cut centrally and a thin slip laid on saline wick electrodes. Action potentials recorded on oscillograph via resistance-capacity coupled amplifier. Blood pressure recorded from femoral artery by condenser manometer. Records from above downwards: time trace 20 ms, electroneurogram of this slip of sinus nerve, blood pressure. Calibration lines for pressures of 150 and 100 mm Hg are shown. A = Cat breathing air spontaneously. B = Cat breathing 10 per cent O_2 in N_2 spontaneously. The large spikes, about 7 mm in the diagram, are baroceptor discharges; the smaller (2 mm) spikes are chemoreceptor discharges. Note the increase in chemoreceptor activity during hypoxia. (Heymans C, Neil N 1958 Reflexogenic areas of the cardiovascular system. London, Churchill)

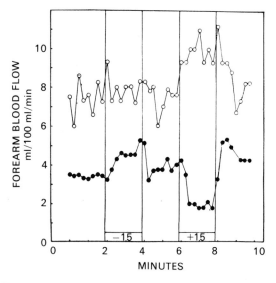

Fig. 8.16 Blood flow in normal (●) and nerve-blocked (○) forearms during pressure breathing. During the two periods indicated, the subject breathed air at pressures 15 mm Hg below and 15 mm Hg above atmospheric pressure, respectively. (Blair D A et al. 1959 Clinical Science 18:9)

Exercise reflexes

When a subject exercises his muscles, strong local vasodilatation is brought about by metabolites in the active muscles. However, in other tissues, such as the

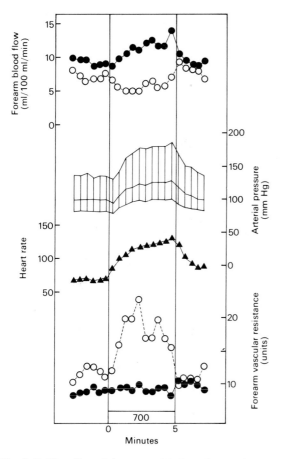

Fig. 8.18 The effect of deep nerve block on forearm blood flow and forearm vascular resistance during 5-min leg exercise. Nerve-blocked forearm (●); normal forearm (○); heart rate (▲). The rectangle represents the period of leg exercise. The increase in oxygen consumption above the resting level during exercise was 700 ml. (Blair D A et al. 1961 Circulation Research 9: 264–274)

muscles that are not taking part in the exercise, there is a reflex vasoconstriction. Figure 8.18 shows the changes that occurred when a subject exercised his legs on a bicycle ergometer. Blood pressure and heart rate rose. Blood flow rose in the forearm, the sympathetic nerves of which had been blocked, probably because the increase in the arterial blood pressure drove more blood through the tissue. However, in the normally innervated forearm, the blood flow fell slightly in spite of the rise in mean arterial pressure. This showed that the peripheral vascular resistance in the forearm rose reflexly during leg exercise. This reflex helps to redistribute blood from the non-active to the active muscles during exercise. The efferent limb of the reflex consists of sympathetic vasoconstrictor fibres but the nature and location of the receptors on the afferent limb and the reflex centre are not known.

If all the sympathetic vasoconstrictor fibres are blocked pharmacologically, exercise cannot be sustained for long. The peripheral vasodilatation produced by the exercise causes such a fall in total peripheral resistance that the arterial pressure falls dramatically and unconsciousness ensues.

Emotional stress reflexes

When a subject is frightened or given difficult mental arithmetic to do, vasodilatation occurs in muscle (Fig. 8.19). This response is reduced or abolished by blocking the sympathetic nerves supplying the tissue and by atropine. These results indicate that sympathetic cholinergic vasodilator nerves are involved in the response. It is likely also that adrenaline released from the adrenal medulla contributes to the response.

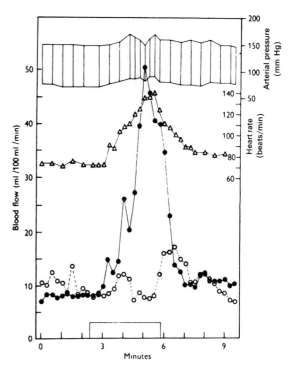

Fig. 8.19 Results showing that active cholinergic vasodilator nerves to human muscle contribute to the vasodilatation in the forearm muscles during stress. ○, hand blood flow; ●, forearm blood flow; △, heart rate. During the time represented by the rectangle it was suggested to the subject that he was suffering from severe blood loss. (Blair D A et al. 1959 Journal of Physiology 148:633)

Lung inflation reflexes

Taking a deep breath causes a reflex vasoconstriction in the skin of the peripheral parts in man. It does not occur if the sympathetic fibres have been severed. In fact, a large number of relatively trivial stimuli, such as a sudden noise, a pinch or the inflation of a cuff on an arm, can cause well-marked reflex vasoconstrictions in the hand. The muscle blood vessels are not involved in these responses. Some of these responses form part of the alerting reaction in man but their physiological significance is obscure.

Hormonal control

Vascular resistance can be affected by circulating vasoactive substances. Some of the more important humoral agents that affect resistance vessels are mentioned below. They can affect smooth muscle tone by acting directly on receptors on the membranes of smooth muscle cells or indirectly by affecting receptors on endothelial cells, which elicit the release of vasoactive agents from the endothelial cells.

Adrenaline and noradrenaline

When the splanchnic nerves are stimulated the initial rise of blood pressure is probably due to vasoconstriction in the abdominal organs. This is followed about half a minute later by a second rise due to the liberation of adrenaline and noradrenaline from the adrenal medulla. A similar effect is described in asphyxia (p. 157). Again, when the pressure in the carotid sinus is reduced the rise of arterial blood pressure that follows is due partly to the reflex activity of the vasoconstrictor nerves and partly to liberation of adrenaline and noradrenaline. Liberation of these hormones also occurs in flight or fight reactions or when the subject is exposed to emotional stress.

When it is injected intravenously into an animal adrenaline produces an immediate and transient fall of arterial pressure at once succeeded by a sudden rise. The increase in blood pressure lasts but a few minutes. Adrenaline causes constriction in the cutaneous and other vessels; however, at the same time the blood vessels of the skeletal muscles dilate so that the total peripheral resistance is slightly lowered (Fig. 8.20). The increased cardiac output must therefore be responsible for the rise in systolic pressure; the mean blood pressure may not be altered.

Injection of noradrenaline is not followed by an initial fall in arterial pressure and the rise in systolic pressure is greater than that after adrenaline. In spite of the reduction in cardiac output brought about through the aortic and carotid sinus reflexes the mean blood pressure rises. Noradrenaline is therefore a general vasoconstrictor (Fig. 8.20), and may be used as such in clinical medicine. The α and β receptors, on which adrenaline and noradrenaline act, are described in Chapter 16.

Noradrenaline is normally present in the walls of the arteries and veins, and in the heart; the aorta of the rabbit, for example, contains an average amount of 0.5 μg per gram. The noradrenaline in the walls of

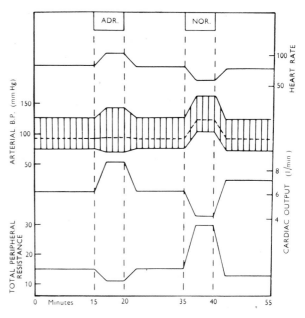

Fig. 8.20 The effects of intravenous infusions of adrenaline and noradrenaline on heart rate, arterial blood pressure, cardiac output and total peripheral resistance. (Barcroft H, Swan H J C 1953 Sympathetic control of human blood vessels. Arnold, London)

vessels is thought to lie in stores associated with vasoconstrictor nerve endings. These stores are mobilised when the constrictor nerves are stimulated, and can be depleted by certain drugs, such as reserpine. Certain substances such as nicotine, and (in the presence of atropine) acetylcholine, cause vasoconstriction in the vessels of the rabbit ear. This vasoconstriction is due to the release of noradrenaline from the artery wall, since it does not occur in the ears of rabbits treated with reserpine.

Angiotensin

The octapeptide angiotensin II (Chap. 12) produces generalised vasoconstriction and thus increases arterial pressure. It also stimulates the production of aldosterone (Chap. 26) and therefore tends to increase the volume of the extracellular fluid and the blood volume.

Kinins

A number of peptides are powerful vasodilators. Bradykinin formed during the active secretion of sweat and salivary glands enormously increases the blood flow in these secreting tissues. The intra-arterial injection of as little as 0.01 μg may, and 0.1 μg always does, increase the blood flow in the forearm (muscle blood flow) or in the hand (blood flow through the skin); intravenous infusion of bradykinin produces large increases in blood flow in both forearm and hand and a visible flushing of the face. The kinins may take part in the vasodilatation associated with the activity of all tissues, not only glandular tissues.

Histamine

Histamine has very pronounced effects on the circulation. When injected intra-arterially or intravenously it causes vasodilatation of the resistance vessels, flushing of the skin and a fall in arterial pressure. It also increases the permeability of the capillaries, which then permit loss of protein and fluid from the circulation (see also Chap. 5).

Prostaglandins

Prostaglandins are naturally occurring fatty acid derivatives that can be synthesised by most tissues of the body. Whereas prostaglandins of the F series tend to increase blood pressure, those of the E series lower blood pressure and increase blood flow by reducing peripheral resistance. Prostaglandins may be considered local hormones but there is no agreement on their normal role in regulating the circulation.

THE CAPILLARIES OR EXCHANGE VESSELS

The circulatory system conveys substances in solution to and from the capillaries where the exchanges between blood and tissue cells take place. The capillaries are minute vessels of the order of 10 μm in diameter connecting arterioles with venules but differing from them in having no muscular coat. Single capillaries differ in diameter, length, and in the nature of their connections with the smallest arteries and veins. Each capillary consists of a tube of endothelium composed of a single layer of flat cells, about 30 μm by 10 μm. The edge of one cell is fitted closely into the edge of its neighbour by slight overlapping or by interdigitations that leave only a very narrow slit between adjacent cells. Each endothelial cell possesses mitochondria and other organelles like those in other cells; its thickness varies from 0.2 μm at the periphery to 3 μm at the bulge containing the nucleus.

With the aid of the electron microscope three types of capillary structure have been described. A *continuous (non-fenestrated) capillary* is one in which endothelium is an apparently continuous sheet. Though no channels can be seen by ordinary electron microscopy, intercellular slit-like pores can be identified by the use of a tracer, which when injected into the blood passes out through the pores and enables them to be visualised. These capillaries are found in many tissues, including muscle and the central nervous system, and it is known that their walls behave as porous membranes. A *fenestrated capillary* has walls that show *intra*cellular fen-

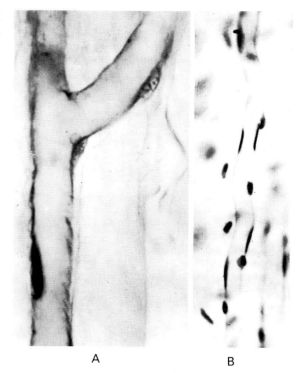

A   B

Fig. 8.21 (A) Branching capillary in frog's muscle showing two Rouget nuclei and one endothelial nucleus. (B) Mesenteric capillary of the rat showing Rouget nuclei on the wall. Endothelial nuclei are also shown. × 1000. (By courtesy of H P Gilding.)

estrations. The holes are usually less than 0.1 μm in diameter. Such capillaries are seen in renal glomeruli, choroid plexus and ciliary body and are thought to permit large and rapid transfer of fluid across their walls. Since there is little protein in glomerular filtrate, these capillaries cannot be freely permeable to protein. A *discontinuous (sinusoid) capillary* is one in which there are large gaps between adjoining endothelial cells. Such capillaries are found in the liver, spleen and bone marrow. They permit the passage of macromolecules and blood cells across their walls.

A basement membrane about 25 nm thick completely surrounds the endothelial tube and outside it is a pericapillary sheath supporting the vessels and continuous with the surrounding connective tissue matrix. Embedded in the pericapillary sheath, or possibly attached to the external surface of the endothelium, are at intervals large branched cells called *pericytes* or *Rouget cells* (Fig. 8.21).

Zweifach, by microscopic observation of the circulation in the capillary beds of the dog's omentum and the mesoappendix of the rat, has shown that the capillaries are arranged in functional units (Figs. 8.22 and 8.23). A metarteriole, which contains muscular

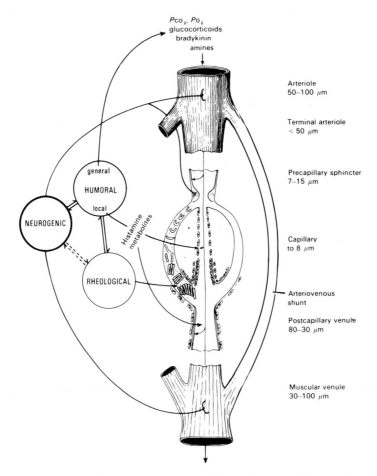

Fig. 8.22 Diagrammatic representation of the normal microcirculation and its control (After Stalker A L 1970 Journal of Clinical Pathology 23 (Suppl. 4):11)

elements, leads into a *thoroughfare channel*, or *AV-bridge*, larger than a true capillary but resembling it in having no muscle tissue in its walls. The thoroughfare channels, which may be as long as 1.5 mm lead directly from arterioles to venules while the true capillaries, shorter in length, open from them and from the metarterioles and arterioles themselves.

The true capillaries may be open or closed according to the needs of the tissue for at the origin of each capillary there is a *precapillary sphincter* by means of which blood flow through the capillary may be slowed or arrested. The precapillary sphincter is a functional one; anatomically it may only be represented by the last smooth muscle cells. The capillaries themselves are probably not contractile. In tissues such as muscle, which require a very variable blood flow, the proportion of true capillaries to thoroughfare channels is high (of the order of four to one) while in others, in which the flow is relatively much more constant, there is a higher proportion of thoroughfare channels.

Whereas the arterioles are mainly under nervous control the more peripheral metarterioles are mainly, but not entirely, under hormonal control; the precapillary sphincters are almost entirely under hormonal control. It is thought that at rest the metabolic needs of a tissue can be met by exchange through thoroughfare channels and that when the tissue becomes active the precapillary sphincters open according to the metabolic needs.

Capillary pressure

Mean capillary pressures were first measured in 1930 by Landis (Fig. 8.24). He used micropipettes about 10 μm in diameter and inserted them into capillaries in the nail bed. The tubes were linked to a mercury manometer and the pressure at which blood flowed neither into nor out of the micropipette was taken as the mean capillary pressure. The average pressure (Fig. 8.24) in the arterial limb was 32 mm Hg with a range of 21 to 44 mm Hg: the summit of the loop gave a mean

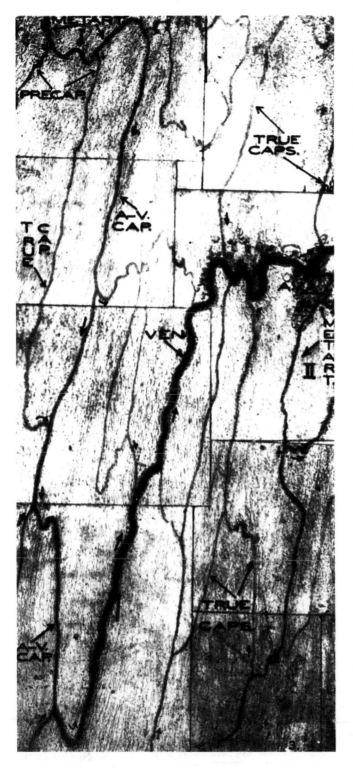

Fig. 8.23 Topographical veiw (approx. × 100) of a portion of capillary bed in the meso-appendix of a rat photographed during moderate hyperaemia to render visible most of the blood vessels in the field. Prominently displayed is the venule that drains this region. Two metarterioles, I and II, are shown, I starting at upper left and II at middle of right margin. Metarteriole I, along its course, gives off three precapillaries with sphincters, then passes down as the AV capillary, which gives off one precapillary at its right, and further down receives, in succession, two post-capillaries. At lower left corner it joins with another AV capillary to form the non-muscular venule. The venule courses up as a prominent vessel and passes out of the figure at the right after receiving several post-capillaries. The true capillaries carry the flow between pre- and post-capillaries. Metarteriole II, shortly after appearing at the right of the figure, is connected with a neighbouring venule by a short anastomosing vessel (AVA), which may serve to short-circuit the blood of this region. (Chambers R, Zweifach B W 1944 American Journal of Anatomy 75:173

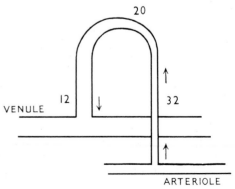

Fig. 8.24 Average pressures in mm Hg in a skin capillary in man. (After Landis E M 1930 Heart 15:213)

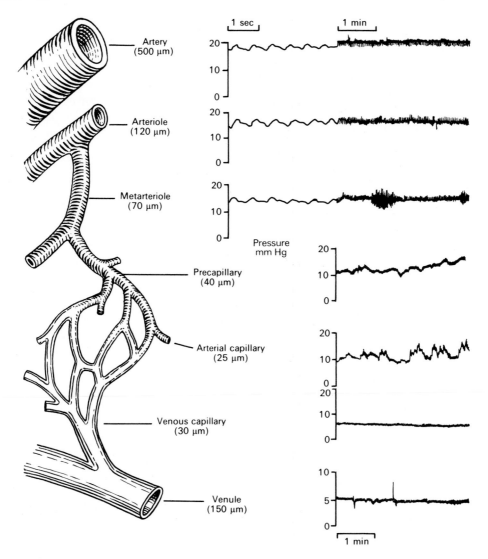

Fig. 8.25 Pressure records obtained at various points in the microcirculation. (Wiederhielm C A et al. 1964 American Journal of Physiology 207:173)

pressure of 20 (range 15 to 32) and the venous end a mean of 12 mm Hg (range 6 to 18). There is thus a considerable gradient of pressure along the capillaries near the root of the nail. The pulse pressure at the arteriolar end of the loop was at least 5 to 10 mm Hg and at the venous end usually zero. Because of the inertia of the mercury column, the fluctuations in capillary pressure with the heart-rate could not be measured but newer methods (Fig. 8.25) have allowed these changes to be observed.

Blood flow in capillaries

When the frog's tongue, lung, or web of the foot is observed under a microscope a network of vessels is seen. In the arterioles the red cells move forward in jerks corresponding to the beats of the heart but the pulsatile nature of the flow is lost in the capillaries unless there is peripheral vasodilatation. If the capillaries are narrow the red cells follow one another in single file and may become deformed (Fig. 8.26), but they recover their shape on reaching a wide vessel. The capillaries show great variations in calibre, with corresponding alterations in flow. In the venules the red blood cells pass along in a steady axial stream, leaving a clear peripheral stream of colourless plasma.

The capillaries in the nail bed of the human finger are easily observed under the microscope if the skin is illuminated by an oblique beam of light. A drop of oil

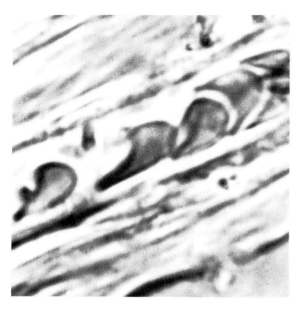

Fig. 8.26 Red cells in a mesenteric capillary of the dog: direction of flow left to right: rate of flow 1 mm per sec: magnification × 3000: exposure time 5 μs. The red cells that are biconcave discs in the large vessels become paraboloid with a bell-shaped hollow in the capillaries. The leading part becomes convex and the trailing part becomes concave so that the shape resembles a thimble or parachute. Further details are to be found in Guest M M et al. 1963 Science, New York 142:1319. (By courtesy of M. Mason Guest)

makes the skin more translucent by replacing the air in the surface layers of the epidermis. The capillaries are of the order of 10 μm in diameter but the capillary loops vary greatly in size, in shape and in lumen, the venous side being usually much wider than the arterial side. Spontaneous alterations in the capillary diameter and the rate of flow of corpuscles occur often at the bases of the nail, and frequently in the back of the hand, capillaries opening and closing in the absence of any apparent stimulus. Thus although the pulsatile flow characteristic of the arterial system is absent in the capillaries, the flow through these vessels is anything but continuous.

The velocity of blood flow in capillaries, about 0.5 mm/s, is about 1000 times lower than that in the aorta. This is because the total cross-sectional area of the capillary bed is so enormous. It is not because the capillaries offer very much resistance to flow. The slow flow in the capillaries provides time for exchange to take place between the plasma and tissue fluid.

Capillary permeability

The rate at which fluid passes through the capillary membrane is determined not only by its permeability under different conditions but also by the pressure and

flow within it. In defining capillary permeability it is necessary to know (a) the volume or mass of substances passing through (b) unit area in (c) unit time, under the influence of (d) unit hydrostatic or osmotic pressure (e) per unit thickness of membrane. Finally, the rate of fluid transfer is affected by the hydrostatic and osmotic pressures of the fluid outside the capillary. There are therefore considerable difficulties in the way of understanding the factors that govern the passage of materials across capillary walls, and it is seldom that all these factors are known.

Various possible routes across the capillary endothelium have been identified by electron microscopy including pinocytic vesicles, various types of fenestration and larger intercellular gaps. Fluids, ions, metabolites, proteins and even blood cells are known to cross the endothelium but there is no agreement about the exact route taken by each.

After injection of plasma dyed with sulfoflavin, which has a high affinity for plasma proteins, fluorescence indicating the passage of protein is seen only at the venous end of long capillaries (Fig. 8.27). This is not a contradiction of the Starling hypothesis described in Chapter 3, which is concerned with the passage of small molecules. It is likely that there is an increase in the size of the pores, that is a 'gradient of permeability', from small arteries to small veins.

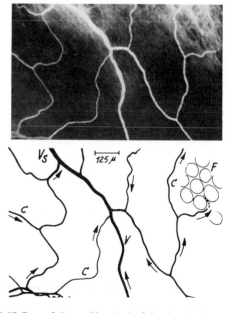

Fig. 8.27 Part of the capillary bed of the duodenal mesentery of a cat 10 minutes after the injection of albumin-conjugated fluorescein isothiocyanate. The dye escaped mainly from the venule V-V$_s$. F = fat globules. C = capillary. V$_s$ = collecting vein. (Hauck G, Schröer H 1969 Pflügers Archiv European Journal of Physiology 312: 32–44)

Normally there is a dynamic balance between loss of fluid from the capillaries and reabsorption into the capillaries and removal of excess by the lymphatics so that fluid does not accumulate. If, however, the venous pressure is increased the balance is upset and fluid accumulates.

Tracer studies indicate that the quantities of fluid and dissolved substances that exchange across the capillary walls each day are enormous. It has been estimated that, in man, about 100 000 litres of fluid can pass out of and back into the vascular system every 24 hours. The bulk of this exchange is due to simple diffusion forces. The fluid exchange dependent on the hydrostatic and colloid osmotic pressure gradients and the lymphatic system accounts for only a tiny fraction (about one five-thousandth) of the total.

Capillary fragility

Capillary permeability and capillary fragility (or resistance) refer to different, and probably distinct, properties of the capillary wall. In clinical usage 'capillary fragility' refers to the production of minute haemorrhages (*petechiae*) in the skin when the capillary pressure has been raised in the forearm by the application of a venous occluding pressure to the upper arm by a sphygmomanometer cuff, or to the production of petechiae by the application of suction to the skin.

There may be a striking lack of association between increased capillary permeability and increased fragility. Thus, the oedema fluid of inflammation contains few red cells but a great deal of protein representing, therefore, an almost pure increase in permeability. On the other hand, the petechiae that occur in certain blood diseases consist chiefly of red cells with little or no oedema fluid or protein.

Despite the fact that the walls of capillaries are so thin, they can withstand very large distending pressures. For example, when a person is standing without making rhythmical contractions of his leg muscles, the pressure in the capillaries in his feet rises to about 100 mm Hg. This is because of the hydrostatic effect of the column of blood above the feet. The law of Laplace explains why this pressure does not burst the capillaries. The tension in the wall of a cylindrical tube (T) depends on the pressure difference across the wall of the tube (P) and the radius of the tube (r), that is T = Pr. In a capillary high internal pressures do not increase the wall tension very much because the radius is so small.

Control of capillary exchange

This is the term applied to the spontaneously occurring periodic relaxation and constriction of the thoroughfare channel and of its precapillaries (p. 118). In uninjured resting tissue the blood-flow through the thoroughfare channel is fairly constant and its hydrostatic pressure relatively high. Vasomotion of the precapillary offshoots, manifested by an opening and closing of their sphincters, governs flow through the true capillaries. The fluid exchange in the capillary bed is thus greatly influenced by vasomotion. This delicately balanced activity depends on vasoconstrictor nervous influences and on humoral factors, both vasodilator and vasoconstrictor. The origin in the tissue itself of some of the humoral

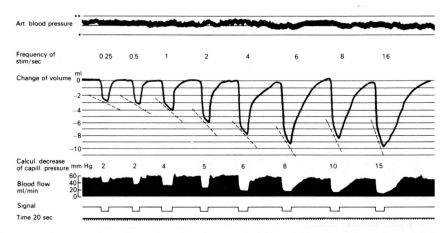

Fig. 8.28 Effects on resistance and capacitance vessels and net transcapillary fluid shift produced in the hindquarters of a cat by maximal lumbar vasoconstrictor fibre stimulation at different frequencies. Changes in blood flow reflect effects on resistance vessels (inflow and outflow pressures kept constant). The initial and rapid decreases in volume reflect effects on capacitance vessels and the subsequent slower and continuous decreases in volume (slopes indicated by dashed lines), transcapillary influx of extravascular fluid. Reductions in mean hydrostatic capillary pressure calculated in approximate figures. (Mellander S 1960 Acta Physiologica Scandinavica 50 (Suppl. 176):35)

factors provides a local mechanism for the distribution of blood and, therefore, the extent and duration of fluid exchange.

The capillaries are not innervated but the vessels upstream and downstream from them are. Nervous influences, by controlling the inflow and outflow from the capillary beds, can control the hydrostatic pressure in the capillaries and thus the net movement of fluid across the capillary wall. Stimulation of the vasoconstrictor fibres to a muscle vascular bed (Fig. 8.28) causes three main effects, (1) a decrease in blood flow due to constriction of the arterioles, (2) a decrease in the volume of blood contained in the muscle due to constriction of the capacity vessels and (3) mobilisation of fluid from the tissue spaces into the blood. The third effect is thought to be due to the fall in capillary pressure that follows constriction of the precapillary resistance vessels.

THE VEINS OR CAPACITY VESSELS

Veins have thinner walls, less elastic tissue and a larger internal diameter than the corresponding arteries and they are more easily distended than arteries. They have valves made of folds of internal endothelium. The veins have two main functions. They transport blood at high velocity and low energy cost from the tissues back to the heart. Secondly, by alterations of tone in the smooth muscle in their walls they adjust the capacity of the circulation to match the blood volume and so regulate the filling pressure of the heart.

Venous pressure

The venous pressure in man is best measured directly by connecting a long thin, flexible cannula, introduced into a vein, to a manometer filled with a solution of isotonic saline. Measurement of the hydrostatic pressure within a vein, say at the level of the elbow, is of little value since the figure obtained depends on the position of the vein relative to the heart. If the arm is raised the pressure falls and if the arm is lowered it rises. The upper level of fluid in the manometer tube does, however, occupy a constant relation to the level of the heart, or to the sternal angle, which is a convenient reference point whose relation to the heart is reasonably constant. Thus if there is no obstruction or constriction between the manometer tube and the right atrium the difference in level between the height of the meniscus and the sternal angle represents the pressure in the right atrium. As a rule this lies between zero and −2 cm of water but there is a great deal of individual variation in *central venous pressure*, values as high as 9 and 12 cm being found not infrequently in apparently healthy young men; values over 20 cm H_2O may be found in congestive heart failure. The pressure in the atria and in the great veins is not constant but varies with the cardiac cycle and with respiration. It also varies with the position of the patient, being somewhat higher if the patient is recumbent.

The *internal jugular vein* may be made to act as its own manometer since it usually has no functioning valves. The vessel collapses at the point at which the external pressure (that is the atmospheric pressure) is greater than the internal pressure (the venous blood pressure). The upper level of the column of blood in the internal jugular vein is identified by the upper level of outward venous pulsation and is conventionally measured from a horizontal plane passing through the sternal angle (Fig. 8.29), which is arbitrarily taken as the reference point. With the patient propped up, his head supported on a pillow, the level is from 0 to 3 cm above this line and the jugular venous pressure is therefore said to be 0 to 3 cm (of blood). Higher values are found when the heart is failing or when the blood volume is much increased. The use in this way of the *external jugular vein* as a manometer is unreliable.

The venous pressure in the superficial veins of the dorsum of the foot with the subject erect and motionless

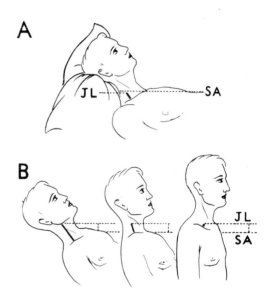

Fig. 8.29 The upper diagram, A, represents the level of blood in the internal jugular vein when the subject is lying with the head supported on pillows. The upper level of the column of blood in the jugular vein (JL) lies a little below the level of the sternal angle (SA). In the lower diagram, B, the upper level of the column of blood in the internal jugular vein is above the sternal angle, indicating an increase of venous pressure. Note that as the position of the patient alters the upper level of the column of blood occupies· different positions in the neck although its relation to the sternal angle remains the same. (Lewis T 1949 Diseases of the heart. Macmillan, London)

is from 70 to 100 mm Hg, which is the same as the calculated hydrostatic pressure from the right atrium. On exercise, owing to the action of the muscle pump (p. 90), the reading falls to less than 30 mm Hg. If, however, the leg veins are varicose, with incompetent valves, there may be little difference between the readings during exercise and at rest.

Venous pulse

At rest the flow of blood in the larger veins is continuous except near the heart. The variations of atrial pressure usually pass back a short way into the great veins near the heart since they are not equipped with valves. A volume pulsation at the root of the neck in the internal jugular vein is therefore often seen in normal people. The pulsations of the internal jugular vein, which lies deep to the sternomastoid muscle, are seen as lateral, not as vertical movements. The venous pulse can be recorded by placing a metal cup on the right side of the neck above the sternal end of the clavicle. A rubber tube leads from the cup to a manometer and a suitable recorder. Such a record is shown in Figure 8.30; it cannot be fully analysed unless either an electrocardiogram or a record of the arterial pulse is made simultaneously.

In the venous pulse there are three positive waves during each cardiac cycle. The a wave is produced by atrial systole. It is replaced by a rapid fluttering movement when the atria flutter and disappears when they fibrillate (p. 68). The a wave becomes more prominent when the pressure in the right side of the heart is raised because of valvular disease or chronic lung disease, and is very prominent should the right atrium contract against a closed tricuspid valve as sometimes happens with complete heart block. The a wave is followed shortly by the c wave. In the jugular pulse this is a disturbance imparted to the recording apparatus by the pulse in the underlying carotid artery. Some time later the v wave appears. This is due to the gradual increase of venous pressure during ventricular systole and the summit of the v wave is coincident with the opening of the mitral and tricuspid valves. The first negative wave, between a and c, is the result of atrial diastole. The trough between c and v is produced by descent of the heart during ventricular systole and the third negative wave (after v) is due to the sudden release of pressure in the veins as the tricuspid valve opens.

The tracing of the jugular pulse in Figure 8.30 should be compared with the record of the changes in intra-atrial pressure obtained from a manometer communi-

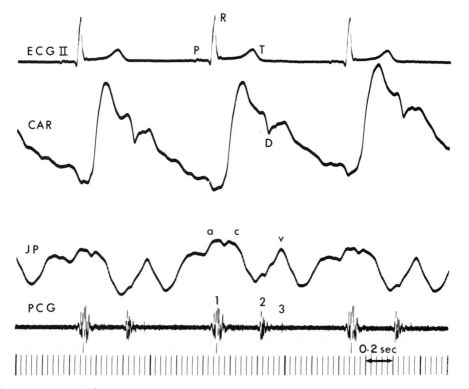

Fig. 8.30 Simultaneous records from a normal male aged 22 years. From above downwards: electrocardiogram (standard lead II; ECG II), external carotid arteriogram (CAR), jugular phlebogram (JP) and apical phonocardiogram (PCG). D marks the dicrotic notch, a, c, v the three main peaks of the phlebogram. 1, 2, 3 First, second and third heart sounds.

cating directly with the interior of the right atrium (Fig. 7.15).

Veins as transport vessels

After passing slowly through the capillaries the blood speeds up as it passes through the venules and veins because the total cross-sectional area of the venous bed is so much smaller than that of the capillaries. The blood is transported from the periphery to the heart with little expenditure of energy. The pressure gradient of about 10 mm Hg is enough to return blood from a small vein in the arm to the right atrium because the veins offer little resistance to blood flow.

Gravity can affect the transport function of the veins. Above heart level, gravity aids the return of blood to the heart. Below heart level the hydrostatic pressure of the dependent blood tends to distend the venous system. The tendency to impair the venous return to the heart is counteracted by the muscle pump. When muscles in the leg contract they compress the veins lying in the fascial planes between them. Because of the system of valves the blood is normally driven towards the heart.

Veins at capacity vessels

The volume of blood accommodated in veins depends on the pressure gradient across their walls (*transmural pressure*). Small changes in transmural pressure can produce large changes in the internal dimensions of veins. When the transmural pressure is low, for example below 5 mm Hg, the venous lumen appears on cross-section as a flattened ellipse and holds little or no blood. With modest increases in transmural pressure, the venous cross-section becomes more and more circular and its capacity rises rapidly. Further increases in transmural pressure when the cross-section has become circular cause little further increase in capacity; at this stage the venous walls are quite stiff.

Although the veins are easily distensible and have little muscle in their walls they should not be thought of as simple inert tubes. They have a resting tone and are capable of constriction to maintain the central venous pressure in spite of a reduction in blood volume.

Contraction of the smooth muscle in the walls of the veins has a number of effects. It reduces the capacity of the venous system to hold blood at any particular venous pressure. By raising the mean pressure in the venous system it tends to raise the filling pressure of the heart. The resulting increase in filling leads to stronger contractions and an increase in cardiac output. The rise in mean venous pressure also tends to cause capillary pressure to rise with a consequential increase in the formation of tissue fluid.

The term *venous tone* is often used to describe the degree of contraction of venous smooth muscle. When

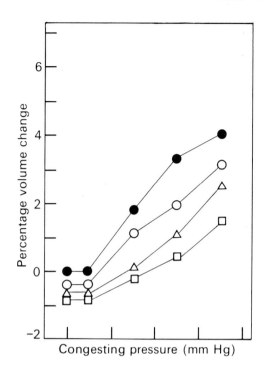

Fig. 8.31 Pressure–volume curves illustrating the effect of intra-arterial infusions of adrenaline on the high- and low-pressure capacity vessels of the forearm. Infusion of saline, ●; adrenaline infusions 0.1 μg/min, ○; 0.4 μg/min, △; 1.0 μg/min, □. Increasing doses of adrenaline progressively decrease the resting volume of the forearm and the distension of the forearm caused by raised venous pressure. This suggests that adrenaline constricts capacity blood vessels. (Glover W E et al. 1958 Journal of Physiology 140:113)

the smooth muscle is contracted, venous tone is said to be high. In these conditions venous distensibility is reduced; higher venous pressures are required to fill the veins to particular volumes so that their pressure–volume curves become flatter (Fig. 8.31).

Measurement of venous tone
There is no completely satisfactory way of doing this but a number of methods may be employed. One is to compress both ends of a superficial segment of a vein under the skin that does not show any side branches opening from or draining into it. If the pressure in the segment is measured through an indwelling needle or catheter, venoconstriction is signalled by a rise, and venodilatation by a fall of pressure in the segment (see Fig. 8.34). Another method is to expose the venous system to gradually increasing or decreasing steps of pressure and construct pressure–volume curves. Flattening of the pressure–volume curves indicates venoconstriction (Fig. 8.31). A third method is to fill the veins to a constant high pressure by venous congestion.

A decrease in the volume of the tissue at constant venous pressure indicates venoconstriction. It is important to realise that distension by itself is not evidence that the smooth muscle in the venous wall has relaxed. The dilatation of veins in parts of the body below heart level is a passive consequence of the increase in transmural pressure and not, of course, due to relaxation of the venous muscle. Further, when resistance vessels dilate, the increased inflow of blood into the capacity vessels raises the pressure in these vessels and distends them.

Venomotor responses

Since the venous system is mainly concerned in integrated responses of the entire circulatory system, the responses of the venous system are usually integrated through vasomotor nerves or hormones.

Local factors

The local application of cold causes venoconstriction, which may be intense and prolonged. This constriction may be greater than the constriction of the arterioles and account for the oedema seen in hands being rewarmed after exposure to cold. Local hypoxia and carbon dioxide excess relax venous smooth muscle, but these responses may be outweighed by the reflex effects of these stimuli acting centrally.

The pharmacological properties of the circular and longitudinal smooth muscle of the veins are different and species variation is considerable. Adrenaline and noradrenaline both cause venoconstriction (Fig. 8.31) due to the stimulation of α-receptors, which are predominant in this muscle. Isoprenaline, which stimulates β-receptors, causes relaxation of venous muscle. Both histamine and 5-hydroxytryptamine cause venoconstriction. The female sex hormones oestradiol and progesterone reduce spontaneous activity in veins and make their contractions weaker. Nitrites and adenylic acid cause venodilatation.

Nervous factors

Most of the stimuli that cause constriction of the resistance vessels seem also to cause constriction of the capacity vessels. As mentioned in the section on exchange vessels, stimulation of the sympathetic nerves to a tissue causes a fall in blood flow and blood capacity in that tissue. Stimuli that are thought to cause reflex venoconstriction include systemic hypoxia and hypercapnia, carotid sinus hypotension, body cooling, emotional stress, the shifting of blood away from the chest, exercise and the taking of deep breaths. Reflex venodilatation has been described in carotid sinus hypertension, fainting and sleep.

When a subject exercises his legs on a bicycle ergometer the capacity of the forearm veins is reduced

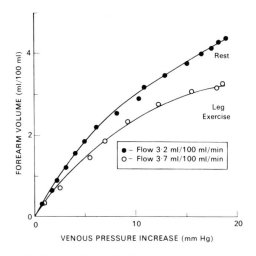

Fig. 8.32 Typical relationship between increase in forearm volume and pressure in a large forearm vein at rest (●) and during supine leg exercise (○). Note that forearm blood flow was similar in both circumstances. (Bevegard B S, Shepherd J T 1968 Journal of Applied Physiology 20:1)

(Fig. 8.32). The response is graded to the severity of the work. This does not occur if the sympathetic nerves to the arm have been cut. It can be demonstrated that the venoconstriction is generalised and occurs also in the muscles taking part in the exercise. Such an increase in venous tone is likely to play an important part in the circulatory adaptation to exercise. When the resistance vessels in the exercising muscles dilate the capillary and post-capillary pressures rise. If this were not accompanied by an adjustment of tone in the capacity vessels, blood would tend to pool in them. This tendency is opposed by the pumping effect of the contracting muscles. The increase in venous tone acts in the same direction.

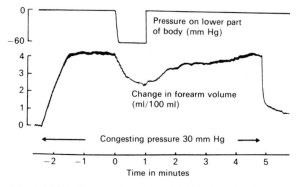

Fig. 8.33 The increase in volume of a forearm after congestion by a cuff as a pressure of 30 mm Hg. When the volume becomes constant, the lower body is exposed to a negative pressure of 60 mm Hg and the arm volume falls. When the suction is removed from the body the forearm volume does not return to its previous level for 4 minutes. (After Ardill B V et al. 1968 Journal of Physiology 194:627)

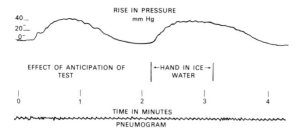

Fig. 8.34 Pressure changes recorded from a segment of a superficial vein of the forearm that had been isolated between wedges and kept at constant volume. (Duggan J J et al. 1953 Circulation 7:869)

Stimuli that shift blood away from the chest cause reflex reductions in venous capacity. Thus venoconstriction has been reported after the Valsalva manoeuvre and on exposing the entire lower part of the body to a pressure below atmospheric. Figure 8.33 shows this response, which is abolished by drugs that block the sympathetic nerves to the arm. This type of response would help to maintain the filling pressure of the heart when blood tended to pool in the lower extremities.

Figure 8.34 shows the result of an experiment in which pressure was measured in a segment of superficial forearm vein. With the subject at rest, the pressure in the segment was about 0 mm Hg. When he became anxious about the nature of the forthcoming test, the pressure rose to about 40 mm Hg and then fell again. Immersing one hand in ice water had a similar effect. The increase in vasomotor tone during emotional stress would help to prevent pooling of blood in the extremities that might result from the concomitant dilatation of the resistance vessels.

SYNCOPE

Syncope, usually called fainting, means a transient loss of consciousness due to reduction in cerebral blood flow. At the same time skeletal muscular tone is diminished and the patient slumps or falls to the ground if unsupported; the faint is thus usually self-limiting.

Cerebral blood flow is remarkably constant over a wide range of blood pressure (p. 379), and fainting only occurs when the fall of blood pressure is severe. The reduction in blood pressure is usually the result of either a reflex vasomotor depression that produces marked vasodilatation or the loss of the baroceptor reflexes that normally maintain cerebral perfusion in the upright posture. Fainting therefore occurs most frequently when the person is upright and consciousness usually returns quickly when he lies flat, unless the syncope is caused by a failure of cardiac output caused

for example by ventricular fibrillation or arrest or by extreme bradycardia, as in heart block (p. 70).

The commonest cause of fainting is probably strong emotions, particularly conflicting ones, such as those aroused by seeing a road traffic accident or surgical operation. Such emotions cause vasodilatation of skeletal muscle, perhaps because of an increase in circulating adrenaline and the activation of cholinergic vasodilator fibres. The heart rate is often low, and this bradycardia is abolished by atropine, so the syndrome of bradycardia, muscle vasodilatation and systemic hypotension with fainting was named *vaso-vagal syncope* by Lewis. Pallor, 'cold' sweating, nausea and yawning may be associated with fainting, and other precipitating factors may include fatigue, hunger or standing in a crowded room. Syncope can also be induced by depletion of the circulating blood volume. A sudden loss of blood may lead to syncope: in blood donors it is uncommon when less than 400 ml of blood are withdrawn, but occurs in about half the subjects if 1 litre is removed (Fig. 8.35).

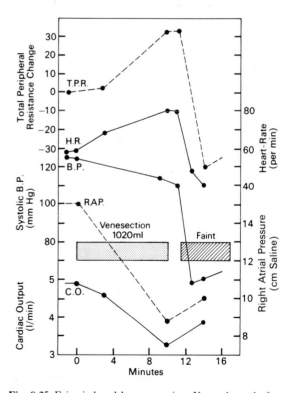

Fig. 8.35 Faint induced by venesection. Up to the end of the venesection, arterial pressure was maintained by peripheral vasoconstriction (increased total peripheral resistance) in spite of a decreasing cardiac output. During the faint, the cardiac output increased slightly, and the fall in blood pressure was, therefore, due to decrease in peripheral resistance. (Barcroft H et al. 1944 Lancet 1:189)

When a subject stands up, blood is normally prevented from pooling in the legs under the influence of gravity by reflex adrenergic vasoconstriction. If for some reason the vasoconstriction fails to oppose the tendency of the blood to pool, *orthostatic hypotension* with syncope may result. This is a common complication induced by the adrenergic-blocking drugs used to treat high blood pressure (hypertension), and sometimes after the reduction of blood volume and sodium produced by powerful diuretic drugs.

Rarely syncope is caused by cardiac inhibition due to reflex vagal effects triggered by pressure on the carotid sinus, by micturition and sometimes by prolonged coughing that virtually amounts to a Valsalva manoeuvre.

PERIPHERAL CIRCULATORY FAILURE

There are two main ways in which the circulatory system may fail to provide the tissues with a blood flow that is adequate for their needs. The primary fault may lie in the heart so that it is unable to deliver an adequate cardiac output despite an adequate filling pressure (see p. 98); this is called *central circulatory failure* or *cardiogenic 'shock'* and occurs, for example, after myocardial infarction and pulmonary embolism. On the other hand, the basic fault may lie peripherally so that the circulation cannot provide an adequate filling pressure for the otherwise normal heart; this is called *peripheral circulatory failure*. Both types of failure can result in underperfusion of the tissues with consequent inadequate function of organs such as the kidney, brain and liver. However, the conventional distinction between central and peripheral circulatory failure is a crude oversimplification. The whole circulatory system, heart, arteries, arterioles, capillaries, venules and veins, functions as an integrated whole; a break-down in any one part can hardly fail to influence events in other parts of the system.

Shock is also the term given to the clinical condition in which the patient is pale, cold and sweaty. The pulse is rapid and the arterial pressure is low, with a systolic level often less than 80 mm Hg and a small pulse pressure. The cardiac output is reduced. The patient has little pain or interest in his surroundings. Physical and mental activities are depressed, the metabolic rate reduced and the temperature low.

The most important factor in peripheral circulatory failure is a disproportion between the blood volume and the volume of the vascular bed; the blood volume and the central venous pressure are usually both reduced. This reduction may be caused by sudden external loss of blood, by pooling of blood in capillary beds, as a result of plasma loss from extensive burns, or because of loss of extracellular fluid (as in diabetic keto-acidosis or severe gastroenteritis). These are all examples of *hypovolaemic shock*. Peripheral circulatory failure also occurs in some cases of self-poisoning with hypnotic drugs that cause paralysis of the vasomotor centres and relaxation of the venous system, leading to a reduction of the central venous pressure. The so-called 'traumatic shock' that occurs after road accidents or under battle conditions is probably the result of a combination of several of these factors. Peripheral circulatory failure may also occur in some bacterial infections, particularly those involving gram-negative organisms ('bacteraemic' shock), but its underlying mechanism is not yet clear.

An unusual type of circulatory failure occurs as a result of adrenocortical insufficiency, either in Addison's disease (Chap. 26) or when adrenal function has been suppressed by previous corticosteroid therapy: severe hypotension develops when the patient is subjected to stress such as severe infection or an operation and is associated with an inadequate rise in the level of corticosteroids in the plasma.

FURTHER READING

Abbond F, Shepherd J T (eds) 1983 Peripheral circulation and organ blood flow. In: Handbook of physiology — the cardiovascular system, vol IV. American Physiology Society, Washington, DC

Bevan J A, Godfraind T, Maxwell R A, Vanhoutte P M (eds) 1979 Vascular neuroeffector mechanisms. Raven, New York

Cliff W J 1976 Blood vessels. University Press, Cambridge

Folkow B, Neil E 1971 Circulation. Oxford University Press, London

Hainsworth P, Mary D A S G, McWilliam P N 1987 Cardiogenic reflexes. University Press, Oxford

Johnson R H, Spalding J M K 1974 Disorders of the autonomic nervous system. Blackwell Scientific, Oxford

McDonald D A 1974 Blood flow in arteries, 2nd edn. Arnold, London

Roberts C (ed) 1972 Blood flow measurement. Sector, London

Russell W J 1974 Central venous pressure: its clinical use and role in cardiovascular dynamics. Butterworth, London

Shepherd J T, Vanhoutte P M 1975 Veins and their control. Saunders, London

Shepherd J T, Vanhoutte P M 1979 The human cardiovascular system; facts and concepts. Raven, New York

Wells R 1973 The microcirculation in clinical medicine. Academic, New York

Zweifach B W 1973 Microcirculation. Annual Reviews of Physiology 35: 117–150

9

Respiration

Oxygen can diffuse from the watery environment to all parts of a unicellular organism, but as the size and complexity of the animal increases during its evolutionary development from an aquatic to a terrestrial environment the distance between the surface and the internal organs becomes too great for diffusion alone. Respiration has then to occur and it can be divided into two phases; external respiration in the lungs and internal respiration at the tissue level connected by the circulation (Fig. 9.1). Carbon dioxide produced by metabolism in the tissues is carried back to the lungs and excreted. In this chapter we consider first how the air is carried to the blood–gas interface in the alveoli (*ventilation*), where gas transfer takes place, and then how the blood is distributed to the lungs in the pulmonary circulation (*perfusion*).

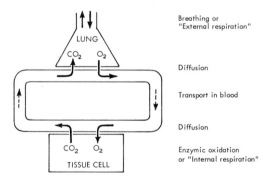

Fig. 9.1 Respiratory processes

Anatomy of the respiratory tract

The respiratory tract begins at the nose or mouth and ends in the alveoli. It is divided into two parts — the conducting tubes and the gas exchange system. The principal function of these conducting tubes is to carry fresh air (containing 21 per cent O_2) down to the alveoli from the environment during inspiration and to get rid of CO_2 during expiration.

The very vascular epithelium lining the nose warms and humidifies the inspired air. Air inspired at 6°C can reach 30°C by the time it reaches the back of the nose and it rises to body temperature at the bifurcation of the trachea, where it has also become fully saturated with water vapour. The nose also acts as a filter for particles more than 10 μm in diameter, which are caught on the mucus produced by goblet cells and then cleared by cilia before being swallowed. Intense irritation or stimulation of the nasal passages results in the reflex closure of the larynx and the cessation of breathing. This is a protective reflex to prevent foreign substances entering the lungs.

The connecting passages (Fig. 9.2) consist of a series of branching tubes and extend from the trachea via the major bronchi and the bronchioles to the terminal bronchioles, which are the smallest airways that do not take part in gas exchange. Inspired gas usually travels thus far by bulk flow and the rest of the way along the respiratory bronchioles, alveolar ducts and into the alveoli by diffusion. This system of dividing tubes means that airflow is greatest in the trachea but falls rapidly as the cross-sectional area of the tubes increases. This increase is the result of the tubes becoming much more numerous even though their diameter decreases (Fig. 9.3). The first sixteen generations of conducting airways have a volume of about 150 ml (the *anatomical dead space*), whereas the remaining eight or so generations of gas exchange areas in the primary lobule have a volume of 2750 ml. As airflow falls, then particulate matter that has been inhaled settles out on the mucosa. Ciliary action carries the mucus and particulate material back up to the trachea (the muco-ciliary 'escalator') whence it is cleared by coughing. Ciliary activity is important in clearing the tracheo-bronchial tree of inhaled bacteria and it continues independent of all nervous connections. Cilia are hair-like processes 1–5 μm long on the free border of the epithelial cell. Adjacent cilia beat synchronously about twenty times a minute, propelling the surface mucus along at about 2 cm a minute. Ciliary activity can be depressed by various noxious substances, and in patients who suffer from chronic bronchitis, for example, damage to their

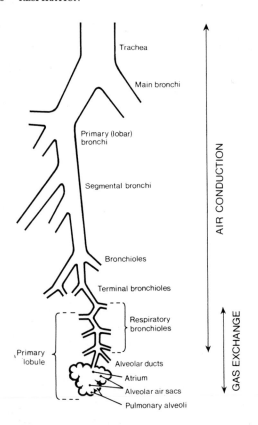

Fig. 9.2 The air passages. There are approximately 23 orders of branching between the bifurcation of the trachea and the alveolar sacs. In man there are about 130 000 primary lobules, each containing 2000 alveoli

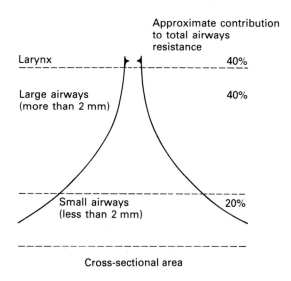

Fig. 9.3 Diagrammatic representation of the increase in cross-sectional area of the air passages and the resultant distribution of airways resistance. The 'trumpet' shape indicates an enormous increase in airway cross-section as the alveoli are approached. The drop in gas flow rate explains why the small airways contribute so little to the overall airway resistance despite their small size and enormous number

muco-ciliary clearance results in retained sputum and repeated infections. About 100 ml of tracheo-bronchial mucus containing albumin and immunoglobulins is produced each day even in normal individuals although patients with chronic bronchitis may produce considerably more. Inhaled particles of less than 10 μm in diameter may reach further down the respiratory tract and are removed by the phagocytic activity of the macrophages that roam the alveoli.

The trachea and major bronchi are surrounded by cartilaginous rings deficient in their posterior aspect that prevent these tubes from collapsing during expiration and keep the trachea patent on moving or turning the neck. As the tubes become smaller the cartilaginous support becomes more sparse and it is replaced by fibrous tissue and elastin. Internal to this there are helical bands of smooth muscle, which are responsible for controlling the diameter of these small bronchi. These smaller bronchi are easily distensible but may collapse during straining or coughing.

The bronchial smooth muscle is supplied by both the cholinergic and adrenergic nervous systems. Stimulation of the vagus results in bronchoconstriction, whereas the sympathetic nervous system is composed mostly of β_2 receptors which when stimulated produce bronchodilatation. This explains why adrenaline or β_2 agonists are used for the treatment of the bronchoconstriction seen in asthma. Other substances may induce bronchoconstriction such as histamine or prostaglandin $F_{2\alpha}$, whereas PGE_2 inhalation produces bronchodilatation. The latter two prostaglandins probably produce their effects by stimulating the cholinergic or β_2 receptors, respectively. The administration of atropine to persons with normal airways produces only a small bronchodilation, suggesting that there is only slight vagal tone controlling normal airway calibre. Drugs that block beta-adrenergic receptors have little effect in producing airway narrowing in normal people, but may exaggerate bronchospasm in an asthmatic. During inspiration the small airways are pulled open by the rib cage and diaphragm as they expand, whilst during expiration the airways tend to collapse. In any patient with airways obstruction the situation is exaggerated, with wider swings in pleural pressure; it can be seen why patients with asthma or chronic bronchitis find it easier to breathe in than out.

The respiratory bronchioles have scattered alveoli in their walls, which makes them the first portion of the gas-exchanging region. From there the inspired gas reaches the alveolar sacs and alveolar duct, which are

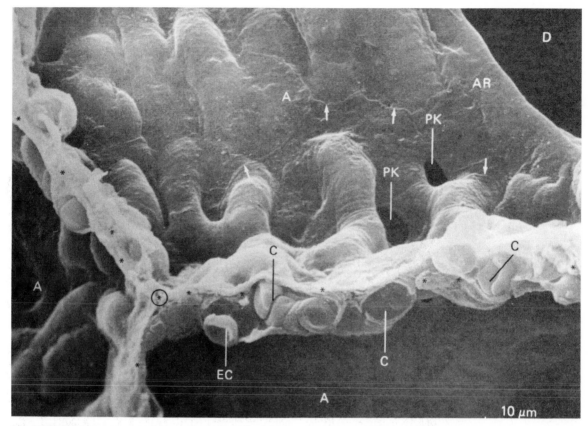

Fig. 9.4 Alveolar septum seen from surface and on cross-section in scanning electron micrograph. On the section face, the capillaries (C), marked by erythrocytes (EC), are seen to be meandering from one side of the septum to the other, the flat septal 'midplane' being marked by connective tissue fibres (indicated by asterisks). The same pattern is apparent on the surface view, where capillaries are seen to 'dip into the depth', i.e. to the other side of the septum. Note alveolar entrance ring (AR) at free edge of septum, junction between three septa (encircled asterisk), and inter-alveolar pores (PK). Arrows indicate terminal bars in alveolar epithelium. D = alveolar duct; A = alveolus. (By courtesy of E R Weibel)

lined by alveoli. In the human lung there are between 250 million and 300 million alveoli, which range in size from 70 μm at the base of the lung to 300 μm in diameter at the apex. Adjacent alveoli are connected by small pores (pores of Kohn, Fig. 9.4), which help to prevent collapse if the main entry point for gas is obstructed. The total area of the alveolar membrane is between 70 and 80 m^2 — about the size of half a tennis court. This large area and the thinness of the barrier between the air sacs and blood (only 0.5 μm) enables gases to diffuse into the blood very rapidly in a healthy lung; complete equilibration can be achieved between the inspired gas and the capillary blood within a second. On the alveolar side the membrane is a thin cytoplasmic extension of a Type I cell that is juxtaposed to the endothelial cell of the pulmonary capillary.

The passage of fluid across the capillary is governed by Starling's equation (p. 20) as it is in other tissues. The capillary hydrostatic pressure tends to force fluid out into the alveolus whilst the osmotic gradient tends to suck fluid back into the circulation. The interstitium is also drained by lymphatics, which deal with any net flow of fluid into the alveolar space. In left-heart failure, when the capillary hydrostatic pressure is raised, it is easy to see why the alveoli can become rapidly filled with fluid (*pulmonary oedema*).

Work of breathing

Like every other tissue, the lungs and respiratory muscles consume O_2 which can account for up to 4 per cent of the total O_2 uptake by the body. Work must be done to get air to enter the lungs, but expiration is a passive process and involves little oxygen consumption unless it is a forced manoeuvre, such as a cough. This work used for inspiration has to overcome (a) the tendency of the lungs to collapse (elastic recoil or elastic resistance), (b) the resistance to airflow through the airways (airway resistance), and (c) resistance to movement of the tissues themselves (tissue resistance). In disease states any one of these three may increase, so increasing the work done. The large airways account for 80 to 90 per cent of airway resistance, and in asthma narrowing of the bronchi results in a greatly increased work of breathing. Normally, in quiet breathing, about 4 J is expended in respiration, of which only 40 per cent is used to overcome airway and tissue resistance. If a normal subject is asked to breathe through a narrow tube to increase airway resistance by 25 per cent this results in an unpleasant feeling of increased respiratory effort and distress (*dyspnoea*). This sensation is not mediated through the vagus but may arise in the muscles or joint receptors of the chest wall.

Mechanics of breathing

The lungs are covered by a single layer of flattened cells (the visceral pleura), which also extends to the inner surface of the chest wall (parietal pleura). The two pleural membranes are separated by a thin layer of serous fluid that reduces friction and makes it difficult to separate them. The lung would collapse due to its inherent elastic recoil if the pleurae were separated and does so when air (*pneumothorax*) or fluid (a *pleural effusion*) is introduced into the pleural cavity. As the lungs tend to contract away from the chest wall, the pressure at rest, within the pleural cavity is negative relative to atmospheric (0 to -2 cm H_2O), becoming more negative as the chest wall moves out during inspiration (-2 to -4 cm H_2O). During forced inspiration pleural pressure may reach -40 cm H_2O.

The movement of air into and out of the lungs (*ventilation*) is brought about by alterations in the size and volume of the thoracic cavity, with the lungs passively following these changes. Three sets of muscles may be used to bring about changes in intrathoracic volume — the diaphragm, the intercostal muscles, and the accessory muscles of respiration.

The diaphragm is the most important muscle during quiet breathing. It is dome-shaped and its contraction during inspiration results in its central portion being pulled down towards the abdomen. In expiration the muscle relaxes and the abdominal pressure helps to return it to its former position. The diaphragm is innervated by the phrenic nerve, originating from the third, fourth and fifth cervical nerve roots. If the spinal cord is transected below this level respiration can still continue by using the diaphragm alone. If the phrenic nerve is cut or interrupted by tumour, for example, then that side of the diaphragm moves only passively (*paradoxically*) on respiration. During quiet breathing the diaphragm moves about a centimetre but the movement can be increased to 10 cm or more during deep breathing.

The intercostal muscles are important in deeper breathing or in patients with lung disease. Their movements are of two kinds: 'pump handle', in which the sternal end of the downward sloping rib is raised, and 'bucket handle' in which the middle of the rib is moved upwards and outwards. The electrical activity of these muscles has been recorded and it has been shown that the external intercostals contract on inspiration and the internal group on expiration.

The accessory muscles include the muscles of the anterior abdominal wall, the scaleni and sternomastoids. The abdominal muscles show no electrical activity except during forced expiration. They contract when ventilation is high or during coughing or straining. The scaleni may be used in the same situations to raise and fix the first two ribs; the sternomastoids help to raise the sternum, increasing the antero-posterior diameter of the chest. In very deep breathing, extension of the vertebral column may also help to increase the intra-thoracic volume. In normal respiration the circumference of the chest increases by about 2 cm, whereas in active inspiration using the accessory muscles the increase may be as much as 10 cm. On expiration the volume of the thorax decreases because of the elastic recoil of the lungs and the passive relaxation of the ribs and diaphragm.

It will be apparent that during quiet breathing the diaphragm is responsible for about 75 per cent of a normal tidal breath (V_T), whereas the ribs and accessory muscles may be responsible for about two-thirds of a vital capacity (VC).

Measurement of ventilation

The volume of air breathed in or out during normal quiet respiration is about 500 ml and is called the *tidal volume* (V_T). The amount breathed in over a minute is called the *minute ventilation* (Ve) and is the product of V_T and the number of breaths per minute (frequency or f).

$$V_T \times f = Ve$$

In normal man a tidal volume of 500 ml at a respiratory frequency of 10 breaths per minute gives a minute ventilation of 5 litres per minute. However, not all the gas in the tidal volume reaches the alveoli, since 150 ml occupies the anatomical dead space (V_D) of the conducting tubes. This leaves 350 ml of the breath that enters the primary lobule, and from the figures quoted above this would be 350×10 or 3.5 litres per minute of alveolar ventilation (VA).

$$\frac{(V_T - V_D) \times f = \dot{V}_A \text{ (alveolar minute ventilation)}}{(500 - 150) \times 10 = 3500}$$

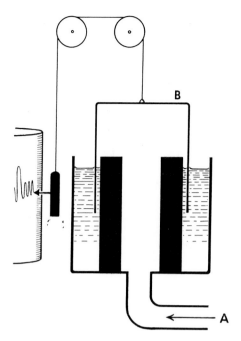

Fig. 9.5 Spirometer. The subject breathes in and out through A into the bell B, which is counterbalanced and effectively weightless. The movement of the bell is recorded

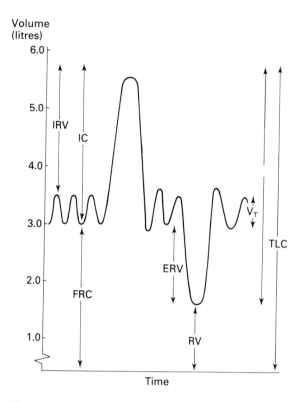

Fig. 9.6 Record from a normal subject breathing into a spirometer. The tidal volume (V_T) is shown prior to a maximal inspiration from functional residual capacity (FRC). This volume is the inspiratory capacity (IC), which is composed of V_T and inspiratory reserve volume (IRV). After further normal respiration a maximal expiration is made to residual volume (RV) and the volume exhaled is the expiratory reserve volume (ERV). The vital capacity (VC) extends from maximal inspiration to maximal expiration. Neither the residual volume, functional residual capacity nor the total lung capacity can be measured directly from a spirometer

The commonest method for measuring tidal volume uses a *spirometer* (Figs. 9.5 and 9.6). This consist of a closed drum situated above a water seal and counterbalanced so that it is effectively weightless. If the subject breathes into the spirometer for any period then a special circuit is attached so that the CO_2 produced is absorbed and O_2 is added to maintain its concentration the same as that in air. An alternative method for measuring air flow and hence tidal volume is a *pneumotachograph* (Fig. 9.7). This consists of a wire mesh, with a pressure sensor on each side, through which the subject breathes. When air flows through the pneumotachograph the pressure across the wire mesh falls. The higher the flow, the greater the pressure difference, which is directly proportional to the flow. Since volume is the integration of flow, tidal volume can be calculated. For example, if the flow rate were 1 litre per second and it was maintained at that constant rate for half a second, the volume that has passed the pneumotachograph is 500 ml. The spirometer and the pneumotachograph require the subject to breathe through a mouthpiece and wear a nose clip, both of which will alter the normal breathing pattern. Less cumbersome methods, such as recording thoracic dimensions with a strain guage or thoracic diameter with a magnetometer, are better but pose problems of accurate calibration.

Figure 9.6 shows the record obtained from a normal subject connected to a spirometer. Tidal respiration is shown (V_T). At the end of expiration the volume of gas in the chest is called the *functional residual capacity* (FRC) and is about 2900 ml in a normal adult. A maximal inspiratory effort from FRC is called the *inspiratory capacity* (IC) and is composed of 500 ml of V_T and 2000 ml of *inspiratory reserve volume* (IRV). After further quiet respiration, a maximal expiration from FRC results in 1300 ml (*expiratory reserve volume*, ERV) of air being expelled. This point of maximal exhalation still leaves about 1600 ml of *residual volume* (RV) in the chest. This residual volume cannot be expelled because of the mechanical restrictions of the chest wall and diaphragm. The functional residual capacity acts as a buffer to rapid changes in alveolar gas composition, since the 350 ml of alveolar ventilation per breath are distributed in 2900 ml of FRC. Neither the

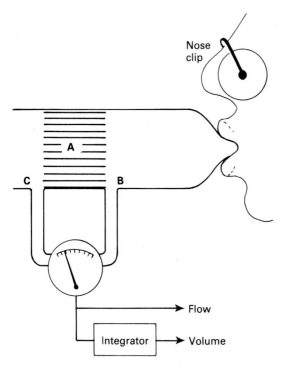

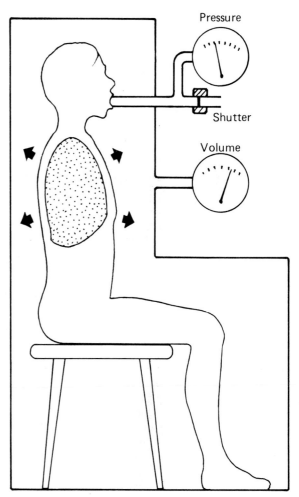

Fig. 9.7 Pneumotachograph. Diagrammatic representation of a pneumotachograph. The subject, who wears a nose-clip, breathes in and out through a tube that contains a wire mesh (A). During expiration the resistance of the wire mesh makes the pressure at B slightly higher than that at C and this is detected by a sensitive pressure manometer. The pressure difference is proportional to flow, and using an integrator the volume of air that has passed through the instrument can be calculated

Fig. 9.8 The whole body plethysmograph. The subject is seated in a sealed box and breathes through a tube that contains a shutter which is closed at functional residual capacity (FRC). The subject then makes panting efforts and this results in a fall in the pressure recorded at the mouth (ΔP). This change in pressure will cause very small changes in the size of the lungs, which, in turn, change the pressure within the closed box. This can be calibrated and allows the change in volume of the lungs, although very small, to be calculated (ΔV)

residual volume nor functional residual capacity can be measured directly from a spirometer.

Methods for measuring lung volumes

Two approaches are currently used for the determination of residual volume (RV) and functional residual capacity (FRC) and the commoner uses a dilution principle. The subject is connected to a spirometer containing helium (or hydrogen) at the end of expiration (FRC). The CO_2 is absorbed by soda lime and the O_2 replenished so that the volume of the spirometer and the patient's lungs remain the same. During quiet breathing the helium is distributed between the spirometer and the patient's lungs. Knowing the initial volume of the spirometer, the original concentration of helium and the eventual concentration of helium in the lungs and spirometer, we can calculate the initial volume of the lungs (FRC) in which the helium has been diluted. A maximal expiration gives one the expiratory reserve volume and the residual volume can then be calculated by subtraction. The normal value for FRC

is a reflection of the balance between the tendency of the lungs to deflate (elastic recoil) and the thoracic cage to expand.

The other method used to measure lung volume is the *whole body plethysmograph*. This consists of a sealed box in which the subject sits (Fig. 9.8). The subject, who wears a nose-clip, breathes the air within the box through a mouth-piece containing a shutter that can completely close the airway. At functional residual capacity this shutter closes and the subject makes panting movements although no air can enter or leave the lungs. During an inspiratory attempt the pressure on the mouth side of the shutter falls (ΔP) and this is transmitted to the air within the subject's chest. The negative pressure causes the volume of gas in the chest (FRC) to expand; the amount of expansion depends on the magnitude of the change in pressure (ΔP) and the volume of gas in the thorax. The increase in volume of gas in the chest may be very small but it does result in compression of gas within the plethysmograph and this can be accurately measured (ΔV). Using Boyle's law, and by simple re-arrangement of the formula, FRC can be calculated

$$\text{FRC} = \frac{(\Delta V)}{(\Delta P)} \times \text{barometric pressure}$$

The FRC measured by the plethysmograph is often larger than that measured by helium dilution in patients with lung disease because air may be 'trapped'. In emphysema, for example, there may be alveoli and air sacs that are dilated but do not connect with the bronchi; their volume is not measured by the helium technique, but is by the plethysmograph.

Vital capacity (VC) is composed of inspiratory capacity and expiratory reserve volume and may be obtained from the spirometer. Its value depends on the age, height, weight, sex and ethnic origin of the subject; the values obtained have to be compared with tables compiled from a normal population. It is also dependent upon position and as one might imagine vital capacity is greater in the sitting than in the lying posture because of the lower position of the diaphragm.

Vital capacity (VC, 3800 ml) and residual volume (RV, 1600 ml) added together give *total lung capacity* (TLC, approximately 5400 ml).

TESTS OF LUNG FUNCTION

One of the simplest tests of lung function is to ask the patient to produce a forced vital capacity (FVC). The subject takes a maximal inspiration and then exhales into spirometer as fast and as hard as he can down to residual volume. The results from a normal subject are shown in Figure 9.9. The FVC for this subject was 5 litres, of which 4 litres was expelled in the first second (forced expiratory volume in the first second: FEV_1)

$$\frac{FEV_1}{FVC} = \frac{4.0}{5.0} \times 100 = 80 \text{ per cent}$$

Figure 9.10 shows the trace for a patient with airways obstruction. His FVC is also 5 litres but he can only expel 2 litres in the first second ($FEV_1/FVC = 2.0/5.0$

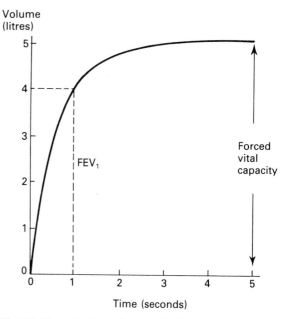

Fig. 9.9 Normal spirometric trace of a forced vital capacity (*FVC*), the FEV_1 being 80 per cent of the FVC

= 40 per cent). His expiratory time is about 6 s and this sort of trace indicates severe airways obstruction such as that seen in asthma or chronic bronchitis. The FEV_1/FVC should normallly be greater than 70 per cent; although values of 90 per cent are obtainable in fit young people the pecentages will fall with age.

Figure 9.10 the trace from a patient with a restrictive defect is also shown. Here the FVC is reduced but the

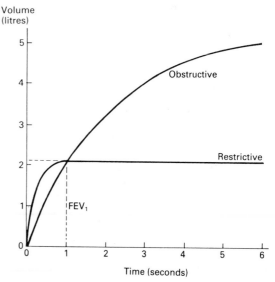

Fig. 9.10 Spirometric traces of FVC for two patients, one with an obstructive defect and one with a restrictive defect

amount exhaled in the first second (FEV_1) is still over 70 per cent of the vital capacity (FVC). This record is from a patient with lung fibrosis whose lungs are smaller than normal. In fact the fibrosis may strengthen the small airways, preventing their collapse and so theoretically increasing the FEV_1/FVC percent. Other causes of a restrictive defect include thoracic deformities (for example, kyphoscoliosis) and a previous operation to remove a lung (pneumonectomy).

The spirometer is used in hospitals or laboratories to measure FEV_1 and FVC but another measure of airways resistance can be obtained from a Wright's peak flow meter. This essentially consists of a vane in a tube through which the subject blows. The subject is asked to exhale at maximum flow rate and the deflection of the vane is proportional to the peak flow. Simple plastic versions of this instrument can be given to patients with asthma to use at home and record their peak flow rate at different times of the day; the records can help the physician to arrange treatment to suit the patient's needs.

More complex tests of airways function

The spirometer and peak flow meter give an overall estimate of *airways resistance* but this can be measured more accurately by using the body plethysmograph (p. 132). Flow at the mouth is recorded with a pneumotachograph and the driving pressure (pleural pressure minus mouth pressure) can be measured by using the plethysmograph or an intra-oesophageal balloon to measure pleural pressure. The latter, if positioned correctly, gives a reasonably accurate estimate of intra-pleural pressure.

Compliance is a measure of the distensibility of the lungs and is defined as the change in volume produced by a unit change in pressure. If the lungs are of low compliance or 'stiff', then for a fixed pressure change there is only a small change in volume, such as is seen in inflating a tubeless car tyre. If the lungs had a high compliance then the same change in pressure would result in a larger change in volume (such as inflating a paper bag). It can be measured under either static or dynamic conditions. The pressure measured is the trans-pleural pressure, usually obtained by taking the pressure difference between the oesophagus and the mouth. If the measurements are made at the end of inspiration there is no air flow and so no pressure is being used to overcome airway resistance. Measurements made under dynamic conditions include those of viscous resistance of the tissues and include airway resistance. In normal man 500 ml of air is moved into the lung for a change of pressure of 3.5 cm H_2O. This gives a compliance of 0.14 l/cm H_2O. Normal ranges are 0.09–0.26 l/cm H_2O. In the newborn the lungs are remarkably stiff at the first breath, the value being

0.005 l/cm H_2O. As one might expect the lungs get stiffer as one gets older (compliance decreases) as the elastic tissue is replaced by collagen.

Flow/volume loops

The previously described simple tests correlate well with large airways narrowing but we can obtain more information about smaller airways by studying a flow/volume loop. The patient performs a maximal forced vital capacity; both the flow and volume are usually recorded from a pneumotachograph and plotted one against the other as shown in Figure 9.11. A normal subject achieves a flow rate of more than 8 litres per second for only a short period and then the majority of the vital capacity is expelled at a much lower flow rate. The first portion of the manoeuvre is effort-dependent but later the flow becomes determined by the lung's elastic recoil, which is trying the prevent the small airways from collapsing, and by the airways resistance of the larger bronchi farther upstream. In obstructive

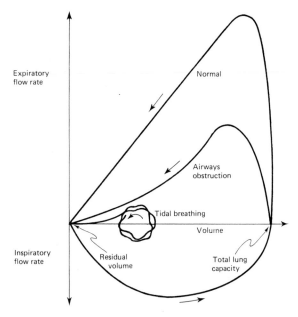

Fig. 9.11 Flow volume loop.   Record obtained from a pneumotachograph of flow rate and volume. The central small irregular loops represent normal tidal breathing (tidal volume — VT_T); they are dissimilar in shape to the later forced manoeuvre because it is under conscious control and the subject is breathing through a mouthpiece. The volunteer expires down to residual volume (RV) and then takes a maximal inspiration to total lung capacity (TLC). In a rapid expiration that follows, the flow rate is high but falls as most of the volume is expelled down to residual volume again. Also shown is the trace from a patient with airways obstruction in whom the peak flow cannot be achieved and there is a convexity of the curve towards the volume axis. This part of the curve is theoretically due to some units emptying more slowly behind narrowed airways

lung disease the downward curve of the flow volume loop is hollowed out, whereas in restrictive lung diseases such as lung fibrosis the fibrotic retraction of the small bronchi produces a flatter curve, that is, a higher flow rate at that lung volume.

Closing capacity

A subject expires down to residual volume and then inspires oxygen. During the next slow expiration the nitrogen content of the expired gas can be analysed by using a rapidly responding gas analyser (Fig. 9.12). The exhaled nitrogen appears in four phases. The first (phase I) contains no nitrogen because the gas is from the anatomical dead space. Phase II reflects the mixed interface between the dead space and alveolar gas. Phase III represents alveolar gas, and at the end of expiration a sudden sharp increase in nitrogen concentration is seen. The volume of gas still residing in the lungs is then called the *closing capacity* and comprises residual volume and closing volume. The explanation is thought to be that the oxygen during inspiration is preferentially distributed to the lower lobes and during exhalation, when the closing capacity is reached, the lower airways collapse, resulting in gas from the upper zones being expelled; this gas is relatively richer in nitrogen since it has been less diluted by inhaled oxygen. The reason for the distribution of inspired oxygen to the lower lobes is that the alveoli in this region are less well distended and because of the shape of the compliance curve it is easier to inflate these alveoli of a lower volume than those of larger volume (p. 137). The same phenomenon can be demonstrated if a bolus of tracer gas (argon or helium) is inhaled at the end of inspiration and then the concentration is followed during the slow exhal-ation. Closing volume is a sensitive index of small airways disease and increases with age. In patients with severe disease closing volume may be as great or greater than functional residual capacity, implying that small airways may close at the base of the lung during a normal expiration in these people.

Measurements of expired gas

We have seen above that the inspired ventilation is about 5 litres per minute and we can calculate that a subject at rest takes up about 250 ml O_2 per minute and produces 200 ml CO_2. This means that expired ventilation volume is slightly less than inspired volume. The O_2 uptake ($\dot{V}O_2$) and CO_2 produced ($\dot{V}CO_2$) are a reflection of the demands and waste products of internal respiration and the ratio of these two is called the *respiratory quotient* or RQ

$$RQ = \frac{\dot{V}CO_2}{\dot{V}O_2} = \frac{200}{250} = 0.8$$

The normal value for RQ depends somewhat upon the metabolic fuel being used to produce energy. On exercise both the volume of O_2 taken up and the volume of CO_2 produced increases and providing the subject has reached a steady state the RQ remains at about 0.8.

Early methods for the measurement of O_2 and CO_2 involved the collection of an accurately measured volume of expired gas, the absorption of CO_2 by potassium hydroxide and then the remeasurement of the

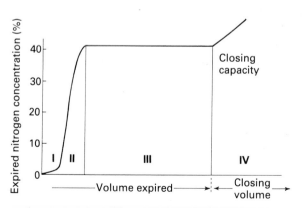

Fig. 9.12 Expired nitrogen concentration recorded after a single breath of pure oxygen. Initially the expired gas contains no nitrogen and is from the dead space (phase I) and then the nitrogen concentration rises (phase II) followed by an almost constant alveolar plateau (phase III), which represents alveolar gas. Finally there is a rise in gas concentration after the closing capacity has been reached (phase IV)

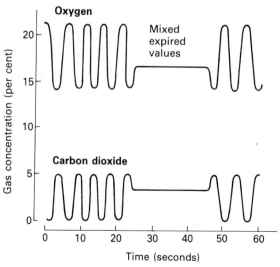

Fig. 9.13 Analysis of expired gas using a rapid gas analyser. O_2 and CO_2 traces are shown as a normal subject breathes through a mouthpiece. Half way through, the analyser is switched to a mixing box for expired gas and this collects both dead space gas (i.e. room air) and alveolar gas. The value obtained is a reflection of the ratio of the two

volume. Oxygen was absorbed by alkaline pyrogallol and the remaining volume is mostly nitrogen with minute traces of inert gases. This is Lloyd's modification of Haldane's volumetric method. Nowadays more rapid analysers are used, such as a *mass spectrometer*. Figure 9.13 shows the trace for O_2 and CO_2 obtained from one of these instruments sampling the gas at the mouth. The values obtained at the end of expiration (end tidal) should be most representative of true alveolar gas.

Table 9.14 shows the normal composition of inspired gas, mixed expired gas collected in a bag (containing both dead space gas and alveolar gas), and end tidal or alveolar gas. The mixed expired gas contains both alveolar gas and inspired gas that was occupying the dead space and therefore the values are somewhere between those of inspired and alveolar gas. The figures for nitrogen suggest that it is present in higher concentrations in alveolar gas but this is not so because no nitrogen exchange has taken place. Expired ventilation is less in volume than inspired ventilation because the value of the respiratory quotient (RQ) results in an apparently higher nitrogen concentration in the lesser volume.

Table 9.14 Composition of lung gases of different sources

Gas	Gas concentrations (%)		
	Oxygen	Carbon dioxide	Nitrogen
Inspired	20.9	0.3	79.0
Mixed expired	16.9	3.5	79.6
End tidal (alveolar)	14.5	5.5	79.9

Measurements of dead space

Anatomical dead space
The early anatomists measured the volume of the conducting tubes by filling them with a resin and found the anatomical dead space to be about 150 ml. This method is impractical in live subjects and methods were developed to measure dead space by analysing gas concentrations during expiration. If we know from a pneumotachograph or a spirometer the volume of gas exhaled before the change in gas concentrations (i.e. phase II of Fig. 9.13) this correlates with anatomical dead space.

However, a more important measurement is that of the *physiological dead space* described by Bohr. This is composed of the anatomical dead space (V_D) together

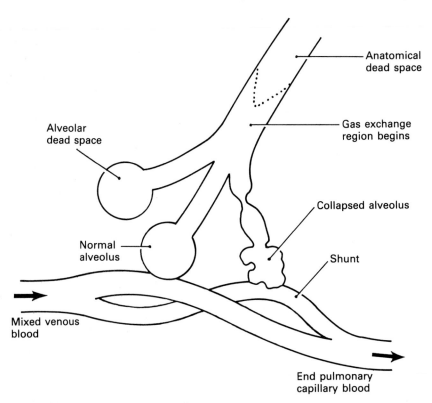

Fig. 9.15 Schematic diagram of potential extremes of ventilation perfusion mismatching. The alveolus on the left has no blood supply and wasted ventilation (alveolar dead space), the middle one has both ventilation and perfusion, but the one on the right has no ventilation but normal blood flow (right-to-left shunt, 'venous admixture'). All combinations of these extremes may be seen in abnormal lungs

with the dead space that results form wasted ventilation (Fig. 9.15). One can see that if inspired gas enters an alveolus that has no blood flow it contributes nothing to gas exchange. This can be estimated by measuring the dilution of alveolar gas by dead space gas to give the mixed expired value. Suppose, for example, the mixed expired value for CO_2 were half the end tidal value, then the dead space would be half the tidal volume. Bohr measured the physiological dead space by assuming that the end tidal CO_2 should accurately represent the end capillary CO_2 tension. If the end tidal value were less than that of the arterial value this would represent dilution by alveolar dead space. Expressing this mathematically:

$$\text{Bohr physiological dead space} = V_T \frac{(Pa_{CO_2} - Pe_{CO_2})}{(Pa_{CO_2})}$$

where Pa_{CO_2} is end capillary of arterial carbon dioxide tension and Pe_{CO_2} is mixed expired carbon dioxide tension

In this equation arterial carbon dioxide tension is substituted for end tidal P_{CO_2} and in both it is assumed that the inspired P_{CO_2} is zero. In effect, if the arterial and end tidal CO_2 tensions are not the same, this is an indication of wasted ventilation, or if arterial CO_2 tension is greater than the end tidal P_{CO_2} then this would indicate wasted perfusion, that is, a right-to-left shunt (Fig. 9.15). One can see that ventilation of an alveolus that is not perfused represents the grossest example but all variations of mismatching will contribute to the physiological dead space.

Uneven ventilation

As has been inferred, all parts of the lung are not equally ventilated. In upright man the weight of the lung will tend to compress the basal alveoli. However, if we ask a subject to inhale an inert radio-active gas (xenon-133), it can be shown that ventilation is best at the bases of the lung. The explanation lies in the pressure/volume curves of the lung (Fig. 9.16). To demonstrate this best experimentally, a pair of excised

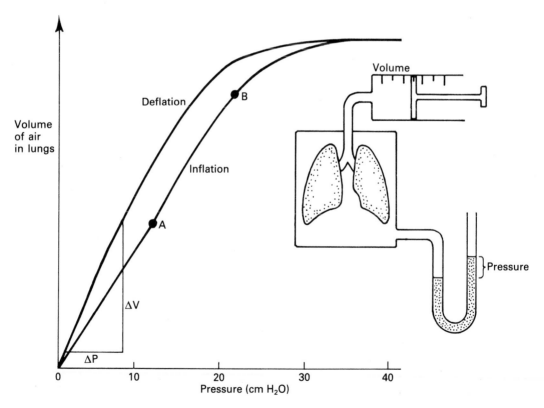

Fig. 9.16 Pressure–volume curve for a pair of rat lungs suspended in an airtight box and inflated in stages with air from a syringe while the pressure in the box is recorded. The volume of gas moved into or out of the lungs at each step during inflation or deflation is shown. The curves obtained are not identical (see text) and the slope ($\Delta V/\Delta P$) is the compliance of the lung. Point A might represent an alveolus at the base of the lung and point B at the apex. For the same change in pressure the alveolus at A will expand more in volume than that at B because of the differences in compliance.

animal lungs are placed in a sealed box and by changing the pressure surrounding them (i.e. the pleural pressure) we can measure the volume of gas taken in for each change in pressure. Figure 9.16 shows that the shape of the pressure volume loop is different during inflation and deflation. This behaviour is known as hysteresis — the volume at any given pressure during deflation is larger than during inflation. The slope of the pressure volume curve or the volume change per unit pressure change is the compliance. One can see that if the volume is smaller (point A) at the base of the lung

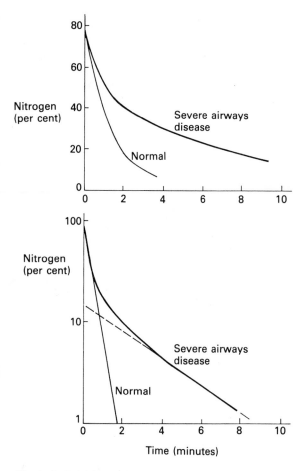

Fig. 9.17 Multiple-breath nitrogen washout. Upper portion shows the nitrogen washout recorded from a gas analyser when the subject breathes 100 per cent O_2. The trace shows one curve obtained from a normal person and one from a patient with airways disease. The lower figure shows the plot of the nitrogen concentration on a logarithmic scale against time for the two traces. In a normal subject the clearance of N_2 is linear but in an abnormal lung there are two components — one fast and one slow — showing that some alveoli are emptying more slowly. Often the same graph is drawn against breath number instead of time to make allowances for different patterns of ventilation

then the same change in pressure will result in a greater increase in the volume of this alveolus compared with one at the apex (point B). The shape of the curve determines that the lung is easier to inflate at low lung volumes than at high lung volumes, but the situation becomes reversed when we consider very low lung volumes.

Information about differences in regional ventilation can be obtained by using radio-active isotopes but other techniques will also indicate uneven ventilation. The multiple-breath nitrogen washout test involves the analysis of nitrogen whilst the subject breathes oxygen. The results are shown for a normal and an abnormal lung in Figure 9.17. Normal lungs give an almost linear plot of nitrogen concentration against breath number on semi-logarithmic paper whilst in diseased lungs the plot becomes divisible into two components; well-ventilated alveoli have a rapid clearance, whereas poorly ventilated units have a much slower time course. Similar information can be derived from the analysis of a single expiration during the same test. The alveolar plateau (phase III of Fig. 9.12) in a uniformly ventilated lung would show no end-tidal rise in nitrogen concentration. However, if ventilation is uneven, O_2 distribution is uneven and a terminal rise in nitrogen concentration is seen.

VENTILATION IN UNUSUAL ENVIRONMENTS

Fetal and neonatal respiration

Over the last few years it has been shown by ultrasound that the fetus makes respiratory movements of the chest wall in utero as early as the 12th week of gestation. If the fetus becomes jeopardised in utero and the arterial Pa_{O_2} falls or the Pa_{CO_2} rises, then fetal respiration is depressed; this information is now used in the early detection of babies at risk. At birth much of the amniotic fluid present in the lungs is expelled during the passage through the birth canal but at the first gasp a violent respiratory effort is needed to expand the lungs. Pleural pressures of -90 cm H_2O have been recorded. Once the air–liquid interface has been created the compliance of the lungs is reduced and the work of breathing diminishes. Most of the fetal lung fluid is absorbed into the interstitium of the lung and then passes into the pulmonary lymphatics. The surface tension of lung fluid is lowered by *surfactant* — a dipalmitoyl lecithin that is secreted by the Type II cells in the alveoli. Surfactant has a very low surface tension, which is less than that of washing-up liquid and enables the alveoli to be easily distended because it lowers compliance. However, it is unique in that the surface tension increases as the surface area increases. Without this property, by Laplace's Law (pressure = 2 ×

surface tension/radius), a small bubble or alveolus will have a higher intra-alveolar pressure than a larger one and that would ultimately cause all the smaller units to collapse into one enormous alveolus. If the infant is premature, pulmonary surfactant may not have been produced in sufficient quantity to prevent hyaline membrane disease. Considerable respiratory effort is then needed to overcome the increased compliance and this is evident by the pronounced rib recession, hypoxaemia and rapid respiratory fatigue. The newborn has a tidal volume of about 17 ml at a frequency of 30 breaths per minute giving a minute ventilation of 540 ml. Respiratory frequency is remarkably irregular at birth, with a range of 14–60 breaths per minute, but settles within a few days.

Artificial ventilation
If ventilation ceases then the arterial P_{O_2} falls rapidly so the normal oxygen content drops from 200 ml/litre of blood to 150 ml/litre in 60 seconds and to zero within 5 minutes. A precipitous fall is prevented to some extent by the O_2 present in the residual volume gas in the lungs. However, the cerebral cortex cannot withstand such severe O_2 lack and consciousness is lost within a few seconds. Irreversible brain damage occurs within 2 or 3 minutes of the respiratory arrest. It is therefore imperative that some form of ventilation be started as soon as spontaneous respiration stops. All students should be familiar with mouth-to-mouth or mouth-to-nose methods of resuscitation. It is important to check that the airway is clear and that the ventilation is effective by watching the chest movements. Expired air, with about 15 per cent oxygen, is adequate as inspired air for the patient, provided that the lungs can be inflated at a rate of about 10 breaths per minute. If external cardiac massage is necessary as well a useful rule is to apply cardiac massage four or five times for every inflation.

Mechanical ventilation
Mechanical ventilation is used more and more frequently for patients during major surgery when muscle relaxants are given, after major surgery during a period in an intensive care unit, and for patients with high spinal-cord paralysis who are unable to breath spontaneously. Ventilators are designed either to give a fixed volume at a pre-determined rate or deliver a variable volume until a certain pressure is achieved. The majority of patients are now ventilated through a tube passed either through the nose or mouth and a seal is achieved by inflating a cuff in the trachea. The satisfactory state of a patient on a ventilator can be assessed by measuring the arterial blood gases and adjusting the settings accordingly.

PULMONARY CIRCULATION

The primary function of the lungs is gas exchange, which is carried out by a network of capillaries surrounding the alveoli. The blood vessels of the lungs consist of two sets originating from different sources and performing functions of a different character. One set is derived from the pulmonary artery and gives rise to the alveolar capillaries; the other set takes origin directly or indirectly from the aorta, and furnishes the nutrient vessels of the lungs by way of the bronchial arteries.

The lung blood vessels
The main pulmonary artery divides into two, one to each lung. Within each lung the pulmonary artery follows the bronchi in all their sub-divisions and breaks up into arterioles and a network of capillaries situated in the walls of the air spaces (Fig 9.18). Structurally the pulmonary artery is a predominantly elastic vessel with

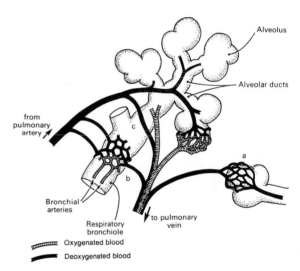

Fig. 9.18 General scheme of a primary lobule showing vascular communications between the pulmonary and bronchial vascular systems in the region of the respiratory bronchiole and some intra-pulmonary causes of venous admixture with arterial blood. The latter include the following (1) Uneven alveolar ventilation of different parts of the lungs. Under-ventilation of alveoli with a normal pulmonary capillary blood flow (indicated by adjacent lobule (a)) leads to hypoxaemia. (2) Venous blood from the bronchial circulation draining into the pulmonary veins (b). (3) Pulmonary artery-pulmonary vein shunts (c). The bronchial artery blood flow is exceedingly difficult to measure but is probably about 1 per cent of the pulmonary flow. The bronchial circulation has few veins of its own, the drainage is mainly as at (b) into the pulmonary veins, which go to the left atrium. The bronchial arteries also supply a small amount of blood to mediastinal structures, which drain into the azygos vein and right atrium (By courtesy of M de Burgh Daly.)

a thin medial coat. After entering the lungs the pulmonary arteries become less elastic and more muscular. Maximum muscularity appears in vessels of 100–200 μm diameter; between 100 and 30 μm diameter the vessels rapidly lose their muscle coat.

The capillaries are each about 8 μm diameter and 8 μm long and form a dense network or mesh with an estimated area of 30–50 m² (Fig. 9.19). An alternative way of depicting the alveolar capillaries is to consider the vascular bed as consisting of two endothelial sheets of tissue held apart by 'stays' or 'posts' of septal tissue. This 'sheet-flow' concept appears to a red cell as an underground parking garage with floor, ceiling and intervening support posts. The capillary vessels are so short and communicate so frequently with one another that the concept of a 'sheet' is more helpful than the notion of a series of tubes.

The air in the alveoli is separated from the blood in the capillaries by 0.3–0.7 μm (Fig. 9.20). In disease, however, the potential space between them may be occupied by oedema fluid or an inflammatory exudate so the distance through which O_2 and CO_2 have to

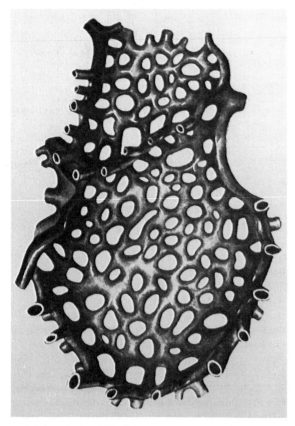

Fig. 9.19 The network of capillaries in the walls of the alveoli (Miller W S 1947 The Lung, 2nd edn. C C Thomas, Illinois)

diffuse is greatly increased. All the pulmonary capillary blood returns by the pulmonary veins, containing oxygenated blood, to the left atrium. The pulmonary circulation is in series with the systemic circulation and therefore the outputs of the left and right ventricles must be equal except for very short periods when circulatory adjustments are taking place. Otherwise the lungs would either become overfilled with blood or depleted of blood depending on the relative outputs of the two ventricles (p. 71).

The *bronchial arteries* enter each lung and break up into two or three branches that accompany each of the larger bronchi and bronchioles. Their capillary networks supply arterial blood to the smooth muscle wall of the whole length of the bronchial tree as far as the respiratory bronchioles, and to intrapulmonary nerves and nerve ganglia, pleura, interstitial lung substance and lymphoid tissue, and are the vasa vasorum of the pulmonary arteries. Blood is carried away from the broncial circulation by two routes: first, by true bronchial veins draining blood from the first two dividing points of the bronchial tree into the right atrium, and second, by broncho-pulmonary veins, which drain blood from the venous plexus surrounding the bronchi and bronchioles as far as the respiratory bronchioles into the pulmonary veins (Fig. 9.18).

Not only do the systemic and pulmonary vascular systems anastomose on the venous side of the pulmonary circulation, but also at a capillary level (Fig. 9.18). Blood from the systemic circulation can therefore reach the pulmonary circulation by way of the bronchial vascular system. Under normal circumstances no bronchial blood flows through the pulmonary capillaries but only joins the pulmonary circulation downstream from the capillaries. The clinical significance of these anastomotic channels is that in forms of congenital heart disease associated with stenosis (narrowing) of the main pulmonary artery, patent interventricular septum and arterial hypoxaemia, these channels, together with precapillary anastomoses that are probably not normally patent, open up enormously. The effect of this is to increase the bronchial artery blood flow from a normal value of 1 to 2 per cent of the left ventricular output to as much as 20 per cent. This blood now goes through the pulmonary capillaries so that the systemic arterial (hypoxic) blood is given a 'second chance' of being oxygenated.

The lungs receive a nerve supply from both the parasympathetic and sympathetic divisions of the autonomic nervous system. The pulmonary circulation (pre- and post-pulmonary capillary blood vessels), the bronchial circulation and the bronchial smooth muscle receive a nerve supply from the vagus and sympathetic nerves. In addition there are now believed to be three functionally different types of receptors in the lungs:

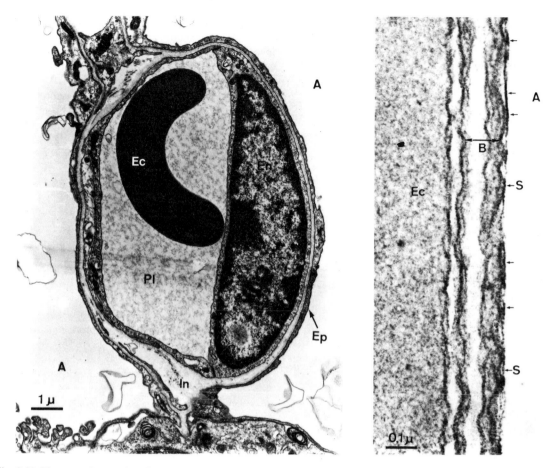

Fig. 9.20 Electron micrographs of monkey lung. The picture on the left shows two alveoli (A) with the capillary between them in cross-section. Ep, epithelium; In, interstitial space; En, endothelial cell; Pl, plasma; Ec, erythrocyte. (Weibel E R 1969 In: Fishmann A P & Hecht H H (eds) The Pulmonary Circulation and Interstitial Space, University of Chicago Press, Chicago, p. 11). The picture on the right shows the alveolar endothelium of rat lung at higher magnification. B, tissue barrier (endothelium, interstitial space and epithelium). S, surfactant (arrows point to osmophilic surface layer) (By courtesy of Joan Gil.)

pulmonary stretch-receptors in the walls of the airways (responsible for the Hering–Breuer respiratory reflex (p. 155); lung irritant receptors (for example, those in the wall of the trachea responsible for the cough reflex (p. 155); and juxta-pulmonary capillary receptors ('J'-receptors) situated in the interstitial space next to the pulmonary capillaries. The afferent fibres conveying the information to the central nervous system run largely in the vagus nerves.

The ensemble of the respiratory bronchiole and its subdivisions (Figs. 9.2 and 9.18), together with its accompanying pulmonary and bronchial blood vessels, lymph vessels and nerves, forms a *primary lobule*.

Pressures in the pulmonary blood vessels
The pressure in the pulmonary artery in man can be measured directly by catheterisation through the right side of the heart. The values for pulmonary arterial pressure are as follows: systolic, 20–23 mmHg, which is the same as the right ventricular systolic pressure; diastolic, 5–9 mmHg; and mean pressure, 11–15 mmHg. Typical pressure waves are shown in Figure 9.21.

When studying pulmonary haemodynamics, it is often important to know that the value of the left atrial pressure, which may be measured by passing a catheter into the pulmonary artery and then advancing it until it can pass no further and oxygenated blood can be withdrawn from it. Its tip must block a small branch of the pulmonary artery and the pressure may be recorded. This is known as pulmonary arterial *wedge pressure* and usually corresponds fairly closely with the pressure in the left atrium. Although the method is relatively simple it can give values for pulmonary wedge pressure that do not agree with those in the left atrium,

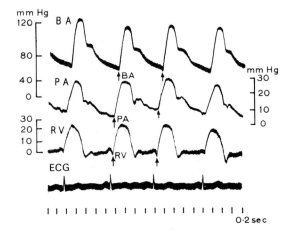

Fig. 9.21 Simultaneous records of pressure in brachial artery (BA), pulmonary artery (PA) and right ventricle (RV) obtained by optical manometers attached to cardiac catheters. An ECG, leads II, is also shown. (By courtesy of A Cournand.)

and a more reliable method is to measure the left atrial pressure directly by transatrial septal catheterisation through the right atrium (p. 81). The mean left atrial pressure varies from 0 to 5 mmHg, so the pressure gradient across the lungs, pulmonary arterial pressure minus left atrial pressure, is 12 mmHg. The blood flow through the lungs is about 5 litres per minute at rest, and therefore the resistance to blood flow offered by the pulmonary circulation (see formula on p. 106) is only about one-eighth that of the systemic circulation.

The pressure in the lung capillaries must lie between the pulmonary arterial pressure and the left atrial pressure, and is about 8 mmHg. This pressure is much lower than that in the capillaries of the systemic circulation. The osmotic pressure exerted by the plasma proteins is, however, the same in the two vascular territories, so the tendency for fluid to remain within the pulmonary capillaries or for fluid to enter them from the alveolar spaces is greater than in the systemic capillary bed. In failure of the left ventricle, the left atrial pressure rises and this rise is transmitted backward to the pulmonary capillaries. When the capillary pressure reaches 20–30 mmHg, fluid passes into the alveoli resulting in pulmonary oedema.

Flow in the pulmonary blood vessels

Mean blood flow through the pulmonary circulation of man may be measured by the Fick, dye dilution or thermal dilution methods, and the normal value at rest, expressed as cardiac index, is 3.2 litres per min per m² body surface area. The output of the right ventricle is not distributed equally between two lungs because of their different size; about 45 per cent passes through the

left lung and 55 per cent through the right. The pulmonary circulation time, that is the time taken for the blood to pass from the pulmonary artery to the left atrium is about 5 seconds, of which about 0.75 second represents the time the blood takes to traverse the pulmonary capillaries at rest. During strenuous exercise the latter figure is reduced to about 0.3 second, which is still long enough for adequate gas exchange to occur. The pressure is pulsatile not only in the pulmonary arteries (Fig. 9.21) but also in the pulmonary capillaries and veins.

Distribution of pulmonary blood flow

The mean pressure in the pulmonary artery of 11–15 mmHg is equivalent to 15–20 cm of blood and is barely sufficient to perfuse the vessels in the apices of the lungs, which are about 15 cm above the level of the pulmonary artery when the body is erect. On the other hand the pressure in the arteries in the bases of the lungs is equal to the pressure in the pulmonary artery plus the hydrostatic pressure of about 15 cm of blood, the vertical distance of the vessels below the pulmonary artery. The lower parts of the lungs (Fig. 9.22) are therefore relatively better perfused. The blood flow in different parts of the lungs varies therefore with their vertical position in relation to the level of the pulmonary artery. Thus in a person lying supine the apices and bases of the lungs are equally perfused, but the vessels in the posterior parts of the lungs are better perfused than those in the anterior parts.

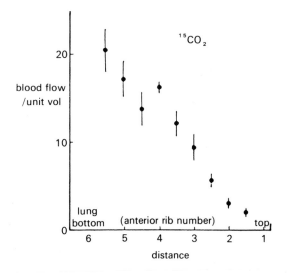

Fig. 9.22 Distribution of blood flow in the normal upright lung as measured with radioactive CO_2. Data from 16 normal subjects; means and standard errors of clearance rates. Note that blood flow decreases steadily from the bottom to the top of the lung, there being virtually no flow at the apex. (West J B 1970 Ventilation, blood flow and gas exchange, 2nd edn. Blackwell Scientific, Oxford)

The blood flow through the various parts of the lungs can be investigated quantitatively. The subject is seated between a pair of scintillation counters sensitive to the radiation from a particular anteroposterior volume of lung. If he takes a single breath of CO_2 containing $^{11}CO_2$, the counting rate rises quickly, indicating the amount of gas coming into the part of the lung being investigated. If he holds his breath, the $^{11}CO_2$ is carried off in the pulmonary circulation and so the count falls, the rate of fall indicating the rate of blood flow. Such experiments (Fig. 9.22) show that the blood flow is maximal at the bases of the lungs and is minimal (nearly zero) at the apices of the lungs when the subject is in the upright position. In exercise the flow increases in all parts of the lungs due to an increase in cardiac output and pulmonary arterial pressure, but especially in the apical regions so that the flows now become more even. In diseases of the heart in which pulmonary blood flow is augmented or in which the left atrial and pulmonary venous pressures are increased, the pulmonary flow is also more evenly distributed within the lungs.

It must be realised that if the pulmonary vessels behaved as a series of rigid tubes, the siphon effect would ensure that blood flow in all parts of the lungs was uniform. In vivo, the vessels are very distensible and collapsible and this is responsible for the blood being delivered in the lungs unevenly largely because of gravitational effects. This can be accounted for by consideration of the mechanical effects of the pressure inside and outside the vessels, that is the transmural pressure.

The lungs may be arbitrarily divided into three zones by the relative sizes of the pulmonary arterial, pulmonary venous and alveolar pressures (Fig. 9.23). In *zone 1* there is little blood flow because the pulmonary arterial pressure is less than the alveolar pressure to which the collapsible vessels are exposed. In *zone 2* the pulmonary arterial pressure exceeds the alveolar pressure, but the alveolar pressure is higher than the pulmonary venous pressure. In this situation the vessels are partly compressed (Fig. 9.23) and the blood flow is proportional to the difference between the pulmonary arterial and alveolar pressures, rather than between the pulmonary arterial and pulmonary venous pressures. This situation has been compared with a sluice or waterfall and has given rise to the term 'sluice' or 'waterfall' effect. In *zone 3* the pulmonary venous pressure exceeds the alveolar pressure so the blood flow is determined by the difference between the pulmonary arterial and pulmonary venous pressures. Thus the blood flow increases down this zone because the transmural pressure increases, thereby distending the vessels.

Figure 9.24 shows that, in addition to the variation in blood flow from the apex to the base of the lung, ventilation also varies, but not to such a great extent.

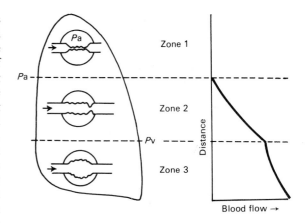

Fig. 9.23 Scheme that accounts for the distribution of blood flow in the lung. In zone 1, alveolar pressure (P_A) exceeds pulmonary arterial pressure (P_a) and no flow occurs, presumably because collapsible vessels are directly exposed to alveolar pressure. In zone 2, pulmonary arterial pressure exceeds alveolar pressure, but alveolar exceeds venous pressure (P_v). Here the vessels are partly compressed and flow is determined by the arterial–alveolar pressure difference, which steadily increases down the zone. In zone 3 venous pressure now exceeds alveolar pressure and flow is determined by the arterial–venous pressure difference, which is constant down the line. However the pressure across the walls of the vessels increases down the zone so that their calibre increases and so does the flow. (After West J B 1977 Ventilation, blood flow and gas exchange, 3rd edn. Blackwell Scientific, Oxford)

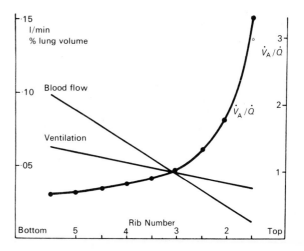

Fig. 9.24 Distribution of ventilation, blood flow and ventilation–perfusion ratio up the normal upright lung. Because blood flow falls more rapidly than ventilation with distance up the lung, the ventilation–perfusion ratio rises, slowly at first, then rapidly. (West J B 1977, Ventilation, blood flow and gas exchange, 3rd. edn. Blackwell Scientific, Oxford)

So far as oxygenation of the blood is concerned, an important factor is the ratio of ventilation to blood flow in different parts of the lungs, known as the alveolar ventilation ($\dot{V}$A)–pulmonary capillary blood flow ($\dot{Q}$C) ratio or the ventilation–perfusion ratio. This varies from 3.3 at the apex to 0.63 at the base of the lungs (Fig. 9.24).

Pulmonary blood volume

The total blood volume in the body is about 5 litres of which 1.8 l, or 1.14 l per m² body surface area, are within the thorax — the intra-thoracic blood volume. The pulmonary blood volume is 1.18 l, or 0.77 l per m² or 29 per cent of the total blood volume. The estimate of pulmonary blood volume includes about 100 ml in the pulmonary capillaries.

The pulmonary blood volume is not constant but varies widely under a variety of conditions, the changes being brought about by the transference of blood from the lungs to the systemic circulation and vice versa. While these changes are occurring the outputs of the two ventricles must momentarily be unequal. Because the volume of blood in the lungs can vary so much and is apparently in excess of that required for respiratory function, the concept has arisen that the lungs act as a blood reservoir. The reserve blood in the lungs is important in determining the diastolic filling of the left side of the heart and thus the stroke volume and output of the left ventricle.

Complex changes in the pulmonary circulation occur during normal breathing. With the fall of intra-thoracic pressure during inspiration there is an increased filling of the right ventricle and therefore an increased right ventricular output. The mean pulmonary arterial pressure rises, causing distension of the pulmonary blood vessels and an increase in pulmonary volume. At the same time the capacity of the pulmonary vascular bed increases but, in spite of the increased pulmonary artery inflow volume, the pulmonary venous outflow decreases, resulting in a reduction in left ventricular outflow and a small fall in systemic blood pressure. In expiration the increased volume of blood in the lungs is expelled through the pulmonary veins with the result that the left ventricular output increases, causing a rise in systemic blood pressure. Simultaneously the higher intra-thoracic pressure reduces the return of blood to the right ventricle and the mean pulmonary arterial pressure falls.

Other factors modify pulmonary blood volume. It is greater in the supine than in the erect position. The application of intermittent positive pressure artificial respiration reduces pulmonary blood volume, as does venesection. Procedures such as warming the body, general and spinal anaesthesia, and injection of systemic vasodilator drugs, for example, amyl nitrate and nitro-

glycerine, cause displacement of appreciable quantities of blood from the thorax. Thus changes in vascular tone in the systemic circulation causing changes in systemic blood volume lead to inverse changes in pulmonary blood volume.

The volume of blood in the lungs increases if a back-pressure is imposed on the pulmonary circulation by a rise in left atrial pressure, such as results from mitral stenosis. In left ventricular failure, the left atrial pressure and the pulmonary blood volume increase.

Regulation of pulmonary blood vessels

It is evident, then, that an important determinant of the pulmonary arterial pressure is the cardiac output. Thus in exercise, when cardiac output increases several-fold, there is usually an accompanying rise in pulmonary arterial pressure (Fig. 9.25).

Active changes in calibre of the pulmonary blood vessels can also occur, thereby altering pulmonary vascular resistance and pulmonary arterial pressure. Vasoconstriction is caused by the stimulation of sympathetic fibres going to the lungs, and by injections of adrenaline, noradrenaline and 5-hydroxytryptamine. Certain reflexes also modify the pulmonary vascular resistance; thus stimulation of the carotid sinus baroreceptors causes a decrease in pulmonary vascular resistance, whereas stimulation of the carotid body

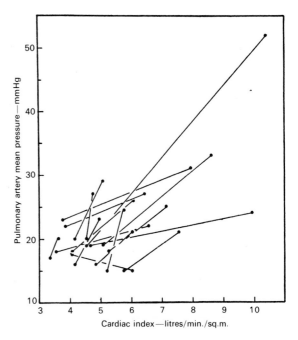

Fig. 9.25 Mean pulmonary arterial pressure and cardiac output at rest and during the fifth minute of exercise in 16 normal subjects. Individual resting and exercise values are joined. (From Donald K W et al 1955 Clinical Science 14:37)

chemoreceptors increases pulmonary vascular resistance. There is still doubt, however, about the functional significance of the sympathetic innervation to the lungs in man.

A particularly potent constrictor agent is hypoxia. Acute hypoxia causes a rise in pulmonary arterial pressure from constriction of the small pulmonary vessels involving both arterioles and venules. This is the result of a direct effect of hypoxic alveolar air or of unsaturated blood in the vessels. An increase in cardiac output is also partly responsible for the rise in pulmonary arterial pressure. Chronic hypoxia at high altitudes causes a rise in pulmonary arterial-pressure (Table 9.26); the pressure returns to normal if the subject is brought down to sea level. At high altitudes breathing is much deeper than at sea level (p. 159) and a reduction of intra-thoracic pressure (p. 130) combined with increased capillary pressure may account for pulmonary oedema in mountain climbers and in mountain cattle (Brisket disease). Chronic disease of the lungs with hypoxia leads to generalised pulmonary

Table 9.26 Pressure in pulmonary artery in relation to altitude and arterial hypoxia

Altitude		Mean pulmonary arterial pressure	Arterial oxygen saturation
(ft)	(m)	(mmHg)	(%)
0	0	13	97
5 280	1610	16	95
10 150	3094	25	92
14 900	4542	28	78

After J H K Vogel et al 1962 Lancet 2: 233

vasoconstriction, persistent increase in mean pulmonary arterial pressure and, ultimately, to failure of the right ventricle. Localised hypoxia in poorly ventilated areas of the lungs causes local vasoconstriction, so that blood is diverted to better aerated parts of the lung. An increase in alveolar P_{CO_2} also causes pulmonary vasoconstriction.

Dilatation of the pulmonary blood vessels occurs in response to injections of acetycholine.

FURTHER READING

Daly I de B 1966 Pulmonary and bronchial vascular systems. Arnold, London

Gibson G J 1984 Clinical tests of respiratory function. McMillan, London

Guz A 1975 Regulation of respiration in man. Annual Review of Physiology 37: 303–323

Macklem P T 1978 Respiratory mechanics. Annual Review of Physiology 40: 157–184

Weibel E R 1973 Morphological basis of alveolar capillary gas exchange. Physiological Review 53: 419–495

West J B 1974 Respiratory physiology — the essentials. Williams and Wilkins, Baltimore

West J B 1982 Pulmonary pathophysiology — the essentials. Williams and Wilkins, Baltimore

West J B 1983 Ventilation, blood flow and gas exchange, 4th edn. Blackwell Scientific, Oxford

10

Respiratory gases and the control of breathing

Transport of gases in the blood

To understand the way in which gases are carried in the blood we must first explain what is meant by *gas tension* and *gas content*. In the gaseous phase the partial pressure of a gas (P) is given by its percentage of the total pressure. For example, oxygen occupies 20.9 per cent of dry room air at a barometric pressure of approximately 760 mmHg: that is, the partial pressure of O_2 (Po_2) is $20.9/100 \times 760 = 160$ mmHg. If room air is allowed to equilibrate with a solution then at equilibrium the number of O_2 molecules entering the liquid would be the same as those leaving it and the partial pressure of O_2 in the liquid would also be 160 mmHg. We refer to this as the *tension* of the gas in the liquid or gaseous phase. The actual amount of O_2 dissolved in the water can be calculated from its solubility coefficient. Each millilitre of water contains 0.00003 ml of oxygen for every mmHg partial pressure to which it is exposed (Henry's Law). For the example above, the oxygen content of 1.0 ml of water exposed to a partial pressure of 160 mmHg would be $0.00003 \times 160 = 0.0048$ ml per ml H_2O at 37 °C. In the lungs the end-capillary blood is nearly in equilibrium with the gas present in the alveolus at an oxygen tension of 100 mmHg and so the tension of gases in the end-capillary blood (P_c) are approximately the same as those in alveolar air (P_A). The same calculation indicates $0.00003 \times 100 = 0.003$ ml O_2 per ml of solution as the amount of gas that can be carried in solution assuming there were no haemoglobin to facilitate transport. Table 10.1 indicates the contents of the three important respiratory gases in saline in equilibrium with air with those for arterial and venous blood.

For O_2 and CO_2 the contents in arterial and venous blood are much higher than those in a simple salt solution, suggesting that they are both carried in combination. For nitrogen, however, the contents in all three fluids are the same, showing that there is no carrier for this gas in blood.

We could draw an analogy between the *tension* and *content* of the gas in solution and the *voltage* and *current* delivered by a battery. Both a small transistor battery

Table 10.1 Content of oxygen, carbon dioxide and nitrogen in saline in equilibrium with air at body temperature compared with corresponding figures for arterial and venous blood. All results expressed as ml per litre of solution or blood.

Medium	Oxygen	Carbon dioxide	Nitrogen
Saline	3	26	9
Arterial blood	190	540	9
Venous blood	140	580	9

and a car battery can deliver 12 volts but the latter has considerably more current.

Estimation of oxygen and carbon dioxide in blood

We can estimate the total gas content of a solution or in blood by exposing it to a vacuum and measuring the total amount of gas evolved. Haldane, in his classical experiments, used potassium ferricyanide to release the O_2 into a closed sealed container and measured the volume evolved and then used tartaric acid to drive off the CO_2. In the Van Slyke apparatus the blood is put into acidified air-free ferricyanide solution and subjected to a vacuum. The ferricyanide releases the O_2, the acid drives off the CO_2 and the vacuum extracts the nitrogen. The gas evolved is analysed by absorbing first the CO_2 and then the O_2.

If the amount of O_2 dissolved in plasma (0.3 ml/l) is subtracted from the total O_2 carried in the blood then a figure for the *oxygen content* carried by haemoglobin is obtained. If a further estimation is performed on the same blood, which has been shaken with O_2 to saturate it fully with the gas, we have determined the *oxygen capacity*. The *percentage saturation* of the first sample is given below:

$$\text{Oxygen saturation} = \frac{\text{oxygen content}}{\text{oxygen capacity}} \times 100$$

Since the light transmissions of haemoglobin and oxyhaemoglobin are different the oxygen saturation can be determined by shining a light through a vascular bed

— the ear lobe or a finger may be used. The light is absorbed by two photoelectric cells, one of which is covered by a blue and the other by a red filter. The ratio of the currents is related to the blood oxygen saturation. The instrument used is called an *oximeter* and has been used to follow changes in oxygen saturation in various clinical states such as during sleep and in pilots flying at high altitudes. It has the advantage that it is simple and non-invasive.

In current clinical practice O_2 and CO_2 tensions are usually measured by special O_2 and CO_2 electrodes. It is important that blood samples are not full of air bubbles and that they are analysed fairly soon after they have been taken, because metabolism will continue in the red cells and so alter the gas tension values. Samples may be stored on ice if delay is inevitable. In the oxygen analyser (Fig. 10.2) blood is placed opposite a platinum electrode covered by a polyethylene membrane permeable to oxygen molecules. These receive electrons from the electrode forming either H_2O_2 or OH^- ions. The current created is detected by a silver/silver chloride electrode placed in saturated potassium chloride. In the CO_2 electrode developed originally by Severinghaus (Fig. 10.3) the CO_2 tension is detected by a pH-sensitive glass electrode covered with cellophane and soaked in bicarbonate solution. The CO_2 passes through a teflon membrane that is permeable to CO_2 molecules but not to hydrogen ions. Once CO_2 is adjacent to the electrode it combines with water to form hydrogen ions and the pH change is proportional to the CO_2 tension in the blood. These electrodes have been modified subsequently so that they can be inserted into various tissues experimentally and more recently cutaneous sensors of Po_2 and Pco_2 have been developed. These

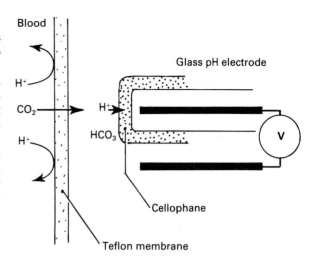

Fig. 10.3 Carbon dioxide electrode shown schematically. CO_2 will penetrate a teflon membrane whereas hydrogen ions will not. Once past the membrane the CO_2 dissociates to form hydrogen ions, which will be measured by the glass pH electrode. The fall in pH will be proportional to the CO_2 tension in the blood.

methods offer considerable advantages over arterial sampling Po_2 and Pco_2 analysis but demand that the skin be adequately vasodilated and the results may be affected by changes in local blood flow.

Transport of oxygen

Oxygen is carried to the periphery both as dissolved oxygen and in combination with haemoglobin. As we have seen, the amount dissolved in solutions obeys Henry's law, that is, the amount dissolved depends upon the partial pressure of the gas to which it is exposed. One litre of plasma from normal arterial blood contains about 3 ml of dissolved oxygen. This is clearly inadequate to meet the tissue demands since an adult at rest consumes about 250 ml of O_2 every minute and would therefore need a cardiac output of about 83 l/min. Haemoglobin consists of four haem molecules attached to the protein globin (p. 26); it is the protein fraction of the globin that determines which particular form of haemoglobin is present. Normal adult haemoglobin (HbA) consists of two alpha and two beta chains. Each haem group is a binding site for one O_2 molecule and therefore each haemoglobin molecule can combine with up to four molecules of oxygen. When some of the binding sites are occupied a change occurs in the arrangement of protein subunits and affinity for O_2 molecules is then further increased. This co-operation between the four binding sites for oxygen is an example of an allosteric effect. We can investigate the avidity of oxygen for haemoglobin by constructing an *oxygen dissociation curve*. If we take a series of glass vessels

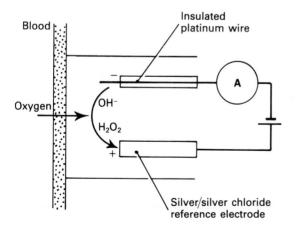

Fig. 10.2 Diagrammatic representation of an oxygen electrode. Oxygen molecules having passed through a polyethylene membrane receive electrons from a platinum electrode, forming OH^- or H_2O_2. The current that passes to the reference silver/silver chloride electrode is proportional to the oxygen tension in the blood.

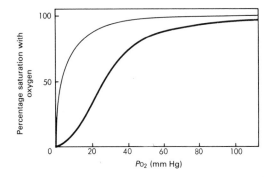

Fig. 10.4 Oxygen dissociation curves of myoglobin (thin line) and haemoglobin (thick line) at $P_{CO_2} = 40$ mmHg.

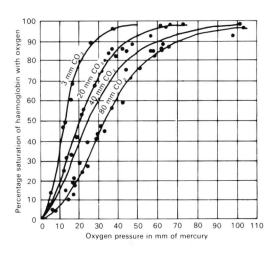

Fig. 10.5 Oxygen dissociation curves of human blood exposed to partial pressures of 3, 20, 40 and 80 mmHg of CO_2.

containing a small amount of blood and shake them continuously in a water bath at 37°C, exposing each one to a different O_2 tension, we can measure the oxygen saturation (that is, the oxygen content of the sample divided by oxygen capacity of the sample and expressed as a percentage) at different O_2 tensions. Figure 10.4 shows the relationship obtained between O_2 saturation and P_{O_2}. It is sigmoid in shape; this relationship has the advantage that it makes the O_2 uptake in the lungs efficient because virtually all the haemoglobin binding sites become full even before the O_2 tension has reached that in the alveoli (100 mmHg). The position of this sigmoid curve can be expressed by stating the P_{O_2} at which the haemoglobin is 50 per cent saturated (P_{50}). For normal arterial blood in man the P_{50} is about 26 mmHg. Also in Figure 10.4 the dissociation curve for myoglobin, which has only one haem moiety, is shown — it is a simple hyperbola with a P_{50} of about 6 mmHg. Myoglobin can thus accept oxygen from haemoglobin and deliver it to the mitochondria with considerable reserve even when the tissue P_{O_2} is very low.

Several factors influence the availability of oxygen in peripheral tissue, or, in effect, the position of the oxygen dissociation curve defined by its P_{50} value: P_{CO_2} (the *Bohr effect*), [H⁺], temperature and 2,3-bisphosphoglycerate (2,3 BPG).

In 1910, Bohr showed that the position, and therefore the amount of oxygen given up for the same oxygen tension, depended upon the P_{CO_2} in the gas mixture, and the higher the P_{CO_2} the further to the right the curve was shifted (Fig. 10.5). Shortly afterwards, Barcroft found that this displacement could be produced by any acid, so that a rise in H⁺ ion concentration (or fall in pH) shifted the curve in the same direction. A rise in temperature also shifts the dissociation curve to the right. These shifts are advantageous because blood will give up its oxygen more readily. These effects are most clearly illustrated by the example

of skeletal muscle in which all three factors operate together to increase the amount of oxygen released from the blood. Similarly, in the lungs the Bohr effect means that more oxygen will be taken up since the blood is exposed to a lower alveolar CO_2 tension ($P_A{CO_2}$), and this is enhanced by the fall in H⁺ concentration as the blood traverses the pulmonary capillary.

Another factor that has an important influence on the oxygen dissociation curve is the concentration of 2,3-BPG. The reduced haemoglobin molecule can bind one molecule of 2,3-BPG fairly tightly in a site between its two beta chains, whereas oxyhaemoglobin, with its different molecular configuration, binds BPG poorly, if at all. The presence of 2,3-BPG stabilises the reduced haemoglobin and its affinity for oxygen is diminished — shifting the oxygen dissociation curve to the right. The concentration of 2,3-BPG inside the red cell is not constant and increases in anaemia and in situations of chronic hypoxia, whether due to residence at high altitude or to the presence of chronic lung or heart disease. As a result the unloading of oxygen is facilitated in peripheral tissues. If blood is stored at 37°C for 24 hours most of the BPG is lost and this is why it is stored at low temperatures, but despite this, progressive reduction in 2,3-BPG occurs.

In man the oxygen tension in systemic arteries ($P_a{O_2}$) is about 95 mmHg, the $P_a{CO_2}$ is about 40 mmHg, and arterial blood is 95 to 98 per cent saturated with oxygen when it leaves the pulmonary capillaries. In mixed venous blood the oxygen tension has fallen to 40 mmHg and this still represents 70 per cent saturation. When fully saturated each gram of haemoglobin can carry 1.39 ml of O_2. Table 10.6 shows the data we have derived so far concerning oxygen carriage in the blood.

Table 10.6 Oxygen carriage in blood

Oxygen	Arterial blood	Mixed venous blood
Partial pressure (mmHg)	95	40
Content (ml per 100 ml whole blood)	19	14
Haemoglobin concentration (g per 100 ml)	14.4	14.4
Capacity (ml/100 ml blood; 14.4 × 1.39)	20	20
Saturation (%)	95	70

The speed of the reaction between oxygen and haemoglobin is important because of the limited time available for oxygenation in the pulmonary capillary. This can be measured experimentally by driving a dilute haemoglobin solution or blood through one jet into a mixing chamber and salt-solution containing O_2 through another. The mixture is then forced rapidly along a narrow capillary and the combination of O_2 with haemoglobin can be assessed spectroscopically from the colour change. If a solution of haemoglobin is used 50 per cent saturation is achieved in about 0.003 s but if a suspension of red cells is used then 50 per cent saturation is achieved in 0.07 s. The slower rate is because O_2 has to penetrate the red cell membrane before it is able to attach itself to haemoglobin. In the normal human lung the red cells spend 0.5–0.75 s in the gas-exchange capillary and therefore the rate of this reaction

is unimportant in determining arterial P_aO_2. However, in anaemia or on severe exercise the rate of pulmonary blood flow is increased and one can imagine that the rate of reaction might become important. The release of oxygen in the tissues is also extremely rapid; 50 per cent can be released within 0.038 s.

The carriage of carbon dioxide in blood

As indicated already, CO_2 is carried not only in simple physical solution obeying Henry's Law but also in combination. At body temperature CO_2 is about 20 times more soluble than O_2, and at a P_{CO_2} of 40 mmHg 1 litre of saline would contain 26 ml of CO_2 whereas 1 litre of whole blood can carry between 500 and 600 ml. We can construct a CO_2 dissociation curve in a way similar to that of oxygen (p. 148) by exposing known amounts of blood to various partial pressures of CO_2 and measuring the gas *content* and *tension* in each sample. The results are shown in Figure 10.7 for both oxygenated and deoxygenated blood. Once present in solution it can be carried in three ways: (a) by the formation of bicarbonate, (b) in combination with plasma proteins, or (c) in combination with haemoglobin in the red cells.

First, it can be slowly hydrated to form bicarbonate and hydrogen ions as shown in the equation below:

$$H_2O + CO_2 = H_2CO_3 = H^+ + HCO_3^-$$

The reaction is extremely slow because it lacks a catalyst.

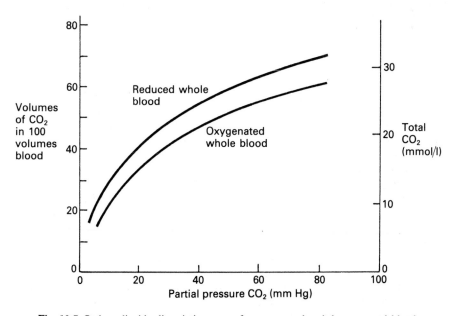

Fig. 10.7 Carbon dioxide dissociation curve for oxygenated and deoxygenated blood.

Secondly, also in plasma some CO_2 is taken up by plasma proteins to form carbamino compounds:

$$CO_2 + \text{protein-}NH_2 \quad = \text{protein-NHCOOH}$$
$$= \text{protein-NHCOO}^- + H^+$$

The H^+ produced in the reaction are buffered by plasma proteins and phosphates.

When CO_2 diffuses into the red cell it is very rapidly converted into bicarbonate and hydrogen ions, as shown below, by the enzyme carbonic anhydrase present in the red cell. This enzyme, discovered by Roughton, increases the speed of this reaction some 13,000 times compared with that in plasma. The hydrogen ions formed are buffered by the protein part of the haemoglobin molecule:

$$CO_2 + H_2O \rightleftharpoons H_2CO_3 \rightleftharpoons H + HCO_3$$

$$H^+ + KHb = K^+ + HHB$$

The speed of the reaction that forms bicarbonate means that the concentration of HCO_3^- ions is much greater in the red cells than in the plasma and accordingly HCO_3^- passes back into the plasma by diffusion. Since the cations such as Na^+ and K^+ cannot pass easily through the red cell membrane, other anions (particularly Cl^-) pass into the cell to maintain electrical neutrality (the Hamburger shift). This results in a lower Cl^- concentration in venous blood (by about 2 per cent) than in arterial blood. This explains why two-thirds of the CO_2 carried in the blood is carried as HCO_3^- in the plasma although the majority of the buffering occurs in the red cells. When venous blood is oxygenated in the lung the chloride shift is reversed. If we inhibit the enzyme carbonic anhydrase by the drug acetazolamide the rapid conversion of CO_2 is inhibited in the red cells and blood CO_2 tension rises.

The third way in which CO_2 is carried is in combination with haemoglobin to form carbamino-haemoglobin:

$$CO_2 + \text{Hb-}NH_2 = \text{Hb-NHCOOH}$$
$$= \text{HbNHCOO}^- + H^+$$

This rapid reaction does not require a catalyst. Although the carbamino-haemoglobin accounts for less than 10 per cent of the total CO_2 carried in blood it is mobile and easily exchanged and so of importance physiologically. This explains why about one-quarter of the change in CO_2 content between arterial and venous blood can be accounted for by the change in CO_2 bound as carbamino-haemoglobin.

The hydrogen ions produced by the carriage of CO_2 are buffered by both haemoglobin and by phosphate esters in the red cells. It has been shown that at normal

metabolic rates the red cell haemoglobin can accommodate all the H^+ ions produced without a change in intracellular pH but at higher metabolic demands the other buffering systems are used.

The amount of CO_2 that can be carried in whole blood is influenced by the O_2 tension in the blood (the Haldane effect, Fig. 10.7). Just as deoxygenated blood can carry more CO_2 than oxygenated blood, so reduced haemoglobin can carry more carbamino-bound CO_2 than oxyhaemoglobin. The importance of haemoglobin in the carriage of CO_2 can be shown in its effects on breathing oxygen under pressure. At 3 atmospheres of pure oxygen the alveolar O_2 tension ($P_A O_2$) is given by $3 \times (P_B - P_{CO_2} - P_{H_2O})$ or $3 \times (760 - 40 - 47)$ giving an alveolar P_{O_2} of 2193 mmHg. From Henry's law (p. 147) the amount of oxygen carried in 100 ml of plasma would be 2193×0.003 or 6.6 ml. This would be sufficient, then, to provide oxygen for the metabolic needs of the body at rest and there would be no need for oxyhaemoglobin to part with its oxygen. Since the CO_2-carrying capacity of oxyhaemoglobin is less than that of haemoglobin, the tissue P_{CO_2} rises and stimulates the respiratory centre. This paradoxical stimulation of ventilation with its consequent lowering of alveolar and arterial P_{CO_2} is also seen to a smaller extent when pure oxygen is breathed at normal atmospheric pressure, though an initial fall in ventilation is more commonly seen due to the withdrawal of the normal peripheral chemoreceptor drive (p. 153).

Table 10.8 shows how CO_2 is carried in the various components of blood. As can be seen, about 75 per cent CO_2 is carried in the plasma. The factors involved in the transport of CO_2 and of O_2 have been summarised by Roughton in Figures 10.9 and 10.10, which illustrate the gases' uptake and release in the peripheral tissues and lungs.

Table 10.8 Carbon dioxide carriage in blood

	Arterial blood	Mixed venous blood
CO_2 tension (mmHg)	40	46
CO_2 content (ml/litre blood)		
In 600 ml of plasma		
In solution	15	18
As bicarbonate	340	362
Total	355	380
In 400 ml of red cells		
In solution	9	8
As bicarbonate	93	99
As carbamino-haemoglobin	23	33
Total	125	140
Total CO_2 content	480	520

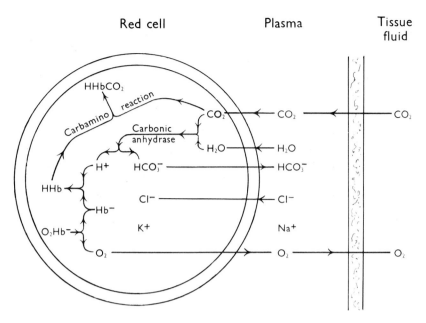

Fig. 10.9 Schematic summary of the chemical processes that occur when haemoglobin parts with its O_2 and takes up CO_2 in the tissues.

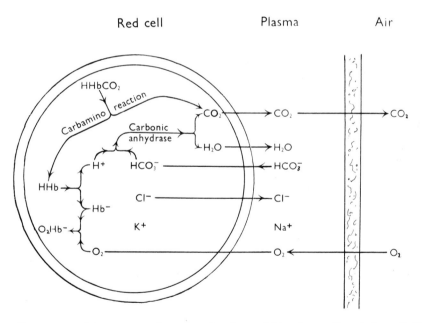

Fig. 10.10 Schematic summary of the processes that occur when haemoglobin takes up O_2 and gives off CO_2 in the lungs.

CONTROL OF BREATHING

Although we may not be consciously aware of it we are continually altering our breathing by changes in the depth of each breath and in its duration. This is so that we can carry out our normal activities such as talking and eating. The actual characteristics of a breath are determined by the outputs from the respiratory centres situated in the pons and medulla. There are many inputs to this centre and Dornhorst has described the respiratory centre as a computer that receives information from the brain, muscles and tissues via nerves

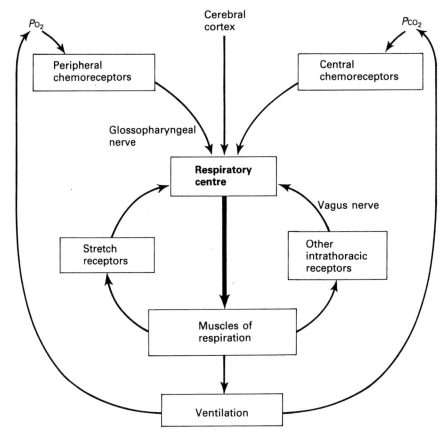

Fig. 10.11 Diagrammatic representation of the inputs to the respiratory centre that generate the output to the respiratory muscles.

and from the blood by chemical stimuli and from which it calculates the demand for ventilation. A diagrammatic representation of the inputs to this computer is shown in Figure 10.11. We will first consider the important chemical input from the blood via the chemoreceptors to this computer.

Chemical regulation of respiration

The chemical regulation of respiration is maintained by central and peripheral chemoreceptors. Chemoreceptors are cells responsive to changes in gas or hydrogen ion concentration. There are two main groups, one of which is situated in the medulla and responds principally to CO_2 and the other group is found in the carotid and aortic bodies and responds principally to O_2.

Central chemoreceptors

The central chemoreceptors are situated in the medulla. If the CO_2 tension in arterial blood rises it also causes a rise in tissue CO_2 tension, which stimulates the central chemoreceptors to increase ventilation. There is good

evidence that the chemoreceptor cells sensitive to CO_2 are separate from those cells of the respiratory centre itself, although the chemoreceptor cells have not been localised histologically. Undoubtedly ventilation is increased when arterial P_aCO_2 rises and since the rise in P_aCO_2 in arterial blood and an increase in H^+ concentration in the CSF both stimulate the medullary chemoreceptors, it is pertinent to ask whether the effect of CO_2 is specific or whether it is due simply to the alteration of intracellular pH. Pappenheimer perfused the cerebral ventricles of goats with CSF of different PCO_2 and bicarbonate concentrations and found that ventilation was best stimulated by H^+ concentration close to the surface of the medulla. In intact man the increase in ventilation appears to be more related to arterial P_aCO_2. This may well be due to the fact that carbon dioxide passes rapidly through cell membranes whereas hydrogen ions penetrate cell membranes slowly. Since H^+ is formed when CO_2 penetrates the cell membrane the final stimulus may in fact be an increase in the H^+ concentration within the chemoreceptor cells. The slow rise and fall in H⁺ in CSF fits in very well with the slower rise or fall in the depth and rate of respiration on breathing gas mixtures rich in CO_2 and their removal, rather than with changes in arterial $P\text{CO}_2$.

Carotid body chemoreceptors

Chemoreceptors sensitive to changes in $P_a\text{O}_2$ in arterial blood are found in carotid and aortic bodies but in man the carotid bodies are by far the more important. They do respond slightly to changes in arterial CO_2 or H⁺ concentration but these have more profound effects on the central group of chemoreceptors. The carotid bodies are structures about 5 mm in diameter situated at the junction of the internal, external and common carotid arteries. Although they weigh only about 10 mg they are exquisitely sensitive to *hypoxia* (hypoxaemia, low $P_a\text{O}_2$); their blood flow is the highest of any organ in the body when related to organ weight and they are ideally suited to detect changes in arterial $P_a\text{O}_2$. Lack of oxygen results in hyperventilation but after denervation or removal of the carotid bodies the same degree of hypoxia produces very little, if any, change in breathing.

The carotid bodies consist of a large number of glomus cells surrounded by a large collection of nerve endings. They are supplied by efferent sympathetic fibres from the superior cervical ganglia and other efferent fibres from the vagus and glossopharyngeal nerves. Afferent impulses pass in the carotid sinus nerve via the glossopharyngeal nerve to the brain stem. If humans are given pure O_2 to breathe respiration is depressed and this implies that even at a normal $P_a\text{O}_2$ there is some information being fed to the brain stem from the carotid bodies. The carotid bodies contain acetylcholine, dopamine and catecholamines, which could act as transmitters to stimulate the nerve endings but the exact nature of the transmitter is still unknown. Hypoxia and *hypercapnia* (raised $P_a\text{CO}_2$) cause an increase in blood flow through the carotid body but a fall in oxygen consumption so long as the sympathetic nerves are intact. After section of these nerves total blood flow may increase by about 30 per cent. Stimulation of the sympathetic nerves to the carotid body reduces the blood flow and increases chemoreceptor discharge in response to hypoxia and also increases the tidal volume. Recordings from the carotid sinus nerve suggest that the discharge from the carotid body is inversely related to the oxygen usage and not to its blood flow. Since sympathetic nervous activity is increased by limb movements it has been proposed that the increase in respiration occurring a few seconds after the beginning of exercise may be related to an increase in chemoreceptor activity. Chronic hypoxia decreases the dopamine content of the carotid body in experimental animals and the complex interaction between the sympathetic nerves, blood flow and chemoreceptor discharge requires considerably more research. The aortic bodies, which are situated around the arch of the aorta in humans, have very little effect on respiration and are more concerned with cardiovascular reflexes (p. 94).

Also within the carotid sinus are the baroreceptors responsible for conveying information to the brain about systemic blood pressure (p. 93). A rise in blood pressure tends to depress respiration. This may be seen in an animal into which adrenaline is injected; as the blood pressure rises, breathing may stop (adrenaline apnoea). Similarly, if the two common carotid arteries are clamped the pressure within the carotid body falls and this results in an increase in respiration and blood pressure. Section of the carotid sinus nerve abolishes this response. The effects of catecholamines do not appear to be mediated directly via the respiratory centre since injection into the vertebral or internal carotid arteries does not produce apnoea.

The respiratory centre

The organisation of the respiratory centre is complex. Information about its input and output have been obtained from a variety of experiments in which nerves providing afferent information have been cut or sections have been made through various parts of the brain stem. Micro-electrodes have also been used to stimulate or record from localised areas of the brain stem in animals. The results of all these studies have been interpreted in a variety of ways and several alternative models have been constructed in an attempt to explain all the findings.

In experiments in anaesthetised animals sections can be cut progressively from above down to mid-brain and result in no change in respiration. This does not imply that we have no control from higher centres on the pattern of respiration; we obviously must have, since we control our respiration when speaking. Figure 10.12 shows the results that Lumsden obtained with progressive caudal sections of the brain stem in cats. If he sectioned the lower medulla at level 6 respiration ceased because the output of the respiratory centre travels via the phrenic nerve (C3, C4 and C5) and intercostal nerves to the intercostal muscles. The respiratory centres lie between levels 1 and 6. Sectioning the vagi of an experimental animal with an intact brain stem removes the afferent information to the brain stem from the stretch receptors within the chest and respiration becomes slower and deeper, an outcome suggesting that the pulmonary stretch receptors (p. 155) have an important modifying role on the inherent rhythm of the respiratory centre. Section of the brain stem between levels 2 and 3 produces prolonged inspiration (apneusis), which prompted the suggestion that the

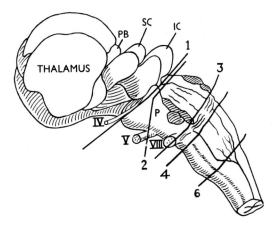

Fig. 10.12 Diagram (not to scale) of the brain stem of a cat to show the position of sections that produced the alterations in respiratory rhythm. PB, pineal body; SC and IC, superior and inferior colliculi; P, pons; IV, V, VIII, cranial nerves. (Lumsden T 1923 Journal of Physiology 57: 153, 354; 58: 81, 111)

respiration. These experiments were conducted with the vagus nerve cut on both sides. If the vagal fibres, which pass mainly to the lower part of the medulla, are left intact breathing remains regular. Thus to maintain rhythmic respiration the respiratory centres in the caudal part of the medulla must be influenced either by the pneumotaxic centre or by afferent impulses travelling in the vagi.

Microelectrodes have been used to record or stimulate localised areas of the brain stem. The results of these studies have been interpreted in a variety of ways and Burns has suggested that there are two independent networks of neurones, inspiratory and expiratory, with a reciprocal innervation between the two (Fig. 10.13).

Von Euler (Fig. 10.14) has suggested that the rhythmic pattern of breathing may be related to the generation of an increasing inspiratory drive from some neurones (inspiratory ramp generator) whose output then drives a second neuronal pool and which also receive afferent information from the lungs by the vagus. The output from the neuronal pool therefore increases with time during inspiration and when a threshold level is reached a further group of neurones is triggered, which then turns off inspiration (the inspiratory off-switch). It is this last centre that seems

upper group of neurones (the control or pneumotaxic centre) are responsible for a lower (caudal) group. Section at level 4 further caudally results in gasping

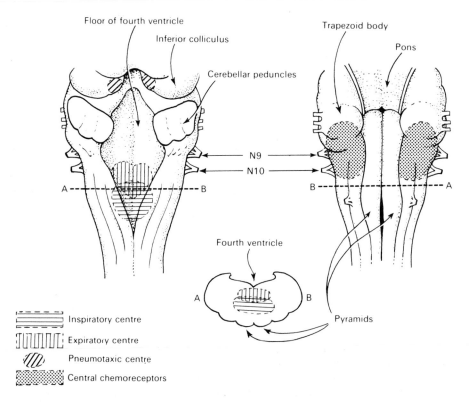

Fig. 10.13 Diagrams of the medulla and pons of the cat to show the areas involved in control of respiration. (Compiled from diagrams by various authors)

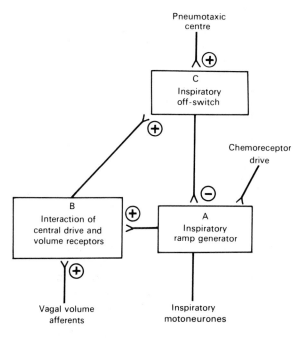

Fig. 10.14 Simplified model of the brain stem mechanisms responsible for the generation of rhythmic breathing movements. The neurones in the ramp generator (A) slowly increase their inspiratory activity and are influenced mainly by the chemoreceptor drive. This activity interacts with information about the volume of the lungs arriving through the vagus (B), and this eventually reaches the threshold of the off-switch (C). When that discharges, the inspiratory ramp generator is reset. (After J. G. Widdicombe).

to receive an input from the pontine pneumotaxic centre.

Undoubtedly the respiratory centre has an inherent rhythm of its own. However, stimulation of certain parts of the cortex increase respiratory movements whereas stimulation of other cortical areas inhibits them. As one might expect, cooling the medulla slows respiration and pyrexia increases it. During sleep the respiratory centre becomes less active and alveolar ventilation is reduced increasing the $P_a\text{CO}_2$ value. The output of the respiratory centres passes via both sides of the spinal cord down to the cervical and thoracic segments for the phrenic and intercostal nerve roots.

Reflex regulation of respiration
Undoubtedly the most important input to the respiratory centre is the information provided by the central chemoreceptors in the medulla. The activity of the respiratory centre is modified by afferent impulses that are arriving continuously in the vagus nerve from stretch receptors in the lung and chest wall, in the glosso-

pharyngeal nerves from the carotid body and carotid sinuses and, thirdly, from the cerebral cortex. When the lungs expand, stretch receptors present in the airways increase their discharge rate and this information inhibits the respiratory centre. Inflation of the lungs or stimulation of the central cut end of the vagus nerve in an anaesthetised animal arrests inspiration. This inhibition of respiration by inflation of the lung was first described in 1868 by Hering and Breuer and is called the Hering–Breuer inflation reflex. After section of the vagus in animals inspiration becomes prolonged and the frequency of respiration is reduced. In man, however, the blocking of both vagi by a local anaesthetic does not alter the pattern of respiration but it does substantially affect the degree and pattern of response to respiratory stimuli like CO_2 and reduces the unpleasant sensation associated with rebreathing and breath-holding, suggesting that receptors for these mechanisms are present within the chest. If a subject is asked to breathe through a resistance in the mouthpiece, tidal volume increases immediately without a change in respiratory rate. The response is too quick for any change in blood gas tensions and is not abolished by vagal blockade. It seems likely that the information is coming from receptors in the chest wall. Many other reflex alterations of breathing have been described and may arise from the receptors in the lungs, heart or large vessels. It has been shown that there are juxta-capillary receptors (J receptors) in the lungs (p. 141) that are probably responsible for information about lung collapse or increased capillary pressure within the lungs; these send their impulses via the vagus to increase respiration. Venous distension of the great veins close to the heart also results in a stimulation of respiration. Swallowing inhibits breathing via the glossopharyngeal nerve. Application of cold water to the skin results in hyperventilation but if the face is stimulated by very cold water apnoea occurs. Although this effect has been demonstrated in man, the *diving reflex* is more obvious in diving animals, in which it results in a redistribution of a reduced cardiac output preferentially to the heart and brain and the blood flow to muscles that can tolerate anaerobic metabolism is virtually zero. This redistribution of blood enables a diving mammal to swim considerable distances underwater without returning to the surface for air.

The cerebral cortex has an effect on respiration in the performance of various involuntary manoeuvres. A *cough* is a sudden expiratory effort, usually initiated by tracheal receptors or irritant receptors deeper in the airway, against a closed glottis, which then opens and intrabronchial material is expelled. The intra-tracheal pressure may reach 100 mmHg and the air velocity 500 mph. A *sneeze* is the same reflex but the stimulus is from the nasal passages and the airflow is directed through the nose with the mouth closed.

Relation between ventilation and blood gases

Carbon dioxide

Carbon dioxide stimulates ventilation by acting principally on the central chemoreceptors and alveolar ventilation (V_A) and P_aCO_2 are inversely related. If we double alveolar ventilation we halve P_aCO_2, providing CO_2 production is unaltered. Research workers have tried to use ventilation as an overall index of the output of the respiratory centre. The ventilatory response to CO_2 can be measured in two ways but it is important to prevent any hypoxic stimulus during the test and so the gas contains a high O_2 content to silence the peripheral chemoreceptors. Either CO_2 is added to the inspired gas and measurements made of end-tidal CO_2 tension and ventilation (p. 136) — the steady-state method — or the subject rebreathes into a closed circuit and the CO_2 is allowed to accumulate (rebreathing method). Figure 10.15 shows the CO_2 response line obtained using the steady-state method and from which the slope (sensitivity) and intercept (threshold) can be measured. These have been shown to be altered in various disease states.

The overall effect of the increase in ventilation in response to CO_2 is to minimise the change in P_aO_2 and is a good example of the body's homeostatic mechanisms. For most purposes the important measurement is arterial PCO_2 and this is measured in hospital practice by electro-chemical methods (p. 147). Where these methods are not available, indirect methods may be used. End-tidal PCO_2 should be an equilibrium with end pulmonary capillary PCO_2 and measurements of end-tidal CO_2 tension should be similar to arterial values. Unfortunately, there are difficulties in obtaining true alveolar air (p. 136) particularly in abnormal lungs. An alternative indirect approach has been based on the premise that P_aCO_2 is about 6 mmHg less than mixed venous tension. The mixed venous PCO_2 (P_vCO_2) can be estimated by a rebreathing technique. The subject is asked to breathe into a bag containing one or one and a half litres of oxygen for about 90 seconds or until an increase in the depth or rate of respiration is noticed. The bag then contains a mixture of gases with a CO_2 tension slightly higher than that in mixed venous blood. After a suitable recovery period the subject rebreathes the gas mixture in the bag for a further 20 seconds to achieve exact equilibration between the bag and mixed

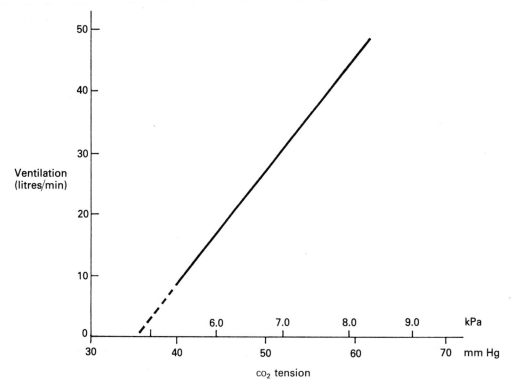

Fig. 10.15 The ventilatory response to CO_2 using the steady-state method. CO_2 is added to the inspired gas and the minute ventilation is measured. The slope indicates sensitivity to CO_2 and intercept on the CO_2 axis the threshold of the response.

venous blood before recirculation occurs. Analysis of the CO_2 in the bag gives the mixed venous CO_2 tension and some workers subtract 6 mmHg to obtain an estimate of arterial P_{CO_2}.

Oxygen

Alveolar oxygen tension (P_aO_2) is not regulated as precisely as P_aCO_2. At sea level the inspired oxygen can be lowered from 21 to 13 per cent without any marked alteration in breathing. Not only are the peripheral chemoreceptors least sensitive in this range but also any increase in ventilation lowers arterial P_{CO_2} and so reduces the central chemoreceptor drive to breathe. Below this level the subject becomes cyanosed (see below) with a bluish tinge in their tongue, lips and fingers. The ventilatory response to hypoxia can be measured either by a steady-state or rebreathing technique but it has to be somewhat more complicated than that for CO_2 because of the necessity to keep P_aCO_2 constant by adding CO_2. In patients with lung disease the end-tidal oxygen tension may not be representative of the arterial gas tension and so measurements of oxygen saturation using an ear oximeter (p. 89) are to be preferred. Some typical results are shown in Figure 10.16. The relation between P_aO_2 and ventilation is an hyperbola but the latter is linearly related to oxygen saturation.

DISORDERS OF RESPIRATION

Asphyxia

Asphyxia is the simultaneous lack of O_2 and increase in CO_2 in the blood seen, for example, in a person who develops acute airway obstruction or if he were to rebreathe his expired gas in a confined space with no fresh air. Respiration is stimulated in both depth and rate until it becomes violent gasps. Consciousness is lost and convulsions follow. Respiration then becomes slower and deeper, then more infrequent before death ensues in a few minutes.

Hypoxia

Hypoxia is a clinical term for a lack of oxygen supply to the tissues. As we have seen already it may arise from many causes — high altitude, diseases of the heart or lungs or an inadequate amount of haemoglobin in the blood. The effects of hypoxia are predominantly on the brain, causing confusion, restlessness, hallucinations and loss of consciousness. There are four types: hypoxic, anaemic, stagnant and histotoxic.

In *hypoxic hypoxia* the arterial P_{O_2} is low; this state may be due to chronic lung disease, respiratory muscle failure with inadequate ventilation or as a result of right-to-left shunts in congenital heart disease. The arterial desaturation stimulates the peripheral chemoreceptors to increase ventilation (p. 94) and cardiac output

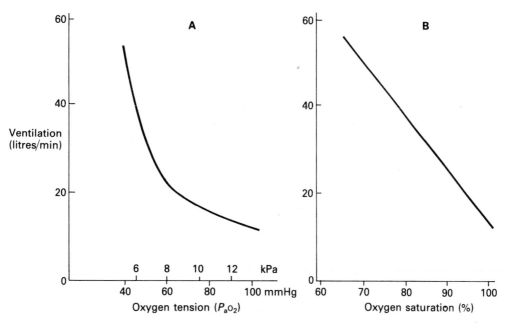

Fig. 10.16 The ventilatory response to hypoxia. As the subject breathes a hypoxic gas mixture CO_2 is added to the gas to maintain the alveolar and arterial CO_2 tension constant. In part A the ventilatory response is plotted against the oxygen tension and is hyperbolic. If plotted against oxygen saturation measured by an oximeter the relation is linear (B).

increases in an attempt to improve tissue oxygenation. If the hypoxaemia persists it also stimulates production of erythropoietin from the kidney (secondary polycythaemia). In chronic lung disease the low arterial O_2 tension results from a poor alveolar P_aO_2 and this will provoke pulmonary vasoconstriction (p. 145), pulmonary hypertension, right ventricular muscle hypertrophy and eventually heart failure.

In *anaemic hypoxia* the amount of oxygen-carrying haemoglobin is reduced either by anaemia or because the haemoglobin binding sites are already full. The latter state is most commonly due to carbon monoxide, which has an affinity for haemoglobin 250 times greater than oxygen. The arterial oxygen tension is normal but the content is reduced. Even inhalation of 0.1 per cent carbon monoxide may produce dangerous hypoxia. Blood from a non-smoker may contain up to 0.4 per cent carboxyhaemoglobin whereas a smoker's blood may contain 10 per cent or more. Carbon monoxide binds even more avidly to myoglobin than to haemoglobin so that tissue oxygen transport may be affected to an even greater extent, with subsequent damage to the oxygen-dependent cells in the central nervous system. The cardiac output is increased but ventilation is stimulated little because the chemoreceptors are sensitive to O_2 tension not content. Anaemia also increases 2,3-BPG (p. 148), shifting the oxygen dissociation curve to the right; this also enables more oxygen to be given up at a lower tissue P_O_2. Drugs such as chlorates and nitrates may convert haemoglobin into methaemoglobin and it is then unable to carry oxygen; anaemic hypoxia results.

Stagnant hypoxia is caused by either intense local vasoconstriction or a poor cardiac output. The arterial blood may have a normal P_aO_2 but the oxygen extraction is very high because of the low blood flow and the blood emerges from the vascular bed almost completely desaturated.

Histotoxic hypoxia is rare but if seen is most often due to cyanide poisoning. Cyanide poisons the cytochrome system so the cells cannot utilise the oxygen; little of the gas is removed on its passage through the vascular bed and arterio-venous oxygen differences are small.

Cyanosis

Cyanosis is a clinical term that refers to a bluish discoloration of the skin produced by abnormally large amounts of reduced haemoglobin in the blood. It is usually apparent if there is more than 5 g of reduced haemoglobin/dl of blood in the circulation. It may also be seen if the haemoglobin contains abnormal pigments such as met- or sulphhaemoglobin. Cyanosis is described as *central* or *peripheral*. Peripheral cyanosis may be seen in the fingers and outer surfaces of the lips on a cold day in normal people in whom it is due to local vasoconstriction such that oxygen extraction has

resulted in at least 5 g of deoxygenated haemoglobin/dl of blood in the capillaries and is an example of stagnant hypoxia (above). The arterial P_O_2 is normal. In central cyanosis the desaturated blood is present in arterial blood usually as a consequence of chest or heart disease and is best seen in the mucous membranes inside the mouth. If central cyanosis is present then peripheral cyanosis must be present as well. Central cyanosis is mostly associated with an arterial P_O_2 below about 50 mmHg, although in patients with polycythaemia the oxygen-carrying capacity of the blood is increased to say 24 g/dl; this may mean that with a normal arterial blood gas tension only 19 g/dl is saturated and the patient appears centrally cyanosed.

Oxygen therapy

The administration of 100 per cent oxygen to patients with a low arterial P_aO_2 (*hypoxaemia*) might seem rational as it will raise alveolar P_aO_2 from about 100 mmHg to about 650 mmHg. This would increase the oxygen content of the plasma from 0.3 to 1.8 g/dl. However, there is evidence that too high a concentration of inhaled oxygen may damage the lung; it is prudent to use oxygen therapy to raise the arterial P_O_2 to normal values and the actual percentage delivered (whether by mask or nasal cannulae) should be increased until this is achieved.

In some patients with long-standing chronic bronchitis there may be both a low arterial oxygen tension and a high arterial P_{CO_2} (hypoxaemia and *hypercapnia*). If maintained over a long period this results in a resetting of the central chemoreceptor response to carbon dioxide so that these patients depend on their hypoxic drive alone to breathe. If oxygen is administered indiscriminately to such a patient it raises arterial P_O_2; since the patient is using this stimulus to breathe, ventilation will be reduced. In turn this leads to accumulation of CO_2 and the signs of *carbon dioxide narcosis* may occur — vasodilatation, a bounding pulse with warm extremities, confusion, coma and convulsions. For this reason, oxygen is administered cautiously to some hypoxic patients and blood gas tensions must be measured frequently.

Breath holding

The influence of the cortex over the respiratory centre is shown during a period of voluntary breath holding (apnoea). At the end of an inspiration the breath can be held for 30 to 50 seconds (the breath-holding time) but the subject is then forced to breathe when the alveolar P_aCO_2 reaches 47 to 50 mmHg. If breathing is resumed the respiratory distress is relieved almost immediately. If the subject breathes a gas mixture that contains a hypoxic and hypercapnic combination (8.2 per cent O_2 and 7.5 per cent CO_2; P_{CO_2} = 53 mmHg) the relief of respiratory distress is still seen despite continuing hypoxia and hypercapnia. Also the period of voluntary apnoea may be prolonged if the vagus nerves are blocked; it has been suggested that the desire to breathe arises from afferent impulses from the stretch receptors in the lungs and chest wall. Other factors are known to influence the breath-holding time such as a short period of overbreathing (voluntary hyperpnoea) often used by divers to prolong their dive underwater. This hyperventilation cannot increase the arterial blood oxygen saturation significantly because the haemoglobin is at least 95 per cent saturated, but it does reduce the initial blood P_aCO_2 and so lengthens the time before CO_2 reaches the breaking-point threshold. For the same reasons breathing O_2 during the period before diving does not greatly increase the period of apnoea. Several drowning accidents have been reported in which the victim hyperventilated before diving in an attempt to prolong the duration of underwater swimming. Such exercise after hyperventilation may reduce the blood P_aO_2 to levels that cause loss of consciousness before the P_aCO_2 rises to the necessary threshold. There is thus no doubt that the CO_2 tension of blood is the main factor determining the length of a held breath but when there is hypoxia as well the breaking point may be reached somewhat sooner.

Athletic sprinters often hold their breath, especially over short distances such as 100 metres and subsequently are unable to hold their breath for any period because of the accumulation of H^+ derived from the anaerobic generation of lactic acid as well as the necessity to excrete the CO_2.

Respiratory gases in divers

As a diver descends through the water the gas mixture he inspires comes under increasing pressure. For example, the oxygen tension in air at atmospheric pressure is 160 mmHg but at a depth of 38 metres it is 760 mmHg and the effect of O_2 on a diver breathing at this depth would be the same as if he were breathing pure oxygen at atmospheric pressure at the surface. Thus during descent increasing amounts of respiratory gases diffuse into the body tissues and are dissolved in them. Nitrogen is five times more soluble in lipid than in water, so fats, including nervous tissue, take up relatively more nitrogen during compression. When a diver ascends the partial pressures of gases in his body are reduced. If decompression is too rapid the gases come out of solution in the tissues and blood, forming bubbles that result in mild pain or severe problems ('the bends'). Gas bubbles in the brain may result in paralysis of the limbs or convulsions. They may block end arteries to bones; workers with chronic decompression sickness may develop aseptic necrosis of bone. This disorder may be prevented by carefully controlled

decompression; if the bends do occur the treatment is to recompress the diver and then decompress him more slowly. The most serious effects on the nervous system may be permanent.

Man at high altitude

All over the earth oxygen accounts for 21 per cent of the total gas inspired but as one ascends to high altitude the reduction in barometric pressure results in a reduction in the O_2 tension in inspired air. At sea level the percentage of O_2 can be reduced from 21 to 13 per cent with little change in ventilation because the arterial chemoreceptors are least sensitive over this range. When man ascends to high altitude the alveolar and arterial PO_2 fall so that ventilation is stimulated and P_aCO_2 is reduced. In consequence the pH of the blood and CSF rises (*respiratory alkalosis*). This returns to normal once the transport of HCO_3^- out of the CSF has occurred. The kidneys, in a slower compensatory adaptation, excrete more bicarbonate to restore the arterial pH to its normal value. Hence continued residence at high altitude produces acclimatisation; when this is complete the arterial P_aO_2 is somewhat reduced, with a concomitant reduction in P_aCO_2 and a normal pH (*compensated respiratory alkalosis*). The reduction in P_aO_2 also produces a rise in erythropoietin output from the kidney, which increases the haemoglobin concentration in peripheral blood. This unfortunately results in an increase in blood viscosity and it has been argued that the increased 'stickiness' of the blood may be detrimental. Residents at high altitude develop enlarged carotid bodies and right ventricular hypertrophy as a consequence not only of alveolar hypoxia producing pulmonary vasoconstriction (p. 145) but also as a result of the increase in blood viscosity. The changes in PO_2 and PCO_2 of alveolar air and in the oxygen saturation in the blood at various altitudes are shown in Figure 10.17. If humans climb to about 18 000 ft (6498 m) the drop in inspired PO_2 is equivalent to breathing 10 per cent oxygen at sea level. At the summit of Mount Everest (29 000 ft, 10 469 m) the inspired PO_2 is approximately 50 mmHg. Despite the hyperventilation that occurs the arterial PO_2 is probably about 32 mmHg. Wagner and West have suggested that the ability to climb to the top depends on the barometric pressure at the time of the ascent. It is rare for people to be able to climb to the top of Everest without supplementary oxygen and this can only be achieved if the barometric pressure is high.

Jet passenger aircraft fly at a height of 6 to 14 kilometres (20 000 to 46 000 ft) and supersonic aircraft fly at altitudes of 18 to 21 kilometres (59 000 to 69 000 ft), where the atmospheric pressure is only 33 mmHg. Though the cabin is pressurised the usual cabin pressure is equivalent to that at 1.5 km; provided that

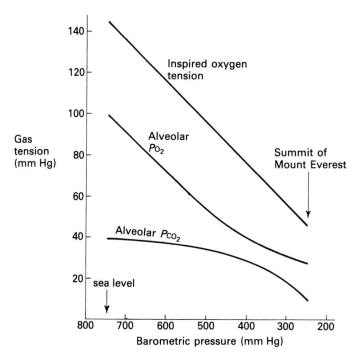

Fig. 10.17 The effect of altitude on the inspired O_2 tension and resultant alveolar gas tensions for O_2 and CO_2 at sea level to the summit of Mount Everest (29 000 ft). The alveolar values differ from a straight line because of the hyperventilation. The data from the summit of Everest were derived from the American Medical Research Expedition to Everest in 1981 and gave an alveolar Po_2 of 28 mmHg and a P_aCO_2 of 7.5 mmHg at a barometric pressure of 253 mmHg.

the occupants of the plane start on the upper flat part of the oxygen dissociation curve (Fig. 10.3) this reduction in barometric pressure would only reduce oxygen saturation from 95 per cent to about 93 per cent. However, patients with chronic chest or heart disease would be unable to tolerate the reduction in oxygen saturation since they may well be on the steep part of the oxygen dissociation curve. If the pressurisation of the cabin were lost, the sudden fall in barometric pressure would cause a sudden desaturation and loss of consciousness; for this reason oxygen masks are available.

FURTHER READING

Berger A J, Mitchell R A, Severinghaus J 1977 Regulation of respiration. New England Journal of Medicine 297: 92–97, 138–143, 194–201

Heath D, Williams D R 1981 Man at high altitude. Churchill Livingstone, Edinburgh

Pappenheimer J R 1967 The ionic composition of cerebral extracellular fluid and its relation to control of breathing. The Harvey Lectures 1965–1966 61: 71–94

Purves M J 1975 The peripheral arterial chemoreceptors. University Press, Cambridge

West J B 1983 Ventilation/blood flow and gas exchange, 4th edn. Blackwell Scientific, Oxford

11

Energy balance and exercise

The potential energy of a foodstuff can be determined by measuring the amount of heat produced when the foodstuff is burned in a *bomb calorimeter*. The 'bomb' is a strong cylindrical steel vessel that can resist very high internal pressures. A weighed amount of the foodstuff is placed in the bomb, which is then filled with oxygen under pressure. The foodstuff is ignited electrically and the amount of heat produced by oxidation is calculated from the rise in temperature of the known volume of water surrounding the bomb and the water equivalent of the calorimeter.

The unit of heat used in nutrition was until recently the kilocalorie (kcal) or Calorie. However, with the introduction of SI units it is now usual to use joules (J) as a measure of heat. One kilocalorie is equal to 4184 J, or 4.184 kJ; 1 MJ (megajoule) = 10^6 J. One joule per second is one watt (W).

The energy derived from the complete combustion of the usual mixture of carbohydrates in human foodstuffs has been found to be 17 kJ per g. The value for fat is 39 kJ per g. In the bomb carbohydrates and fats are oxidised to CO_2 and H_2O just as they are in the body. In the bomb protein is oxidised to CO_2, H_2O, and oxides of nitrogen and other elements but in the body it is incompletely oxidised, part being excreted as urea, which has an appreciable energy value. When the potential energy of the urea excreted is subtracted from the figure for the complete oxidation (23 kJ per g) a physiological value of 17 kJ per g is obtained for protein.

METHODS FOR ESTIMATING ENERGY OUTPUT

Direct calorimetry

To determine energy expenditure by direct calorimetry the subject is placed in a calorimeter, a small room with heavily insulated walls. The heat generated by the subject is taken up by water pumped through a series of pipes that pass through the calorimeter. By multi-plying the difference in temperature between the ingoing and outgoing water by the volume of water flowing his heat output can be obtained; the oxygen consumption can be read on a meter. By its use Atwater showed many years ago that over several days energy expenditure balances energy intake within 1 per cent or so. He also showed that measurements by direct calorimetry agreed well with measurements by indirect calorimetry, which is much more convenient, relatively cheap, and very nearly as accurate.

Indirect calorimetry

In indirect methods the heat output of the subject is calculated from his oxygen consumption. Because the relation between oxygen consumption and heat production depends on the type of food being oxidised, we must briefly consider the *respiratory quotient* (RQ), which is by definition the *volume* of CO_2 produced divided by the *volume* of O_2 used in the same time.

The oxidation of carbohydrate can be represented by the equation

$$C_6H_{12}O_6 + 6\ O_2 = 6\ CO_2 + 6\ H_2O + heat$$

The respiratory quotient is 6/6, that is 1.0. Oxidation of the fat triolein is represented by the equation

$$C_{57}H_{104}O_6 + 80\ O_2 = 57\ CO_2 + 52\ H_2O + O + heat$$

Its RQ is 57/80 or 0.71; the RQ of human fat is 0.72. The RQ for an average protein is 0.80. A subject on an ordinary mixed diet containing carbohydrate, fat and protein has an RQ of the order of 0.85. In other words the RQ gives a clue to the type of food being oxidised at any given time if we assume that the CO_2 collected and measured is derived solely from the oxygen taken into the body during the same period.

The calorific values of O_2 used by the body in the combustion of mixtures of fat and carbohydrate for different levels of the RQ are shown in Figure 11.1.

The RQ can lie outside the limits 0.7 to 1.0. When

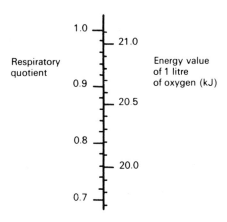

Fig. 11.1 A nomogram from which may be read off the energy value of a litre of oxygen (at STP) at non-protein RQS from 0.7 to 1.0.

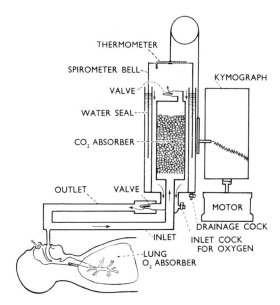

Fig. 11.2 Diagram of recording spirometer. The subject wears a nose-clip and breathes through a mouthpiece that is connected to the apparatus by two tubes. He breathes in oxygen through the inspiratory valve and breathes out into the CO_2 absorber and then, through the expiratory valve, into the spirometer bell. A pump may be introduced in place of the valves shown in the diagram to ease the circulation of air through the CO_2 absorber. The amount of oxygen used is recorded on the revolving drum by the pen attached to the counterweight. (Courtesy of J B de V Weir)

carbohydrate is transformed into fat the non-protein RQ is greater than 1, since CO_2 is produced and O_2 is not used.

$$13\ C_6H_{12}O_6 \rightarrow C_{55}H_{104}O_6 + 23\ CO_2 + 26\ H_2O.$$

In one experiment, overfeeding of thin men with carbohydrate gave a respiratory quotient as high as 1.3. Conversely, when fat is being transformed to carbohydrate in excess of that being oxidised, the RQ is less than 0.7 because oxygen is used up without a corresponding production of CO_2.

Closed circuit methods
The subject is kept in an airtight chamber through which a continuous circulation of air is maintained by a rotary blower. O_2 is added through a meter to make good the O_2 used in metabolism; the water in the expired air is caught in a sulphuric acid trap in the ventilation circuit; the CO_2 is caught in a soda-lime trap and is estimated by weighing or by a chemical method.

The subject remains within the chamber for a period of several hours; since his oxygen consumption and CO_2 output are measured his RQ can be calculated. Protein metabolism can be estimated by measuring the nitrogen content of the urine excreted during the time of the experiment.

Simpler methods have been evolved for clinical use. The Benedict–Roth spirometer (Fig. 11.2) consists of a gasholder (spirometer bell) that is filled with O_2. As the O_2 is used up by the subject the level of the gasholder falls and from the record of its movements on the rotating drum the amount of oxygen consumed in a given period can be measured. Because the expired CO_2 is not measured, the RQ cannot be calculated but an arbitrary value of 0.8 is usually assumed. At this RQ

the calorific value of O_2 is 20.2 kJ per litre, and by multiplying this value by the number of litres of O_2 consumed the energy output during the experimental period is obtained with an error of no clinical importance (Fig. 11.3).

Open circuit method
In the open circuit method the subject's nose is closed by a clip and he breathes through a mouthpiece fitted with valves so that he inspires atmospheric air and expires through a wide tube into a rubberised canvas or polythene bag (Douglas bag) of capacity 100 or 200 litres (Fig. 11.4). The volume of the air in the bag is measured with a gas meter.

For the calculation of the metabolic rate when using the Douglas bag method it is necessary to find only (1) the volume of the expired air and (2) the percentage of oxygen in the expired air. For the usual range of protein intake, that is where protein contributes 10 to 15 per cent of the total energy, Weir has shown that the energy value of a litre of expired air is $0.209\ (O_i - O_e)$ kJ where O_i is the percentage of oxygen in the inspired air (normally 20.9) and O_e is the percentage of oxygen in the expired air. The following example illustrates the method.

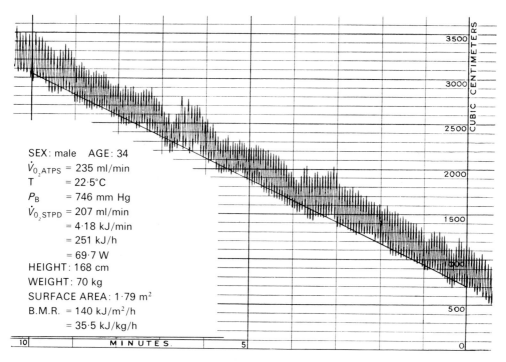

SEX: male   AGE: 34
$\dot{V}_{O_2,ATPS}$ = 235 ml/min
T   = 22·5°C
P_B = 746 mm Hg
$\dot{V}_{O_2,STPD}$ = 207 ml/min
       = 4·18 kJ/min
       = 251 kJ/h
       = 69·7 W
HEIGHT: 168 cm
WEIGHT: 70 kg
SURFACE AREA: 1·79 m²
B.M.R. = 140 kJ/m²/h
       = 35·5 kJ/kg/h

Fig. 11.3 Chart of oxygen consumption and data for the estimation of BMR obtained with the apparatus shown in Figure 11.2 V_{O_2} = rate of oxygen consumption; ATPS = atmospheric temperature and pressure saturated with water vapour; STPD = standard temperature and pressure, dry; P_B = barometric pressure. The calculations are explained in the text. Note that as the spirometer bell falls the writing lever rises; the zero time on this chart is on the right and the graph must be read from right to left.

Fig. 11.4 The subject is wearing a 100-litre capacity Douglas bag that is partly filled with expired air. The cylindrical box attached to the mouth-piece contains valves so arranged that the subject breathes in atmospheric air and breathes out through the corrugated tubing into the bag.

The subject breathed into a Douglas bag for 10 minutes. The volume of the expired air was 80.3 litres at 16.8°C and 750 mmHg atmospheric pressure, equivalent to 73.2 litres at STPD. The expired air contained 16.9 per cent oxygen. From Weir's formula the energy value of a litre of this expired air is 0.209 (20.9 − 16.9) or 0.84 kJ. The energy output was therefore 73.2 × 0.84 = 61.5 kJ in 10 minutes or 369 kJ per hour. The subject weighed 50 kg and his height was 163 cm; his surface area obtained from the formula on this page was 1.52 m² and his metabolic rate was therefore 369 ÷ 1.52 = 243 kJ per m² per hour = 68 W per m².

Because of its limited capacity the Douglas bag can be used for only 2 or 3 minutes if the subject is carrying out strenuous activity. It is often more convenient to use the Max Planck respirometer. This apparatus, weighing less than 4 kg, is a small, accurately built gas meter. It measures directly the volume of expired air and at the same time diverts a small fraction (0.3 or 0.6 per cent) of the air into a rubber bag for subsequent analysis. The energy expenditure can be calculated from Weir's formula.

So many figures for the energy expenditure during different kinds of activity are now tabulated in the literature that reasonably accurate estimates (as distinct from laborious measurements) of the energy expended in different jobs can be made by an observer equipped with stop-watch, paper and pencil who records the duration of each kind of activity.

BASAL METABOLIC RATE

The output of energy and the rate of oxygen consumption depend on many factors including body size, muscular activity, the nature and amount of food eaten, changes in environmental and body temperature, thyroid activity and emotional excitement. To reduce the influence of these factors to a minimum and allow a valid comparison of the metabolism of one individual with that of another, it is desirable to measure the metabolism under basal conditions. It is well known, however, that it is difficult, especially for an untrained subject, to achieve the necessary mental and physical relaxation. The oxygen consumption measured in the morning while the subject is lying relaxed and warm in bed 12 to 15 hours after the last meal, gives the *basal metabolism*. A certain amount of energy must continually be produced to maintain essential processes such as the beating of the heart, the breathing and the maintenance of the body temperature.

The heat production of animals of various sizes is closely correlated with the surface area of the body but not with the body weight (Table 11.5). Small animals have a greater surface area per unit of weight than large ones and therefore a relatively greater surface from which heat can be lost. These observations led to the convention established many years ago by which the basal metabolism of large and small persons was standardised by referring it to the surface area of the body. The basal metabolic rate (BMR) is expressed as kJ per m^2 per hour.

The surface area of the body was determined directly by Du Bois by clothing his subjects in thin, wax-impregnated garments. The formula giving the best fit to his data is:

$$S = W^{0.425} \times H^{0.725} \times 0.007184$$

where S is the surface area in m^2, W is the nude weight in kg, H is the height in cm. In practice S is usually determined by the use of standard tables and nomograms based on this formula. The surface area of an adult man is of the order of 1.8 m^2. Because of the scatter of the data it is likely that the value obtained from the formula for any one person deviates appreciably from his true value and that the error in estimation of surface area may be greater than that in estimating oxygen consumption.

The *basal metabolic rate* (BMR) is usually expressed as a percentage of the standard value of a subject of the same sex and age. Variations within the range from 85 to 115 per cent or, as it is usually expressed, minus 15 to plus 15 per cent are accepted as being within normal limits. Occasionally healthy persons deviate more than 20 per cent above or below the standard. The test has therefore little diagnostic value.

Figures 11.6 and 11.7 show how the BMR and total energy requirements vary with age.

For a man the average BMR is about 167 kJ/m^2/h (46 W/m^2) and for a woman about 150 kJ/m^2/h (42 W/m^2). The lower figures for women are probably due to the greater fat content of the female body.

In babies there is a small range of environmental temperature, namely 36° to 38° in the newborn, 32° to 37° at 1 week, in which the metabolic rate at rest is at a minimum. In this range the basal oxygen consumption of newborn infants is about 4.8 ml/min/kg. On the second day it is about 6.6 ml/min/kg. By the seventh day the oxygen consumption reaches 7 ml/min/kg and remains about 7.2 ml/min/kg for the first 18 months.

Table 11.5 Energy expenditure by different species

Animal	Weight (kg)	kJ/day	
		Per kg	Per m^2 surface
Pig	128.0	80	4510
Man	64.3	134	4360
Dog	15.2	216	4347
Goose	3.5	279	4046
Fowl	2.0	297	3946
Mouse	0.018	2736	4971

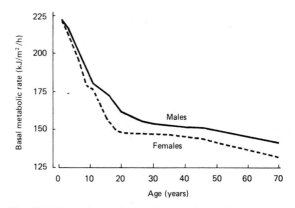

Fig. 11.6 Mean figures for basal metabolic rate in kJ/m^2/hour or W/m^2 from the age of 1 year. (After Davidson S, Passmore R 1966 Human nutrition and dietetics, 3rd end. Livingstone, Edinburgh)

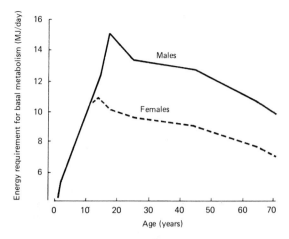

Fig. 11.7 The total daily energy requirement for basal metabolism from 1 year onwards. (After Davidson S and Passmore R 1966 Human nutrition and dietetics, 3rd edn. Livingstone, Edinburgh)

The total energy to be supplied in the food is 500 kJ/kg in the first 3 months gradually decreasing to 420 kJ/kg at the end of the first year.

Adipose tissue, having a rich blood supply, is not metabolically inert but it contributes relatively little to the metabolic rate. The oxygen uptake of a person at rest is probably mostly due to the activity of the non-fatty tissues or fat-free mass, FFM. The fat-free mass has a density of 1100 kg/m³ but the density of the whole body is less because fatty tissue has a lower density (900 kg/m³) than the other tissues of the body. A thin man has a density of the order of 1075 kg/m³, a plump man about 1046 kg/m³. Density is measured by weighing the subject in air and then, after maximum expiration, by weighing him in water during complete submersion, due allowance being made for the residual volume of air in the lungs (Chap. 9). From the figure for density the FFM can be calculated. Passmore measured the resting oxygen consumption of 49 medical students (Table 11.8) and found that although there was a significant sex difference in oxygen consumption referred to surface area, the difference in oxygen consumption per kg of lean body mass was not significant. This method is obviously unsuitable for routine

Table 11.8 Resting oxygen consumption in a group of normal students

	ml/m² per min	ml/kg lean body mass per min
24 men	141	4.22
25 women	115	4.31

(From MacMillan M G et al. 1965 Lancet 1:728)

use but it has been shown that skinfold thickness measured by suitable callipers gives a fairly good indication of body fat and FFM. The correlation coefficient of skin fold thickness with body density is usually between 0.7 and 0.9. Triceps skinfold thicknesses of 20 mm for men and 23 mm for women are probably good cut-off points for obesity: these correspond to body fats of about 28 per cent for men and 34 per cent for women.

Specific dynamic action (SDA)

After food is absorbed the metabolic activities of the body are stimulated and heat production increases. Thus a person whose metabolism under basal conditions is 7.1 MJ/day actually needs more than 7.1 MJ of food to maintain himself in equilibrium. The metabolism of 7.1 MJ of food raises his energy output to about 7.9 MJ. This increase in metabolism is termed the *specific dynamic action*.

The mechanical efficiency of the human body

The efficiency of a steam engine or an internal combustion engine is given by the ratio of the useful work done to the total potential energy (PE) of the fuel used. Thus

$$\text{efficiency} = \frac{\text{useful work}}{\text{PE of fuel}} = \frac{\text{useful work}}{\text{useful work} + \text{heat}}$$

The difference between the total potential energy and the useful work appears as heat. The efficiency of the petrol engine is of the order of 25 per cent.

In man the situation is different since metabolism must continue even at complete rest, when no external work is done. In these circumstances the efficiency is obviously zero. Values approaching the true efficiency can be obtained if a very large mass of muscles is brought into action. In such experiments the subject pedals a stationary bicycle connected to an ergometer to measure the external work; the oxygen consumption is measured at the same time to find the potential energy of the fuel used. The gross efficiency in such experiments is of the order of 10 to 20 per cent when care is taken to avoid, or correct for, an oxygen debt (p. 169).

ENERGY EXPENDITURE

Food provides energy for three main purposes. First it is required to maintain basal bodily activities such as heart beat, breathing, muscle tone and body temperature. A man weighing 70 kg has an energy output for basal purposes of 318 kJ/h or 7.7 MJ per day.

Additional food, 1.5 to 2.0 MJ per day, is needed to cover the expenditure of energy in everyday activities, such as sitting, standing, walking and dressing; a further allowance, depending on the nature of the occupation, has to be made for work carried out. Men engaged in hard muscular work may expend as much as 1.6 MJ/h.

Such simple calculations have been found to be misleading for three main reasons. First, the energy expenditure varies considerably from minute to minute in any particular job — few people work steadily at a given rate for an hour. Secondly, even within one sort of job, say domestic work or light engineering, the work varies from sedentary to heavy. Thirdly, very high expenditure cannot be kept up for long. The average man doing physical work for 8 hours a day is not likely to show evidence of fatigue if the intensity of the work and the length of the rest pauses are adjusted to give an average energy expenditure of less than 21 kJ/min. This is equivalent to walking on the level at 3.8 miles per hour (6 km/h). If he works twice as hard, he must have rest pauses equal to the actual working time. If we allow 2.1 MJ for sleep and 5.9 MJ as energy expendi-

Table 11.9 Energy output and intake of a clerk over 1 week (Ian C., age 29, ht. 165 cm, wt. 66 kg)

Activity	Total time spent		kJ/min	Total MJ
	hr	min		
In bed	54	4	4.7	15.4
Daytime dozing	1	43	5.7	0.6
Recreational and off work				
Light sedentary activities	31	14	6.2	11.8
Washing, shaving, dressing	3	18	12.5	2.5
Light domestic work	7	14	12.5	5.4
Walking	8	35	27.6	14.2
Gardening	2	48	20.1	3.4
Standing activities	6	45	6.5	2.6
Watching football	2	10	8.4	1.1
Total recreational and off work	62	32		41.0
Working				
Sitting activities	22	22	6.9	9.2
Standing activities	25	27	7.9	12.4
Walking	1	22	27.6	2.3
Total working	49	41		23.9
Grand total	168			80.8
Daily average	24			11.5
Food intake (daily av. determined by diet survey)				11.0

(From Garry R C et al. 1955 Studies on expenditure of energy and consumption of food by miners and clerks. Medical Research Council Special Report, 289. HMSO, London)

Table 11.10 Energy output and intake of a coal miner over 1 week (John H., age 32, ht. 175 cm, wt. 67 kg)

Activity	Total time spent		kJ/min	Total MJ
	hr	min		
In bed	58	30	4.4	15.4
Recreational and off work				
Light sedentary activities	38	37	6.6	15.4
Washing, shaving, dressing	5	3	13.8	4.2
Walking	15		20.5	18.5
Standing	2	16	7.5	1.0
Cycling	2	25	27.6	4.0
Gardening	2		20.9	2.5
Total recreational and off work	65	21		45.6
Working				
Loading	12	6	26.4	19.1
Hewing	1	14	28.0	2.1
Timbering	6	51	23.8	9.8
Walking	6	43	28.0	11.3
Standing	2	6	7.5	1.0
Sitting	15	9	7.0	6.4
Total working	44	9		50.0
Grand total	168			110.7
Daily average	24			15.8
Food intake (daily av. determined by diet survey)				16.7

(From Garry et al as in Table 11.9)

ture off duty, the total energy expenditure (including 10 MJ for 8 hours of work) for this upper limit activity is of the order of 18 MJ/day. This is much less than was at one time given as the daily requirements for blacksmiths or lumbermen but even these strong men must have rest pauses, which bring down their average requirements in spite of their high peak performance.

Tables 11.9 and 11.10 show the results of investigations of energy expenditure in a sedentary worker and in a heavy manual worker. To assess the requirements accurately, detailed minute-to-minute diaries of their activities were kept for a complete week because omission of weekend activities gives a false impression of the average needs. About one-third of the day is spent asleep. The amount of muscular movement in sleep varies from person to person, but it is considerable and no one sleeps like the proverbial log. On average the energy requirement is at the basal level — for an adult man 5.4 kJ/min. The performance of personal necessities, such as dressing and undressing, requires in different people 10 to 17 kJ/min. An average adult walking on the level at 2 miles per hour (3 km/h) needs 12 kJ per minute; at 4 miles per hour (6.5 km/h) he requires 24 kJ per minute. Walking up an incline of 15 per cent at 2 miles per hour (3 km/h) requires 25 kJ/min. Mental 'work', for example adding or multiplying figures, has no significant effect on metabolism. Light indoor recreations may require up to 17 kJ/min while hard exercise may involve 84 kJ/min. Domestic work varies between 8 and 33 kJ/min. Typing requires about 5.9 kJ/min. Christensen's gradings of severity for different forms of work are generally accepted:

Unduly heavy	over 2.5 litres oxygen per min = 850 W
Very heavy	over 2.0 litres oxygen per min = 680 W
Heavy	over 1.5 litres oxygen per min = 510 W
Moderate	over 1.0 litres oxygen per min = 340 W
Light	over 0.5 litres oxygen per min = 170 W

His observations on Swedish ironworkers led him to point out that in a hot environment grading by oxygen uptake does not measure the real stress on the subject. Pulse rate then becomes a better indicator of stress and the above gradings would correspond to pulse rates of: over 175, 150 to 175, 120 to 150, 100 to 125 and 75 to 100, respectively.

MUSCULAR EXERCISE

Internal energy stores allow very high levels of activity for about 20 s, reaching nearly 2 horsepower (1.4 kW) in trained men sprinting 200 m. Longer activity depends on chemicals brought to the muscles and only about a quarter of this output of power can be maintained. Although skeletal muscles are the principal tissues concerned in exercise, many other systems are involved in the adaptation to physical work.

The initiation and co-ordination of movement depend on the nervous system; the extra fuel and oxygen requirements of the muscles are supplied by appropriate adjustment of the cardiovascular and respiratory systems. These adjustments are initiated by chemical, mechanical and thermal stimuli associated with the neuromuscular activity; they are carried out through the nervous system and the endocrine system. Not only must an exercising man supply his muscles with metabolic substrates from the liver, intestine and lungs, while transporting metabolites to the lungs and kidneys for excretion, but he must also increase the blood supply to the skin in order to dissipate the extra heat generated.

The adaptation to exercise depends on the type and the severity of the work that is performed and on the state of training of the individual. Muscular work may be thought of in two categories: 'dynamic work', in which muscles contract through some distance against a resisting force (as in running or cycling) and 'static work' in which the muscles contract to support a load or exert a force without movement.

Skeletal muscle metabolism

The immediate source of energy for muscular contraction comes from the hydrolysis of ATP. However, the ATP concentration in muscle is sufficient only for a limited number of contractions and therefore if the muscle is to work for a significant length of time a continuous supply of ATP is necessary.

At the beginning of light muscular work, the oxygen requirements are not met, because blood flow and oxygen transport do not increase to the required level instantaneously. For the first few minutes, therefore, anaerobic sources of energy are used. However, after this interval, aerobic metabolism takes over and energy is derived from oxidative breakdown of glucose and free fatty acids.

During heavy work when the oxygen supply cannot meet the demand, anaerobic glycolysis occurs, with the production of lactic acid. Three reactions are important under these circumstances (Fig. 11.11):

$$\text{adenosine triphosphate (ATP)} \rightarrow \text{adenosine diphosphate (ADP)} + \text{phosphate}$$
$$\text{creatine phosphate} \rightarrow \text{creatine} + \text{phosphate}$$
$$\text{glycogen} \rightarrow \text{pyruvate} \rightarrow \text{lactate}$$

Carbohydrate, fat and proteins are utilised in exercise as sources of energy. It has usually been assumed that protein is not used as a fuel if the supply of carbohydrate and fat are adequate. The relative amounts of carbohydrate and fat metabolised are determined by the type of exercise performed: whether it is continuous or intermittent, brief or prolonged, light or heavy (as compared with the maximum aerobic power). Other factors are the state of physical training, the previous diet and the state of health of the subject. The type of work influences the metabolic response, particularly the ratio of carbohydrate to fat, because of the availability of oxygen. If it is inadequate, the usable fuel is restricted to carbohydrate, which is metabolised to lactate, the accumulation of which not only impairs muscle function but also inhibits the mobilisation of fatty acids. The oxidation of fatty acids spares glycogen stores but cannot completely replace glucose as a source of energy and can only support about 65 per cent of the individual's aerobic capacity. However, the sparing of glycogen by fatty acids is not always observed and

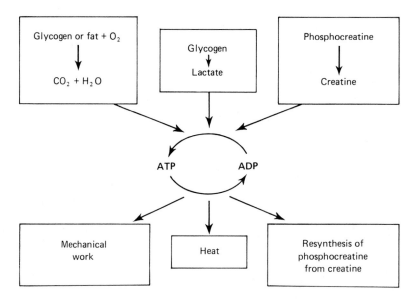

Fig. 11.11 Energy sources for muscle contraction.

depends upon many factors such as the work intensity, the state of nutrition and the previous diet of the individual. Fatty acids arise from adipose tissue by lipolysis and an equilibrium exists between lipolysis and esterification, the degree of lipolysis depending on the level of free fatty acids in the blood, so that when utilisation is increased more fatty acids are released from adipose tissue. The catecholamine concentration in blood increases during exercise so that lipolysis is stimulated. Blocking the action of catecholamine with a β-receptor blocking agent (propranolol) reduces the availability of free fatty acids and the RQ shifts to near 1.0. In addition to catecholamines, other hormones are involved in the response to exercise; concentrations of glucagon, cortisol and growth hormone are raised. Insulin levels, on the other hand, tend to fall. Such responses increase glucose production by gluconeogenesis in the liver and by lipid mobilisation.

Although amino acids are liberated by muscle during exercise, proteins are not regarded as significant fuels in exercise. Recent work has shown that there is an increase in leucine oxidation in moderate exercise in fasting individuals, but nitrogen excretion in the urine only occurs over many hours after exercise.

Physical capacity and effort
The ability to perform physical work depends upon the transformation of chemically bound energy into mechanical energy. This function is limited by the physical capacity of an individual. The performance of an individual depends not only on the type of exercise, dynamic or static, but also on the intensity and duration

of effort and also whether the exercise is continuous or intermittent. The strength of a muscle group determines the force developed during a maximal voluntary static contraction and seems to be related to the cross-sectional area of muscle.

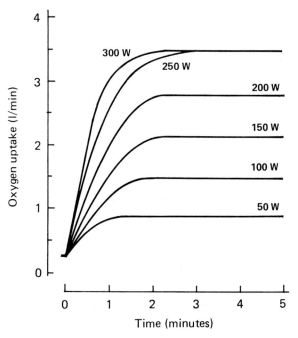

Fig. 11.12 Increase in oxygen during exercise on a bicycle ergometer with different work loads performed for five minutes. (After Åstrand P-O, Rodahl K 1977 Textbook of work physiology. McGraw-Hill, London)

In static exercise the effort associated with a maximal voluntary contraction (MVC) cannot be sustained for more than about 60 seconds, even in well-motivated subjects, but if carried out at 10 per cent of the MVC it may be continued almost indefinitely. In the case of dynamic exercise the effort can be endured longer, and fatigue delayed, if the exercise is performed at the same intensity but intermittently.

The upper limit of dynamic work is set by the maximal oxygen uptake that the individual can attain and this is determined by fitness, age and sex (Fig. 11.12). It is measured in terms of energy output per unit of time and is termed the maximal aerobic power. If a given task demands an oxygen uptake of 2 l/min then an individual with a maximal oxygen uptake of 4 l/min has a satisfactory margin so that anaerobic work would not be required.

Oxygen uptake

The steady state and oxygen debt

The oxygen uptake increases slowly during the first minutes of submaximal dynamic exercise to a steady state at which the oxygen uptake corresponds to the energy demands of the tissues (Fig. 11.13). The slow increase at the beginning of exercise is due to the time taken for adjustments of the oxygen transporting systems. The deficit achieved in the early stages of exercise must be repaid at the end of exercise as the 'oxygen debt'. Myoglobin stores, ATP and phosphocreatine levels are restored fairly quickly while lactic acid removal is the main factor in the slower component of the return of oxygen uptake to the pre-exercise level. Other factors, such as the increased metabolic demand of heart and respiratory muscles and elevated metabolism (metabolism increases by about 13 per cent for every degree rise in temperature) also contribute to the slower component. In the repayment of the oxygen debt, for every two moles of lactate produced 1.7 is re-

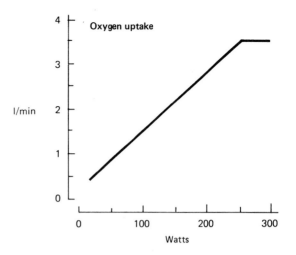

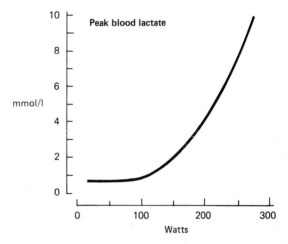

Fig. 11.14 Oxygen uptake and blood lactate levels at the end of five minutes work at different loads as described in Figure 11.12.

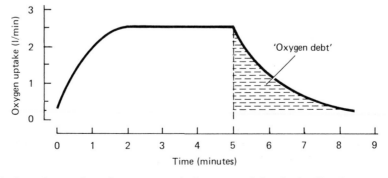

Fig. 11.13 During the first minutes of exercise oxygen uptake increases and then levels off as the oxygen uptake reaches a level adequate to meet the needs of the tissues. At the end of exercise oxygen uptake gradually decreases as the 'oxygen debt' is paid off.

synthesised in the liver and 0.3 oxidised to CO_2 and H_2O in cardiac and skeletal muscle. Figure 11.14 illustrates the linear increase in oxygen uptake, measured after 5 minutes duration at different work loads up to 300 W. At this intensity any increase in work load does not increase oxygen uptake further because the maximal aerobic power has been reached at 3.5 l/min. The increased work output from 250 to 300 W is accomplished anaerobically.

Intermittent Work

If the work period lasts for less than 10 seconds then the energy for the activity is derived from aerobic metabolism by using oxygen bound to myoglobin. Lactic acid levels do not rise. During the recovery phase of intermittent exercise, these stores are rapidly replenished but it is the length of the work period and not the rest pauses that predetermines the moment of onset of fatigue.

Considerable argument exists over whether dynamic endurance activity is limited by 'peripheral' or 'central' factors. The ability of the oxygen transport system to deliver oxygen and the ability of skeletal muscles to utilise oxygen have been designated 'peripheral' factors and the ability of the heart to generate a sufficient cardiac output 'central' factors.

Peripheral factors limiting oxygen uptake

In dynamic exercise, the arteriovenous oxygen difference increases as more oxygen is extracted from the blood, so the oxygen content of mixed venous blood may fall as low as 4 ml/100 ml during maximal dynamic exercise. The oxygen content of the blood leaving maximally exercising skeletal muscle may be less than 1 ml/100 ml. It is the ability of the muscles to utilise

Table 11.16 Characteristics of type 1 and type II muscle fibres

Characteristics	Type 1	Type II
Concentrations of oxidative enzymes	High	Low
Concentration of myosin ATPase	Low	High
Concentration of lactate dehydrogenase	Low	High
Recruitment in dynamic exercise:		
low or moderate intensity	From the onset	At exhaustion
severe intensity	From the onset	From the onset
Recruitment in isometric exercise	< 20% maximum	> 20% maximum

From Bassey and Fentem, as in Table 11.15

oxygen that determines to a great extent the total oxygen during exercise. This ability is related to the development of mitochondria within the cells. Certain muscle fibres (slow-twitch or Type I) appear to be better suited to this function, as shown in Tables 11.15 and 11.16, and fast-twitch or type II fibres have a greater capacity for anaerobic metabolism, although a proportion of these fibres also exhibit a well-developed oxidative system. Almost all muscles contain a proportion of both of the main fibre types; successful long-distance runners have a higher proportion of type I fibres and weight-lifters and sprinters have a higher than average proportion of type II fibres.

Table 11.15 Characteristics of slow and fast muscles

Characteristic	Slow	Fast
Macroscopic appearance	Red	White
Twitch characteristics	Slow	Fast
Fibres types	Mainly type I	Mainly type II
Function	Mainly postural and dynamic endurance exercise	Mainly isometric work or high-intensity, dynamic exercise
Anaerobic capacity	Moderate	High
Capillary supply	High	Low
Tolerance of sustained work (endurance)	High	Low

(From Bassey E J, Fentem P H 1981 In: Principles and practice of human physiology. Academic, New York)

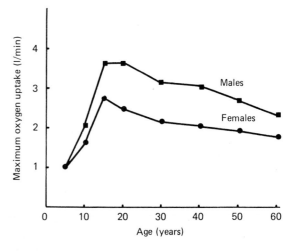

Fig. 11.17 The effect of age and sex on the maximum oxygen uptake, measured on a treadmill or bicycle ergometer. (After Åstrand P-O, Rodahl K 1977 Textbook of work physiology. McGraw-Hill, London)

A further factor increasing the supply of oxgyen to the muscles is the increase in functioning capillaries. Up to 500 capillaries/mm^2 may be open during intense physical activity, which not only reduces the diffusion distance but also increases the surface area available for the exchange of nutrients. The capillary density is higher around slow-twitch fibres than fast-twitch fibres. The maximal oxygen uptake is influenced by age and sex. In the untrained individual it is maximal in the late teens and then declines over the years (Fig. 11.17).

Central factors limiting oxygen uptake
There is a linear relation between heart rate and oxygen consumption and in severe dynamic exercise the cardiac output increases due to an increase in heart rate and a doubling of stroke volume. The regulation of the cardiac output and the heart rate were considered in Chapter 7.

Since the heart rate is determined largely by the work load, the central limiting factor to aerobic work is the extent to which the stroke volume can be augmented.

Pulmonary ventilation
Ventilation rises in exercise from about 6 l/min to 200 l/min, in extreme cases, in almost rectilinear fashion. An increase in the alveolar to arterial Po_2 difference is seen in strenuous exercise and is unexpected, because the inequalities in ventilation and perfusion decrease with exercise. The Va/Q ratio becomes more uniform due to increase in pulmonary artery pressure. Thus decrease in gaseous exchange may be explained by a shorter transit time in the pulmonary capillaries and by venous shunting, perhaps due to increased flow through the bronchial circulation. In practice, pulmonary ventilation is rarely limiting to endurance work at sea level. However, the increased use of the muscles of breathing requires an increasing proportion of the total blood flow and up to 10 per cent of the total oxygen uptake.

Hyperpnoea in exercise
Although the feedback mechanism of chemical control is known to be important in the regulation of breathing at rest, it cannot be responsible for the hyperpnoea of exercise. Increase in breathing during mild-to-moderate exercise occurs in the absence of any change of arterial Po_2, Pco_2 or pH. The mechanism of this hyperpnoea is still not certain; one theory is that at the same time as impulses travel from the motor cortex to active muscles, collateral branches to the brain stem stimulate breathing. Another theory is that impulses from proprioreceptors in the active muscles and joints travel to the respiratory centre to stimulate it. Increased chemoreceptor sensitivity to CO_2 and increased body tempera-

ture may also be contributory factors. In strenuous exercise, the blood pH does fall, because the rise in blood lactic acid concentration gradually depletes the bicarbonate buffer concentration in the blood.

The increase in pulmonary ventilation is brought about by a combination of increase in tidal volume and in respiratory rate. However, in long-term exercise the tidal volume does not exceed 50 per cent of the vital capacity, and further increase in ventilation can only be achieved by increase in rate. In short-term exercise, the tidal volume can approach the vital capacity.

Cardiovascular adjustments
With the onset of muscular activity, and perhaps even before it, the blood flow through the active muscles increases dramatically: an increase in flow of more than 10 times is not unusual in fast muscle. The increase in flow is brought about by metabolites of active muscle that act on the pre-capillary sphincters. There are a number of candidates, which include organic molecules (AMP and adenosine), inorganic ions (H^+, K^+ and PO_4^{3-}) and low Po_2, high Pco_2. The effect may well be due to the summation of several factors, and the increase in extracellular fluid osmotic pressure may itself have an effect. These local factors override what would otherwise be a vasoconstrictor action of noradrenaline released from sympathetic endings. The latter provides a mechanism for the redistribution of blood from inactive splanchnic areas and skin to active muscle.

Relaxation of pre-capillary sphincters allows the perfusion of many more capillaries, and not only does the blood flow through the muscle increase, but the mean diffusion distance from capillaries to active muscle fibres is reduced so that the gas exchange becomes more efficient. The number of capillaries that can be opened up in this way becomes greater when a muscle is trained. The blood flow through a muscle is also affected by the frequency of contraction of the active muscle fibres; blood cannot flow freely through capillaries and veins that are compressed by the continuous contraction of neighbouring muscle fibres, but intermittently contracting fibres may, by their pumping action, actually enhance the blood flow.

The increase in blood flow through muscles during even moderate exercise is so great that it can be met only by an increase in the cardiac output. Redistribution of flow can only satisfy a part of the requirements of the muscles, and the cutaneous vasoconstriction passes off anyway when the body temperature begins to rise. Table 11.18 shows the increase in cardiac output that may occur during exercise of varying severity.

Cardiac output rises in direct proportion to the increase in oxygen consumption over a wide range of exercise levels. Despite a large increase in the cardiac output, the arterial blood pressure rises less than might

Table 11.18 Approximate figures for the cardiac output and oxygen consumption during exercise of varying severity

Exercise	Cardiac output (l/min)	Total oxygen consumption of body (l/min)	Arteriovenous oxygen difference (ml/100ml)
Rest	5	0.25	5
Walking 3.2 km/h (2 mph)	10	0.8	8
Walking 8 km/h (5 mph)	20	2.5	12
Running 12 km/h (7.5 mph)	25	3.0	12
Very severe exercise (max. athletic effort)	34	4.0	13

These values apply to calm conditions. Walking or running against a wind increases the oxygen consumption markedly. For example walking at 3.2 km/h against a gale may cost 2 litres/min. (Pugh LGCE 1971 Journal of Physiology 213:225)

be expected during exercise, and may actually fall, since the total peripheral resistance is substantially reduced.

The increase in cardiac output during exercise is due to increases in both heart rate and stroke volume. An average young man with a resting heart rate of 65 beats/min and a stroke volume of 90 ml might have a maximal cardiac output during severe exertion of about 25 l/min, with a heart rate of up to 190/min and a stroke volume of 130 ml. In a trained subject, however, the pulse rate rises less (Fig. 11.19), and more of the increase in cardiac output is obtained by increasing the stroke volume.

The increase in venous return that results from the pumping action of contracting muscles and of increased respiratory movements is undoubtedly important, but during exercise a normal heart does not significantly increase its diastolic volume. The increased stroke volume is due to a more complete emptying by a more forcible systolic contraction. There is an increase of sympathetic activity very early in exercise. The heart muscle contracts more strongly with an increase in the rate of shortening and relaxation so that the duration of systole is decreased. Increased venous return ensures that filling keeps pace with increasing cardiac output so that the heart muscle remains at an optimal degree of stretch for maximal contraction.

The increase in force of ventricular contraction and the increase in heart rate are both results of reflex control through the autonomic nervous system. At the onset of exercise the main effect is a reduction of the cardio-inhibitory action of the vagus, but within a heart beat or two the increase in heart rate and stroke volume are largely due to increased activity in the cardiac sympathetic nerves and later to circulating adrenaline.

In summary, the increased cardiac output is achieved by a combination of three mechanisms: the increase in

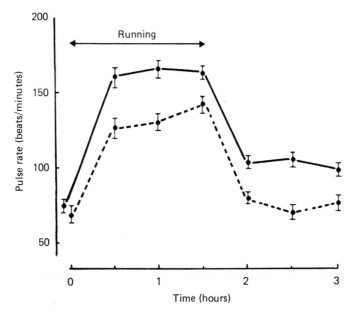

Fig. 11.19 Mean and standard deviation of the mean of observations in nine athletes (●-----●) and 18 untrained subjects (●———●) before and after running for 1.5 hours. The athletes ran much faster than the non-athletes. The athletes had a lower heart rate than the untrained subjects both during and after exercise. (Johnson R H et al. 1969 Lancet 2:452)

heart rate, Starling's Law and an increased inotropic state of the cardiac muscle. The latter two mechanisms contribute about equally to the increase in cardiac output and operate to double the stroke volume despite an increase in heart rate.

Fatigue and exhaustion

Fatigue is a state that occurs after exercise has been continued for some time and is associated with a decrease in performance capacity. It may have a physical or a psychological basis, which are at times difficult to distinguish.

The physiological basis of fatigue depends on the nature of the exercise undertaken. Thus prolonged submaximal work lasting several hours in a fasting subject may be limited by the symptoms associated with hypoglycaemia and by ionic imbalance. In intense work the loss of tension within the muscle and the subjective feelings of fatigue are related to the accumulation of lactic acid. Because of the increased acidity, glycolysis is inhibited and further energy transformation ceases. In the presence of oxygen both the pyruvic acid and the derivatives of free fatty acids are oxidised in the tricarboxylic acid cycle and the electron transfer pathway involving mitochondrial enzymes. Even though the enzymes involved in oxidative metabolism seem to function at oxygen tensions of only 1 or 2 mmHg, anaerobic metabolism is always a feature of high-intensity exercise. Another reason for a decrease in developed tension in certain situations is a failure of the excitation-contraction coupling mechanism of skeletal muscle. After severe exercise, the muscles may go into spasm or cramp, or there may be tremor due to inability to relax the muscle completely. The urine may contain albumin, haemoglobin, epithelial casts and red and white blood cells. After exercise sufficiently strenuous to cause damage to muscle fibres, myoglobin (molecular weight 1700) may also be found in the urine. Despite these alarming features, exhaustion of this type virtually never causes any lasting damage.

FURTHER READING

Astrand P-O, Rodahl K 1977 Textbook of work physiology. McGraw-Hill, London

Bassey E J, Fentem P H 1981 Work physiology. In: Edholm O G Weiner J S (eds) Principles and practice of human physiology. Academic Press, New York, pp. 19–110

Bove A A, Lowenthal D T (eds) 1983 Exercise medicine. Academic Press, New York

Durnin J V G A, Passmore R 1967 Energy, work and leisure. Heinemann, London

12

The kidney

The kidneys are often regarded as excretory organs that rid the body of the non-volatile products of metabolism, such as urea, uric acid, sulphates and phosphates. Their major function, however, is probably the regulation of the composition and volume of extracellular fluid. The mammalian kidney achieves this regulation by filtering large volumes of fluid from the blood plasma and then selectively reabsorbing from the filtrate, or secreting into it, various ions, metabolites and water.

A third function of the kidney is as an endocrine organ. Several hormones, such as renin, erythropoietin and calcitriol (p. 363) are produced in the kidney; some act locally but others affect the function of other organs.

RENAL ANATOMY

In man the two kidneys lie one on either side of the vertebral column and in the healthy adult each weighs between 115 and 170 g and measures 11–13 cm in length. On the medial side of each kidney is an indentation, the hilum, and through this pass the major renal vessels, lymphatics, nerves and the pelvis of the ureter.

The internal arrangement of a kidney can be seen on a bisected specimen (Fig. 12.1). The outer layer, the cortex, appears red or brown in a fresh specimen; inside that is the much paler medulla. The medulla is made up of a series of pyramids the apices of which, the papillae, project into the upper end of the ureter. Each

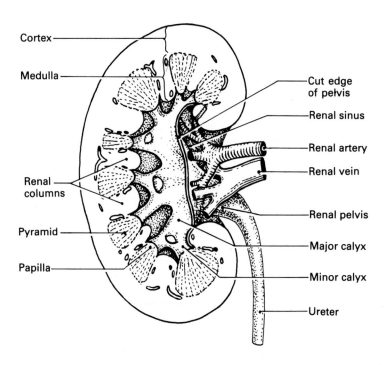

Fig. 12.1 Human kidney bisected to show cortex, medulla, calyces and papilla

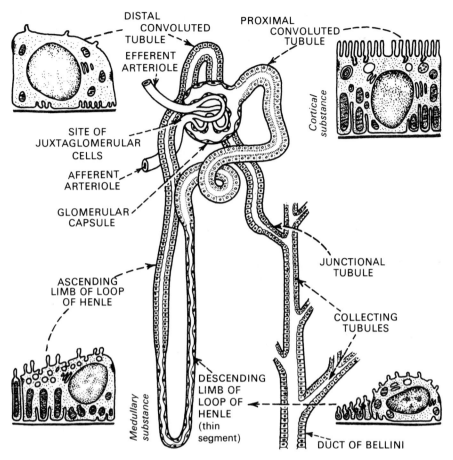

Fig. 12.2 Diagram illustrating ultrastructural features of different parts of the nephron. Only the major divisions of the nephron are shown (After Rhodin J 1958 International Review of Cytology 7:485)

papilla projects into a minor calyx. Minor calyces join together to form major calyces, which unite to form the pelvis of the ureter.

The functional unit of the kidney is the nephron (Fig. 12.2). Each human kidney contains about one million nephrons with a number of functionally distinct parts.

Glomerulus

Each nephron begins with a glomerulus, in which a clump of capillaries, derived from an afferent arteriole, join to form an efferent arteriole and invaginate the tubule to form Bowman's capsule. Glomeruli are found throughout the cortex but usually do not appear on the kidney surface.

Proximal convoluted tubule

The proximal convoluted tubule leads fluid away from Bowman's capsule. It is lined by cuboidal cells containing many mitochondria. The cells are joined to each other at the mucosal pole by tight junctions. These, together with the lateral intercellular spaces, comprise a low-resistance pathway for passive transport of fluid and low-molecular-weight solutes. A thick carpet of microvilli increases the mucosal surface available for transport while the extensive interdigitations between adjacent cells increase the area of the baso-lateral membrane. These structural characteristics are frequently found in leaky epithelia that transport large volumes of salt and water. The proximal convoluted tubule is sited solely within the renal cortex but it becomes the proximal straight tubule, or *pars recta*, which dips down towards the renal medulla and becomes the descending limb of the loop of Henle.

Loop of Henle

The cells of the thin part of the descending limb of the loop of Henle are flattened, with rudimentary microvilli, few mitochondria and few interdigitations between cells, suggesting that little active reabsorption of salt and water takes place at this site. After projecting to a variable distance into the medulla, the loop of Henle turns back on itself to form the thin ascending limb, which has similar characteristics to the descending limb. The thick part of the ascending limb of the loop of Henle begins at the junction of the inner and outer medullary segments and the cells of this area have many mitochondria and extensive lateral interdigitations.

Juxtaglomerular apparatus

The thick part of the ascending limb lies between the afferent and efferent arterioles at the pole of the glomerulus. At this point, it forms a special structure, called the juxtaglomerular apparatus (Fig. 12.3). The cells of the thick ascending limb are specialised where they abut on the arteriolar walls and are termed the *macula densa*. The juxtaglomerular cells of the afferent arteriole contain many granules, some of which are thought to contain renin.

Distal convoluted tubule and collecting ducts

Although, conventionally, the distal tubule is said to begin at the juxtaglomerular apparatus, the epithelium is similar to that of the cortical part of the thick ascending limb of Henle's loop. Distal tubular cells are cuboidal and have fewer microvilli and mitochondria than proximal tubular cells but have extensive lateral interdigitations. Distal tubules drain into connecting tubules, which in turn drain into cortical collecting tubules, then cortical and medullary collecting ducts; the cells have progressively fewer mitochondria, microvilli and lateral interdigitations. It is likely that these histological variations reflect variations in function.

Although we have described a 'typical' nephron, there are at least three different populations. Cortical nephrons have glomeruli in the superficial cortex and short loops of Henle, which project only into the outer part of the medulla (Fig. 12.4). The thin ascending limb of the loop of Henle is very short or absent. Juxtamedullary nephrons have rather larger glomeruli, which

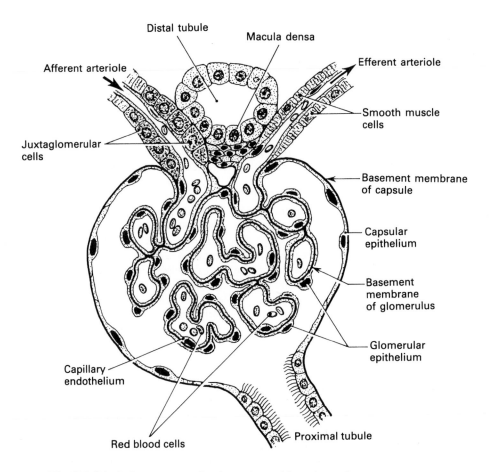

Fig. 12.3 Principal components of a glomerulus and juxtaglomerular apparatus.

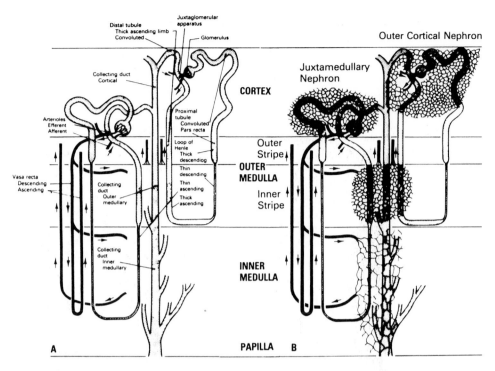

Fig. 12.4 Outer cortical and juxtamedullary nephrons and their blood vessels. A shows the major vessels and parts of the nephron; B shows capillary networks superimposed on the tubules. (From Valtin H 1983 Renal function, 2nd edn. Little Brown, Boston, by courtesy of author and publisher)

are situated near the corticomedullary border, and very long loops of Henle stretching down to the tips of the papillae. A third population of nephrons have intermediate characteristics.

It might be imagined from the foregoing description that each nephron is tightly packed and easily distinguished from other adjacent nephrons. Nothing could be further from the truth. Many proximal and distal convoluted tubules are jumbled haphazardly in the kidney cortex so that if one views the surface of the kidney it is impossible to identify tubules from any given nephron.

Blood supply

Each renal artery successively divides to form interlobar, arcuate, interlobular arteries and finally, afferent arterioles. The afferent artery gives rise to the glomerular capillaries, which join to form the efferent arteriole, which in turn supplies capillaries surrounding the complex mass of tubules in the cortex (Fig. 12.4). These capillaries eventually drain into the venous system, the arrangement of which parallels that of the arteries. Thus the kidney is another example of a portal system in which two sets of capillaries are arranged in series. Because of this arrangement, events occurring in the first capillary bed, the glomerulus, have consequences for the second set of peritubular capillaries. It is often said that each proximal (and distal) tubule is supplied by capillaries derived exclusively from its own efferent arteriole, but the evidence for this is not good.

The blood supply to the renal medulla is derived from the efferent arterioles of the juxtamedullary glomeruli (Fig. 12.4). The first branches descend as the *vasa recta* deep into the medulla and then return. There are a number of branching capillary networks between these descending and ascending limbs. Eventually both cortical and medullary system drain into the cortical venous system.

Nerve supply

The afferent and efferent arterioles are abundantly supplied with sympathetic nerves; while both alpha and beta receptors have been demonstrated, the alpha efferents appear to predominate. Dopaminergic nerves also supply the arterioles. The juxtaglomerular apparatus and proximal convoluted tubule are innervated by sympathetic nerves.

RENAL CLEARANCE

The extent to which a substance appears in the urine depends on three processes: filtration, reabsorption and secretion (Fig. 12.5). A measure of the kidney's handling of a substance is expressed as its renal *clearance*.

Clearance can be defined as the volume of plasma that is cleared of a substance in one minute and can be calculated as the amount of the substance excreted divided by its plasma concentration; that is

$$C = \frac{UV}{P}$$

when U = concentration in urine, V = urine volume in ml/min, P = concentration in plasma, and C = clearance in ml/min.

Blood flowing through the kidney is seldom completely cleared of a substance, so the clearance is a theoretical not a real volume.

Measurement of clearance can give useful information on whether a substance is absorbed from or secreted by the kidney. For example, if a substance is neither reabsorbed nor secreted by the tubule (Fig. 12.5), but is freely filtered at the glomerulus, the clearance of that substance is equivalent to the volume of plasma filtered through the glomerulus, the *glomerular filtration rate* (GFR). If the clearance of a substance exceeds the GFR then net secretion has occurred; if clearance is less than GFR either net reabsorption has occurred or the substance is not freely filterable.

RENAL BLOOD FLOW

The amount of blood that perfuses the kidneys in man is about 1200 ml/min (20 to 25 per cent of the cardiac output), which is far more than is necessary for their metabolic needs. The renal circulation is a portal circulation with a relatively high pressure in the glomerular capillaries, and a low pressure in the peritubular capillaries. Most of the resistance to flow arises in the afferent and efferent arterioles; about 60 per cent in the afferent, and 30 per cent in the efferent.

Renal plasma flow (RPF) can be measured by using clearance techniques. If a substance is totally extracted from the plasma going to the kidneys so that there is none in the plasma in the renal vein, then the clearance of that substance is equal to RPF. Para-aminohippuric acid (PAH) is a substance that in many circumstances approaches this ideal. If PAH is infused intravenously into subjects, at low plasma concentration all the PAH is extracted in one pass through the kidneys; some is filtered at the glomerulus and the remainder is secreted into the tubular lumen. The plasma concentration of PAH has to be fairly low because there is a maximum amount of PAH that the renal tubules can secrete — the tubular maximum (Tm_{PAH}) — and if the plasma concentration rises too high the Tm_{PAH} is soon exceeded (Fig. 12.6). The Tm_{PAH} in humans is about 0.4 mmol/min, although there is considerable variation between subjects.

In fact PAH is never totally absent from the renal veins since some of the blood going to the kidney

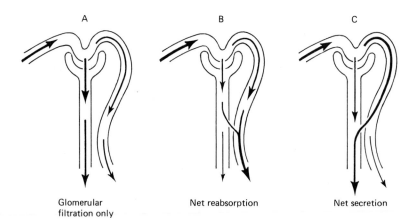

| A | B | C |

Glomerular filtration only   Net reabsorption   Net secretion

Fig. 12.5 Diagram showing the source of substances appearing in the urine. Some substances such as inulin (A) are freely filtered at the glomerulus and neither reabsorbed nor secreted by the tubule. Net reabsorption (B) occurs when substances such as sodium previously filtered into Bowman's space are reabsorbed; their output in the urine is less than the amount filtered. Some substances (such as PAH) are secreted by the tubular cells (C), and the amount appearing in the urine is greater than the amount filtered.

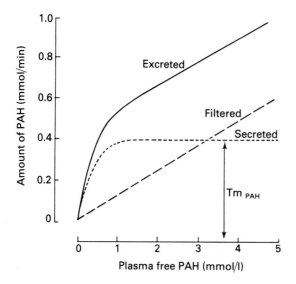

Fig. 12.6 Approximate rates of filtration, excretion and secretion (excretion–filtration) in humans at increasing plasma concentrations of PAH. The maximum amount of PAH that can be secreted (Tm_{PAH}) is about 0.4 mmol/min.

supplies the capsule, perirenal and intrarenal fat or other non-filtering areas, and so the clearance of PAH measures effective renal plasma flow. Normal figures for an adult are around 625 ml/min.

It can be seen that the measurement of renal blood flow may be a complicated procedure. In animals electromagnetic flow meters can be placed round the renal artery and the flow measured directly, but this is not applicable to humans. Because of these difficulties it has become fashionable to measure renal blood flow in a clinical context by using isotope renograms. Iodohippuric acid labelled with [131]I (Hippuran) is injected intravenously and it is handled in the kidney like PAH. Gamma counters are placed over the kidneys with the patient lying supine and the counts they record are displayed graphically against time (Fig. 12.7). Three phases of the graph can be distinguished: (a) the rising phase, which is mainly due to delivery of blood to the kidney and hence reflects renal blood flow; (b) a tissue phase, when the isotope is mainly within the cells and tubules of the kidney; and (c) a washout phase. Although a renogram can give useful data, especially if the two kidneys are compared (Fig. 12.8), the results cannot be expressed in terms of flow in ml/min, nor is it possible to distinguish different types of disease from the shape of the graph.

The methods so far described can detect blood flow changes but they do not indicate how blood is distributed to different parts of the kidney. The best evidence at present indicates that 93 per cent of the total renal blood flow goes through cortical peritubular

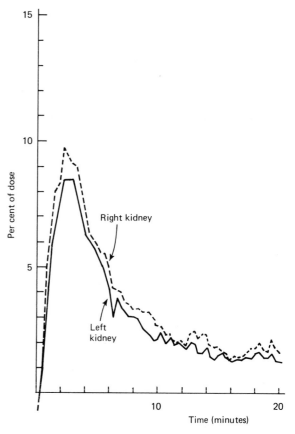

Fig. 12.7 Tracing of a normal isotope renogram. Three phases are described: a rising 'vascular' phase, a plateau 'tissue' phase, and a descending 'excretory' phase. It is not possible to correlate precisely each phase with a function. (Courtesy of H E Testa).

capillaries, some 6 per cent goes through capillaries in the outer medulla and 1 per cent or less reaches the papilla. It must be remembered, however, that all this blood has passed first of all through the glomeruli in the cortex.

There is also evidence that the blood flow can be selectively directed towards the cortical or the juxtamedullary glomeruli.

Factors affecting renal blood flow
Many of the factors that alter renal blood flow also alter GFR (p. 183). One of the most important influences on renal blood flow is a phenomenon known as *autoregulation*. When renal arterial pressure is altered in the range 80 to 160 mm Hg, renal blood flow changes little; above and below these pressures blood flow varies with renal artery pressure (Fig. 12.9). This stabilisation of blood flow is presumably caused by adaptations in arteriolar resistance, but the mechanism is not estab-

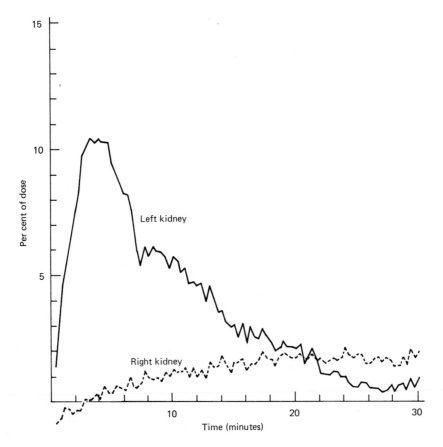

Fig. 12.8 Isotope renogram from a patient with minimal function of the right kidney. (Courtesy of H E Testa.)

lished. It may be that the arterioles are stretched by increasing arterial pressure and respond by contraction — the *myogenic theory* — or that each juxtaglomerular apparatus regulates the blood flow to its own nephron depending on flow in the distal tubule.

Stimulation of sympathetic nerves reduces the blood supply to the cortical glomeruli, but the juxtamedullary glomeruli remain relatively well perfused. The smooth muscle of the descending vasa recta is also supplied by sympathetic nerves and so sympathetic stimulation reduces medullary blood flow, which enhances the efficiency of the counter-current concentrating mechanism (p. 195).

GLOMERULAR FILTRATION

About 20 per cent of the plasma passes through the glomerular membrane into Bowman's capsule and forms the glomerular ultrafiltrate.

The forces involved in filtration at the glomerulus are the same as those operating to transfer fluid across a capillary (Chap. 3). The major force causing filtration is the substantial hydrostatic pressure of the blood in the glomerular capillaries. Because there are relatively few branches between the aorta and glomerular capillaries and because of the effects of the efferent arterioles, the glomerular capillary pressure, 50 to 60 mm Hg (7 to 8 kPa), is higher than in normal capillaries.

Opposing this is the oncotic pressure of the plasma proteins, which do not pass through the filter and the hydrostatic pressure of the fluid in Bowman's space. The relationship between these forces is expressed as

$$P_{UF} = (P_{GC} - P_T) - OsmP_{GC}$$

where P_{UF} is the ultrafiltration pressure, P_{GC} and P_T refer to hydrostatic pressure in the glomerular capillaries and tubule, and $OsmP_{GC}$ to oncotic pressure in glomerular capillaries.

However, unlike other capillaries, the fluid transport into Bowman's space is so great that the concentration of the plasma proteins rises markedly. In addition, the

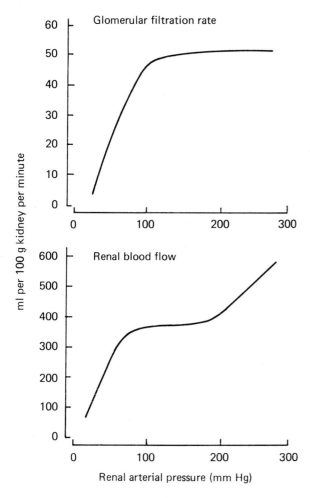

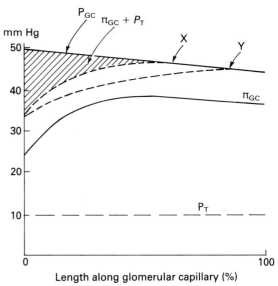

Fig. 12.10 The forces available for filtration at points along a glomerular capillary. Hydrostatic pressure in the capillaries P_{GC} falls only slightly along its length while oncotic pressure of the plasma proteins (π_{GC}) rises. Pressure inside Bowman's space (P_T) remains constant. It can be seen that the forces opposing filtration ($\pi_{GC} + P_T$) come into equilibrium with the hydrostatic force causing filtration at X (filtration equilibrium); the force available for filtration is represented by the shaded area. If glomerular plasma flow increases, the filtration equilibrium moves to point Y and it can be seen that the force available for filtration increases.

Fig. 12.9 Changes in GFR and RBF in dogs when renal arterial pressure is altered. The 'plateau' regions are said to be achieved by autoregulation. (After Shipley R E, Study R S 1951 American Journal of Physiology 167:676)

presence of the efferent arteriole ensures that the fall in hydrostatic pressure is minimal along the glomerular capillary. The profile of changes along the glomerular capillary is shown in Figure 12.10.

Filtration membrane

The filtration membrane consists of three components: the endothelium of the glomerular blood vessels, the basement membrane and the epithelial cells of Bowman's capsule, called *podocytes* because they have numerous foot processes (Fig. 12.11). The endothelium appears to have holes some 50 to 100 nm across and offers no mechanical barrier even to quite large molecules. The basement membrane is a continuous filamentous layer, fused with both the endothelium and the podocytes. The podocytes are attached to the base-

ment membrane by foot processes or *pedicels*. Adjacent pedicels are separated by filtration slits, 25 nm wide, which are bridged by a thin diaphragm.

Water and electrolytes and other molecules up to a molecular weight of about 10 000 pass freely through the filtration membrane. Thus the glomerular filtrate is a solution with a composition similar to plasma except that most protein is absent. Low-molecular-weight proteins such as β_2-microglobulin are filtered at the glomerulus, but most of these are reabsorbed in the proximal convoluted tubule.

It is not only the size of the molecule that determines whether a molecule is filtered; the shape and charge are also important. Positively charged molecules are filtered in preference to negatively charged molecules — even when these are smaller. This electrical barrier may comprise the glycoprotein matrix supported by the fenestrae in the endothelium and the slit pores between the pedicels (Fig. 12.11) together with the proteoglycans contained in the basement membrane. Thus while free haemoglobin can penetrate the glomerulus, albumin, which has more negative charges but a similar molecular weight, can normally only pass with great difficulty and is virtually excluded from the final urine. One conse-

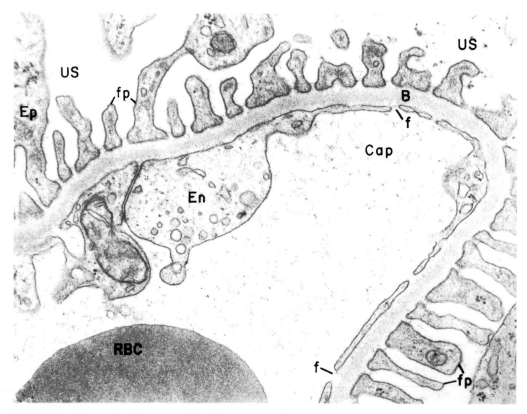

Fig. 12.11 Peripheral area of a glomerular capillary from a normal rat. The capillary wall has three distinct layers: the endothelium (En) with its periodic interruptions of fenestrae (f), the basement membrane (B) and the foot processes (fp) of the epithelium (Ep). Cap = capillary lumen, US = urinary spaces, RBC = red blood cell × 32 000. (Courtesy of M G Farquhar.)

quence of the failure of the membrane to exclude haemoglobin is that after intravascular haemolysis or crush injuries free haemoglobin is filtered into Bowman's space, and as it progresses down the tubule, reabsorption of water and salts causes its concentration to rise until it forms a gel that blocks the tubule.

Glomerular filtration rate

The amount of fluid filtered at the glomerulus is a very important measurement both in renal physiology and in the assessment of renal function in patients. GFR can be assessed by measuring the clearance of a substance that is freely filtered at the glomerulus, not bound to plasma proteins, neither reabsorbed nor secreted by the renal tubule, and not metabolised by the cells. Of the substances available inulin (a polyfructose of molecular weight 5500) is nearly ideal; for clinical assessment creatinine, which is produced endogenously, is used.

To measure inulin clearance it is necessary to infuse a solution of inulin intravenously until the plasma level is constant and then to collect a timed urine sample,

usually over a period of 3 to 5 hours, and to measure the urine and plasma concentrations. Using the formula

$$C_{in} = \frac{U_{in}V}{P_{in}}$$

the clearance of inulin can be calculated. This test is impractical in clinical investigation since it involves a long intravenous infusion.

Creatinine is a substance produced from the muscles of the body in relatively constant daily amounts. Thus with creatinine there is no need for an infusion. The disadvantages of creatinine, however, are (a) that a small amount of creatinine is secreted by the renal tubule and (b) that the conventional methods of analysis measure other substances in plasma besides creatinine. In normal subjects these errors cancel and there is a good agreement between the clearances of inulin and creatinine.

Over recent years, more use has been made of plasma creatinine measurements alone. Since the amount of creatinine produced is similar from day to day, the amount excreted must be fairly constant and the formula

$$C_{Cr} = \frac{U_{Cr}V}{P_{Cr}}$$

can be arranged such that

$$C_{Cr} \propto \frac{1}{P_{Cr}}$$

This relationship is shown in Figure 12.12. Thus, the plasma creatinine can be monitored in order to follow changes in GFR.

Other techniques involving single injections of substances have also been pioneered for measuring GFR. These include the excretion of radioactively labelled vitamin B_{12} and radioactive renograms using a variety of substances like DTPA (diethylenetriamine-penta acetic acid). Renograms cannot give measurements of GFR (see Fig. 12.8) but they may give a general indication that 'renal function' is impaired without being able to specify which of the renal mechanisms is involved. Measurement of plasma clearance of DTPA (by giving a single injection and taking multiple timed blood samples) can give a reasonably quantitative measure of GFR.

Using these techniques the GFR has been measured in large numbers of normal individuals and has been found to be about 125 ml/min for an adult.

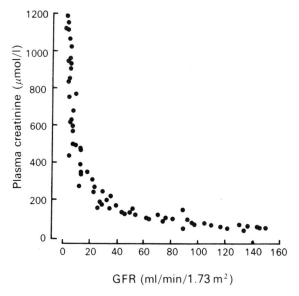

Fig. 12.12 Relation between plasma creatinine concentration and glomerular filtration rate in normal persons and in patients with chronic renal disease. (Courtesy of M Allison)

Filtration fraction

The filtration fraction is the proportion of the fluid passing to the glomerulus that is filtered. It can be calculated from the GFR and RPF, both of which are measured by using clearance techniques. The filtration fraction in humans is about 20 per cent. This means that the concentration of the substances not filtered at the glomerulus, notably red blood cells and albumin, rises along the length of the glomerular capillaries and may be 25 per cent higher in the efferent than in the afferent arteriole.

Factors affecting GFR

The GFR is about 125 ml/min for a subject with a body surface area of 1.73 m^2. The bigger the individual the higher the GFR is likely to be; because of their larger size, men usually have a higher GFR than women. The GFR tends to be higher in the secretory phase of the menstrual cycle than in the proliferative phase; pregnancy may increase GFR by 50 to 100 per cent. It is often said that GFR is constant in any one individual, but this is not so. There can be minute-to-minute variations due to changes in a number of factors. If RPF is increased the GFR rises proportionately. From the consideration of the forces and permeability of the membrane given earlier this is not immediately apparent, but it must be realised that increasing RPF alters the point at which equilibrium occurs (e.g. from X to Y in Fig. 12.10), and this increases the mean ultrafiltration pressure without altering hydrostatic pressure in the glomerular capillaries. Once filtration disequilibrium has been reached (i.e. when pressure equilibrium does not occur before the end of the glomerular capillaries) the effect of changing RPF becomes much less marked.

Constriction of the afferent and efferent arterioles might also alter GFR. Afferent arteriolar constriction decreases both glomerular plasma flow and glomerular capillary pressure; both contribute to a decrease in GFR. Constriction of the efferent arteriole has variable effects. It leads to a direct increase in glomerular capillary pressure, which would tend to increase filtration, but decreases plasma flow, which has the opposite effects. Which of these effects predominates at any one time is impossible to predict.

Stimulation of renal sympathetic nerves can have dramatic effects. Usually afferent arterioles are preferentially constricted, resulting in a decreased blood flow, a decreased filtration pressure and a reduced GFR. It has been suggested that stimulation of dopaminergic nerves could have the opposite effect.

It might be expected that changing the systemic arterial pressure would greatly alter the GFR, but this is not usually so because of the phenomenon of auto-regulation described earlier (p. 179). One might expect changes in plasma oncotic pressure to produce a dramatic effect on GFR but this does not seem to occur, perhaps because the permeability of the filtration membrane is itself altered by the protein.

The mesangium

If a glomerulus is sectioned it can be seen that the centre of the tuft of capillaries is occupied by special cells, the *mesangial cells* (Fig. 12.13). These cells are phagocytic and engulf protein and also immune complexes that escape from the capillaries. It may be that they can also alter GFR. They contain contractile elements that alter the shape and/or the volume of the cells and by altering their contact with the glomerular capillaries may alter the area available for filtration. A number of hormones such as vasopressin are known to cause constriction of mesangial cells and so may indirectly affect the amount of fluid filtered.

TUBULAR FUNCTION

The amount of any substance reabsorbed or secreted by the tubular epithelium (X) is the difference between the amount filtered by the glomeruli and the amount in the urine. The amount filtered is the product of the GFR and the plasma concentration of unbound substance; the amount in the urine is the product of the urine flow rate and the concentration of the substance in the urine.

Thus,

$$X = (GFR \times P) - (U \times V)$$

If X is positive, reabsorption exceeds secretion; if X is negative, the opposite is true. Table 12.14 shows some

Table 12.14 Typical adult figures for the amounts of various substances filtered at the glomerulus and the final amounts excreted in the urine

Compound	Amount filtered (mmol/day)	Amount excreted (mmol/day)
Sodium	26 000	150
Potassium	900	150
Calcium	270	3.5
Magnesium	200	6
Chloride	19 000	200
Sulphate	65	25
Urea	900	440
Uric acid	30	4
Glucose	900	<5

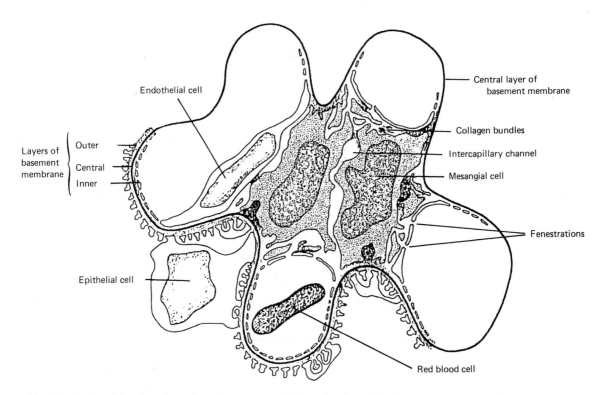

Fig. 12.13 Mesangial region of rat glomerulus, surrounded by capillaries. (After Latta H 1973 In: Orloff J, Berliner R W (eds) Handbook of Physiology 8: Renal Physiology, p. 19

typical figures. Such figures only give an overall picture and give no indication of what happens in the different parts of the nephron. For example, there is net reabsorption of potassium in the proximal tubule but, usually, net secretion in the distal segments. In addition, of course, each net flux is probably the difference of two individual fluxes, one reabsorptive and one secretory.

Proximal tubule
In general the proximal convoluted tubule is concerned with reabsorption of large quantities of solutes and water; probably about two-thirds of the filtered load of sodium and water and slightly more of potassium. Reabsorption is against a very small electrochemical gradient and the epithelium is considered to be leaky (p. 175). However, mechanisms for changing reabsorption in the proximal tubule may not alter the final output in the urine because once the fluid has left the proximal tubule it still has to pass through the loop of Henle, distal tubule and collecting ducts, where it can be further modified. So the final, precise control of urinary composition cannot be effected by proximal tubular control mechanisms.

Another function of the proximal tubule is the reabsorption of various organic substances. Glucose and amino acids are almost entirely reabsorbed in the first part of the proximal tubule. Such protein as is filtered is usually reabsorbed in the proximal tubule, as is the small amount of albumin filtered. Hydrogen ions and ammonia are secreted along the length of the proximal tubule as well as in the distal nephron.

Organic acids and bases are also secreted in the proximal tubule, particularly in the pars recta. The functional significance of this is not known but the same mechanism is used for excretion of drugs such as penicillin and probenecid and for such substances as diodrast, PAH and phenol red, which have been used to assess renal function.

Loop of Henle
Many of the functions of the loop of Henle are related to concentrating mechanisms; the loop reabsorbs a considerable amount of salt and water (p. 195).

Distal tubule
In contrast to the proximal tubule, the distal tubule has a relatively tight epithelium, which reabsorbs small amounts of solutes against a large electrochemical gradient. Because the distal tubule and the collecting duct are the last parts of the nephron they have a dominant influence on the final composition of the urine and many of the control mechanisms are sited here.

The secretion of potassium is a major function, contrasting with potassium reabsorption in the proximal tubule. Hydrogen ions and ammonia are secreted in the distal as well as the proximal tubule.

Collecting system
The collecting duct system has many properties in common with the distal tubule. Sodium reabsorption takes place against a considerable gradient. In addition, the collecting ducts traverse the hypertonic renal medulla and water can be reabsorbed back into the blood, while other low-molecular-weight substances leak from the medullary interstitium to the lumen of the collecting duct.

Transport processes
Substances can cross the renal epithelium by passing across the cells (transcellular route) or between the cells via the tight junctions and lateral intercellular spaces (paracellular route). Transport across the cells usually involves carrier-mediated transport across at least one membrane and may be energy dependent (Chap. 2) while transport between cells occurs by diffusion down electrical or chemical gradients. Another means of transport — *solvent drag* — depends on small solutes passing through the same channels as water molecules and being 'dragged' by water movement, however that is caused.

SODIUM TRANSPORT

In man some 25 mol of sodium is filtered each day and more than 99 per cent is reabsorbed (Table 12.14). Most of the reabsorption takes place in the proximal tubule.

Reabsorption in the proximal tubule
The proportion of the filtered sodium reabsorbed in the proximal tubule of man is not known though figures for animals vary from 50 per cent in rats to 80 per cent in monkeys. Absorption occurs via transcellular and paracellular routes; at least 70 per cent of reabsorption is transcellular. Some of the mechanisms are similar to those described for the small intestine (p. 275).

Sodium enters the cell by moving passively down its concentration and electrical gradients. Some sodium entry is coupled to hydrogen ions and a small amount (less than 10 per cent) is coupled to glucose and amino acid entry into the cell (Fig. 12.15). There is some dispute as to whether sodium and chloride are co-transported into the proximal tubular cells, but such evidence as is available in mammals suggests that this is not so. At the basolateral cell membrane, sodium is actively transported against both electrical and chemical gradients by the Na^+, K^+-ATPase.

Passive reabsorption must occur down an electrochemical gradient. However in the proximal convoluted

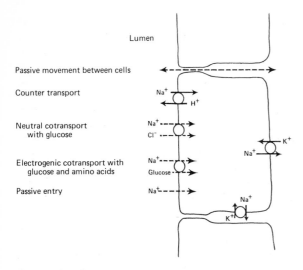

Lumen

Passive movement between cells

Counter transport   Na$^+$ H$^+$

Neutral cotransport   Na$^+$
with glucose   Cl$^-$
    K$^+$
    Na$^+$

Electrogenic cotransport with   Na$^+$
glucose and amino acids   Glucose

Passive entry   Na$^+$
    Na$^+$
    K$^+$

Fig. 12.15 Possible routes and mechanisms of sodium movement across the proximal convoluted tubule. Coupled transport is indicated by the circles and energy requiring processes by solid lines.

tubule there is no concentration gradient so that the small electrical gradients between the tubular lumen and the interstitium are important. In the first part of the proximal tubule the tubule is 5 mV negative with respect to the interstitium and little passive sodium reabsorption occurs. In the last two-thirds of the proximal tubule, however, the potential difference is 2 mV (tubule *positive*) and so some passive movement can occur. The positive potential arises because early preferential bicarbonate reabsorption (p. 192) leaves a higher concentration of chloride ions in the lumen than in the interstitium; movement of negative chloride ions down this concentration gradient leaves the lumen positive. Some sodium also moves by solvent drag.

Reabsortion in the loop of Henle
About 25 per cent of the filtered sodium is thought to be reabsorbed by the loop of Henle and the loop has plenty of 'spare capacity' so that if proximal tubular reabsorptlon falls, the loop can reabsorb more sodium. Transport of sodium across the thin parts of the loop of Henle is probably passive, although there is some evidence of a weak active transport system in the thin ascending limb.

In the thick ascending limb coupled transport of sodium and chloride occurs across the luminal membrane, probably on a protein carrier that has transport sites for 1 sodium, 1 potassium and 2 chloride ions. Sodium is actively extruded at the basolateral membrane by Na$^+$, K$^+$–ATPase but some of the potassium leaks back into the tubular lumen and this results in the thick

ascending limb having a potential gradient of about 7 mV with the lumen positive.

The absorption of electrolytes in the thick ascending limb is not coupled with absorption of water; this is an important mechanism in creating a hypertonic medulla (see p. 195) and a hypotonic tubular fluid. For this reason the thick ascending limb and adjacent parts of the distal tubule are often called the diluting segment.

Reabsorption in the distal tubule and collecting ducts
About 8 per cent of the filtered load of sodium is actively reabsorbed in the distal parts of the nephron, though the proportion can be varied. While some co-transport of sodium and chloride takes place across the mucosal membrane, counter transport with hydrogen ions is more important. Sodium is then actively transported across the basolateral membrane by Na$^+$, K$^+$-ATPase. Sodium reabsorption and potassium secretion are related (p. 188).

As the collecting ducts pass through the renal medulla, the gradient of sodium concentration between the interstitial fluid and the lumen increases. Although there is usually a small net reabsorption there is evidence that sodium leaks back into the lumen from the hypertonic medulla.

Control of sodium reabsorption
The amount of sodium consumed in a normal human diet is between 50 and 150 mmol/day. This is the most that needs to be lost (by all routes) to keep an adult in sodium balance. When one considers that in the kidney 25 mol of sodium are filtered and the controllable part of sodium excretion needs to be between 0.2 and 0.6 per cent of this, the magnitude of the problem becomes apparent.

Sodium is the principal cation in extracellular fluid (p. 18). If too much sodium is retained in the body, water is also retained and the extracellular fluid volume increases. If too much sodium is excreted the extracellular fluid volume contracts. Regulation of sodium is thus intimately related to regulation of the body's extracellular fluid volume.

Basically the body has to be defended against two major threats to sodium homeostasis: spontaneous increases in GFR and alterations of sodium intake in the diet. Excessive loss of salt by other routes, such as sweating, has the same effect as a reduced dietary intake.

Spontaneous changes in GFR
A rise in GFR leads to a rise in the amount of sodium filtered. Unless a compensatory increase in sodium reabsorption takes place excess sodium would be lost. For example, in pregnancy GFR increases by 50 to 100 per cent and an extra 12 to 25 mmol sodium must be

reabsorbed if the body's sodium stores are not to be depleted.

It is thought that the increase in sodium reabsorption is due to a phenomenon known as *glomerulo-tubular balance*. This means that the proximal tubule absorbs a constant fraction of the filtered sodium. The underlying mechanism is not known; suggested factors include the change in the flow rate within the tubule, the increase in the oncotic pressure or the fall in hydrostatic pressure in the peritubular capillaries, and increases in angiotensin II levels.

Changes in sodium intake

The changes in sodium reabsorption that occur in response to an altered sodium intake are very different from those occurring in response to spontaneous changes in the GFR. For example, an increase in GFR is one of the major responses to an increase in sodium intake. The mechanism of this response is not clear but may be due to the effects of volume receptors since an increase in sodium intake leads to a rise in ECF volume and perhaps an increase in blood pressure.

The rise in GFR in this situation is not associated with an increase in sodium reabsorption. This lack of glomerulo-tubular balance may reflect the fall in plasma oncotic pressure that is associated with a rise in ECF volume. In addition increasing blood pressure may lead to dilatation of the afferent and efferent arterioles, an increase in the flow through the peritubular capillaries and a further fall in the oncotic pressure. The fall in oncotic pressure in these capillaries decreases the uptake of fluid and sodium, and so increases sodium excretion.

Aldosterone production from the adrenal cortex is decreased when the sodium intake is increased, and increased when sodium intake decreases. The usual way this is achieved is through the renin-angiotensin system (p. 206), but a large reduction of plasma sodium (more than 20 mmol/l) may stimulate the adrenal cortex directly. Aldosterone (p. 206) increases sodium reabsorption and potassium secretion by the distal tubule and collecting duct.

Changes in GFR and aldosterone cannot account for all the changes in sodium excretion that occur and a number of natriuretic factors have been described. These include a specific natriuretic hormone, which has not yet been positively identified or characterised, a number of vasodilators, parathyrin, prostaglandins and kinins. Some of these may act because of their effects on renal vasculature, but some, such as prostaglandins, may also have a direct effect on tubular reabsorption. The recently isolated atrial natriuretic factor probably mainly has a vascular action although some actions on tubules are now reported. Its precise physiological role has yet to be determined.

Stimulation of nerves supplying the kidney has a number of effects on sodium excretion. Stimulation of nerves supplying the afferent arteriole causes constriction and a reduction in filtration, while stimulation of nerves to the juxtaglomerular apparatus increases renin production and hence angiotensin II and aldosterone concentration. A direct increase in reabsorption can be produced by stimulating nerves supplying the proximal tubules. Renal nerves may increase sodium and water reabsorption by redistributing renal blood flow preferentially to the long juxtamedullary nephrons since they normally reabsorb more sodium and water than the short cortical nephrons. Such effects have only been demonstrated in experimental animals.

Diuretics

An increase in urine production above normal is known as a diuresis. Drugs that increase urine flow are known as diuretics. Many diuretics act because they alter sodium transport; clinically they are useful in reducing an abnormally high extracellular fluid volume in a number of conditions. Technically water itself is a potent diuretic, since it increases urine flow, as is alcohol, which acts by preventing secretion of vasopressin (p. 307).

Osmotic diuretics

The presence of any non-absorbable substance within the renal tubule exerts an osmotic force reducing fluid reabsorption. Mannitol is probably the commonest administered osmotic diuretic, but glucose can act as an osmotic agent when, in diabetes mellitus, not all the tubular glucose can be reabsorbed. This prevents water reabsorption and at the same time increases sodium excretion and increases potassium excretion.

Thiazide diuretics

Thiazides produce a natriuresis and chloruresis that is not dependent on the acid–base status of the individual. They act by inhibiting sodium reabsorption in the cortical part of the diluting segment, but may also inhibit sodium reabsorption in proximal tubule. Once they have reduced extracellular fluid volume, thiazides reduce GFR.

Loop diuretics

These are the most potent diuretics available at present; the group includes frusemide, ethacrynic acid and bumetanide. Their major action is on transport processes in the thick ascending limb of the loop of Henle. Since up to 25 per cent of the filtrate is reabsorbed in the loop of Henle it is obvious that these can produce a profound diuresis. Because they interfere with mechanisms responsible for generating osmotic gradients in the medulla, these agents produce an isosmotic urine. It has been reported that they have minor actions on the proximal tubule and the juxtaglomerular apparatus. Potassium secretion is increased by two mechanisms: inhibition of the sodium/potassium/chloride co-transport system prevents potassium reabsorption, while an increase in distal fluid flow enhances potassium secretion. Calcium reabsorption in the loop of Henle is also inhibited and calcium excretion increases.

Secretion of loop diuretics occurs by the organic anion transport system in the proximal tubule and so they interfere with urate secretion. The drugs are active at the luminal membrane and so secretion is a necessary prerequisite for their action.

Potassium-sparing diuretics

These are three chemically unrelated compounds — spironolactone, triamterene and amiloride — which act on the distal nephron and cause potassium retention. All are relatively weak diuretics the actions of which are enhanced by combination with other more potent agents.

Spironolactone is a true antagonist for aldosterone; it inhibits it and so only exerts an effect when aldosterone secretion is high. Triamterene acts in the same part of the nephron but is able to cause an effect even in adrenalectomised individuals, so it does not act by competing with aldosterone. The actions of spironolactone and triamterene are additive.

Amiloride at very low concentrations blocks specific channels through which sodium crosses cell membranes. At higher concentrations sodium/hydrogen exchange is inhibited. This action in the distal tubule probably accounts for its diuretic action. Recently it has also been demonstrated that amiloride inhibits Na^+, K^+–ATPase.

POTASSIUM

Most reabsorption of potassium takes place in the proximal tubule while secretion of potassium occurs in the distal tubule and collecting ducts. In most physiological conditions there is net reabsorption of potassium by the kidney; usually the amount of potassium excreted is 10 to 20 per cent of that filtered.

The proximal convoluted tubule reabsorbs some 80 per cent of the filtered potassium, though the means whereby this is achieved is not certain. Some reabsorption is said to occur by an active transcellular mechanism but the direct evidence for this is sparse.

Potassium is also reabsorbed in the thick ascending limb of Henle's loop, by the co-transport system that transfers two chloride ions for one sodium ion and one potassium ion. By the end of the loop of Henle all but 5 to 10 per cent of the filtered potassium has been reabsorbed.

In the distal tubules and collecting ducts, potassium is both reabsorbed and secreted. Different mechanisms are involved and possibly even different cells; either net secretion or net reabsorption takes place depending on which transport system predominates. Reabsorption probably occurs through mechanisms similar to those in the thick ascending limb of the loop of Henle. Potassium is, however, generally secreted in the distal tubule. It was once assumed that potassium secretion and sodium reabsorption were directly linked in the distal tubule; a carrier molecule was postulated to reabsorb sodium across the luminal cell membrane and secrete either potassium or hydrogen ions. This is now known not to be the case.

Intracellular potassium concentration is high (although not known with any accuracy) when compared with that in the tubular interstitial fluids. This favours passive potassium movement across both luminal and basolateral membranes (Fig. 12.16); the precise amount that crosses each membrane depends on the permeability of that membrane to potassium. This leakage of potassium generates a negative potential inside the cell; this is partly offset across the luminal membrane by sodium diffusing into the cell. Sodium is actively secreted from the cell across the basolateral membrane by a sodium

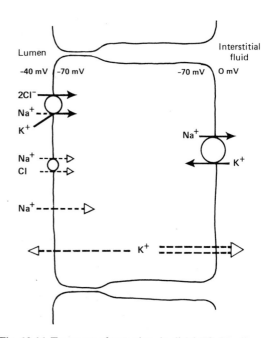

Fig. 12.16 Transport of potassium in distal tubule cells. Sodium enters the cell and is pumped out, in exchange for K^+, at the basolateral membrane by the sodium pump. Some K may be reabsorbed on a Na^+:K^+:$2Cl^-$ co-transport system. Potassium leaves the cells through conductive pathways. Some authors suggest that reabsorption from and secretion into the tubular lumen occur in different cells.

pump (p. 11) which, at the same time, delivers potassium into the cell, so serving to maintain the high intracellular potassium that is necessary for diffusion, particularly across the luminal membrane. The net result is that potassium is pumped into the cell across the basolateral membrane and then diffuses across the luminal membrane.

Similar processes seem to exist in collecting ducts but the net fluxes are smaller. One additional mechanism needs to be considered. Because there is a high concentration of potassium in the renal medulla some may diffuse passively into the collecting duct lumen. How important this route is in practice is not known.

Control of potassium excretion

There is no known control mechanism for potassium reabsorption in the proximal tubule and probably no physiological control in the loop of Henle; some diuretic drugs such as frusemide probably interfere with reabsorption at this site as they inhibit the co-transport process. In the distal segments of the nephron four important factors must be considered: flow rate along the nephron, aldosterone, changes in acid–base balance and changes in potassium intake.

One of the limiting factors to potassium secretion is the concentration of potassium in distal tubular fluid; the higher it is the less potassium can diffuse out from the cell. Consequently, any factor that increases tubular flow rate will increase potassium secretion, because it reduces the potassium concentration in the tubule. This is probably the means whereby most diuretics that act on the proximal tubule or on the loop of Henle increase potassium secretion.

Aldosterone increases potassium excretion as well as increasing sodium reabsorption either because of its effect on luminal membrane permeability or because of its effect on Na^+, K^+–ATPase activity enhancing intracellular potassium concentration (p. 320).

Acute changes in acid–base balance have a profound effect on renal potassium excretion. Acute metabolic acidosis leads to a reduced potassium secretion and acute metabolic alkalosis leads to increased potassium secretion. Chronic changes in acid–base status are much more difficult to interpret, however, since they have other effects on the kidney. For example, chronic metabolic acidosis inhibits reabsorption of salt and water by the proximal convoluted tubule, leading to an increased flow in the distal tubule; in turn the increase in distal flow increases the potassium loss (see above) and this masks the normal diminution of secretion that acidosis would be expected to cause. The precise mechanism for potassium secretion that is affected by an acute change in acid–base status is not known.

Most acute changes in potassium intake evoke a response via aldosterone. Other changes occur as plasma potassium concentration rises increasing delivery to Na^+, K^+–ATPase in the basolateral membrane of the distal tubular cells or because of a general increase in cellular potassium, which would increase passive diffusion across the luminal membrane.

HYDROGEN ION (HYDRION)

The body produces many acidic waste products during metabolism. Of these the most important quantitatively is CO_2, which is eliminated in the lungs. A number of fixed or non-volatile acids also have to be eliminated and the major route is through the kidney. If the kidney is unable to deal with these excess acids, as happens in chronic renal failure, then the patient becomes acidaemic and may die because of the cellular effects of increased hydrion concentration.

Mechanism of hydrion secretion

The production of hydrions is similar in all renal tubular cells (Fig. 12.17). Water molecules are split and the hydrions are secreted while the hydroxyl ions combine with CO_2 under the influence of carbonic anhydrase to form bicarbonate (hydrocarbonate) ions

$$H_2O \rightleftharpoons H^+ + OH^-$$
$$OH^- + CO_2 \rightleftharpoons HCO_3^-$$

Conventionally this has been represented as two separate steps, hydration of CO_2 (under the influence of carbonic anhydrase) and subsequent ionisation to give hydrions and bicarbonate ions. The end result is the same.

Hydrions are secreted across the luminal membrane of the cell. A carrier has been demonstrated that exchanges hydrogen and sodium ions, but whether this accounts for all the hydrion secretion is not known; it certainly does not account for all the sodium reabsorption. The energy for hydrion secretion is derived from the sodium gradient (p. 10).

Sodium that enters the cell through an exchange mechanism is pumped across the basolateral cell membrane by the sodium pump (p. 11). Bicarbonate ions formed in the cell also pass across the basolateral membrane. This may be because the basolateral membrane is very much more permeable to bicarbonate ions than the apical membrane, or because bicarbonate is exchanged for another anion such as chloride, using a carrier in the basolateral membrane. The net result is that for each hydrion secreted the kidney manufactures a bicarbonate ion that is available for buffering in other body fluids. It is important to recognise that this is the result whatever the fate of the secreted hydrions.

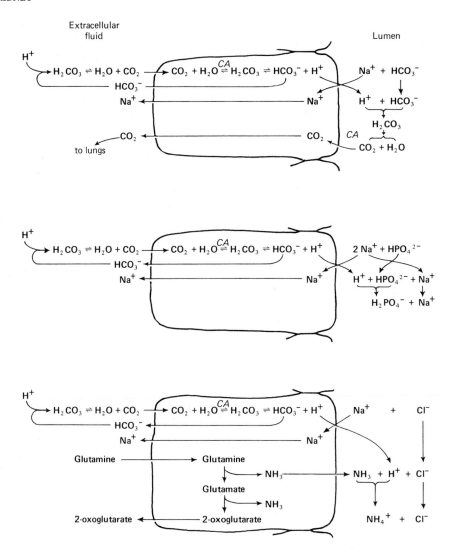

Fig. 12.17 Mechanisms for the production and secretion of hydrogen ions. Carbonic anhydrase (CA) is not only within cells but is also attached to the luminal surfaces of the tubular cells.

Most of the hydrions secreted into the luminal fluid are buffered in one of three ways (Fig. 12.17). The importance of these buffers varies in different parts of the tubule. In the early part of the proximal tubule hydrions predominantly react with bicarbonate in the glomerular filtrate and form carbonic acid, which dissociates to form water and CO_2. Both of these are easily reabsorbed across the tubular epithelium. Carbonic anhydrase has an important role in the hydration of CO_2.

In the blood, and also in the glomerular filtrate, the principal forms of phosphate are HPO_4^{2-} and $H_2PO_4^-$, in a ratio of 4:1. Secretion of hydrion results in buffering by conversion of HPO_4^{2-} to $H_2PO_4^-$. This process takes place mainly in the distal tubule but also to a small extent in the proximal tubule. Hydrions excreted in this way are the major component of the 'titratable acid', which is measured when urine is titrated to pH 7.4 by addition of alkali.

Ammonia is produced in the tubular cells by deamination of glutamine or other amino acids. Glutamine is filtered at the glomerulus and almost completely reabsorbed in the early parts of the proximal tubule. The remainder of the tubule obtains its glutamine by uptake from the blood. In tubular fluid, ammonia and hydrion combine to form ammonium ions to which the tubular epithelium is not permeable; ammonium ions therefore remain trapped in the tubule. This process is known as *diffusion-trapping*.

In the proximal convoluted tubule bicarbonate is the

major buffer for the hydrions secreted. The pH of fluid from the end of the proximal tubule is 6.6 to 6.7 but most of the change from the glomerular filtrate pH of 7.4 occurs early in the tubule; bicarbonate concentration falls most rapidly at the same site (p. 192). Some titratable acid is formed and some ammonia is secreted. The proximal convoluted tubule is the major site for hydrion secretion.

In distal tubules ammonia secretion and titratable acid are much more important than bicarbonate as buffering mechanisms. Because the total quantity of buffer has been reduced, however, the pH may fall further and reach 6.0. The major site of ammonia secretion is difficult to determine. Most ammonia is produced in proximal tubular cells. Because of the anatomical arrangements of the tubules in the renal cortex it is likely that of the ammonia produced by cells of the first part of the proximal convoluted tubule some diffuses into the proximal tubule while some diffuses to surrounding tubules, particularly those that have a lower pH.

The final urinary pH may vary from 4.5 to 8.4 depending on diet, time of day, and a number of other factors. Final secretion of hydrions seems to take place in the collecting ducts but as yet little is known about this.

Control of hydrion secretion

The amount of hydrion secreted depends to a large extent on the pH of body fluids. If the pH of body fluids is low then the urine has a low pH, no bicarbonate, a high titratable acid and a high ammonium ion concentration; if the pH of body fluids is high the urine has a high pH, variable amounts of bicarbonate, a low or even negative titratable acid and few or no ammonium ions.

Control seems to be exerted mainly through the effects of CO_2 directly on renal tubular cells. An increased P_{CO_2} of plasma results in greater hydrion secretion and more bicarbonate manufactured (a compensated respiratory acidaemia), whereas a decreased P_{CO_2} in plasma produces the opposite effect (a compensated respiratory alkalaemia). Damage to the kidney produces retention of hydrion and a reduction of bicarbonate (a metabolic acidaemia).

Alterations in plasma potassium concentration also have effects on acid secretion. As plasma potassium concentration rises, cellular concentration of potassium increases and the cell becomes alkaline, fewer hydrions are available for secretion; less bicarbonate is reabsorbed from the tubular fluid and a more alkaline urine results. The converse sequence occurs if the plasma concentration of potassium falls.

As plasma pH falls the amount of ammonia secreted is increased, perhaps as much as tenfold from a normal value of 50 mmol/day to 500 mmol/day. The precise stimulus for this increase and the mechanism by which it is achieved still require elucidation; there are probably multiple sites in the glutamine metabolic pathway that could be regulated. A cascade of different regulatory sites has been proposed, some of them involving induction of enzyme production.

Effects of carbonic anhydrase inhibitors

Carbonic anhydrase has a central role in acid secretion by the kidney (Fig. 12.17) as well as being important in erythrocytes, the gastrointestinal tract, the choroid plexuses and the ciliary body. If carbonic anhydrase inhibitors such as Diamox (acetazolamide) are given to patients, the relationship between urinary and plasma pH is broken. Because little hydrion can be secreted the urinary pH is alkaline, there is no titratable acid, little ammonia secretion, and considerable bicarbonate excretion. At the same time the plasma pH falls. It thus appears that carbonic anhydrase is essential for the mechanisms necessary to protect the body from major changes in pH.

DIVALENT CATIONS

Calcium

Calcium levels in the extracellular fluid are precisely controlled. Plasma contains about 2.5 mmol/l calcium, of which about 40 per cent is bound to proteins and so cannot be filtered by the glomerulus. Most of the filtered calcium is reabsorbed in the proximal tubule and thick ascending limb of the loop of Henle. In the proximal tubule calcium reabsorption parallels the reabsorption of sodium and water. Up to 60 per cent may be reabsorbed passively via the paracellular route, though some is reabsorbed by an active transcellular route. Entry into the cells is probably passive, while exit from the cells may be by a calcium/sodium countertransport system or may be directly linked to a calcium ATPase. In the thick part of the ascending limb and in the distal tubule there is an active transport system which in the thick ascending limb is very powerful.

Calcium reabsorption is controlled by parathyrin and calcitriol. Parathyrin inhibits calcium reabsorption in the proximal tubule and enhances reabsorption in the loop of Henle and distal tubule. The net effect is increased reabsorption of calcium. However, since the effects of parathyrin on bone are to increase plasma calcium concentration (p. 360), the net effects are to increase the filtered load of calcium and in spite of the increased reabsorption more is excreted and this may cause formation of renal stones. Calcitriol also stimulates net reabsorption of calcium by the kidney, in part by inhibiting the effect of parathyrin on the proximal convoluted tubule and in part by a direct action on the tubule. The effects of calcitonin on the kidney are not yet understood.

Magnesium

The normal plasma concentration is 1 to 2 mmol/l, of which 80 per cent is ultrafilterable. Only 3 per cent of the filtered load is excreted (about 4 to 7 mmol/day). Reabsorption of magnesium by the proximal convoluted tubule is not great, estimates vary from 0 to 30 per cent of the filtered load, and so the concentration rises until at the end of the proximal convoluted tubule the concentration of magnesium is 50 per cent higher than in the glomerular filtrate. Most reabsorption takes place in the thick ascending limb of the loop of Henle but the mechanism is not clear. It appears to be voltage dependent and is limited, so that magnesium reabsorption appears to exhibit a tubular maximum. Parathyrin enhances tubular reabsorption of magnesium as of calcium, in the loop of Henle and distal tubule. In addition aldosterone increases magnesium excretion; the mechanism is unknown.

ANIONS

Chloride

Chloride ions can move passively in some parts of the renal tubule, following chemical or electrical gradients, but the proportions that move transcellularly and paracellularly are not known. Two other major mechanisms must also be considered, co-transport with sodium or exchange for other anions. When ions move transcellularly the negative interior of the cell hinders entry into the cell but aids exit.

In the proximal convoluted tubule, some passive reabsorption occurs. Preferential bicarbonate reabsorption in the very early part of the tubule leads to a raised chloride concentration and a gradient from the tubule to the peritubular fluid. This gradient could account for some chloride movement via paracellular pathways and also some passive sodium movement, since the movement of negatively charged anions renders the inside of the renal tubule positive. This probably cannot account for more than 30 per cent of the transport, however. Exchange of chloride for other ions occurs by mechanisms similar to those in red blood cells (Chap. 10). This is also important for bicarbonate transport.

In most distal segments of the nephron, particularly in the thick ascending limb of Henle's loop, co-transport with sodium (and potassium) is probably the most important mechanism for chloride reabsorption.

Bicarbonate

When hydrogen ions are secreted, bicarbonate ions are produced in the cells (p. 190). These excess bicarbonate ions leave the cell by counter transport with chloride at the basolateral border. Recent evidence suggests a cotransport system for Na^+ and HCO_3^- at the basolateral border.

It has always been assumed that bicarbonate ions in the glomerular filtrate are reabsorbed by hydrion secretion (p. 189) although it is possible that some bicarbonate is reabsorbed intact by way of a chloride–bicarbonate exchanger. Whatever the mechanism, most of the bicarbonate is preferentially reabsorbed in the early part of the proximal tubule and its concentration rapidly falls to about 6 mmol/l. Reabsorption of bicarbonate in other segments of the nephron has not been studied, but must occur since its concentration in the final urine can be very low.

Phosphate

Phosphate is one of the major breakdown products of protein metabolism. Phosphate ions in the plasma are freely filtered at the glomerulus and thereafter 80 per cent are reabsorbed. Much of this reabsorption occurs in the proximal convoluted and proximal straight tubules, although small amounts can be reabsorbed in the thick ascending limb and distal parts of the nephron. The mechanism for reabsorption involves co-transport with sodium, utilising the sodium gradient as an energy source. The divalent form HPO_4^{2-} is preferred by the transport system.

Parathyrin increases phosphate excretion by decreasing reabsorption in all segments of the nephron. In the proximal tubule calcitriol acts by increasing phosphate reabsorption, but only when parathyrin is present, and it is thought to act by inhibiting the production of cAMP by the parathyrin. Diet and systemic pH changes also modify phosphate reabsorption; the mechanisms appear to be independent of parathyrin.

Sulphate

Sulphate is also a breakdown product of protein metabolism. The kidney has a limited ability to reabsorb sulphate ions but usually this is exceeded. Although net reabsorption takes place in the proximal tubule, both secretion and reabsorption occur. Reabsorption occurs by two steps, a sodium/sulphate co-transport at the luminal membrane and anion exchange at the peritubular membrane. Nothing is known of any controlling mechanism.

Organic anions

Certain organic anions are reabsorbed in the nephron, others are secreted and some such as urate undergo both reabsorption and secretion. Many drugs are handled by these same mechanisms so that renal damage can contribute to drug toxicity.

Reabsorption of organic anions

Many of the organic anions that are reabsorbed by the tubule are metabolic substrates that are freely filterable at the glomerulus; they include citrate, lactate, malate, α-oxoglutarate, acetoacetate, β-hydroxybutyrate, and amino acids. The mechanism of transport, secondary active transport dependent on the sodium gradient across the luminal membrane, is probably similar for all of them. Transport at the basolateral membrane has not been fully characterised, but for many there may also be uptake into the cell across this membrane; the anions would then be used in cellular metabolic processes. If the metabolic machinery cannot deal with all the anions their concentration rises and passive diffusion through the carrier-mediated system at the basolateral membrane takes place.

Secretion of organic anions

The secretory system is common to a variety of structurally unrelated anions such as para-aminohippurate (PAH), phenol red, penicillin, thiazide diuretics, glucuronides and sulphate esters, and various radio-opaque dyes used for visualising the urinary tract. The secretion of PAH has been widely studied and is typical of the system. Its handling is summarised in Figure 12.7 (p. 179). The secretion, which is easily demonstrated, occurs predominantly in the proximal straight tubule. It depends on uptake of PAH from the plasma by a carrier-mediated process in the basolateral membrane. While the uptake mechanism is not dependent on a sodium gradient, the presence of a sodium gradient enhances both the maximal rate of transport of PAH and the affinity of the carrier. The normal carrier mechanism probably involves exchange of PAH for an intracellular anion, although whether this must also be an organic anion or whether an inorganic anion will suffice, is not known. Probenecid interferes with the uptake process probably by forming a relatively stable, slowly dissociating complex with the carrier. Competition for the carrier occurs with all members of this group.

Once inside the cell PAH moves across the luminal membrane down its diffusion gradient; this may involve a carrier or be merely diffusion trapping (see below).

Diffusion trapping

A number of weak acids and bases diffuse across the luminal membranes of the renal cell in their undissociated form, but are then trapped in the lumen by being converted to their ionised form, which cannot cross the cell membranes. The degree of ionisation depends on the pH of tubular fluid and whether the substance is a base or an acid. Weak bases such as ammonia are ionised and trapped in an acid tubular fluid (p. 190). Conversely weak acids such as aspirin or barbiturate may be trapped in an alkaline tubular fluid. Sodium bicarbonate may be administered to patients who have swallowed an overdose of salicylate or phenobarbitone to aid the excretion of these drugs and hence the rate at which they can be cleared from the plasma.

Urate

Excess urate in plasma results in deposition of urate crystals in various tissues, resulting in gout. The high plasma levels of urate may occur because of increased production or because of the kidney's inability to secrete a normal load. Increased amounts of uric acid in the urine may cause uric acid stones.

Urate is filtered by the glomerulus, but is both reabsorbed and secreted during passage through the proximal tubule. The net result is usually reabsorption. Reabsorption can be inhibited by certain drugs, such as probenecid, salicylates and diuretics given in high doses. These are sometimes called uricosuric agents and are useful in the treatment of gout.

GLUCOSE

Glucose is freely filtered in the glomerulus and is then reabsorbed. The amount reabsorbed depends on the filtered load. Normally about 95 per cent of the glucose is reabsorbed by the first part of the proximal tubule, but when the filtered load of glucose is greatly increased, either by an increase in plasma glucose or by an increase in the filtration rate, considerable amounts of glucose escape from the proximal tubule to be reabsorbed in the loop of Henle, in the distal convoluted tubule and in the collecting duct.

If plasma glucose concentration is sufficiently high (usually above 10 mmol/l) then easily measurable amounts of glucose appear in the urine (Fig. 12.18). The maximum amount of glucose reabsorbed by the kidney (Tm_G) is dependent on glomerular filtration rate and the degree of extracellular fluid volume expansion.

The mechanism for the reabsorption of glucose is similar to that described for transport of glucose in the small intestine (p. 268). Uptake at the luminal cell membrane occurs on a common carrier with sodium and utilises the sodium gradient as a source of energy. Glucose leaves the cell via the basolateral membrane, probably by facilitated diffusion. The transport mechanism is unaffected by insulin, glucagon or any of the other hormones that alter uptake of glucose by cells elsewhere in the body.

The presence of abnormal amounts of glucose in the urine is called *glycosuria*. This occurs either when the filtered load of glucose is increased, as in diabetes mellitus (p. 295), or when the renal tubules are damaged and unable to reabsorb the normal filtered load. Glycosuria frequently occurs in pregnancy; not,

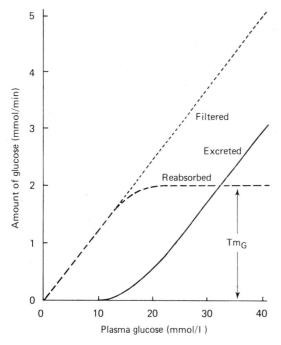

Fig. 12.18 Rates of filtration, excretion and reabsorption (filtration–excretion) in humans with different plasma glucose concentrations. The maximum amount of glucose that can be reabsorbed (Tm_G) is about 2 mmol/min. The plasma concentration at which glucose is first detectable in the urine (threshold concentration) is about 10 mmol. There is considerable 'splay' at the lower end of the excretion curve. This is said to be due to different nephrons having slightly different capacities to reabsorb glucose.

as might be expected, because of the increased filtered load but because of alteration in glucose handling in distal parts of the nephron.

AMINO ACIDS

Amino acids are transported across the luminal cell membrane of proximal tubular cells by sodium-dependent uptake processes, which are similar to those described for the small intestine (p. 269). Several carrier systems are involved; one transports predominantly acidic amino acids such as glutamic and aspartic acid; a second transports the basic amino acids, cysteine, ornithine, arginine and lysine; a third transports the amino acids proline and hydroxyproline, while all the other amino acids have a common transport mechanism. Patients with *cystinuria* lack the carrier that transports the basic amino acids, and may develop cystine stones in the urinary tract. Most amino acids are transported from the renal cell across the basolateral membrane into the interstitial fluid, possibly by facilitated diffusion. The transport of glutamine, which is

needed in large quantities to generate ammonia for secretion into the tubular fluid (p. 190), is unusual in that the luminal and basolateral membranes appear to have identical sodium-dependent uptake mechanisms.

PROTEIN

Although the concentration of albumin in glomerular filtrate is very low (usually about 200 mg/l compared with 40–50 g/l in plasma), this would be a significant drain on the body protein stores if reabsorption did not occur. At a filtration rate of 180 litres/day 36 g of protein would be lost each day; measured losses are less than 200 mg/day. Most reabsorption occurs in the proximal convoluted tubule, and is by a process of pinocytosis. Reabsorption of protein-rich fluid causes the cells to be packed with protein-containing vesicles.

Many smaller proteins are also filtered, including many hormones that are not bound in plasma (such as angiotensin, glucagon, insulin) and a protein derived from broken down cell membranes in the body (β_2-microglobulin). These are selectively reabsorbed: the larger molecules by pinocytosis, while the smaller ones are degraded to amino acids or small peptides, which are then reabsorbed.

TRANSPORT OF WATER

Although the glomerular filtrate is produced at about 125 ml/min, the rate of urine flow can vary between 0.3 and 20 ml/min. Thus, the tubules reabsorb a large but variable amount of water.

Water moves across the epithelium in response to hydrostatic or osmotic pressure gradients. Osmotic gradients are quantitatively more important since a difference of 1 mmol/kg is equivalent to a hydrostatic pressure difference of 17 mm Hg (2.3 kPa). The amount of water absorbed or secreted depends on the magnitude of these gradients and the permeability of the tubular epithelium to water; in more distal segments of the nephron, water permeability is under hormonal control.

About 67 per cent of the reabsorption occurs in the proximal convoluted tubule and is coupled to solute reabsorption. In the loop of Henle and distal segments of the nephron, water and solute reabsorption are not closely linked in the same segment. These later segments are responsible for setting up the underlying mechanism that enables the kidney to produce either a concentrated or a dilute urine.

Water reabsorption in the proximal tubule is driven by osmotic gradients. These arise partly because the tubule can generate a small osmotic difference and partly because the effective osmolality, which takes into account the reflection coefficients of the ions on either side (p. 14), is some 15 mmol/kg higher in peritubular than in luminal fluid. Absorption of water in all other nephron segments depends on the presence of large osmotic gradients in the renal medulla and delivery of a hypotonic fluid to the distal convoluted tubule.

Role of the loop of Henle in the creation of a hypertonic medulla

The loop of Henle is essential for the production of a hypertonic urine. Among the vertebrates only mammals and some birds can produce hypertonic urine; only in these species are there structures equivalent to the thin limbs of the loop of Henle. In addition the maximum extent to which different animals are able to concentrate urine increases as the thickness of the medulla increases relative to the cortex. For example, the desert rat, which can concentrate its urine to an osmolality of 6000 mmol/kg has a very long loop of Henle and a thick medulla, whilst the aquatic beaver has a relatively thin medulla, relatively short loops of Henle and a much lower maximum urine osmolality. Thus, animals with a high proportion of nephrons with long loops of Henle produce the most concentrated urine.

Measurement of the osmolality of fluid obtained by micropuncture of single nephrons show that at the beginning of the loop of Henle the fluid is isotonic (or isosmotic with normal plasma), at the tip of the loop it is hypertonic, while at the end of the loop it is hypotonic. Plasma obtained from blood vessels surrounding

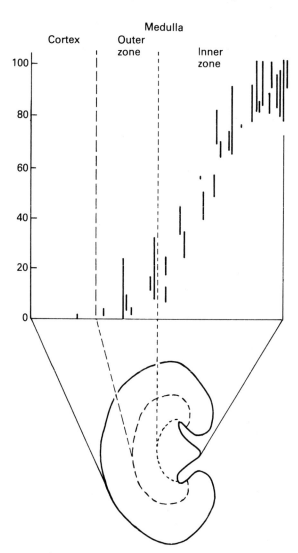

Fig. 12.19 Osmolality of tissue and tubular fluid at different depths in the medulla of dehydrated rats. Zero on the ordinate represents isotonicity with plasma and 100 represents the maximal osmolality at the papillary tip. (After Wirz H et al. 1951 Helvetica Physiologica Pharmacologica Acta 9:196)

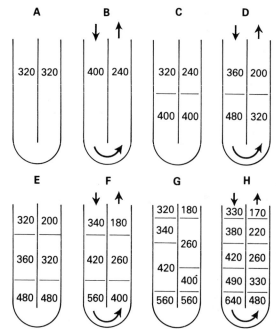

Fig. 12.20 Diagrammatic representation of counter-current multiplier in Henle's loop. It is supposed that fluid with an osmolality of 320 mmol/kg water enters the loop. Reabsorption of solute from the ascending limb and of water from the descending limb can establish a difference of 160 mmol/kg water. A. Both limbs full of isotonic fluid. B. Result of reabsorption. C. Movement of fluid part way round the loop; isotonic fluid enters the descending limb. D. Results of reabsorption. E. Further movement of fluid. F. Results of reabsorption. G. Further movement of fluid. H. Reabsorption. It should be noted that in real life movement and reabsorption occur simultaneously. (From Mills J N 1963 In: Creese R (ed) Recent advances in physiology, 8th edn. p. 261)

the loop of Henle deep in the medulla show that plasma in those vessels had an osmolality equivalent to that in the adjacent loop of Henle. Indeed, the medulla of the kidney as a whole becomes progressively more hypertonic the nearer one gets to the tips of the papillae (Fig. 12.19).

The loop of Henle is responsible for the hypertonicity of the medulla and it achieves this by behaving as a counter-current multiplier. This is shown diagrammatically in Figure 12.20, in which the process is artificially divided into a series of discrete steps. It is supposed that fluid at an osmolality of 320 mmol/kg enters the loop and that some active process generates a difference in osmolality between the two limbs. This leads to a situation as in (B). If fluid flow occurs, the fluid in the lower part of the loop will then be equally hypertonic

in both limbs (C), and the same active process can now establish a new gradient (D). This progresses until there is a large gradient extending along the loop of Henle. Thus, the loop generates a high osmolality in the medulla without any part being subject to a high transmural gradient.

The mechanism by which these osmotic differences arise vary in the two limbs. Changes in osmolality can occur either because solute moves or because water moves. In the ascending limb of the loop, which is relatively impermeable to water, the major reason for change in osmolality is removal of solute, whereas in the descending limb, which has a much higher water permeability, most of the change is due to abstraction of water. Basically solute is transferred to the interstitial fluid by the ascending limb and this raises the osmo-

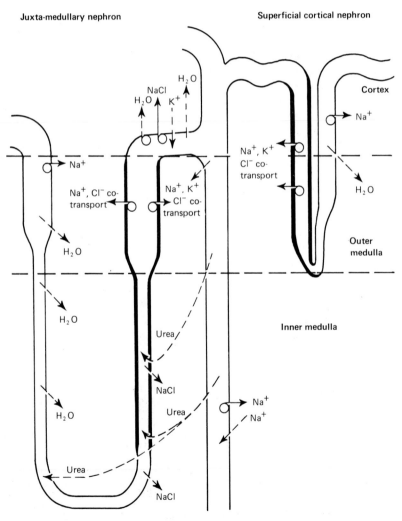

Fig. 12.21 Movement of water, ions and urea in the loop of Henle. Passive movements are shown by dashed lines while energy-dependent processes are shown by circles and solid lines.

lality of the interstitial fluid and water moves down its osmotic gradient from the descending limb. Some solute enters the descending limb (mainly sodium, chloride and urea) but at the tip of the loop of Henle, although the osmolality of tubular fluid is the same as that in the surrounding interstitial fluid, the concentration of sodium is higher and the concentration of urea is lower. As fluid passes into the thin ascending limb more urea enters (passively) while sodium chloride leaves. This sodium reabsorption is generally thought to be passive, although a weak active sodium transport system has also been proposed (Fig. 12.21).

In the thick ascending limb of the loop there is considerable sodium and chloride reabsorption, probably by a co-transport mechanism (see p. 10) and, since the epithelium is impermeable to water, a hypotonic fluid enters the distal convoluted tubule.

Water reabsorption in the distal tubule and collecting ducts

What happens to water movement in the distal tubules and collecting ducts depends not only on the gradient generated by the counter-current multiplier but also on the permeability of the membrane to water. This permeability can be modified by vasopressin (p. 307), which alters the permeability of the luminal membrane, mainly of the cortical collecting tubules and collecting ducts. Tubular fluid has become isotonic by the time it reaches the collecting ducts provided that vasopressin is present. Thereafter the osmolality of the tubular fluid matches the osmolality of the hypertonic medulla through which it passes, because water permeability is so high that it allows very rapid equilibration. Thus the osmotic gradient across the collecting duct wall is relatively small. The maximum urinary osmolality that can be achieved is the maximum osmolality that can be generated in the medulla by the loop of Henle.

If vasopressin is absent, however, the fluid at the end of the distal tubule is more hypotonic than that at the beginning because sodium and chloride are still reabsorbed but water is not. Thereafter the osmolality may alter little in the collecting duct because the small amount of solute reabsorption is balanced by some reabsorption of water. This occurs in spite of the low water permeability because the presence of a large gradient (the medullary interstitium is still hypertonic, though not to the same extent) across the collecting duct wall ensures some reabsorption.

Role of the vasa recta

The vasa recta, derived from the efferent arterioles of juxtamedullary nephrons (see p. 177) supply blood to the medulla. If they were not arranged in a loop configuration then the flow of blood would dissipate the gradient that is so laboriously built up by the loop of Henle. Because of their arrangement they act as counter-current *exchangers*.

There is no active transfer of solutes but the prevailing gradients drive water to leave and solute to enter the descending limbs of vasa recta as they progress through more and more concentrated medullary interstitial fluid approaching the papilla; solute leaves and water enters the ascending limbs as they return to the cortex (Fig. 12.22). This results in diffusible solutes such as sodium chloride and urea being trapped in the medulla while water effectively short-circuits it.

In addition excess water reabsorbed from the collecting ducts is effectively removed. For maximal concentration of urine the blood flow through the vasa recta must be minimal; when flow in the vasa recta is increased solutes are washed out of the medulla and

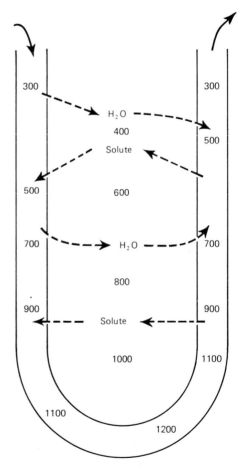

Fig. 12.22 Solute and water movement in the counter-current exchange system of the vasa recta. Note that the ascending limb and the tissue are in equilibrium but that flow down the descending limb presents hypotonic fluid to the medulla. Water effectively short-circuits the loop while solute is recycled and hence retained. Solid lines indicate direction of fluid flow.

medullary osmolality is decreased, as is the concentrating ability.

It has been shown that the vasa recta are responsive to vasopressin so that in the antidiuretic state when vasopressin is high, blood flow to the vasa recta is reduced and maximum osmolalities can be achieved.

Urea and the concentrating mechanism

Urea is passively reabsorbed from the nephron. Because the proximal tubule is not as permeable to urea as to water, the concentration of urea rises along the proximal tubule and by the end it may be 1.5 times the concentration in plasma.

As fluid descends to the tip of the loop of Henle water is removed and this increases the urea concentration. In addition, because the medullary interstitial fluid has a high urea concentration some urea diffuses into the loop of Henle. Even when the fluid reaches the tip of the loop its urea concentration is still less than in the surrounding medulla and so some urea also enters the thin ascending limb of the loop (Fig. 12.21).

Thus by the time the fluid reaches the distal tubule its concentration of urea is considerably higher than in the plasma or surrounding interstitial fluid and may account for 50 mmol/kg of the total osmolality of 100 mmol/kg. Reabsorption of water from the distal tubule, under the influence of vasopressin, again increases the urea concentration, which may achieve 40 times that of the surrounding plasma. Some urea diffuses across the collecting duct to enter the medullary interstitium and, although the permeability of urea is less than that of water, both are increased by vasopressin. By the time the tubular fluid reaches the end of the collecting ducts the concentrations of urea in the fluid and in the medullary interstitium are almost equal. This results in a high medullary urea concentration, which accounts for its uptake in the loop of Henle. Urea is thus recycled and this has the effect of conserving other osmotically active urinary constituents such as sodium and chloride.

The importance of urea to the concentrating mechanisms has been shown both theoretically and practically. Mathematical models of the counter-current system will not work with a single solute and need two solutes such as urea and sodium chloride. Children who have low plasma urea concentrations do not concentrate urine as well as adults (p. 199) and this is made much worse if protein malnutrition reduces the urea concentration still further. Such malnourished children have had their concentrating ability restored either by feeding protein or by adding urea to the diet!

Free-water clearance

When the kidney produces urine that is more dilute than plasma a higher proportion of water from the glomerular filtrate is excreted than of osmotically active substances. This excess is termed *free water*. The rate of clearance of free water is important since it shows how rapidly the kidneys are changing the balance between water and osmotically active substances in the body fluids. Free water clearance (C_{H_2O}) is calculated as follows:

$$C_{H_2O} = V - C_{osm}$$

where V is the urine volume and C_{osm} is the clearance of osmotically active solutes. This in turn can be expressed:

$$C_{osm} = \frac{U_{osm} \, V}{P_{osm}}$$

where U_{osm} and P_{osm} are the urinary and plasma osmolalities respectively. It can be shown therefore that:

$$C_{H_2O} = V\left(1 - \frac{U_{osm}}{P_{osm}}\right)$$

Free water clearance can be positive (in a dilute urine) or negative (in a concentrated urine).

THE KIDNEY AS AN ENDOCRINE ORGAN

The kidney produces components of the *renin-angiotensin system* (p. 206), erythropoietin (p. 30), calcitriol (p. 363) and local hormones such as prostaglandins and kinins.

The kidney produces a number of prostaglandins. PGE, PGA$_2$ and PGF$_{2\alpha}$ are produced by the interstitial cells in the renal medulla and PGI$_2$ is produced in the cortex. All have vasodilator actions on the kidney. They may be secreted only in response to cell damage or other hormones. There are complex interactions at the glomerulus between prostaglandins and angiotensin II, vasopressin, kinins, acetylcholine; in general prostaglandins oppose the action of these agents. In addition, prostaglandins increase the permeability of the collecting ducts to sodium, chloride and calcium ions and interact with ADH in controlling water permeability.

The kidney produces an enzyme called kallikrein, which is one of the wider family of kallikreins. Kallikreins act on circulating globulins called kininigens to produce a number of kinins such as bradykinin. All kinins are vasodilators and so may alter sodium reabsorption (p. 186). Kallikrein or one of its derivative kinins is also thought to have direct natriuretic properties (although whether it has these independent of the changes that occur in renal blood flow is not known).

Both kallikrein and prostaglandins are natriuretic factors (p. 187).

NEONATAL RENAL FUNCTION

During fetal life the major function of the kidney is to produce amniotic fluid; the homeostatic functions of the kidney are subserved by the placenta. Even when related to the body surface area, the filtration rate is low and reabsorption of fluid and salt may be 97 per cent of the filtered load instead of the 99.5 per cent in an adult. At birth mean arterial blood pressure is reduced and this further reduces GFR and RPF. Over the first few months of extrauterine life, however, GFR steadily increases. This is partly due to an increase in blood pressure and partly due to cortical nephrons becoming functional; even at birth many nephrons on the surface of the kidney have no blood flow and so are non-functional. Adult levels of GFR (expressed per m^2) are reached by 2–3 years of age (Fig. 12.23). Loss of 3 to 4 per cent of the filtered sodium load would be catastrophic after birth since the major source of sodium in the fetus (the placenta) has been removed. Although a negative sodium balance does occur for the first 2 days of life, there is a rapid fall in fractional excretion of sodium and intake balances output by the end of the first week. Most of the reabsorptive and secretory mechanisms are immature in the newborn but the kidney is rapidly able to achieve homeostasis. Excretion of sodium and water loads is slower than in adults however; a high salt load may be poorly tolerated. Secretion of PAH is decreased in the neonate; this gives rise to particular problems in that it cannot be assumed that all the PAH is extracted in a single passage through the kidney and so C_{PAH} cannot be used as an index of RPF.

Because most of the protein in the neonate's diet is used in the manufacture of new protein to sustain growth, little is catabolised to give urea, and plasma levels of urea are lower than in the adult. Because of this the neonate cannot excrete a highly concentrated urine. Feeding protein-rich artificial milk can elevate plasma urea and increase the concentrating ability to adult levels, as can feeding urea. There is no evidence for a reduced secretion, or activity, of vasopressin.

RENAL FUNCTION DURING PREGNANCY

During pregnancy there are substantial changes in renal function. GFR and RPF are both increased by up to 50 per cent in the first three months of pregnancy and there is a proportionate or greater increase in tubular reabsorption of salt and water. The volume of extracellular fluid increases and is probably accompanied by an increased plasma volume, although this is disputed. It is likely that these changes are hormonally mediated (since they also occur in transplanted kidneys). Part of the increased reabsorption is due to an increase in the length of the proximal tubule; whether other parts of the tubule also grow is not yet known. The functional significance of these changes is not known. It may be that they are incidental to changes that occur in the cardiac output; however, changes in renal plasma flow are greater than changes in blood flow to any organ other than uterus and breasts.

Plasma osmolality in pregnant women is less than in comparable control groups, but plasma vasopressin levels are normal; it is postulated that this is due to resetting of the osmoreceptor mechanism, which now functions about a new, lower mean. Similar arguments can be applied to volume control. In the face of a significant increase in the volume of extracellular fluid in pregnancy, renal mechanisms do not operate to excrete more salt and water. The volume receptor mechanism is set to a new, higher level. How this relates to pre-eclamptic toxaemia in pregnancy is not yet known.

During pregnancy increased amounts of glucose are found in the urine. It has been suggested that this is due to an increased filtered load or a decreased reabsorptive capacity of the tubule; in either case the loss would be

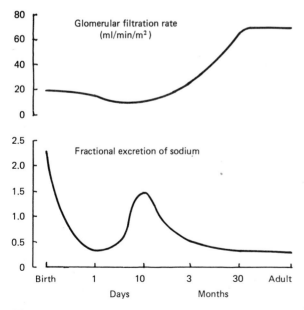

Fig. 12.23 Changes in GFR and sodium excretion after birth. Note that the time scale is logarithmic and that adult levels are achieved by about 2 years. (After Green R 1985 In: Case R M (ed) Variations in human physiology. Manchester University Press.)

exaggerated if minimal damage occurred to the tubules. Direct experimental evidence in the rat (which also excretes increased amounts of glucose in the urine during pregnancy) has demonstrated that neither of these mechanisms obtains. There is alteration of glucose handling by the loop of Henle and the collecting duct and the change in the 5 per cent glucose reabsorption that normally occurs at these sites is sufficient to account for the amount of glucose excreted by pregnant rats. It is likely that similar changes take place in human pregnancy.

RENAL FUNCTION IN THE ELDERLY

After the third or fourth decade of life GFR decreases progressively until by the age of 70 it may have been reduced to 60–70 per cent. This reduction probably arises because of vascular damage and loss of functioning nephrons. This means that the kidney has a reduction of its reserve capacity. Many drugs are excreted via the kidney; elderly patients on 'normal' doses of such drugs tend to have high plasma concentrations.

The normal diurnal variation of urine production and GFR is disturbed and increased amounts of urine are produced at night. This frequently results in older people having to pass urine during the night (nocturia).

RENAL DISEASES

Normal kidneys have a large functional reserve; 75 per cent of renal tissue can be removed without detriment to the individual. After the loss of one kidney in a healthy individual the remaining kidney immediately compensates, initially by an increase in blood flow and filtration rate; over a period of weeks, however, the remaining kidney grows (compensatory hypertrophy) — not by increasing the number of nephrons but by increasing the size of the glomeruli and the length of the tubules. Such renal growth depends on a number of factors; one of the most important appears to be a specific renal growth factor, which is produced by the action of an enzyme derived from the remaining kidney on a circulating plasma protein.

It is possible to divide renal diseases into those causing glomerular damage (or dysfunction) and those causing tubular damage, but both types of damage may occur. Diseases affecting only the tubules are uncommon. Loss of the homeostatic function of the kidney is the major consequence of renal disease. There is a limit to the increases in hydrion and potassium concentrations that can be tolerated by the body; loss of the major site of control for potassium and fixed hydrion excretion results in a steady increase in their plasma concentrations. Death can be due to an excess of either of these ions. Loss of the excretory function of the kidney can cause a rise in plasma urea concentration but this of itself is not usually life threatening. Loss of the ability to excrete certain drugs results in a higher plasma concentration than could be expected in normal individuals and may cause toxic symptoms.

Diseases of renal tubules
These may have a genetic basis, as in cystinuria, in which the transport protein for cystine, ornithine, arginine and lysine is lacking from the proximal tubules, or in nephrogenic diabetes insipidus, in which the vasopressin receptors on the collecting system are reduced or absent.

Tubular diseases may be acquired. Toxic damage can be caused by a number of drugs (including gentamicin or kanamycin). Acute tubular necrosis can also result from a reduction in the blood supply to the nephron; lack of blood supply to the nephron is linked to a reduced glomerular blood flow. Blockage of the ureter or of the tubules both cause defective reabsorption and probably defective secretion; the permeability of paracellular pathways is increased and leakage, even of inulin, may occur. Blockage of the nephron may occur after crush injuries to large volumes of muscle; the increase in plasma myoglobin leads to an increase in filtered myoglobin, which is concentrated along the tubule and finally solidifies within the lumen of the nephron.

Diseases of glomeruli
Glomerular dysfunction arises either from a reduction of blood flow to the glomerulus or from damage to the filtration membrane. Reduction of blood flow may result from pre-renal mechanisms (such as a general reduction in blood pressure after trauma), from renal damage to glomerular vessels (such as occurs in hypertension or damage from antigen–antibody reactions), or from purely mechanical obstruction and causes a reduction in GFR and insufficient flow through the renal tubule for it to perform its homeostatic functions adequately.

Damage to the filter is probably caused by disease processes, many of them depending on immune mechanisms, which lead to an alteration of the charge on the glycoproteins that form part of the filtration barrier. The major detectable result is albuminuria. When the albumin loss can be balanced by increased manufacture in the liver, signs of this disease are minimal. Prolonged exposure to abnormally high concentrations of protein may eventually damage the glomerulus and then cause a reduction in blood flow.

The kidney and hypertension

Richard Bright reported in 1827 an association between damaged kidneys and left ventricular hypertrophy. The relation between the kidneys and high blood pressure (hypertension) is complicated because hypertension can itself cause renal damage and some kidney diseases cause hypertension.

Theoretically high blood pressure could be caused either by a primary increase in peripheral resistance mediated by angiotensin II or the catecholamines (which may be derived from the sympathetic nerves), or by an increased cardiac output, which, long-term, usually depends on an increase in extracellular fluid volume. As we have seen previously, sodium handling is very important in homeostatic mechanisms controlling extra-cellular volume. About 90 per cent of cases of hyper-tension have no demonstrable cause; these are called 'essential' hypertension but its cause is unknown.

Renoprival hypertension

Patients who have insufficient functioning renal tissue to maintain life (and who must be supported by dialysis) or patients who have had both diseased kidneys removed prior to transplantation, develop hypertension. It was originally suggested that this was due to excessive sodium retention because the major route for sodium excretion had been removed. It is now clear that removal of the kidneys removes some anti-hypertensive factor(s). The prostaglandins that are manufactured in the kidney are one possible antihypertensive agent. It is thought for example that during pregnancy increased secretion of prostaglandins prevents the rise in blood pressure one would normally associate with the increased aldosterone and renin concentrations; if pros-taglandin production is impaired then hypertension results and this has been postulated as a mechanism responsible for development of pre-eclamptic toxaemia in pregnancy.

Renovascular hypertension

Reduction of blood flow to the kidney by a narrowing of one of the renal vessels caused an increase in renin secretion which, via angiotensin II, is thought to increase peripheral resistance and, possibly by its effects on the blood pressure control centres in the brain, to increase blood pressure through neural pathways. In addition, of course, it would also increase aldosterone secretion and increase extracellular fluid volume.

If the normal kidney remains it develops damage due to the hypertension, which alters the stimuli to its juxtaglomerular apparatuses; the damaged kidney then maintains the hypertension even if the renal artery sten-osis is corrected (Fig. 12.24).

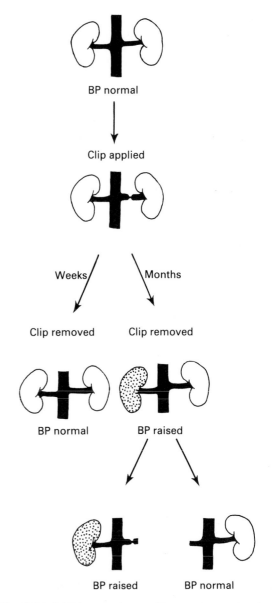

Fig. 12.24 Goldblatt experiments. Hypertension produced by partial stenosis of a renal artery. If the stenosis is removed within weeks the BP reverts to normal. If the stenosis remains for months then hypertensive changes occur in the non-stenosed kidney (shaded) and this maintains the hypertension after the renal artery stenosis has been removed. Cure can only be effected by removal of the previously non-stenosed kidney.

Hypertension due to excess mineralocorticoids

Increased secretion of aldosterone from an adenoma in the zona glomerulosa of the adrenal cortex, or even increased secretion of glucocorticoids that have some mineralocorticoid activity, can both cause increased retention of salt and thus hypertension. Steroid hormones used in the treatment of conditions such as rheumatoid arthritis may have similar effects.

Essential hypertension

Although it has long been known that essential hypertension could be ameliorated by reducing salt intake, it is not known whether excessive salt retention by itself causes hypertension. One recently proposed hypothesis postulates the presence of a naturally occurring inhibitor of Na^+, K^+–ATPase. When Na^+, K^+–ATPase is inhibited, the intracellular concentration of sodium rises and as a consequence in the kidney more sodium is excreted.

It is thought that production of this natriuretic substance (perhaps the natriuretic hormone) is stimulated either by increased salt intake or in certain individuals by an inability of the kidney to handle sodium normally, and acts in a negative feedback control system to reduce sodium reabsorption in the nephron. Because of its general effects on Na^+, K^+–ATPase, however, it would cause an increase in intracellular sodium in all the cells of the body. This would be particularly important in arteriolar smooth muscle cells and sympathetic neurones, in which the decreased gradient for sodium entry would reduce the sodium/calcium exchange that normally helps to maintain a low intracellular calcium concentration. Therefore there would be a rise in intracellular calcium, which would cause constriction of the arteriolar muscle or an increased secretion of catecholamines from sympathetic nerves, both of which would result in increased peripheral resistance and hypertension.

Therefore, reduction of salt intake (by reducing the circulating natriuretic hormone), sympathectomy or drugs that interfere with catecholamine secretion would all be expected to have beneficial therapeutic effects in essential hypertension; they do.

Effects of hypertension

Hypertension causes arteriolar damage in most tissues and the kidney is no exception. The changes in renal arterioles reduce blood flow to the kidney, which causes further hypertension and initiates a sequence of events that results in renal failure.

Treatment of renal failure

Treatment of renal diseases should be directed to its primary cause, if that is possible. However, once irreversible renal failure has occurred dialysis or transplantation of a normal kidney is needed. The normal homeostatic function is taken over either by a machine or by the donated kidney.

Many different forms of dialysis are used. They all depend on exposing the blood to dialysis fluid across a partially permeable membrane. Sometimes artificial membranes like cellophane are used, but sometimes use is made of the great area of the patient's own peritoneum as a dialysis membrane. The principles of dialysis are simple; solute fluxes occur passively across the membrane and so if the dialysis fluid has a normal concentration of sodium, no potassium and a high pH this encourages outward movement of potassium and hydrion. Although these principles are simple there are many practical problems.

MICTURITION

Passage of urine from kidney to bladder

Urine is excreted from the collecting ducts into the pelvis of the kidney. It is propelled by propagated contractions down the pelvis and ureter and enters the bladder in regular squirts. These contractions keep the pressure in the renal pelvis low so that tubular function remains unimpaired. The electrical basis of ureteric contractions consists of regular depolarisations of the smooth muscle of the pelvis and ureters, which commence every 10 seconds from a pacemaker in the minor calyces and travel down the renal pelvis and the ureter at a rate of 2 or 3 cm/s. The ureters pass obliquely through the thick muscular wall of the bladder and run for a few centimetres under the bladder epithelium before opening in the trigone of the bladder. This design allows increases in pressure within the bladder to compress the ureters and prevent the reflux of urine up the ureters. If the ureter is obstructed, the ureteric pressure may rise to 50 mmHg (7 kPa). This causes pain, but the kidney is partly protected by a reflex constriction of the renal arterioles (uretero-renal reflex), which reduces urine production by the kidney on the affected side.

The bladder and urethra

The bladder consists of three principal components (Fig. 12.25); the body, which is composed mainly of the detrusor muscle; the *trigone*, a small triangular area on the posterior and inferior aspects of the bladder through which both the ureters and urethra pass; and the *bladder neck* or outlet to the urethra.

The bladder is lined by transitional epithelium, which is impermeable to passage of water and electrolytes. The epithelium is adherent to the network of smooth muscle that constitutes the detrusor muscle. At the base of the bladder the smooth muscle fibres pass around the upper urethra for about 2 cm, forming what has been called the *internal sphincter*. It is not certain whether continuous tone of this muscle is important for maintaining continence. The loop of muscle around the urethra may be just an extension of the bladder muscle, which is stretched as the bladder fills, closing the urethra, but

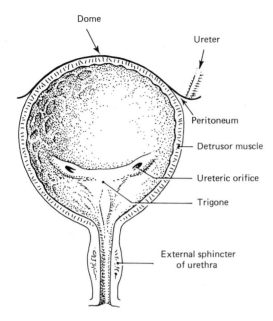

Fig. 12.25 Anatomy of the bladder in a woman.

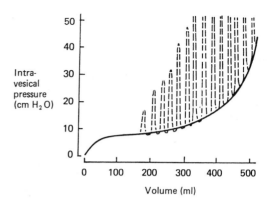

Fig. 12.26 A normal cystometrogram (recording of pressure within the bladder). The solid line shows the basal pressure. The acute pressure waves (micturition contractions) are caused by micturition reflexes.

is pulled open by contraction of the detrusor muscle during micturition.

The smooth muscle of the bladder receives its parasympathetic supply from the pelvic nerves and its sympathetic supply from the thoracolumbar outflow via the paravertebral chain and hypogastric plexus. Stimulation of the parasympathetic nerves contracts the detrusor and inhibits the internal sphincter while sympathetic stimulation relaxes the detrusor and contracts the internal sphincter.

Beyond the bladder neck, the urethra passes through the urogenital diaphragm, which contains a layer of muscle known as the *external sphincter*. This sheet is continuous with the levator ani and is under voluntary control via the pudendal nerves. Contraction of both muscles prevents incontinence by compressing the upper part of the urethra. Increases in intra-abdominal pressure, for example induced by coughing, cause sharp reflex contractions of these muscles, even during sleep, so preventing incontinence.

Urination

The basal pressure changes very little as more urine enters the bladder up to about 400 ml. This is probably due to a reflex relaxation and aids the passage of urine into the bladder from the ureters. Above about 400 to 500 ml the pressure rises more sharply, and acute increases in pressure, lasting from a few seconds to more than a minute, may be superimposed on the tonic pressure changes (Fig. 12.26). These contractions probably occur as a result of a reflex initiated by stretch receptors in the bladder wall and conveyed to the sacral cord and back via the pelvic nerves.

When the person wishes to urinate, the cortical centres facilitate the sacral centres to inhibit the activity of the external urethral sphincter and to facilitate detrusor contraction. The contraction of the detrusor probably pulls the bladder neck open, overcoming any inherent contraction of the internal sphincter. The passage of urine through the external urethra causes a discharge of afferent fibres in the pudendal nerve, which reinforces the excitation of the parsympathetic neurones, increasing and maintaining the contraction of the detrusor muscle until voiding is complete.

Atonic bladder
Interruption of the reflex arc by injury to the sacral cord or destruction of the sensory fibres to the cord abolishes the micturition reflex and results in an atonic bladder, which fills to capacity and overflows a few drops at a time.

Automatic bladder
Disconnection of the sacral micturition centre from the brain by lesions in the upper part of the spinal cord causes initially an atonic bladder due to lack of facilitatory influences from the brain. Then after a few weeks or months, this gives way to an automatic bladder, in which the bladder empties reflexly as soon as it is filled to a critical capacity. Micturition in these patients can often be elicited by scratching the skin of the abdomen or the thigh. This provides a means by which patients with spinal lesions can regain some control of micturition.

FURTHER READING

Abrams P, Feneley R, Tarrens M 1983 Urodynamics. Springer, Berlin

Andreoli T E (ed) 1980–83 Renal physiology. In: Annual Review of Physiology, Vols 40, 43, 44, 45. Annual Reviews, Palo Alto

Brenner B M, Rector F C (eds) 1981 The kidney, 2nd edn. Saunders, Philadelphia

de Wardener H E 1985 The kidney, 5th edn. Churchill Livingstone, Edinburgh

Orloff J, Berliner R W (eds) 1973 Handbook of physiology 8: Renal Physiology. American Physiological Society, Washington, DC

Pitts R F 1974 Physiology of the kidney and body fluids, 3rd edn. Yearbook, Chicago

Valtin H 1983 Renal function: mechanisms preserving fluid and solute balance in health, 2nd edn. Little Brown, Boston

13

Control of extracellular fluid volume and the regulation of fluid and electrolyte balance

Extracellular fluid volume is about 12 litres in a 70-kg man; its main cationic component is sodium. Regulatory mechanisms are usually so powerful that if there is retention of sodium, water is automatically retained, thus maintaining the osmolality of extracellullar fluid constant (see below); conversely, if sodium is lost, then water is also lost. Maintenance of extracellular fluid volume is therefore very closely linked to the total amount of sodium in the body.

Blood volume is the volume of fluid contained in the heart and blood vessels. For lean men it averages 79 ml/kg but varies according to weight and sex. Fatty tissue has a smaller than normal vascular volume, so obese subjects and women (who have, on average, a greater proportion of their body weight as fat) have a lower than predicted blood volume. Plasma, which is part of the extracellular fluid, comprises 60 per cent of the total blood volume, while cells are 40 per cent.

An increased blood volume eventually leads to an increased arterial pressure in spite of a number of regulatory mechanisms (p. 105). Because of this there is a link between blood pressure and sodium content of the body and hence of the diet.

Since the plasma volume is in equilibrium with the interstitial fluid, changes in plasma volume rapidly result in corresponding changes throughout the extracellular fluid compartment. So the effect of addition to or loss of fluid from the cardiovascular space is spread over a much larger volume. This constitutes one of the body's defences against changes in blood volume. For example, an increased plasma volume increases the capillary pressure, which enhances leakage of fluid from the capillaries into the interstitial spaces (p. 20). This mechanism provides an overflow compartment to deal with rapid increases in blood volume, and prevents blood pressure from rising excessively.

REGULATION OF BLOOD VOLUME

In order to maintain adequate perfusion of all organs, it is important that blood volume is kept relatively constant, in spite of possibly large changes in fluid and electrolyte intake. Many of these important homeostatic mechanisms involve the kidney. In general, an increase in blood volume enhances excretion of urine while a decreased blood volume reduces urine output. It must be realised, however, that if blood volume is reduced the kidney can only minimise further loss of fluid, it is unable to restore blood volume. Thirst (p. 208) is therefore an important part of the regulatory system.

When the blood volume is expanded rapidly the tone of large veins is reduced so there is a bigger reservoir in which blood can be stored. In addition, some of the fluid is passed to the interstitial fluid compartment. These are only short-term measures and do nothing to restore extracellular fluid volume to normal.

The volume of circulating blood is sensed by a number of 'volume' receptors, which alter renal excretion by altering GFR or tubular reabsorption of salt and water or both.

Volume receptors

There are volume receptors situated centrally and peripherally. Many of the central receptors are present in the walls of the atria in the heart and respond to stretch of the atria. Some of these receptors send impulses to the brain via the vagus nerves, but others result in secretion, probably of atrial natriuretic peptides (ANP), which are found in secretory granules in the atrial myocytes. If the increase in blood volume is sufficiently large to cause blood pressure to increase, stimulation of high-pressure baroreceptors in the carotid arteries, aorta and pulmonary arteries may contribute to the effect of atrial volume receptors.

The macula densa also acts as a peripheral volume receptor, although in addition to responding directly to stretch it may respond to other changes that are consequent on changes of extracellular fluid volume, such as changes in fluid flow in distal nephron or sympathetic nervous stimulation.

Mechanism of renal effects

Changes in blood volume cause changes in GFR and

perhaps changes in tubular reabsorption. If blood volume increases, GFR increases and tubular reabsorption may be decreased so that the excretion of salt and water is increased. If blood volume decreases, the converse is true.

Changes in GFR

An increase in blood volume increases GFR; this overrides the normal autoregulatory mechanisms (p. 183). The changes in GFR may be a result of altered stimulation of the renal nerves. Stimulation of atrial volume receptors increase the number of impulses in the vagal afferents and results in a decreased rate of impulses in the sympathetic nerves to the kidney, which results in dilatation of afferent and efferent arterioles and an increased GFR. Recently it has been shown that ANP has a direct effect on blood vessels and particularly on the renal vasculature so that its release from the atria in response to stretch may be the most important factor causing renal vasodilatation. Some changes in GFR may also result from changes in angiotensin II production (see below).

Changes in proximal tubular handling

When extracellular fluid volume is altered, glomerulotubular balance (p. 187) is disturbed. Thus an increased GFR in response to an increased extracellular fluid volume does not result in an appropriate increase in reabsorption by the proximal tubule, i.e. the fraction of the filtered load that is reabsorbed is decreased. The converse is true when GFR decreases.

This may be explained in a number of ways. Stimulation of renal nerves when blood volume is reduced has been shown to have a direct effect enhancing proximal tubular fluid reabsorption. In addition, stimulation of renal nerves may redistribute glomerular filtration from superficial nephrons (which lose relatively more salt) to deeper juxtamedullary nephrons (which retain relatively more salt).

Blood volume expansion is frequently associated with reduced plasma protein concentrations, especially if the volume expansion has been rapid. The reduced plasma protein concentration reduces the oncotic force in peritubular capillaries (which helps transport reabsorbed fluid from the proximal tubule) thus reducing proximal tubular fluid reabsorption.

Angiotensin II has been shown to have a direct effect on proximal tubular reabsorption, stimulating reabsorption at physiological concentrations.

Renin–angiotensin–aldosterone

When blood volume is reduced, renin is released from the macula densa of the juxtaglomerular apparatus in the kidney (Fig. 13.1). This effect is mediated in three ways. First, a reduction in renal perfusion pressure (particularly pulse pressure) has a direct effect on the afferent arterioles. Secondly, the reduction in GFR consequent on reduced extracellular fluid volume leads to a reduced flow of fluid and electrolytes past the macula densa. A reduction in flow by itself increases renin secretion but whether this is mediated by an alteration in the stretch of the macula densa cells or whether it is due to a change in some constituent such as sodium or chloride is not yet known. Thirdly, an increased sympathetic discharge to the juxtaglomerular apparatus results in increased renin secretion.

Renin is a proteolytic enzyme that hydrolyses circulating angiotensinogen (produced in the liver) to angiotensin I, a decapeptide. Further hydrolysis of angiotensin I to angiotensin II, an octapeptide, is carried out by converting enzyme that is present in both lungs and juxtaglomerular apparatus.

Renin has no direct action in the kidney, but angiotensin II is the most potent naturally occurring vasoconstrictor known. It acts on peripheral adrenergic neurones to facilitate catecholamine synthesis and so influences the activity of the sympathetic nervous system. The physiological importance of angiotensin II in normal control of blood pressure is not established; in patients with severe contraction of extracellular fluid volume, it may play a major part in maintaining arterial blood pressure. The major vascular effect of angiotensin II, however, is to constrict the afferent and efferent arterioles in the kidney and this reduces GFR. It also increases reabsorption of salt and water from the proximal renal tubule.

Another major action of angiotensin II, and one that is partially shared by angiotensin I, is a stimulation of aldosterone production by the adrenal cortex. Angiotensin II is further degraded to angiotensin III, a heptapeptide, which also stimulates aldosterone secretion but is a less effective vasoconstrictor than angiotensin II. It can be seen then that the juxtaglomerular apparatus has a central role in preventing excess salt and water losses whenever extracellular fluid volume is reduced.

Aldosterone secretion, as well as being stimulated by angiotensin, may also be stimulated by a large decrease (greater than 20 mmol/l) in the plasma concentration of sodium or by a rise in plasma potassium concentration (p.189). Its secretion is also increased by the secretion of ACTH from the adenohypophysis, which is stimulated via central volume receptors by extracellular fluid depletion.

The major actions of aldosterone are on the distal tubule and cortical collecting ducts of the kidney; it enhances sodium reabsorption and potassium secretion either by increasing the permeability of the luminal cell membrane, by increasing the activity of Na$^+$, K$^+$–ATPase at the basolateral cell membrane, or by

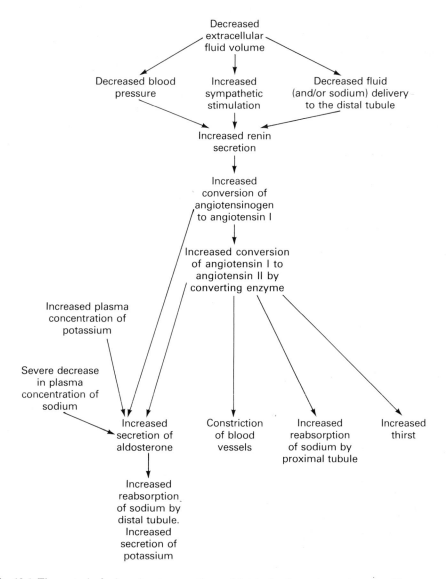

Fig. 13.1 The control of salt and water excretion and intake by the renin–angiotensin–aldosterone system.

increasing oxidative metabolism, so producing more energy for the sodium pump, or by a combination of these. Aldosterone is an important physiological regulator of sodium reabsorption, helping to prevent excess sodium loss. If aldosterone levels are increased, as in Conn's syndrome or primary hyperaldosteronism, it ceases to have an effect after a time because other mechanisms increase sodium excretion.

Vasopressin
The role of vasopressin in the day-to-day control of blood volume is not established. If there is a dramatic fall in blood volume and blood pressure, there is a massive outpouring of vasopressin from the neurohypophysis, which helps to restore blood pressure by a direct effect on arterioles and which also reduces excretion of water by the kidney. This complements the action of aldosterone. In these special circumstances, the defence of plasma osmolality is abandoned in favour of the defence of plasma volume.

Natriuretic hormone(s)
For many years it was thought that GFR and aldosterone could account for all the changes in sodium excretion that occurred. It is now known that many other substances alter sodium excretion. Whether these

are true natriuretic hormones is not known; they include parathyrin, kinins, prostaglandins and a number of other vasodilators. Their physiological role in the control of sodium excretion is uncertain.

In addition, it is postulated that a natriuretic hormone that inhibits Na⁺ K⁺–ATPase (perhaps in all cells) is normally increased when extracellular fluid volume is increased. This could reduce sodium reabsorption in the proximal tubules, loops of Henle, distal and collecting tubules of the kidney. Tubular functions have also been described for ANP but it is not established as a major determinant of sodium reabsorption. In addition, stimulation of atrial volume receptors is postulated to release a diuretic substance from a site in the brain; the nature of this substance is not yet known.

Salt appetite

Many animals have a well-developed salt appetite, preferring salted foods or saline to drink if they become volume depleted. In man, there is little evidence that such a mechanism exists, but this may reflect the tremendous excess of salt normally present in the human diet. The problem is not usually of obtaining enough salt but of getting rid of the excess that is normally consumed.

WATER BALANCE

The concentration of sodium and other solutes in the plasma depends on the total amount of water and the total amount of solutes. Control of extracellular fluid volume, which is relatively slow, controls the total amount of sodium in the body. Control of the amount of water in the body depends mainly on mechanisms for maintaining plasma osmolality constant; these respond in a matter of minutes. During dehydration, vasopressin decreases water loss by the kidney, and thirst mechanisms increase the water supply.

Vasopressin response

The details of vasopressin manufacture and release are given in Chapter 24. Basically, a decrease in plasma osmolality (caused for example by drinking a litre of water) decreases the stimulus to vasopressin secretion and permits the excretion of copious amounts of dilute urine. An increase in plasma osmolality increases the stimulus to vasopressin secretion that results in increased water reabsorption from the renal tubules and the excretion of small amounts of concentrated urine (Fig. 13.2).

Thirst

Thirst is the second control mechanism for fluid balance. The control centres for thirst are thought to

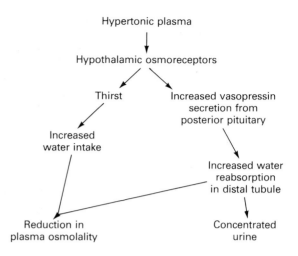

Fig. 13.2 The role of vasopressin in the control of plasma osmolality. Details of vasopressin release and actions are given in Chapter 24.

be situated in the hypothalamus (thirst centres). Electrical stimulation or injection of hypertonic solutions into these areas cause drinking; destruction of the thirst centres abolishes the desire to drink.

The commonest physiological stimulus to thirst is an increase in osmolality of the extracellular fluid, and the cells in the thirst centres respond by shrinking or swelling; it is not known whether the cells concerned are the same as the osmoreceptors concerned with vasopressin secretion.

Role of renin and angiotensin

Thirst is induced after severe haemorrhage and may be mediated by release of renin and angiotensin II (p. 206). Renin is thought to cross the blood-brain barrier whilst angiotensin II cannot; however it may be that the most sensitive areas in the subfornical organ and the organum vasculosum of the lamina terminalis are functionally outside the blood–brain barrier. The thirst centres themselves also contain all the precursors, including converting enzyme, necessary for the manufacture of angiotensin II. It therefore seems likely that renin is able to produce angiotensin II in the brain. Angiotensin is thought to act on receptors in the surface of the third ventricle and causes intense thirst.

Monitoring fluid intake

When water is ingested in response to a thirst stimulus, it takes at least an hour to be absorbed and exert its maximum effect on plasma osmolality. If the hypothalamic osmoreceptors were the only sensors concerned in the mechanism, this would result in 'overdrinking'. There seems to be a mechanism that turns off the thirst centres. The stimuli include distension of the stomach, moistening of the oral mucosa and passage of fluid over the posterior pharynx, but the precise significance of each is not known. Many animals rely heavily on this mechanism; the camel is able to drink enough in a few minutes to replenish its substantial fluid losses so that plasma osmolality returns precisely to normal values. The evidence that this has an important role in man is less convincing.

CONTROL OF POTASSIUM

It is essential that the plasma potassium concentration is maintained between 3 and 6 mmol/l. Variations outside these limits have severe consequences for functioning of muscle, particularly heart muscle, and the nervous system.

The only known hormone that controls potassium excretion is aldosterone, although recently suggestions have been made that vasopressin may have some effect. An increase in plasma potassium concentration causes an increased secretion of aldosterone by a direct effect on the adrenal cortex. This mechanism operates when plasma potassium concentration is less than 7 mmol/l but further increases have no further effect on aldosterone secretion. Aldosterone stimulates secretion of potassium by the distal tubule (p. 189). In patients with aldosterone-secreting tumours of the adrenal cortex (Conn's syndrome), plasma potassium concentrations may fall to very low levels.

However, a number of other factors alter potassium excretion including acid-base balance (p. 189) and flow in the distal convoluted tubule (p. 189). In addition, it should be remembered that the major store of potassium is intracellular and movement of potassium into or out of cells has great effects on plasma potassium concentration. For example, in untreated diabetes mellitus, potassium is lost from cells and excreted in the urine. When insulin is administered to diabetic patients, glucose enters cells and potassium enters as well. Thus the treatment can cause severe hypokalaemia. Conversely, in patients with a dangerously high concentration of potassium in their plasma one emergency measure to reduce it is by infusion of glucose and insulin.

FURTHER READING

Catto G R D, Smith J A R 1981 Clinical aspects of renal physiology. Blackwell Scientific, Oxford

Fitzsimons J T 1979 The physiology of thirst and sodium appetite. University Press, Cambridge

Linden R J, Kappagoda C T 1982 Atrial receptors. University Press, Cambridge

Morgan D B (ed) 1984 Electrolyte disorders. Clinics in Endocrinology and Metabolism 13: 231–342

Richards P, Truniger B 1983 Understanding water, electrolyte and acid–base balance. Heinemann, London

Sullivan L P, Grantham J J 1982 Physiology of the kidney, 2nd edn. Lea & Febiger, Philadelphia

Valtin H 1984 Renal function: mechanisms preserving fluid and solute transport in health, 2nd edn. Little Brown, Boston

Willatts S M 1984 Fluid and electrolyte disorders: water. British Journal of Hospital Medicine 32: 8–14

14

Acid–base balance

The oxidation of food yields about 13 mol of carbonic acid per day. In addition, about 70 mmol of phosphoric acid and sulphuric acid and appreciable amounts of organic acids, such as lactic, acetic, propionic and butyric acids are produced daily. Despite the large amounts of acid produced each day, the hydrogen ion concentration ([H⁺]) of extracellular fluid (ECF) is maintained between 36 and 44 nmol/l. The maintenance of [H⁺] within this fairly narrow range is essential for the optimal functioning of most chemical reactions within the body, particularly those involving specialised proteins such as enzymes or carriers. Deviations from

this range can cause severe alterations in many metabolic processes and values above 141 or below 22 nmol/l are incompatible with life.

The [H⁺] in body fluids is often expressed as the pH, where pH is equal to the negative logarithm to the base 10 of [H⁺] in mol/l. Thus a low pH corresponds to a high [H⁺] or *acidaemia*, while a high pH corresponds to a low [H⁺] or *alkalaemia*. A nomogram for converting [H⁺] to pH is shown in Figure 14.1. The normal pH range of the extracellular fluid is between 7.36 and 7.44, which corresponds to a [H⁺] of between 44 and 36 nmol/l.

The pH of venous blood is slightly less than the pH of arterial blood, because the extra amounts of CO_2 in venous blood dissolve to form carbonic acid.

The intracellular pH varies from tissue to tissue, but is usually slightly less than the extracellular pH. This is probably because of the rapid production of CO_2, which is hydrated to carbonic acid within the cells.

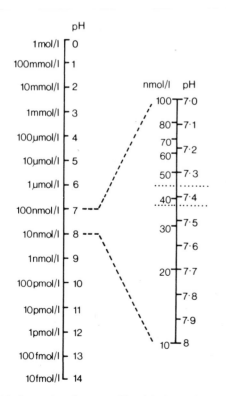

Fig. 14.1 Comparison between pH and hydrogen ion concentration in aqueous solutions. The dotted lines indicate the normal range for arterial blood plasma.

MAINTENANCE OF A NORMAL pH

The pH of the body fluids is maintained at a constant level by several mechanisms. Acid–base buffer systems combine with excessive hydrogen ion to minimise acidaemia, and release H⁺ when the pH starts to rise, minimising alkalaemia.

If the [H⁺] in the ECF changes, the rate and depth of respiration alters, changing the excretion of CO_2 and the removal of hydrogen ion; a fall in pH of the blood (acidaemia) increases in the respiratory rate, lowering the P_{CO_2}, which removes the H⁺ from the ECF by causing it to associate with HCO_3^-.

A change in [H⁺] in the blood also causes the kidneys to excrete either an acid or an alkaline urine, which helps to restore the pH of the body fluids to normal. These processes vary in their rates of action. Neutralisation by buffers may take just a fraction of a second, whereas it takes 1 to 15 minutes for the respiratory system to adjust a sudden change in [H⁺] and several hours or even days for the kidney to mitigate a disturbance of [H⁺].

Buffers

An acid–base buffer usually consists of two or more chemical compounds in solution that act to prevent changes in [H⁺] when either acid or base is added to the solution. If acid is added to water the pH changes very rapidly to a low value. If, however, a few drops of a buffer are added to the water and then acid is added, the H⁺ combines with the buffer and the pH of the solution changes very little. The amount of acid that has to be added to a solution to change the pH by a nominal amount, for example one pH unit, is known as the *buffer capacity*.

Buffers are usually solutions of weak acids or weak bases that are 50 per cent dissociated at or near the pH range of ECF. The pH at which the buffer is 50 per cent dissociated is known as the pK. Three major buffer systems exist in the ECF: protein compounds, phosphate buffers and the bicarbonate/carbonic acid system.

Proteins

Tissues and plasma proteins make the greatest contribution to the buffer capacity of the body. They possess at least two different systems. One is the carboxy group (R–COOH), which can dissociate in solution to an anion and H⁺.

$$R-COOH \rightleftharpoons R-COO^- + H^+ \qquad (1)$$

The undissociated carboxyl is capable of donating hydrogen ion while the dissociated anion, which can accept hydrogen ion as the reaction moves to the left, is its conjugate base.

Another buffer system is the ammonium group R–NH₃⁺, which dissociates as follows:

$$R-NH_3^+ \rightleftharpoons R-NH_2 + H^+ \qquad (2)$$

R–NH₃⁺ is the acid and R–NH₂ is its conjugate base. The addition of H⁺ to these systems causes both of these reactions to move to the left so that H⁺ is mopped up and the pH changes very little. In contrast, the addition of alkali removes hydrogen ion, and causes both reactions to move to the right, releasing more H⁺ from the hydrogen ion 'store'. Protein is a good buffer because it contains large numbers of these two systems and has the capacity to remove or release large amounts of hydrogen ion according to the body's requirements. Moreover, since the pK of some of the protein buffers is around 7.4, the system can work well at the pH of body fluids.

Haemoglobin

Haemoglobin plays a particularly important role in buffering plasma. In addition to the groups described above, haemoglobin also possesses another buffer system: the imidazole groups on the histidine molecules (Fig. 14.2), particularly at the C terminals of the beta chains (p. 26).

The buffering potential of the imidazole group is greater when haemoglobin is in the reduced form (Fig. 14.2). This is because the imidazole grouping in reduced haemoglobin is a much weaker acid and is related to the change in the shape of haemoglobin molecule and the association of the C-terminal histidines with aspartate groupings. This property increases the ability of haemoglobin to buffer acid in the tissues as it loses oxygen and becomes exposed to large amounts of carbonic acid. Conversely, as the haemoglobin becomes oxygenated in the lungs, the imidazole groupings become stronger acids, and hydrogen ion is released from the haemoglobin.

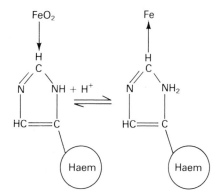

Oxyhaemoglobin   Reduced haemoglobin

Fig. 14.2 The effect of oxygenation and reduction on the buffering action of the imidazole group of haemoglobin. Oxygenation causes the imidazole group to become more acidic.

Carriage of carbon dioxide in the blood

Much the largest amount of acid produced in the body is in the form of carbonic acid, produced by the hydration of CO_2. When CO_2 is produced in the tissues it dissolves in plasma, where one of three things happens to it.

A small proportion remains dissolved in plasma, where it can combine with water to produce carbonic acid.

$$CO_2 + H_2O \rightleftharpoons H_2CO_3 \qquad (3)$$

In practice the equilibrium of this reaction is far to the left, so that the concentration of dissolved CO_2 is about 1000 times that of carbonic acid. The carbonic acid then ionises to bicarbonate and hydrogen ions.

$$H_2CO_3 \rightleftharpoons HCO_3^- + H^+ \qquad (4)$$

The H^+ are buffered in the plasma while the HCO_3^- remain.

Some CO_2 forms carbamino compounds with plasma proteins, and this reaction also results in the release of H^+.

$$R-NH_2 + CO_2 \rightleftharpoons R-NH-COO^- + H^+ \qquad (5)$$

Most of the CO_2 diffuses into the erythrocytes, where it rapidly hydrates to carbonic acid by the action of the large amounts of carbonic anhydrase in the red cells. This rapid hydration allows the red cells to take up rapidly the large amounts of CO_2 that are formed in the tissues. Carbonic acid then ionises to form H^+ and HCO_3^-. This reaction proceeds because the reaction products are removed as soon as they are formed. Bicarbonate diffuses out into the plasma while H^+ is buffered by the haemoglobin, the buffering capacity of which is increased by the loss of oxygen (as described earlier).

In the lungs the reverse happens: the association of oxygen with haemoglobin converts it into a stronger acid, releasing H^+, which combines with HCO_3^- to produce more carbonic acid. As the HCO_3^- in the cell is used up, more enters from the plasma to combine with the released H^+. Carbonic acid is dehydrated by carbonic anhydrase to release CO_2, which diffuses out of the erythrocytes and into the alveoli. In this way the elimination of CO_2 removes H^+ from the blood.

Action of the bicarbonate/carbonic acid buffer system
The carbonic acid/bicarbonate system provides a moderately weak buffer system in the plasma.

$$H_2CO_3 \rightleftharpoons H^+ + HCO_3^- \qquad (4)$$

An increase in $[H^+]$ drives the reaction to the left, lowering the HCO_3^- and forming undissociated carbonic acid. Conversely, the addition of extra base to the plasma combines with hydrogen ions, driving the reaction to the right and making carbonic acid dissociate. Although this system is not the important buffer system in the blood, the relation between P_{CO_2}, bicarbonate ion concentration ($[HCO_3^-]$) and pH provides a simple clinical means for determining the acid–base status of the extracellular fluid. This relation is expressed mathematically by the Henderson–Hasselbalch equation.

Henderson–Hasselbalch equation
Carbonic acid in solution is in equilibrium with bicarbonate and hydrogen ions. According to the law of mass action, the concentration of carbonic acid in solution is proportional to the product of $[H^+]$ and $[HCO_3^-]$.

$$[H_2CO_3] \propto [HCO_3^-][H^+] \qquad (6)$$

Or, to put it another way, the product of the concentrations of H^+ and HCO_3^- divided by the concentration of carbonic acid is equal to a constant:

$$K = \frac{[HCO_3^-][H^+]}{[H_2CO_3]} \qquad (7)$$

Since the concentration of carbonic acid in plasma is proportional to that of dissolved CO_2, the term $[CO_2]$ can be substituted for $[H_2CO_3]$

$$K' = \frac{[HCO_3^-][H^+]}{[CO_2]} \qquad (8)$$

Taking the logarithm of both sides of the equation we have:

$$\text{Log } K' = \frac{[H^+][HCO_3^-]}{[CO_2]} \qquad (9)$$

Since the logarithm of the product of two quantities is equal to the sum of the logarithms of each:

$$\text{Log } K' = \text{Log }[H^+] + \text{Log }\frac{[HCO_3^-]}{[CO_2]} \qquad (10)$$

Transposing Log K' and Log H:

$$-\text{Log }[H^+] = -\text{Log } K' + \text{Log }\frac{[HCO_3^-]}{[CO_2]} \qquad (11)$$

Since $-\text{Log } H^+ = pH$ and $-\text{Log } K' = pK$

$$pH = pK + \log \frac{[HCO_3^-]}{[CO_2]} \qquad (12)$$

Since the concentration of CO_2 dissolved in plasma is equal to the product of the partial pressure of CO_2 and a constant describing the solubility of CO_2 in plasma (a);

$$pH = pK + \text{Log }\frac{[HCO_3^-]}{aP_{CO_2}} \qquad (13)$$

Since the values of the two constants pK and a are known, the equation can be used to calculate any one of the variables, P_{CO_2}, $[HCO_3]$ or pH, by knowing the other two.

$$pH = 6.10 + Log \frac{[HCO_3^-]}{0.0301 \ P_{CO_2}} \qquad (14)$$

pH/Bicarbonate diagram

The relation between pH, $[HCO_3^-]$ and P_{CO_2} can be expressed in a useful diagrammatic form, shown in Figure 14.3. The pH units are plotted on the abscissa and the bicarbonate concentration is plotted on the ordinate. The P_{CO_2} can be plotted as a series of isobars. Knowing any two of the variables, it is possible to read off the other from the diagram.

The pH/bicarbonate diagram is useful in explaining the acid–base disturbances that can occur in man (Fig. 14.4). Under normal resting conditions, the pH of arterial blood lies between 7.36 and 7.44, the P_{CO_2} between 35 and 45 mm Hg (4.6 to 6.0 kPa), and the bicarbonate concentration between approximately 24 and 28 mmol/l.

DISORDERS OF ACID–BASE BALANCE

Respiratory acidaemia

A man with respiratory failure is unable to excrete sufficient CO_2 from the lungs so large amounts of CO_2 become hydrated to yield abnormally large amounts of bicarbonate and hydrogen ion.

$$CO_2 + H_2O \rightleftharpoons H_2CO_3 \rightleftharpoons H^+ + HCO_3 \quad (15)$$

Much of the H^+ is buffered so that the pH falls only slightly, while the $[HCO_3^-]$ may increase considerably, as shown in Figure 14.4.

Respiratory alkalaemia

If a person is anxious and overbreathes, the P_{CO_2} falls, causing corresponding reductions in both $[H^+]$ and $[HCO_3^-]$. The buffer systems ensure that $[H^+]$ falls by a few nmol/l, causing a small increase in pH while the $[HCO_3^-]$ falls by several mmol/l, a thousand-fold differ-

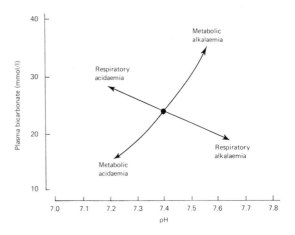

Fig. 14.4 The relation between bicarbonate concentration and pH in plasma. The arrows indicate typical values found in uncompensated alkalaemia or acidaemia.

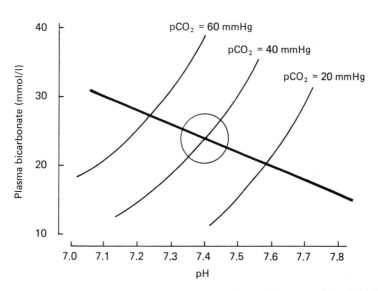

Fig. 14.3 The relation between the bicarbonate concentration, pH and P_{CO_2} of the extracellular fluid. The curved lines join points at which P_{CO_2} are the same. The straight line indicates the buffer line for plasma. The circle indicates the normal limits.

ence (Fig. 14.4). This state is known as respiratory alkalaemia.

Buffer capacity of body

Since carbonic acid dissociates into equal amounts of H^+ and HCO_3^-, increasing the P_{CO_2} must liberate equal amounts of these ions. While the H^+ is buffered, HCO_3^- remains in the extracellular fluid and the change in $[HCO_3^-]$ is equal to the increase in $[H^+]$ that would have occurred if hydrogen ion had not been buffered. Thus comparison of the increase in $[HCO_3^-]$ with the increase in $[H^+]$ provides an index of the buffer capacity of the body. Analysis of Figure 14.4 shows that going from respiratory acidaemia to respiratory alkalaemia causes a difference of 10 mmol/l in bicarbonate concentration and a change in pH from 7.7 to 7.2, equivalent to a change of 40 nmol/l. Converting these changes to the same units, this represents a buffer capacity of 10 000 000/40.

Metabolic acidaemia

Metabolic acidaemia is caused by the addition of H^+ to the extracellular fluid or the removal of base. This may result from the formation of metabolic acids, as in lactic acidosis or diabetic ketoacidosis, or from the inability of the kidney to excrete acid. Excess H^+ in the extracellular fluid is buffered by bicarbonate as well as the more powerful protein buffers. Equation 16 is shifted to the left, lowering the $[HCO_3^-]$ and moving the equilibrium as shown in Figure 14.4. The P_{CO_2} changes little because the plasma $[CO_2]$ is already very large compared with plasma $[H_2CO_3]$, so a large change in carbonic acid has a negligible influence on $[CO_2]$.

$$H_2CO_3 \rightleftharpoons HCO_3^- + H^+ \qquad (16)$$

Metabolic alkalaemia

The addition of base to the extracellular fluid, for example after ingestion of excessive amounts of alkali for duodenal ulcer or the removal of H^+ by vomiting, causes dissociation of carbonic acid, releasing more bicarbonate and resulting in a shift in the equilibrium (Fig. 14.4).

$$H_2CO_3 \rightleftharpoons HCO_3^- + \begin{array}{c} H^+ \\ \downarrow \\ H^+ + OH^- = H_2O \end{array} \qquad (17)$$

Again the P_{CO_2} is initially unchanged. A similar sequence occurs as a result of the direct removal of H^+, such as in vomiting. This state is known as metabolic alkalaemia.

Table 14.5 shows that these four common disturb-

Table 14.5 Changes in arterial blood composition in uncompensated acid–base disturbances

Disturbance	pH	$[HCO_3]$	P_{CO_2}
Respiratory acidaemia	lowered	raised	raised
Metabolic acidaemia	lowered	lowered	unchanged
Respiratory alkalaemia	raised	lowered	lowered
Metabolic alkalaemia	raised	raised	unchanged

ances in acid–base balance can be distinguished simply by the changes that occur in pH, $[HCO_3^-]$ and P_{CO_2}.

Respiratory compensation

The pH changes in acidaemia and alkalaemia are normally less than indicated in Figure 14.4 because the body attempts to correct changes in pH by compensatory alterations in respiratory and renal function. Consider for example metabolic acidaemia. The increase in $[H^+]$ of the ECF stimulates the central chemoreceptors and increases the rate and depth of respiration (p. 152). This lowers the P_{CO_2} and carbonic acid concentration, causing association of HCO_3^- and H^+ and lowering both the $[H^+]$ (raising the pH to near normal), and $[HCO_3^-]$ (Fig. 14.6).

$$CO_2 + H_2O \rightleftharpoons H_2CO_3 \rightleftharpoons H^+ + HCO_3^- \qquad (18)$$

In metabolic alkalaemia, the reverse occurs: respiration becomes slow and shallow, the retained CO_2 causes the $[H^+]$ to rise and the pH to fall, and the $[HCO_3^-]$ increases even more (Fig. 14.6).

Renal compensation

Respiratory acidaemia or metabolic acidaemia or alkalaemia, which is not of renal origin, may be partially compensated by changes in the renal excretion of hydrogen ion. For example, the renal correction for

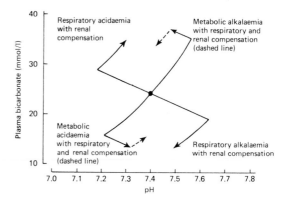

Fig. 14.6 The relation between the pH and bicarbonate concentration in the extracellular fluid with compensated acidaemia or alkalaemia.

respiratory acidaemia causes an increase in renal hydrogen ion excretion, lowers plasma $[H^+]$ and increases $[HCO_3^-]$ (Fig. 14.6; see below).

Mechanism of renal excretion of acid

The kidneys are capable of removing up to 500 mmol of acid (or alkali) per day. This rate of excretion cannot be achieved by filtration of H^+ alone since the concentration in the plasma is in the nanomolar range. Instead, H^+ is rapidly generated in the tubular cells by hydration of CO_2, under the influence of carbonic anhydrase, and actively secreted into the tubular lumen in exchange for sodium ion. The secretion of H^+ by the tubule is proportional to the P_{CO_2}. The tubular epithelium is permeable to H^+. Diffusion of H^+ back into the plasma is normally prevented by the combination of H^+ with buffers in the tubular fluid. The three mechanisms involved in the excretion of hydrogen ions are described on page 190.

Regulation of renal excretion of hydrogen ions

The control of H^+ secretion is largely exerted through the effects of CO_2 on the renal tubular cells. An increased plasma P_{CO_2} (respiratory acidaemia) increases H^+ secretion while at the same time increasing the apparent reabsorption of bicarbonate. Since the rate of H^+ secretion exceeds the buffering capacity of the filtered HCO_3^-, more HCO_3^- is returned to the blood than is filtered, so increasing the $[HCO_3^-]$; the excess H^+ is buffered by ammonia and phosphate.

In metabolic acidaemia caused by conditions other than renal failure, plasma $[HCO_3^-]$ is lower and hence the filtered HCO_3 is much less than the normal amounts of H^+ secreted. The surplus H^+, however, can be excreted because it combines with phosphate and ammonia in the tubular lumen. Ammonia is particularly important; acidaemia increases the production of ammonia tenfold, from 50 mmol/day to 500 mmol/day. Since the secretion of hydrogen ion automatically leads to the addition of bicarbonate to the ECF, irrespective of whether or not the secreted hydrogen ion is buffered by bicarbonate, acid is expelled from the ECF while bicarbonate is added.

In metabolic alkalaemia, the amount of filtered bicarbonate exceeds the amount of acid produced. Thus, although all the acid is buffered and lost from the body, surplus base is excreted in an alkaline urine.

FURTHER READING

Arruda J A L 1981 Acid–base. Seminars in Nephrology 1: 3
Catto G R D, Smith J A R 1981 Clinical aspects of renal physiology. Baillére Tindall, London
Davenport H W 1974 The ABC of acid base chemistry, 6th edn. University of Chicago Press, Chicago
Kirtzman M A, Battle, D C 1983 Acid–base disorders. Medical Clinics of North America 67: 751–932
Porter R, Lawrenson G 1982 Metabolic acidosis (Ciba Foundation Symposium 87). Pitman, London
Richards P, Truniger B 1983 Understanding water, electrolytes and acid–base balance. Heinemann, London
Rose B D 1980 Clinical physiology of acid–base and electrolyte disorders. McGraw Hill, New York

15

Nutrition

The food we eat is composed of animal and plant tissues or products derived from them. Its oxidation provides the energy needed for metabolism, for the maintenance of body temperature and for muscular activity. In addition, food provides essential materials that cannot be synthesised in the body.

The daily energy requirements are derived from carbohydrates, fats and proteins. A normal daily diet contains about 350 g of carbohydrate, 120 g of fat and 70 g of protein and provides 11.6 MJ of energy.

Protein requirements

The growing child needs enough protein to provide the amino acids out of which new tissue protein is constructed. The adult needs protein to replace tissue lost by wear and tear, to build up new tissue protein after injury or a wasting illness, and to supply amino acids essential for the synthesis of enzymes and certain hormones.

Nitrogen balance

The proteins of the tissues of the body are continuously broken down into their constituent amino acids. Most of these are re-used to build new protein molecules, although about 20–30 g is used for the production of other chemicals, notably the substrates of the tricarboxylic acid cycle. It is therefore necessary to have a supply of protein to replace that being destroyed. The extent to which this replacement is achieved can be assessed accurately by measuring the nitrogen balance, whereby the intake of nitrogen in the diet is compared with the amount of nitrogen lost from the body in the urine and faeces. Nitrogen losses from the skin (1 g/day) and menstrual blood (approximately 1 g/day) must also be taken into account.

One gram of nitrogen is equivalent to about 6.25 g of protein. A subject eating a diet containing carbohydrate and fat but no protein has an obligatory nitrogen loss of 2–3 g/day and is in negative nitrogen balance. An intake of 2–3 g/day nitrogen does not necessarily restore a positive balance because urinary losses increase as the nitrogen intake is increased. Up to 5 g of nitrogen may be needed before a positive nitrogen balance is restored.

Much of the nitrogen is lost by the conversion of amino acids to substances such as pyruvate, which is converted to glucose (gluconeogenesis) or to acetyl CoA. Acetyl CoA can either be built up to fatty acids or be oxidised in the tricarboxylic acid cycle to yield energy. If the diet contains adequate amounts of fat and carbohydrate, less protein is converted to energy-rich substrate. Carbohydrate and fat are therefore said to have a protein-sparing action since nitrogen balance is achieved at a lower level of nitrogen intake than if the diet were to consist almost entirely of protein.

A physical injury, such as a fracture of bone or a surgical operation, is immediately followed by a period of negative nitrogen balance, which reaches its maximum about a week after the injury. This increased loss of nitrogen is largely derived from the breakdown of muscle protein, probably stimulated by hormones such as glucocorticoids (p. 318). Adequate nutrition before and after surgical operations is therefore very important.

Essential amino acids

The nutritional value of a protein depends upon its amino acid composition. Most amino acids can be synthesised within the body, usually from other amino acids; their presence in the diet is therefore not essential. Other amino acids cannot be synthesised in the amounts needed for normal growth and must be supplied in the diet. These *essential amino acids* are lysine, tryptophan, phenylalanine, leucine, isoleucine, threonine, methionine, valine and histidine. About 1 g of each is the minimum daily requirement.

People who eat diets lacking only one of the essential amino acids are unable to synthesise normal body proteins and become protein deficient, despite having a normal nitrogen intake. Since they are unable to utilise the protein ingested, growth is impaired and the output of nitrogen in the urine and faeces exceeds the intake; they are in negative nitrogen balance. The requirement for essential amino acids is greater in growing children.

Most animal proteins are 'complete'; that is they contain all the necessary amino acids in the appropriate proportions for utilisation by man. Plant proteins are often 'incomplete', since they lack certain essential amino acids. Thus people living on a strictly vegetarian diet may become protein deficient. However, vegetarians can have a complete protein intake if they mix cereals and pulses in their diets, since proteins from different plant sources lack different essential amino acids.

Kwashiorkor

The clinical syndrome usually thought to be associated with protein lack is kwashiorkor, which affects millions of children in developing countries. It most commonly occurs in infants after weaning and particularly when given an inadequate and predominantly carbohydrate diet. Many of the children also have an inadequate energy intake and the disorder is known as *protein-energy malnutrition*. The affected child stops growing, loses weight and becomes listless, apathetic and irritable. The skin and hair may become depigmented, and oedema associated with low plasma levels of albumin often develops. The relative importance of protein lack and energy lack in this syndrome is controversial since children respond both to protein supplementation and to the restoration of a normal energy intake. Untreated kwashiorkor is often fatal.

Fat requirements

The fat in the diet is important, not only because of its high energy value, but also because it is the vehicle for the fat-soluble vitamins A, D, E and K and because it contains the essential fatty acids, linoleic acid and arachidonic acid, which cannot be synthesised by the tissues. Arachidonic acid is the precursor for the production of prostaglandins, prostacyclin and thromboxane (p. 233).

The fat content of human diets varies widely according to climate, race and dietary custom. In western countries the fat intake per day is between 80 and 150 g (35 to 40 per cent of the total energy intake). In developing countries, fat may contribute as little as 15 per cent of total energy. A diet that contains a high ratio of saturated to unsaturated fats may possibly predispose to atheroma and death from heart attacks and strokes. Most animal fats are saturated while most vegetable fats contain a higher proportion of unsaturated lipid.

Carbohydrate requirements

Carbohydrate provides an important source of rapidly available energy and is particularly important when a person undertakes heavy work.

The proportion of carbohydrate in the diet varies widely. In western countries less than 50 per cent of the energy intake may come from carbohydrate. Since carbohydrate foods derived from cereals are cheap, they constitute a larger proportion of the diet in developing countries.

Not all the carbohydrate we eat is in a form that can be digested in the small intestine. Pulses (beans and peas), for example, contain polysaccharides that are not broken down in the small intestine, but pass into the colon, where they are fermented by anaerobic bacteria to short-chain fatty acids (acetic, propionic and butyric acids), which are rapidly absorbed. Up to 10 per cent of the starch in the diet escapes absorption in the small intestine and is fermented in the colon.

Dietary fibre

The unabsorbable proportion of carbohydrate or glycoprotein, which cannot be digested in the small intestine, is collectively known as *dietary fibre*. It includes wheat bran, cellulose, lignin and gel-forming polysaccharides, such as pectin and guar gum.

Modern 'western' diets contain a large amount of refined 'white' flour and sucrose, and little dietary fibre. The excessive intake of refined carbohydrate and relative lack of fibre is thought by some to contribute to the high prevalence in western society of disease such as diabetes mellitus, obesity, gallstones, atheroma, dental caries, constipation, diverticular disease of the colon and carcinoma of the colon. Such conditions are rare in rural Africans living on diets rich in 'fibre'.

The recognition of the possible relation between fibre intake and disease has led to measures to increase the proportion of unavailable carbohydrate in the diet. The use of wholemeal flour and the addition of wheat bran is thought to prevent constipation or colonic diverticular disease by making the stool softer, bulkier and easier to pass. This effect may be related to the water-holding properties of 'fibre' and to the increase in bacterial numbers caused by a greater supply of bacterial substrate.

The addition of viscous polysaccharides, such as guar gum and pectin, to the diet delays the absorption of glucose in the small intestine and may have a role in the management of diabetes mellitus. Addition of viscous polysaccharides also causes food to empty slowly from the stomach, producing earlier satiety. In this way viscous polysaccharides may help obese people to reduce food intake.

The effect of starvation

When the body is deprived of food it calls first on its stores of carbohydrate and fat for the provision of energy. Stores of carbohydrate, glycogen in liver and muscle, are small and soon exhausted but fat stores may be enough to meet the needs of the body for several

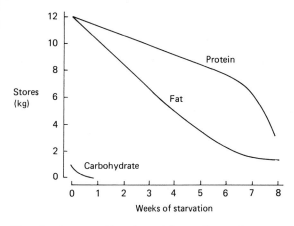

Fig. 15.1 The quantities of stored foodstuffs at different times of total starvation.

weeks (Fig. 15.1). However, in the absence of a ready supply of carbohydrate, the oxidation of fat produces more acetyl CoA than can be utilised by the tricarboxylic acid cycle. This excess acetyl CoA is converted into ketone bodies. Long before the reserves of nonnitrogenous fuel are exhausted, the tissue proteins begin to be broken down to provide energy. When the fat stores are exhausted muscle protein is the sole source of energy. Thus, nitrogen excretion is low in the early stages of starvation, but it rises after the exhaustion of carbohydrate and fat stores. Death is preceded by a further sharp rise in nitrogen excretion.

The vitamins

The vitamins are organic compounds with a variety of chemical structures. They are essential components in metabolic processes and need to be present in the diet in small amounts for the normal functioning of the body. Vitamins are found in both plant and animal foods. The latter are an important source of vitamins that are normally stored in the tissues. In their absence a 'biochemical lesion' develops, which may be accompanied by structural changes in various tissues. The amounts required are usually quite small, but requirements are increased during growth, pregnancy and lactation. Some of the vitamins may be synthesised in the body, but only in amounts that are insufficient to satisfy metabolic needs. Although it is important to understand the metabolic role of each vitamin and how its lack affects body function, diets in poor communities are often deficient in several vitamins, as well as protein and calories; the signs and symptoms of people with inadequate nutrition reflect all of the deficiencies.

Vitamins A, D, E and K are fat soluble, while the vitamins of the B group and vitamin C are water soluble. Deficiency may result from reduced intake as well as from impaired absorption (p. 273). Table 15.2 lists the characteristics of the more important vitamins. Their absorption from the intestine is discussed in Chapter 21.

Minerals

The metabolism of calcium and phosphorus is discussed in Chapter 29. Iron metabolism is described in Chapter 4 and iodine metabolism in Chapter 25. This section is concerned with other minerals.

Magnesium

The adult human body contains about 25 g (1000 mmol) of magnesium, about half being in the bones and half in the cells. Magnesium is an essential component of intracellular enzymes, and an essential cofactor in all reactions involving ATP. It is also necessary for the integrity of intracellular organelles such as ribosomes and mitochondria.

The extracellular concentration of magnesium is 1.8 to 2.5 mmol/l. An increased extracellular magnesium level occurs, for example, in renal failure; it depresses activity in the nervous system and impairs skeletal muscle contraction.

The minimum daily requirements of magnesium for an adult are about 250 mg (10 mmol) but a simple dietary deficiency of magnesium is unknown in man since green vegetables and cereals contain large amounts of magnesium. Magnesium depletion with low plasma magnesium levels occurs in patients with excessive intestinal losses due to diarrhoea, particularly after resection of large amounts of small intestine. Such patients suffer from increased irritability of the nervous system (tetany or epileptic fits) and cardiac arrhythmias. Magnesium depletion causes low plasma levels of calcium.

Copper

A normal adult has about 100 mg (1.6 mmol) of copper in his body. Any excess of absorbed copper is removed from the blood by the liver cells and is excreted in the bile. The copper content of plasma is normally 13 to 24 μmol/l and most of this is bound to *caeruloplasmin*, an α_2-globulin.

Copper is a component of cytochrome oxidase, which is involved in the final step for the reduction of molecular oxygen. It is also a component of enzymes such as tyrosinase, ascorbic acid oxidase, monoamine oxidase and lysyl oxidase (essential for the synthesis of collagen and elastin), as well as enzymes concerned with phospholipid synthesis.

Copper deficiency is not known in adults, but in infants an anaemia may occur that responds to treatment with copper and iron. Copper excess occurs in *Wilson's disease* (hepatolenticular degeneration) in which

Table 15.2 The sources, requirements and storage action of the principal vitamins and the effects of their deficiency

Vitamin	Source	Daily requirement	Body stores	Action	Deficiency
A	Liver, eggs, milk butter and margarine. Vegetables and fruit (carotene)	750 μg	Liver stores last several months	Formation of retinal pigment — rhodopsin. Cell growth especially epithelial cells.	Night blindness, eczema, acne, keratinisation of the cornea. Damage to respiratory epithelium. Hypospermia.
B_1 (thiamin)	Lean meat, beans, nuts, outer portion of grain. Wholemeal flour. Yeast extract.	1 mg	25 mg in heart, brain, liver and kidney.	Thiamine pyrophosphate is a coenzyme in decarboxylation of alpha-oxo-acids, such as pyruvic acid.	Decreases glucose utilisation. Beri beri: peripheral nerve dysfunction, cardiac failure, peripheral vasodilatation.
Niacin	Liver, kidney and muscle. Yeast and outer portion of grain.	12 mg		Nicotinamide adenine dinucleotide (NAD) or NAD phosphate (NADP) are hydrogen acceptions in biological oxidation systems.	Pellagra — diarrhoea, dermatitis. Soreness of the tongue and mouth. Dementia.
Folic acid	Liver. Fresh green vegetables. Produced by colonic bacteria.	200 μg		Methyl-tetrahydrofolate is a coenzyme in the transfer of 1-carbon units and plays a part in DNA synthesis.	Disturbance in DNA synthesis. Megaloblastic anaemia.
B12	All foods of animal origin especially liver	2 μg	Liver stores last 4 years	5-adenysyl cobalamin is a hydrogen acceptor and an essential coenzyme in DNA synthesis	Megaloblastic anaemia Subacute combined degeneration of the spinal cord. Peripheral nerve damage
C (ascorbic) acid)	Fresh fruits and vegetables	45 mg		A powerful reducing agent — important in all oxidative reactions. Especially in formation of collagen and mobilisation of iron	Scurvy — poor wound healing, abnormal bone formation, capillary fragility (swollen, bleeding gums).
D (calciferol)	Fatty fish (herring, salmon, sardines)	2.5 μg	Stores in fat and muscle, may last several years	Precursor of calcitriol (Chap. 29) and therefore essential for active calcium absorption in the gut	Rickets and osteomalacia
K	Green plants synthesised by colonic bacteria.		Minimal	Necessary for formation of clotting factors in liver.	Serious bleeding after injuries.

caeruloplasmin is deficient and copper is deposited in the brain, liver and other tissues including the cornea; disorders of movement and cirrhosis of the liver result.

Zinc

Zinc is a component of at least 80 enzymes, including carbonic anhydrase, which is essential for the carriage of CO_2 in the blood and in the secretion of hydrogen ions by the kidneys.

Good sources of zinc are herrings, eggs, nuts, beef and liver but most foods contain significant amounts. A daily intake of at least 13 mg is recommended. Only one-third of the ingested zinc is absorbed; the rest is lost in the faeces.

Zinc deficiency may occur in patients with malabsorption or when the diet contains large amounts of cereal rich in phytic acid, which binds divalent cations in the gut lumen. Zinc deficiency causes impaired growth, delayed sexual development and atrophy of the thymus with impairment of cell-mediated immunity (Chap. 5).

Fluorine

Fluorine is concentrated in bones and teeth; a small proportion appears to improve the stability of hydroxapatite crystals. The optimal intake of fluoride appears to be between 1.0 and 2.0 mg daily. Drinking water is the principal source of fluoride but other sources are seafood, tea (one cup provides about 0.2 mg) and toothpaste. Fluoride deficiency leads to dental caries and to decreased bone mass (osteoporosis, p. 351). Excess of fluoride, as occurs in some parts of India with a concentration in the water greater than 4 mg/l, may cause discolouration of the enamel of the teeth. Severe excess may cause crippling bone changes.

A healthy diet

Most people in western countries eat far more food than they need. In particular the 'western diet' contains excessive amounts of fat, particularly saturated fats, salt, refined sugar and alcohol, but contains little unrefined carbohydrate. This diet has evolved for several reasons: the availability of a large variety of foods, the greater attractiveness and tastiness of refined foods, the increase in wealth, the decline of the formal meal and its replacement by frequent snacks, rich in sugars and readily available carbohydrate, and the pace and pressures of life, which lead to a neurotic pattern of eating or drinking in order to obtain emotional satisfaction rather than to satisfy hunger.

This diet may be an important factor in the pathogenesis of the so-called 'diseases of civilisation'. An excessive intake of saturated fats is thought to contribute to atheroma. An excessive intake of sucrose may contribute to dental caries. Lack of dietary fibre

Table 15.3 Current intake of various foodstuffs in western countries compared with recommended intake.

Food	Current estimated intake in UK and other western countries		Long-term recommendations	
	Amount (g)	Percentage of total energy intake	Amount (g)	Percentage of total energy intake
Fat	128	38	101	30
Saturated fatty acid	59	18	33	10
Sucrose	104	13	54	75
Fibre	20		30	
Salt	10		7	
Alcohol	26	6	18	4
Protein	84	11	84	11
Carbohydrate	343	45	419	55

(p. 217) causes constipation and may lead to diverticular disease of the colon and perhaps gallstones and arterial disease. An excessive intake of salt may contribute to hypertension. An excessive intake of alcohol causes chronic liver disease.

The recommended adult intake of these foodstuffs is outlined in Table 15.3 and has been compared with the current daily intake of a normal person. Adoption of the ideal diet would necessitate the following changes. The energy content of the diet should maintain the body weight constant and at the ideal level for the height and sex of the person. The actual amount of energy depends on the energy expenditure. The fat intake, particularly the consumption of saturated fats, derived from dairy products and fatty meat, should be reduced. The sucrose intake from confectionery and soft drinks should also be restricted. To compensate for these reductions, the intake of carbohydrate in the form of wholemeal bread, vegetables and fruit should be increased and the diet should contain at least 30 g fibre per day. The salt and alcohol content of the diet should be restricted.

THE COMPOSITION OF FOOD

Milk

The human infant starts life on a diet consisting solely of milk. Human and cow's milk differ in composition and average values are given in Table 15.4.

Milk is an excellent source of protein, calcium and phosphorus but it is deficient in iron. However, infants are born with a store of iron sufficient to prevent anaemia if weaning starts within about four months.

Table 15.4 Composition of human and cow's milk per 100 g

Content	Human milk	Fresh summer cow's milk
Energy value	289 kj	272 kj
Water	87.1 g	87.6 g
Protein	1.3 g	3.3 g
Casein: whey proteins	1:3	4:1
Fat	4.1 g	3.8 g
Carbohydrate (lactose)	7.2 g	4.7 g
Calcium	34 mg	120 mg
Iron	70 μg	50 μg
Phosphorus	14 mg	95 mg
Sodium	14 mg	50 mg
Potassium	58 mg	150 mg
Retinol and carotene	35 and 22 μg	35 and 22 μg
Thiamin	20 μg	40 μg
Niacin	220 μg	80 μg
Ascorbic acid	3.7 mg	2 mg

After Paul A A, Southgate D A T 1978 McCance and Widdowson's The Composition of Foods, 4th edn. HMSO, London

Milk is an important source of vitamins A and D. The chief proteins of milk are casein and the whey proteins alpha-lactalbumin and beta-lactoglobulin. Milk goes 'sour' and curdles if kept at room temperature because bacteria in it multiply and produce lactic acid, which renders casein insoluble.

Milk products
Cream contains a high proportion (40 to 50 per cent) of fat. It is prepared by separating the fat from milk either by gentle centrifugation or by allowing it to rise in the surface. Milk from which the cream has been removed is known as *skim milk*.

When cream is submitted to prolonged shaking (churning) the globules coalesce to form a solid mass of *butter*, which is, like cream, an important source of the fat-soluble vitamins, especially vitamin A. It contains 65 per cent saturated fats.

Cheese is made by coagulating the proteins of milk with rennet (an enzyme prepared from calf stomach) at 30°C. Most of the fat is included in the coagulated mass, which is pressed out and allowed to 'ripen' under the influence of bacteria. The characteristic texture and taste of the finished cheese depends on the particular bacteria and moulds involved in the ripening process. Cheese is a good source of protein, fat and mineral elements such as calcium.

Yoghurt is manufactured by inoculating sterilised skim milk (or whole milk) with bacteria that produce lactic acid, and culturing it at 37°C.

Margarine
Margarine is prepared from blends of vegetable oils or animal fats. After hydrogenation the mixture acquires a consistence similar to that of butter. Soft margarines contain 25 to 50 per cent of polyunsaturated fatty acids compared with 2 per cent for butter. Vitamins A and D are added to margarine in Britain.

Meat and offal
Meat is skeletal muscle. When fresh meat is allowed to 'hang' glycogen disappears and acids such as lactic acid are produced; they soften the muscle fibres and make the meat more tender. Liver and kidney are both rich in nucleoprotein and contain less fat than most meat. Liver is rich in vitamin A and in iron.

Fish
Fish is an important source of protein. White fish such as cod, haddock and plaice contain only a small proportion of fat (less than 2 per cent), but herring, mackerel and salmon contain 5 to 18 per cent of fat and provide useful amounts of the fat-soluble vitamins A and D.

Eggs
Eggs are a good source of proteins, vitamins and minerals. An average egg (62.5 g) supplies 327 kJ of energy, 6.4 g of protein, 5.9 g of fat (including 30 mg cholesterol) 30 mg of calcium, 1.6 mg of iron, 80 μg of vitamin A, 1 μg of vitamin D and 0.06 mg of thiamin.

Cereals
The main constituents of cereals are starch (about 70 per cent), water (about 15 per cent) and protein (about 11 per cent). The amount of fat varies widely (0.5 to 8 per cent) from one cereal to another, being particularly high in oatmeal. The inorganic matter, about 2 per cent, consists chiefly of calcium, phosphorus and iron.

The endosperm in the centre of the wheat grain (Fig. 15.5) is mainly starch with some protein, but the outer layer of the endosperm contains the important protein mixture, gluten, as well as minerals and nicotinic acid. The germ is particularly rich in vitamins of the B group.

In the process of milling the degree of extraction, that is the percentage of the whole grain retained in the flour, can be varied widely. Wholemeal flour (92 to 100 per cent extraction) contains a large proportion of indigestible fibrous matter, vitamins and minerals. White flour (72 per cent extraction) has the advantage of good keeping qualities but much of the mineral, vitamin, protein content has been removed. In Britain, white flour is fortified with calcium, iron and thiamin. Wheatmeal flour (85 per cent extraction) used in the manufacture of most brown bread retains some of the B vitamins, minerals and fibre.

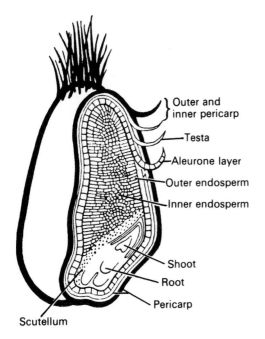

Fig. 15.5 Longitudinal section through a grain of wheat. (From McCance R A 1946 Lancet 1:77)

Bread

When wheat flour is kneaded with water a sticky mass of dough is formed by the formation of disulphide bonds in soluble proteins, such as gluten. Traditionally the dough is made to rise by the addition of yeast, which ferments the sugars in the flour to release gas. During baking the starch grains are ruptured and caramelised products are formed in the crust.

Gluten is a mixture of proteins, mainly gliadins and glutelins, and the flours made from these cereals produce a dough on the addition of water. Oatmeal and maize flour contain less gluten and therefore can be made into bread only with difficulty. The intestinal mucosa of patients with coeliac disease is damaged by the alpha-gliadin of wheat, causing villous atrophy and malabsorption.

Fruit and vegetables

Green vegetables are good sources of dietary fibre as well as minerals, ascorbic acid and carotene, the precursor of vitamin A.

Potatoes consist mainly of starch granules that swell up and burst on cooking. Potatoes also provide about one-quarter of the ascorbic acid intake, a small amount of vegetable protein, and useful amounts of iron and fluorine.

The pulses (beans, peas, lentils) are good sources of vegetable protein (20 to 25 per cent of the dry matter). When fresh (but not when dried) they supply ascorbic acid and carotene. They contain much undigestible polysaccharide, which makes the intestinal contents more viscous, delaying access of glucose to the epithelium and slowing its absorption. For this reason, pulses have been recommended for use in diabetic diets.

Most fruits are of little nutritional value except as sources of ascorbic acid. When ripe they contain varying amounts of sucrose and fructose; the banana is unique in supplying starch as well. Sugar manufactured from cane or sugar beet is almost pure sucrose. Since it contains no vitamins or minerals it is said to provide 'empty' calories.

Beverages

Chocolate and cocoa have a relatively high protein, fat and carbohydrate content and have thus a high energy value, but the energy value of tea and coffee depends entirely on the added sugar and milk. A cup of tea or coffee contains 100 to 150 mg of the stimulant caffeine. Cocoa is a source of iron.

Alcohol

Ethanol (ethyl alcohol) has a potential energy of 29 kJ/g. It is absorbed quickly from the intestine, especially if accompanied by a carbonated fluid such as soda water. Ethanol diffuses rapidly into the brain where it has a depressant action; deep coma occurs when the blood alcohol concentration exceeds 90 mmol/l. Alcohol is oxidised in the liver by alcohol dehydrogenase, which converts it to acetaldehyde; this is in turn oxidised to acetic acid, which enters the metabolic pool as acetyl-CoA. Both of these reactions require NAD (Fig. 15.6).

After an alcoholic drink the blood level falls slowly; only 150 mmol (7 g) can be metabolised per hour, the limiting factor being the availability of NAD. Small amounts of alcohol (3 per cent of the intake) are excreted in the urine and breath.

Alcoholic drinks lower the blood glucose level by inhibiting hepatic glycogenolysis and by potentiating the insulin-releasing properties of carbohydrate.

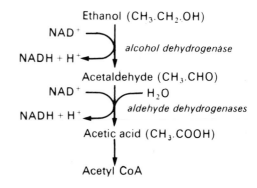

Fig. 15.6 Pathway for the oxidation of ethanol ('alcohol').

Beer is made by fermentation by yeast of a solution of sugars and other nutrients derived from a carbohydrate source, usually barley in Europe, but many other cereals are used. Since yeast cannot break down carbohydrates larger than trisaccharides, the cereal is allowed to germinate in the complex process of malting to produce hydrolytic enzymes that break down starch and other polysaccharides. Beer contains, in addition to 4 to 6 per cent of alcohol, a little carbohydrate and some vitamins of the B group derived from the yeast.

Spirits contain about 40 per cent alcohol, fortified wines (such as sherry and port) 20 per cent and ordinary wines 10 to 15 per cent alcohol.

Effects of cooking

The chemical composition of food may be considerably altered in the process of cooking. Cooking renders most foodstuffs more palatable and digestible and destroys bacteria. The most obvious effect of cooking is the coagulation of protein, for example during the boiling of an egg.

When meat is cooked water is lost, soluble protein is coagulated and collagen is converted to gelatin. As a result meat fibres shrink and become softer and looser so that the meat is easier to chew. When meat is boiled, soluble constituents, such as inorganic salts, gelatin and soluble organic substances responsible for flavour are lost. Loss of soluble materials is much less during roasting and baking, and less still during grilling and frying, in which the heat is usually applied for a short time and the surface is rapidly sealed by the heat. The starch granules of cereals and potatoes swell up during cooking and burst; they are more easily digested in this form. Cooking loosens the cellulose framework of vegetables.

Cooking has little effect on any of the vitamins except thiamin and ascorbic acid. Thiamin is destroyed by heat and does not survive the temperature used for example in the baking of biscuits. It is, however, not destroyed in the baking of bread unless sodium bicarbonate is added. As much as 60 per cent of the ascorbic acid content of foods may be lost during cooking; some is destroyed by the enzyme ascorbic acid oxidase liberated from damaged cells during the preparation of vegetables, some dissolves in the water in which vegetables are cooked, and some is destroyed by heat, especially in an alkaline medium. Vegetables should therefore be prepared immediately before they are to be used and cooked for as short a time as possible in the minimum of water.

Effects of freezing

Freezing is a very useful method of storing food, especially meat and vegetables. The rate of freezing is important. The disruption of the cells is considerably

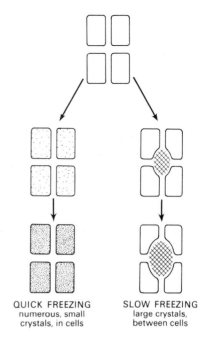

QUICK FREEZING
numerous, small
crystals, in cells

SLOW FREEZING
large crystals,
between cells

Fig. 15.7 Differences between slow freezing and rapid freezing in the size of ice crystal formed and therefore the extent to which cells are damaged. (After Cook D J 1974 British Nutrition Foundation Bulletin 11: 39)

greater with slow freezing than with quick freezing because much larger ice crystals are formed (Fig. 15.7). During the freezing stage the organic and inorganic constituents are concentrated in a diminishing volume of unfrozen water and this concentration may cause changes in the nutritional value of the food. For example, the transient high concentration of copper leads to the oxidation of vitamin C; loss of up to 50 per cent may occur during freezing and thawing.

During the prolonged storage of frozen foods, slow oxidation of fats makes food taste rancid and destroys vitamin A. Oxidation may be minimised by reducing the oxygen content within the package, for example by packaging in nitrogen or in a vacuum or by the use of antioxidants. During storage the ATP of meat is rapidly converted to inosine 5-phosphate, which is said to improve its flavour.

APPETITE AND HUNGER

Appetite is the desire for food and is associated with the feeling of pleasure associated with eating certain items of food. Hunger is usually taken to mean the craving of food following abstinence. Satiety is the lack of any desire to eat more food it is often associated with a sensation of fullness.

Hunger and satiety centres

The stimulation of the lateral hypothalamus of an experimental animal causes the animal to eat voraciously; while, destruction of this area suppresses any desire for food and causes starvation. Stimulation of the ventromedial hypothalamus induces satiety, while destruction of this region is associated with an enormous appetite and causes obesity. These experiments suggest that there is a hunger centre in the lateral hypothalamus and a satiety centre in the ventromedial hypothalamus. These centres are concerned with the desire to eat but do not co-ordinate the muscular activities associated with eating. If the brain is sectioned between the hypothalamus and mesencephalon, the animal salivates, licks its lips, chews and swallows in response to food but it cannot regulate the amount of food eaten.

The limbic system, comprising the amygdala, infra-orbital cortex, cingulate gyrus and hippocampal gyrus, appears to play an important role in the animal's drive to search for food when it is hungry, and in the emotional associations with food. It is concerned with the quality of food eaten and with a dislike for a food that has been previously associated with an unpleasant experience. In man, the association of emotions with eating is reflected in the compensatory eating associated with anxiety and the loss of appetite that may accompany emotional depression.

Factors regulating food intake

Food intake may be regulated by nutritional factors that are associated with the maintenance of normal amounts of nutrient stores and by alimentary factors concerned more with the capacity of the alimentary tract to digest and absorb a certain meal.

Nutritional regulation

Reduction in blood glucose is associated with sensations of hunger. These sensations are abolished if glucose is infused intravenously to increase plasma glucose. Increases in concentrations of plasma glucose enhance the electrical activity of the ventromedial nucleus of the hypothalamus (the satiety centre), while decreasing the electrical activity in the lateral nucleus (the hunger centre). Unlike other areas in the hypothalamus, the ventromedial nucleus is able to concentrate glucose. The evidence therefore suggests that the glucose level in the hypothalamus is one factor controlling appetite.

Increases in amino acid concentration in the plasma reduce feeding, though the effect is not as great as that of glucose.

The overall amount of feeding by normal people varies inversely with the amount of adipose tissue. The mechanism for this effect may be related to the long-term plasma concentration of free fatty acids since these are directly related to the amount of adipose tissue. This mechanism is not effective in obese people.

Alimentary control

An animal with a gastrostomy, which drains food from the stomach to the exterior, eats considerably more than a normal animal. This finding suggests that receptors in the stomach or small intestine, but not in the mouth, are important for inducing satiety.

The importance of gastric signals in regulating food intake is demonstrated by the following observations in experimental animals. Inflation of balloons in the stomach induces satiety. Inhibition of gastric emptying by tightening a noose around the pylorus reduces food intake, but if food is removed from the stomach of such an animal, it quickly consumes enough food to make up for the amount removed. The signal involved in these responses is transmitted by a hormone, since injection of food into a second stomach, transplanted from another animal, causes inhibition of eating even if the normal stomach is empty.

Signals from the small intestine are also important. The infusion of food into the intestine of an animal with a gastrostomy inhibits its ingestion. This effect may be mediated by CCK-Pz (p. 260), since this hormone is released from the duodenum and upper jejunum when food is present and since an injection of exogenous CCK-Pz induces satiety.

Obesity

Obesity is caused when energy intake in the form of food exceeds the energy that is expended. Each 9.3 kJ of excess energy intake yields 1 g of stored fat. Clearly obesity may result from an increase in food intake or from a reduction in energy expenditure. When sportsmen cease taking regular exercise, they often become obese, even though they may be eating less than they did when they were more active. This weight gain is probably related to the reduction in energy expenditure.

Several specific abnormalities have been proposed to explain obesity, but the importance of none of them has been established.

Brown adipose tissue

A large proportion of the adipose tissue in newborn babies is metabolically very active and fat is oxidised to release energy as heat. This brown adipose tissue may be important in maintaining body temperature in neonates (p. 530). Some brown adipose tissue remains in the adult especially around the kidneys and possibly around the great vessels. Some workers have suggested that this tissue may burn off surplus energy in lean adults but recent research has suggested that the amount of energy produced by brown adipose tissue in adults is small; it is unlikely that it would account for the differences in energy balance between lean and obese adults.

Psychogenic obesity

Food intake is closely related to emotional states. Some people are known to gain large amounts of weight during periods of stress while others lose weight when they are stressed. Several theories have been put forward to explain these variations. In some people, eating is associated with feelings of comfort and security.

Hypothalamic obesity

People with hypothalamic tumours may develop progressive obesity, but most obese people have no demonstrable hypothalamic abnormality. An obese person who has reduced his weight to normal becomes hungry more readily than a normal person; this suggests that the hypothalamic centre may be set to inhibit eating at a higher level of nutrient storage than in normal people.

FURTHER READING

Barker B M, Bender D A 1982 Vitamins in medicine, 4th edn Heinemann, London

Brown J J, Lever A F, Robertson J I S, Semple P F 1984 Should dietary sodium be reduced: the sceptics position. Quarterly Journal of Medicine NS53: 427–437

Garrow J, Blaza S 1982 Energy requirements in human beings. In: Neuberger A, Jukes T H (eds) Human nutrition: Current issues and Controversies. MTP Press, Lancaster, p. 1–21

Garrow J S 1981 Treat obesity seriously. Churchill Livingstone, Edinburgh

James W P T (ed) 1984 Obesity. Clinics in Endocrinology and Metabolism 13: 435–663

Paul A A, Southgate D A T 1978 The composition of foods, 4th edn. HMSO, London

Taylor O A (ed) 1985 Trace elements in human disease. Clinics in Endocrinolgy and Metabolism 14: 513–764

Waterlow J C (ed) 1982 Nutrition of man. British Medical Bulletin 37

Waterlow J C 1983 Nutrition in the third world. In: Saunders K B (ed) Advanced Medicine 19. Pitman, London, p. 144–155

16

The control of visceral function

Visceral function is controlled by the autonomic nervous system, the endocrine glands (Chaps. 23–29) and local transmitter substances released in response to injury or changes in metabolic activity. Their local action is termed *paracrine*.

The autonomic nervous system and the endocrine system co-ordinate the function of different organs for homeostasis and for specific functions such as reproduction or response to injury. Both systems work by way of chemical transmitters; the endocrine glands release their transmitters (hormones) directly into the blood whereas autonomic nerve endings release their transmitters at the target organs. The specificity of the endocrine response depends upon the presence of a specific receptor on the target cell. The specificity of the autonomic response depends on the site of release of the transmitter since many types of cell have receptors for autonomic neurotransmitters.

Neurotransmitters released from autonomic nerves are quickly removed or inactivated at their sites of action. In contrast, hormones are removed from the circulation by metabolism in the liver and excretion in the bile and urine. Thus the autonomic nervous system provides a rapid and sensitive control of, for example, blood flow and heart rate; the endocrine system exerts a slower control of, for example, salt and water balance, plasma concentrations of calcium and intermediary metabolism.

THE AUTONOMIC NERVOUS SYSTEM

The autonomic nervous system regulates the motor and secretory functions of the gut, the contraction of the heart, the tone of blood vessels, blood flow, blood pressure, the contraction of bronchioles, the contraction of the urinary bladder, thermoregulation and the diameter of the pupil and visual accommodation.

The activity of the autonomic nervous system is controlled by centres in the hypothalamus, brain stem and spinal cord. Although it is not under conscious control, its activity is influenced by the cerebral cortex

and limbic system. The control of autonomic function is mediated by visceral reflexes; events occurring at one site lead to motor or secretory responses at the same or different sites. These are described elsewhere and include the baroreceptor reflex responsible for controlling the arterial blood pressure and cardiac output (p. 92), the cephalic phase of the gastric secretion (p. 257), and the micturition and defaecation reflexes (p. 202 and p. 251).

The nerve endings of autonomic nerves differ from those of somatic nerves (p. 490) in that they contain numerous bulbous enlargements or varicosities within which are vesicles containing the neurotransmitters. When an action potential spreads over the nerve endings, the depolarisation of the membrane causes an influx of calcium ions from the extracellular fluid. This causes the transmitter vesicles to migrate to the membrane; the transmitters are released into the tissue fluid and diffuse to nearby target sites.

The autonomic nervous system consists of two major divisions, the *sympathetic* and *parasympathetic* nervous systems. Both divisions contain both afferent and efferent nerves. The efferent nerves of both systems contain two kinds of neurone; the preganglionic neurone connects the central nervous system with the cell body of the postganglionic neurone, which travels to the effector cell. All preganglionic nerves are termed *cholinergic* because acetylcholine is released from their nerve endings and interacts with specific receptors on the postganglionic membrane. Most postganglionic parasympathetic fibres also secrete acetylcholine; some secrete other transmitters, notably vasoactive intestinal polypeptide (VIP). Most postganglionic sympathetic fibres release noradrenaline (norepinephrine) and are termed *adrenergic*, but sympathetic fibres supplying the sweat glands and the vasodilator fibres to striated muscle release acetylcholine. Recent evidence suggests that depolarisation of all postganglionic sympathetic nerve endings releases acetylcholine, which then liberates noradrenaline.

Acetylcholine and noradrenaline are synthesised at the nerve endings but are very rapidly inactivated after release. VIP is produced in the cell body, travels down the axon by the process of *axoplasmic flow*, and is stored in vesicles within the bulbous varicosities.

After cutting the autonomic nerve supply, an organ becomes very sensitive to the presence of the lost transmitter, probably because of an increase in the number of receptors.

Receptor interaction
The transmitters released from autonomic nerve endings interact with specific protein receptors, situated on the membranes of the target cells. This interaction either

alters the permeability of the membrane to specific ions such as calcium, or activates an enzyme such as adenylate cyclase, which promotes the formation of cyclic AMP (Chap. 23). Calcium or cyclic AMP then function as *'second messengers'*, leading ultimately to changes in the metabolic activity of the cell, to changes in the permeability of the cell membrane, or to contraction.

The parasympathetic nervous system
Figure 16.1 illustrates the organisation of the parasympathetic nervous system. Approximately 75 per cent of all parasympathetic nerve fibres are in the vagus nerves

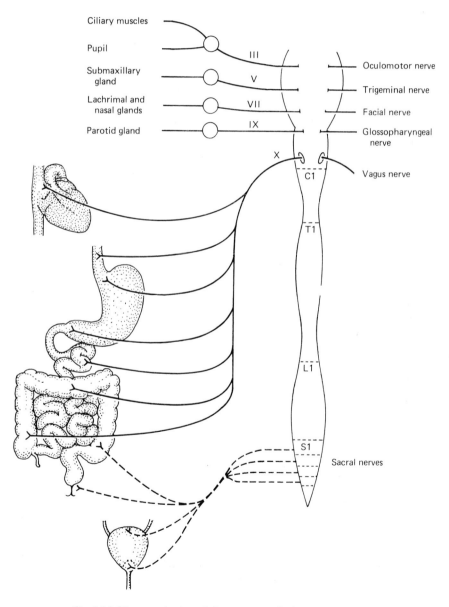

Fig. 16.1 The organisation of the parasympathetic nervous system.

supplying the heart, the lungs, the oesophagus, stomach, small intestine, proximal half of the colon, the liver, the gall bladder, the pancreas and the upper portions of the ureters. The afferent fibres in the vagus nerve outnumber the efferent fibres by 9:1.

Parasympathetic fibres also travel in the ophthalmic nerves to supply the pupillary sphincters and the ciliary muscles of the eye, in the seventh nerve to supply the lachrimal, nasal and submaxillary glands and in the ninth nerve to supply the parotid gland. The pelvic parasympathetic fibres form the pelvic nerves, which leave the sacral plexus on each side and supply the descending colon, rectum, external genitalia, bladder and lower parts of the ureters.

Acetylcholine receptors

Acetylcholine interacts with two different types of cholinergic receptors, *nicotinic* and *muscarinic*. The reason for these names is that muscarine, a poison from toadstools, activates the muscarinic receptors without affecting the nicotinic receptors, whereas nicotine only activates the nicotinic receptors. Nicotinic receptors mediate transmission between the preganglionic and postganglionic neurones of both sympathetic and parasympathetic nerves. Muscarinic receptors are mainly found on the cell membranes of tissues supplied by parasympathetic nerves. They are also present on postganglionic sympathetic nerve endings, where they may augment or induce the release of noradrenaline.

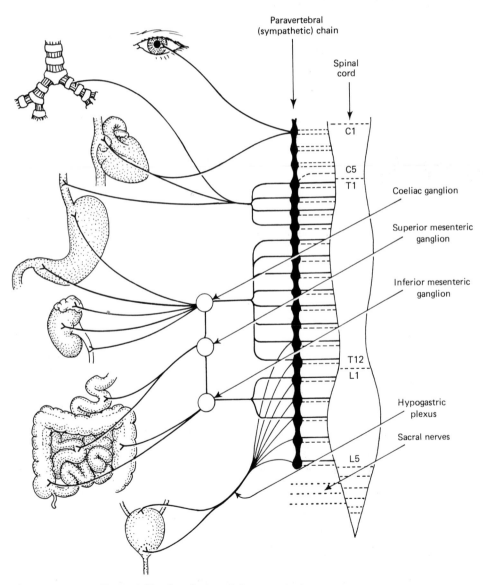

Fig. 16.2 The organisation of the sympathetic nervous system.

Deactivation of acetylcholine

After acetylcholine is released from cholinergic nerve endings it is quickly hydrolysed by cholinesterase to acetic acid and choline. Choline is then taken up into the nerve terminal by active transport and is used together with acetic acid to make new acetylcholine. It is thought that acetylcholine is then stored in vesicles.

The sympathetic nervous system

The sympathetic nerves originate in the spinal cord between T1 and L2 (Fig. 16.2). The cell body of the preganglionic efferent neurone lies in the lateral horn of the spinal cord and its axon passes through the anterior root of the cord into a spinal nerve. As soon as the spinal nerve leaves the spinal column, the preganglionic fibres leave it and pass via white *rami communicantes* into the sympathetic chain of ganglia lying parallel to the vertebral column. The sympathetic fibres then take one of three courses; they may either synapse in the ganglia they enter, or they may pass up or down the chain to synapse at another level or they may pass out of the chain and synapse in the peripheral ganglia such as the coeliac ganglion or hypogastric plexus (Fig. 16.3). The postganglionic fibres often travel with blood vessels to the target organs. Sensory sympathetic fibres can make connections with the efferent fibres either in the sympathetic chain or in the cord itself.

The adrenal medulla

The adrenal medulla is part of the sympathetic nervous system and is derived embryologically from the neural crest. The cells of the adrenal medulla are equivalent

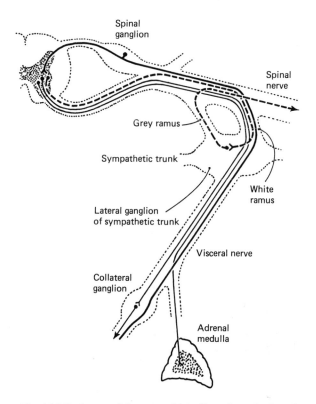

Fig. 16.3 Pathways of the sympathetic fibres from the lateral horn of the grey matter of the spinal cord. Some preganglionic fibres (dashed lines) arising in the lateral horn pass to a lateral ganglion in the sympathetic chain, where they synapse with cells that give rise to postganglionic fibres. Others (thin lines) pass to a collateral ganglion, such as the coeliac or hypogastric ganglia, or to the adrenal medulla. The thick continuous line represents afferent fibres from the viscera. The spinal nerve contains, in addition to the postganglionic sympathetic fibres shown in this diagram, afferent and efferent somatic fibres, and is therefore known as a mixed nerve.

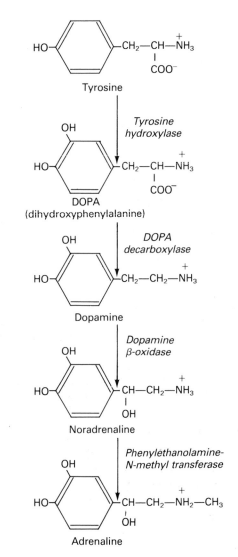

Fig. 16.4 The metabolic pathway involved in the production of noradrenaline.

to post-ganglionic neurones and are known as *chromaffin* cells. These cells synthesise the catecholamines, *noradrenaline* (norepinephrine) and *adrenaline* (epinephrine) in a ratio of about 1:4.

In the metabolic pathway shown in Figure 16.4, the activity of the rate-limiting enzyme, tyrosine hydroxylase, is regulated by a negative feedback from noradrenaline and dopamine. The conversion of noradrenaline to adrenaline requires a high concentration of glucocorticoids. Glucocorticoids are present in the adrenal medulla because it is supplied with arterial blood that has drained through the adrenal cortex.

The secretory activity of the adrenal medulla is controlled by the activity in preganglionic cholinergic fibres of the splanchnic nerves.

Actions of adrenaline

While the adrenal medulla is not essential for life, its major role is the production of adrenaline in response to an emergency ('fight or flight').

As a result of fear or injury, large parts of the sympathetic nervous system become activated simultaneously, increasing the ability of the body to perform vigorous muscular exertion to combat or escape from the source of danger, the 'fight or flight' reaction. The arterial blood pressure increases, blood flow is diverted to muscles, brain and heart and away from visceral organs, metabolism is increased, resulting in rises in blood glucose and free fatty acids and an increase in muscle glycolysis, muscle contraction is faster and stronger, mental activity is sharper, the rate of blood coagulation is accelerated, the pupils dilate and the bronchioles expand to allow the intake of more air.

Adrenergic receptors

The receptors for catecholamine hormones, adrenergic receptors, are of two types, alpha and beta. Noradrenaline, secreted from sympathetic nerve endings, combines mainly with alpha receptors, and has only a small effect on beta receptors. Adrenaline, on the other hand, combines with both types of receptors to about the same extent. This fact explains the physiological differences between the actions of adrenaline an noradrenaline

Table 16.5 Actions of adrenaline and noradrenaline

Action	Adrenaline	Noradrenaline
Systolic blood pressure	Increased	Increased
Diastolic blood pressure	Reduced	Increased
Heart rate	Increased	Reduced
Gut motility	Reduced	—
Pupils	Dilated	Dilated
Hepatic glycogenolysis	Increased	—
Plasma free fatty acids	Increased	Increased

Table 16.6 Adrenergic receptors and function

Alpha receptor	Beta receptor
Vasoconstriction	Vasodilatation (β_2)
Vasodilatation (α_2)	Cardioacceleration (β_1)
Iris dilatation	Increased myocardial
Intestinal relaxation	strength (β_1)
Intestinal sphincter contraction	Intestinal relaxation (β_2)
	Uterus relaxation (β_2)
Pilomotor contraction	Bronchodilatation (β_2)
Bladder sphincter contraction	Thermogenesis (β_2)
	Glycogenolysis (β_2)
Intestinal absorption (α_2)	Lipolysis (β_1)
	Bladder relaxation (β_2)

(Table 16.5). Thus the effect of sympathetic stimulation on certain tissues or organs depends upon whether the receptors are of the alpha or beta type.

Table 16.6 gives a list of the functions mediated by alpha receptors compared with to those mediated by beta receptors. In general, alpha interactions appear to cause contraction of smooth muscle, whereas beta interactions cause relaxation of smooth muscle, stimulate the heart and increase metabolic activity.

Beta receptors are subdivided into beta$_1$ and beta$_2$ receptors. Most beta receptors on cardiac muscle are beta$_1$ receptors, while beta$_2$ receptors predominate on bronchial smooth muscle. This knowledge has lead to the development of specific beta$_2$ agonists, such as salbutamol, which is used to dilate the bronchi of patients with asthma without stimulating the heart, and specific beta$_1$ antagonists, which are used to suppress cardiac arrhythmias without causing bronchiolar constriction.

Alpha receptors are sub-divided into alpha$_1$ and alpha$_2$ adrenoreceptors. Alpha$_2$ receptors are situated on the intestinal enterocyte and may mediate the effect of sympathetic stimulation on salt and water absorption. They are also situated on the sympathetic nerve endings, where they control the amount of noradrenaline present in the synaptic cleft by inhibiting its release. One alpha$_2$ agonist, clonidine, is used to treat high blood pressure.

Deactivation of catecholamines

Most of the noradrenaline released from nerve endings is rapidly taken up into the nerve endings intact and stored in the transmitter vesicles; some is destroyed by enzymes such as monoamine oxidase, which is found in the nerve endings, and a little diffuses into the blood.

The actions of catecholamines released into the blood are terminated in part by their metabolic degradation (Fig. 16.7) and in part by their uptake by tissues. Metabolic degradation by the enzyme *catechol-o-methyl*

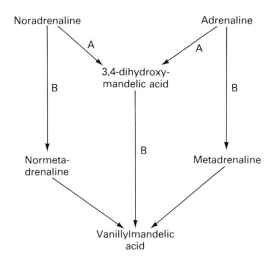

Fig. 16.7 Pathways for the catabolism of the catecholamines leading to the production of vanillylmandelic acid (VMA; 3-methoxy, 4-hydroxy mandelic acid). The enzymes are A: monoamine oxidase, B: catechol-O-methyl transferase.

transferase, which is present in all tissues, produces metadrenaline, normetadrenaline and vanillylmandelic acid, which are excreted in the urine. Only about 5 per cent of catecholamines released into the blood is excreted in the urine unchanged.

Diseases of the adrenal medulla

Tumours of the chromaffin cells of the adrenal medulla are known as phaeochromocytomas. These tumours produce noradrenaline or adrenaline in varying proportions but noradrenaline almost always predominates. The clinical result of such tumours is therefore hypertension, which, in most patients, is sustained, but may be paroxysmal. Patients with increased adrenaline secretion may develop hyperglycaemia.

The diagnosis of a phaeochromocytoma can be made by measurement of the urinary excretion of catecholamines and in particular vanillylmandelic acid, metadrenaline and normetadrenaline. Although phaeochromocytomas account for only a very small proportion of patients with hypertension, it is important that they should be identified as their hypertension can be cured by removal of the tumour.

Effects of stimulation of the sympathetic and parasympathetic nervous systems

Table 16.8 summarises the effects of stimulating the parasympathetic or sympathetic nervous systems. In some cases the two systems are antagonistic. For example, parasympathetic stimulation increases the activity of the smooth muscle of the gut and the bladder, whereas sympathetic stimulation reduces it;

parasympathetic stimulation slows the heart, sympathetic stimulation speeds it up.

Sympathetic and parasympathetic tone

The sympathetic and parasympathetic systems are continually active and exert a nervous tone on the organs and tissues. This effect gives flexibility of control; the sympathetic tone normally keeps peripheral arterioles constricted to about half their maximal diameter. Increasing the degree of sympathetic stimulation causes increased vasoconstriction but inhibition of the sympathetic tone can cause vasodilatation. Without constant sympathetic tone, constriction would be possible but never dilatation.

Cutting the sympathetic supply to a blood vessel causes vasodilatation, though after several days the intrinsic tone of the smooth muscle itself may adapt to restore a normal degree of vasoconstriction.

LOCAL HORMONES

Histamine

Histamine is synthesised by the decarboxylation of histidine in the mast cells of the tissues or in the basophils of the blood. It is stored within the cell in granules, which are released from the cell surface.

Histamine increases capillary permeability and dilates the capillaries by constricting the postcapillary sphincter and relaxing the precapillary sphincter. These effects are part of the inflammatory response to injury (p. 52). Histamine also contracts the smooth muscle of bronchi or gut and stimulates the secretion of gastric acid. Two types of histamine receptor have been identified. H_1 receptors mediate the effects of histamine on smooth muscle and on capillaries; H_2 receptors mediate the effects of histamine on gastric acid secretion.

Serotonin

Serotonin is found in blood platelets, in the brain and in the gut wall. The serum obtained from clotted blood has vasoconstrictor properties due to the release of serotonin from damaged platelets.

In the gut, serotonin is found in serotoninergic nerves and in argentaffin cells. It can cause intestinal secretion and contraction of smooth muscle.

Serotonin is synthesised from dietary tryptophan. After release it is degraded by monoamine oxidase in the tissues to 5-hydroxyindoleacetic acid (5-HIAA). Measurement of urinary 5-HIAA is used clinically to diagnose tumours of the argentaffin cells of the small intestine (*carcinoid tumour*), which may release large amounts of serotonin and cause flushing of the face and bronchoconstriction.

Table 16.8 Autonomic effects on various organs of the body

Site	Effect of sympathetic stimulation	Effect of parasympathetic stimulation
Eye		
Pupils	Dilated	Constricted
Ciliary muscle	Slight relaxation	Contracted
Glands (nasal, lachrimal, parotid, submaxillary, gastric, pancreatic)	Vasoconstriction and slight secretion	Stimulation of thin, copious secretion (containing many enzymes for enzyme-secreting glands).
Sweat glands	Copious sweating (cholinergic)	None
Apocrine glands	Thick, smelly secretion	None
Heart		
Muscle	Increased rate Increased force of contraction	Slowed rate Decreased force of atrial contraction
Coronaries	Dilated (β_2) Constricted (α)	Dilated
Lungs		
Bronchi	Dilated	Constricted
Blood vessels	Mildly constricted	? Dilated
Gut		
Sphincter	Decreased peristalsis and tone Increased tone	Increased peristalsis and tone Relaxed
Liver	Glucose released	Slight glycogen synthesis
Gallbladder and bile ducts	Relaxed	Contracted
Kidney	Decreased output	None
Bladder		
Detrusor	Relaxed	Excited
Trigone	Contracted	Relaxed
Male genitalia	Ejaculation	Erection
Systemic blood vessels		
Abdominal	Constricted	None
Muscle	Constricted (adrenergic alpha) Dilated (adrenergic beta) Dilated (cholinergic)	None
Skin	Constricted	None
Blood		
Coagulation	Increased	None
Glucose	Increased	None
Basal metabolism	Increased up to 100 per cent	None
Adrenal cortical secretion	Increased	None
Mental activity	Increased	None
Piloerector muscles	Excited	None
Skeletal muscle	Increased glycogenolysis Increased strength	None

Prostaglandins

The prostaglandins are a group of fatty acid derivatives that are synthesised from the essential fatty acid, arachidonic acid (Fig. 16.9).

Prostaglandins are formed in large amounts by inflammatory cells and may play an essential role in mediating the inflammatory reaction. As arachidonic acid is a component of all cell membranes, prostaglandins may function to mediate and amplify the effect of interactions with membrane receptors. Prostaglandins

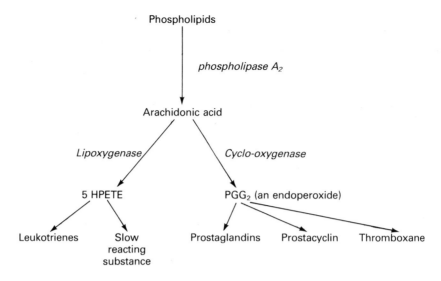

Fig. 16.9 Important products of arachidonic acid metabolism.

are rapidly inactivated by enzymes found in all tissues, though the lung and the liver are particularly active in removing them from the plasma. Prostaglandins have many actions in all tissues of the body, though their physiological roles are still uncertain. In many cases different prostaglandins have opposing actions. For example, prostaglandins of the PGA and PGE series reduce blood pressure while PGF prostaglandins increase it. The opposing actions of prostacyclin (PGI) and thromboxane on blood clotting are described in Chapter 4.

The kinins

The kinins are a group of peptides liberated from plasma proteins (*kininogens*) by endogenous enzymes (kininogenases or *kallikreins*). The principal kinin in plasma is *bradykinin*.

The kinins cause vasodilatation and hypotension when administered systemically. Their physiological function is not known, but they may have a role in some antigen–antibody reactions and in haemostasis.

FURTHER READING

Burn J H 1975 The autonomic nervous system. Blackwell Scientific, Oxford

James V H T 1979 The adrenal gland. Raven Press, New York

Leftowitz R, Caron M C, Stiles G L 1984 Mechanisms of membrane-receptor interaction: biochemical, physiological and clinical insights derived from studies of the adrenergic receptors. New England Journal of Medicine 310: 1570–1579

Sever P S, Roberts J C, Snell M E 1980 Phaeochromocytoma. Clinics in Endocrinology and Metabolism 9: 543–568

17

The mouth

The oral cavity and tongue are covered by a stratified squamous epithelium richly supplied with pain, tactile and temperature nerve endings and in the case of the tongue, taste buds are distributed over its surface. When food enters the mouth, impulses from these nerve endings indicate that the food is acceptable and mastication begins. Chewing breaks up the solid parts of the food and mixes it with the saliva that is reflexly secreted.

THE TONGUE

The tongue plays an important role in the physiology of the mouth. Its highly developed sensory innervation and its precision of movement enables it to locate and retrieve food that lodges in any part of the mouth. The tongue acts together with the saliva as a cleansing device and is important in articulation. The acute sensory equipment of the tongue and lips allows food and drink

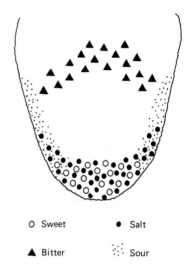

O Sweet   ● Salt

▲ Bitter   Sour

Fig. 17.1 A map of the tongue to show the four areas particularly sensitive to the four differently tasting substances.

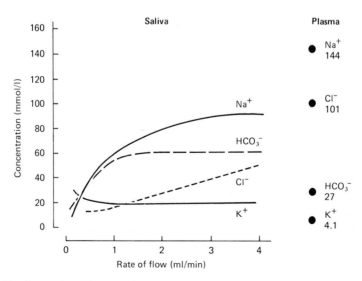

Fig. 17.2 Human parotid saliva produced by parasympathomimetic stimulation. (After Thaysen J H 1954 American Journal of Physiology 178:155)

to be sampled and the ingestion of noxious or scalding substances to be avoided.

Taste

The receptors responsible for the appreciation of taste are the taste buds. These are distributed mainly on the tongue but are also found in the epithelium of the soft and hard palate, the epiglottis and the pillars of the fauces. Before the receptors can be stimulated, the substance to be tasted must be in solution. The saliva acts as the solvent for the solids in the food.

Only four primary modalities of taste can be appreciated — sweet, sour(acid), salt and bitter — and the receptors are distributed on the surface of the tongue as shown in Figure 17.1. It is common experience that the fine details of taste cannot be experienced unless the olfactory receptors are also functioning, for example, taste may be lost during a common cold.

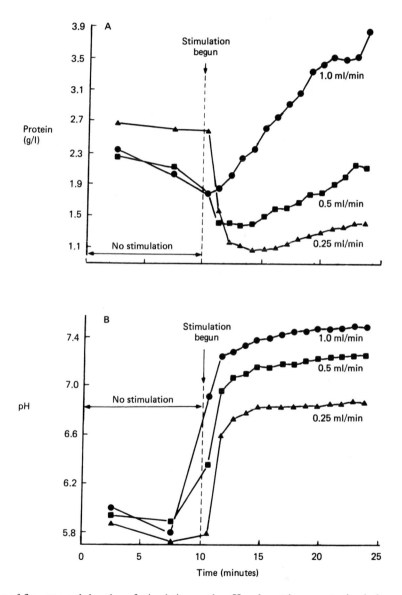

Fig. 17.3 The effect of flow-rate and duration of stimulation on the pH and protein concentration in human parotid saliva from 10 subjects (A) and 15 subjects (B). For the first 10 minutes the salivary flow was unstimulated, but during the final 15 minutes constant flow-rates were achieved by sucking a sour substance. The pH reached almost steady values within about 5 minutes of stimulation whereas the protein levels were still rising after 15 minutes. It is clear that an analysis taken within a few minutes of stimulation would produce very different results from those made, say, after 15 minutes. (After Dawes C 1969 Archives of Oral Biology 14:277)

THE SALIVA

Saliva is produced by three pairs of salivary glands —
the parotids, the submandibular and the sublingual
glands — together with numerous small glands scattered
in the oral mucosa. It is an opalescent slimy fluid, the
main constituent of which is water containing about 1
per cent of solids. It is not useful to list the constituents
of saliva because its composition is so variable and
depends upon so many factors, such as the rate of
salivary flow (Fig. 17.2), the duration of stimulation and
the relative contributions from the various glands each
producing its own characteristic secretion. In general,
the concentrations of sodium and the major anion bicarbonate increase with the rate of flow, as does the protein
content (Figs. 17.2 and 17.3).

pH and buffering

The main buffer in saliva is bicarbonate and as its
concentration is a function of the rate of flow, the pH
is also flow dependent; it varies from about 5.4 to 7.5
at the highest rates. Calcium and phosphate are also
important constituents of saliva as an equilibrium exists
between the tooth mineral (hydroxyapatite) and the
calcium ions of the saliva. At pH values above 6.0,
saliva ia sufficiently saturated to prevent the dissolution
of the enamel, but if the saliva becomes more acid than
this, the enamel dissolves; bicarbonate may thus be of
importance in protection against caries.

Organic constituents

The two most important organic constituents of saliva
in relation to digestion are amylase and glycoproteins.

Amylase

The parotid gland is the principal source of salivary
amylase, which has an optimum pH of 6.8 and requires
chloride for full activity. Amylase hydrolyses the 1–4
β-glycoside links in starch and glycogen, with the
production of maltose, maltotriose and some glucose.
The α(1–6) branches are not attacked and therefore
some α-dextrins remain. Although the food does not
remain long enough in the mouth for the amylase to
have much effect there, hydrolysis continues in the
centre of the food bolus in the stomach until it is inactivated by pepsin and hydrochloric acid.

Glycoproteins

These compounds are complexes of carbohydrate and
protein and give the saliva its characteristic sliminess.
Thus they are important as lubricants and aid in
chewing, swallowing and articulation.

Other organic compounds

A considerable number of proteins are secreted in the
saliva; the significance of many of these is as yet
unknown. They include hormones, enzymes, blood
clotting factors, immunoglobulins and traces of many
of the plasma constituents. Lysozymes, peroxidases
and immunoglobulins together with the blood clotting
factors are thought to play a role in the defence against
bacterial infection and injury.

SALIVARY GLANDS

The salivary glands are compound racemose glands.
The glandular cells are arranged in acini, each of which
consists of a single layer of cells around a central cavity
into which the cells discharge their secretions
(Fig. 17.4). In man, an acinus may be entirely mucous
(secreting glycoproteins), as in the subligual, or entirely
serous (secreting enzymes), as in the parotid, or mixed,
as in the submandibular gland. Small intercalated ducts
from a number of adjacent acini join together to form
striated ducts lined by tall cells, the basal membranes
of which have numerous infoldings that produce the
characteristic striated appearance. These ducts drain

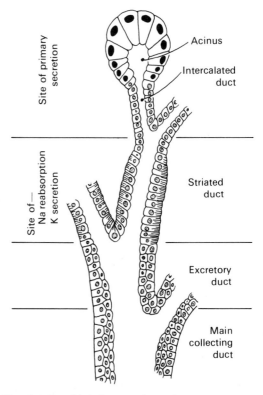

Fig. 17.4 Simplified diagram of an acinus and ducts of a
salivary gland.

into larger excretory ducts, which in turn connect with a large collecting duct opening into the mouth. The ducts and acini are surrounded at intervals by myo-epithelial cells. These are contractile and serve to support the glandular elements and allow secretion at high pressures, even as high as the blood pressure if salivary flow is obstructed.

Innervation

The salivary glands are supplied by both parasympath-etic and sympathetic nerves (Fig.17.5). The secretory acini always have a parasympathetic innervation and also, in most cases, a sympathetic innervation. Each acinus may be supplied by several fibres but it is not necessary for each cell to be innervated directly since the acinar cells are electrically linked so that the influ-ence of each nerve ending spreads to adjacent cells.

Myoepithelial cells lie close to the acinar cells and, being in close contact with the intra-acinar nerve endings, they probably receive the same pattern of

innervation as the acinar cells. When activated they increase duct pressure and therefore salivary flow. The striated duct cells of the cat's submandibular gland seem to have a dual sympathetic and parasympathetic inner-vation since membrane potential changes are seen after stimulation of either of these nerves. This innervation may not be direct. The nerve endings may terminate near acinar cells and the action of the transmitters may pass to the duct cells by electrical coupling. The blood vessels receive a sympathetic constrictor innervation and a parasympathetic dilator innervation. The transmitters at the parasympathetic junctions are acetylcholine and vasoactive intestinal polypeptide (VIP), which is prob-ably stored in the same terminal. The transmitter at the sympathetic nerve ending is noradrenaline.

Control of secretion and blood flow

Stimulation of the parasympathetic nerves causes not only profuse salivary secretion but also vasodilatation.

Reflex salivation is normally evoked by the food in

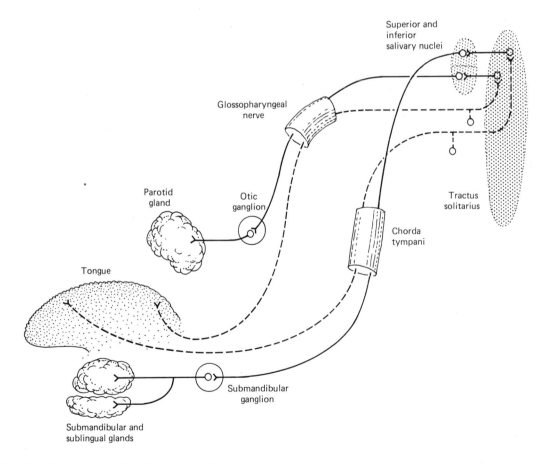

Fig. 17.5 Nerve supply to the salivary glands. Parasympathetic efferent neurones, continuous line. Afferent pathways from taste buds, interrupted line.
End Tape

the mouth stimulatinq taste buds and by impulses from sensory nerves in the teeth, muscles and oral epithelium in response to masticatory movements. Stimuli acting on the 'sour' taste buds appear to be most potent. However, even chewing paraffin wax can stimulate a salivary flow of up to 250 ml per hour from a resting level of 2 to 10 ml per hour. Receptors in the oesophagus can detect a bolus that might lodge there and, besides initiating peristalsis, can induce salivary secretion. It is possible to condition salivary secretion in man, though it is not clear whether the so-called mouth-watering at the thought, sight or smell of food is a conditioned reflex or merely an awareness of saliva already in the mouth.

Salivary secretion is reduced in conditions that lead to tissue dehydration. Exercise and emotional stress also depress salivary secretion, perhaps, in part, as a result of a reduction in salivary blood flow.

The vasodilatation that accompanies parasympathetic nerve stimulation seems to be mediated by more than one mechanism. The first of these involves the enzyme kallikrein, which is produced by the salivary glands. It appears in the saliva and also the interstitial fluid. This enzyme acts on specific plasma proteins (kininogens) to split off vasodilator kinins such as bradykinin.

Vasodilatation is also mediated directly by parasympathetic fibres, which may be both cholinergic and non-cholinergic; the non-cholinergic transmitter is VIP. The receptors for initiating secretion are cholinergic and blocked by atropine, those mediating vasodilation are non-cholinergic and resistant to atropine.

Secretory Mechanisms

Electrolyte secretion

Secretion by the salivary glands is a two-stage process, with first a primary secretion by the acini and second a modification of the composition of this secretion as the saliva passes through the duct system. The primary secretion by the acinus has sodium and chloride concentrations equal to or slightly greater than those in plasma but a potassium concentration that may be appreciably greater (8 mmol/l). The primary driving force is the active extrusion of sodium into the secretory canaliculus; water follows passively down the osmotic gradient so created. Chloride also follows passively but potassium seems to be actively transported. The secondary stage occurs as the primary fluid flows along the duct system where the secretion is modified by the reabsorption of sodium and chloride and the secretion of potassium and bicarbonate without any further secretion of fluid. As the reabsorption of sodium and potassium is in excess of the secretion of potassium and bicarbonate and the ductal epithelium has a low water permeability, this mechanism accounts for the hypotonicity of saliva and its relation to flow rate. At low flow rates, more time is given to the removal of ions from the primary fluid, so the osmolality is low, whereas at higher rates of flow less time is available and the osmolality of saliva approaches isosmolality. These alterations in the composition of the primary secretion occur largely in the striated ducts (see Fig. 17.4).

Protein secretion

The salivary glands synthesise and secrete many proteins, including the enzymes amylase and kallikrein as well as glycoproteins.

Amino acids are taken up across the basal membranes of the acinar cells. Within the rough endoplasmic reticulum they are brought together in the synthesis of the various proteins, which are then transported to the Golgi complex and finally stored in the secretory granules. After stimulation of the cell, the proteins including amylase are released into the lumen by exocytosis. During stimulation of the glands, the cells are almost depleted of secretory granules but they reappear several hours after stimulation ceases.

FURTHER READING

Ferguson D B 1981 The environment of the teeth. In: Frontiers of Oral Physiology, Vol. 3. Karger, Basel

Jenkins G N 1970 The physiology of the mouth. Blackwell Scientific, Oxford

Kawamura Y 1974 Physiology of mastication. In: Frontiers of Oral Physiology, Vol. 1. Karger, Basel

Lavelle, C L B 1975 Applied physiology of the mouth. John Wright, Bristol

Osborn J W, Armstrong W G, Spiers, R L 1982 A Companion to Dental Studies, Vol. 1, Book 1. Blackwell Scientific, Oxford

Young J A, Case R M, Conigrave A D, Novak I 1980 Transport of bicarbonate and other ions in salivary secretion. Annals of the New York Academy of Science 341: 172–190

18

Gastrointestinal motility

The contractile activity of the gastrointestinal tract propels food down the gut at an optimal rate for digestion and absorption to take place and mixes the intestinal contents, ensuring the contact between enzymes and complex food substances and increasing access of nutrients to the absorptive epithelium. In the colon, the predominant pattern of motor activity creates the stagnant conditions needed for the bacterial fermentation of carbohydrate.

GASTROINTESTINAL MUSCLE

From the upper part of the oesophagus to the lower end of the rectum, the muscle of the gut comprises a thick layer of circular smooth muscle, an outer thinner layer of longitudinal smooth muscle and a thin sheet of muscle lying just underneath the epithelium, the muscularis mucosae. The muscle of the upper third of the oesophagus and the external anal sphincter is striated. Networks of nerves (plexuses) lie between the longitudinal and circular muscle layers (myenteric plexus) and between the circular muscle and muscularis mucosae (submucous plexus). Branches from these networks supply the smooth muscle.

Structure of smooth muscle
Smooth muscle is made up of narrow cells, 4 to 10 μm wide and 500 to 700 μm long, tapering toward their ends. Each cell has a single centrally placed nucleus. These cells are arranged in bundles, with their longitudinal axes lying in the same direction. Although each smooth muscle cell is anatomically distinct, it is coupled electrically to other cells through *gap junctions* so that a whole area of smooth muscle behaves as a single unit or *syncytium* (Fig. 18.1).

Smooth muscle contraction
The contractile apparatus of smooth muscle cells consists of actin filaments and myosin molecules most of which lie parallel to the long axis of the cell but are not so regularly arranged as in striated muscle. It is

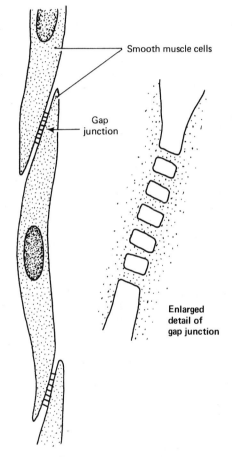

Fig. 18.1 Smooth muscle cells of the gastrointestinal tract showing the gap junctions between the cells. The insert shows enlargement of a gap junction to illustrate the intercellular connections.

generally believed that contraction of smooth muscle operates on the sliding filament principle, similar to that described for striated muscle (p. 494). Contraction is brought about by the sequential attachment, pivotal movement, dissociation and reattachment of myosin cross bridges with the reactive sites on the thin actin filaments. Contraction is initiated by the release of calcium into the sarcoplasm from binding sites on the smooth muscle membrane. Calcium then activates an enzyme on the myosin cross-bridge (*myosin light-chain kinase*), which phosphorylates the myosin bridge so that it can react with actin. Contraction in smooth muscle occurs more slowly than in striated muscle, where calcium is released rapidly from special cisternae in the sarcoplasmic reticulum, and initiates contraction by binding to a special protein on the actin filament and uncovering sites that bind to myosin.

Electrical basis of smooth muscle contraction

At rest, the interior of a smooth muscle cell is approximately 50 mV negative compared with the outside. This potential difference is caused by the selective permeability of the cell membrane to potassium, and to a lesser extent chloride; small amounts of potassium leak from a high concentration within the cell to a low concentration outside, while chloride diffuses down its concentration gradient in the opposite direction. Smooth muscle, like striated muscle, contracts in response to depolarisation of the cell membrane. Unlike striated muscle the smooth muscle of many parts of the gut undergoes spontaneous regular depolarisation and repolarisation (slow waves), the amplitude of which may be modified by neurotransmitters or hormones. In this respect the electrical activity of smooth muscle resembles the spontaneous activity of cardiac muscle.

The ionic basis of spontaneous depolarisation and repolarisation is unclear, but it is thought that depolarisation may be caused by increases in permeability of the membrane to calcium and sodium, while the repolarisation is caused by increases in permeability to potassium.

The frequency of the slow wave varies in different parts of the gut, and may be driven by the spontaneous activity of one or more pacemaker regions. Waves of depolarisation then propagate along the gut via the gap junctions between smooth muscle cells in a manner comparable with conduction in unmyelinated nerves (p. 392); the electrical field induced by depolarisation at one site initiates depolarisation at an adjacent site.

Electro-mechanical coupling

The regular fluctuation of the membrane potential is the basis for muscle contraction (Fig. 18.2). Only one contraction is associated with each slow wave. This contraction travels down the stomach and intestine at the same rate as the wave of depolarisation. However, unlike cardiac muscle, a contraction does not occur with every electrical cycle. It is likely that contractions only

Myoelectric activity

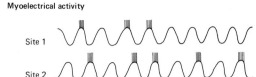
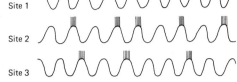

Intraluminal pressure

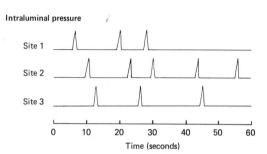

Fig. 18.2 The relationship between myoelectrical slow waves (recorded by extracellular electrodes), spike potentials and smooth muscle contractions in the small intestine.

occur when the membrane potential exceeds a threshold, which allows calcium to enter the sarcoplasm rapidly and initiate the contractile process. In some areas, such as the small intestine, the rapid entry of calcium is observed as a series of very rapid spikes superimposed on the slow wave; the number of spikes is proportional to the force of the contraction. In other areas, such as the body of the stomach or the internal anal sphincter, spike potentials do not occur and the force and duration of contraction is related to the amplitude and duration of the depolarisation.

Chemical transmitter substances probably act to vary the amplitude of depolarisation in relation to the threshold potential. Thus agents that increase the degree of depolarisation increase the incidence of bursts of spike potentials and the degree of coupling between an electrical and a mechanical event. This not only increases the frequency of contractions but also the distance of propagation along the gut.

Sphincters are special areas of smooth muscle that remain tonically contracted for most of the time. However, sphincters also exhibit electrical slow waves that are associated with corresponding oscillations in intraluminal pressure. Presumably the membrane potential in a tonically contracted sphincter muscle remains above the threshold required to initiate a contraction. Sphincter relaxation requires the release of a transmitter, which hyperpolarises the muscle.

NEURAL CONTROL OF GASTROINTESTINAL MOTILITY

Although the intrinsic electrical activity of the smooth muscle provides the basis for all intestinal movements, it is modified and regulated by neurohumoral transmitters. The nerve fibres supplying smooth muscle run for long distances (up to 10 cm) among the muscle cells, and have a number of swellings or 'varicosities' along their length, which contain the transmitter substance. These varicosities release transmitter into the extracellular fluid bathing a group of muscle cells. The tight electrical coupling between adjacent smooth muscle cells then allows the concerted depolarisation and contraction of a whole region of muscle.

The nervous control of intestinal contraction is co-ordinated at three levels: the enteric (intrinsic) nervous system, the prevertebral ganglia, and the central nervous system via the vagus and splanchnic nerves.

Enteric nervous system

The intrinsic nervous system is a complicated organisation of ganglion cells and their respective axons and interneurones, and is largely concentrated as networks between the longitudinal and circular smooth muscle layers and in the submucosa. This system of interconnected neurones releases a number of transmitters including acetylcholine, vasoactive intestinal polypeptide (VIP), somatostatin, serotonin and cholecystokinin, and contains the 'wiring' for the patterns of movement required during digestion and absorption.

Peristalsis is a co-ordinated series of events responsible for moving food along the gut. It can be initiated by distension of the intestine by, for example, a food bolus. It comprises a contraction of circular muscle just proximal to the bolus, associated with a relaxation distally. In contrast, the longitudinal muscle relaxes just proximal to the bolus and contracts distally, pulling the intestinal wall over the bolus (like pulling a vest over the head). These events are propagated downstream, pushing the bolus along. The components of the peristaltic reflex are co-ordinated by the enteric nerve networks (Fig. 18.3). For example, the linkage of an inhibitory neurone caudal to an excitatory neurone allows for the phenomenon of descending inhibition, which precedes a peristaltic wave. Disconnecting the

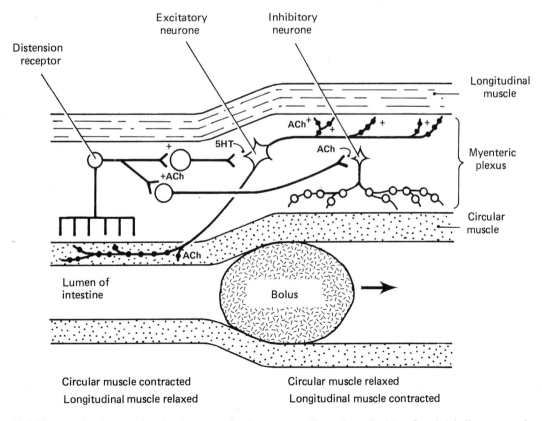

Fig. 18.3 The postulated connections in the myenteric plexus to co-ordinate the peristaltic reflex. (+) indicates an excitatory synapse; (–) an inhibitory synapse. Ach = Acetylcholine. 5HT = 5-hydroxytryptamine.

gut from its extrinsic nerve supply does not radically alter its ability to propel food.

Prevertebral ganglia

The prevertebral ganglia of the sympathetic nervous system receive and process information from both the gut and central nervous system and modify the activity of quite separate and distinct areas of the gut. They provide an important integrative system, which may be responsible for a variety of enteric responses or reflexes. For example, the inhibition of gastrointestinal motor activity during painful distension of the gut is probably integrated via the prevertebral ganglia.

Central nervous system

The gut is connected to the brain and spinal cord through the vagus and pelvic parasympathetic nerves and splanchnic sympathetic nerves (Fig. 18.4). These long tracts and their central connections provide a route for modification of gut activity by the central nervous system during, for example, stress or nausea. They also provide a route whereby sensory information from the

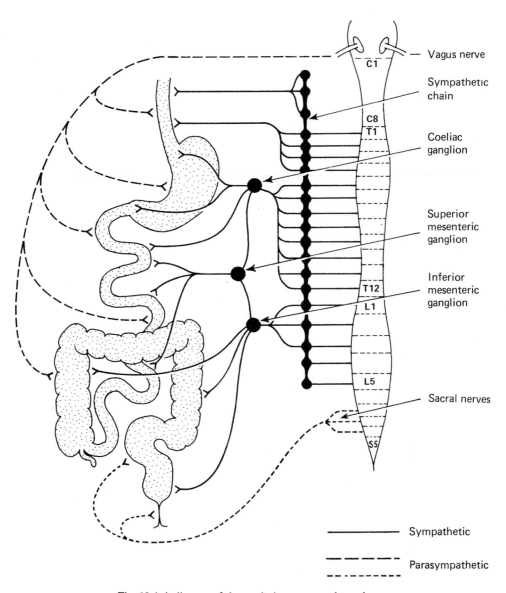

Fig. 18.4 A diagram of the extrinsic nerve supply to the gut.

gut can be integrated with information received from other organs to result in a co-ordinated response in several regions of the gut as well as in other systems.

The vagus nerve

Approximately 90 per cent of nerve fibres in the vagus nerve are sensory. Sensory nerve endings are present in the mucosa and the muscle. Mucosal nerve endings adapt rapidly to mechanical stimuli. Only a brief burst of impulses is generated when a static stimulus is applied, but if the stimulus is moved backwards and forwards over the receptor field, a continuous discharge is evoked. These endings can therefore function as contact receptors detecting the passage of solids or semi-solids. Nerve endings in the muscle respond to increases in tension and adapt slowly. They signal the distension induced by an increase in volume as well as by contraction of adjacent muscle fibres. As volume receptors, they are thought to initiate, for example, the relaxation of the gastric fundus that takes place as food enters the stomach or passes down the oesophagus.

Vagal responses to stimulation may be excitatory or inhibitory and can exhibit reciprocal organisation so that one group of neurones may be excited while another is inhibited.

Until recently, it was thought that stimulation of the parasympathetic supply to the gut induced contraction of most of the gastrointestinal smooth muscle but relaxed the sphincters, while stimulation of the sympathetic nerves relaxed most of the smooth muscle but contracted the sphincters. This simple scheme had to be revised after it was found that stimulation of the vagus nerve in the presence of atropine, which blocks muscarinic receptors, caused relaxation of certain areas of the gut, particularly the sphincters. Thus, in addition to cholinergic and adrenergic nerves there is a third category of non-cholinergic, non-adrenergic inhibitory neurones. The identity of the transmitter released from the ends of these neurones is still not established, though the most likely candidates are vasoactive intestinal polypeptide (VIP) or ATP.

Other transmitters

Endogenous opiates are thought to act on the myenteric nerve plexus to inhibit the release of acetylcholine and lead to relaxation in many areas of the intestine; however, they contract the circular muscle of the colon by a direct action on smooth muscle. Serotonin (5-hydroxytryptamine) is an important neurotransmitter in the myenteric plexus and may play a key role in the peristaltic reflex (Fig. 18.3). Other peptides such as 'substance P', CCK-Pz (p. 260) and somatostatin (p. 302) are also present in the myenteric plexus but their role is unclear. Endocrine substances may also directly modify contraction of smooth muscle. For

example, gastrin increases electro-mechanical coupling in the stomach and enhances contractile activity.

THE OESOPHAGUS

The oesophagus is a tube about 25 cm long and about 2 cm in diameter joining the pharynx to the cardia of the stomach. The muscle layer consists predominantly of striated muscle in the upper third, smooth muscle in the lower third, and both striated and smooth muscle fibres in the middle third.

The oesophagus at rest is closed above and below by sphincters. The upper oesophageal or cricopharyngeal sphincter produces a band of high pressure, about 50 to 80 mmHg above atmosphere. This normally prevents air passing into the oesophagus during inspiration, and helps to prevent the aspiration of oesophageal contents into the lungs.

The lower oesophageal sphincter (LOS) can be demonstrated as a high-pressure zone (15 to 40 mmHg above gastric pressure), 2 to 6 cm in length. The tonic contraction of the LOS is increased by stimulation of the sympathetic nerves and by the hormone gastrin. Relaxation can be induced by stimulation of the vagus via inhibitory fibres that are neither cholinergic nor adrenergic. The LOS normally prevents the reflux of acid into the oesophagus and increases its tone whenever the intra-abdominal pressure rises. This function is

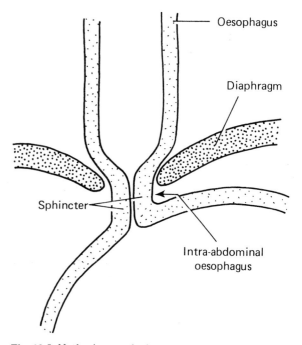

Fig. 18.5 Mechanisms at the lower oesophagus to prevent reflux of acid.

supported by the pinching action of the hiatal fibres of the diaphragm around the lower oesophagus during inspiration, and the presence of a length of intra-abdominal oesophagus, which is compressed during an increase in intra-abdominal pressure (Fig. 18.5).

Weakness or inappropriate relaxation of the LOS leads to reflux of gastric acid and symptoms of heartburn and acid regurgitation. Acid reflux may damage the mucosa of the lower oesophagus, and lead eventually to scarring and narrowing of the oesophageal lumen, which may cause difficulty in swallowing.

Swallowing

Swallowing (deglutition) is initiated voluntarily. The mouth is closed and the food bolus is forced into the pharynx by an upward and backward movement of the tongue caused mainly by the contraction of the mylohyoid and styloglossus muscles. The passage of the bolus through the back of the mouth stimulates receptors on the fauces and the posterior pharyngeal wall, initiating an involuntary sequence of events that propels the bolus

through the pharynx and oesophagus. A contraction commences on the posterior pharyngeal wall as the soft palate is forced back against it. The contraction then travels down and drives the bolus into the pharynx, which appears to come up to meet it (like a snake going for its prey) because of the elevation of the larynx. The same action stretches the upper oesophageal sphincter, which relaxes as the bolus approaches. Aspiration of food into the lungs is prevented by the elevation of the larynx, increasing its angulation with the pharynx, the contraction of the laryngeal constrictors, the inhibition of respiration, and the folding of the epiglottis over the laryngeal opening by the bolus as it passes over the back of the tongue. When the bolus is safely past the cricopharyngeus, the larynx and epiglottis resume their original positions and the vocal folds open.

The deglutition reflex is co-ordinated by the swallowing centre situated in the medulla and pons and acting through the seventh, ninth, tenth and twelfth cranial nerves to produce a precisely timed sequence of events. Once the food has reached the end of the

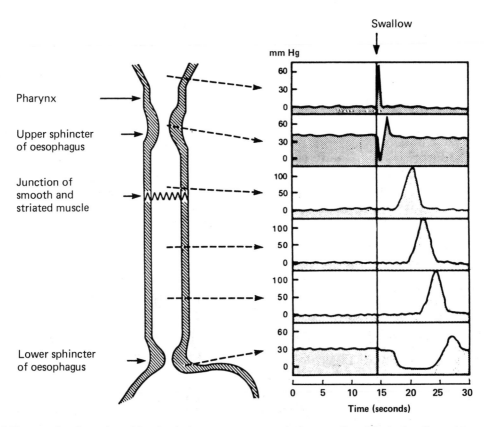

Fig. 18.6 Pharyngeal and oesophageal intraluminal pressures at rest and after a swallow. The broken lines with arrows indicate the level from which the pressure tracings were drawn. Pressure scales indicate the approximate normal values for pressure at each level at rest and in swallowing (from Christensen J 1983) In Christensen J, Wingate D L (eds) A guide to gastrointestinal motility. Wright, Bristol)

striated oesophagus, vagal activity acting through the intrinsic nerve plexuses continues the peristaltic wave down the oesophagus (Fig. 18.6).

The peristaltic wave of contraction moves down the oesophagus at the rate of 2 to 4 cm/s, accelerating towards the lower half of the oesophagus. 'Secondary' peristaltic waves may, however, commence in the mid or lower oesophagus, possibly stimulated by the presence of food or refluxed gastric contents. When the bolus of food arrives at the lower oesophagus, the LOS relaxes to allow it to enter the stomach.

THE STOMACH

The stomach receives food, stores it and converts it to a semi-liquid, partially digested slurry called chyme, which it delivers into the duodenum at a controlled rate.

The stomach consists of an expanded portion, the *fundus*, which functions as a reservoir; the body of the stomach or *corpus*, which is the main site for acid secretion; the *pyloric antrum*, which secretes the hormone gastrin and grinds the food up into smaller particles; and the *pylorus*, which functions as a sieve to let through small particles of food while keeping back larger particles (Fig. 18.7).

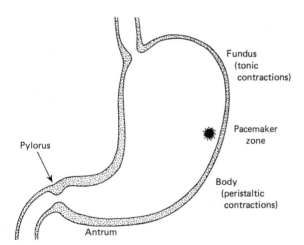

Fig. 18.7 The different parts of the stomach to indicate the thickness of the muscle wall and the type of contractile activity.

The gastric fundus
The fundus of the stomach does not undergo phasic or intermittent contraction but shows changes in the tone of the smooth muscle.

As food is eaten, swallowed and enters the stomach the muscle fibres of the gastric fundus increase in length

to accomodate the food, so that the intragastric pressure remains nearly constant at values not very different from those found in the empty stomach (about 7 mmHg). This phenomenon is known as *receptive relaxation* and is mediated by the activity of non-cholinergic, non-adrenergic vagal inhibitory nerves. Receptive relaxation can be initiated by gastric distension (gastric phase), oesophageal distension (oesophageal phase) and also by the sight, smell or taste of food (cephalic phase). As the meal leaves the stomach, the smooth muscle recovers its tone and continues to maintain a near-constant intragastric pressure. Unlike the body of the stomach, the smooth muscle cells of the fundus do not exhibit regular fluctuations in membrane potential. Instead, contraction is associated with a slow depolarisation to a new level.

The gastric corpus and antrum
When food is present in the stomach, waves of contraction develop in the corpus at a maximum rate of 3 to 4 per minute. These waves merely indent the wall of the corpus, but as they sweep down towards the antrum they progressively narrow and may obliterate the lumen, pressing food material up against the pylorus. Particles that are sufficiently small pass through the pyloric aperture into the duodenum but the rest of food bolus is squirted forcibly back through the advancing peristaltic wave into the stomach (Fig. 18.8). In this way, antral peristalsis mixes and grinds the gastric contents, breaking up large particles and reducing gastric contents to a semi-liquid slurry.

The pyloric aperture acts like a sieve, allowing small particles through, but keeping larger particles behind. However, the pyloric diameter is adjustable; constriction may be mediated by nerve fibres releasing enkephalins, while dilatation may be mediated by nerve fibres that release VIP. The nature of the luminal contents influence pyloric diameter; fats and hyperosmotic substances also interact with duodenal receptors to reduce antral contractility and pyloric diameter.

The electrical basis of antral contractions
Waves of depolarisation commence at a rate of about 3 per minute from a pacemaker zone high on the greater curvature of the stomach. As the electrical coupling of smooth muscle cells is faster in a circular direction than in a longitudinal direction, a circular band of depolarisation develops rapidly and progresses more slowly to the pylorus. These regular waves of depolarisation set the pattern from which contractions can arise. Intracellular recordings of muscle from the gastric body show an initial sharp depolarisation, followed by a plateau (Fig. 18.9). The magnitude and duration of contraction is directly related to the amplitude and duration of the plateau potential. In the terminal antrum, contrac-

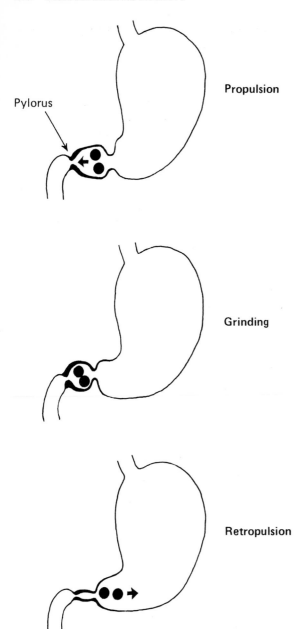

Pylorus

Propulsion

Grinding

Retropulsion

Fig. 18.8 The grinding activity of the contractions in the antrum and pylorus, (after Kelly K A, In: Johnson L (ed) Physiology of gastrointestinal tract. Raven Press, New York, p. 400)

tions are associated with the generation of spike potentials. The coupling between electrical depolarisation and muscular contraction increases when food is in the stomach, and experimentally when gastrin and acetylcholine are administered. Electro-mechanical coupling and contractile activity are decreased by secretin.

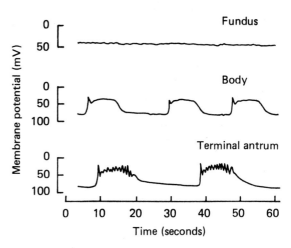

Fig. 18.9 The intracellular electrical recordings from the fundus, body and terminal antrum of the dog stomach. Note that the fundus has no regular depolarisations. The body of the stomach has a spike and plateau pattern whereas the terminal antrum shows numerous spikes superimposed on the plateau phase.

The control of gastric emptying

Physical nature of food

Liquids empty from the stomach more quickly than solids (Fig. 18.10). The emptying of liquids is directly proportional to the pressure gradient between the stomach and duodenum and inversely proportional to the resistance of the pylorus. It is often assumed that the duodenal pressure and pyloric resistance are constant and that the pressure exerted by the gastric fundus has the dominant influence on the emptying of liquid. The rate of emptying of liquid from the stomach

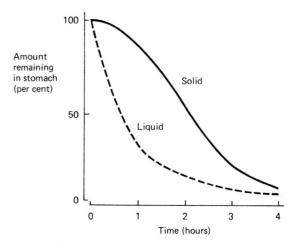

Fig. 18.10 The pattern of gastric emptying of the liquid components of a meal compared with the solid components.

is approximately proportional to the square root of the volume of fluid remaining in the stomach at any one time. Fats that are easily liquified may leave the stomach later than aqueous fluids when the subject is in the upright posture because they float to the top of the fluid gastric contents.

Solids have to be ground to particles small enough to leave the stomach. Thus emptying of solids depends on the particle size and the ease with which they may be reduced to small particles; solids like porridge and mashed potato leave the stomach more rapidly than a pancake or omelette, which have more cohesion. Mushrooms are very resistant to gastric disruption and may take several hours to pass into the duodenum.

Effect of the vagus nerve

The vagus has different effects on the emptying of solids compared with liquids. Stimulation of the vagus nerve increases antral contractility and accelerates the emptying of solids. On the other hand, vagal stimulation relaxes the gastric fundus and slows emptying of liquids. After section of the vagus nerve, which may be performed to reduce acid secretion in patients with duodenal ulcer, emptying of solids is slowed while emptying of liquids is faster than before the operation.

Feedback mechanisms

Gastric emptying is regulated by the chemical composition of gastric effluent via receptors in the upper small intestine. The presence of hypertonic fluids, acid, fat and tryptophan in the duodenum activates feedback mechanisms that regulate the force and frequency of antral contractions, fundic tone and the resistance of the pylorus and duodenum. These mechanisms are thought to involve nervous reflexes as well as the release of hormones.

Acid solutions empty more slowly from the stomach than neutral solutions because of the presence of pH receptors sensitive to acid in the duodenum. This mechanism ensures that acid is delivered to the duodenum at a constant rate. Receptors in the duodenum sensitive to changes in osmolality also influence gastric emptying. In general, the more hypertonic the solution, the slower it is emptied from the stomach, but an isotonic solution of sodium chloride is emptied faster than water. The slowing of gastric emptying by fat is brought about by receptors sensitive to long-chain fatty acids. The optimal chain length for the slowing of gastric emptying appears to be 14 carbon atoms, and unsaturated fats are more effective than saturated fats.

The amino acid tryptophan slows gastric emptying by interacting with specific duodenal receptors; tryptophan is the only amino acid known to have such an effect.

In general, these mechanisms mean that meals consisting predominantly of carbohydrates are generally emptied faster than meals consisting predominantly of proteins, which in turn are emptied faster than meals consisting predominantly of fats.

Vomiting

Vomiting is an integrated set of physiological events culminating in the forcible expulsion of gastric contents. It consists of three phases; nausea, retching and gastric evacuation (Fig. 18.11).

Nausea is a psychological experience that is difficult to define. It is associated with inhibition of gastric tone and contractility, the development of duodenal or jejunal contractions, which may migrate back towards the stomach, and the reflux of duodenal contents into

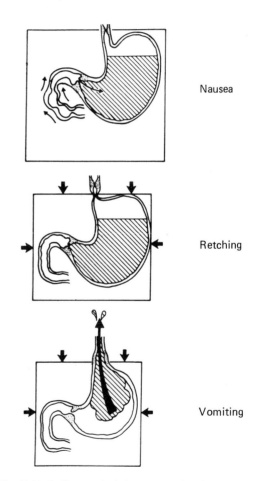

Fig. 18.11 A diagram depicting the physiological events that occur during the three phases of vomiting. Nausea (top) is associated with relaxation of gastric tone and reflux of intestinal contents into the stomach. During retching (middle), spasmodic contractions of the diaphragm and abdominal musculature force the cardiac portion of the stomach into the chest. During the expulsion phase of vomiting (bottom) the lower oesophageal sphincter is relaxed and abdominal and diaphragmatic contractions expel gastric contents into the oesophagus and through the mouth.

the stomach. Salivation and yawning are common during nausea.

Retching consists of intermittent forceful contractions of the diaphragm and abdominal muscles, which force the cardiac portion of the stomach up into the thorax, abolishing the length of intra-abdominal oesophagus that normally guards against reflux of gastric contents into the oesophagus (p. 243). Both the LOS and the striated muscle fibres around the diaphragmatic opening are contracted during retching. The upper oesophageal sphincter is open during each retch but promptly recovers its tone.

Vomiting is the forcible expulsion of the gastric and oesophageal contents through the mouth and can only occur when the cardia is raised, the hiatal fibres of the diaphragm are relaxed and the upper and lower oesophageal sphincters are open. The propulsive force for vomiting comes from the abdominal muscles and diaphragm, and experiments in animals have shown that it is possible for vomiting to occur even after the stomach has been replaced by a rubber bag.

The vomiting centre

The act of vomiting appears to be co-ordinated by a bilateral vomiting centre, which lies in the medulla near the tractus solitarius at the level of the dorsal motor nucleus of the vagus (Fig. 18.12). Appropriate motor reactions are then transmitted from this centre through the fifth, seventh, ninth, tenth and twelfth cranial nerves to the upper gastrointestinal tract and through the spinal nerves to the diaphragm and abdominal muscles.

Vomiting can be initiated by many stimuli (Table 18.13); most act directly on the vomiting centre.

Changes in body chemistry are thought to induce vomiting by stimulation of the chemoreceptor trigger zone (CTZ), which lies at the floor of the fourth ventricle. Ablation of the CTZ abolishes the vomiting caused by the parenteral administration of copper sulphate but does not prevent vomiting caused by the introduction of copper sulphate directly into the stomach.

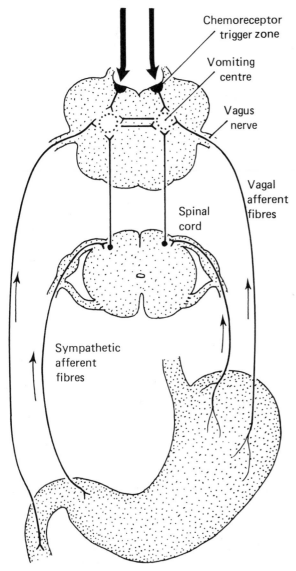

Fig. 18.12 A diagram illustrating the cerebral centres and visceral afferent pathways involved in vomiting.

Table 18.13 Causes of vomiting

Cortical factors
  Emotion
  Pain
  Raised intracranial pressure
  Migraine

Vestibular factors
  Rotation, for example in motion sickness

Visceral factors
  Pharyngeal irritation
  Effect of chemical composition of food on gastric and
    intestinal chemoreceptors
  Distension of any abdominal hollow viscus
  Obstruction of any abdominal smooth muscle tube
  Peritonitis

Alterations in body chemistry
  Diabetic ketoacidosis
  Renal failure
  Drug ingestion
  Alcohol ingestion
  Liver failure

THE SMALL INTESTINE

The movements of the small intestine mix the digestive juices with chyme, expose the chyme to the greatest possible surface area of intestinal epithelium so that absorption may be maximal, and regulate the passage of food down the small intestine to allow optimal absorption to take place before the next meal is ingested. When a solid meal is eaten it takes about four hours to reach the caecum and another four hours for all the residues to enter the colon. The transit of food through the upper small intestine is fast, but it slows down as residues reach the ileum.

Electrical basis of small bowel contraction

The electrical activity of intestinal smooth muscle consists of slow waves and spike bursts (Fig. 18.2). Slow waves are regular oscillations in the resting membrane potential of smooth muscle cells. They are present all the time and occur at a higher frequency in the upper small intestine than in the lower (12 per minute in the duodenum diminishing to 8 per minute in the ileum). The frequency gradient down the small intestine is determined by a series of pacemakers, each controlling a length of intestine distally. Neither the position of each pacemaker nor the length of bowel controlled is fixed anatomically. Slow waves are propagated distally at a rate of between 1 and 2 cm/s.

Spike bursts consist of a series of up to 20 rapid fluctuations in membrane potential, superimposed on the slow wave. Spike bursts do not occur with every slow wave, but when they do occur they are associated with a contraction, the strength of which appears to be related to the number of spike potentials. Contractions and spike bursts are propagated distally at the same rate as the slow wave.

Patterns of movement

The patterns of motor activity in the small intestine differ according to whether they are recorded after ingestion of a meal or during a period of fasting.

Motor activity after meals

After a meal is ingested contractions of the small intestine are irregular. Most contractions travel only a short distance down the gut before disappearing and being replaced by other contractions. This activity mixes the chyme with the digestive enzymes, increases the contact of nutrients with the absorbing surface and moves the intestinal contents onwards. Other types of motor activity may be seen in this phase; radiological studies with radio-opaque 'meals' have demonstrated that 'pendular movements', that is movements of contents backwards and forwards for short distances, may occur, as well as retroperistalsis and propulsion of food over long distances.

The motor pattern in the ileum differs from that in the rest of the small intestine. The transit of material through the ileum is slower than through the jejunum and for long periods ileal motility consists of regular contractions with little or no propulsive function. Large complex contractions may develop shortly after ingestion of a meal and appear to move through the ileum, spilling residues into the colon.

Small bowel transit

The composition of a meal may influence the rate at which it passes through the small intestine. Unabsorbed carbohydrates accelerate transit because they retain fluid in the intestinal lumen by virtue of their osmotic activity, increasing the volume and flow of intestinal contents and inducing peristalsis. Unabsorbed fat slows transit by interacting with specific receptors in the ileum (Fig. 18.14).

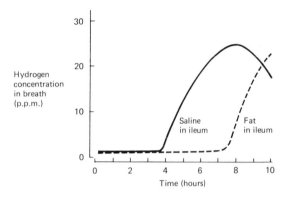

Fig. 18.14 The effect of infusion of a lipid emulsion into the ileum on the mouth to caecum transit time. The latter is demonstrated by the rise in breath hydrogen concentration that occurs when unabsorbed carbohydrate residues from a meal reach the colon and are fermented by bacteria.

Intestinal activity while fasting

During fasting the motility of the small intestine exhibits a recurrent pattern known as the migrating motor complex (MMC). The MMC consists of periods of quiescence (phase I) with few spike potentials or contractions associated with slow waves, periods of intermittent activity (phase II), with regular spike potentials and contractions and short periods of regular activity (phase III), with spike potentials and contractions associated with every slow wave (Fig. 18.15). The MMC recycles with a period of between 1 and 2 hours and migrates slowly down the small intestine at a rate of about 4 cm/min. Phase III lasts about 10 minutes and is thought to sweep remnants of the previous meal into the colon and to reduce the number of bacteria that would otherwise accumulate. The MMC often commences in the stomach, clearing the solid residues of the last meal into the small intestine.

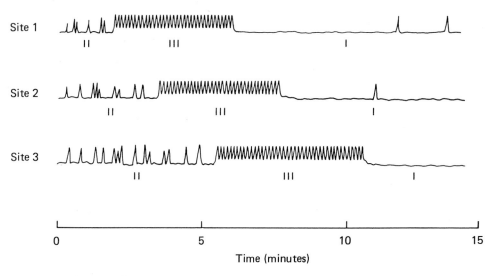

Fig. 18.15 A record of intraluminal pressure recorded at three sites in the small intestine in a fasted subject, showing the phases of the migrating motor complex.

The MMC is disrupted within minutes of eating a meal. This disruption is thought to be mediated by activity in the vagus nerve.

THE LARGE INTESTINE

The calibre of the colon is greater than that of the small bowel, being widest at the caecum and becoming narrower towards the rectum. The smooth muscle of the colon consists of an inner continuous circular layer and an outer longitudinal layer that is gathered into three longitudinal strands (*taeniae coli*). The taeniae coli join together to form a continuous longitudinal layer in the rectum.

Colonic movements
For most of the time colonic movements consist of ring-like contractions of both longitudinal and circular muscle, which cause the relaxed area between the contractions to bulge outwards in *haustrations*. These ring-like contractions may travel either forwards and backwards or they may simply disappear and then reform (Fig. 18.16). The haustral contractions mix the faecal material, exposing it to the absorbing surface and may also function as 'baffles' to slow the flow through the colon.

The sigmoid colon has a high degree of tonic and phasic motor activity and may act to hold colonic contents back in the descending colon so that they may

be slowly solidified. The observation that the contractile activity in the sigmoid may be increased in some patients with constipation and absent in some patients with diarrhoea supports this hypothesis. This type of colonic motor activity retains material in the proximal colon of normal people for periods of at least 36 hours, creating the stagnant conditions for bacterial proliferation and carbohydrate fermentation.

From time to time, and particularly after the ingestion of food and before defaecation the colon develops a different mode of activity (Fig. 18.16). Contraction rings disappear and the colon becomes narrower and shorter. This sets the scene for the appearance of large contractions or *mass movements*, which propel contents rapidly towards the rectum. Mass movements usually commence in the descending colon and force faeces into the rectum. They occur with increased frequency and commence more proximally in patients with diarrhoea.

The electrical basis of colonic motility
This is incompletely understood and is complicated by the fact that the same part of the colon may demonstrate at least two different frequencies of slow-wave activity. However, as in the small intestine, bursts of spike potentials are associated with contractions. Two types of spike bursts are recognised. Short spike bursts (SSB), less than 5 seconds in duration, are thought to be the electrical counterpart of ring-like or haustral contractions, whereas long spike bursts (more than 10 seconds in duration) may be the electrical counterpart of mass movements.

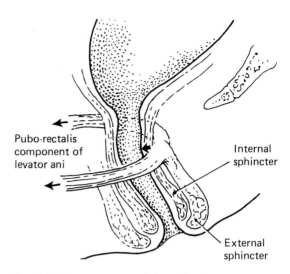

Fig. 18.17 The components of the anal sphincter mechanism.

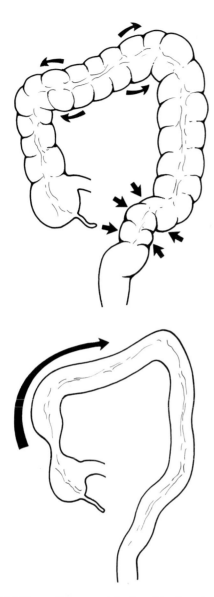

Fig. 18.16 Types of motor activity found in the colon. Above: 'Holding pattern' with ring-like contractions that move slowly in either direction. Below: 'Mass movements' in which the ring contractions disappear and a single peristaltic wave drives the intestinal contents towards the anus.

DEFECATION

The rectum can be regarded as a reservoir that retains faeces just prior to defecation. It is often empty when the rest of the colon is full of faecal material. The anal canal is approximately 3 cm long and is lined by squamous epithelium, which has a rich sensory innervation.

The anal sphincter consists of two concentric sphincters (Fig. 18.17). The internal sphincter is a continuation of the circular smooth muscle of the rectum and like all smooth muscle sphincters, it remains tonically contracted for most of the time. The intrinsic nerve supply to both rectum and internal anal sphincter comes from the enteric nerve plexuses, while the extrinsic nerve supply comes from the pelvic parasympathetic outflow and from the thoracolumbar sympathetic outflow via the prevertebral ganglia and hypogastric plexuses.

The external anal sphincter consists of striated muscle and is continuous above with the puborectalis (the innermost loop of the levator ani). It receives its nerve supply from the pudendal nerve. Continence for faeces is maintained by the tonic contraction of the sphincters and by the acute forward angulation between the rectum and anal canal caused by the contraction of the puborectalis. Increases in intra-abdominal pressure enhance the contraction of the puborectalis and external anal sphincter, increasing the anorectal angle and the anal resistance.

The act of defecation has many similarities to micturition (Chap. 12). Distension of the rectum initiates reflex contraction of the rectal wall and relaxation of the internal anal sphincter (the defecation reflex). Increasing the distension may induce a series of rectal contractions and internal sphincter relaxations. However, this does not normally give rise to defecation unless the striated muscle of the puborectalis and external sphincter is relaxed.

The act of defecation is normally under voluntary control. The desire to defecate may be signalled by the presence of faeces in the rectum, which stimulates receptors in the rectum and pelvic floor. If conditions are appropriate, these signals may facilitate relaxation of the external sphincter and puborectalis muscles. The anorectal angle becomes straight and allows contraction of the abdominal muscles to expel the faeces (Fig. 18.17).

FURTHER READING

Christensen J, Wingate D L 1983 A guide to gastrointestinal motility. Wright, Bristol

Akkermans L M A, Johnson A G, Read N W 1984 Gastric and gastroduodenal motility. Praeger, Eastbourne

Johnson L J 1981 Physiology of the gastrointestinal tract. Chapters 6–16 and 58, Raven Press, New York

19

Gastric secretion

The gastric mucosa consists of simple branched tubular glands packed tightly together and arranged perpendicularly to the surface. Groups of glands, usually four, open into *gastric pits*, which in turn open on to the mucosal surface (Fig. 19.1). In the mucosa of the distal part of the stomach (the pyloric area) the glands are lined by mucus-secreting cells only. In the mucosa of the remainder of the stomach, the glands are lined not only with mucous cells but also with *parietal* (oxyntic)

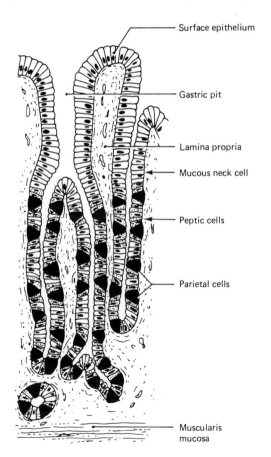

Surface epithelium

Gastric pit

Lamina propria

Mucous neck cell

Peptic cells

Parietal cells

Muscularis mucosa

Fig. 19.1 Structure of gastric mucosa of the body of the stomach to show types of cells found within a gastric gland

cells and *peptic* (chief or zymogen) cells. The different cell types are arranged as illustrated in Figure 19.1. The glands have three parts: base, neck and isthmus. The neck region contains irregularly shaped mucous cells with basal nuclei and most of the parietal cells. A few parietal cells are also found in the isthmus and basal regions. Peptic cells (zymogen cells with granular cytoplasm) are present in the base of the glands. Special staining techniques reveal a few scattered argentaffin cells in the basal region. The gastric pits and the mucosal surface throughout the stomach are lined with charateristic mucus-laden, columnar epithelial cells with basal nuclei.

The mucosal structure is the result of a dynamic equilibrium between the production and destruction of mucosal cells. These cells are produced by cellular division, probably from common 'mother' cell in the glandular neck. From this region gradually maturing cells pass up to the surface or down into the glands. The cells take 2 to 3 days to migrate from the neck region to the surface; the oldest surface cells are extruded into the gastric lumen and are digested. Estimation of the DNA content of gastric washings shows that, in normal people, about half a million cells are lost per minute. The cells that pass downward are probably destroyed eventually in the base of the glands. The mechanisms controlling cell proliferation are not fully understood but they are known to be influenced by hormones such as growth hormone and gastrin and also by vagal stimulation and by dietary factors that affect somatic growth.

Acid secretion

The gastric juice contains hydrochloric acid secreted by the parietal cells. Electron microscopy of the parietal cell at rest reveals large numbers of mitochondria an extensive cytoplasmic smooth membrane system of tubular and vesicular components (tubulovesicles) and relatively few canaliculi with few villi. When acid is being secreted, the tubulovesicles migrate and become incorporated into the canalicular surface so that canaliculi become a prominent feature of the cell structure.

Histochemical studies of biopsy specimens of gastric

mocosa reveal high concentrations of the flavoprotein enzymes and of cytochrome oxidase in the parietal cells. These enzymes are presumably important for the production of the large amounts of energy needed to elaborate a concentrated acid solution.

Uncontaminated parietal cell secretion has not yet been obtained because gastric juice is a mixture of secretions from a variety of cell types. However, maximal stimulation with gastrin might be expected to yield a concentration of acid in the juice closely approximating that of the secretion of the parietal cells. Such a secretion can be collected in humans by continuous suction through a tube passed from the nose or mouth through the oesophagus into the stomach; contamination by swallowed saliva may be prevented by simultaneous aspiration of saliva through another tube placed in the mouth.

The output of acid from the stomach when maximally stimulated is proportional to the number of parietal cells in the mucosa, the parietal cell mass. In humans, the maximal hydrogen ion secretion per hour is approximately 1 mmol per ml of mucosa or 20 mmol per 10^9 cells. The maximal concentration of hydrogen ion in the gastric juice varies between 140 and 160 mmol/l. The main anion is chloride and at low rates of acid secretion the hydrogen ion is replaced by sodium. Other ions, such as calcium, magnesium, phosphate and potassium are present in small amounts, of which potassium is the most abundant at a concentration of about 10 mmol/l.

Mechanism of HCl secretion
The concentration of hydrogen ions in parietal cell secretion is a million times greater than that in the plasma and an active process requiring the utilisation of energy must therefore be involved. The fundamental reaction in the parietal cell secreting acid is

$$H_2O \rightleftharpoons H^+ + OH^-$$

H^+ is secreted on the luminal surface (through the canalicular membranes) and the OH^- is secreted over the serosal membrane. OH^- is not secreted as such but combines with CO_2 to form bicarbonate. Thus, with isolated gastric mucosa, it has been demonstrated that for every hydrogen ion secreted into the fluid bathing the luminal side of the mucosa, an equivalent of alkali

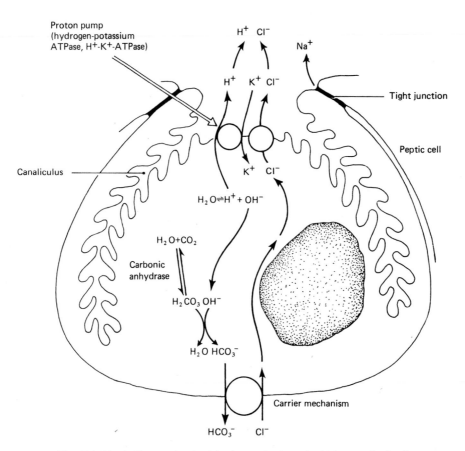

Fig. 19.2 Metabolic steps involved in the production of acid by a parietal cell

was secreted over the serosal surface. This provides an explanation for the observation in man that, shortly after a meal, the pH of the arterial blood rises and the amount of acid secreted by the kidney decreases, the so-called *alkaline tide*.

The energy for the secretion of H⁺ arises from ATP. If energy-rich phosphate compounds are made unavailable by dinitrophenol, cell respiration continues but acid secretion is inhibited. Proof that ATP is the only energy source for acid secretion was demonstrated in the following way. Acid secretion can be studied in vitro by using isolated gastric glands. The addition of ATP to such a suspension does not stimulate acid secretion because it cannot gain access to the cell. However, if the glands are subjected to a high voltage discharge or to a solution of digitonin, the basolateral membrane of the parietal cell is made permeable to ATP. If, after such treatment, ATP is added to a suspension of gastric glands, acid secretion is stimulated even under anoxic conditions, thus demonstrating that energy for secretion comes from ATP and not from some oxidation–reduction system.

Carbonic anhydrase

After transport of hydrogen ion into the canaliculus, hydroxyl ion accumulates in the parietal cell. It combines with CO_2 under the influence of carbonic anhydrase to form bicarbonate, which is secreted into the blood (Fig. 19.2). The inhibition of carbonic anhydrase causes an inhibition of acid secretion due to the rise in pH within the parietal cell as a result of the accumulation of hydroxyl ion.

Enzyme secretion

The only gastric enzymes of any consequence in digestion are the pepsins, a group of enzymes that hydrolyse proteins. The gastric pepsins are a complex of at least seven enzymes each with its own specific chemical characteristics. These enzymes are secreted from the chief cells as inactive precursors, the *pepsinogens*, and are activated by acid and by pepsin itself. They are unusual enzymes in that their pH optima are in the range 1.5 to 3.5. The pepsins are endopeptidases that hydrolyse peptides at several specific peptide bonds, the most susceptible involving the amino acids tyrosine and phenylalanine. Peptic digestion is not essential to life; after complete removal of the human stomach, digestion of proteins in the intestine proceeds quite well.

Secretion of mucus and bicarbonate

Mucus is secreted by the surface cells of the stomach as a gel that adheres to the gastric mucous membrane. It functions as a lubricant, facilitating the passage of food, and protects the mucosal surfaces from damage by the solid and liquid shear forces that are brought to bear on it during digestion. The mucus also behaves as a barrier that protects the underlying cells from erosion by the acid and pepsin of the gastric juice. The HCl is able to diffuse through the mucus gel but becomes neutralised within the gel layer by bicarbonate secreted by the mucosa, possibly from the same cells that secrete the mucus. The mucus gel layer thus functions as a mixing barrier, with prevents bicarbonate secretion being dissipated by mixing with the bulk of luminal acid. The higher pH adjacent to the mucosa also inhibits the action of pepsin and affords further protection. Although mucus lines the whole of the mucosal surface, including the gastric pits, it does not line the gastric glands. It is not yet known how the glands are protected from the acid and pepsin they contain.

Gastric mucus is a high-molecular-weight glycoprotein consisting of polymers, each composed of four subunits containing a protein backbone to which are attached a large number of carbohydrate side-chains. About one quarter of the protein backbone of each subunit is, however, non-glycosylated. Although the carbohydrate covering protects the underlying protein from proteolysis, the polymer can be split into its water-soluble subunits at the non-glycosylated region by proteolytic enzymes such as pepsin and trypsin. In ABO blood group secretors the terminal sugar residues of the gastric mucus are the same as those that determine the specificity of the ABO blood groups on the red cell surface (p. 53): in the case of blood group A this is *N*-acetyl-galactosamine and in blood group B it is galactose.

The viscous character of gastric mucus depends on the presence of glycoprotein in the polymeric form, so enzymes and chemicals that split the mucus into its glycoprotein subunits also destroy the physico-chemical properties responsible for its physiological function. The surface of the mucus layer in contact with the gastric chyme is no doubt continually being solubilised by pepsin and replaced from beneath by newly secreted mucus. The mucus must also be formed at a suitable rate because strong non-covalent intermolecular interactions between the polymers are necessary to form a gel and these interactions increase as the glycoprotein concentration increases.

Intrinsic factor

Intrinsic factor is a glycoprotein secreted by the parietal cell that binds to vitamin B12 in the stomach and is needed for the absorption of vitamin B12 in the terminal ileum. Stimulants of acid secretion increase the rate of secretion of intrinsic factor and the amount secreted usually greatly exceeds that required for the complete absorption of the dietary cobalamin.

Human big gastrin (G34)

Pyro.Leu.Gln.Pro.Gln.Gly.Pro.Pro.His.Leu.Val.Ala.Asp.Pro.Ser.Lys.Gln.
Gly.Pro.Trp.Leu.Glu.Glu.Glu.Glu.Ala.Tyr.**Gly.Trp.Met.Asp.Phe.**
                                                   |
                                                   R

Human little gastrin (G17)

Pyro.Gly.Pro.Trp.Leu.Glu.Glu.Glu.Glu.Glu.Ala.Tyr.**Gly.Trp.Met.Asp.Phe.**
                                             |
                                             R

Fig. 19.3 Amino acid sequence of big gastrin (G34) and little gastrin (G17). Note the five residues at the C-terminal end for G34, G17 and CCK-Pz are common. Pyro = pyroglutamyl. R = H or SO_3H

Stimulation of the parietal cell

Secretion by parietal cells is regulated by acetylcholine from post-ganglionic terminals, by the peptide hormone gastrin from the pyloric antrum and duodenum, and by histamine from histaminocytes near the lamina propria. All three agents acting singly induce acid secretion from the parietal cell, which has receptors for each of these stimulants. When two of these secretagogues act together, the acid response is greater than the sum of the individual responses, a result indicating that there is considerable potentiation. On eating a meal gastrin is released into the circulation and the vagus increases its discharge to the parietal cells but there is no evidence that histamine release is also increased. It now seems that histamine is released continuously and potentiates the action of gastrin and acetylcholine.

Gastrin

Gastrin is a peptide synthesised and released from cells in the pyloric antrum and duodenum. It exists in several forms but the most physiologically important are the heptadecapeptide, often called *little gastrin* (G17), and a peptide of 34 residues (G34), called *big gastrin*.

All the physiological actions of the gastrin molecule are possessed by the C-terminal tetrapeptide (indicated in heavy type), which appears to be the 'action centre' of the molecule. *Pentagastrin*, a synthetic analogue containing five amino acids (the C-terminal tetrapeptide of gastrin with β-alanine added at the N-terminal), is used in medicine for testing the secretory capacity of the stomach (Fig. 19.3).

THE CONTROL OF GASTRIC SECRETION

When a meal is eaten, secretion of both acid and pepsinogen by the stomach begins, the acid output approaching that which can be achieved by exogenous stimulation with histamine or pentagastrin. The peak is reached at about 90 minutes after the meal and

declines gradually to pre-stimulation levels at about 240 minutes (Fig. 19.4).

It has been customary to classify gastric secretion into a number of phases according to the site at which the stimuli act. It must however be realised that these phases not only follow one another in sequence but they also overlap to some extent.

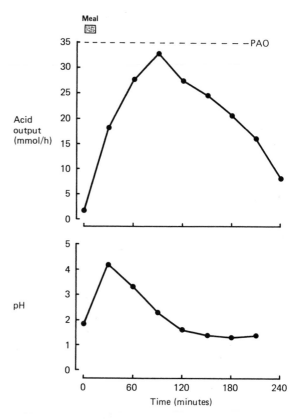

Fig. 19.4 Acid secretion after a meal in a normal man. The pH of the gastric content is shown below. PAO is the peak acid output following a maximal dose of histamine or gastrin pentapeptide (After Feldman M, Richardson C T 1981 In: Johnson L R (ed) Physiology of the gastrointestinal tract. Raven Press, New York, p. 697)

The cephalic phase

The sight, smell and taste of food initiate this phase of gastric secretion, through conditioned and unconditioned reflexes. The magnitude of the response is greatest if the meal is appetising. It can be studied in man by sham feeding, in which a subject chews an appetising meal but instead of swallowing, he spits it out so that the food does not enter the stomach. At the same time, the gastric juice secreted is aspirated through a nasogastric tube. After a short latent period, acid and pepsinogen secretion begins with acid secretion reaching a peak of between 22 and 80 per cent of the peak acid output within 30 minutes and remaining elevated for more than a further hour. A significant response can be obtained from a purely psychic stimulus in which gastric secretion occurs in respose to the sight of food in a hungry individual even though no food enters the mouth (Fig. 19.5).

The afferent pathways for these reflexes are similar to those involved in salivation but the efferent pathways are quite distinct. The cephalic phase of acid secretion is abolished either by vagotomy or by very small doses of atropine. In addition to the direct influence on acid and pepsinogen secretion by the cholinergic vagal innervation, an indirect effect on acid secretion can also occur, for vagal impulses also liberate gastrin from the antral gastrin-producing cells (G-cells).

The gastric phase

When a meal enters the stomach, the gastric phase begins and gastric secretion is stimulated by further reflex action and the liberation of gastrin.

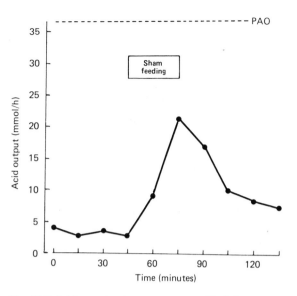

Fig. 19.5 Acid secretion in response to modified sham feeding in 22 healthy subjects (After Feldman M, Richardson C T 1981 In: Johnson L R (ed) Physiology of the gastrointestinal tract. Raven Press, New York, p. 698).

Reflexes of the gastric phase

Distension of the body of the stomach by the ingested meal stimulates gastric secretion. The receptors for this reflex are in tension receptors in the muscle layers of the stomach wall, and both afferent and efferent fibres are carried in the vagus nerves. The vago-vagal reflex acts directly on oxyntic and peptic cells; it does not liberate gastrin from pyloric G-cells. Vagal section does

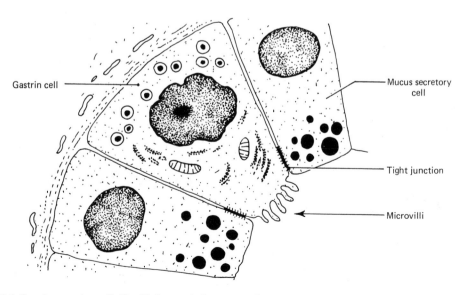

Fig. 19.6 Gastrin-secreting cell (G-cell) from pyloric antrum. On either side mucus-secreting cells can also be seen.

not completely abolish the gastric secretion resulting from distension. The remaining response is the result of a local reflex that lies entirely within the stomach wall.

Gastrin-producing cells and gastrin release

Gastrin-containing G-cells are found in the surface epithelium of the mid-zone of the pyloric glands and in the mucosa of the upper part of the small intestine. These cells contain numerous basal granules and from their apical surface microvilli protrude into the gut lumen (Fig. 19.6). The neurotransmitter for the vagal release of gastrin in man has not been identified with certainty, but it does not appear to be acetylcholine and may be one of the other peptides found in the pyloric mucosa, such as bombesin.

Protein in the food is the most important stimulant for gastrin release. Undigested protein has only a weak action, whereas peptic digestion products, particularly certain amino acids such as phenylalanine, are very effective. After a meal, the two forms of gastrin, G34 and G17 can be detected in plasma. The increment of serum G17 gastrin rises to a peak 20 to 30 min after a meal and then gradually declines over the next hour to an hour and a half. The G34 component of the response reaches a peak much later and declines more slowly (Fig. 19.7).

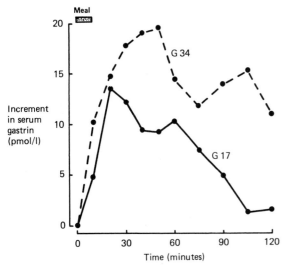

Fig. 19.7 Increment in serum levels of two forms of gastrin after a meal in a normal subject (After Taylor I L et al. 1979 Gut 20:957)

Inhibition of gastrin release

Gastrin-stimulated acid release is inhibited when the pH of the contents of the pyloric antrum fall below about 2.5. This inhibition is due to the suppression of gastrin release. During the course of a meal, the pH of the stomach contents changes. It is high over the first 60 to 70 minutes (even in the face of a high rate of acid secretion) because of the buffering action of the food, but it falls towards the end meal even though the rate of acid secretion is falling. By 120 minutes after the meal, the pH is about 1.5 and gastrin release is suppressed (Fig. 19.4). The mechanisms responsible for the inhibition of gastrin release by luminal acid are not known. Acid could act directly on the luminal surface of the G-cells as microvilli project from these cells into the lumina of the pyloric glands. An alternative suggestion is that the somatostatin-producing D cells in the mucosa respond to luminal acid by producing somatostatin, which inhibits gastrin release from adjacent G-cells (a paracrine action).

Intestinal phase

Stimuli coming from the intestine make a small contribution to the gastric secretory response. Chyme reaching the duodenum has two effects depending upon the nature of the meal, it can stimulate or inhibit gastric secretion. The major contribution of the small intestine to the control of gastric function is one of inhibition both of secretion and of gastric emptying so that the passage of the liquified chyme from the stomach does not overload the duodenum either by excess volume, acidity, osmolality or fat. This negative feed-back is mediated by both neural and humoral pathways but neither the neural mechanism nor the chemical messengers have yet been identified.

FURTHER READING

Blair E L 1974 Control of gastric emptying and acidity. In: Linden R J (ed) Recent advances in physiology, No. 9. Churchill Livingstone, Edinburgh

Gregory R A 1982 Regulatory peptides of gut and brain. British Medical Bulletin 38: 271–276

Johnson L R (ed) 1981 Physiology of the gastrointestinal tract. Raven Press, New York

Mignon M, Vatier J, Ruskoné A, Merrouche M, Bonfils S 1983 Gastric acid secretion in response to food. In: Young J A (ed), Gastrointestinal physiology, IV. International Review of Physiology, Vol. 28, University Park Press, Baltimore.

20

The pancreas

The pancreas is both an endocrine and an exocrine gland. It is composed largely of cells concerned with the synthesis and secretion of the digestive enzymes. The cells that have an endocrine function are scattered throughout the substance of the gland in small groups called the *islets of Langerhans* and secrete the hormones insulin, glucagon, somatostatin and pancreatic polypeptide directly into the dense capillary network that surrounds them (Chap. 23).

The exocrine cells are pyramidal in shape and are arranged around a small lumen in *acini* (Fig. 20.1), which are connected to the duct system like a bunch of grapes. The apical portion of each cell is filled with membrane-bound *zymogen granules*, which are the inactive precursors of the digestive enzymes. Each acinus leads into an intercalated duct, which joins others to form the intralobular ducts; these finally empty into the main pancreatic duct, which drains into the second part of the duodenum. The intercalated ducts possess cells that are invaginated into the lumen of the acinus so that on section they appear to be in the centre of the acinus, hence the term centro-acinar cell. The ductule cells possess no zymogen granules, have sparse cytoplasm with few endoplasmic reticulum cisternae, but they have many mitochondria. The external secretion is a mixture of two secretions; one arises from the acini and consists largely of enzymes, while the other comes from ductules and centro-acinar cells and contains only electrolytes. Each group of cells has its own controlling system.

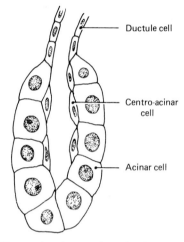

Fig. 20.1 Pancreatic acinus to show the three types of cells

Stimulants for pancreatic secretion
Secretion is influenced both by neural and by hormonal mechanisms. Stimuli that affect mainly the acinar cell provoke a viscid secretion rich in enzymes. Such stimuli are cholinergic, mediated by reflexes in the vagus nerves and by two hormones, *cholecystokinin-pancreozymin* (CCK-Pz) and gastrin. The centro-acinar and ductule cells are stimulated by secretin to produce an electrolyte secretion poor in enzymes.

Human CCK — Pz

Tyr—Ile—Gln—Gln—Ala—Arg—Lys—Ala—Pro—Ser— Gly—Arg—Met—Ser—Ile—Val—Lys—Asn—Leu—Gln—Ser—

                                                                         R
                                                                      |

Leu —Asp—Pro—Ser—His—Arg—Ile—Ser—Asp—Arg— Asp—Tyr—Met—Gly—Trp—Met—Asp—Phe—NH$_2$

Human Gastrin 17

                                                 R or H
Glp—Gly—Pro—Trp—Met—Glu—Glu—Glu—Glu—Glu— Ala—Tyr—Gly—Trp—Met—Asp—Phe—NH$_2$

Fig. 20.2 Amino acid sequence of gastrin compared with CCK-Pz to show similarities of the amino-terminal portion.

Cholecystokinin-pancreozymin

This is a polypeptide hormone of 33 residues, the five C-terminal residues being identical with those of gastrin (Fig. 20.2). It is because of this common sequence that CCK-Pz and gastrin share some properties, such as the ability to stimulate pancreatic enzyme secretion. At one time it was thought that two hormones existed, one that stimulated enzyme secretion (*pancreozymin*) and a second that caused the gallbladder to contract (*cholecystokinin*). It is now known that these activities are caused by the same polypeptide, which is produced in cells in the duodenum and jejunum. These cells are pear-shaped, contain granules of the preformed hormone and lie between the columnar cells of the mucosa with apical processes projecting into the intestinal lumen.

CCK-Pz is released by digestion products of both proteins and fats, the aromatic amino acids and the fatty acids being the most potent.

Gastrin

Gastrin has been discussed in Chapter 19. Although gastrin stimulates the release of enzyme it is a less powerful stimulus than CCK-Pz.

Cholinergic stimuli

Reflex excitation of the vagus stimulates enzyme secretion by the pancreas through the liberation of acetylcholine from post-ganglionic terminals, an effect that is abolished by a previous intravenous injection of the anti-muscarinic agent atropine.

Secretin

Secretin is responsible for the stimulation of electrolyte secretion. It is a polypeptide of 27 residues and has its cell of origin in the intestinal crypts of the duodenum and jejunum. It is released by acid and by bile salts in the lumen of the small intestine (Fig. 20.3).

Vasoactive intestinal polypeptide

This peptide has many roles in the body. It is released from vagal postganglionic terminals in the pancreas and in some animals, stimulates both electro-lyte secretion and pancreatic blood flow. Its importance in the control of secretion in man is uncertain. Its effect on the pancreas is due to its structural similarities to secretin.

Interaction between stimuli

While it is true that electrolyte and enzyme secretion are controlled by separate mechanisms, there is considerable interaction between the various stimuli, with potentiation occurring particularly between vagal action and CCK-Pz on the one hand and secretin on the other.

The composition of pancreatic juice

Electrolytes

Pancreatic juice is an isotonic, alkaline solution, the principal ions of which are sodium, potassium, bicarbonate and chloride. The cations are secreted at concentrations close to those in plasma and are independent of the rate of secretion. The major anion is bicarbonate, which increases its concentration with increasing rates of secretion. The concentration of chloride decreases as the flow rate increases, so that the sum of $[Cl^-]$ and $[HCO_3^-]$ remains constant and independent of secretion rate (Fig. 20.4). Some calcium is also secreted; part of this is ionised with a concentration about one-quarter of that in plasma, the remainder is secreted bound to some of the enzymes.

The enzymes

Enzymes are synthesised on the ribosomes of the rough endoplasmic reticulum of the acinar cell. They pass into the cisternal spaces from which vesicles, containing the enzymes, bud off and pass to the Golgi region of the cell. The vesicles coalesce and grow into mature zymogen granules. When the gland is stimulated to secrete, the membranes that surround the zymogen granule fuse with the apical membrane of the cell and the contents are extruded (exocytosis) into the lumen of the acinus. The pancreatic enzymes are hydrolases and are secreted in parallel. They lack co-enzymes and

	1	2	3	4	5	6	7	8	9	10	11	12	13	14	15
Human VIP	His	Ser	Asp	Ala	Val	Phe	Thr	Asp	Asn	Tyr	Thr	Arg	Leu	Arg	Lys
Secretin	His	Ser	Asp	Gly	Thr	Phe	Thr	Ser	Glu	Leu	Ser	Arg	Leu	Arg	Glu

	16	17	18	19	20	21	22	23	24	25	26	27	28	29
Human VIP	Gln	Met	Ala	Val	Lys	Lys	Tyr	Leu	Asn	Ser	Ile	Leu	Asn	NH_2
Secretin	Ser	Ala	Arg	Leu	Gln	Arg	Leu	Leu	Gln	Gly	Leu	Val	NH_2	

Fig. 20.3 Amino acid sequence of secretin and of vasoactive intestinal peptide.

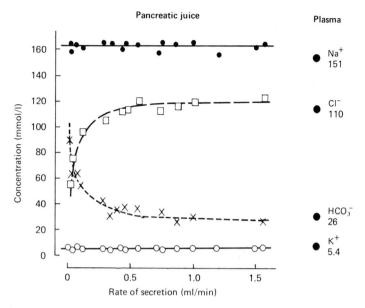

Fig. 20.4 Composition of pancreatic juice and its relationship to the flow rate in the cat. (After Bro-Rasmussen F et al 1956 Acta Physiologica Scandinavica 37:97)

Table 20.5 Principal digestive enzymes produced by the pancreas

Amylolytic:
α-Amylase

Proteolytic:
Trypsinogen
Chymotrypsinogen
Proelastases and elastases
Pro-carboxypeptidases

Lipolytic:
Lipase
Co-Lipase

Nucleolytic:
Ribonuclease
Deoxyribonuclease

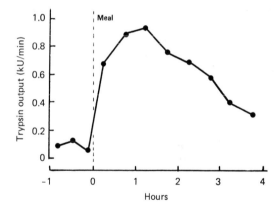

Fig. 20.6 Enzyme response to a meal in man.

are classified according to the type of molecule they hydrolyse (Table 20.5).

CONTROL OF PANCREATIC SECRETION

The control of pancreatic secretion in man is less well understood than that of gastric secretion. The reasons for this difference are mainly the inaccessibility of the organ and the difficulty of recovering pancreatic secretion from the duodenum.

The response to a meal

After a meal has been ingested, the pancreatic response reaches a peak in about 1 to 1½ hours and then declines to basal levels by three to four hours after the beginning of the meal. Unlike the stomach, where acid secretion can be monitored quite easily, it has not been possible to estimate the electrolyte response to the meal. However, the secretion of enzymes can be measured (Fig. 20.6). As with gastric secretion, control can be classified under three phases — cephalic, gastric and intestinal.

Cephalic phase
The cephalic phase (Fig. 20.7) begins the response to the meal by the stimuli of taste, smell and sight of food initiating reflexes whose efferent neurones, travelling in the vagus nerves, release acetylcholine directly on to the

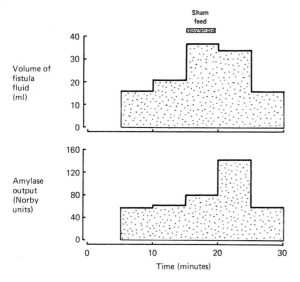

Sham feed

Volume of fistula fluid (ml)

Amylase output (Norby units)

Time (minutes)

Fig. 20.7 Pancreatic response to sham feeding in a patient who had had a total gastrectomy and had a pancreatic fistula.

acinar cells from postganglionic neurones. It is likely that the gastrin released from the pyloric antrum by vagal action also stimulates the secretion of pancreatic enzymes. The stimulation of pancreatic secretion continues when the food enters the stomach to initiate the gastric phase.

Gastric phase
Distension of the body of the stomach by the meal initiates a *gastro-pancreatic reflex*, the receptors for which are tension receptors in series with the gastric muscle

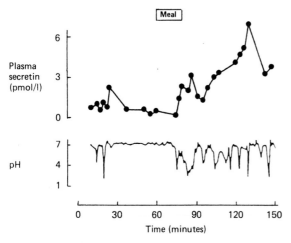

Meal

Plasma secretin (pmol/l)

pH

Time (minutes)

Fig. 20.8 Plasma secretin concentration and intraduodenal pH in a normal subject before and after the ingestion of a protein-rich meal (After Shaffalitzky de Muckadell O B, Fahrenkrug J 1978 Gut 19:812).

fibres whose afferent and efferent neurones lie entirely in the vagus nerves. The meal also releases gastrin. Thus the effectiveness of the gastric phase depends on the volume of the meal and its protein content. Up to this point, the stimuli act on the acinar cell producing a viscid juice rich in enzymes. It is not until food enters the small intestine that fluid and electrolyte are secreted to any extent.

The intestinal phase
This phase is initiated as soon as the stomach begins to empty; its magnitude depends on the rate of emptying and on the chemical composition of the chyme. It is usually stated that the intestinal phase is quantitatively the most important of the three phases; although this is probably true in the case of electrolytes, it has not been confirmed for enzyme secretion. The stomach

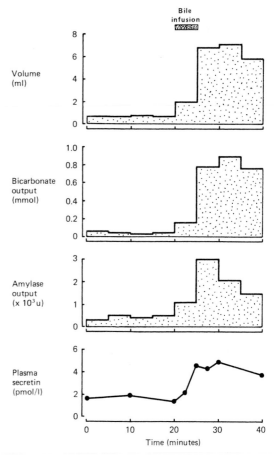

Bile infusion

Volume (ml)

Bicarbonate output (mmol)

Amylase output (x 10³u)

Plasma secretin (pmol/l)

Time (minutes)

Fig. 20.9 The volume, electrolyte and amylase secretion collected by cannulation of the pancreatic duct in six human subjects, before and after the infusion of 6 g of isosmolar bile into the duodenum. The rise in plasma levels of immuno-reactive secretin is also shown. (After Osnes M et al 1978 Gut 19:180).

empties its contents into the duodenum in spurts; each spurt is reflected, at least in the first part of the duodenum, by a transient fall in pH, which falls below the threshold (pH 4.5) for the release of secretin (Fig. 20.8). Accompanying these episodes of acidity are intermittent increases in the plasma secretin concentration that are sufficient to stimulate bicarbonate secretion by the pancreas. In addition, the emptying of the gallbladder delivers bile salt into the small intestine and this in turn releases secretin (Fig. 20.9) The amounts of secretin released during the course of a meal are quite small but the action of the hormone is potentiated both by vagal action and by CCK-Pz.

The digestion products of the protein and fat content of the food have two effects: they release CCK-Pz, which in turn excites enzyme secretion through its hormonal action and, at the same time, they stimulate chemoreceptors that initiate an entero-pancreatic reflex with both afferent and efferent neurones in the vagus nerve.

Inhibition of pancreatic secretion

Recent experiments suggest that digestion products, particularly fats, acting from terminal ileum and colon, inhibit pancreatic secretion towards the end of a meal, in which both humoral and nervous mechanisms participate.

FURTHER READING

Creutzfeldt W (ed) 1984 The exocrine pancreas. Clinics in Gastroenterology 13: 655–1005

Howat H T, Sarles H (ed) 1979 The exocrine pancreas. Saunders, Philadelphia

Scratcherd T 1981. The control of pancreatic exocrine secretion. In: Jewell D P, Lee (eds) Topics in gastroenterology. Blackwell Scientific, Oxford, pp. 193–213

Solomon T E 1984 Regulation of pancreatic secretion. Clinics in Gastroenterology 13: 657–678

21

Intestinal absorption and secretion

The small and large intestines together form a long tube adapted for the digestion and absorption of nutrients and the absorption of salt and water. Approximately 90 per cent of food is normally absorbed in the small intestine during a relatively brief passage of about five hours. The remainder passes into the colon, where it stays for up to three days, during which time most of the fluid, sodium and carbohydrate is extracted.

Anatomy

The enormous absorptive capacity of the small intestine is made possible by the vast surface area produced by myriad microscopic finger- or leaf-like *villi* (Fig. 21.1) upon which are situated the absorptive cells or *enterocytes* and occasional mucus-secreting goblet cells Patients with villous atrophy due to coeliac disease have a completely flat epithelium and can suffer severe malabsorption.

The luminal surface of each enterocyte is increased by *microvilli* (Fig. 21.2) from which extend a network of hair-like structures termed the *glycocalyx*. The glycocalyx and the microvilli, often known as the epithelial brush border, contain many of the enzymes responsible for the terminal digestion of carbohydrate and protein, while the special carrier proteins necessary for the absorption of hexose sugars, amino acids, vitamins, minerals and electrolytes are situated on the surface of the microvilli. The core of the microvilli contains contractile filaments that may aid absorption by pumping absorbed material into the cytosol.

The enterocytes are joined together at their luminal poles by tight junctions (Fig. 21.2). The tight junctions and the lateral intercellular spaces contain the channels through which most water and electrolytes cross the epithelium.

Mitosis takes place in the depressions between the villi, known as the crypts. These are lined by immature enterocytes, which are thought to secrete water and electrolytes into the lumen. As these enterocytes mature, they migrate slowly up the crypts to the villus to take the place of effete enterocytes that are constantly being extruded from the villous tips. Climbing the

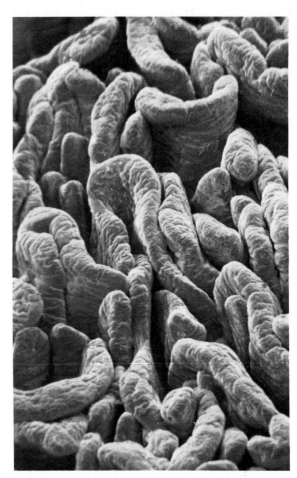

Fig. 21.1 Scanning electron micrograph ($\times$ 72) of the small intestinal surface in a normal subject (by courtesy of K G Carr and P G Toner).

villous escalator, they acquire more microvilli and develop the enzymes responsible for digestion and absorption. The time for a cell to migrate up the villus and be extruded at the tip is about 5 days. Normally the mitotic rate matches the extrusion rate and the length of the villus remains constant. A reduction in

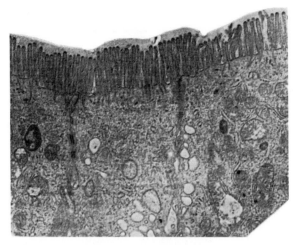

Fig. 21.2 Transmission electron micrograph ($\times$ 80 000) of the surface of a human small intestinal enterocyte showing microvilli (MV), glycocalyx (G) and the tight junctions between the cells (TJ).

villous length occurs during starvation (which slows mitosis) and in coeliac disease (in which mature cells are destroyed). The crypts also contain Paneth cells, which probably secrete bacteriolytic enzymes, and enterochromaffin cells, which are thought to release neuroendocrine transmitters.

The small intestine is subdivided into the duodenum (the first 25 cm), the jejunum (the next 125 cm) and the ileum (the last 75 cm). This division is somewhat arbitrary, but certain important differences exist between the three regions. The duodenum is retroperitoneal and contains submucosal glands (Brunner's glands). The duodenum and jejunum contain prominent semi-lunar folds that amplify the surface area. The ileum has smaller villi and fewer folds. The transit of chyme through the ileum is slow compared with that in the jejunum. This fact may allow sufficient epithelial contact for substances that are transported slowly across the epithelium to be absorbed. The ileum also has special mechanisms for absorbing vitamin B12 and bile salts.

Colon
The colon is adapted for the extraction of salt and water and for the bacterial salvage of unabsorbed carbohydrate by conversion to readily absorbable short-chain fatty acids. These processes require that the material remains in the colonic lumen for at least two days. The colon is a commodious, sacculated tube. Its surface is flat, but punctuated by openings leading to closely packed tubular pits, analogous to the crypts in the small intestine. Mitosis takes place at the base of these pits. The epithelium consists predominantly of

columnar cells, called *colonocytes*, and mucus-secreting goblet cells, with a few endocrine cells. There are many more goblet cells in the colon compared with the small intestine, presumably because mucus is needed to lubricate the passage of the solidifying faecal material and because much of it is destroyed by bacterial action.

MECHANISMS OF ABSORPTION

Absorption is the process whereby material passes from the intestinal lumen to the blood draining the intestine. It involves movement to the cell surface, passage across the enterocyte (transcellular route) or between adjacent enterocytes (paracellular route), and transport away from the epithelium by the blood or lymph.

Movement to the cell surface
Contractions of the circular and longitudinal muscle layers mix luminal contents (Chap. 18), increasing the interactions between food and digestive enzymes and bringing the products of digestion close to the epithelium. Mixing is impaired if the intestinal contents are very viscous, and this is probably the mechanism by which viscous polysaccharide food gums (guar, pectin) inhibit glucose absorption. Contraction of the villi may also aid absorption by mixing the lumen contents adjacent to the epithelium and by pulling nutrients down to encounter transport sites on the sides of the villi (Fig. 21.3).

Convection brings nutrients close to the epithelium, but they can only reach the transport sites on the membrane surface by simple diffusion through the layer of fluid that lies adjacent to the epithelial surface and is known as the unstirred water layer. Water-soluble substances such as glucose or amino acids diffuse easily across this barrier; fat-soluble substances such as triglycerides cannot cross this layer unless converted into a water-soluble form. The association of lipids with

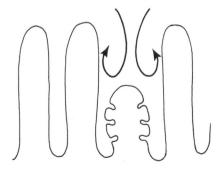

Fig. 21.3 Villous contraction drawing luminal contents into the spaces between the villi. Nutrients are thus exposed to absorptive sites on the sides as well as the tips of the villi.

bile acids to form micelles (p. 269) renders them water-soluble and able to cross the unstirred layer.

Transport across the enterocyte

Passage across the cell involves crossing two lipid membranes. Lipids can diffuse through the membranes, the rate of transport depending on the oil/water partition and on the concentration gradient. Water-soluble substances, however, can only cross lipid membranes by diffusing through aqueous gaps or pores in the membrane or by combining with a membrane-bound carrier protein (Chap. 2).

Transport between enterocytes

The lateral spaces and tight junctions provide low resistance (high conductance) channels for the passive transport of water-soluble substances of small molecular radius across the epithelium. Such substances either diffuse down concentration or electrochemical gradients or are carried along with water movement in response to hydrostatic or osmotic forces ('*solvent drag*'). Very large molecules may · also be able to permeate the epithelium in small quantities. These macromolecules probably pass through the large gaps of the villous tips, where cells are being shed (*the extrusion zones*).

Transport away in the blood or lymph

The villus is supplied by a central arteriole, which divides at the villous tip into capillaries forming a network under the epithelium and carrying blood down to veins at the root of the villus (Fig. 21.4). These capillaries are very leaky, and it is assumed that after passing across the epithelium, water-soluble substances rapidly equilibrate with the plasma in the vascular spaces.

Most fats are packaged within the enterocyte with a protein coat to form chylomicrons. These lipoproteins are not water-soluble; they pass into the extracellular spaces at the centre of the villi (the lamina propria) and are cleared from the villi via lymphatic channels called lacteals. Since lymphatic vessels contain valves, the pumping action of villous contractions may propel chylomicrons down the lacteals. Chylomicrons eventually pass via the thoracic duct to enter the subclavian vein in the neck.

The effect of intestinal motor activity on absorption

Gastrointestinal motor activity regulates intestinal absorption by controlling the exposure of nutrients to digestive enzymes and the absorptive epithelium.

Gastric emptying

Emptying of food from the stomach occurs at a rate appropriate for optimal absorption of nutrients. The rate of absorption of substances such as glucose and

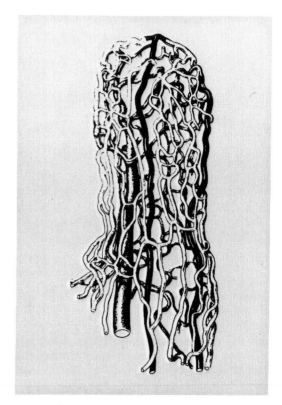

Fig. 21.4 The vascular anatomy of a human villus. The dark vessels are the arteries and veins; the light vessels are the capillaries. (From Spanner R 1932 Handatlas und Lehrbuch der Anatomie des Menschen, Academis Verlagsgesellschaft, Leipzig).

certain drugs that are rapidly transported across the duodenal epithelium is limited by the rate of delivery from the stomach.

Contact area

After the first portion of the meal has left the stomach, it passes rapidly along the small intestine. The rest of the meal appears to travel down the small intestine more slowly. The spreading out of the initial part of the meal probably enhances the initial rate of absorption by exposing nutrients to a large number of absorptive sites.

Residence or contact time

Normally food remains in the small intestine for about 6 hours. This is normally enough time for absorption of about 90 per cent of nutrients to occur. Excessive motor activity may reduce the time food spends in the intestine and leads to incomplete absorption. The degree of impairment of absorption depends on how rapidly a substance is transported across the epithelium; the absorption of slowly transported substances is

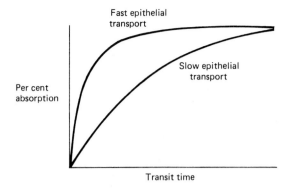

Fig. 21.5 The relation between the transit time down the small intestine and the degree of absorption of two substances: one that is rapidly transported and one that is slowly transported across the intestinal epithelium.

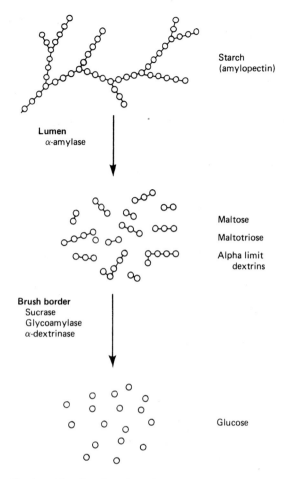

Fig. 21.6 The digestion of starch.

limited by transit time to a greater extent than the absorption of rapidly transported substances (Fig. 21.5).

The presence of unabsorbed food, particularly fat, in the ileum activates a mechanism to slow small bowel transit (Chap. 18). As food remains longer in the small intestine the degree of absorption is increased.

Mixing

Contractions of the muscle layers (Chap. 18) mix intestinal contents and enhance absorption by increasing the interaction between food and digestive enzymes and between products of digestion and the intestinal epithelium.

Absorption of carbohydrate

Most of the carbohydrate in the diet is in the form of starch but most diets also include sucrose, lactose and fructose.

Luminal digestion

Starch is largely broken down in the intestinal lumen by pancreatic amylase to maltose, maltotriose and alpha-limit dextrins (Fig. 21.6). The enterocytes have no carrier systems for absorption of these oligosaccharides, and only very small amounts can diffuse across the epithelium. Instead, the oligosaccharides and the dietary disaccharides, lactose and sucrose are hydrolysed to their constituent monosaccharides by enzymes situated within the glycocalyx or on the surface of the microvilli (Table 21.7).

This arrangement means that the monosaccharides are released in high concentrations adjacent to their carrier sites, a feature that may explain the observation that sugar absorption is faster when carbohydrate is present in the lumen as disaccharide than as monosaccharide.

Table 21.7 The brush-border enzymes concerned with the digestion of dietary carbohydrate

Enzyme	Substrate	Product
Alphadextrinase	Alpha limit dextrins	Maltose and maltotriose
Sucrase	Sucrose	Glucose and fructose
	Maltose Maltotriose	Glucose
Glycoamylase	Maltose Maltotriose Alpha limit dextrins	Glucose
Lactase	Lactose	Glucose and galactose

Lactase deficiency

The brush-border enzymes responsible for the terminal digestion of starch and the hydrolysis of sucrose are present at high concentrations and remain throughout life. Lactase is present at much lower concentrations and in most of the world's population falls to very low levels soon after weaning. In northern Europeans, however, lactase persists throughout life. If a person who has lost lactase drinks milk, the lactose remains in the intestinal lumen, retains fluid and may cause an osmotic diarrhoea.

Glucose and galactose absorption

Glucose and galactose are absorbed rapidly from the small intestine by an active carrier-mediated process, which requires the presence of sodium in the luminal fluid. It is thought that sodium and glucose (or galactose) combine with a common carrier on the brush-border membrane. The active entry of sugars into the cell from the mucosal surface is propelled by the energy supplied by the diffusion of sodium down its electrochemical gradient from a high luminal concentration to a low cellular concentration. This is known as the sodium gradient hypothesis (Fig. 21.8).

The sodium gradient across the brush-border membrane is maintained by the activity of an outwardly directed sodium pump situated on the basolateral membrane of the cell. This 'pump' is thought to be a sodium-potassium ATPase, which utilises the energy gained from the breakdown of ATP to pump sodium out of the cell and to pump potassium into the cell in a ratio of 3:2. Glucose and galactose are transported out of the cell at the basolateral pole by carrier-mediated facilitated diffusion that does not require the presence of sodium.

The active carrier-mediated absorption of glucose and galactose resembles enzyme interactions and obeys saturation kinetics; it is possible to define the maximum rate of transport (J_{max}) and an apparent Km (the concentration of substrate at which transport is half the J_{max}) (Fig. 21.9). As with enzyme kinetics, J_{max} can be regarded as the capacity of the transport system while the apparent Km reflects the affinity of the carrier for the substrate. Substances with a lower apparent Km have a greater affinity for the carrier system than those with a high Km.

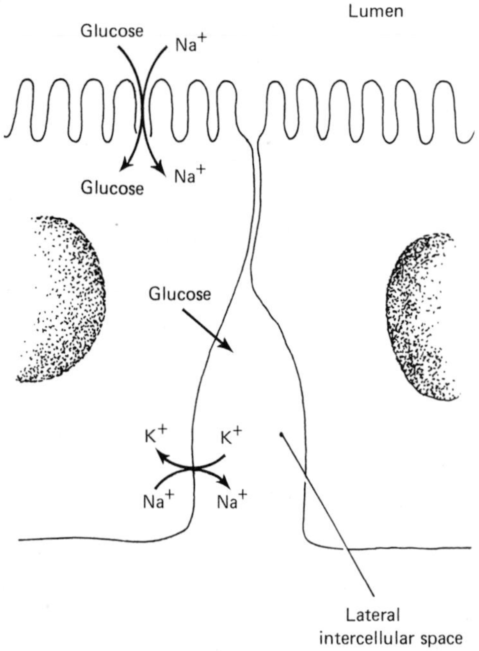

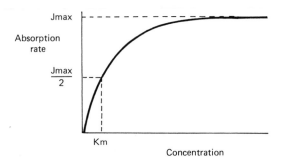

Fig. 21.9 The kinetics of active carrier-mediated absorption of glucose or galactose.

Fructose absorption

Fructose is absorbed by facilitated or carrier-mediated diffusion (Chap. 2). Between 20 and 50 per cent of the fructose that is absorbed from human small intestine is converted within the enterocytes to glucose.

Absorption of protein

Protein, available for digestion in the small intestine, is derived not only from food, but also from desquamated cells and secreted enzymes.

Intraluminal digestion

Initial digestion of protein occurs in the stomach through the action of pepsin, secreted from the chief

Fig. 21.8 The sodium gradient hypothesis for the absorption of glucose. Glucose and sodium combine with a common carrier situated on the brush border membrane. The entry of glucose into the cell is linked to the diffusion of sodium into the cell down its concentration gradient. The sodium concentration in the cell is kept low by an outwardly directed sodium pump, expelling sodium into the lateral intercellular space in exchange for potassium; glucose leaves the cell by facilitated diffusion.

cells of the gastric glands (p. 255). Most digestion, however, takes place in the small intestine by the action of pancreatic proteases. Endopeptidases, such as trypsin, chymotrypsin and elastase, hydrolyse the peptide bonds in the middle of the peptide chain, breaking it up into smaller units. Exopeptidases then remove amino acids sequentially from the carboxyl terminal. This leaves a mixture of small peptides (2 to 6 residues in length) and amino acids.

Pancreatic proteases are secreted as inactive precursors and are activated by hydrolysis of specific peptide bonds. Enterokinase, secreted from the duodenal and jejunal epithelium, activates trypsin, which then helps to activate the other enzymes.

Some of the small peptides are broken down in the brush border by amino-peptidases, which remove amino acids sequentially from the amino terminal. This yields a mixture of free amino acids and tri- or dipeptides; all of these can then be absorbed by active sodium-dependent, carrier-mediated processes.

The mechanisms that mediate the intact absorption of di- or tripeptides are independent of those that mediate the absorption of free amino acids. Nitrogen uptake is faster when protein is fed as a mixture of peptides than as an equivalent amino acid mixture.

Peptides, taken up by the enterocytes, are largely broken down to their constituent amino acids by peptidases within the cell.

Absorption of amino acids

Free amino acids are absorbed across the mucosal membrane of the enterocyte by carrier-mediated, sodium-dependent active transport processes similar to those described for glucose and galactose. Separate carrier systems are thought to exist for the neutral (monoamino-monocarboxylic), basic (diaminomonocarboxylic) and acidic (monoamino-dicarboxylic) amino acids, and for the imino acids (proline and hydroxyproline). Patients with the congenital absorption defect known as *Hartnup disease* cannot absorb certain neutral amino acids, but can absorb basic or acidic amino acids normally, while patients with *cystinuria* have a defect in absorption of basic amino acids, but absorb neutral and acidic amino acids normally. In each case, the amino acid that cannot be absorbed when presented in the free form may be absorbed normally as components of dipeptides.

Amino acids cross the serosal membrane by facilitated diffusion and leave the intestine in the portal blood. Some changes in amino acid content occur within the intestinal cell. Aspartic acid and glutamic acid are transaminated to alanine, cystine is converted to cysteine and arginine is converted to aspartic acid.

Absorption of fat

Most of the fat in the diet is in the form of triglycerides. The diet also includes phospholipids, cholesterol and the fat-soluble vitamins A, D, E and K.

Triglyceride molecules are insoluble in water and tend to aggregate together in droplets. In the presence of protein, gastric contractions disperse these droplets into a fat emulsion with a particle size of 200 to 5000 nm.

Fat digestion

Between 10 and 30 per cent of dietary triglyceride is digested by *lingual lipase* secreted from von Ebner's glands near the back of the tongue. There is also a lipase secreted from the stomach, but in man this only hydrolyses short-chain triglycerides (less than 10 carbon atom chain length). Most triglyceride digestion takes place in the small intestine as a result of the action of pancreatic lipase. This enzyme is inactive in the presence of physiological concentrations of bile acids, which line up along the oil–water interface and displace lipase from the triglycerides. The enzyme, *colipase*, which is secreted from the pancreas with lipase, is not displaced from the oil–water interface and activates lipase by anchoring it to its substrate. Colipase is secreted as the precursor procolipase, which needs to be activated by trypsin before fat digestion can take place.

Triglycerides resemble a tuning fork in structure, with the fatty acid chain in the 2 position as the handle and the chains in the 1 and 3 positions as the prongs. Triglycerides within oil droplets are thought to line up in ordered ranks. Lipase splits off the fatty acids at the 1 and 3 positions, leaving the monoglyceride (Fig. 21.10). This exposes the carboxyl and alcohol groupings on the fatty acid and monoglyceride, allowing water to penetrate the oil phase and causing the droplet to swell (*viscous isotropic phase*). Pairs of these chains then line up and are brought into intraluminal solution by combining with bile acid in a physico-chemical complex called a *mixed micelle*. This is a stable water-soluble collection of bile acids, fatty acids, 2-monoglycerides, cholesterol, phospholipids and fat-soluble vitamins between 3 and 10 nm in diameter. The molecules are arranged so that the hydrophilic groups lie towards the outside in contact with the watery medium and the hydrophobic groups are on the inside (Fig. 22.10, p. 285). Mixed micelles form spontaneously when the products of fat digestion exist with a concentration of bile acids above a critical micellar concentration of 2 to 5 mmol/l. Non-polar lipids such as cholesterol and fat-soluble vitamins remain in the interior of the micelle between the lipid chains.

The pancreas secretes other enzymes that hydrolyse fats. Phospholipase A_2 hydrolyses phospholipids at the 2 position to yield fatty acid and lysophospholipid. It

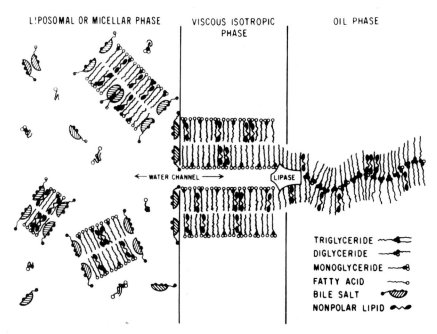

Fig. 21.10 The 'zipper model' of fat digestion (from Patton J 1982 In Johnson L R (ed) Physiology of the Gastrointestinal Tract. Raven Press, New York, p. 1138). A detailed illustration of the structure of a mixed micelle is given in Fig. 22.10, p. 285.

is secreted as a proenzyme and is activated by the tryptic removal of a seven–amino acid fragment at the N-terminal. Pancreatic non-specific lipase, also known as cholesterol esterase, can hydrolyse triglyceride at the 2 position and can also hydrolyse cholesterol esters and vitamin esters. Both of these enzymes are much more active on dispersed or micellar fat, and so require the presence of bile acid for their full activity.

Human milk contains a lipase that assists its own digestion. This enzyme is protected against pancreatic proteolysis by bile acids, which are also needed for its hydrolytic activity. Its absence from cow's milk is one of the nutritional advantages of infant feeding with breast milk (p. 349).

Epithelial absorption of fat
The micelle is important for the absorption of fat because it presents the fat to the epithelium in a dispersed water-soluble form that can readily diffuse through the layer of unstirred water to reach the cell surface. There the micelle is disrupted and the lipids are thought to partition first into the aqueous phase and then diffuse through the lipid membrane into the cell. Some cholesterol and vitamin K may be actively transported into the cell on a carrier. The bile acid returns to the lumen where it may form more micelles with the fat emulsion.

Long-chain fatty acids and 2-monoglycerides are re-converted to triglyceride inside the enterocyte by enzymes in the smooth endoplasmic reticulum (Fig. 21.11). Upon entering the cell, the long-chain fatty acids combine with a specific fatty acid binding protein. This combination keeps the intracellular concentration of fatty acid low, facilitating the diffusion of more free fatty acid into the cell; it is also needed for the synthesis of triglyceride. In the major synthetic pathway, fatty acid is first activated by fatty acid CoA ligase. The combination of fatty acid with first the monoglyceride and then the diglyceride is catalysed by monoglyceride and diglyceride acyltransferases. The triglyceride droplet so formed combines with lipoprotein formed from phospholipid and apoprotein B (synthesised within the cell) to form a globular mass called a *chylomicron*. The chylomicron is packaged in a secretory vesicle and crosses the lateral cell membrane by exocytosis. Chylomicrons are transported away from the villus via the lacteals rather than the portal blood. One explanation for this is that lipid-soluble chylomicrons pass through the capillary membrane and become concentrated in the lamina propria at the villous tip. They escape from this site by being pumped down the lacteals when the villus contracts.

Lysophospholipids, cholesterol, vitamin A and 25 per cent of vitamin D are esterified in the enterocyte but vitamins K and E remain unaltered. They are all packaged together with triglyceride as chylomicrons and

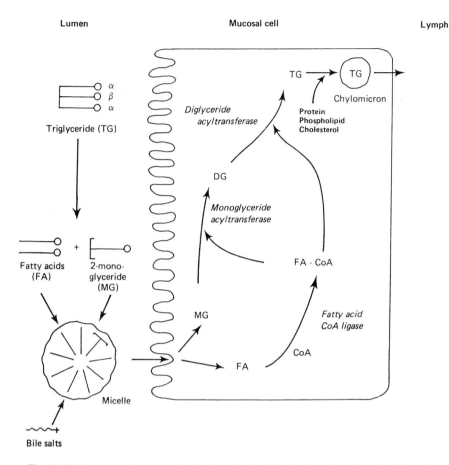

Fig. 21.11 The events that occur in the intestinal cell during the absorption of triglyceride.

leave the intestine in the lymph. Some cholesterol is synthesised within the enterocyte, but the amount is reduced if the diet is rich in cholesterol.

Absorption of triglyceride is impaired by a deficiency of pancreatic enzymes or bile acids, by a reduction in intestinal surface area as in coeliac disease, or by lymphatic obstruction. There is also a rare congenital defect of fat absorption called *abetalipoproteinaemia*, in which apoprotein B synthesis is deficient and as a result triglyceride accumulates within the enterocyte as visible fat droplets. All such disorders cause weight loss and excessive amounts of fat in the stool (*steatorrhoea*).

Medium-chain triglycerides (MCT; 8 to 14 carbon chain length) can circumvent many of the steps involved in the digestion and the absorption of long-chain triglyceride. They do not need to be hydrolysed by pancreatic lipase, they are more soluble in aqueous solutions and can diffuse through the unstirred layer without the assistance of bile acids, they are able to enter the enterocyte intact, and they leave the villus by the blood stream rather than the lacteal vessels. Thus feeding

MCT can provide an important source of dietary lipid when absorption of long-chain triglyceride is impaired.

Absorption of bile acids
No specific mechanism for the absorption of bile acids exists in the jejunum; once the micelle has unloaded its fat, bile acids diffuse back into the lumen where they may form more micelles with the fat emulsion. This shuttling of fat across the unstirred layer probably occurs several times before most of the bile acids are finally absorbed in the terminal ileum by an active carrier-mediated sodium-dependent mechanism similar to that responsible for glucose or amino acid absorption. A small amount of unconjugated bile acid is absorbed passively in the jejunum.

Enterohepatic circulation of bile acid
The absorbed bile acids pass in the portal blood to the liver where they are again incorporated into the hepatic bile, which is stored in the gall bladder and re-excreted

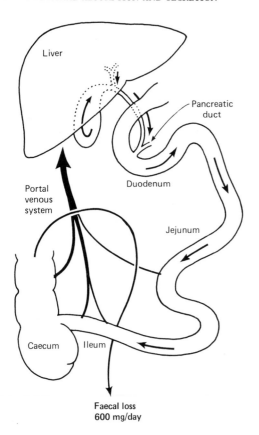

Fig. 21.12 The enterohepatic circulation of bile acids. Loss of bile acid in the faeces is normally balanced by synthesis from cholesterol in the liver. Most bile acids are actively reabsorbed in the terminal ileum, though small amounts of unconjugated bile acids are absorbed by non-specific mechanisms in the jejunum or colon.

into the duodenum. This is known as the enterohepatic circulation of bile acids (Fig. 21.12). The total bile acid pool is approximately 5 to 10 mmol (2 to 4 g) and recirculates between 3 and 12 times daily (about 3 times during digestion of a large meal). Approximately 5 per cent of bile acids escape absorption in the ileum and enter the colon, where they are deconjugated and dehydroxylated by bacteria to the monohydroxy (lithocholate) and dihydroxy (deoxycholate) bile acids. Lithocholate acid is very insoluble and is lost in the faeces but deoxycholate is fat-soluble and can pass through the colonic membrane into the portal blood to the liver where it joins the bile acid pool.

The passage of small amounts of bile acid into the colon stimulates colonic secretion and propulsion and may act as 'nature's laxative' to promote a regular bowel action. The bile acids that are lost in the faeces are replaced by synthesis in the liver.

Absorption of nutrients in the colon

The colon can be regarded as a fermenting vat, full of bacteria, most of them anaerobic. The large capacity of the colon, the stagnation of its contents and the ready availability of an energy source from unabsorbed food provide an environment ideal for bacterial proliferation. These bacteria use their own enzymes to metabolise luminal nutrients to products that may be absorbed in the colon and contribute to the energy intake of the host.

Carbohydrate

A significant proportion of dietary carbohydrate escapes absorption in the small intestine and passes into the colon. This includes the complex polysaccharides that comprise dietary fibre and are resistant to digestion by pancreatic enzymes, up to 10 per cent of the starch and contributions from mucus and extruded epithelial cells. There are no specific carrier mechanisms for the absorption of sugars in the colon and the relatively impermeable epithelium inhibits absorption by diffusion. However, unabsorbed carbohydrate can be converted by bacteria to short-chain fatty acids (SCFA), which are rapidly absorbed across the colonic epithelium. Absorption of SCFA in the large intestine probably contributes between 10 and 20 per cent of basal energy requirements in man.

Protein

Organic nitrogen enters the colon from exogenous dietary sources and from endogenous sources such as desquamated cells, enzymes, mucus, and urea, which diffuses into the colon from the blood. Much of the nitrogen that enters the colon is probably taken up by bacteria and incorporated into bacterial protein. However, about 25 per cent of the urea produced in the body is degraded by colonic bacteria to ammonia, which can be absorbed into the portal blood by non-ionic diffusion and reconverted in the liver to non-essential amino acids.

Fat

Little is known of the digestion and absorption of fat in the colon, but many bacterial species possess lipases that can digest triglyceride. Colonic bacteria can hydrolyse fatty acids to hydroxy fatty acids, which resemble castor oil. Hydroxy fatty acids induce colonic secretion and may be responsible for diarrhoea associated with fat malabsorption.

Gastrointestinal gas

The gastrointestinal tract contains about 250 ml of gas, consisting almost entirely of nitrogen, hydrogen, methane and CO_2 (Fig. 21.13). Smelly substances, such

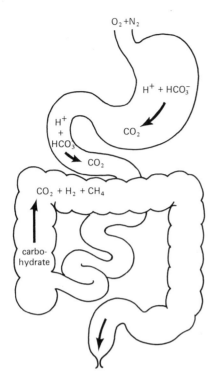

Fig. 21.13 The origin of gas in the bowel. Nitrogen and oxygen enter in swallowed air and CO_2 is formed in the stomach and duodenum by neutralisation of acid with bicarbonate. Fermentation of carbohydrate by anaerobic bacteria in the colon yields hydrogen, methane and CO_2.

as hydrogen sulphide, are only present in trace quantities.

Source of gas

Nitrogen enters the gut in swallowed air. It also diffuses down its concentration gradient from the blood, where the partial pressure of nitrogen is approximately 500 mmHg, to parts of the intestine that contain other gases, where the partial pressure of nitrogen may be near zero.

Very large amounts of CO_2 may be produced in the stomach and duodenum by neutralisation of gastric acid with bicarbonate secreted into the duodenum, stomach or saliva, but nearly all of this CO_2 is absorbed in the small intestine. Hydrogen and methane cannot be produced by mammalian cells but can be produced in large amounts together with CO_2 in the colon as a result of the bacteria fermentation of unabsorbed carbohydrate. Hydrogen is rapidly absorbed into the blood stream and excreted in the breath. Measurement of breath hydrogen concentrations are used in clinical practice to signal the arrival of a meal containing unabsorbed carbohydrate at the colon (see Fig. 18.14,

p. 249) and to demonstrate the malabsorption of carbohydrate. Methane is only produced in about 30 per cent of healthy subjects, presumably because most people do not harbour methanogenic bacteria.

Composition of faeces

Faeces normally contain about 80 per cent water and 20 per cent solids. The solids comprise bacteria (70 per cent), undigestable cell wall remnants and fibre, fat, protein, inorganic matter, bile pigment and extruded epithelial cells.

Up to 7 g of fat is excreted daily in the stools of healthy subjects. Most of this is in the form of magnesium or calcium soaps. About half of the fat in faeces comes from bile and from desquamated and bacterial cells during intestinal transit.

The brown colour of faeces is caused by stercobilin and urobilin, produced by the action of colonic bacteria on bilirubin. The odour of faeces varies from one person to another and in the same person at different times. It depends on the composition of bacterial flora and on the food eaten. The offensive components include indole, skatole, mercaptans and hydrogen sulphide.

Absorption of vitamins

The absorption of fat-soluble vitamins is described with the absorption of fat (p. 269). Little is known of the absorptive mechanisms for most water-soluble vitamins, though active-transport systems have been described for ascorbic acid and for thiamin. Colonic bacteria produce several water-soluble vitamins (folate, cobalamin and pyridoxine) but the extent to which these are absorbed is uncertain. The mechanisms for cobalamin and folate absorption have been extensively studied.

Cobalamin

Absorption of cobalamin (vitamin B_{12}) in man is a complicated process requiring the binding of the vitamin to a specific glycoprotein, *intrinsic factor* (IF), secreted by the parietal cells of the stomach. The complex of cobalamin and IF then travels down the intestine and binds to the enterocytes of the ileum, where it is absorbed by endocytosis. Cobalamin separates from the intrinsic factor within the cell and binds to another glycoprotein, *transcobalamin II*, which is thought to be necessary for transport in the portal blood and for subsequent binding to target cells. One remarkable feature of cobalamin absorption is the long delay between binding of the complex and appearance of cobalamin in the portal blood.

Failure to absorb cobalamin causes *pernicious anaemia*, associated with a failure of red blood cell maturation and neurological abnormalities (p. 41). Since the liver normally contains considerable stores of cobalamin it may take as long as 3 years before malabsorption of cobalamin causes pernicious anaemia. The commonest cause of pernicious anaemia is lack of secretion of intrinsic factor due to gastric resection or gastric atrophy. Pernicious anaemia may also occur after ileal resection or disease, or because of overgrowth of the small intestine by bacteria that split the cobalamin-IF complex and utilise cobalamin.

Folate

Most folic acid exists in the diet as pteroylpolyglutamic acid in which pteroic acid is linked to a chain of glutamic acid molecules (Fig. 21.14). Pteroylpolyglutamic acid is hydrolysed to the monoglutamate in the glycocalyx or mucosal surface of the jejunal enterocyte. Monoglutamate can then be absorbed by a saturable mechanism and is converted to methyltetrahydrofolate in the enterocyte. The uptake of monoglutamate by the enterocyte is facilitated by a slightly acid environment (pH 6) in the luminal fluid adjacent to the epithelium.

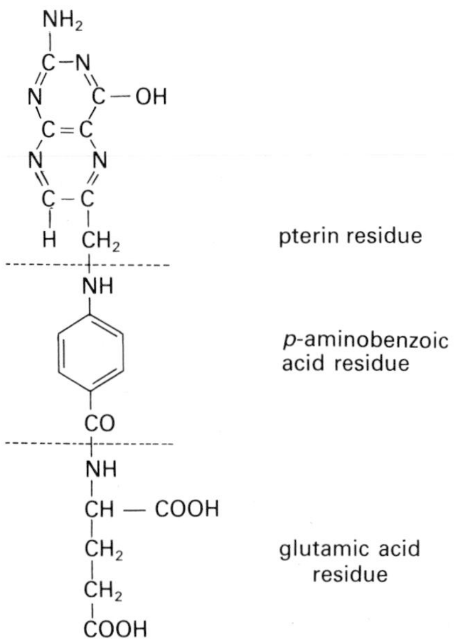

Fig. 21.14 Structure of folic acid. In the tissues, the molecule usually has several glutamic acid residues.

Calcium absorption

Absorption of calcium occurs predominantly in the upper small intestine. Most calcium is transported across the enterocyte and the rate of uptake is limited by carrier-mediated entry at the brush border. This process is enhanced by calcitriol, the activated form of vitamin D produced in the kidney (p. 363). Calcium is actively extruded at the basolateral pole of the enterocyte.

Calcium absorption is stimulated by glucose and other sugars, and inhibited by substances such as fats, oxalates, phosphates and phytates, which form insoluble complexes with calcium in the gut lumen.

Iron absorption

Iron is absorbed in the upper small intestine and its absorption is strongly influenced by intraluminal factors. Gastric acid and reducing agents such as ascorbic acid facilitate iron absorption by converting ferric salts to the more soluble ferrous salts. Bicarbonate and possibly other constituents of pancreatic juice inhibit iron absorption probably by favouring the formation of insoluble precipitates. This may be prevented by bile, which tends to keep iron in solution by forming low-molecular-weight ligands with it. Phytates, phosphates, oxalates and carbonates also form insoluble precipitates with iron, decreasing its absorption, while certain sugars and amino acids increase iron absorption by increasing its solubility. The absorption of haemoglobin iron is not affected by the same intraluminal factors as that of other forms of dietary iron. It is broken down by pancreatic enzymes to haem, which is absorbed intact, releasing the free iron inside the enterocyte.

Inorganic iron is absorbed by the epithelium of the duodenum and upper jejunum by a process that is closely regulated according to body requirements. Uptake of iron at the mucosal membrane occurs by an active carrier-mediated transport mechanism. The iron is then either diverted to a soluble pool, from which it is transferred across the serosal membrane, or it forms a complex with a protein, *apoferritin*, within the cell to become insoluble ferritin. Iron travels in the plasma loosely bound to a beta globulin, transferrin. A large proportion of the iron absorbed is taken up by the bone marrow and is used in the formation of haemoglobin.

Excess iron combines with apoferritin in all cells of the body, but particularly in the liver, to form ferritin. When stores of ferritin are saturated, iron is not released from transferrin and further uptake from the enterocyte is inhibited. In consequence, more iron is converted to ferritin in the enterocyte and is lost when the cell is extruded at the villous tip. In situations of iron deficiency iron is readily removed from the transferrin, facilitating uptake from the intestinal epithelium.

Transport of fluid

About 9 litres of fluid containing about 50 g of sodium enter the gut each day. Approximately 1.5 litres come from the diet. The remainder comes from salivary, gastric, pancreatic, biliary and intestinal secretions. The major part of this fluid (about 8 litres) is absorbed in the small intestine; some is absorbed in the large intestine (about 1 litre) and only a very small proportion is voided in the stool (about 0.1 litre). If larger volumes enter the gut, the intestine can adapt to absorb as much as 20 litres a day.

Standing gradient hypothesis for water absorption

Fluid is absorbed from the intestine in response to osmotic gradients set up by the active transport of sodium, hexose sugars and amino acids. According to the standing gradient hypothesis, the transport of sodium and non-electrolytes across the enterocyte establishes a hypertonic zone in the spaces between the cells (lateral intercellular spaces), particularly towards the apices, where the lateral membranes are close together. This encourages water to flow into these spaces from the lumen mainly through the so-called 'tight' junctions (Fig. 21.15), which connect adjacent cells at their mucosal poles but also through the cells themselves. The distension of the lateral spaces by the osmotic influx of water increases the hydrostatic pressure, and fluid moves in the direction of least resistance towards the capillary. Continued transport of solute into the apices of the lateral spaces maintains the osmotic force. Backflow into the lumen is restricted by the tight junctions between the cells. This mechanism allows absorption of water to take place against an adverse lumen-to-plasma osmotic gradient as long as the osmolality in the lateral space is higher than in the lumen.

While the standing gradient hypothesis offers a plausible explanation for water absorption in epithelia such

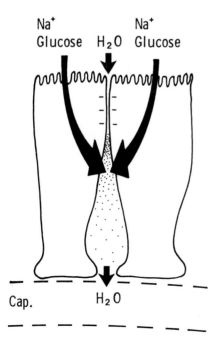

Fig. 21.15 The standing gradient hypothesis to explain fluid absorption from the gut.

as the gall bladder and colon, which are relatively impermeable, it is perhaps less satisfactory for epithelia such as the jejunum, where the leakiness of the 'tight' junctions would allow more water and electrolytes to leak back into the lumen.

Transport of electrolytes

Passive transport through aqueous channels

Most passive movement of electrolytes across the epithelium is thought to take place through aqueous channels between adjacent cells (paracellular route). These aqueous channels in the human jejunum (0.7 to 0.9 nm in diameter) are larger than those in the ileum (0.4 nm) or the colon (0.2 nm). This difference explains why fluid is absorbed more rapidly in the jejunum than in the remainder of the intestine, and why most of the absorption of sodium, potassium and small non-electrolytes such as urea in the jejunum is coupled to the osmotic influx of water by the process of solvent drag. It also explains the rapid osmotic equilibration of hypotonic or hypertonic solutions in the lumen of the duodenum and jejunum. On the other hand, the presence of large paracellular aqueous channels also means that active transcellular absorption of sodium in the jejunum cannot take place against high electrochemical gradients since the actively transported ions would tend to leak back between the cells into the lumen.

In the ileum, where aqueous channels are narrower, fluid cannot be absorbed as rapidly as in the jejunum, and solvent drag is a less important mechanism for absorption of electrolytes. Thus total absorption of sodium is less rapid, but transcellular absorption of sodium can take place against higher concentration gradients in the ileum than in the jejunum.

In the colon, where aqueous channels are even smaller, nearly all the sodium is absorbed by the active transcellular route and continues to be absorbed even at luminal concentrations as low as 15 mmol/l (a tenfold plasma-to-lumen concentration gradient) and adverse electrical gradients of up to 80 mV. The tightness of the aqueous channels also enables very high osmolalities to be generated within the lateral spaces, allowing water to be extracted from the faecal mass against large transepithelial osmotic gradients. Although this mechanism may not permit rapid absorption of salt and water, faecal material usually remains in contact with colonic mucosa for several days, which is more than enough time to solidify the stool and extract most of the sodium.

Thus, the properties of the paracellular aqueous channels dictate that the more proximal regions of the intestine are adapted to the rapid absorption of a large quantity of fluid and electrolytes while the more distal regions of the intestine are adapted for extraction of salt and water against high electrochemical and osmotic gradients.

Transcellular Ion Transport

Most electrolytes can only cross the intestinal cells by an active process involving expenditure of energy. This is because intracellular ion concentrations are either much higher or much lower than the extracellular concentrations in the plasma and lumen and the cytosol is some 40 mV negative to plasma and luminal fluids. Thus although an electrolyte may be able to cross one membrane by simple or facilitated diffusion, an active mechanism is needed to cross the other.

Jejunum

The absorption of salt and water from the jejunum is greatly increased in the presence of actively transported sugars, amino acids and peptides. Sodium interacts with the non-electrolyte on a common carrier mechanism on the mucosal membrane. The energy for the transfer of both into the cell is provided by the inwardly directed sodium gradient (p. 10). Sodium is then pumped out of the cell into the lateral intercellular space by an ion exchange mechanism, thought to be coupled to a specific sodium- and potassium-dependent ATPase. The osmotic gradient set up by the transcellular passage of sodium and sugars or amino acids then encourages water and more electrolytes to enter via the paracellular route. This mechanism accounts for the important therapeutic effect of glucose and electrolyte solutions in countering fluid losses and preventing fluid and electrolyte depletion in severe diarrhoeal states such as cholera.

In the absence of actively transported sugars and amino acids, active jejunal absorption of sodium is thought to be electrically neutral and mediated via a sodium/hydrogen ion exchange pump at the mucosal membrane (Fig. 21.16). Hydrogen ion is generated within the cell from CO_2 and H_2O by the action of carbonic anhydrase, and is accompanied by the formation of bicarbonate, which leaves the cell to enter the plasma. Increasing the luminal concentration of bicarbonate encourages sodium absorption by neutralising the hydrogen ion and increasing the movement of hydrogen ion from cell to lumen in exchange for sodium. The result is an apparent increase in sodium and bicarbonate absorption by a mechanism similar to that for hydrogen ion secretion by the renal tubules (Chap. 14).

Ileum

In the ileum the coupling of active transcellular sodium transport with sugar and amino acid absorption does not contribute to the net transfer of sodium across the epithelium. This can be explained by a tighter paracellular pathway, which not only allows less sodium to enter by solvent drag but also means that active sodium transport generates a larger potential difference (PD) across the epithelium, causing sodium that has entered the lateral space via the cellular route to diffuse back into the lumen via the paracellular route.

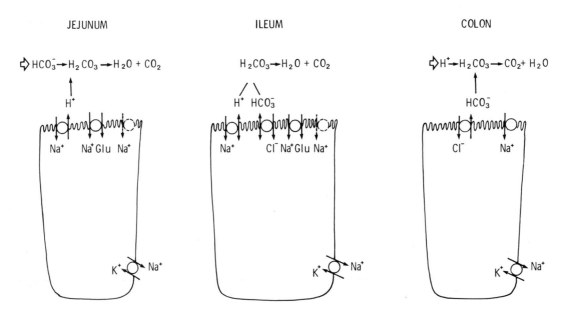

Fig. 21.16 The mechanisms for transcellular absorption of electrolytes across the epithelium of the jejunum, ileum and colon. In the jejunum, the hydrogen ion secreted from the enterocyte is neutralised by the bicarbonate secreted in the pancreatic juice or bile. In the colon, the bicarbonate ion is neutralised by hydrogen ion, generated by fermentation of carbohydrate to volatile fatty acids.

Table 21.17 Comparison the composition of ileal effluent and faeces and typical amounts of fluid and ions entering and leaving the colon

Component	Concentrations (mmol/l)		Amount		Amount absorbed in colon
	Ileum	Stool	Entering colon	Leaving colon	
Water	—	—	1000 ml	100 ml	900 ml
Sodium	130	10	130 mmol	1 mmol	129 mmol
Potassium	5	150	5 mmol	15 mmol	−10 mmol
Chloride	100	30	100 mmol	3 mmol	97 mmol
Bicarbonate	35	0	35 mmol	0 mmol	35 mmol
Acetate/propionate	0	50	0 mmol	5 mmol	−5 mmol

Negative sign = net secretion or net production

Most electrolyte absorption in the human ileum occurs by a double exchange process, which does not change the transepithelial PD (Fig. 21.18). The absorption of sodium in exchange for hydrogen ion is coupled with the absorption of chloride in exchange for bicarbonate. In addition, some sodium may be absorbed by an active mechanism that is not coupled to the transport of another ion and so generates a PD across the epithelium.

Potassium is transported across the intestinal epithelium by diffusion or solvent drag along the paracellular route.

Colon

The colon absorbs sodium and chloride and secretes bicarbonate against electrochemical gradients. Sodium is absorbed by an active carrier-mediated mechanism that is not linked to the transfer of hydrogen and is not influenced by the intraluminal presence of glucose, amino acids or bicarbonate. The rate of absorption is stimulated by increased plasma levels of aldosterone.

Chloride is absorbed by the colonic epithelium in exchange for bicarbonate. Potassium is the dominant cation of faecal fluid (Table 21.17). The surprisingly large epithelial conductance for potassium (approximately ten times that for sodium and chloride) suggests the existence of specific channels for potassium in the epithelium, while the accumulation of potassium in the colonic lumen is favoured by the high electrical gradient (lumen negative) set up by sodium transport. It is also possible that dead or damaged epithelial cells and mucus rich in potassium contribute to the high luminal potassium concentrations.

INTESTINAL SECRETION OF WATER AND ELECTROLYTES

The intestinal epithelium can secrete as well as absorb fluid and electrolytes; net salt and water transport can be regarded as the balance between an absorptive flux on the one hand and a secretory flux on the other. Absorption is thought to take place on the villi, while the crypts are the sites for secretion. Intestinal secretion may lubricate intestinal contents and wash detached brush border enzymes and immunoglobulins into the lumen. It may also serve as a protective mechanism to flush out toxins or pathogens that may damage the epithelium.

Mechanisms of secretion

Most fluid secretion is initiated by an increase in the permeability of the mucosal membrane of the enterocyte to chloride ion. Chloride enters the lumen from a high concentration within the cell accompanied by sodium, which leaks from the hypertonic lateral space into the lumen. This provides the osmotic force for flux of water, largely from the lateral spaces.

This mechanism, however, cannot sustain continuous secretion from an epithelium in vivo unless the lateral intercellular space continuously refills with fluid from the serosal side. Thus increases in capillary permeability or capillary hydrostatic pressure (filtration pressure) or both must accompany intestinal secretion.

NEUROENDOCRINE CONTROL OF FLUID AND ELECTROLYTE TRANSPORT

When the small intestine of a normal subject is perfused with a plasma-like solution, it usually absorbs salt and water. However, the rate of absorption varies widely from subject to subject and in the same subject on different test days. Some apparently normal subjects may secrete fluid into the small intestine rather than absorb it. The mechanisms of this physiological variation are unknown but it is likely that the autonomic nervous system is important. Sympathetic stimulation is thought to promote fluid absorption while vagal stimulation is thought to cause fluid secretion.

It is probable that intestinal transport is mainly controlled by local reflexes. For example, distension of the lumen or tactile stimulation induces intestinal secretion, and the secretory response to cholera toxin may be partly mediated by a nervous reflex leading to the release of vasoactive intestinal polypeptide (VIP).

Action of transmitter substances in the intestinal mucosa

A large number of polypeptides and other chemical transmitters are present in the small intestinal wall and can alter intestinal transport. Some of these substances (enkephalin, acetylcholine, noradrenaline, somatostatin and VIP) are found within nerves, while the remainder are found in cells within the mucosa or submucosa (serotonin, histamine prostaglandins).

Vasoactive intestinal polypeptide (VIP) is a very potent intestinal secretagogue. It is found in enteric neurones and can be released by vagal stimulation and by stimulation of intramural nerves. It interacts with receptors on enterocytes and may be the major neurotransmitter mediating intestinal secretion. Patients with tumours secreting VIP have voluminous diarrhoea.

Prostaglandins are produced from arachidonic acid (p. 233) and act directly on the cell to stimulate intestinal secretion and increase production of cyclic AMP. They can be released by distension of the gut wall, vagal stimulation and mucosal injury. They probably mediate intestinal secretion induced by local stimuli, and may serve to amplify the effects of other secretagogues. They are thought to contribute to the diarrhoea caused by inflammatory diseases of the bowel or by irradiation.

Adrenaline and noradrenaline act directly on the enterocyte (via alpha$_2$ receptors) to enhance absorption and reduce secretion.

Endogenous opiates probably enhance absorption and inhibit secretion by acting on enteric ganglia to inhibit the release of acetylcholine and/or VIP from postganglionic neurones.

Dihydroxy bile acids and hydroxy fatty acids are perhaps important in the induction of colonic secretion of fluid and electrolytes. These substances are formed in the colon by bacterial degradation of bile acids and lipids. They enter the colon in large quantities in disease in which the digestion or absorption of fat is inhibited or after resection of the ileum which impairs absorption of bile acid.

The cellular control of intestinal secretion

The cellular action of intestinal secretagogues appears to be mediated by an increase in intracellular levels of calcium. This occurs in two ways. Substances such as VIP and cholera toxin interact with a receptor on the cell surface, resulting in the activation of adenylate cyclase and formation of cyclic AMP. The latter releases

calcium from intracellular stores, increases calcium uptake into the cell from the extracellular fluid, and activates protein kinases, which may ultimately increase chloride permeability. Secretagogues such as serotonin or acetylcholine interact with a receptor on the cell membrane to cause hydrolysis of phospholipid components within the cell membrane and the opening of channels to allow the entry of calcium (Fig. 21.18). Calcium is then thought to activate a specific calcium-dependent regulator protein, called calmodulin, which in turn activates protein kinases to result in enhanced chloride permeability. Some bacterial toxins can interact with a receptor on the mucosal surface, activating guanylate cyclase and producing cyclic guanosine monophosphate (GMP), which also activates protein kinase.

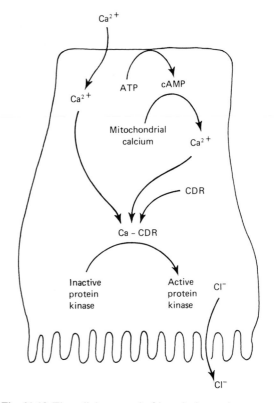

Fig. 21.18 The cellular control of intestinal secretion. Neurotransmitters such as vasoactive intestinal polypeptide (VIP) interact with a receptor on the serosal membrane of the cell to activate adenylate cyclase. This increases the production of cyclic AMP, releases calcium from mitochondrial stores and activates protein kinases. Other transmitters, such as acetylcholine (ACh) or serotonin (5HT) interact with serosal receptors to increase cellular uptake of calcium. Intracellular calcium interacts with calmodulin (CDR) to form CaCDR, which activates protein kinases and by a series of steps, which are not understood, increases the permeability of the mucosal membrane to chloride.

FURTHER READING

Hadova B, Green J R, Starchi E E, Houri H P 1981
Biochemical mechanisms in congenital enzyme deficiencies
in the small intestine. Clinics in Gastroenterology
10: 671–690

Johnson L R (ed) 1982 Physiology of the gastrointestinal
tract. Raven Press, New York

Phillips S F, Wingate D L 1979 Fluid and electrolyte fluxes
in the gut. Advances in Internal Medicine 24: 429–453

Polak J M, Bloom S R, Wright N A, Butler AG (eds) 1984
Physiology of the Gut. Scandinavian Journal of
Gastroenterology, Supplements 82, 87 and 93

Silk D B A 1982 Disorders of nitrogen absorption. Clinics in
Gastroenterology 11: 47–72

Wrong O M, Edmonds C J, Chadwick V S 1981 The large
intestine. MTP Press, Lancaster

22

The liver and bile

The liver is the largest internal organ, weighing 1500 g in the adult, or approximately 2 per cent of the total body weight.

The liver cells are arranged in units or lobules. Each lobule is a cylinder, several millimetres in length and one millimetre in diameter. It has a central vein that eventually drains into the hepatic veins and peripheral portal tracts, each containing a branch of the hepatic artery, a branch of a portal vein, a bile duct and lymphatic vessels. The liver parenchymal cells or *hepatocytes* are arranged in plates one or two cells thick radiating like the spokes of a wheel between the portal tracts and the central vein (Fig. 22.1). These plates are separated by spaces, the *sinusoids*, which convey a mixture of hepatic arterial blood and portal venous blood from the portal tracts to the central vein. The sinusoids are lined by endothelial cells, some of which, the Kupffer cells, are macrophages, capable of phagocytosis of foreign material. Between the liver cells are bile canaliculi (Fig. 22.1) which convey bile to the bile ducts.

The endothelial lining of the sinusoid has large gaps or pores to allow nutrients in the blood to gain access to the hepatocyte, and to allow material such as plasma proteins synthesised in the hepatocyte to get out into the blood. Thus the normal Starling equilibrium does not operate in the liver and fluid readily leaks out into the extracellular fluid in the spaces of Disse (Fig. 22.1). These are drained by large numbers of lymphatic vessels, which return fluid from the liver via the thoracic duct to the subclavian vein. The liver produces between a third and a half of all the lymph in the body under resting conditions.

Approximately 1.5 litres of blood perfuse the liver every minute. Seventy per cent of this is partially oxygenated portal blood containing nutrients and hormones coming from the digestive tract and spleen. The remainder is oxygenated blood from the hepatic artery. Entry of blood to the sinusoids is controlled by sphincters around both hepatic artery and portal vein radicles (Fig. 22.1).

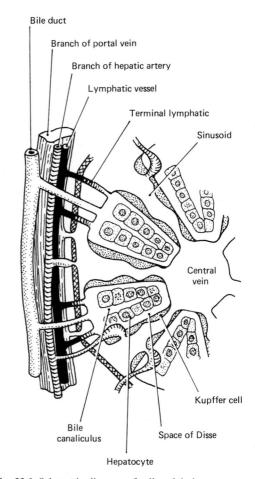

Fig. 22.1 Schematic diagram of a liver lobule.

FUNCTIONS OF THE LIVER

The many functions of the liver include the metabolism of carbohydrates, amino acids, lipids, and ethanol, the synthesis of plasma proteins, the formation and excretion of bile, the storage of glycogen, vitamins and iron, the removal of antigens absorbed from the gastrointestinal tract, and the excretion of drugs, hormones, toxins and waste products of metabolism.

Carbohydrate metabolism

The liver stores carbohydrate as glycogen and has a major role in regulating blood glucose concentrations (Chap. 23). After a meal, when blood glucose levels are high, insulin causes glucose to enter the hepatocytes, where it is converted into glycogen and stored. Between meals, glucagon, secreted from the pancreas, breaks down glycogen and maintains plasma glucose levels above 4 mmol/l. The liver also possesses the enzymes to metabolise fructose and galactose, absorbed from the intestine.

The liver converts amino acids to pyruvate and substrates of the tricarboxylic acid cycle, which can be metabolised to supply energy, converted to glucose (gluconeogenesis), or converted to fat.

Fat metabolism

Fat is stored in adipose tissue as triglyceride. When required as an energy source, it is split by lipase to free fatty acids (FFA), which enter the blood and are carried to the tissues for oxidation. The oxidation of fat can take place in most cells but it is most rapid in the liver. The liver cannot utilise all the acetyl CoA that results from fatty acid oxidation. The excess is converted to acetoacetic acid and β-hydroxybutyric acid (the *ketone bodies*), which are released into the blood and transported to other tissues. The ketone bodies can then be reconverted in most cells to acetyl CoA, which enters the tricarboxylic acid cycle to provide energy. In this way, rapid oxidation of fatty acids in the liver supplies energy-rich substrate for all the cells of the body.

After meals, excess protein and carbohydrate that has been absorbed can be converted by the liver into fat. This involves the metabolism of glucose and amino acids to acetyl CoA, which is in turn converted to malonyl CoA and then to fatty acids and triglycerides. Triglycerides and cholesterol and phospholipids combine with apoproteins synthesised by the hepatocyte to form *lipoproteins*, mainly VLDL (very low density lipoproteins). They are secreted in this form into the blood and travel to the adipose tissue, where the triglyceride is split by lipoprotein lipases to yield fatty acids, which are taken up by the cell and resynthesised into triglyceride. This action is promoted by insulin and leaves the lipoprotein depleted of triglyceride but rich in cholesterol esters (LDL, low density lipoprotein). Unused FFA are also taken up as triglyceride in lipoproteins and conveyed to the adipose tissue. If the liver cells are damaged, lipoprotein synthesis may be impaired and triglyceride accumulates in the hepatocytes as fat droplets (fatty liver).

The liver also synthesises cholesterol and phospholipids. About 80 per cent of the cholesterol is converted to bile acids; the remainder is transported in the blood as high density lipoproteins (HDL) and VLDL. Phospholipids are also conveyed to the tissues as lipoproteins (HDL and VLDL). Phospholipids and cholesterol are essential for the formation of membranes in all cells of the body.

Protein metabolism

Transamination

The liver can synthesise all the non-essential amino acids by the process of transamination, whereby the amino radical of one amino acid is transferred to an appropriate alpha-oxo-acid to produce another amino acid. In the example shown in Figure 22.2, an amino radical from glutamate is transferred to oxaloacetate, yielding aspartate.

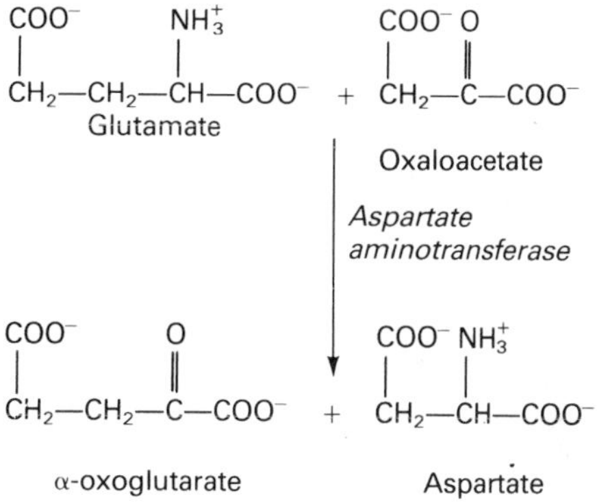

$$CH_2-CH_2-\underset{NH_3^+}{\overset{COO^-}{CH}}-COO^- + CH_2-\underset{O}{\overset{COO^-}{C}}-COO^-$$

Glutamate Oxaloacetate

Aspartate aminotransferase

$$CH_2-CH_2-\underset{O}{\overset{COO^-}{C}}-COO^- + CH_2-\underset{NH_3^+}{\overset{COO^-}{CH}}-COO^-$$

α-oxoglutarate Aspartate

Fig. 22.2 Synthesis of aspartate from oxaloacetate by transamination.

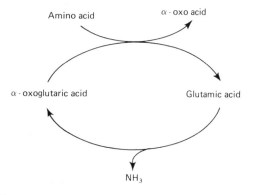

Fig. 22.3 One method for the deamination of amino acids.

Deamination

The liver is the major site for the deamination of amino acids before they are used for energy or converted into carbohydrates and fats. Most deamination occurs by the process shown in Figure 22.3.

The amino group is transferred first to α-oxoglutaric acid, which becomes glutamic acid. The glutamic acid can transfer the amino group to other substances or can release it as ammonia.

Production of ammonia

Ammonia is also formed in the renal tubule (from glutamine) and from the colon (by bacterial degradation of urea and possibly proteins). Ammonia is toxic and may be partly responsible for the impairment of cerebral function that occurs with liver failure (hepatic encephalopathy).

The liver converts ammonia into urea by a cyclical process (Fig. 22.4) and removes it from body fluids.

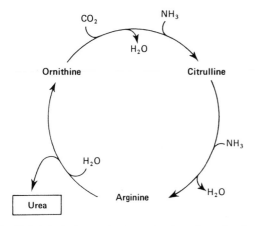

Fig. 22.4 Principal steps in the production of urea by the liver.

Synthesis of proteins

All the plasma proteins except the immunoglobulins are synthesised in the liver. Approximately 10 to 14 g of albumin is synthesised per day to replace the 6 to 10 per cent of the plasma albumin pool (140 g) that is degraded daily.

The liver is responsible for the synthesis of most of the blood clotting factors, including factors I, II, V, VII, IX and X. Synthesis of factors II, VII, IX and X requires vitamin K. Fibrinolytic factors (p. 37) are also produced by the liver.

Proteins responsible for the transport of lipids, hormones and some minerals are synthesised in the liver. These include the apoprotein component of plasma lipoproteins, thyroxine-binding globulin, sex hormone binding globulin, transferrin, and caeruloplasmin. The latter is responsible for the carriage of copper.

Plasma enzymes, such as lecithin–cholesterol acyl transferase, which catalyses the transfer of long-chain fatty acid from lecithin to free cholesterol on the surface of the lipoprotein particles, and enzyme inhibitors, such as α₁-antitrypsin, are produced in the liver.

Detoxification

Many drugs are metabolised by the liver, and the stages in drug metabolism have been classified as phase I and phase II reactions. In a phase I reaction, the drug undergoes oxidation, reduction, or hydrolysis, and in a phase II reaction either the drug or the product of a phase I reaction is conjugated with glucuronic acid, glycine, or sulphate. Such transformations produce metabolites that are more polar (and therefore more water-soluble) than the parent drug. The conjugates are excreted either into the bile or into the urine.

The drug-metabolising enzymes of the liver are associated with the smooth endoplasmic reticulum, forming the non-specific 'mixed function oxidase system'. One feature of this system is the increase in enzyme activity that follows the long-term administration of a substrate drug, a process known as *enzyme induction*. Drugs that act as enzyme inducers include barbiturates and ethanol. Enzyme induction is not specific; for example, the long-term administration of a barbiturate enhances the rate of metabolism of the anticoagulant drug warfarin.

A drug taken by mouth and absorbed from the gastrointestinal tract must pass through the liver before entering the systemic circulation. Metabolism of the drug in the intestinal mucosa or liver during this initial transit is referred to as 'first-pass metabolism' and may lead to peripheral blood levels of the drug lower than those obtained from the same dose given into a peripheral vein.

In some cases, metabolism in the liver yields a more active compound. For example, the corticosteroid drug prednisone is reduced in the liver to the active metabolite prednisolone, and metabolism of the immunosuppressive agent azathioprine produces the pharmacologically active product 6-mercaptopurine. Some vitamins undergo conversion in the liver to metabolically active forms, for example pyridoxine is converted to the active coenzyme, pyridoxal-5'-phosphate.

Inactivation of hormones

The liver is the principal site of inactivation of many hormones, including insulin, glucagon, cortisol, aldosterone, testosterone, oestrogens and thyroid hormones.

Metabolism of ethanol

Ethanol is metabolised mainly by alcohol dehydrogenase to acetaldehyde, which is itself further oxidised in the mitochrondria of the hepatocytes.

Storage

The liver stores energy in the form of glycogen. Hepatic stores of vitamin B12 are sufficient to last up to four years. Copper and iron (as ferritin in the Kupffer cells), the fat-soluble vitamins A, D and K, and the water-soluble vitamins, riboflavin, nicotinamide, pyridoxine and folic acid, are all stored in the liver.

Antigen clearance

All the blood draining the gut passes through the liver sinusoids. This blood contains bacteria and other foreign proteins and the Kupffer cells lining the sinusoids play a part in their removal (Chap. 5)

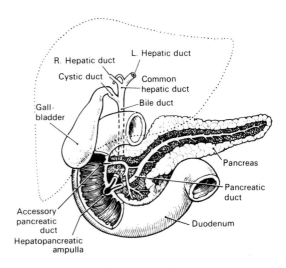

Fig. 22.6 Anatomy of the extrahepatic bile ducts, gall-bladder, pancreas and duodenum.

BILE

Bile is secreted by the hepatocytes into the bile canaliculi, a series of narrow spaces between adjacent liver cells. The surface area of the canaliculi is increased by microvilli that protrude into the canalicular lumen (Fig. 22.5). The canaliculi drain via bile ductules into the bile ducts, which run in the portal tracts; the bile ducts themselves discharge into the right and left hepatic ducts, which unite to form the common hepatic duct at the hilum of the liver (Fig. 22.6).

The gall-bladder is a sac-like structure with a capacity of 30 to 50 ml. It consists of smooth muscle lined by columnar epithelium. It fills and empties via the cystic duct, which joins the common hepatic duct to form the bile duct; this in turn empties into the duodenum through the ampulla of Vater. At the point of entry into the duodenum, the bile duct and the adjacent pancreatic duct are surrounded by a circular band of smooth muscle, the choledocho-duodenal sphincter (sphincter of Oddi).

Table 22.7 Concentration of the constituents of hepatic and gall-bladder bile (mmol/l)

Compound	Liver bile	Gall-bladder bile
Bile salts	26	145
Bilirubin	0.7	5.1
Cholesterol	2.6	16
Fatty acids	3.6	29
Lecithin	0.5	3.9
Na^+	145	130
K^+	5	12
Ca^{2+}	5	23
Cl^-	100	25
HCO_3^-	28	10

Composition of bile

Bile is an aqueous solution of organic compounds and electrolytes. Its composition is shown in Table 22.7. Bile is secreted into the canaliculi and modified during passage through the biliary ductules (see below). In the gall-bladder, electrolytes and water are reabsorbed, concentrating the bile approximately 10 to 15 times. Despite this concentration the osmolality of gall-bladder bile is similar to that of plasma, approximately 300 mmol/kg, and the pH lies between 6 and 8.5.

Bile acids

Each bile acid molecule consists of a non-polar, hydrophobic steroid nucleus and a polar, hydrophilic side chain and hydroxyl groups. Bile acids are synthesised in the hepatocyte from cholesterol. The rate-limiting step in bile acid synthesis is 7α-hydroxylation of chol-

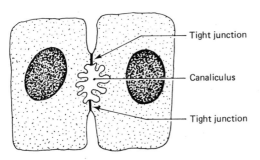

Fig. 22.5 Cross-section of a bile canaliculus formed by two hepatocytes.

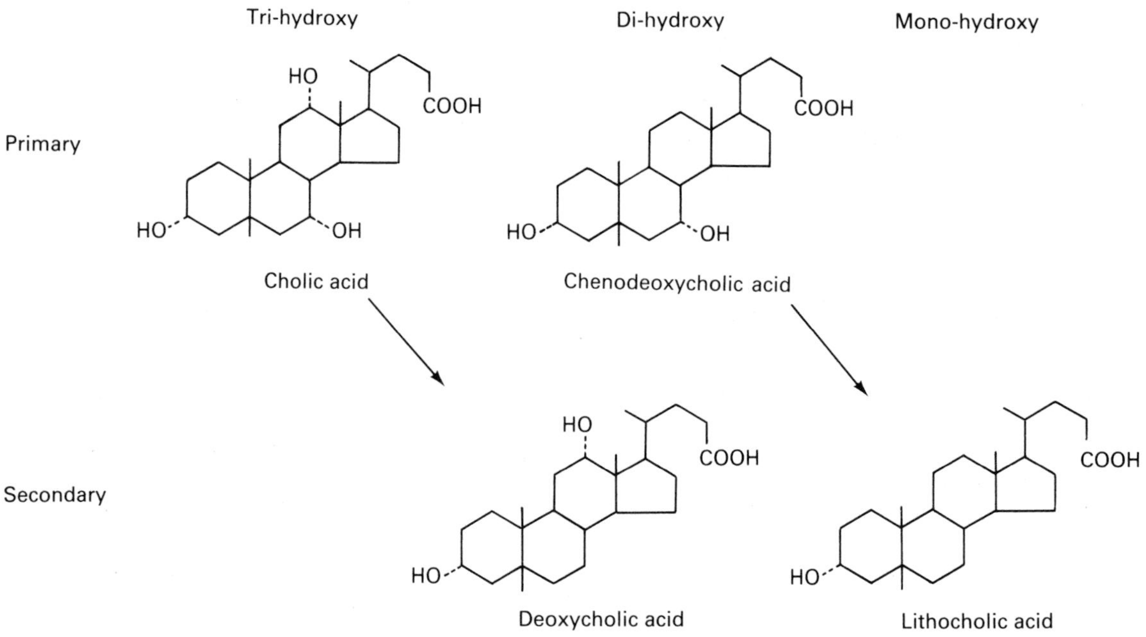

Fig. 22.8 The principal bile acids.

esterol. The principal bile acids are shown in Figure 22.8. The primary bile acids, *cholic acid* and *chenodeoxycholic acid* are synthesised in the hepatocyte, conjugated with either glycine or taurine (Fig. 22.9) and secreted by an active sodium-dependent mechanism into the canaliculus. Most of these bile acids are eventually reabsorbed in the ileum, returning via the portal blood to the hepatocytes, whence they are re-excreted. This process is known as the *enterohepatic circulation of bile acids* (p. 272). The return of bile acids to the hepatocyte controls the amount of new bile acids synthesised by negative feedback inhibition of the enzyme cholesterol 7α-hydroxylase. In other words, as more bile acids are returned to the liver, synthesis of new bile acids is suppressed. This mechanism helps to maintain bile acid production at a constant level.

The primary bile acids that escape reabsorption in the ileum are deconjugated and dehydroxylated in the 7α position by colonic bacteria to form the secondary bile acids deoxycholic acid and lithocholic acid (Fig. 22.9). A proportion of the secondary bile acids are reabsorbed and reconjugated and form part of the bile acid pool; the remainder are excreted in the faeces.

Bile acids combine with cholesterol and phospholipid, also secreted into the canaliculus to form aggregations called micelles, in which the bile acid molecules package the lipid so that the polar groups on the outside in the aqueous phase and the non-polar groups are on the inside or lipid phase (Fig. 22.10). Cholesterol is in-

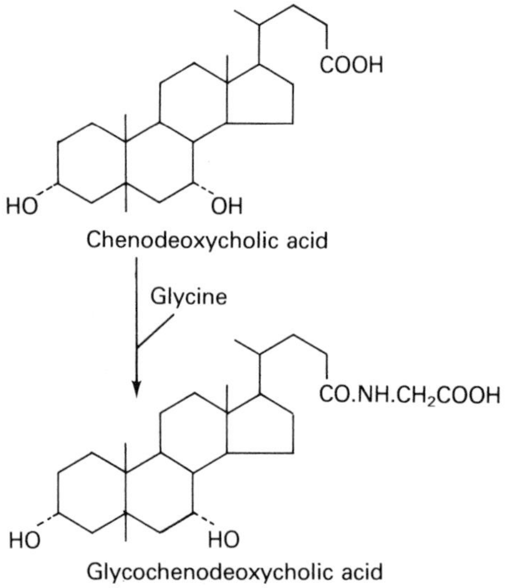

Fig. 22.9 Conjugation of chenodeoxycholic acid with glycine.

soluble in water but the association with bile acid and phospholipid renders it soluble. A micellar solution remains stable only if the relative proportions of the constituents remain within certain limits. Outside these limits, either the phospholipid, the cholesterol, or both, come out of solution. The relative concentrations of bile acids, phospholipid and cholesterol can be shown

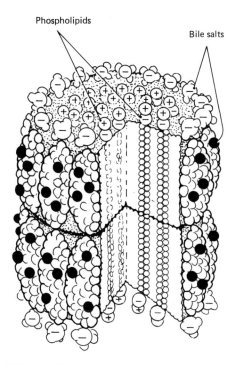

Phospholipids

Bile salts

Fig. 22.10 A mixed micelle.

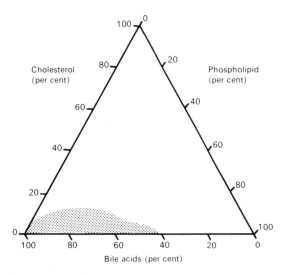

100   0

Cholesterol (per cent)

80

60

40

20

0

100   80   60   40   20   0

Bile acids (per cent)

20

40

60

80

100

Phospholipid (per cent)

Fig. 22.12 Solubility of cholesterol in bile. Only bile samples that lie within the shaded area are unsaturated with cholesterol.

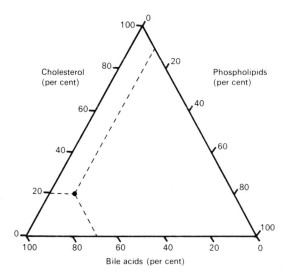

100   0

Cholesterol (per cent)

80

60

40

20

0

100   80   60   40   20   0

Bile acids (per cent)

20

40

60

80

100

Phospholipids (per cent)

Fig. 22.11 Molar composition of bile plotted on triangular co-ordinates. The point A represents a bile sample with a molar composition of 10 per cent phospholipid, 20 per cent cholesterol and 70 per cent bile acids.

graphically on a system of triangular co-ordinates (Fig. 22.11). The molar concentration of each constituent is expressed as a percentage of the total molar concentration of the solution and plotted along the appropriate axis. The composition of the mixture is represented by a point that lies at the intersection of three lines (Fig. 22.11); only mixtures with compositions that lie in the lower left-hand corner of the triangle (Fig. 22.12) can exist in micellar solution. In subjects who regularly produce bile supersaturated with cholesterol, the cholesterol may be deposited in the gallbladder as gallstones.

Bile pigments

Bilirubin is an orange pigment produced by the breakdown of haem in the macrophages (p. 51). It is carried in the plasma bound to albumin and taken up into the hepatocytes by carrier-mediated or 'facilitated' diffusion (p. 8). Within the cell, bile acid binds to a protein known as *Y protein*, and is then conjugated with glucuronic acid. It is secreted by active transport into the canaliculus and excreted with the bile into the duodenum.

Bilirubin is degraded by colonic bacteria to urobilinogen, some of which is absorbed into the blood; most is re-excreted in the bile but some is excreted in the urine. Urobilinogen remaining in the gut is converted to stercobilin, which is responsible for the brown colour of the faeces.

Failure of the body to excrete the bilirubin produced by red cell destruction (haemolysis) causes *jaundice*. Jaundice can result from excessive haemolysis, which overwhelms the liver's excretory capacity, or from damage to hepatocytes (hepatocellular jaundice) or from blockage of the bile ducts (obstructive jaundice).

Bile secretion

The formation of bile involves the uptake or synthesis of a variety of substances by the hepatocytes, their discharge into the bile canaliculi and the modification of the composition of bile during its passage through the bile ducts and gall-bladder. Active secretion of solutes, particularly bile acid and sodium into the canaliculi, creates an osmotic gradient, which encourages the passive transfer of water into the canalicular lumen from the ECF through the tight junctions (Fig. 22.5).

About 5 litres of bile are secreted every day. Sodium bicarbonate is secreted into the bile as it passes through the ductules. This ductular secretion is under the control of hormones, particularly secretin.

In the gall-bladder, sodium, chloride, and bicarbonate are actively reabsorbed, increasing the osmolality in the spaces between the epithelial cells. Absorption of water from the gall-bladder is driven by this osmotic gradient in a manner identical to that described for the intestine (p. 275). This process results in a ten- to fifteen-fold increase in the concentration of non-absorbable organic solutes. The daily output of bile into the duodenum is about 500 ml

The control of gall-bladder contraction

Filling of the gall-bladder depends on the positive pressure gradient caused by the active secretion of bile while the sphincter of Oddi is contracted and the gall-bladder wall relaxed.

Secretion of bile into the duodenum requires the contraction of the gall-bladder and the relaxation of the sphincter of Oddi. Both events occur when food enters the duodenum. The presence of fat or protein in the duodenum releases cholecystokinin-pancreozymin (CCK-Pz) from the duodenal epithelium. This hormone contracts the gall-bladder, an action that is greatly augmented by concomitant release of secretin or vagal stimulation. The sphincter of Oddi relaxes when the gall-bladder contracts. The relaxation of the sphincter may be partly due to a direct action of CCK-Pz and partly due to a reflex from the gall-bladder to the sphincter of Oddi.

Since the common bile duct travels obliquely through the duodenal wall, bile flow is inhibited by duodenal contractions. Thus bile often enters the duodenum in squirts during relaxation of the duodenal muscle around the sphincter.

FURTHER READING

Bacon B R, Tavill A S 1984 Role of the liver in normal iron metabolism. Seminars in Liver Disease 4: 181–192

Blumgart L H 1982 The biliary tract. Churchill Livingstone, Edinburgh

Cooper A D 1985 Role of the liver in the degradation of lipoproteins. Gastroenterology 88: 192–205

Everson G T, Kern F 1983 Bile acid metabolism. In: Thomas H C, MacSween R N M (eds) Recent advances in hepatology. Churchill Livingstone, Edinburgh pp. 171–181

Sherlock S 1981 Diseases of the liver and biliary system, 6th edn. Blackwell Scientific, Oxford

Strange R C 1984 Hepatic bile flow. Physiological Reviews 64: 1055–1102

Whitmer D I, Hauser S C, Gollan J L 1984 Mechanisms of formation, hepatic transport and metabolism of bile pigments. Progress in Clinical and Biological Research 152: 29–52

Wright R, Alberti K G M M, Karran S, Millward-Sadler G H 1979 Liver and biliary disease. Saunders, Philadelphia

23

Hormones and the control of metabolism

The endocrine glands secrete hormones that enter the circulation, are carried to distant tissues and modify their function. The production of such hormones is not confined to the recognised endocrine glands, for secretin and cholecystokinin (p. 260) produced by the intestine are hormones; hormones are produced by the kidney (p. 198) and enough noradrenaline may be liberated at nerve-endings to produce distant effects.

HORMONES

Three main groups of hormones are recognised. *Protein and peptide hormones* are produced by the hypothalamus and pituitary (Chap. 24), by the intestine and pancreas and by the parathyroid glands (Chap. 29). *Steroid hormones* include those produced by the adrenal cortex (Chap. 26) and the sex hormones produced by the gonads (Chap. 27). Calcitriol, a sterol derived from vitamin D (Chap. 29), is usually included in this group. Finally, a group of hormones are derivatives of the amino acid tyrosine. These include the thyroid hormones (Chap. 25) and the catecholamines: noradrenaline, adrenaline and dopamine (Chap. 16).

Synthesis and secretion

Protein and peptide hormones are produced initially by ribosomes as larger precursors often known as pre-pro-hormones. The 'pre'-fragment is the 'signal sequence' of amino acid residues that are formed first in translation and direct the growing peptide chain into the lumen of the endoplasmic reticulum, where it is later cleaved off. Post-translational modifications such as the formation of disulphide bridges and the addition of carbohydrate moieties take place in the endoplasmic reticulum and the Golgi apparatus. The completed pro-hormone is stored in vesicles within the cell, often together with a precursor of the peptidase, which, when activated, breaks the pro-hormone down to give the definitive hormone. The hormone is secreted from the cell by exocytosis. An example of a pro-hormone is pro-insulin (p. 292). Many of the smaller peptide hormones are produced by specific cleavage of large precursor proteins, for example, β-lipotrophin (p. 308).

Steroid hormones are produced from cholesterol, which is either obtained in the diet or is synthesised from acetate in the smooth endoplasmic reticulum. All steroid-producing cells contain fat droplets, which mainly contain cholesterol esters. The further enzymic steps leading to the production of the hormones take place either in the mitochondria or in the smooth endoplasmic reticulum.

Our knowledge of the mechanisms whereby endocrine cells are stimulated to secrete hormones is very incomplete. In many cases the stimulus is another hormone, the actions of which may be mediated by changes in the calcium concentration within the cell, which, in turn, cause the exocytosis of intracellular vesicles of hormones.

Many hormones are now known to be secreted in a pulsatile manner (p. 301 and p. 305). The recognition of this fact is important for two reasons. First, measurement of the level of a hormone in a single sample of plasma may not reflect the average levels over a day. Secondly, attempts to replace or mimic hormonal actions may be unsuccessful without pulsatile administration.

Feedback inhibition

The control of the secretion of individual hormones will be discussed later, but one general point should be mentioned here. The secretory activity of many endocrine cells is modified by plasma levels of a substance produced by the target tissue. For example, a rise in the plasma levels of cortisol (p. 301) leads to a fall in the production of ACTH by the pituitary and so to a reduction in cortisol secretion.

Transport

Some hormones, notably the thyroid hormones and the steroids, are present in the plasma bound to highly specific *binding proteins*. Such proteins include thyroxine-binding globulin and *transcortin*, which transports cortisol. Many hormones are also loosely bound to other circulating proteins such as albumin. Hormones bound to proteins are in equilibrium with the free hormone, but the amount of free hormone may be a small fraction of the total. The protein-bound hormone acts as a store from which free hormone can be released as rapidly as it is used. It is the concentration of the free hormone not the total plasma concentration that determines its physiological activity. Changes in the concentration of binding proteins alter the amount of bound hormone and may change greatly, but without any change in the concentration of free hormone. Thus assays that measure total plasma hormone levels may be misleading in the assessment of the physiological activity of the hormone in plasma.

Actions

The physiological actions of hormones have been explored in a number of ways. Surgical removal of an endocrine gland or the administration of drugs that inhibit hormone synthesis have been used to study the effects of hormone deficiency. Grafting experiments or injections of active extracts of the gland have been used

in attempts to restore to normal a hormone-deficient animal. Administration of large amounts of hormones to normal animals has induced conditions of hormone excess. The results of such experiments can be compared with observations made on patients with

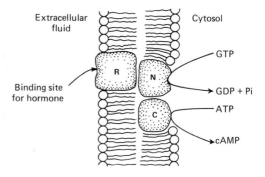

Fig. 23.1 Proteins involved in the activation of adenylate cyclase by a peptide or catecholamine hormone. The binding of the hormone to the receptor protein (R) leads to the binding of GTP to the nucleotide binding protein (N). In turn this activates adenylate cyclase (C). (From Paterson C R 1983 Essentials of human biochemistry. Pitman, London)

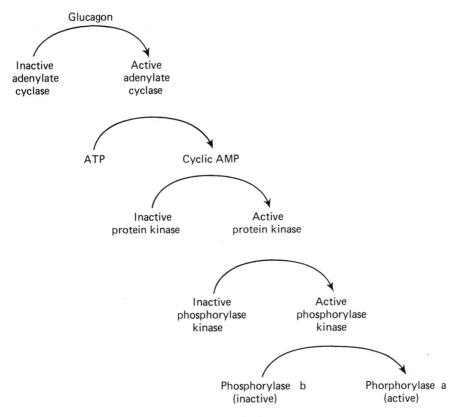

Fig. 23.2 Part of the response by the liver to glucagon leading to increased breakdown of glycogen by causing the production of the active (phosphorylated) phosphorylase. An additional change (not shown) is a conversion of active (dephosphorylated) glycogen synthase to an inactive (phosphorylated) form, so decreasing glycogen synthesis.

endocrine diseases, since disorders due to overactivity or destruction of the various endocrine glands are well recognised. The effects of over-secretion by an endocrine gland may be relieved or cured by the surgical removal of part of the overactive tissue. On the other hand the operative removal of too much tissue or the destruction of an endocrine gland by disease gives rise to a 'deficiency syndrome' that is controlled, but not cured, by 'replacement therapy' with the deficient hormone or another substance with a similar action.

Our knowledge of hormonal mechanisms is still incomplete but it is becoming clear that the first step is the binding of the hormone to a specific receptor. In the case of protein, peptide and amine hormones the receptor appears to be on the cell membrane, while steroid and sterol hormones enter cells and bind to specific proteins within the nuclei. The thyroid hormones also enter cells but the details of their receptor, probably a protein associated with DNA in the nucleus, are not yet certain (p. 314).

One of the major advances in endocrinology in the last decade has been the recognition of disorders in which the primary defect is not over-production or under-production of a hormone, but is, instead, a failure of the binding of a hormone to its receptors or a failure of a hormone-receptor complex to bring about the normal changes in cellular metabolism (p. 303).

The cell membrane

The peptide hormones and the catecholamines have specific binding sites on the outer surface of the plasma membrane. In the case of some, but not all, of these hormones, binding leads to the activation of the enzyme adenylate cyclase and the production within the cell of a 'second messenger', cyclic AMP. This mechanism has been particularly clearly demonstrated in the action of ACTH (p. 301), in the action of adrenaline on beta receptors (p. 230) and in the action of glucagon in inducing glycogen breakdown (p. 293). The response to these hormones involves at least three membrane proteins, as shown in Figure 23.1.

The increase in levels of cyclic AMP within a cell activates protein kinases which in turn stimulate the phosphorylation of enzymes and the modification of their activity. An example of the mode of action of glucagon is given in Figure 23.2. A similar mechanism applies even when a hormone modifies the permeability of a plasma membrane (Fig. 23.3).

In some instances, the binding of a hormone to its receptor leads to a rise in the concentration of calcium within the cytosol. The best known example of this form of hormone action is that of adrenaline on the alpha-adrenergic receptors in the liver. The calcium becomes bound to a specialised protein, *calmodulin*, which in turn leads to the modification of intracellular

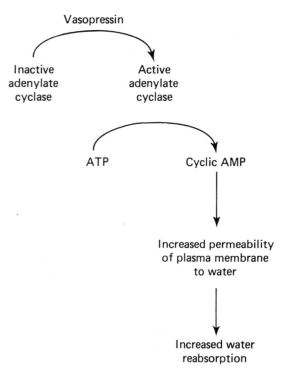

Fig. 23.3 Probable mechanism of the action of vasopressin on the cells of the distal tubule and collecting ducts of the kidney.

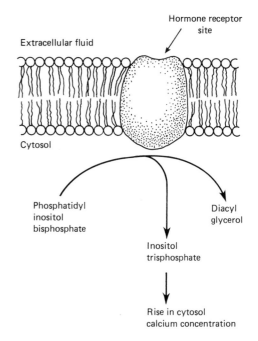

Fig. 23.4 Role of inositol trisphosphate in the mediation of the action of hormones that act by increasing intracellular calcium concentrations.

enzyme activities. It is now known that the rise in intracellular calcium is mediated by the production of inositol trisphosphate (Fig. 23.4).

Insulin and perhaps other growth-promoting hormones act by binding to receptor proteins that are transmembrane proteins. The cytosolic component of the receptor is a protein kinase and its activation may represent the first step in the action of insulin, as described later (p. 293).

Intracellular actions

Steroid and sterol hormones enter a cell and bind to receptor proteins within the nucleus. The effect of this binding is to stimulate or inhibit the synthesis of a particular protein. For example, calcitriol (p. 363) specifically stimulates the production, in cells of the intestinal mucosa, of a protein required for the active transport of calcium. Both thyroxine (T_4) and tri-iodothyronine (T_3) enter the cell but there is growing evidence that the principal physiological effects of thyroid hormone result from the direct binding of T_3 to non-histone proteins in the nucleus (p. 314).

CONTROL OF ENERGY METABOLISM

The supply of energy in the diet is intermittent but the tissues have a continuous requirement for energy. Mechanisms are therefore needed to store energy and to release it in such a way that undue fluctuations in the plasma levels of glucose and other energy-supplying compounds do not occur.

Energy stores

A limited amount of carbohydrate can be stored as glycogen in the liver and in muscles. Liver glycogen can be broken down to free glucose, which enters the blood. Muscle glycogen is not converted to glucose but is used directly within the muscle as an energy source (p. 167). The adipose tissue represents the major energy reserve in man (Table 23.5). A third energy source, particularly in prolonged starvation, is provided by proteins, particularly in muscle.

Table 23.5 Energy reserves in a 70-kg man (in MJ) (After Cahill G F 1976 Starvation in man. Clinics in Endocrinology and Metabolism 5:397)

	Triglyceride	Glycogen or glucose	Available protein	Total
Adipose tissue	564.3	0.3	0.2	565
Muscle	1.9	5.0	100.3	107
Liver	1.9	1.7	1.7	5

Control mechanisms

Metabolic pathways involved in the storage of energy or in the release of energy from stores are controlled at

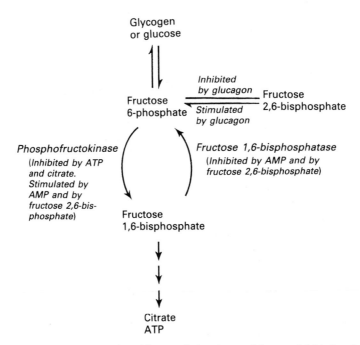

Fig. 23.6 The factors controlling the interconversion of fructose 6-phosphate and fructose 1,6-bisphosphate, key reactions in the regulation of glycolysis and reverse glycolysis.

several distinct levels. At the level of the individual cell, metabolic pathways are largely controlled by allosteric mechanisms. Thus the rate-limiting step in the glycolytic pathway is that controlled by phosphofructokinase, which is inhibited by ATP and stimulated by AMP. Other factors described below are also important in controlling this pathway. Similarly, the key step in the reverse reaction of gluconeogenesis, that catalysed by fructose 1,6-bisphosphatase, is inhibited by AMP.

In addition to such effects many key reactions are controlled by plasma levels of various hormones, particularly glucagon, insulin, adrenaline, cortisol and growth hormone. Thus in glycolysis, phosphofructokinase is stimulated by fructose 2,6-bisphosphate while the reverse reaction, catalysed by fructose 1,6-bisphosphatase, is inhibited by this substance. Intracellular levels of fructose 2,6-bisphosphate are in turn controlled by glucagon (Fig. 23.6).

Similarly, the enzymes involved in the synthesis or breakdown of glycogen are subject both to allosteric control within the cell and to control by the action of hormones, notably glucagon and adrenaline. Part of the mechanism of action of these hormones was shown earlier; the cascade shown in Figure 23.2 provides a means whereby small amounts of cyclic AMP can cause the rapid transformation of phosphorylase from the b to the a form.

The active phosphorylase kinase, which activates phosphorylase and so increases glycogen breakdown, also inactivates glycogen synthase. In this way the synthesis of glycogen is active when glycogen breakdown is inhibited and inactive when glycogen breakdown is stimulated.

In the liver the control of glycogen metabolism is essential for the control of plasma glucose levels within the range 4.0 to 8.0 mmol/l. It is now clear that, in addition to the hormonal effects just described, glucose itself has a direct effect on phosphorylase a; infusion of glucose into a rat leads to the conversion of phosphorylase a into the inactive phosphorylase b within a minute.

In muscle, electrical stimulation leads to glycogen breakdown so that glucose 6-phosphate and therefore ATP is available at the time of a muscle contraction. Stimulation of muscle (Chap. 37) leads to the inflow of calcium ions; these bind to the proteins *calmodulin* and *troponin C*, in which, in turn, bind to and activate phosphorylase kinase. This activates phosphorylase and inactivates glycogen synthase so that glycogen breakdown and ATP synthesis are increased. This coordination between muscle contraction and its energy supply is illustrated in Figure 23.7.

The principal hormones controlling energy metabolism are insulin, glucagon, adrenaline, cortisol and growth hormone.

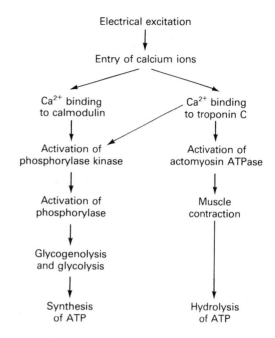

Fig. 23.7 Coordination of glycogen breakdown with contraction of skeletal muscle. (After Picton C et al. 1981 Cell Calcium 2:281)

Insulin

Insulin is a protein secreted by the pancreatic islets (islets of Langerhans). Its main role is in the co-ordination of the metabolic response to meals.

Source

Pancreatic islets contain three histologically distinct types of cells (Fig. 23.8). The rim of glucagon-secreting A cells surrounds large areas of insulin-secreting B cells. Here and there, but mainly among the A cells are D cells, which produce somatostatin.

Like other peptide hormones, insulin is formed first as a precursor, *pre-pro-insulin*. The signal sequence of 16 amino acid residues is removed to give the 84-residue protein *pro-insulin*; this is transported to the Golgi complex where it is split to give insulin and the C-peptide (Fig. 23.9). Insulin is stored in granules in the cytoplasm.

Structure

The insulin molecule consists of two peptide chains (Fig. 23.9), an A chain of 21 residues and a B chain of 30 residues. The chains are linked by two disulphide bridges.

In practice amounts of insulin are expressed in units, one unit being approximately 40 μg.

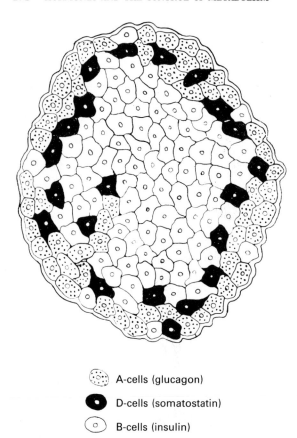

A-cells (glucagon)

D-cells (somatostatin)

B-cells (insulin)

Fig. 23.8 The typical cellular composition of an islet of Langerhans to show the distribution of the different cell types. Islet cells for which a function has not yet been established are omitted. (From Orci L, Unger R H 1975 Lancet 2:1243, by courtesy of authors and editor)

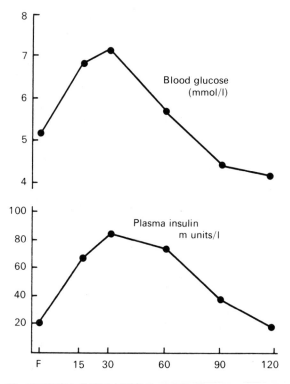

Fig. 23.10 Blood glucose and plasma insulin responses to the administration of 50 g of glucose by mouth in 34 normal subjects. F = fasting level. (From Buchanan K D, McKiddie M T 1967 Diabetologia 3:46, by courtesy of authors and publisher)

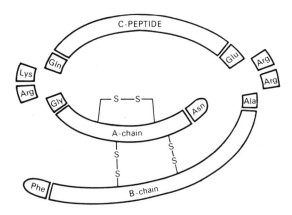

Fig. 23.9 Conversion of pro-insulin to insulin by the action of protease enzymes.

Table 23.11 Factors influencing release of insulin from the B-cells of the pancreas

Stimulation
Increase in plasma glucose

Increase in plasma levels of certain amino acids such as arginine

Glucose in intestine (probably mediated by GIP)

Other gastro-intestinal hormones such as gastrin, secretin and pancreozymin

Glucagon from A cells of the pancreas

Parasympathetic stimulation

Inhibition
Adrenaline

Sympathetic stimulation (β receptors)

Somatostatin from D cells of pancreas

Secretion

Insulin release from the B cells of the pancreas is mediated by changes in the membrane potential associated with an influx of calcium ions into the cell. A rise in plasma glucose levels is a major stimulus for insulin release (Fig. 23.10). However, the rise in plasma insulin is greater when glucose is adminstered by mouth than intravenously. It is probable that a gut factor is responsible and the most likely is thought to be gastric inhibitory polypeptide (GIP); many other factors also influence B cell activity (Table 23.11). Some pro-insulin is secreted with insulin; about 10 per cent of the total insulin-like activity measured by radioimmunoassay in plasma is due to pro-insulin.

Actions

The best known action of insulin is its effect on the plasma glucose (Fig. 23.12), but insulin has many important actions on cells in all tissues (Table 23.13). Its role in the overall regulation of energy metabolism is described later.

The mode of action of insulin at a cellular level has recently become clearer. The receptor for insulin is a protein kinase with a specificity for tyrosine residues.

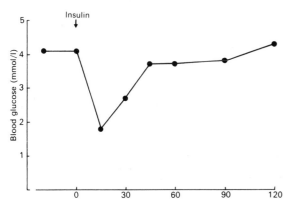

Fig. 23.12 Changes in blood glucose concentration after the intravenous injection of insulin in a dose of 0.15 units/kg. (Courtesy of T E Isles and H Barker)

Table 23.13 Principal actions of insulin on cells

Membrane effects
Uptake of glucose increased

Uptake of amino acids increased

Uptake of fatty acids increased

Uptake of Mg^{2+} and K^+ increased

Metabolic effects
Increased synthesis of DNA and RNA

Increased protein synthesis

Increased synthesis of glycogen (in liver and muscle)

Increased synthesis of triglycerides (in adipose tissue)

Increased synthesis of cholesterol (in liver and gut)

Increased fatty acid synthesis (in liver)

Decreased protein breakdown (in muscle)

Decreased glycogenolysis (in liver)

Decreased gluconeogenesis (in liver and kidney)

Decreased ketone production (in liver)

Decreased triglyceride breakdown (in adipose tissue)

It is a transmembrane protein with the binding site for insulin on the outer surface and the protein kinase activity on the inner surface of the plasma membrane. As a result of the binding of an insulin molecule, the tyrosine kinase is activated. The role of the tyrosine kinase is still unclear but one possibility is that it phosphorylates intracellular proteins. If this is so, then no second messenger may be involved in the action of insulin.

Metabolism

Insulin is degraded rapidly by the liver and has a half-life in the plasma of about five minutes.

Glucagon

Glucagon (*pancreatic glucagon*) is a peptide of 29 amino acid residues secreted by the A cells of the pancreas. It is produced initially as a precursor, pro-glucagon. Glucagon-like peptides often known as *enteroglucagon* are found in various parts of the gastrointestinal tract, but do not have actions on metabolism similar to glucagon.

Secretion

Glucagon is secreted in response to hypoglycaemia and its principal role is the prevention of hypoglycaemia during fasting. In addition, glucagon and insulin are released together after a protein meal; in this way the insulin release provoked by the rise in plasma levels of amino acids does not cause hypoglycaemia. Glucagon secretion is stimulated by adrenaline.

Actions

Glucagon stimulates the breakdown of liver glycogen to release glucose. It also stimulates gluconeogenesis and reduces fatty acid synthesis (Table 23.14). Glucagon stimulates insulin release. The mode of action of glucagon at the cellular level is now well understood (Fig. 23.2).

Adrenaline

Adrenaline (epinephrine) is produced by the adrenal medulla in response to hypoglycaemia or stress (p. 230). Its major metabolic actions are on muscle, where it increases glycogen breakdown, and on adipose tissue, where it stimulates triglyceride mobilisation. Its other metabolic actions are summarised in Table 23.14. The cellular mode of action of adrenaline on glycogen breakdown is shown in Figure 23.2.

Growth hormone

The secretion of growth hormone (somatotrophin) is stimulated by hypoglycaemia. While the principal actions of growth hormone are on the growth of tissues (p. 302) it also causes a rise in plasma glucose by

Table 23.14 The actions of glucagon, adrenaline, cortisol and growth hormone

Site, action	Glucagon	Adrenaline	Cortisol	Growth hormone
Liver				
Glycogen synthesis	↓	↓	↑	↑
Glycogen breakdown	↑	↑		
Gluconeogenesis	↑	↑		
Glucose release	↑	↑	↑	↑
Ketone body production	↑	↑		
Amino acid catabolism	↑		↑	
Fatty acid synthesis	↓	↓		
Muscle				
Fatty acid utilisation		↑		↑
Glycogen breakdown		↑		
Glucose uptake		↓	↓	↓
Protein synthesis			↓	↑
Adipose tissue				
Fatty acid release		↑	↑	↑
Triglyceride synthesis				↓

increasing glucose release from the liver and decreasing glucose uptake by muscles (Table 23.14).

Somatostatin

This hormone was first recognised as a hypothalamic factor inhibiting growth hormone production (growth hormone release inhibiting factor, GHRIH; p. 302). It is now clear that somatostatin is also produced in the D-cells of the pancreas, and probably other parts of the gastrointestinal tract.

Somatostatin is a peptide with 14 amino acid residues. Its release in the pancreas is stimulated by high plasma glucose levels and by high amino acid levels. Within the pancreas it probably acts locally in a paracrine manner in 'switching off' insulin production by the adjacent B-cells and glucagon production by adjacent A-cells. Its action may therefore be as a 'fine adjustment' in the control of plasma glucose.

Other hormones

The physiology of cortisol is described in Chapter 26. Its production increases slowly in hypoglycaemia or after stress. It may be regarded as a long-term defence

against hypoglycaemia, since it raises the plasma glucose by increasing gluconeogenesis from amino acids derived from muscle. Other metabolic actions of cortisol are summarised in Table 23.14.

The thyroid hormones (Chap. 25) increase gluconeogenesis, glycogenolysis and amino acid production from muscle protein and so tend to raise the blood glucose level. However, they also stimulate insulin secretion and overall have little effect on plasma glucose.

INTEGRATION OF ENERGY METABOLISM

The tissues of the body are interdependent in their energy metabolism. The brain, for example, is ordinarily dependent on glucose for its energy needs. Other tissues, such as erythrocytes, leucocytes, the skin and exercising muscle also require glucose but metabolise it to lactate even when aerobic. The lactate is cleared and reconverted to glucose by the liver and by the cortex of the kidneys. The normal turnover of lactate is about 1500 mmol/day; the liver is able to clear some 3400 mmol daily. Further integration between the tissues can be seen when the effects of meals and fasting are examined.

Effects of meals

After a meal including carbohydrates, fats and protein, insulin levels in the plasma rise and glucagon secretion diminishes. Glucose is taken up by the liver and synthesised to glycogen. Glucose also enters adipose tissue to form triglycerides, enters muscle to form glycogen and provides a source of energy in other tissues.

At the same time amino acids are taken up partly by the liver to form glycogen and partly by muscle to form protein. Triglycerides from the diet, largely reformed into chylomicrons (p. 270), are partly stored in adipose tissue, partly used for energy by muscle and partly taken up by the liver, where they are converted to very low density lipoproteins (VLDL), which pass in the blood to adipose tissue. All these steps are promoted by insulin.

Between meals

Between meals plasma levels of insulin fall and blood levels of glucagon levels rise. Blood levels of glucose, essential for the normal functioning of the brain, are maintained by the mobilisation of glycogen in the liver. The energy needs of muscle and most other tissues are met by the release of fatty acids from adipose tissue.

After an overnight fast

After an overnight fast much of the liver glycogen has been used up and plasma levels of glucose are maintained by gluconeogenesis from amino acids derived from muscle in response to cortisol. Release of fatty acids from adipose tissue continues; some is used directly as an energy source while others are taken up by the liver and converted to ketone bodies, which are also used as energy sources.

In prolonged fasting

After about two days glucose can only be obtained by gluconeogenesis in the liver (and to a smaller extent the renal cortex) from amino acids derived from muscle. The production of fatty acids and ketone bodies continues. A gradual adaptation of the metabolism of the brain takes place whereby it can obtain an increasing proportion of its energy needs from ketone bodies.

Diabetes mellitus

This disorder is characterised by hyperglycaemia and glycosuria, accompanied by alterations in fat and protein metabolism. It is the result of lack of effective insulin action. In most patients the disease develops spontaneously, probably as a result of a hereditary predisposition. However, insulin deficiency can also occur if the pancreas is destroyed by disease or removed surgically.

There are two main clinical groups of diabetes mellitus, though the distinction between them is not complete.

Type I occurs most commonly with an abrupt onset in patients under 25 years of age. These patients are deficient in insulin; there is little or no insulin in their plasma and no insulin response to a glucose load. They

are liable to ketosis (see below) and require insulin for the control of their diabetes.

Type II develops insidiously in middle-aged, usually obese, patients; symptoms, if present, have often lasted several months before medical advice is sought. Population surveys have shown that many apparently healthy people have mild diabetes of this type. The total amount of islet tissue in the pancreas may be greater than normal and the plasma levels of insulin may be normal or raised. In these patients the fasting level of blood glucose may be normal but after a glucose load the blood level of glucose rises higher than in normal people and remains high longer (Fig. 23.15). Plasma levels of insulin may also start within the normal range but the maximum insulin response may not be seen until 90 or 120 minutes after the administration of glucose. This slow response is quite unlike the brisk response seen in normal subjects (Fig. 23.10). The cause of these abnormalities is still unknown.

Clinical features

The initial symptoms of diabetes develop because large amounts of glucose are excreted in the urine. The loss of so much solute causes an osmotic diuresis (Chap. 12) and a large volume of urine (*polyuria*). In spite of drinking large amounts of fluid (*polydipsia*) the patient is thirsty. These two symptoms alone may persist for many months in maturity-onset diabetes.

In type I, further features develop if treatment is not begun quickly. The tissues, in particular the muscles, are unable to take up glucose in the absence of insulin, so that the diabetic patient feels weak and tired. In adipose tissue triglycerides are broken down and the level of free fatty acids in the blood rises. The disproportionate metabolism of fat in diabetes results in the overproduction of ketone bodies (acetone, acetoacetic acid and β-hydroxybutyric acid), which can be detected in the blood and urine. When this *ketosis* is severe the patient's breath has a characteristic smell. As acetoacetic and β-hydroxybutyric acids are produced faster than they can be metabolised, the patient develops *acidaemia*, which causes hyperventilation (Chap. 10). Along with the abnormal metabolism of carbohydrate and fat there is an excessive breakdown of protein, the amino acids being converted to glucose in the liver.

At this stage, as a result of the ketosis, the patient develops *anorexia* (lack of appetite), nausea and vomiting; the continued loss of water and electrolytes in the urine leads to increasing saline depletion. The 'keto-acidosis' is associated with increasing drowsiness and, if untreated, the patient may become unconscious (diabetic coma) and die from a combination of hyperglycaemia, ketosis and acidaemia. This outcome can be prevented by treatment with insulin and intravenous fluids.

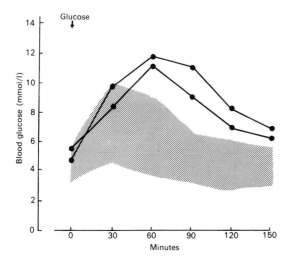

Fig. 23.15 Glucose tolerance tests in two patients with type II diabetes. Although the fasting blood glucose is normal the response to 50 g of glucose is abnormal. The normal range is indicated by the dotted area.

Hypoglycaemia

The amount of insulin that is given to a diabetic and the timing of its administration has to be adjusted to be compatible with his pattern of meals and exercise. If a diabetic receives his usual dose of insulin but misses a meal or takes unaccustomed exercise, he may become hypoglycaemic, with a plasma level of glucose lower than 3.5 mmol/l. Hypoglycaemia can also result from the presence of an insulin-producing tumour in the pancreas.

Any patient with hypoglycaemia may be seen to be behaving oddly; he may be confused and thought to be drunk. In severe cases the hypoglycaemia may cause convulsions and coma. Some patients with insulin-producing tumours learn that they can avoid symptoms by taking carbohydrate-rich snacks; they tend to gain weight.

FURTHER READING

Berridge M J, Irvine R F 1984 Inositol trisphosphate, a novel second messenger in cellular signal transduction. Nature 312: 315–321

Brown B L, Walker S W, Tomlinson S 1985 Calcium calmodulin and hormone secretion. Clinical Endocrinology 23: 201–218

Clayton R N 1983 Hormone-receptor interactions. In: Saunders K B (ed) Advanced medicine 19. Pitman, London, pp. 60–75

Czech M (ed) 1985 The molecular basis of insulin action. Plenum, New York

Daniel P M, Pratt O E, Spargo E 1977 The metabolic homeostatic role of muscle and its function as a store of protein. Lancet 2: 446–448

Dobbs R E, Unger R H 1982 Glucagon: secretion, function and clinical role. In: Freinkel N (ed) Contemporary metabolism, 2nd edn. Plenum, New York, pp. 61–118

Flier J S 1983 Insulin receptors and insulin resistance. Annual Review of Medicine 34: 145–160

Franchimont P (ed) 1986 Paracrine control. Clinics in Endocrinology and Metabolism 15: 1–211

Gale E 1980 Hypoglycaemia. Clinics in Endocrinology and Metabolism 9: 461–475

Lefkowitz R J, Caron M C, Stiles G L 1984 Mechanisms of membrane-receptor regulation. New England Journal of Medicine 310: 1570–1579

Marks V, Rose F C 1981 Hypoglycaemia, 2nd edn. Blackwell Scientific, Oxford

Orci L 1984 Patterns of cellular and subcellular organization in the endocrine pancreas. Journal of Endocrinology 102: 3–11

Stanley J C 1981 The glucose–fatty acid cycle. British Journal of Anaesthesia 53: 123–129

Tepperman J 1980 Endocrine functions of the pancreas. In: Metabolic and Endocrine Physiology, 4th edn. Year Book, Chicago

White D A, Middleton B, Baxter M 1984 Hormones and metabolic control. Arnold, London

Wollheim C B, Sharp G W G 1981 Regulation of insulin release by calcium. Physiological Reviews 61: 914–973

24

The hypothalamus and the pituitary gland

The hypothalamus and pituitary gland function as an integrated unit. The pituitary gland is attached by a stalk to the hypothalamus in the base of the brain. The pituitary gland (hypophysis) has two distinct components: the *adenohypophysis* or anterior pituitary and the *neurohypophysis* or posterior pituitary. The neurohypophysis is derived from neural cells in the floor of the developing third ventricle of the embryo in a region from which the hypothalamus is also formed. The adenohypophysis originates as an out-pocketing of ectodermal cells in the roof of the primitive oral cavity. This group of cells, containing an inner cavity, migrates upward and assumes a position anterior to the neurohypophysis.

The pituitary gland in an adult man weighs about 500 mg; it is slightly larger in women and increases in size during pregnancy. The pituitary fossa is covered by an extension of the dura mater through which passes the pituitary stalk connecting the gland to the hypothalamus. The optic chiasma lies just anterior to this connection. Enlargement of the gland, for example by tumour, results in upward growth towards the base of the brain and may cause pressure on the optic chiasma and consequently defects in the field of vision.

The blood supply to the pituitary gland is derived from the internal carotid artery. The posterior lobe is supplied directly from an arterial ring formed by branches of the two inferior hypophyseal arteries. The branches of the superior hypophyseal arteries supply the hypothalamus and the neural stalk to form a capillary plexus at these sites. A system of portal veins arising from this plexus delivers blood to the anterior lobe, which receives little direct arterial blood supply (Fig. 24.1). Within the anterior lobe the blood enters sinusoids in contact with the hormone-producing cells. This 'pituitary portal system' has great physiological significance since the blood not only provides nutrition for the anterior lobe but also delivers to it humoral substances from the hypothalamus and median eminence.

Hypothalamic neurones of different types liberate hormonal substances from their nerve endings into the

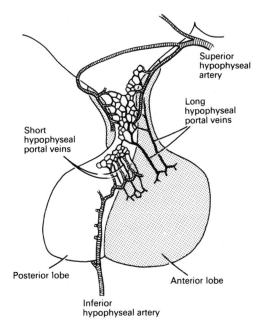

Fig. 24.1 The blood supply of the pituitary gland. The anterior lobe is largely supplied by portal vessels that arise from a capillary plexus in the pituitary stalk. The posterior lobe is supplied directly from the inferior hypophysial artery. The venous drainage of the anterior lobe (not shown) carries with it the hormones produced by the gland.

primary capillary plexus of the hypophyseal portal system in the median eminence, and then these substances are carried by the portal vessels to the anterior pituitary gland (Fig. 24.2) where they stimulate or inhibit the release of the various anterior pituitary hormones (Table 24.3). It is likely that the granules detected in the neurones of the median eminence contain the hypothalamic releasing hormones. The production of the hypothalamic hormones is regulated by monoamine neurotransmitters.

The hypothalamus contains only a few nanograms of releasing hormones. Much smaller quantities are

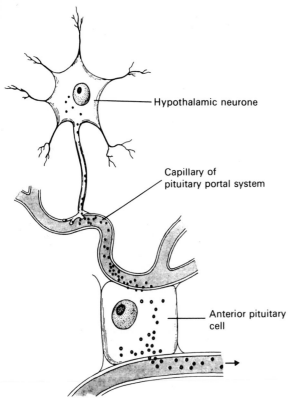

Fig. 24.2 Relation between hypothalamic neurones and anterior pituitary cells. (From Guillemin R, Burgus R 1972 Scientific American 227(5):24)

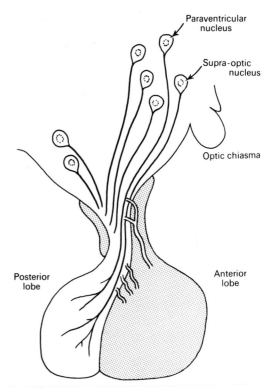

Fig. 24.4 The tracts from the hypothalamus to the pituitary. The paraventricular nucleus and the supra-optic nucleus are thought to be responsible for the elaboration of oxytocin and vasopressin, respectively. The other tracts terminate in the capillary plexus shown in Figure 24.1 and carry the hypothalamic hormones that control the release of the hormones of the anterior pituitary.

Table 24.3 The anterior pituitary hormones and the appropriate hypothalamic releasing hormones or release-inhibiting hormones. The hypothalamic hormones are usually known as factors until their structure has been determined.

Hormone	Structure	Hypothalamic control
Thyroid stimulating hormone (TSH)	Glycoprotein	Thyrotrophin releasing hormone (TRH)
Luteinising hormone (LH)	Glycoprotein	Gonadotrophin releasing hormone (GnRH)
Follicle stimulating hormone (FSH)	Glycoprotein	Gonadotrophin releasing hormone (GnRH)
Growth hormone (GH)	Protein	Growth hormone releasing factor (GRH)
		Growth hormone release inhibitory hormone (somatostatin)
Adrenocorticotrophic hormone (ACTH)	Polypeptide	Corticotrophin releasing hormone (CRH)
Prolactin	Protein	Prolactin release inhibitory factor (PIF) (Dopamine)
		Prolactin releasing factor (PRF)

secreted into the portal vessels, but enough to cause the cells of the anterior pituitary to synthesise and release a thousand or more times that weight of trophic hormones. The trophic hormones in turn cause the target glands to secrete at least a thousand times more hormone.

The two hormones of the posterior pituitary, oxytocin and vasopressin, are manufactured in specialised nerve cells in the hypothalamus — the paraventricular and supraoptic nuclei (Fig. 24.4). The hormones combine with specific binding proteins called *neurophysins* and flow down the axons of the nerve fibres of the hypothalamo–hypophyseal tract to storage cells in the posterior pituitary (Fig. 24.5).

The hypothalamic hormones

The hypothalamus has a major influence on the release and synthesis of the anterior pituitary hormones. Cutting the pituitary stalk leads to a reduction in the secretion of adrenocorticotrophic hormone (ACTH), thyroid stimulating hormone (TSH), luteinising hormone (LH), follicle stimulating hormone (FSH) and growth hormone (GH). As a consequence, the adrenal cortex,

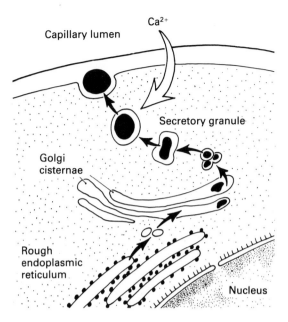

Fig. 24.6 Probable pathway of LH synthesis and release from the anterior pituitary cell. GnRH is thought to increase cell permeability to calcium, which in turn induces exocytosis. (From McCann S J 1977 New England Journal of Medicine 296:797)

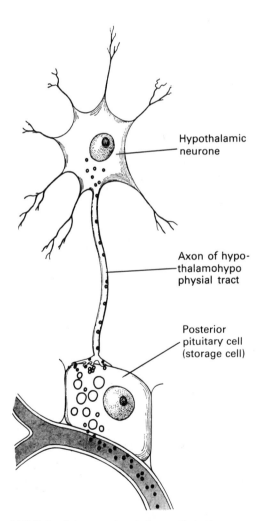

Fig. 24.5 Role of the posterior pituitary cells in the storage of the hormones oxytocin and ADH elaborated by hypothalamic neurones. (From Guillemin R, Burgus R 1972 Scientific American 227(5):24)

thyroid gland and gonads atrophy. Prolactin production increases after section of the pituitary stalk because its secretion is controlled by an inhibitory factor from the hypothalamus.

Evidence from experimental stimulation or from localised lesions indicates that corticotrophin releasing hormone (CRH) is produced in the posterior hypothalamus whereas thyrotrophin releasing hormone (TRH) is formed in the anterior region. The mid-hypothalamic region appears to be the source of gonadotrophin releasing hormone (GnRH). The ventral hypothalamus appears to control the secretion of growth hormone and prolactin. The neurosecretory cells are probably scattered throughout the hypothalamus rather than clustered in specific areas since extensive destruction of the hypothalamus is needed to produce a significant alteration in anterior pituitary function.

It is now generally accepted that the releasing hormones act by combining with specific receptors on the surface of the pituitary cells and activating adenylate cyclase. As a consequence calcium is taken up and in the process called exocytosis the secretory granules fuse with the cell membrane and their cores are extruded (Fig. 24.6). As well as stimulating the release of hormones these hormones probably also stimulate hormone synthesis.

CONTROL OF THE THYROID GLAND

Thyroid stimulating hormone (TSH, thyrotrophin) stimulates the thyroid gland to produce thyroxine (T_4) and tri-iodothyronine (T_3) (Chap. 25). The production of TSH by the anterior pituitary is stimulated by thyrotrophin releasing hormone (TRH) from the hypothalamus.

Thyrotrophin releasing hormone

TRH is a tripeptide (Table 24.7) that, given orally or intravenously, promotes the release of TSH by the anterior pituitary. TRH acts rapidly to release preformed TSH by acting on specific receptors on the plasma membranes of the appropriate cells of the anterior pituitary. Cyclic AMP is the likely intermediate messenger. High circulating levels of T_4 and T_3 block the stimulatory action of TRH on the TSH-producing cells of the anterior pituitary by decreasing the number of TRH binding sites. Conversely, if TRH is given to patients with primary thyroid failure, in whom circulating levels of thyroxine and tri-iodothyronine are low, there is an augmented TSH response (p. 316). Oestrogens also augment the response by increasing the number of TSH-binding sites in the anterior pituitary;

consequently the rise in TSH in response to TRH is greater in women in their reproductive years than in men (Fig. 24.8). Dopamine and somatostatin impair the release of TSH in response to TRH.

TSH is not the only hormone released by TRH. Intravenous infusion of TRH leads to increased production of prolactin but the physiological significance of this is unknown.

Thyroid stimulating hormone

TSH, a glycoprotein of molecular weight 28 000, consists of two dissimilar subunits, α and β. The structure of the α subunit closely resembles that of the α subunits of the other glycoprotein hormones — FSH, LH and human chorionic gonadotrophin (HCG). The β subunit confers on the hormone its biological specificity. The action of TSH is mediated by cyclic AMP; TSH is bound to receptors on the plasma membranes of the thyroid cells.

After hypophysectomy the thyroid gland atrophies and ceases to produce thyroid hormones. The administration of TSH reverses these abnormalities; it increases the weight and size of the thyroid, stimulates glucose oxidation and stimulates the synthesis of RNA and protein. TSH administration causes an increase in the uptake of iodine by the thyroid gland as well as stimulating the synthesis and release of tri-iodothyronine and thyroxine.

With modern immunoradiometric techniques it can be shown that plasma levels of TSH normally range between 0.1 μ/l up to about 5 μ/l. The production of TSH is controlled in part by a negative feedback by the thyroid hormones. TSH secretion has a circadian rhythm with peak values between 10 p.m. and midnight and minimum values at about 11 a.m. Superimposed upon this rhythm are fluctuations that are presumed to reflect the episodic secretion of TRH. The circadian rhythm of TSH levels is also thought to reflect the rhythmic secretion of TRH.

After destruction of the thyroid gland either by disease or by a surgical operation, the level of thyroid hormones in the plasma falls and TSH production is stimulated. It is extremely rare that over-activity of the thyroid gland is caused by over-production of TSH.

Table 24.7 The structures of some of the hypothalamic hormones. pGlu is pyroglutamate.

TRH
pGlu-His-Pro(NH$_2$)

GnRH
pGlu-His-Trp-Ser-Tyr-Gly-Leu-Arg-Pro-Gly-(NH$_2$)

GHRIH (Somatostatin)
H-Ala-Gly-Cys-Lys-Asn-Phe-Phe-Trp

HO-Cys-Ser-Thr-Phe-Thr-Lys

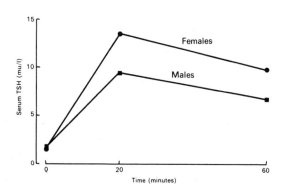

Fig. 24.8 Response in serum TSH levels to the administration of 200 μg of TRH intravenously in 25 normal women and 20 normal men. (After Ormston B J et al. 1971 Lancet 2:10)

CONTROL OF THE ADRENAL CORTEX

ACTH (adrenocorticotrophic hormone, corticotrophin) is a peptide hormone produced by the anterior pituitary and stimulates the release of cortisol from the adrenal cortex (Chap. 26). The production of ACTH is in turn stimulated by corticotrophin releasing hormone (CRH) from the hypothalamus.

Corticotrophin releasing hormone (CRH)

CRH was the first hypothalamic hormone to be described but its structure has only recently been determined. It is a peptide with 41 residues formed by the hydrolysis of a much larger pro-hormone with 196 amino acid residues. The secretion of CRH is influenced by neural impulses from higher centres as well as by circulating levels of ACTH and cortisol. Periodic variations in the secretion of cortisol and ACTH occur from the age of 3 years (p. 320) and reflect cyclical changes in CRH secretion.

ACTH

This is a single-chain peptide of 39 amino acids (Fig. 24.9). The ACTH molecules in different species have minor differences in amino acid composition, but the 24 amino acids at the amino-terminal are identical and are needed for biological activity.

NH$_2$-Ser-Tyr-Ser-Met-Glu-His-Phe-Arg-Trp-Gly-Lys-
-Pro-Val-Gly-Lys-Lys-Arg-Arg-Pro-Val-Lys-Val-Tyr-
-Pro-Asp-Ala-Gly-Glu-Asp-Gln-Ser-Ala-Glu-Ala-Phe-
-Pro-Leu-Glu-Phe-COOH.

Fig. 24.9 Amino acid sequence of human ACTH. The first 24 residues, shown in bold type, are those essential for biological activity.

ACTH has a number of biological effects and is the only hormone known to control the secretion of cortisol by the adrenal cortex. ACTH increases adrenal blood flow, increases the concentration of cholesterol and steroids within the adrenal cortex and increases the output of steroids, especially cortisol, into the circulation. ACTH also stimulates protein synthesis in the adrenal cortex; prolonged ACTH stimulation causes hypertrophy of the adrenal cortex.

ACTH secretion is believed to be controlled mainly by CRF from the hypothalamus. In the absence of CRF, due either to hypothalamic destruction or to

Table 24.10 Factors controlling the release of ACTH

Increased ACTH production
Increased CRH production due to
   Physical stress (particularly exercise)
   Emotional stress
   Hypoglycaemia
   As part of the circadian rhythm

Decreased ACTH production
Decreased CRH production
   Increased ACTH levels ('short feed-back loop')
   Increased cortisol levels ('long feed-back loop')
   As part of circadian rhythm
Increased cortisol levels (direct effect)

interruption of the portal circulation between hypothalamus and pituitary, the secretion of ACTH and consequently that of cortisol is severely impaired. Three major mechanisms appear to control ACTH release and thus cortisol secretion: circadian rhythm, negative feedback and stress (Table 24.10).

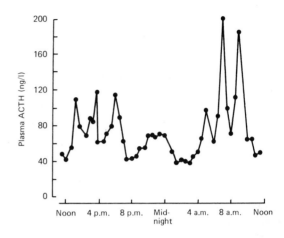

Fig. 24.11 Plasma ACTH levels throughout the day in a normal woman. (Data of Krieger D T 1979 Clinics in Endocrinology and Metabolism 8:467)

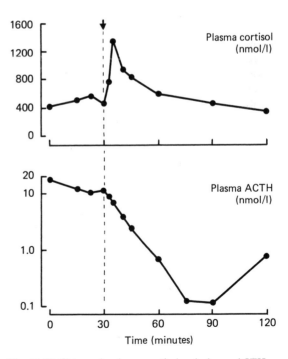

Fig. 24.12 Changes in plasma cortisol and plasma ACTH levels after a single intravenous injection of 5 mg of cortisol into a normal subject. (Data of Daly J R et al. 1974 Clinical Endocrinology 3:335)

Plasma levels of cortisol and ACTH are lowest around midnight and increase to maximal levels about 8 a.m.; levels then fall throughout the day with peaks that may occur around mid-day and 6 p.m. (Fig. 24.11). This periodicity of ACTH secretion is well established from about the age of three and persists throughout life, even in patients without adrenal function. The rhythm is controlled by the pattern of sleep, but several days are needed for the rhythm to adapt to a change, for example to a different time-zone ('jet-lag'). Abnormalities in the circadian rhythm of plasma cortisol occur in some patients with psychiatric disorders such as depression and also in patients with disease of the hypothalamus.

The reciprocal relationship between circulating ACTH and cortisol levels constitutes a major homeostatic mechanism: as cortisol levels rise so ACTH levels fall. ACTH secretion decreases within two minutes of a rise in plasma cortisol (Fig. 24.12).

The neuroendocrine system regulating ACTH secretion can respond to stress with great rapidity; for example ACTH secretion increases in response to surgical stress within a few minutes of the first incision. Many different forms of stress, including fever, noise, pain, fear and hypoglycaemia can cause ACTH release. Such stress factors over-ride both circadian rhythm and feed-back control.

GROWTH HORMONE

Control

The secretion of growth hormone by the anterior pituitary is regulated by the anterior pituitary factors, growth hormone releasing hormone (GRH) and growth hormone release inhibiting hormone on *somatostatin* (Table 24.7). It is thought that there are two forms of GRH in the hypothalamus; peptides with 40 and with 44 residues. The 40-residue peptide has been synthesised and can stimulate the formation of cyclic-AMP in isolated rat pituitary cells. GH production is also stimulated. In the human subject intravenous administration of GRH stimulates GH release within 5 minutes but does not affect the plasma levels of prolactin, TSH, LH or ACTH.

The function of somatostatin is illustrated in Figure 24.13. Somatostatin, a peptide with 14 residues, is

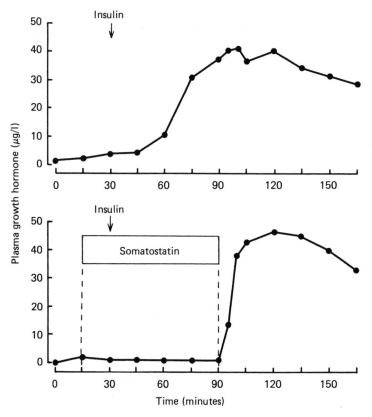

Fig. 24.13 Action of somatostatin in preventing the rise in plasma growth hormone induced by an injection of insulin. Mean values for five normal men. (Data of Gomez-Pan A, Shaw R 1977 Clinics in Endocrinology and Metabolism 6:181)

Table 24.14 Some reported biological actions of somatostatin

Endocrine actions
Inhibits secretion of: growth hormone, TSH, ACTH, gastrin, CCK-PZ, secretin, human pancreatic polypeptide, vasoactive intestinal polypeptide, gastric inhibitory polypeptide, motilin, glucagon, insulin, renin

Non-endocrine actions
Inhibits gastric secretion and emptying
Decreases splanchnic blood flow
Diminishes electrical activity in CNS neurones
Inhibits platelet aggregation

found in many other parts of the central nervous system, in the gut and in the delta cells of the pancreas (p. 294). It is now appreciated that somatostatin has many actions in addition to inhibiting the secretion of growth hormone (Table 24.14). In the control of GH secretion GRH is probably more important than somatostatin since section of the pituitary stalk leads to greatly reduced production of GH.

The mechanism by which somatostatin inhibits secretion is still not clear. Somatostatin has been reported to lower cyclic AMP levels in the pituitary gland and to block the elevation of cyclic AMP during glucose-stimulated insulin release from pancreatic islets. Somatostatin does not appear to act as a conventional systemic hormone since it has a very short half life and a wide variety of actions in different tissues. It has not been demonstrated in plasma. It seems likely that somatostatin acts as a local hormone; in the pancreas, for example, it probably modifies the function of the alpha cells in the immediate vicinity of the cells by which it is produced. Somatostatin release by the hypothalamus is inhibited by glucose and stimulated by insulin. Growth hormone itself has a direct inhibitory effect on somatostatin release, as does somatomedin (see below).

Functions
Human growth hormone (GH, somatotrophin) is a single-chain polypeptide composed of 190 amino acids containing two intra-chain disulphide bridges. GH promotes skeletal growth, as well as increasing growth of muscles, connective tissue and viscera such as liver, kidneys, intestines, pancreas and adrenals.

Secretion
Growth hormone is released in a pulsatile manner; the largest surges occur during the first two hours of sleep at night. The number and magnitude of spontaneous GH pulses depend on age; they increase during the growth spurt of adolescence and decline thereafter. Sleep-associated release of GH is usually absent in adults over 50 years of age.

Mode of action
Growth hormone does not stimulate anabolic processes in cartilage in vitro, but the growth of cartilage is readily stimulated in vivo by GH. This finding led to the demonstration that GH exerts its anabolic effects not directly but by stimulating the release of a second hormonal mediator, *somatomedin*, which acts on the target tissues. It is now known that the somatomedins are a group of small peptides of molecular weight 6000 to 8000. They are produced, particularly in the liver, in response to GH. Their half-life in the circulation is several hours compared with that of GH, which is about 20 minutes.

The major somatomedin in adults is somatomedin C, which was at one time also known as insulin-like growth factor I since it has many actions similar to those of insulin. Like insulin, it promotes glucose uptake and oxidation in muscle and adipose tissue. It also promotes cell division in many tissues.

Somatomedin levels can now be measured in plasma. As might be expected high levels occur in acromegaly when there is excess of growth hormone (below); low levels occur in pituitary insufficiency. Low levels of somatomedin are found, together with high GH levels, in malnutrition and in a rare form of growth impairment, Laron-type dwarfism. This disorder has been attributed to lack of receptors for GH.

Disorders
An increase in circulating levels of GH occurs in response to various stimuli, including exercise, anxiety, hypoglycaemia and the administration of certain amino acids such as arginine (Table 24.15). Hyperglycaemia inhibits GH release. In children pituitary insufficiency causes dwarfism (p. 370); GH lack may also occur because of lack of GRH (p. 302). Excessive production of GH in childhood results in the rare disorder *gigantism*. Excessive production of GH in an adult leads to enlargement of the jaw, hands, feet and viscera in a condition known as *acromegaly* (Fig. 24.16). Growth of long bones is not possible in response to the GH excess

Table 24.15 Factors controlling the production of growth hormone (GH) by the anterior pituitary

Increased GH production
Increased GRH secretion by the hypothalamus
  Exercise
  Anxiety
  Hypoglycaemia
  Rise in plasma amino acid levels
  Sleep

Decreased GH production
Increased somatostatin secretion by the hypothalamus
  Hyperglycaemia

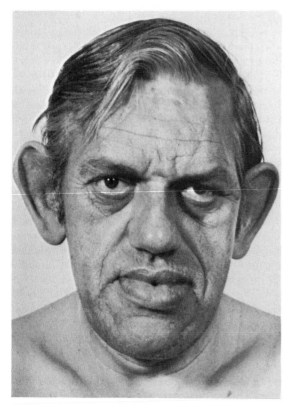

Fig. 24.16 A patient with acromegaly. (Courtesy of C. G. Beardwell)

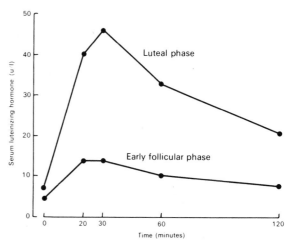

Fig. 24.17 Response of serum LH to an intravenous injection of 100 μg of GnRH. Mean values in ten normal women in whom the study was carried out in the follicular phase and in the luteal phase of the same menstrual cycle. (After Shaw R W et al. 1974 Journal of Obstetrics and Gynaecology of the British Commonwealth 81:632)

since the epiphyses have fused. No recognisable clinical disorder is associated with lack of GH in adults.

THE GONADOTROPHINS

The pituitary gonadotrophins are luteinising hormone (LH) and follicle stimulating hormone (FSH). Their secretion is stimulated by a single hypothalamic hormone, gonadotrophin releasing hormone (GnRH), also known as luteinising hormone releasing hormone (LHRH).

Gonadotrophin releasing hormone

GnRH is a decapeptide (Table 24.7) and is produced in specific areas of the hypothalamus, namely the median eminence and the arcuate and ventromedial nuclei.

The response of the anterior pituitary to GnRH is modified by the circulating levels of the gonadal hormones that are produced in response to LH and FSH. In women the oestrogens, particularly oestradiol-17β, inhibit gonadotrophin production (negative feedback) during most of the menstrual cycle, but the pre-ovulatory discharge of LH is associated with a rise in oestrogen levels. These feedback effects are accompanied by marked changes in responsiveness of the pituitary gland to GnRH. Figure 24.17 compares the response to GnRH in the early or follicular phase of the menstrual cycle, when oestradiol-17β levels are low, with the response in the luteal phase when oestradiol-17β levels are higher. Two major sites within the hypothalamus take up oestradiol-17β, namely the arcuate nucleus and the pre-optic region; both also contain GnRH neurones. Noradrenaline appears to mediate both the stimulatory effect of gonadal steroids in the pre-optic region and the negative feedback thought to be localised in the arcuate nucleus.

Inhibin

Studies in animals and in humans have shown that there is an inverse relation between gametogenesis and the secretion of FSH. The factor involved was named *inhibin* and has now been isolated in a partially purified form from both male and female gonadal tissue. In men the site of production appears to be the seminiferous tubules, although the Sertoli cells also appear to be involved in synthesis and secretion. In women inhibin is secreted by granulosa cells. In the range of doses that are active on FSH secretion, inhibin does not lower basal LH levels.

LH and FSH

Like TSH these hormones are glycoproteins composed of two subunits, α and β. Structurally LH is very similar to HCG (p. 339) and these substances cross-react both biologically and immunologically.

The secretion of the gonadotrophins by the anterior pituitary determines testicular and ovarian function. In women FSH is responsible for the growth and maturation of the ovarian follicle. LH is also needed for normal follicular development and function, but the major action of LH in women is to promote the development and endocrine function of the corpus luteum (p. 328).

In men FSH increases the growth of the seminiferous tubules and stimulates spermatogenesis. In this action LH also appears to be necessary for full effect. LH increases the production of testosterone by the interstitial cells of the testes. The secretion of the gonadotrophins varies at different ages; low levels are found in childhood, with a rise at about the time of puberty (p. 367). After middle age, the germinal and endocrine functions of the ovary diminish (the menopause). In turn this leads to greatly increased levels of LH and FSH, which fall only slowly in later years.

In the ovulatory cycles of women there is a peak of LH and FSH at mid-cycle. FSH levels are also moderately raised during the first few days of the follicular phase and decrease during the days preceding ovulation (p. 331). The secretion of LH and, to a smaller extent, FSH takes place in bursts at irregular intervals throughout the day in both men and women. In women there are between 9 and 14 secretory episodes when LH levels rise sharply two-or three-fold during each 24-hour period (Fig. 24.18). In women the frequency and amplitude of the pulses of LH and FSH secretion vary according to the stage of the menstrual cycle; they are larger but less frequent in the luteal than in the follicular phase.

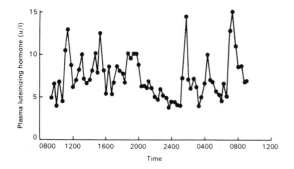

Fig. 24.18 Plasma concentrations of LH sampled every 20 minutes in a normal man. The pulsatile secretion of LH reflects the pulsatile secretion of GnRH by the hypothalamus. The physiological action of GnRH may be mimicked by the pulsatile infusion of GnRH, for example in the treatment of certain types of male infertility caused by azoospermia (Chap. 27). (After Boyar R et al. 1972 Journal of Clinical Endocrinology and Metabolism 35:73)

Regulation of gonadotrophin secretion

Men

The administration of testosterone to men is followed by a rapid fall in plasma LH levels and a smaller fall in plasma FSH levels. The capacity of the pituitary gland to respond to GnRH is not affected by the administration of testosterone; this suggests that the decrease in gonadotrophin levels produced by testosterone is not related to a diminished pituitary responsiveness to GnRH but rather to a reduced hypothalamic production of GnRH. It is likely, therefore, that testosterone acts at the hypothalamic level.

Women

Oestradiol-17β also suppresses LH production but in a different manner: whereas testosterone decreases the number of pulses of LH secretion per day, oestradiol-17β decreases the amplitude of the pulses of LH and has a more marked effect on the secretion of FSH.

The responsiveness of the anterior pituitary to the administration of GnRH varies throughout the menstrual cycle. It is greatest in the pre-ovulatory phase, less marked in the luteal phase and smallest in the follicular phase. The cyclical variation in response is related to changes in endogenous production of oestrogen and progesterone. The administration of exogenous oestradiol-17β to normal women in the follicular phase of the cycle, a time when endogenous oestrogen levels are low, increases the responsiveness to GnRH.

In women oestrogens inhibit FSH secretion whereas they exert a biphasic action on LH: first a negative (or inhibitory) effect followed by a positive (or stimulatory) effect. During the menstrual cycle the oestradiol-17β peak in plasma precedes the rise in LH by between one and three days. This chronological sequence makes it likely that oestrogens stimulate the release of LH at mid-cycle.

Children

The secretion of pituitary gonadotrophins is present from the beginning of infancy. After the separation of the placenta an abrupt fall in circulating levels of HCG, progesterone and oestrogen takes place. This fall stimulates an increase in the secretion of the previously suppressed pituitary gonadotrophins, peak levels being reached at about 2 or 3 months of age both in boys and in girls. The administration of GnRH to re-pubertal children results in a greater rise in FSH and in LH and the response is usually more pronounced in girls. During puberty the plasma levels of the gonadotrophins increase greatly. In girls FSH levels increase during the early stages of puberty and then level off. LH levels rise steadily until just before the beginning of menstruation, when a further rapid increase occurs. The first cycles after the menarche are usually anovular.

PROLACTIN

Prolactin secretion by the anterior pituitary is controlled by two hypothalamic factors, prolactin release inhibiting factor (PIF) and prolactin releasing factor (PRF). Prolactin is unique among the anterior pituitary hormones in that its secretion is under tonic inhibitory control by the hypothalamus. If the connection between the hypothalamus and the pituitary gland is damaged the secretion of prolactin is increased; the secretion of the other anterior pituitary hormones is reduced. It is clear, therefore, that PIF, now known to be dopamine, is dominant in the control of prolactin secretion. TRH releases prolactin from anterior pituitary cells both in vivo and in vitro. It is unlikely, however, that TRH acts as the physiological prolactin releasing factor as prolactin can be released without thyrotrophin, for example during suckling (p. 349). In addition prolactin and thyrotrophin have different circadian rhythms.

Secretion

Prolactin is secreted in a pulsatile manner and plasma levels fluctuate markedly over a short period. Levels of prolactin in plasma increase shortly after falling asleep, and fall again in the morning. Increases also occur during day-time naps. Both physical and emotional stress have been found to raise prolactin levels. The magnitude of the stress-induced increase is higher in women than in men.

Prolactin secretion is inhibited by increased plasma levels of prolactin (short-loop feedback); this effect is mediated through the hypothalamus. Oestrogens also affect prolactin secretion; high levels of oestrogen, as for example in pregnancy, stimulate prolactin production. In vitro studies have shown that oestrogen increase the rate of mitosis of prolactin-secreting cells; this probably accounts for the enlargement of the pituitary seen during pregnancy. Levels of prolactin in plasma are higher in women during the reproductive years than in men or in post-menopausal women.

Many drugs alter the production or action of amines in the central nervous system and prolactin production is frequently affected by drugs such as methyl dopa and drugs used in the treatment of psychological disorders. Raised prolactin levels, with the consequent effect on breast tissue and gonadal function, are commonly seen when these drugs are administered. Conversely any drug that mimics the action of dopamine lowers prolactin levels; *bromocriptine*, a derivative of ergot, is used for this purpose.

Functions

Although it is possible that prolactin is important in a variety of metabolic processes its only established roles in man are concerned with the control of lactation and gonadal function.

Prolactin is one of several hormones including oestrogens, corticosteroids, insulin and thyroxine involved in the initiation and maintenance of lactation (p. 348). Suckling stimulates the production of prolactin so that plasma levels of prolactin remain high throughout lactation, particularly in societies in which no supplementary feeding is usual. These high prolactin levels play a part in reducing the likelihood of conception while lactation is in progress (p. 349).

Prolactin appears to exert a direct inhibitory effect on the ovaries, reducing the production of both oestradiol and progesterone. High levels of prolactin suppress the pulsatile release of GnRH and lead to gonadal dysfunction in both men and women. In men hyperprolactinaemia is an uncommon finding associated with impotence and galactorrhoea (milk production).

THE POSTERIOR PITUITARY

The posterior pituitary gland is a prolongation of the floor of the third ventricle. Approximately 100 000 nerve fibres connect the posterior pituitary with the hypothalamus, particularly the supra-optic and paraventricular nuclei (Fig. 24.4). The two hormones *oxytocin* and *vasopressin* are synthesised in the hypothalamus, oxytocin mainly in the paraventricular nuclei and vasopressin largely in the supra-optic nuclei (Fig. 24.19). They are then incorporated into granules with a binding protein, *neurophysin*, of which two forms, specific for oxytocin and vasopressin, are recognised. The granules pass down the axons of the neurohypophyseal tract to dilated nerve endings in the posterior pituitary from which they enter the blood (Figs. 24.5 and 24.20).

Oxytocin

```
 S————————————————S
 |                |
Cys—Tyr—Ile—Glu—Asn—Cys—Pro—Leu—Gly (NH₂)
```

Vasopressin

```
 S————————————————S
 |                |
Cys—Tyr—Phe—Glu—Asn—Cys—Pro—Arg—Gly (NH₂)
```

Fig. 24.19 The structures of oxytocin and vasopressin. Vertebrates all have the same oxytocin but the structure of vasopressin varies from species to species. Human vasopressin is known as arginine vasopressin.

Table 24.21 Relative potencies of oxytocin and vasopressin

Action	Oxytocin	Vasopressin
Antidiuretic potency	1	200
Milk ejection activity	100	1

fetus itself may have a role to play in its own delivery. The function of oxytocin in men is not known.

The release of oxytocin results from depolarisation of the neurosecretory cells and is mediated through neural pathways the afferent components of which begin in the uterine cervix and the nipple. Oxytocin and vasopressin are usually secreted together although the relative amounts secreted depend on the nature of the stimulus. The half-life of oxytocin is 1 to 4 minutes. It is metabolised in the liver and kidneys.

Oxytocin or a synthetic analogue is used to induce labour or to strengthen uterine contractions in a prolonged labour. Care must be given to the rate of administration since even synthetic analogues of oxytocin have some vasopressin-like properties (Table 24.21). Overdosage may therefore cause water retention.

Vasopressin

Vasopressin in man is also known as arginine vaso-pressin; it is a peptide (Fig. 24.23). Its principal function is the control of water reabsorption in the distal convoluted tubule and the collecting ducts of the kidney (p. 197). The mode of action of vasopressin involves activation of adenylate cyclase and the production of cyclic AMP; theophylline, which inhibits the breakdown of cyclic AMP, has an antidiuretic effect. Patients with diabetes insipidus have low urinary levels of cyclic AMP.

In large doses vasopressin causes contraction of smooth muscle particularly in the blood vessels of the skin and in the splanchnic bed; this leads to a rise in blood pressure. In physiological concentrations, however, vasopressin has little or no effect on smooth muscle.

The secretion of vasopressin provides a homeostatic mechanism to maintain the osmolarity of body fluids within a relatively narrow range. Two main types of receptor have been postulated: hypothalamic receptors sensitive to changes in osmolarity (*osmoreceptors*) and *baroreceptors*, sensitive to changes in blood volume. Baroreceptors are situated in the large thoracic blood vessels and are linked to the hypothalamus by the vagus nerve. Vasopressin is secreted continuously, basal plasma levels are 1 to 5 ng/l. When there is an increase in plasma osmolarity due to dehydration or a fall in blood volume due to haemorrhage, the secretion of vasopressin increases (Fig. 24.22) and the resulting water retention restores the osmolarity or blood volume to normal (Chap. 13). Vasopressin cannot be detected

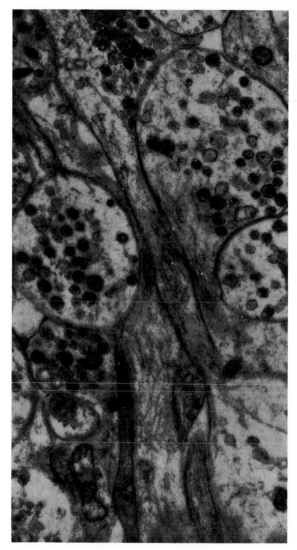

Fig. 24.20 Electron micrograph of the posterior pituitary of the rabbit to show unmyelinated nerve fibres in longitudinal section and a number of neural swellings. Most of the swellings contain granules about 130 nm in diameter with an electron-dense centre; these are known as neurosecretory granules. × 24000. (Barer R et al. 1963 Proceedings of the Royal Society Series B 158:338)

Oxytocin

This peptide hormone has a molecular weight of 1025. It stimulates the myoepithelial cells of the ducts of the breasts to eject milk in response to stimuli from the nipple. Oxytocin levels rise in labour but it is not yet clear whether oxytocin plays a part in the initiation or maintenance of labour; women with damage to the neurohypophyseal tract severe enough to cause diabetes insipidus are able to have a normal labour. Since blood levels of oxytocin are high in umbilical vein blood the

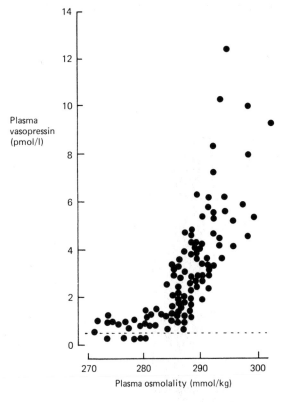

Fig. 24.22 Relation between plasma vasopressin and plasma osmolality in recumbent normal subjects. The horizontal dashed line indicates the detection limit for the assay. (After Robertson G L et al. 1973 Journal of Clinical Investigation 52:2340)

in the plasma in patients with diabetes insipidus or in normal subjects after a water load.

The likely steps involved in the release of vasopressin from the posterior pituitary are as follows. Reception of an appropriate stimulus produces depolarisation of cells in the supra-optic nucleus. The depolarisation propagated down the axons in the neurohypophyseal stalk allows an influx of calcium ions into the neuro-secretory cell. The neurosecretory granules are extruded

through the cell membrane of the axon terminals and enter the capillary blood. Presumably vasopressin and neurophysin dissociate before the effects on the renal tubules can be produced but the site of dissociation is not known.

Vasopressin has a half-life in the plasma of approximately 5 minutes and is metabolised in the liver and kidneys. A lack of vasopressin causes *diabetes insipidus*; a syndrome of excessive vasopressin secretion is also recognised. These disorders are described in Chapter 12.

OTHER BRAIN PEPTIDES

In addition to the releasing and inhibiting factors produced by the hypothalamus and the hormones produced by the anterior and posterior pituitary, a number of other polypeptides are produced in this area. Of particular interest is β-lipotrophin, a single-chain peptide containing 91 amino acids. Various fragments of this molecule and of the ACTH molecule are recognised (Figs. 24.23 and 24.24), including α-*melanocyte stimulating hormone* (α-MSH) and *corticotrophin-like intermediate lobe peptide* (CLIP). These two compounds are found in the human pituitary gland only during fetal life and during pregnancy, when a distinct *intermediate lobe* can be found. γ-Lipotrophin is also secreted by the human pituitary but β-MSH has never been found in humans.

Pharmacological studies of the effects of opiates revealed that the brain itself contained several

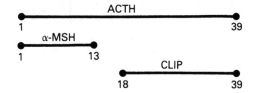

Fig. 24.24 Relationship between the amino acid sequences of ACTH and related peptides. Sequences are numbered from the amino-terminal (N-terminal).

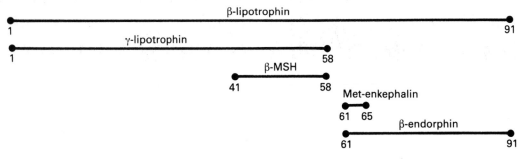

Fig. 24.23 Relationship between the amino acid sequences of β-lipotrophin and related peptides.

Met-enkephalin

H$_2$N-Tyr-Gly-Gly-Phe-Met-COOH

Leu-enkephalin

H$_2$N-Tyr-Gly-Gly-Phe-Leu-COOH

Fig. 24.25 Structures of the enkephalins.

morphine-like factors. Two of these were found to be pentapeptides, *met-enkephalin* and *leu-enkephalin* (Fig. 24.25). The structure of met-enkephalin is contained in β-lipotrophin. The opiate action of the entire 31 amino acid fragment (β-endorphin) was then studied and found to be more potent than met-enkephalin. The release of β-endorphin from the pituitary has been shown to be regulated in parallel with ACTH but the function of β-endorphin is still not known; it is possible that these peptides are involved in the control of mood.

Neurotensin

Neurotensin is a peptide with 13 residues that has been extracted from brain and gut. It increases capillary permeability, dilates arterioles and stimulates gastric acid secretion. It is possible that these actions are mediated by the local release of histamine from mast cells. The physiological role of neurotensin is not clear.

THE PINEAL GLAND

The pineal gland, often visible in X-rays of the skull because of its tendency to calcify, is a small structure about 8 mm long and 4 mm wide lying on the dorsal aspect of the superior colliculi. The gland contains much serotonin (5HT), which is converted to melatonin (*N*-acetyl-5-methoxytryptamine). Melatonin causes constriction of the melanocytes of the frog's skin. In mammals melatonin secretion is increased by exposure to darkness and inhibited by light; melatonin seems to have a role in the control of seasonal behaviour such as mating and hibernation.

In man the function of melatonin is unknown but plasma levels are higher at midnight than at noon and this variation is related to sleep, particularly REM sleep, rather than to darkness. Plasma melatonin levels are high during menstruation and low at the time of ovulation. Tumours that destroy the pineal in boys may cause precocious puberty, while pineal tumours that secrete melatonin are associated with a diminution of gonadal function.

FURTHER READING

Baylis P H 1983 Posterior pituitary function in health and disease. Clinics in Endocrinology and Metabolism 12: 747–770

Bloom F E 1983 The endorphins: a growing family of pharmacologically pertinent peptides. Annual Review of Pharmacology and Toxicology 23: 151–170

Brown E M, Aurbach G D 1982 Receptors and second messengers in cell function and clinical disorders. In: Freinkel N (ed) Contemporary metabolism, Vol. 2. Plenum, New York, pp. 247–299

Clayton R N 1983 Receptors in health and disease. Clinics in Endocrinology and Metabolism 12: xi–xlv, 1–255

Feek C M, Marante D J, Edwards C R W 1983 The hypothalamic pituitary adrenal axis. Clinics in Endocrinology and Metabolism 12: 597–618

Gómez-Pan A, Rodriguez-Arnao M D 1983 Somatostatin and growth-hormone releasing factor: synthesis, location, metabolism and function. Clinics in Endocrinology and Metabolism 12: 469–507

Hall R, Anderson H, Smart G A, Besser M 1980 Fundamentals of clinical endocrinology, 3rd edn. Pitman, London

Hughes J (ed) 1983 Opioid peptides. British Medical Bulletin 39, 1–100

Imura H 1985 ACTH and related peptides. Clinics in Endocrinology and Metabolism 14: 845–866

O'Riordan J L H, Malan P G, Gould R P 1982 Essentials of endocrinology. Blackwell Scientific, Oxford.

Mullen P E, Smith I 1981 The endocrinology of the human pineal. British Journal of Hospital Medicine 26: 248–256

Pasternak G W, Childers S R 1983 The actions of opiates and opioid peptides. In: Turner P, Shard D (eds) Recent Advances in Clinical Pharmacology 3. Churchill Livingstone, Edinburgh, p. 253–279

Phillips L S, Vassilopoulou-Sellin R 1980 The somatomedins. New England Journal of Medicine 302: 371–380, 438–446

Reiter R J (ed) 1984 The pineal gland. Raven Press, New York

Winter J S D 1982 Hypothalamic-pituitary function in the fetus and infant. Clinics in Endocrinology and Metabolism 11: 41–55

25

The thyroid gland

The thyroid gland, which weighs between 15 and 40 g in a healthy adult, consists of an enormous number of closed spherical follicles, the walls of which are composed of a single layer of epithelium (Fig. 25.1). The follicles, which vary in diameter from 0.05 to 0.1 mm, are filled with a protein material, the *colloid*, in which thyroid hormones are incorporated. The gland has a very rich capillary network. Between the follicles are the *parafollicular cells* or C-cells, which produce calcitonin (p. 361).

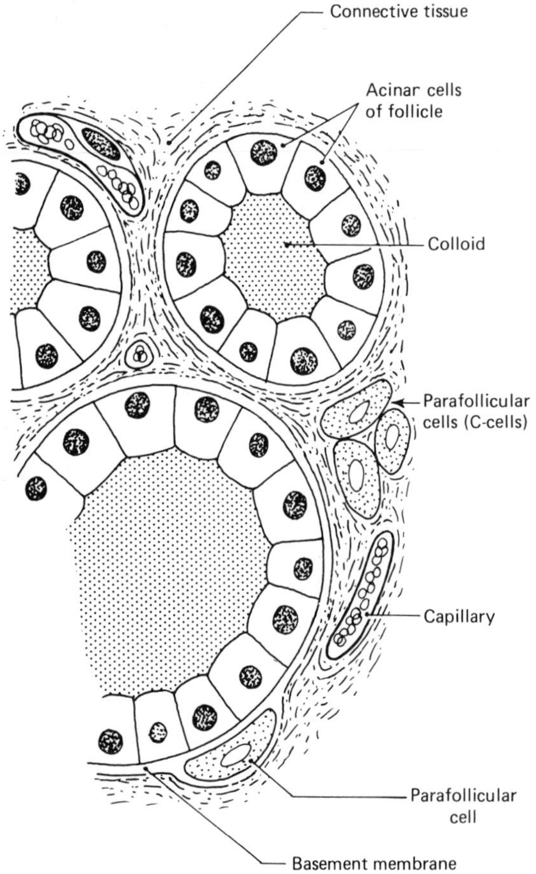

The thyroid gland is not essential to life but it is essential for growth and for physical and mental well-being. The gland begins to synthesise thyroxine about the third month of fetal life. The secretion of thyroid hormones appears to be fairly constant throughout life but the gland enlarges and its secretion is increased at puberty and during pregnancy.

The thyroid gland contains a large amount of iodine (0.06 per cent) almost all of which is firmly bound to protein either in the cells lining the follicles or in the colloid material within them. The characteristic protein of the colloid is thyroglobulin; on hydrolysis it yields several iodine-containing derivatives of tyrosine including mono- and di-iodotyrosine, tri-iodothyronine and tetra-iodothyronine (thyroxine).

THE THYROID HORMONES

The thyroid hormones are thyroxine and tri-iodothyronine (Fig. 25.2). Thyroxine was the first to be

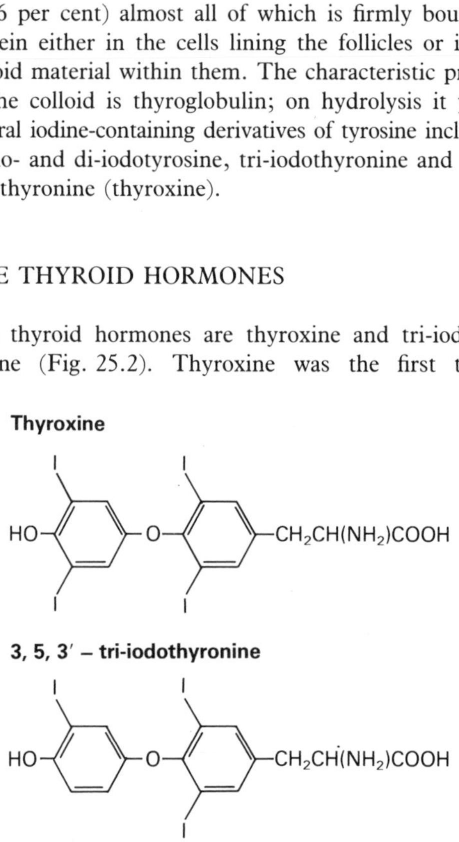

Fig. 25.1 The histological features of the normal thyroid gland. In an inactive gland the amount of colloid is increased and the cells are flattened. In an over-active gland the colloid is reduced and the cells form a tall columnar epithelium.

Fig. 25.2 Structures of thyroxine (T_4) and tri-iodothyronine (T_3)

discovered and is produced in larger amounts. About one-third of the thyroxine secreted by the thyroid is metabolised in the tissues to tri-iodothyronine, which is the active hormone at the cellular level.

Synthesis of thyroid hormones

In the first stage of the formation of the hormones thyroglobulin is synthesised and at the same time inorganic iodide from the plasma is concentrated some 25-fold in the follicular cells. The gland's remarkable powers of accumulating iodide can be demonstrated with ^{123}I (Fig. 25.3). This accumulation is controlled by TSH.

As iodide is absorbed by the follicular cells it is oxidised to iodine ($2I^- \rightarrow I_2 + 2e$) by hydrogen peroxide generated by an enzyme system that includes cytochrome C. The free iodine is immediately taken up by the tyrosine of the thyroglobulin to form mono-iodotyrosine and di-iodotyrosine as residues still incorporated in the protein molecule. These residues then undergo oxidative coupling with the transfer of one side chain to form thyroxine and tri-iodothyronine (Fig. 25.4).

The thyroxine and tri-iodothyronine produced in the gland are still within the structure of the thyroglobulin

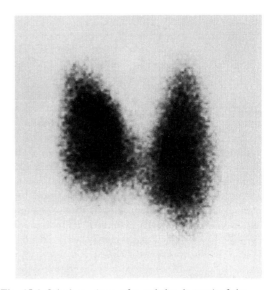

Fig. 25.3 Scintiscan (scan of γ-emitting isotope) of the thyroid gland in a normal 44-year-old woman 4 hours after an intravenous dose of 40 mBq of ^{123}I. (Courtesy of H. W. Gray)

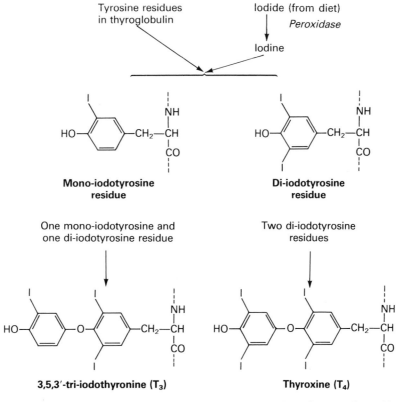

Fig. 25.4 Pathways for the synthesis of thyroxine (T₄) and tri-iodotyrosine (T₃) residues from tyrosine residues on thyroglobulin molecules.

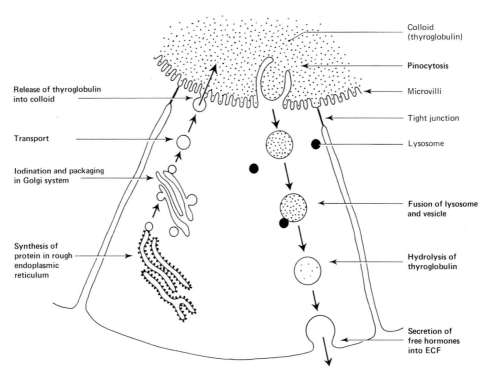

Fig. 25.5 The two steps in the secretion of the thyroid hormones. The thyroglobulin is synthesised in the rough endoplasmic reticulum, iodinated and packaged in the Golgi complex, and transported into the colloid. When the gland is stimulated colloid is taken up by vesicles that fuse with lysosomes. The lysosomal enzymes hydrolyse the thyroglobulin with the production of free hormones, which pass out into the blood.

molecule and are stored in the colloid. When the thyroid is stimulated by TSH the thyroglobulin of colloid is engulfed by the follicular cells and broken down by lysosomal enzymes to yield thyroxine, tri-iodothyronine and mono- and di-iodotyrosines (Fig. 25.5). Figure 25.6 shows the pseudopods involved in pinocytosis. The thyroxine and tri-iodothyronine pass into the plasma while the iodotyrosines are broken down within the cells to yield iodide, which can be used again. These steps are summarised in Figure 25.7.

Tri-iodothyronine is also produced in peripheral tissues by removal of one atom of iodine from thyroxine. It has been estimated that some 80 per cent of the tri-iodothyronine in the blood plasma is produced in this way and only 20 per cent in the thyroid. Thyroxine is also de-iodinated in the tissues to the physiologically inactive $3,3',5'$-tri-iodothyronine (reverse T_3). The factors that control the way in which a particular tissue adjusts T_4 metabolism between the T_3 pathway and the reverse T_3 pathway are not understood.

Control of thyroid activity
The activity of the thyroid gland is regulated by variations in the plasma levels of thyrotrophin (thyroid-stimulating hormone, TSH). The immediate action of this hormone is to release thyroid hormones from the gland. Prolonged stimulation with TSH increases the uptake of iodine from the blood and promotes hyperplasia of the gland.

The output of TSH from the anterior pituitary is itself governed in part by thyrotrophin releasing hormone (TRH), derived from the hypothalamus (p. 300), and in part by the plasma levels of the thyroid hormones. A fall in plasma levels of thyroxine and tri-iodothyronine increases TSH production and a rise diminishes it.

Drugs affecting hormone synthesis
The accumulation of iodide by the thyroid can be reduced by anti-thyroid drugs such as perchlorate and thiocyanate. Drugs such as carbimazole block the oxidation of iodide and cause the accumulation of free iodine in the gland. These effects are summarised in Figure 25.7.

Disorders of thyroid hormone synthesis
A number of rare defects in thyroid hormone synthesis have been described. Some impair synthesis so severely that hypothyroidism (p. 314) results. All lead to

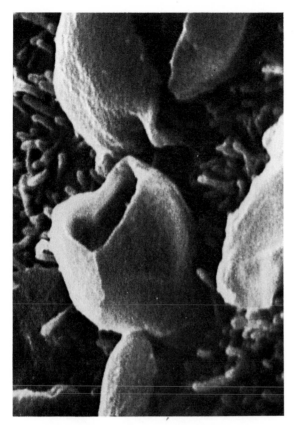

Fig. 25.6 Scanning electron micrograph of pseudopods at the inner surface of follicular cells of the dog thyroid. (Courtesy of P. Ketelbant)

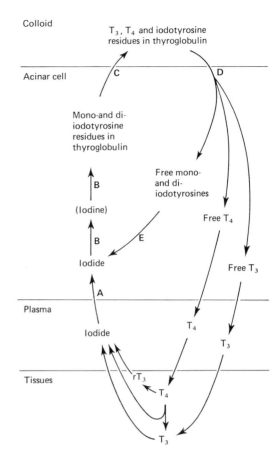

Fig. 25.7 Summary of the metabolism of iodine. The recovery of iodide is not perfect and new iodide must be supplied from the diet. The uptake of iodide (A) is accelerated by TSH and inhibited by carbimazole or thiouracil. The oxidative coupling of mono- and di-iodotyrosine residues (C) is accelerated by TSH as is the breakdown of thyroglobulin to give thyroxine (T_4) and tri-iodothyronine (T_3). The diagram also shows the role of the dehalogenase enzyme in recovering iodide from iodotyrosines (E) and the conversion of T_4 to reverse T_3 (rT_3).

increases in TSH production that in turn cause enlargement of the thyroid gland to give a *goitre*. The defects include disorders of thyroglobulin synthesis, of iodine accumulation, of tyrosine iodination, and of coupling of iodotyrosine residues. One other disorder results from a dehalogenase defect: that is, a lack of the enzyme needed for the de-iodination of unused iodotyrosine, and therefore for the recovery of iodine.

Thyroid hormones in blood

The thyroid hormones are exceptional in that plasma levels remain remarkably constant. In normal adults the plasma level of thyroxine (T_4) is 75 to 140 nmol/l and that of tri-iodothyronine 1.1 to 2.3 nmol/l. More than 99 per cent of both hormones are bound to proteins: thyroxine to thyronine binding globulin (TBG), pre-albumin and albumin, while tri-iodothyronine is bound to TBG and albumin. Only about one-third of the total thyroxine binding capacity is taken up in a normal person. In hyperthyroidism a larger than normal proportion of the binding sites are occupied whereas the opposite is true in hypothyroidism. Many factors,

particularly drugs, affect this binding capacity: oestrogens increase it while corticosteroids and androgens decrease it.

The active components of both thyroxine and tri-iodothyronine in the plasma are the very small fractions that are not bound to proteins: approximately 0.03 per cent of the thyroxine and 0.5 per cent of the tri-iodothyronine.

Actions

The study of the actions of the thyroid hormones has proved very difficult; much of our knowledge is derived only from investigation of the clinical changes found in hypothyroidism and hyperthyroidism. For example the thyroid hormones are essential for normal growth. The only certain action of the thyroid hormones on the intact animal is their effect in increasing the basal metabolic rate. Recently the mechanism of action at a cellular level has become clearer.

Cellular effects

Both thyroxine (T_4) and tri-iodothyronine (T_3) enter the cell and are bound to a variety of proteins. While bound, some T_4 is metabolised to T_3 but some is metabolised in other ways to give inactive products such as reverse T_3 (p. 312). The significance of the binding to cytosol proteins is not clear and there is growing evidence that the principal physiological effects of the thyroid hormones result from the binding of T_3 to non-histone proteins in the chromatin of the nucleus (Fig. 25.8). The binding of T_3 in the nucleus leads to changes in the rate of synthesis of the specific proteins that mediate the effects of the hormone. Extensive changes in intracellular protein concentrations occur in response to T_3 but the precise mechanisms remain obscure.

Several disorders are recognised in which the binding of T_3 to nuclei is defective. In severe cases features of hypothyroidism including delayed bone development occur despite high plasma levels of T_4 and T_3 and high TSH levels. A rare but particularly interesting disorder is thought to result from defects in the receptors for T_3 in pituitary cells. In such cases TSH secretion is not supressed and the excess production of TSH leads to increased production of T_4 and T_3 with signs of clinical hyperthyroidism.

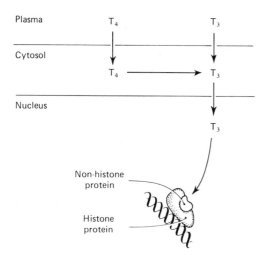

Fig. 25.8 Intracellular events in the actions of the thyroid hormones. After T_3 binds to the receptor protein a structural change takes place in the chromatin that in turn leads to increases in RNA transcription and therefore to changes in protein synthesis.

DISEASES OF THE THYROID GLAND

Iodine deficiency

Iodine is essential for the synthesis of the thyroid hormones and a diet severely deficient in iodine leads to increased TSH production and so to enlargement of the thyroid gland (goitre; Fig. 25.9). This *endemic goitre* is common in certain parts of the world, particularly in the highlands of New Guinea, in the Himalayas and also in parts of central Africa, notably Zaire. In countries such as Zaire, where the staple diet contains antithyroid substances, frank hypothyroidism may occur (Fig. 25.10). In many areas the incidence of goitre has been greatly reduced by the provision of iodine supplements, either by adding potassium iodide to table salt or by administering single injections of iodised oil that persists in the body for about five years. In Zaire mass 'vaccination' with iodised oil has resulted in a great reduction in the incidence of hypothyroidism and mental retardation.

Fig. 25.9 Endemic goitre in Darfur, Western Sudan due to lack of iodine. (Courtesy of D. A. Smith)

Hypothyroidism

Inadequate production of the thyroid hormones can be due either to disorders of the thyroid itself (primary hypothyroidism) or to impaired production of TSH by the anterior pituitary (secondary hypothyroidism). Primary hypothyroidism is most commonly caused in western countries by either autoimmune thyroid disease, in which antibodies to constituents of thyroid

Fig. 25.10 Male adult cretin whose impaired growth and permanent intellectual loss were due to hypothyroidism caused by severe lack of iodine in childhood. (Courtesy of F. DeLange and A. M. Eremans)

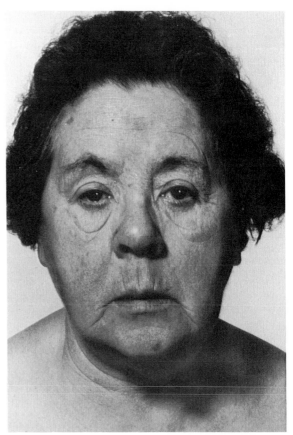

Fig. 25.11 Facial changes in severe hypothyroidism. (Courtesy of D. Borsey)

cells can be demonstrated in the plasma, or loss of functioning tissue resulting from surgical or radio-isotope treatment of hyperthyroidism. Inborn errors of thyroxine synthesis were described earlier (p. 312).

The clinical effects of hypothyroidism in an adult result from the lowered metabolic rate. Patients may be particularly sensitive to cold and need extra clothing. They gain weight, the heart rate falls and they become slow both mentally and physically. The skin may become thickened (Fig. 25.11). In severe cases, psychiatric disorders or coma may develop. Plasma levels of

T_4 and T_3 are low and, if the primary disorder is in the thyroid gland, plasma TSH levels are raised.

In children it is important to diagnose hypothyroidism early because if it is untreated the patients are severely stunted and intellectually impaired (*cretinism*). Since untreated hypothyroidism has such disastrous effects in children and since the condition is seldom clinically obvious at a time when impairment can be prevented, newborn infants are routinely tested to identify affected children.

Hyperthyroidism

This disorder (also known as thyrotoxicosis) occurs in about 0.2 per cent of adult women and a smaller proportion of men. In most cases the cause appears to be the production of a thyroid-stimulating antibody with an action mimicking that of TSH.

The clinical features of hyperthyroidism can be related to the increase in the metabolic rate. Weight is lost as a result of the increased catabolism of tissue protein and stored fat. The patient may be nervous and

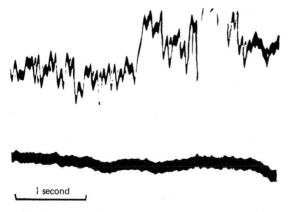

Fig. 25.12 Muscular tremor as shown by the movements of the tip of the index finger in a 20-year-old patient with hyperthyroidism (upper tracing) and in the same patient 45 days after partial removal of the thyroid gland (lower tracing). Lazarus S., Bell G H 1943 Glasgow Medical Journal 140:77)

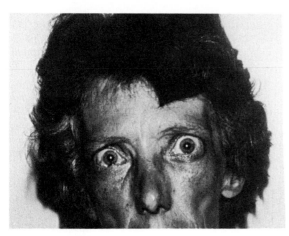

Fig. 25.13 Prominence of the eyes in hyperthyroidism. This sign is due in part to forward displacement of the eyeballs (exophthalmus) and in part to retraction of the upper lid. (Courtesy of R. W. Newton)

excitable and have a tremor (Fig. 25.12). The pulse is rapid and the skin warm and flushed. The eyes may appear particularly prominent (Fig. 25.13) as a result of forward displacement of the eyeballs (*exophthalmos*) and lid retraction. The cause of the eye changes is not known but they may persist long after the other features of hyperthyroidism have been abolished by treatment.

Investigation of thyroid disease

In hyperthyroidism, plasma levels of T_4 or T_3 or both are raised and TSH is ordinarily undetectable. The chronic overactivity of the thyroid leads to underactivity

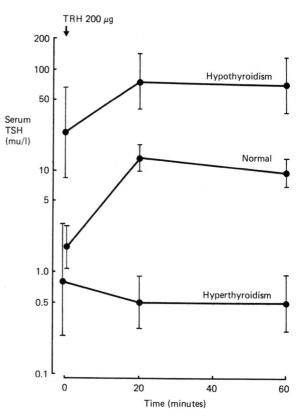

Fig. 25.14 Response in serum thyroid stimulating hormone (TSH) to an intravenous injection of 200 μg of thyrotrophin releasing hormone (TRH) in 25 normal women, 14 hypothyroid women and 17 hyperthyroid women. The vertical lines represent one standard deviation calculated on logarithms of values for serum TSH. TSH values were determined by a radio-immunoassay. (Data of Ormston B J et al. 1971 Lancet 2: 10)

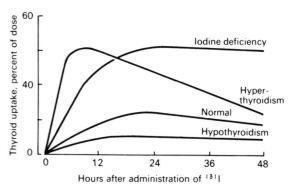

Fig. 25.15 Patterns of uptake of iodine by the thyroid gland in various disorders. After a small oral dose or radioactive iodine (^{131}I or ^{132}I) as sodium iodide, the ^{131}(or ^{132}I) is detected by a suitable counter placed over the thyroid gland.

of the TSH-producing cells of the anterior pituitary, shown by their poor response to TRH (Fig. 25.14). Similarly, in patients with hypothyroidism due to thyroid disease, the TSH response to TRH is greater than normal.

T_4, T_3 and TSH can be measured by radio-immunoassay. Additional information about thyroid function can be obtained by estimating the proportion of an oral dose of radioactive iodine that is taken up by the thyroid gland (Fig. 25.15). In autoimmune thyroid disease (p. 314) antibodies to the thyroid are present in the plasma.

The results of tests of the peripheral effects of thyroid hormones, such as measurement of the basal metabolic rate, are so variable that they are not used in clinical practice.

FURTHER READING

De Visscher M 1980 Comprehensive endocrinology: The thyroid gland. Raven Press, New York

Hall R, Anderson J, Smart G A, Besser M 1980 Fundamentals of clinical endocrinology. Pitman, London

Hetzel B S 1983 Iodine deficiency disorders (IDD) and their eradication. Lancet 2: 1126–1129.

Lancet 1981 Screening for thyroid disease. Lancet 2: 128–130.

Lancet 1983 Thyroid function tests: progress and problems. Lancet 1: 164–165

Laycock J, Wise P 1983 Essential endocrinology, 2nd ed University Press, Oxford

O'Riordan J L H, Malan P G, Gould R P 1982 Essentials of endocrinology. Blackwell Scientific, Oxford

Seth J, Beckett G 1985 Diagnosis of hyperthyroidism: the newer biochemical tests. Clinics in Endocrinology and Metabolism 14: 373–396

26

The adrenal cortex

Each adrenal gland in an adult weighs about 4 g and consists of two distinct kinds of tissue, cortex and medulla. These have quite different embryological origins but their association, found only in mammals, is physiologically important since part of the blood supply of the medulla is derived from the capillary network of the cortex. The adrenal medulla is discussed in Chapter 16.

The adrenal cortex is essential for life and the total removal of both adrenal glands causes death within a few days.

The adrenal cortex is made up of three zones (Fig. 26.1). The outermost, the *zona glomerulosa*, poorly demarcated in man, consists of islands of cells. The *zona fasciculata* forms about three-quarters of the volume of the cortex. Its cells are arranged in cords separated by capillaries and are characterised by an abundance of smooth endoplasmic reticulum and lipid droplets. The *zona reticularis* consists of clumps of smaller numbers of interconnected cells varying in shape, size and number of granules.

The zona glomerulosa produces aldosterone and is controlled mainly by the renin–angiotensin system and by the plasma potassium. The zona fasciculata and the zona reticularis produce cortisol and this activity is controlled by corticotrophin (adrenocorticotrophic hormone, ACTH) derived from the anterior pituitary (p. 301). These two zones also produce the adrenal androgens; the *zona reticularis* is particularly rich in the enzyme sulphokinase, which is required for the production of sulphated steroids. All three zones store cholesterol as esters in lipid droplets. Cholesterol is derived mainly from the diet but may also be synthesised from acetate; it is the precursor for the synthesis of the steroid hormones.

Cortisol

In humans, cortisol is the most important *glucocorticoid*; it affects carbohydrate, fat and protein metabolism.

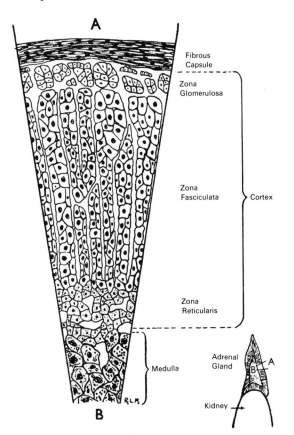

Fig. 26.1 Diagram of adrenal gland showing differentiation into medulla and cortex, the latter being divided into three zones not clearly demarcated from one another. The part of the gland from which the section was taken is shown alongside.

Cortisol

Synthesis and secretion

Cortisol and other adrenal steroids are all synthesised from cholesterol in the smooth endoplasmic reticulum. The synthetic pathway is shown in Figure 26.2. In normal adults between 30 and 90 μmol of cortisol is secreted per day but the secretion rate may be substantially higher at a time of stress. Cortisol secretion is controlled largely by plasma levels of ACTH (p. 301; Fig. 26.3).

The plasma level of cortisol has a marked circadian variation (Fig. 26.4), the highest values occurring between 6 a.m. and 10 a.m. and the lowest values in the late evening. The variation in cortisol level reflects a corresponding variation in ACTH secretion by the anterior pituitary; in turn this probably reflects variation in the release of corticotrophin releasing factor (CRF) by the hypothalamus (p. 301). The circadian rhythm is altered by changes in the pattern of sleeping and waking, provided that the new pattern is maintained for several days. The delayed adjustment of the ACTH/cortisol rhythm may be one factor underlying jet-lag.

Only about 5 per cent of the cortisol in the plasma is free and physiologically active; most of the remainder

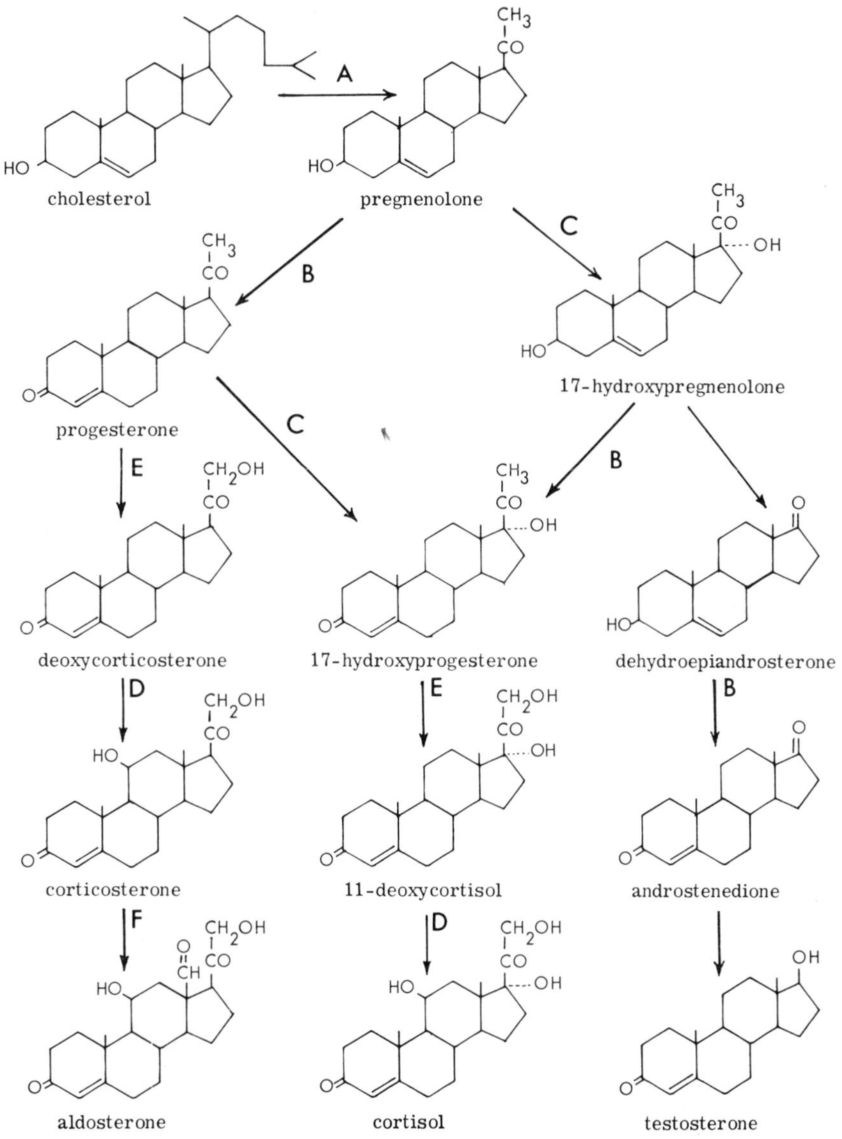

Fig. 26.2 Pathways for the synthesis of adrenal steroids from cholesterol. The enzymes involved are as follows: A, desmolase; B, $\triangle$5-isomerase 3β-hydroxydehydrogenase; C, 17α-hydroxylase; D, 11β-hydroxylase; E, 21-hydroxylase; F, 18-oxidase.

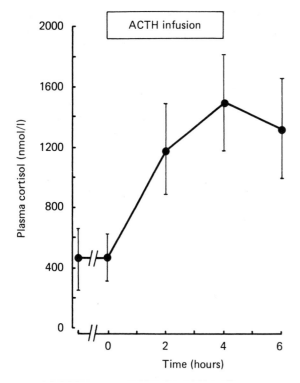

Fig. 26.3 Effect of an infusion of ACTH (75 iu over four hours) on plasma cortisol levels in a group of 18 subjects with no evidence of endocrine disease. Mean values with vertical bars representing one standard deviation. (Data of Greig W R et al. 1969 Postgraduate Medical Journal **45**:307)

is reversibly bound to a specific alpha-globulin, *transcortin*.

Actions

The glucocorticoids enter a target cell, bind to cytoplasmic receptors and migrate to the nucleus as described earlier (p. 290). The way in which the function of the nucleus is changed is not yet clear. Glucocorticoids are important in the regulation of carbohydrate metabolism, with actions largely opposite to those of insulin. They promote the synthesis and storage of glycogen in the liver and at the same time increase gluconeogenesis from protein by increasing protein catabolism. The overall effect is a rise in the plasma glucose level. At pathologically high plasma levels cortisol has an anti-inflammatory action and suppresses tissue response to injury. Cortisol also possesses some mineralocorticoid activity, promoting retention of sodium and water and loss of potassium by the distal tubules of the kidney. Although the mineralocorticoid activity of aldosterone is about 100 times greater than that of cortisol, cortisol none the less makes a significant contribution to mineralocorticoid activity since its secretion rate is substantially higher.

Cortisol has a direct action both on the anterior pituitary and on the hypothalamus to inhibit the production of ACTH, and CRH, respectively (Fig. 24.12, p. 301).

Metabolism

Cortisol in plasma has a half-life of 80 to 110 minutes. It is removed by the liver in which it is inactivated mainly by reduction and conjugation with glucuronic acid to metabolites that are excreted in the urine. A very small amount of cortisol is excreted unchanged; cortisol excretion rises disproportionately when cortisol production is increased.

Aldosterone

Aldosterone, the most potent mineralocorticoid, is produced exclusively in the zona glomerulosa. Its plasma level varies with posture; normal figures for recumbent subjects are in the range 100 to 400 pmol/l, and for ambulant subjects 200 to 700 pmol/l. The aldosterone secretion rate in normal adults on an average

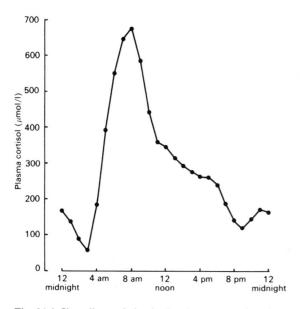

Fig. 26.4 Circadian variation in the plasma level of cortisol.

Aldosterone

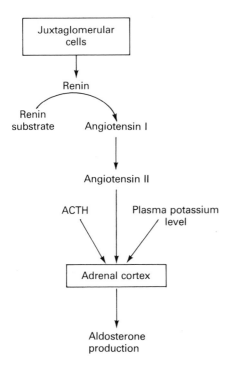

```
┌─────────────────┐
│ Juxtaglomerular │
│      cells      │
└─────────────────┘
        │
        ▼
      Renin
Renin
substrate    Angiotensin I
                 │
                 ▼
           Angiotensin II

   ACTH        Plasma potassium
                    level

        ┌─────────────────┐
        │ Adrenal cortex  │
        └─────────────────┘
                 │
                 ▼
           Aldosterone
           production
```

Fig. 26.5 Summary of factors controlling aldosterone production. For example a fall in plasma volume leads to decreased transmural pressure in the juxtaglomerular apparatus, increased renin production and therefore increased aldosterone production. In turn this leads to sodium retention, which, in turn, helps to restore the plasma volume.

intake of salt is about 400 nmol per day; a high-salt diet suppresses the secretion of aldosterone.

Control of secretion

The major factor controlling aldosterone production is the renin-angiotensin system (p. 206). For example, a fall in ECF volume or saline depletion causes the production of renin by the juxtaglomerular cells of the kidney. In turn this leads to aldosterone production by the steps shown in Figure 26.5. Aldosterone production is also regulated by the plasma potassium level, rising in response to increased potassium levels and falling in hypokalaemia. The effect of potassium is independent of the renin–angiotensin system.

Aldosterone secretion is influenced to a small extent by plasma ACTH levels but this effect is of limited importance since lack of ACTH as a result of pituitary disease does not significantly reduce aldosterone production.

Breakdown

Aldosterone is rapidly removed from the circulation mainly by the liver, which reduces it and conjugates it with glucuronic acid. Some aldosterone is conjugated without reduction. In these ways it is rendered sufficiently soluble to be excreted in the urine.

Actions

The principal sites of action of aldosterone are the distal convoluted tubules and the collecting ducts of the kidney. It increases the reabsorption of sodium and the secretion of potassium and hydrogen ions. As a result of the increased sodium reabsorption, the plasma volume rises and the blood pressure increases.

Like other steroid hormones, aldosterone enters the target cell, binds with a specific receptor in the cytoplasm and migrates to the nucleus. There it promotes the synthesis of a specific protein involved in sodium transport.

Adrenal androgens

Quantitatively the most important androgens secreted by the adrenal cortex in both sexes are dehydroepiandrosterone sulphate, dehydroepiandrosterone and androstenedione. Some androstenedione is converted in the peripheral tissues to the more potent androgens, testosterone and dihydrotestosterone.

Actions

The actions of androgens in the males are described in Chapter 27. In females their significance in normal physiology is not yet clear; as in men they may be important for the maintenance of normal libido. Increasing production of adrenal androgens occurs in both sexes one or two years before obvious sexual maturation and is known as the *adrenarche*.

Other steroids, for example corticosterone, 11-deoxycortisol and 17α-hydroxyprogesterone, are normally also produced in small quantities by the adrenal cortex. These become of importance only when there are deficiencies of the enzymes required for steroid biosynthesis.

Disorders of the adrenal cortex

The metabolic pathways involved in the synthesis of adrenal steroids are shown in Figure 26.2. Inborn deficiencies of each of the enzymes have been recognised. All are rare but the most common is deficiency of the 21-hydroxylase. As this affects the production both of cortisol and of aldosterone it is a life-threatening condition demanding immediate treatment. This disorder, and other conditions causing impaired cortisol production, lead to an increased output of ACTH. In turn this causes adrenal hyperplasia and in some cases, depending on which enzyme defect is present, a greatly increased production of adrenal androgens and masculinisation (Fig. 26.6). This condition is known as congenital adrenal hyperplasia.

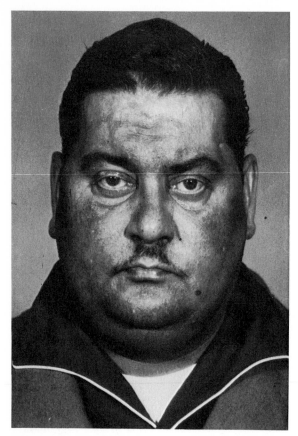

Fig. 26.6 38-year-old man with Cushing's disease. Only a minority of patients show the florid facial appearances seen in this patient. (Courtesy of I. D. Ramsay)

patients maintained in good health by the regular administration of some 20 to 30 mg of cortisol ('hydrocortisone') daily by mouth. Aldosterone is ineffective by mouth and the synthetic mineralocorticoid fludrocortisone is given orally to compensate for the lack of aldosterone.

Inadequate production of glucocorticoids may result from pituitary insufficiency with lack of ACTH. In such cases cortisol is also required but fludrocortisone is not needed. Inadequate aldosterone production due to defects of the renin–angiotensin system has not yet been recognised.

Overactivity of the adrenal cortex

Overactivity of the adrenal cortex may result from a tumour of the cortex itself or from excessive stimulation of the adrenals either by an increased output of ACTH from the pituitary or from the production of an ACTH-like substance by a malignant tumour elsewhere.

Tumours of the adrenal cortex may secrete predominantly cortisol and androgens or, more rarely, aldosterone. Excessive cortisol production gives rises to *Cushing's syndrome*, many of the characteristics of which can also be produced by the administration of large doses of cortisol or synthetic glucocorticoids such as prednisolone. Patients may be obese, have muscle wasting in the arms or legs, osteoporosis with fractures particularly in the vertebrae and hyperglycaemia (Fig. 26.6). Excessive production of androgens may lead to hirsutism and in severe cases to masculinisation. An aldosterone-producing tumour results in hypertension and a low plasma potassium level (*Conn's syndrome*).

Adrenocortisol insufficiency

Both adrenal glands may be destroyed, usually by an autoimmune process or by tuberculous infection; the resulting disorder is known as Addison's disease. The patient complains of weakness, lassitude and loss of weight, and is found on examination to have a low blood pressure and pigmentation of parts of the skin and mucous membranes. Lack of aldosterone leads to excessive losses of sodium and chloride in the urine; a lack of cortisol causes increased secretion of ACTH and hypoglycaemia. The abnormalities can be reversed and

FURTHER READING

Arendt J, Marks V 1982 Physiological changes underlying jet-lag. British Medical Journal 284: 144–146

Hall R, Anderson J, Smart G A, Besser M 1980 Fundamentals of clinical endocrinology. Pitman, London

James V H T, Few J D 1985 Adrenocortical steroids: chemistry, synthesis and disturbances in disease. Clinics in Endocrinology and Metabolism 14: 867–892

Makin H L J (ed) 1984 Biochemistry of steroid hormones, 2nd edn. Blackwell Scientific, Oxford

O'Riordan J L H, Malan P G, Gould R P 1982 Essentials of endocrinology. Blackwell Scientific, Oxford

Reproduction

Reproduction involves transmission to the next generation of genetic material that results in the offspring having the characteristics of the species and of an individual within the species. The genetic material is carried on *chromosomes* in specialised cells called *gametes*. Male gametes, spermatozoa, are produced in the testes, female gametes, ova, are found in the ovaries. The fusion of a spermatozoon with an ovum combines the genetic material from the father and from the mother and begins the process of development that results in the formation of a new individual.

In order that fusion of a spermatozoon and an ovum can take place, a complex series of events has to occur. In the male this involves the constant production of vast numbers of spermatozoa and their storage and transport, as well as the sequence of events that culminates in the delivery of the sperms in a suitable medium to the vaginal fornix often enough to make conception likely. This sequence requires normal libido (which depends on endocrine and psychogenic factors), the erection of the penis (dependent on vascular, nervous and psychogenic factors), penetration, and ejaculation, which involves neuromuscular co-ordination. The ejaculated fluid, *semen*, contains not only spermatozoa but other components produced by the accessory sex organs, especially the prostate and seminal vesicles.

In the female, ova must be released regularly enough to allow conception and the secretions of the genital tract must permit the passage of spermatozoa and their access to the ovum. The lining of the uterus must be in a suitable condition to allow the newly fertilised ovum to embed itself. The embryo has then to be sustained until it is ready for independent existence.

SPERMATOGENESIS

The testes have two main functons: the production of spermatozoa and the production of the male steroid hormones.

The testes develop during embryonic life in the abdominal cavity. The gubernaculum testis connects each to the area of the skin that later forms the scrotum. As development proceeds the testes travel to the scrotum, which they normally reach about the eighth month of intrauterine life. Sometimes this process is delayed and the testes are retained in the abdomen after birth (*cryptorchidism*). The incidence of undescended testis at birth is about 10 per cent and at one year about 2 per cent. Most of those whose testes have not descended by one year need surgical treatment within a year.

Spermatogenesis proceeds normally only when the testes are kept some 2 to 4°C cooler than the temperature within the abdomen. Spermatozoa are not formed when the testes remain in the abdominal cavity. It is thought that the pampiniform plexus of veins contributes to the maintenance of the ideal temperature in the testis by cooling the blood flowing to the testis by a process of counter-current heat exchange. The temperature of the testes is also regulated by the cutaneous muscle of the scrotum, the *dartos muscle*, and the *cremaster muscle* of the cord, which contract when the environment is cold and relax when it is warm and so regulate the distance between the testes and the groin.

Each adult testis contains about 750 convoluted *seminiferous tubules*. On cross-section these tubules, each of which is about 70 cm long and 200 μm in diameter, show a basement membrane on which three irregular layers of epithelial cells can be distinguished (Fig. 27.1). The cubical cells of the outermost layer, the *spermatogonia*, give rise by cell division to the second layer, the *spermatocytes*, which are large cells with large nuclei. Two types of spermatocyte are found in this layer, namely the primary spermatocytes, containing the somatic or diploid number of chromosomes, and the secondary spermatocytes, formed from them by meiosis (Fig. 27.2). The nucleus of the spermatid forms the head of the spermatozoon; the Golgi complex forms the cap or acrosome, which contains proteases. During this transformation the spermatids cluster around the *sustentacular cells* (cells of Sertoli), which contain an androgen-binding protein. The spermatozoa (Fig. 27.3) leave the sustentacular cells and lie around the inner

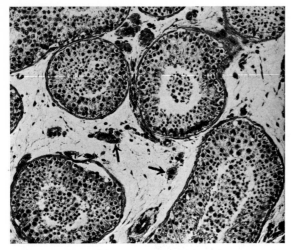

Fig. 27.1 Normal adult male testis. Note especially the intensive proliferative activity in every tubule, the thin basement membranes, and the relatively scanty interstitial (Leydig) cells (examples are arrowed) in the interstitial tissue. This is a surgical biopsy and most of the loose cells in the centre of each tubule are the result of pressure during removal: however, the minute dots of spermatozoon heads can be recognised among them. × 105. (By courtesy of B. Lennox)

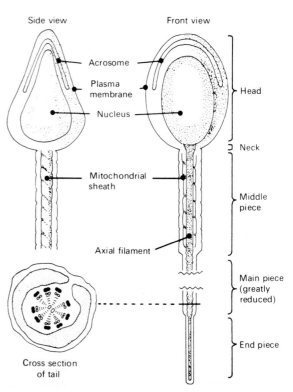

Fig. 27.3 The fine structure of a spermatozoon. (From Gardner D L, Dodds T C 1976 Human histology 3rd edn. Churchill Livingstone, Edinburgh)

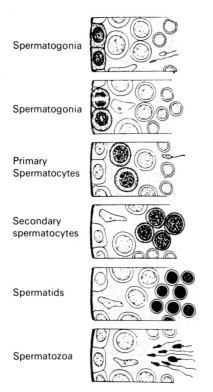

Fig. 27.2 A wave of spermatogenesis in seminiferous tubules, shown diagrammatically. Cells in a single sequence are shown darkened. (From Gardner D L, Dodds T C 1976 Human histology, 3rd edn. Churchill Livingstone, Edinburgh)

margin of the germinal epithelium where they can easily be recognised by their densely staining heads and long curved tails pointing into the lumen of the tubule. At this stage they are immature, being not yet capable of fertilising an ovum. About 500 million spermatozoa are produced per day. The time required for spermatogenesis is about 70 days.

Spermatozoa are first produced at puberty and spermatogenic activity is maintained into old age so that there is no definite end to reproductive life in the male. Both FSH and testosterone are necessary for spermatogenesis. The germinal cells are easily damaged by ischaemia.

From the seminiferous tubules (Fig. 27.4) the spermatozoa pass into the *rete testis*, a series of channels in the fibrous stroma of the posterior part of the testis. About a dozen efferent ductules pass from the upper part of the rete testis into a single canal some 6 m long, which by its convolutions makes up the *epididymis*, in which the spermatozoa mature and are stored until ejaculation takes place. Spermatozoa are also stored in the ampulla of the vas deferens. Production continues whether or not ejaculation occurs; spermatozoa not

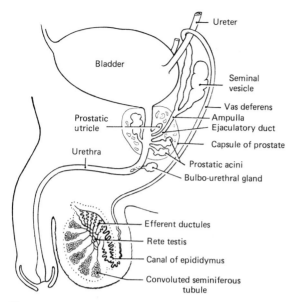

Fig. 27.4 The male sex organs.

ejaculated are reabsorbed in the tubules and in the epididymis.

The vas deferens passes to the *prostate gland* at the base of the urinary bladder. Here it is joined by the duct of the *seminal vesicle* to form the ampulla and the ejaculatory duct, which passes through the prostate and enters the prostatic urethra. The seminal vesicles do not normally store spermatozoa. The prostate, surrounding the first part of the urethra, is a glandular organ containing much smooth muscle tissue and numerous acini that communicate with the prostatic urethra. About 2.5 cm distally in the penile part of the urethra are the openings of the ducts of the two bulbo-urethral glands.

Semen

Semen consists of secretions from the testis, epididymis, the prostate, the seminal vesicles and the bulbo-urethral glands (Cowper's glands). An average ejaculation of 2 to 5 ml of semen contains 40 to 100 million spermatozoa per ml. A figure of 20 million spermatozoa per ml is often quoted as the dividing line between fertility and infertility. However many fertile men have counts below this and many infertile men have higher counts. The principal measurable parameters of semen are volume, pH, sperm count, sperm motility and morphology.

From 60 to 80 per cent of the sperms are of normal shape and, after incubation for one hour at 37°C, 50 per cent are motile. The sperms from the testis collect in the dilated end of the vas deferens until they are swept out by fluid from the seminal vesicles. Less than 10 per cent of the ejaculate is spermatozoa, the remainder

being seminal fluid and prostatic secretions. The volume of the semen is unaffected by bilateral vasectomy. Semen clots soon after ejaculation but it is liquefied shortly after by fibrinolysis; then the spermatozoa become fully motile.

About 70 per cent of the semen is *seminal fluid* produced by the seminal vesicles. This has a pH of about 7.4 and contains fructose, citrate, ascorbic acid, prostaglandins and various enzymes. The fructose is a source of energy for the spermatozoa. The function of the prostaglandins in semen is not known. The seminal fluid acts as an activator and as a diluent for the spermatozoa, which are tightly packed in the epididymis. Seminal fluid contains hyaluronidase, which acts on hyaluronic acid found in mucus and so allows the sperms to pass more readily through the cervix to the uterus and uterine tubes.

The thin prostatic secretion forms about 20 per cent of the volume of semen. It is colourless and slightly acid (pH 6.5) because of the presence of citric acid; it contains substances important for sperm mobility, notably albumin and the proteolytic enzymes fibrinolysin and fibrinogenase. It also contains acid phosphatase and an antibacterial substance of low molecular weight.

Spermatozoa after ejaculation obtain energy from the fructose of the seminal fluid and from glucose derived from the uterine secretions. Spermatozoa are able to oxidise fructose to CO_2 and water if oxygen is available. The spermatozoa within the epididymis are, because of the lack of oxygen and glycolysable sugar, metabolically inactive; they can survive in this situation for perhaps a month. Outside the body, spermatozoa survive only a few hours at body temperature, a few days at 4°C and a few years at − 79°C.

Hormones of the testis

The testis grows a little during the first two years of life and remains about 1 g in weight till about 11 years of age when there is a rapid spurt to 15 g reached at 17 years. The prostate and the other accessory glands increase in size at the same time. The first external sign of puberty is rapid growth of the penis and the development of pubic hair (p. 367), but spermatogenesis begins some months earlier. About the middle of pubescence the larynx enlarges and the pitch of the voice falls about an octave. The vocal folds lengthen by 10 mm, that is by almost half their original length. At this time the skeletal muscles develop rapidly and the pattern of behaviour alters. There is considerable variation in the age of onset of puberty; for most boys it is between 10 and 14.

These changes depend on the testes since they do not occur if these organs are removed before puberty. The castrated patient, known as a eunuch, usually becomes a tall man because of the prolonged period of growth of the long bones. A eunuch is often rather fat, his penis remains small, voice remains unbroken and hair does not grow over the face and abdomen in the typical masculine fashion. Such a person is sterile and seldom has any sexual desire (libido).

Castration after puberty produces muscular weakness and atrophy of the prostate and seminal vesicles. Although psychological changes are common, sexual desire may be retained, but the individual is sterile although he is potent, that is, he is able to copulate.

Testosterone and other androgens

Testosterone, a potent androgen, is usually regarded as the hormone responsible for transforming a boy into a man. It is produced by the *interstitial cells* or Leydig cells, which possess a rich supply of nerves. They lie scattered between the seminiferous tubules (Fig. 27.1). The metabolic pathways for the synthesis of testosterone are described in Figure 27.5. The average concentrations of testosterone in peripheral blood plasma in young men are 9 to 40 nmol/l, falling to about half that after the age of 50, and for women 0.7 to 2.8 nmol/l. Only a small proportion of the testosterone in the plasma is free, that is, not bound to proteins, and therefore physiologically active. Free testosterone is very difficult to measure.

Both follicle stimulating hormone (FSH, p. 304) and luteinising hormone (LH, p. 304) together with testosterone are necessary for spermatogenesis. In other words spermatogenesis depends on interstitial cell function. At puberty LH stimulates the interstitial cells and the plasma testosterone is increased ten times. The output of LH is in turn inhibited by the feed-back action of testosterone, while the output of FSH is thought to be inhibited by a protein hormone *inhibin* produced by the Sertoli cells. When the testes are removed these inhibitory influences are lost. Malnutrition causes a fall in the production of testosterone by inhibiting the production of FSH and LH by the anterior pituitary.

Both in males and females the adrenal cortex produces small amounts of androgens: testosterone, androsterone and dehydroepiandrosterone. The 17-oxosteroids found in the urine after castration come from this source.

Oestrogens

Much of the oestrogen found in the plasma in males is formed by the peripheral conversion of androgens, mainly in the liver. In cirrhosis of the liver increased production of oestrogen occurs. The functional significance of the oestrogen produced in males is not known.

Biological action of androgens

Testosterone and other androgens have actions on most tissues. In the fetus they are responsible for the differentiation of the Wolffian ducts, external genitalia and brain. In the adolescent they are responsible for the physical changes of puberty (p. 367). They stimulate growth, muscular development, libido and aggressive behaviour.

At the molecular level testosterone enters a cell and is converted by the membrane-bound enzyme, 5 α-reductase, to *dihydrotestosterone*, the active metabolite responsible for the development of secondary sexual characteristics. This is then bound to a specific binding protein and the protein–hormone complex enters the nucleus, where it stimulates protein synthesis. In some tissues, notably the brain, pituitary and muscle, testosterone itself is the main intracellular androgen.

Clinical use of androgens

In cases of delayed puberty in boys administration of testosterone produces hair in the typical male distribution and also growth of the larynx. Testosterone is of no value in the treatment of psychogenic impotence but is of clinical value in the rare cases of impotence due to testicular insufficiency.

In undernourished and emaciated persons injection of testosterone has an anabolic effect, nitrogen and other tissue-forming materials such as potassium, calcium and phosphorus being retained. The value of this form of treatment is limited by virilisation, particularly in females. Various derivatives of testosterone, such as

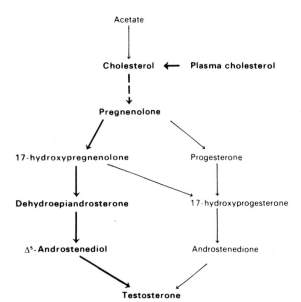

Fig. 27.5 Principal pathways for the synthesis of testosterone in the testis. The pathway shown with heavy lettering and arrows is probably the most important.

methandienone, have a much higher ratio of anabolic to androgenic potency than testosterone and these so-called 'non-virilising androgens' are used clinically.

OVULATION

The internal genital organs in the female consist of the ovaries, the uterine tubes, the uterus and the vagina (Fig. 27.6). The *uterus* communicates through the *uterine tubes* with the peritoneal cavity, while the lower part is continuous through the narrow canal of the *cervix* with the *vagina*, which passes to the exterior. The walls of the uterus contain smooth muscle fibres (the *myometrium*) among which is a considerable amount of fibrous tissue. The mucous membrane or *endometrium* lining the interior is covered by a columnar epithelium that dips down into the stroma of the endometrium to form simple tubular glands. The epithelium, the uterine cavity and the cervical canal is partly ciliated. Mucus secreted by the glands within the cervix plays a part in the transport of spermatozoa. The columnar cells of the cervix give place abruptly, close to its external orifice, to the stratified squamous epithelium covering the vaginal portion of the cervix. The vagina is lined by a stratified squamous epithelium without any glands. During reproductive life the vagina contains *Lactobacillus acidophilus*, which keeps the vaginal pH between 4.9 and 3.5 by producing lactic acid from glycogen. The acid inhibits the growth of pathogenic bacteria that might otherwise invade the vagina.

The uterine tubes (Fallopian tubes) pass towards the ovaries, to which they are loosely attached by an *ovarian fimbria* on each side. Each tube is lined by ciliated epithelium, the cilia of which beat towards the uterus. Smooth muscle, which can show characteristic peristalsis, lies between the mucosa and the serosal layer formed by parietal peritoneum. The tube is more than an anatomical conduit — it is within the tube that the ovum is fertilised and where the embryo develops into a blastocyst ready for implantation. The secretory activity of the mucosa of the tubes ensures optimal conditions for fertilisation and for the transport of ova and spermatozoa.

The ovaries

The ovaries in the adult are oval bodies weighing 2 to 8 g, covered by a cubical epithelium called the *germinal epithelium*. The stroma or framework is particularly dense below the epithelium, where it forms the tunica albuginea. Immediately below this are numerous *vesicular ovarian (Graafian) follicles* in various stages of development or degeneration (Fig. 27.7).

The primordial sex cells arise from the yolk sac and migrate to the genital ridge where they are found under the germinal epithelium. Near the end of fetal life groups of cells from the germinal epithelium form themselves around the sex cells (oogonia) to give the primordial ovarian follicles. No oogonia are formed after fetal life. At birth the ovary contains some 750 000 follicles but most eventually disappear and their oocytes degenerate. About 70 000 follicles are found in the ovaries from 25 to 40 years, but after 40 years less than 10 000 are present.

From puberty onwards a limited number of follicles mature in succession so that various stages of their development may be seen in one adult ovary. In each follicle the primitive ovum or oocyte can be recognised by its larger size. As the follicle begins to mature (Fig. 27.7) the cells investing the ovum multiply rapidly and a cavity filled with *liquor folliculi* appears among them giving the follicle the naked eye appearance of a clear vesicle on the surface of the ovary. The outer layer of investing cells is called the *zona granulosa* and the

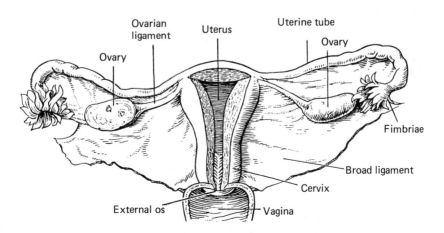

Fig. 27.6 The female genital organs, posterior view.

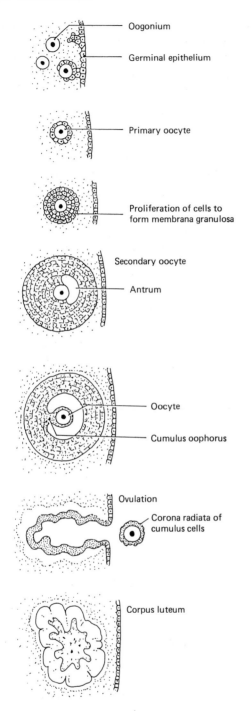

Oogonium

Germinal epithelium

Primary oocyte

Proliferation of cells to
form membrana granulosa

Secondary oocyte

Antrum

Oocyte

Cumulus oophorus

Ovulation

Corona radiata of
cumulus cells

Corpus luteum

Fig. 27.7 The stages in the development of an ovarian follicle (Graafian follicle), ovulation and the formation of a corpus luteum.

layer around the ovum is the *cumulus ovaricus*. The follicle begins to enlarge about the ninth day of the menstrual cycle and in four days grows from 2 to 20 mm in diameter. A digestive enzyme appears in the liquor of the follicle and weakens its surface. Release of the ovum (ovulation) follows thinning of the follicular wall associated with rhythmic contractions of the ovary itself. The ovum when released is surrounded by a mass of some 3000 oestrogen-producing granulosa cells. It is picked up by the specialised cells of the tubal fimbria and is passed, with its attached cumulus cells, into the lumen of the tube where fertilisation can take place. The empty space in the ruptured follicle is filled with serous exudate and a varying amount of blood that is gradually replaced by large cells (*lutein cells*), which are mainly hypertrophied granulosa cells. The resulting structure, the *corpus luteum*, persists up to the twelfth week of pregnancy; if the oocyte is not fertilised it breaks down after 10 to 12 days and menstruation occurs.

High concentrations of oxytocin and vasopressin are found in ovaries; these hormones may play a part in the regulation of the menstrual cycle.

The menstrual cycle

From puberty the endometrium undergoes cyclical changes that result in bleeding from the uterus. This bleeding or *menstruation* lasts 4 to 6 days and recurs every 28 days approximately. In describing the menstrual cycle it is usual to date events from the first day on which bleeding occurs. However, because of the variations in the length of cycles the increasingly common practice is to relate events to the time of ovulation as judged by the peak in plasma LH (Fig. 27.11, p. 331).

During the first half, the *follicular* or *proliferative phase* of the cycle, an ovarian follicle enlarges and comes to the surface of the ovary, ovulation occurring about the fourteenth day. The subsequent 14 days in which the corpus luteum is active are referred to as the *luteal* or *secretory phase*. The corpus luteum degenerates just before the next menstruation (Fig. 27.8) probably as a result of local actions of prostaglandins.

On the first three days or so of the menstrual cycle (Fig. 27.8) the more superficial layers of the endometrium degenerate and are cast off with some bleeding leaving the endometrium about 1 mm thick. The bleeding process has been studied by transplanting small fragments of endometrium into the anterior chamber of the eye of a monkey where they can easily be observed microscopically through the transparent cornea. In the follicular and luteal phases of the cycle the circulation through the spiral arteries supplying the endometrium is continuous. When the time of menstruation approaches, the circulation in the spiral arteries supplying the superficial parts of the endometrium slows down and then stops for some hours so that the endometrium blanches and then degenerates.

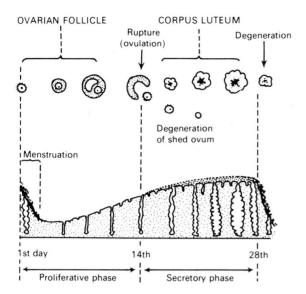

Fig. 27.8 Changes in the endometrium, the follicle and corpus luteum during a normal menstrual cycle.

After a time these arteries open again and blood escapes through the walls of capillaries, venules and arterioles, with the formation of subepithelial haematomata. The cause of the vasoconstriction is not clear.

The menstrual flow consists of blood mixed with mucus and shed endometrial tissue and at first it contains numerous leucocytes. The blood clots and is simultaneously broken down by plasmin formed by the activation of the fibrinolytic system. At the time of menstruation the fibrinolytic activity of the endometrium and the concentration of fibrin degradation products in the plasma are greatest; the local activity of platelets is also inhibited. The volume of the blood lost varies greatly from woman to woman but in 80 per cent is in the range 6 to 60 ml, a loss of 3 to 30 mg of iron and 1 to 12 g of protein. Losses greater than 60 ml are often associated with iron-deficiency anaemia (p. 28).

Histological changes
At the end of menstruation the endometrium is regenerated from the deeper parts of the glands next to the myometrium. During the *phase of proliferation*, from the fifth to the fourteenth day, new capillaries grow out from the spiral arterioles, the endometrial glands progressively increase in length and tortuosity and the cells of the stroma hypertrophy so that at the end of this phase the endometrium is some 3 to 4 mm thick.

During the next 14 days the glands continue to grow, becoming more dilated and convoluted and showing secretory activity. The cells of the stroma enlarge and their glycogen content increases. These premenstrual changes may be regarded as preparation for a fertilised ovum and when they are complete the endometrium is about 6 or 7 mm thick. If the ovum is not fertilised small collections of blood appear in the endometrium and the degenerative changes that result in menstruation begin again.

The endometrium is a major site of prostaglandin synthesis. The level of prostaglandin in the endometrium is low in the proliferative phase and in some animals rises significantly during the luteal phase. It is thought that these prostaglandins are responsible for the contraction of the myometrium during menstruation. Contractions of the vagina occur during menstruation.

Many variations in the bleeding pattern may occur in association with irregularity or failure of ovulation. Menstrual bleeding is absent during pregnancy, may be suppressed during lactation and ceases finally at the *menopause* usually between the ages of 45 and 55.

Ovarian hormones

Oestrogens
In women the principal ovarian oestrogen in reproductive life is oestradiol-17β, which is produced by the granulosa cells (Fig. 27.9) The other oestrogens are oestrone, which can arise from a follicle or from peripheral conversion of oestradiol or androgens in adipose

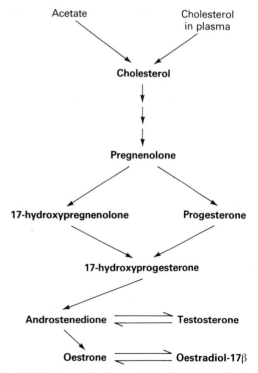

Fig. 27.9 Pathways for the synthesis of oestrogens in the human ovary.

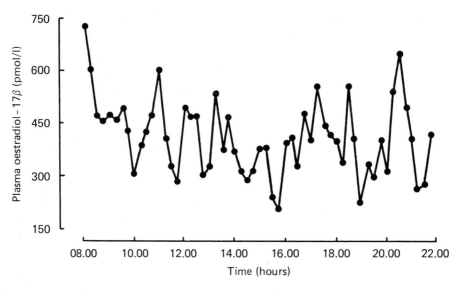

Fig. 27.10 Diurnal and pulsatile variations in the plasma levels of oestradiol-17β in a normal woman. Plasma was taken at 15-minute intervals. (After Lenton E A et al. 1978 Clinical Endocrinology 9:37)

tissue, and *oestriol*, produced by the fetus and by the placenta. Oestriol is the principal oestrogen in pregnancy. The secretion of oestrogens is pulsatile, reflecting the pulsatile (Fig. 27.10) release of the gonadotrophins.

Oestradiol-17β is only slightly active when taken by mouth but oral administration of synthetic oestrogens such as ethinyloestradiol, mestranol and stilboestrol is effective.

All the oestrogens circulate in the plasma bound to specific globulins and are excreted in the bile and urine after being rendered soluble by conjugation in the liver with glucuronides and sulphates. The mode of action of oestrogens at the cellular level in, for example, the breast and the uterus, is still not known.

Progesterone
This hormone is secreted by the corpus luteum and, in pregnancy, by the placenta. Its main action during the menstrual cycle is on the oestrogen-stimulated endometrium, the glands of which develop further and begin to secrete. Progesterone prevents bleeding from the endometrium and a fall in progesterone secretion is probably the signal for the start of menstruation. The slightly higher body temperature in the second half of the cycle is probably due to progesterone. If fertilisation takes place the progesterone-prepared endometrium is loose and oedematous so that it is readily entered by the trophoblast.

In the liver progesterone is reduced to *pregnanediol* and conjugated with glucuronic acid to be excreted in the urine as a biologically inactive glucuronide. About

10 to 40 per cent of injected progesterone can be recovered in the urine and about 5 per cent in the bile as conjugated pregnanediol.

Ovarian androgens
The ovarian stroma produces androgens, particularly androstenedione. Their significance is not fully understood but they may, together with the oestrogens, be responsible for sexual desire or *libido*.

Synthetic 'hormones'
Large numbers of oestrogenic compounds with little chemical resemblance to the naturally occurring steroid hormones have been synthesised. Stilboestrol was one of the first non-steroidal oestrogens to be synthesised. Ethinyloestradiol, which is closely related to oestradiol-17β, is commonly used in the combined oral contraceptive pill. Synthetic oestrogens may be used for the relief of postmenopausal symptoms and have proved of value in the treatment of cancer of the prostate. These synthetic compounds are cheap to make and effective when given by mouth.

The hormonal control of the menstrual cycle
After removal of the ovaries the menstrual cycle is abolished, the vagina atrophies and the vaginal smear consists almost entirely of leucocytes; at the same time the uterus atrophies and the endometrium becomes thin. Treatment with oestrogens causes the walls of the vagina to become cornified (so that the smear contains squamous cells), the vaginal secretion returns to its normal acid pH; the uterine muscle hypertrophies, the

endometrium proliferates and the glands of the cervix begin to secrete again. If oestrogen treatment is stopped or if the dosage is suddenly reduced the uterine mucosa becomes oedematous and about 5 days later there is bleeding from the endometrium. This is called *withdrawal bleeding*. If, however, treatment is continued when the endometrium is showing proliferative changes and progesterone as well as oestrogen is given in suitable

dosage a typical premenstrual endometrium can be produced. Cessation of hormonal treatment is followed as before by bleeding but in this case it takes place in a premenstrual endometrium just as in a normal menstrual cycle. This cycle of hormone administration forms the basis of the action of oral contraceptives.

Since the endometrial changes of the menstrual cycle can be imitated by injection of oestradiol and progesterone, it is a fair assumption that these hormones are responsible for the changes in the normal menstrual cycle; indeed the variations in the plasma levels of oestrogens and progestogens are consistent with this view (Fig. 27.11). Plasma levels of oestradiol reach a peak at about the twelfth day and this peak is the signal to the hypothalamus and pituitary to produce a surge of luteinising hormone, which in turn causes ovulation. The highest values of progesterone are found in the mid-luteal phase of the cycle.

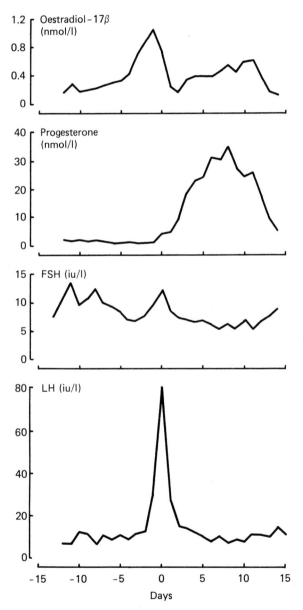

Fig. 27.11 Mean values of serum oestradiol-17β, progesterone, FSH and LH levels in eight normal women. The data in each case are plotted in relation to the day of the LH peak (day 0). (After Leyendecker G et al. 1975 Archiv für Gynaekologie 218: 47)

Gonadotrophic hormones

If the pituitary gland is removed from an immature female animal the gonads remain infantile and since the development of the secondary sex organs, the clitoris, uterus and vagina, is dependent on the hormones of the gonads, these organs also remain immature. The secondary sex organs atrophy after removal of the ovaries in an adult in spite of the presence of the pituitary gland; it is clear therefore that the gonadotrophins produced by the anterior pituitary have no direct influence on the secondary sex organs but only an indirect one through the gonads. In both male and female two gonadotrophins, FSH and LH, are produced by the anterior pituitary and another gonadotrophin is produced by the placenta in pregnancy (*human chorionic gonadotrophin*, HCG). The release of the pituitary gonadotrophins is controlled by the hypothalamic peptide hormone *gonadotrophin releasing hormone* (GnRH; p. 304).

FSH controls the development and maturation of the ovarian follicle in the female. In the follicular phase of the menstrual cycle, oestrogen production increases under FSH control. FSH levels in plasma are at their highest during the follicular phase of the cycle and have a second small peak at ovulation (Fig. 27.11) before falling in the luteal phase. High values are found in postmenopausal women and in patients without functioning gonads; low levels are found in pituitary insufficiency.

The pattern of changes in plasma LH levels in menstruating women is shown in Figure 27.11. It is likely that the peak in LH level induces ovulation and is triggered by the rise in plasma oestradiol. The plasma level of LH is raised in patients with gonadal failure and low in pituitary insufficiency.

Infertility may result from failure of ovulation secondary to lack of gonadotrophins; this condition may be overcome by the administration of FSH and LH to produce a rise in plasma oestradiol levels. Release of the ovum may then be triggered by an injection of human chorionic gonadotrophin (HCG), which has an action similar to that of LH. Excessive stimulation of the ovary can cause multiple ovulation and therefore multiple births.

The hypothalamus therefore appears to control the menstrual cycle. If the woman has a period every 28 days then this periodicity exists in the hypothalamus or its associated nuclei. The cycle can be modified by signals coming back from the gonads, and also by signals coming from the higher centres of the brain, so that stresses of various kinds can affect the menstrual cycle by way of the higher centres and the hypothalamus. It is not uncommon for girls under stress such as leaving home, sitting examinations, or losing a relative to have a disturbance of menstruation even to the point of amenorrhoea (absence of menstruation).

The pituitary gonadotrophins are affected by the gonadal hormones in a negative feed-back system and in general it can be said that the production of FSH and LH is reduced by a rise in the secretion of oestrogens and progesterone by the ovary. The main effect of the synthetic oestrogens and progestogens contained in the contraceptive pill is to reduce the pituitary gonadotrophin secretion and thus inhibit ovulation.

Clomiphene is an anti-oestrogen which binds to the oestrogen receptor sites in the hypothalamus. In so doing it prevents the negative feed-back of oestradiol and thus increases the production of pituitary gonadotrophins, which stimulate the ovary as judged by the increase in output of steroid hormones. It is used to stimulate ovulation in infertile women with ovarian failure.

In young children the secretion of gonadotrophic hormones is very low. It rises slowly throughout childhood until, with approaching puberty, the secretion of both hormones increases rapidly to adult levels. The onset of these pubertal changes is probably related to the achievement of a critical weight of around 37 kg. In later years the normal pulsatile secretion of FSH and LH may be inhibited by weight loss and this is a common cause of amenorrhoea. Less frequent, but more serious, is the severe weight loss of anorexia nervosa, which is invariably associated with amenorrhoea due to lack of gonadotrophins.

The cyclical changes in plasma gonadotrophin levels continue throughout reproductive life; a further increase in gonadotrophin level occurs after the menopause, when the inhibitory influence of the ovarian steroids on gonadotrophin production is reduced.

Time of ovulation

Ovulation in women occurs spontaneously and is not the result of coitus. The finding of an actual ovum is, of course, the best proof that ovulation has recently occurred; human ova can be obtained at operation or with a laparoscope by washing the uterine tubes with saline and collecting the fluid that emerges from the fimbriated end. Ova are found only at the middle of the cycle (about the 15th day) and not at other times. Inspection of human ovaries during abdominal operations show that ovulation usually occurs between the 12th and 15th day of the menstrual cycle. Close monitoring of the cycle by an ultrasound imaging of the follicle itself shows its rupture around the 14th day, when it has reached the diameter of about 2 cm and contains about 10 ml of fluid.

More indirect evidence of ovulation is provided by the change from the proliferative to the secretory phase of the endometrium. This occurs at about the middle of the cycle and is dependent on the corpus luteum. Also the slight fall of body temperature followed by a slight rise, usually less than 0.5°C, which occurs about the middle of the menstrual cycle gives an approximate indication of the time of ovulation. This elevation of body temperature in the second half of the cycle is caused by the thermogenic action of progesterone. A peak in plasma oestrogen levels (and urinary oestrogen excretion) provides another guide to the time of ovulation. This occurs about 24 hours before the rise in plasma LH. In turn the rise in LH level is followed some 24 to 36 hours later by ovulation. Plasma progesterone levels of more than 13 nmol/l by day 21 of a cycle is good evidence that ovulation has occurred.

Changes in the genital tract at ovulation

Under the influence of oestrogen the mucus secreted by the glands within the cervix becomes thin and watery, allowing the passage of spermatozoa. After ovulation the mucus becomes viscid and cellular and penetration by sperm impossible. This is associated with a physiological closure of the utero-tubular junction and so spermatozoa are unlikely to reach the uterine tubes except at the time of ovulation, when the oestrogen effect is maximal.

The cilia of the fimbriae are adapted to pick up the viscous contents of the ovarian follicle and pass them, with the ovum, into the tubal ostium. The tubal mucosa secretes bicarbonate, which is responsible for the dispersal of the cumulus cells of the ovum prior to sperm penetration. Tubal secretions, maximal at the time of ovulation, are the result both of transudation from plasma and of epithelial secretion. The oxygen uptake of spermatozoa increases with exposure to tubal fluids; this increased uptake correlates with tubal bicarbonate ion secretion. The process of sperm capacitation that occurs within the uterine tube before penetration of the ovum is discussed on page 334.

FERTILISATION

The determination of the time of ovulation in woman is important in the study and treatment of infertility. An ovum can be fertilised at a mating that precedes ovulation only if the spermatozoa placed in the genital tract survive until ovulation occurs; fertilisation can occur after ovulation only so long as the ovum remains capable of being fertilised. If, as is likely, the period of viability of both spermatozoa and ova is short, the time of ovulation determines to a large extent the time during which mating is fertile.

Viability of spermatozoa and ova
Microscopic examination of spermatozoa gives little information as to their fertilising power; at most it can be said that semen containing very few spermatozoa or large numbers of abnormally shaped spermatozoa is unlikely to bring about a pregnancy. Normal spermatozoa may retain their motility after their power to fertilise is lost; motile sperms have been found in human cervical mucus three days after coitus and in the uterine tubes seven days after coitus.

The ovum has an even shorter life than the spermatozoon. Histological examination shows that the unfertilised ovum quickly degenerates in the uterine tubes. It is unlikely that the fertilisable life of the human ovum is more than 8 hours.

Coitus
Conception occurs after a fertile mating in which the spermatozoa deposited in the vagina reach an ovum shortly after ovulation. In response to psychological and sensory stimuli the penis becomes erect, increasing in length from about 9.5 to 17 cm by engorgement of the erectile tissue of the corpora cavernosa and spongiosa. The mechanism of this engorgement is not yet fully understood but it seems likely that in the flaccid state much of the arterial blood entering the corpora cavernosa is diverted through 'shunt' arteries to the venous system within the corpora spongiosa. During erection these shunt arteries constrict and the pressure of the blood within the spaces of the corpora cavernosa increases (Fig. 27.12). At the same time smooth muscle within the corpora cavernosa relaxes. It seems likely that vasoactive intestinal peptide (VIP) is the neurotransmitter involved.

During erection the dartos and cremaster muscles also contract and elevate the testes. The testes themselves

Flaccid

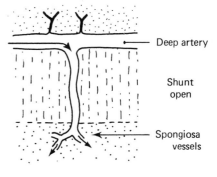

Erect

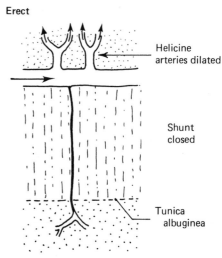

Fig. 27.12 Mechanism of erection (After Wagner G et al. 1982 Lancet 2: 416)

become congested and the skin flushes. The penis is inserted into the vagina and stimulation of the penis, clitoris and vagina is increased by rhythmic voluntary movements.

The nipples of the woman become erect by contraction of their smooth muscle, the areolae and breasts become engorged. The passage of the penis into the vagina is facilitated by the mucus secreted by the cervix and by the glands of Bartholin in the vulva. Later the clitoral glans becomes engorged and the clitoris is retracted against the anterior border of the symphysis pubis. The vagina becomes lengthened and distended. The outer third becomes congested and is described as the orgasmic platform. The uterus is raised.

As physical and psychological stimulation increases the heart rate rises, breathing becomes faster and the blood pressure increases. Semen is moved from the vas deferens, prostate and seminal vesicles into the urethra by contraction of smooth muscle. Coitus culminates both physiologically and psychologically in the *orgasm*, in which semen is ejaculated from the urethra into the upper part of the vagina by rhythmic contractions of bulbocavernosus and ischiocavernosus muscles. The internal sphincter of the bladder prevents retrograde ejaculation. Orgasm in the woman, which may occur simultaneously with the male orgasm, consists of rhythmical contractions of vaginal and uterine muscle and dilatation of the cervix.

After ejaculation of the highly buffered semen the vaginal pH increases to 7 and may not return to pH 4 for ten hours or so. Sperm motility is favoured by a neutral pH and inhibited by a low pH. The unaided random movements of spermatozoa (about 100 μm/s) are insufficient to explain their transport to the uterine tubes, but it is possible that coitus causes uterine contractions that aid the transport of sperm.

Coitus is controlled primarily by the cerebral cortex but the reflex changes in the genitalia are governed by lumbar and sacral spinal centres. Stimulation of the sacral (parasympathetic) outflow in the pelvic splanchnic nerves (p. 227) causes erection of the penis or clitoris by dilatation of their blood vessels. Somatic nerves arising in the sacral region of the cord pass out in the pudendal nerves to the ischiocavernosus and bulbo-cavernosus muscles in both sexes and, therefore, both somatic and autonomic nerves are involved in coitus.

The internal organs of reproduction in both sexes are supplied by sympathetic fibres from the lumbar outflow travelling in the hypogastric nerves. Stimulation of these nerves in non-pregnant women produces a contraction, followed by an inhibition, of the body and cervix of the uterus. After section of the hypogastric nerves in man the power of ejaculation, but not of erection, is lost. Failure of ejaculation was common in patients with high blood pressure who were treated with adrenergic neurone-blocking drugs that prevent the internal sphincter of the bladder from closing. Failure of erection is called *impotence* and can be caused by vascular, neurological or psychological problems.

Fertilisation

Although only one spermatozoon is necessary for the fertilisation of an ovum, pregnancy does not occur unless many millions are deposited in the vagina. The ejaculate (p. 325) usually contains 40×10^6 to 200×10^6 spermatozoa per ml. Only a tiny fraction of this number reaches the site of fertilisation. Recent evidence in studies of in vitro fertilisation show that the optimum number of spermatozoa in a fertilisation medium is about 100 000. This is similar to the number found in the ampulla of one uterine tube after coitus.

Freshly ejaculated spermatozoa are unable to enter the ovum; they acquire this capacity after a few hours'

stay in the reproductive tract of the female. This essential change is known as *capacitation*. It involves an alteration in the membrane potential of the acrosome and occurs over a period of a few hours if the sperms are exposed to genital tract fluid of the mid-cycle female (tubal, uterine or cervical secretions). This phenomenon occurs in vitro and is an essential step in the process of in vitro fertilisation.

Fertilisation involves the mixing of genetic material from the chromosomes of the ovum and the spermatozoon. To do this both germ cells reduce their chromosomes from the normal diploid state (46) to the

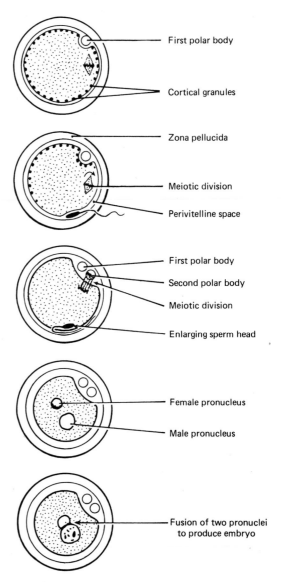

Fig. 27.13 The steps in the fertilisation of an ovum by a spermatozoon. (After Thibault C 1972 International Journal of Fertility 17: 1)

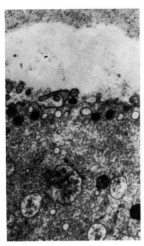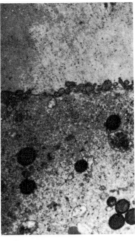

Fig. 27.14 Electron microscope view of the surface of an unfertilised human ovum (left) to show the electron-dense cortical granules. A similar view of an ovum that has been penetrated by a spermatozoon is shown on the right. (Courtesy of Mills J. A. and Oh Y. K.)

haploid (23) by meiotic division. In the ovum this meiotic division is triggered by the penetration of the fertilising spermatozoon through the zona pellucida.

The cumulus cells surrounding the ovum are dispersed partly by the bicarbonate secreted by the tubal mucosa and partly by hyaluronidase produced by the accumulated spermatozoa. The events of fertilisation are shown in Figure 27.13. The fertilising spermatozoon penetrates the zona pellucida by digesting it with an enzyme produced in the acrosome; this enzyme has been called acrosomal proteinase. When the fertilising spermatozoon passes through the zona pellucida into the ovum the zona becomes impenetrable to further spermatozoa. This is achieved by the release of a substance from many cortical granules around the periphery of the ovum itself into the space between the ovum and the zona pellucida (Fig. 27.14).

Once it has entered the ovum the sperm head enlarges to form the male pronucleus. The chromatin left in the ovum, after the second polar body has been extruded, condenses to form the smaller female pronucleus. These two condensations of genetic material move towards one another and fuse to form the nucleus of the fertilised embryo. Mitotic divisions of this cell results in the formation of the blastocyst.

FURTHER READING

Berkovitz G D, Brown T R, Migeon C J 1983 Androgen receptors. Clinics in Endocrinology and Metabolism 12: 155–173

Begley D J, Firth J A, Hoult J R S 1980 Human reproduction and developmental biology. Macmillan, London

Davson H, Segal M B 1980 Introduction to physiology, 5: Control of reproduction. Academic Press, New York

Edwards R G 1980 Conception in the human female. Academic Press, New York

Findlay A L R 1984 Reproduction and the fetus. Arnold, London

France J T 1982 The detection of ovulation for fertility and infertility. In: Bonnar J (ed) Recent advances in obstetrics and gynaecology 14. Churchill Livingstone, Edinburgh, pp. 2151–239

Furlow W L (ed) 1981 Male sexual dysfunction. Urologic Clinics of North America 8: 1–205

Gasden R G 1985 Biology of menopause. Academic Press, New York

Johnson M, Everitt B 1984 Essential reproduction. Blackwell Scientific, Oxford

Lee P A 1983 Ovarian function from conception to puberty: physiology and disorders. In: Serra G B (ed) The ovary. Raven Press, New York, pp. 177–189

Mann T, Lutwak-Mann C 1981 Male reproductive function and semen. Springer, Berlin

Stanhope R, Adams J, Brook CGD 1985 Disturbances of puberty. Clinics in Obstetrics and Gynaecology 12: 557–577

Wagner G 1982 Vascular mechanisms involved in erection and erectile disorders. Clinics in Endocrinology and Metabolism 11: 717–723

28

Pregnancy

Fertilisation usually occurs in the ampulla of the uterine tubes within 12 hours of coitus and the early embryo then passes along the tube into the uterine cavity, undergoing cleavage as it goes (Fig. 28.1). It is thought to implant in the endometrium at the blastocyst stage 5 days after fertilisation. Progress along the uterine tube is facilitated by peristaltic contractions, ciliary activity and epithelial secretions, all of which increase around the time of ovulation.

When an ovum is fertilised the corpus luteum persists instead of degenerating and menstruation does not occur. Failure to menstruate at the expected date is thus

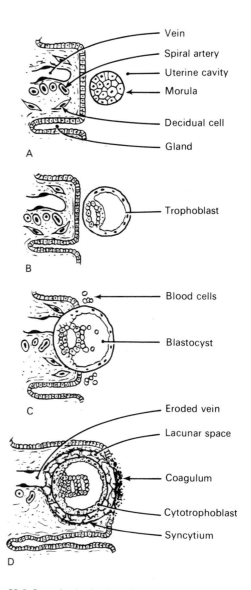

Fig. 28.2 Steps in the implantation of the embryo into the uterine wall.

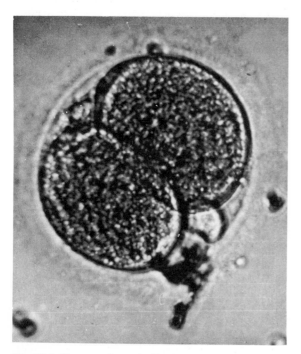

Fig. 28.1 Human embryo, fertilised in vitro, at two-cell stage. The embryo has lost its cumulus cells and is surrounded by the translucent zona pellucida. The two polar bodies can also be seen. (Courtesy of M. Seitz, L. Mastroiani and B. Bracket.)

one of the first presumptive signs of pregnancy. This ensures a continuous production of progesterone to maintain the secretory changes in the endometrium and prevent it from breaking down in menstruation. It is likely that the corpus luteum is maintained by human chorionic gonadotrophin (HCG, p. 339) produced by the blastocyst as it embeds in the endometrium.

Little is known of the factors that control the process of implantation (Fig. 28.2) but HCG produced by the embryo is probably important.

The endometrium continues to grow during pregnancy since there is no menstrual degeneration, and it may eventually reach 10 mm or more in thickness. The superficial layer of the stroma becomes compact and the greatly enlarged stromal cells are known as decidual cells. The value of this decidual reaction is not clear since it occurs a considerable time after implantation. It may protect the uterus against invasion by the trophoblast.

In the decidua basalis under the developing embryo the maternal blood vessels dilate and small finger-like outgrowths of the outer layer of the blastocyst, the chorionic villi, grow into them. This penetration by the villi is aided by obliteration of small arteries of the decidua, causing necrosis and the formation of large spaces in the decidua that fill with maternal blood. The villi are soon invaded by mesoderm carrying fetal blood vessels and so the fetal and maternal circulations are brought very close to one another; the placenta (p. 340) is formed in this way.

The fetus possesses genes derived from its father and therefore has antigens foreign to its mother; its rejection might be expected. It is likely that the placenta plays a part in the protection of the fetus. Fetuses removed from the uteri of pregnant rats or rabbits and transplanted in the abdominal muscles are rejected like any other homografts. Grafts placed in the pregnant uterus of animals survive for a considerable time if surrounded by decidual cells.

MATERNAL CHANGES IN PREGNANCY

The cardiac output increases by up to 40 per cent in pregnancy. Most of the increase in early pregnancy goes to the kidneys; the GFR is markedly increased. Later the uterus receives a larger share. The blood volume also increases: the plasma volume rises much more than does the red cell mass (Table 28.3). The haematocrit and haemoglobin concentration in the peripheral blood falls but this is not a true anaemia. After delivery the blood volume returns to the non-pregnant level in a few hours.

The total body water rises in pregnancy. The reten-

Table 28.3 Typical values for total body water and plasma volume in pregnancy in women without oedema.

Status	Water content (kg)	Plasma volume (ml)
Non-pregnant	30.6	2600
Pregnant		
20 weeks	32.4	3150
30 weeks	34.9	3750
40 weeks	36.4	3600

Partly from Hytten F E, Chamberlain G V P 1980 Clinical physiology in obstetrics. Blackwell Scientific, Oxford

tion of water and sodium may be related to the increased production of oestrogens in pregnancy; oestrogen therapy in women also produces an increase in blood volume. The sodium retention of pregnancy may be due to aldosterone, the urinary excretion of which is some 10 times greater than in the non-pregnant state. The high production of aldosterone is related to increased renin production.

The total gain in weight during pregnancy, about 12.5 kg, is greater than would be expected from the gain in water. The difference can be accounted for by an increase in depot fat of about 3.5 kg and in protein (mainly in the uterus and its contents) of 0.8 kg. Failure to gain weight may be evidence of placental insufficiency and poor fetal growth.

It is difficult to determine the energy requirements in pregnancy. The increased tissue stores amount to about 170 MJ and the cumulative extra need for the metabolism of the fetus and uterus may be about 150 MJ. The increase in maternal fat stores may be used up in breast feeding. In pregnancy the β-cells of the pancreas increase in number and the plasma insulin rises. This suggests that pregnancy puts a strain on carbohydrate homeostasis and indeed pregnancy is occasionally followed by diabetes mellitus.

During pregnancy the respiratory centre is more sensitive to CO_2 and hyperventilation occurs. The arterial P_{CO_2} in pregnancy is about 30 mmHg. Progesterone may be responsible for the changes since injection of progesterone into men and women produces a decrease in alveolar P_{CO_2}.

Hormonal changes

The ovary is necessary in the early stages of pregnancy since progesterone from the corpus luteum is responsible for preparing the endometrium for the reception of a fertilised ovum but after this preliminary stage the ovaries can be removed without disturbing the pregnancy. The placenta provides all the hormones needed for the continuation of pregnancy.

The endocrine function of the conceptus begins early in pregnancy about the time of implantation when the primitive trophoblast secretes HCG, which increases the life span of the corpus luteum; in turn this supplies oestrogen and progesterone necessary for the growth and development of the uterus and fetus. Later the placenta produces its own oestrogens and progesterone in amounts that increase as pregnancy advances. The placenta also produces a number of peptide hormones, notably HCG, human placental lactogen and relaxin.

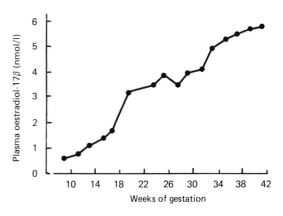

Fig. 28.4 Mean plasma levels of unconjugated oestradiol-17β in 310 normal, pregnancies. (After Tulchinsky D et al. 1972 American Journal of Obstetrics and Gynecology 112: 1095)

Oestrogens

Plasma and urinary levels of oestrogens in the mother rise steadily during pregnancy (Fig. 28.4).

The oestrogens produced by the placenta are formed from precursors synthesised by the fetal adrenal glands (Fig. 28.5). Since the placenta cannot synthesise oestrogens from simple precursors, the production of oestrogens depends on there being a live fetus with functional adrenal glands. After fetal death the urinary excretion of oestriol falls; in the presence of an anencephalic fetus with poorly developed adrenals the oestriol excretion is low. The placenta possesses enzymes lacking in the fetus but the fetus has enzymes lacking in the placenta; the two together, the feto-placental unit, form a complete system for steroid synthesis.

Progesterone

The maternal plasma contains between 30 and 150 nmol/l progesterone in early pregnancy, and as pregnancy advances the level rises to about 500 nmol/l (Fig. 28.6). The plasma progesterone remains high during labour and falls after parturition. The fetus uses

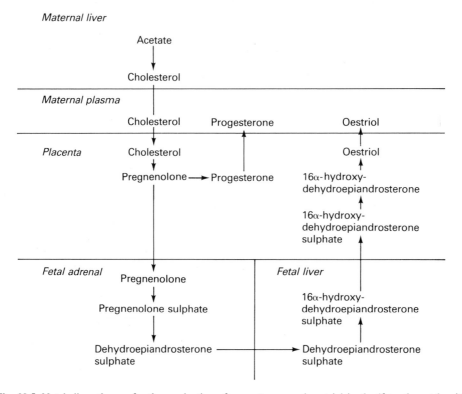

Fig. 28.5 Metabolic pathways for the production of progesterone and oestriol in the 'feto-placental unit'.

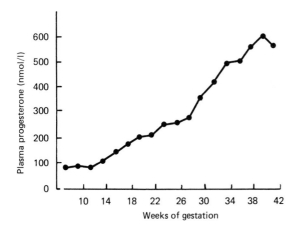

Fig. 28.6 Mean plasma levels of progesterone in 308 normal pregnancies. (After Tulchinsky D et al. 1972 American Journal of Obstetrics and Gynecology 112: 1095)

the progesterone produced in the maternal placenta for the production of corticosteroids.

Human chorionic gonadotrophin

HCG excretion begins about the time of the expected, but missed, menstrual period, rises to a peak about 10 weeks later and then falls to a lower value, around which it fluctuates until the end of pregnancy. The amount of HCG in the serum shows similar changes (Fig. 28.7). HCG production seems to depend on the number of cells of the cytotrophoblast in the placenta; the number of these cells increases rapidly in early pregnancy and then declines until they can scarcely be seen at term.

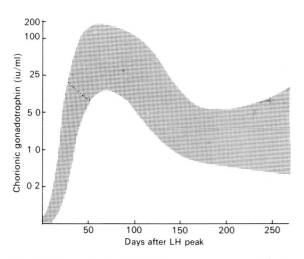

Fig. 28.7 Serum levels of HCG in normal pregnancy plotted on a logarithmic scale. (After Hobson W et al. 1975 Journal of Toxicology and Environmental Health 1: 657)

Human placental lactogen (HPL)

This placental hormone has both prolactin-like and growth hormone-like properties. It is a protein and has structural similarities to both growth hormone and prolactin. It can be detected in the maternal plasma early in pregnancy; levels rise steadily to about 37 weeks and then level off. After delivery HPL disappears from the circulation within 24 hours.

HPL plays a part in the preparation of the breasts for lactation (p. 348). Its growth hormone-like action is responsible for many of the metabolic changes seen in pregnancy such as the increased secretion of insulin, increased insulin resistance and increased plasma fatty acid levels. While plasma HPL levels are often low in patients with placental insufficiency, the range in normal pregnancy is so wide that measurement of plasma HPL is unsatisfactory in clinical evaluation.

Pregnancy diagnosis tests

The rapid rise in HCG excretion early in pregnancy is the basis of these tests. The principle is as follows. HCG prepared from the urine of pregnant women is injected into a rabbit; the rabbit produces antibodies to HCG in its serum. When a suspension of latex particles is coated with HCG and mixed with the serum containing antibodies to HCG agglutination of the particles occurs. If urine containing HCG (that is urine from a pregnant woman) is added to serum containing antibodies to HCG the reaction between the HCG and antibodies to HCG leaves no free antibody. On subsequent addition of latex particles coated with HCG no agglutination occurs. The absence of agglutination indicates that the urine contained HCG and constitutes a positive pregnancy test.

AMNIOTIC FLUID

As pregnancy advances the products of conception increase in size and eventually occupy the whole of the uterine cavity. The growing fetus is bathed by the amniotic fluid, which is contained within the 'bag of membranes' consisting of the amnion and chorion.

The volume of the amniotic fluid is variable: it is detectable at 8 weeks' gestation, a little over 30 ml at 10 weeks' gestation and is about 400 ml at 19 weeks. The highest value, between 37 and 38 weeks' gestation, is between 500 ml and 1100 ml; thereafter there is a steady decrease. The amniotic fluid maintains the fetus in a shock-proof and weightless condition in a constant temperature environment. Amniotic fluid is fairly freely exchanged with the maternal fluids; its protein content approaches that of blood plasma. It is partly a secretory product of the amniotic epithelium and partly derived from fetal urine and lung liquid (p. 346). The fetus swallows amniotic fluid and one cause of excess of amniotic fluid (*hydramnios*) is oesophageal atresia (failure of the canalisation of the oesophagus).

The amniotic fluid is sometimes sampled to detect fetal abnormalities. The bilirubin content of the fluid may be raised in a fetus whose mother has antibodies to its red cells so that haemolysis occurs in the fetus. The concentration of the phospholipid lecithin rises sharply at about 35 weeks' gestation and indicates that the baby's lungs are producing surfactant (p. 346); reduced levels of lecithin in the amniotic fluid indicate that the baby, when born, has an increased liability to severe respiratory distress syndrome. In babies with a neural tube defect (anencephaly or spina bifida) alpha-fetoprotein (AFP), synthesised by the fetal liver and yolk sac, escapes in excessive amounts into the amniotic fluid; the concentration may be 350 mg/l instead of the normal 16 mg/l. A high concentration at 16 weeks may reflect fetal abnormality. More sensitive tests now permit the estimation of AFP in maternal serum.

Amniotic fluid always contains a number of fetal cells and the sex of the fetus can be discovered by examination of their chromatin content. After culture of the cells the chromosome picture may reveal abnormalities such as Down's syndrome (trisomy 21). Biochemical tests may be applied to cultures of cells in the diagnosis of certain inborn errors of metabolism.

THE PLACENTA

The placenta consists mainly of fetal tissue implanted in the decidua of the uterine wall. It is derived by specialisation of the chorion, the outermost layer of the developing embryo, part of which develops a villous structure presenting a large surface area to the maternal tissues. The fetal side consists of two elements — an outer trophoblastic layer, derived from the fetal ectoderm, and an underlying stroma containing a rich capillary circulation derived from mesoderm. The trophoblast is of two types: cytotrophoblast, consisting of distinct cells, and syncytial trophoblast.

The placenta is served by two extensive vascular networks, one fetal the other maternal, which come into very close relationship with each other so that the distance to be traversed by a substance passing from mother to fetus is usually only some 2 to 3 μm. The area available for exchange is large — about 12 m² in the mature placenta. In human placentas the capillaries on the maternal side are replaced by sinusoids without capillary walls so that maternal blood bathes the fetal villi directy (Fig. 28.8). The feto–maternal barrier consists only of chorion and fetal capillary wall.

The chorion has properties similar to those of an epithelium such as that of the small intestine or renal

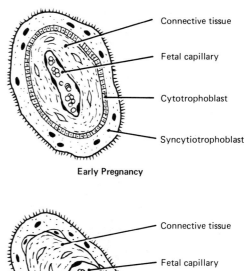

Early Pregnancy

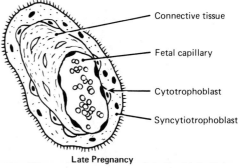

Late Pregnancy

Fig. 28.8 Microscopic structure of chorionic villi in early and late pregnancy. (After D L Gardner, T C Dodds 1976 Human histology, 3rd edn. Churchill Livingstone, Edinburgh)

tubule; it allows free passage of lipid-soluble substances, restricts the movement of polar molecules and actively controls the transfer of ions and other biologically important substances. Besides acting as an organ of external exchange the placenta is the site of synthesis of steroid and protein hormones (p. 338) essential for the maintenance of pregnancy.

The placenta is unique in its rapid development, early senescence and death. It functions well for about 40 weeks but if parturition is delayed the needs of the fetus may not be adequately met. The child born after an excessively long gestation has a reduced chance of survival.

Placental transport

Lipid soluble substances
A lipid-soluble substance crosses the placenta so rapidly that its concentration in the venous effluent on the recipient side is likely to be as high as that in the outflow from the donor side. For a lipid-soluble substance the amount transferred depends only on the blood flow in the two circulations and on the patterns of capillary flow. Transport of this type is said to be

'flow-limited'; in the placenta this designation applies to the exchanges of respiratory gases (O_2, CO_2, N_2), anaesthetics, many drugs, narcotics, alcohol and probably nicotine. The relatively easy access of these substances to the fetus may affect fetal health and development. Thus smoking may cause low birth weight, excess alcohol may cause fetal malformations and narcotics may lead to withdrawal symptoms in the neonatal period.

Oxygen and CO2

The transport of oxygen to the fetus is favoured by two special features of fetal blood that ensure that the amount of oxygen it can carry is almost twice that carried by maternal blood when the P_{O_2} is about 30 mmHg, the normal level in blood leaving the placenta. The first is the relatively high haemoglobin concentration (18 to 20 g/dl at term) and the second is the displacement of the oxygen dissociation curve to the left (Fig. 28.9).

The dissociation curve of the blood of the fetus differs from that of the adult because fetal blood contains a high proportion of fetal haemoglobin (HbF). HbF differs slightly but significantly from HbA in amino acid composition and therefore in its affinity for 2,3-bisphosphoglycerate (2,3-BPG; p. 148). This difference in turn affects the interactions between subunits of the haemoglobin molecule and so the shape of the oxygen curve. The HbE/HbA ratio is about 0.9 at midgestation, 0.8 at term and 0.1 three months after birth.

The fetal P_{CO_2} at which an adequate amount of CO_2 passes to the mother is set at about 48 mmHg as a result of maternal hyperventilation that develops at about 8 weeks of pregnancy, lowering the mother's alveolar P_{CO_2} from 40 to 33 mmHg. This hyperventilation has been shown to be due to the action of progesterone on the maternal respiratory centre.

Water-soluble substances

Urea and other waste products of fetal metabolism cross the placenta from fetus to mother through water-filled channels that allow the passage only of small polar molecules of this type.

Glucose and some amino acids are transported across the placenta by specific carrier mechanisms. Glucose transport depends on a carrier specific for D-glucose, allowing transfer in either direction depending on the concentration difference between fetal and maternal plasma. The carrier provides a rate of transport about a hundred times faster than that of other molecules of similar size and solubility; it is not available to L-glucose or most other monosaccharides. Normally the blood glucose level of the fetus is about 0.6 mmol/l less than that of the mother. The fetus of a poorly controlled diabetic mother may be supplied with excess glucose and become obese; ultimately the placenta may be unable to sustain the overgrown fetus.

The fetus receives about 1 g/kg of nitrogen per day in the form of amino acids. Of this two-thirds are used for growth and the remainder are broken down to release energy; the nitrogen is returned to the mother mainly as urea. Most amino acids, including all the essential ones (p. 216) appear to be actively transported to the fetus as their concentrations in fetal plasma are 1.5 to 5 times higher than in the maternal side. In the rare condition, maternal hyperphenylalaninaemia (or *phenylketonuria*), the level of phenylalanine in the fetus may be more than 10 times the normal level, with disastrous consequences for the development of the fetal brain.

The extent to which fatty acids and other lipids cross the placenta is still controversial. Most of the fetal lipids are synthesised from carbohydrate and amino acid precursors; the essential fatty acids (p. 217), however, must be obtained from the mother.

Most minerals probably reach the fetus by carrier-mediated transport. During a pregnancy the fetal body accumulates 240 mmol of sodium, 700 mmol of calcium and 10 mmol of iron. Most of the iron in the maternal blood is bound to the transport protein *transferrin* (p. 29). Transferrin does not cross the placenta but it appears to interact with placental binding sites leading to transport of iron into the fetus in a bound form.

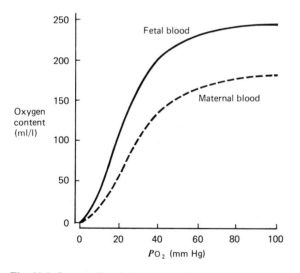

Fig. 28.9 Oxygen dissociation curves. These show the oxygen content of whole blood from human subjects at oxygen tensions between 0 and 100 mmHg (pH 7.4, temp 37°C). Fetal blood has a higher haemoglobin content and therefore higher oxygen capacity than maternal blood. In addition the oxygen affinity of fetal blood, is higher than that of maternal blood so that its dissociation curve is displaced to the left.

The placenta has an important role in the regulation of water and electrolyte balance. While the fetal kidney can affect the distribution of water and electrolytes between the fetal body and the amniotic fluid, the placenta controls the total amounts in the conceptus. The transport, active or passive, of ions such as Na^+, K^+, Cl^-, HCO_3^- and phosphates almost certainly determines the osmotic movements of water and therefore volume regulation. Although active transport of Na^+ and some other ions is likely, details of these mechanisms and of their control by hormones such as vasopressin and aldosterone remain to be discovered. In most species there is an electrical potential difference between the mother and the fetus that probably reflects active ion transport. The fetal lamb is about $30\,mV$ negative to the ewe.

Antibody transfer

Immunoglobulins of the IgG class cross the placenta by a specific transport mechanism and are usually found at a higher concentration in fetal than in maternal plasma. IgA and IgM antibodies are synthesised by the fetus.

These facts have important clinical implications. A high level of IgM in the fetus usually denotes a fetal infection. More specifically, a high level of the IgM antibody to rubella is characteristic of infection of the fetus with rubella. In contrast, antibodies of the IgG class in the newborn infant reflect the mother's exposure to viral infections. Transfer of these antibodies to the fetus provides a measure of protection for the infant against measles and other viral infections in the first few months of life. Less happily, transfer of IgG antibodies to rhesus antigens of red blood cells may cause the haemolysis that is the basis of rhesus haemolytic disease (p. 53).

LABOUR AND DELIVERY

In some 55 per cent of pregnant women labour takes place 280 ± 7 days from the first day of the last menstrual period; in 25 per cent it occurs before the 273rd day and in 20 per cent after the 287th day. Some uterine contractions occur early in pregnancy but they are small and usually separated by periods of an hour or so in which the uterus is quiescent. From the twentieth week the contractions are greater in amplitude and much more frequent, although they remain irregular until the last few weeks of pregnancy when rhythmic contractions begin. The interval between the contraction waves in late pregnancy is usually from 5 to 10 minutes.

In the few days prior to the onset of labour the genital tract is prepared by the hormone *relaxin*. This is produced by the ovaries and has the effect of softening the cervix of the uterus and softening the cartilage of the pubic symphysis.

It is not easy to account for the onset of labour in hormonal terms. The oestrogen and progesterone blood levels continue to rise (p. 338) until parturition has occurred and the final decline in the production of these hormones is the result rather than the cause of parturition.

Oxytocin may play a part in the onset of labour. Certainly infusions of oxytocin may bring on labour; also the sensitivity of the uterus to oxytocin increases steadily throughout pregnancy. However hypophysectomy does not prevent parturition and the maternal plasma concentration of oxytocin is low in pregnancy and in labour. Its concentration in the amniotic fluid, however, increases at term because of increased production by the fetus.

Prostaglandin PGE_2 given by mouth can produce uterine contractions and induce labour, even in early pregnancy, but its effect is even greater when it is delivered directly to the uterus by intrauterine injection. Prostaglandins are detectable in the plasma during labour with peaks associated with each uterine contraction.

The nervous system is not responsible for the uterine contractions of labour. Near full term the onset of labour may be hastened by emotional factors but it is not affected by section of the sympathetic and parasympathetic nerves.

Since the ovaries can be removed early in pregnancy in women without causing abortion and since the corpus luteum begins to degenerate in the third month of pregnancy, the hormones produced in the ovary can have little influence in determining the onset of labour.

Distension of the uterus is unlikely to be an important factor in the onset of labour. The duration of pregnancy remains constant in spite of great variations in size of the fetus and in spite of the presence of excessive amounts of amniotic fluid (hydramnios); even in extrauterine pregnancies in which the embryo is in the uterine tube or abdominal cavity and the uterus is empty the patient may experience labour pains at full term. Furthermore single pregnancies come to an end at a distension that is much less than that obtaining in a multiple pregnancy long before parturition.

On two occasions twin pregnancies have been reported in which one twin was present in each horn of a bicornuate uterus. There was an interval of several weeks between the births of the children. It is difficult to see how conditions at the same time in one woman can be suitable for the maintenance, as well as the termination, of pregnancy unless there is some local factor that triggers off the mechanism of parturition. It has long been suspected that the fetus itself has some influence on the length of gestation. If it has a poorly developed pituitary gland with hypoplasia of the adrenal cortex, gestation is often prolonged. Electrocoagulation of pituitary glands of fetal lambs prolongs gestation for many days. This of course causes adrenal hypoplasia and similarly fetal adrenalectomy also results in prolongation of pregnancy. Conversely infusion of ACTH into fetal lambs is followed by parturition. Cortisol given to the ewe has no effect but given to the fetuses it causes labour. In this way it seems clear that the fetus plays a part in determining the time of its own birth.

Labour

The slight contractions of the uterus that occur throughout pregnancy increase the pressure in the uterine veins and assist the movement of blood through the intervillous placental spaces and so aid the oxygenation of the fetal blood. Towards the end of pregnancy, but before labour begins, the basal amniotic pressure is about 5 mmHg with slow oscillations of 1 to 5 mmHg above this value. At the onset of labour these rhythmic contractions increase and the basal intrauterine pressure rises to 8 or 12 mmHg.

In the *first stage* of labour the intrauterine pressure rises slowly with each contraction to a peak of 30 to 50 mmHg above the basal value and then falls more slowly to the basal level. These contractions, which occur at intervals of 2 to 5 minutes, can be felt by a hand placed on the abdominal wall. When the pressure is above a certain value, which varies with different patients but is in the region 25 to 35 mmHg, the mother is conscious of *labour pain*, that is a pain commencing in the lumbosacral region and radiating to the front and down the thighs. By pressing on the amniotic fluid the uterine contractions dilate first the upper part of the cervical canal and later the mouth of the cervix. The membranes finally rupture and a small quantity of amniotic fluid escapes.

In the *second stage* of labour the intrauterine pressure at the height of a contraction may rise to 110 mmHg and the pressure between contractions is usually about twice that in the first stage. The head of the child is slowly forced through the pelvis and is born, the remainder of the body following almost at once. During this stage voluntary contraction of the abdominal muscles can increase the intrauterine pressure still further to as much as 260 mmHg.

The pressure within the uterus at the height of a contraction may be sufficient to squeeze out the maternal blood from the uterine vessels into the vena cava and even occasionally into the aorta if the intrauterine pressure rises above the arterial pressure. Thus at the height of each contraction the venous pressure is considerably raised; this rise may be dangerous in patients with cardiac disease. The arterial pressure increases slightly during a labour contraction but quite considerably if the abdominal muscles contract at the same time. The fetal heart rate falls during a uterine contraction, the amount of the fall depending on the rise of intrauterine pressure.

After the birth of the child uterine contractions cease for a time, usually 5 to 15 minutes, and then in the *third stage* of labour they begin again and the placenta and membranes are expelled. With the detachment and delivery of the placenta a raw bleeding surface is left but the average loss of blood is only 300 ml. The mechanisms that limit blood loss are not clearly understood. The contraction of the uterus no doubt plays a part; when the child is allowed to suck, oxytocin is released and the uterus contracts firmly but does not go into a prolonged spasm. During the *puerperium*, the period immediately following parturition, the uterus shrinks until, when involution is complete, it is only a little larger than in women who have never been pregnant.

THE FETUS AND ADAPTATION AT BIRTH

Two phases are often distinguished within intrauterine life. In the first 12 weeks the major process is the formation of the internal organs and during this period the conceptus is known as an *embryo*. After 12 weeks the major change is an increase in the size and complexity of organs already formed; the conceptus is known as a *fetus*. This distinction is more apparent than real since many organs continue to undergo obvious morphological changes during the fetal period and well into post-natal life. For example, the cerebral cortex, which is little folded at 12 weeks, undergoes changes leading to the formation of the mature convolutional pattern in the full-term infant. Even at birth the structural maturation of the brain is incomplete; further microscopical changes take place after birth, notably the growth of the neural networks.

The major way in which the fetus differs from the child or adult is in its exchanges with the external environment to permit respiration, nutrition and excretion. In the fetus all these functions are served by the placenta, which was described earlier.

Circulation

The fetal circulation differs from that of the child in two important respects. It provides blood flow to and from the placenta, and it includes right-to-left shunts, allowing the greater part of the systemic venous return to by-pass the lungs. At birth the adaptation consists essentially of the discarding of the placental circulation, the substantial increase in the blood flow through the lungs and the closure of the right-to-left shunt channels.

The fetal circulation is illustrated in Figure 28.10.

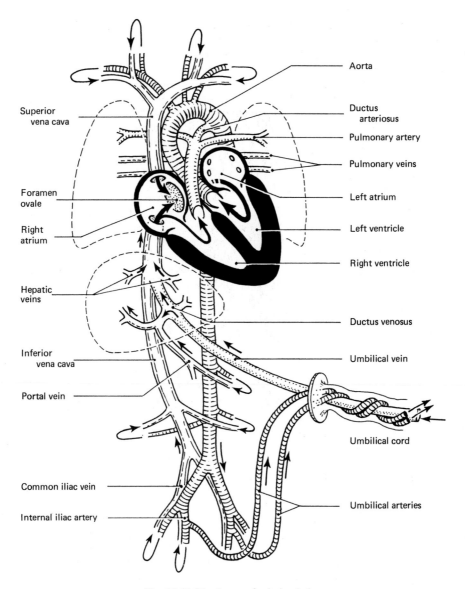

Fig. 28.10 The human fetal circulation.

The arterial supply to the placenta is provided through the umbilical arteries, which arise from the internal iliacs. These arteries have three muscle coats — circular, longitudinal and spiral — and it is stretch on the spiral muscle that normally initiates cord occlusion at birth. The umbilical arteries produce prostacyclin (p. 233), a vasodilator and an inhibitor of platelet aggregation. It may be important for the regulation of the fetal blood flow through the placenta.

The umbilical vein passes from the umbilicus to the porta hepatis, where it joins the portal vein; most of its blood then passes directly to the inferior vena cava through the *ductus venosus*. At birth, the ductus venosus closes, at first temporarily and then permanently; little is known of the mechanism.

Two shunts allow blood to by-pass the lungs: the *foramen ovale* between the atria and the *ductus arteriosus* between the aorta and the pulmonary artery

Foramen ovale
Blood flowing into the heart from the inferior vena cava is split into two roughly equal streams by the crista dividens, the free margin of the inter-atrial septum. One stream goes through the foramen ovale to the left atrium, the other to the right atrium. On the left side

of the foramen ovale there is a thin but strong membrane that is larger than the opening; it has a free upper margin and is attached below. This, the valve of the foramen ovale, is held open in fetal life because the pressure in the inferior vena cava is higher than that in the left atrium. After the onset of breathing this pressure gradient is reversed and the valve closes.

The ductus arteriosus

This is a short, wide vessel connecting the main pulmonary artery to the aorta. In the fetus some 90 per cent of the output of the right ventricle passes through the ductus and only 10 per cent goes to the lungs. This distribution of flow is dictated by the high pressure in the pulmonary artery, which, in turn, results from the high vascular resistance in the small muscular arterioles of the lung. The muscle in the wall of the ductus arteriosus has the unusual property of contracting in response to a rise in Po_2. This means that the amount of oxygen diffusing into the wall of the ductus from blood in its lumen determines whether the vessel is open or closed. This mechanism underlies the initial closure of the ductus after birth. Prostaglandins, particularly PGE_1 and PGE_2, may be involved in the maintenance of the patency of the ductus in intrauterine life.

Changes at birth

Dramatic changes take place in the circulation at the start of breathing. The first and most important change on which the others depend is a reduction in pulmonary vascular resistance. This is brought about by relaxation of the pulmonary arterioles partly in response to the increase in Po_2 and decrease in Pco_2 in the lung, and partly because of some undefined effect of the expansion of the lungs with air. The local increase in oxygen tension is considerable; the highest Po_2 in the fetal lung is some 25 to 30 mmHg compared with about 147 mmHg in the inspired air. The start of ventilation also leads to a fall in Pco_2 from the fetal level of 50 mmHg to about 40 mmHg.

The increased blood flow through the lungs increases the inflow to the left atrium and hence the left atrial pressure. At the same time the cessation of the inflow from the umbilical veins to the inferior vena cava lowers the pressure of the right side of the valve of the foramen ovale. These two changes lead to the reversal of the pressure gradient and closure of the valve.

At the arterial level, the decrease in pulmonary vascular resistance causes a fall in the pulmonary artery pressure and the reversal of flow in the ductus arteriosus, so that blood flows from the aorta to the pulmonary artery. Since the aortic blood is now derived from ventilated lungs its oxygen tension is sone 50 mmHg higher than in the fetus; the diffusion of

oxygen from the ductal blood stream to its muscular coat initiates closure of the ductus.

Thus the changes in the circulation at birth can be seen to be closely interconnected and to be initiated by the decrease in pulmonary vascular resistance, the cessation of placental flow also playing a part. Although these changes begin as soon as the first breath is taken, there is evidence of a so-called transitional circulation in certain circumstances. Thus a failure of ventilation for any reason quickly returns the distribution of the circulation to that of the fetus. The fall in pulmonary artery pressure is not complete immediately; it falls from about 60 mmHg in the fetus to about 35 mmHg at 8 hours and about 25 mmHg at 2 days.

Postnatal changes

The changes in the distribution of blood flow that take place soon after birth are followed in the first few weeks by a more gradual increase in cardiac output and arterial pressure. The proportion of cardiac output going to different organs also changes in this period. Thus the renal blood flow increases about seven-fold, mainly because of a fall in renal vascular resistance.

Permanent changes in the circulation take place more gradually. The muscular wall of the pulmonary arterioles decreases in thickness rapidly in the first two weeks and then more gradually over the next 18 months. Fibrous closure of the foramen ovale begins within a few days of birth; sometimes it never closes completely. Fibrous closure of the ductus arteriosus starts within 24 to 72 hours in small areas of sub-intimal necrosis. In an infant born prematurely, the ductus may remain open for several weeks and then close normally, often at a gestational age close to term. In a few individuals the ductus remains open permanently and needs to be closed surgically. When the ductus is patent, whether temporarily or permanently, shunting is normally in thc direction·opposite to that in the fetus, from aorta to pulmonary artery, causing an increased flow of blood through the pulmonary artery, left atrium and left ventricle.

Respiration

The lungs develop as an epithelial outgrowth from the embryonic foregut. The first rudimentary pouch appears at about 3 weeks after fertilisation and it subsequently undergoes extensive branching; the formation of the tracheobronchial tree is virtually complete by 17 weeks. Initially the epithelium is columnar; it then becomes cuboidal and finally, from about 24 weeks, it develops the two cell-types (described below) characteristic of the periphery of the mature lung. Ciliated cells and cartilage develop in the conducting airways from 10 weeks. At about 24 weeks an interface is formed between the peripheral epithelium and the rapidly growing circulation.

About half the epithelial cells of the lung periphery are large, very thin, flat cells occupying some 90 per cent of its surface area (type I cells); the other half are fat rounded cells occupying only a small proportion of the surface (type II cells). The latter are the site of surfactant synthesis: this material is stored in intracellular lamellar bodies and the number in each cell increases as gestation advances. These cells also contain numerous mitochondria, have a brush border, and may well be involved in the secretion of lung liquid.

Lung liquid

The fetal lungs secrete liquid that keeps the potential air-spaces expanded to about the same volume that they will occupy after inflation with air — about 30 ml/kg body weight. The liquid is produced by a mechanism dependent on the active transport of ions, particularly chloride, into the lung lumen. This is shown by a relatively high concentration of chloride in the lung liquid and by an electrical potential difference between the lung lumen and blood of some 5 to 10 mV, negative on the luminal side. The lung produces 3 to 4 ml lung liquid per kg body weight per hour (some 300 ml/24 hours in a mature fetus). Some enters the amniotic cavity, the remainder is swallowed. About a quarter of the amniotic fluid is probably produced in the lungs.

In response to the stress of labour the fetus secretes adrenaline and noradrenaline from the adrenal medullas and probably from extra-adrenal chromaffin tissue. The plasma adrenaline concentration increases some 50 to 100 fold and this leads to the absorption of lung liquid. A large proportion of the liquid is normally absorbed before delivery but in some instances, particularly when the infant is delivered by Caesarean section, much of the absorption must take place immediately after birth when the surge in adrenaline production continues for a period. Pulmonary adaptation is somewhat delayed in infants delivered by Caesarean section but this is seldom a serious problem. The absorptive process depends on activation of a sodium pump producing net ion movement from the lumen towards the blood. It is not known whether the chloride pump responsible for secretion is inactivated at this stage, nor whether these two ion pumps have a part to play in the physiology of the adult lung.

Surfactant

This complex of lipid and protein reduces surface tension; it must be present at the air–liquid interface when air enters the lungs, otherwise the newly inflated air-spaces would collapse under the force of surface tension. The surfactant in the lung lumen is adsorbed onto the surface within the period of a single inspiration. The infant often holds his breath, with his chest in the inspiratory position, between each of the first few breaths and so increases the time available for surfactant adsorption.

Surfactant is present in lamellar bodies within type II cells from about the 24th week of gestation. From about 30 weeks surfactant is secreted into the lung lumen and thence to the amniotic fluid where it can be detected in samples taken by aspiration through a needle (*amniocentesis*). This procedure is used clinically to assess lung maturity. The synthesis of surfactant can be stimulated by the administration of glucocorticoids or thyroxine to the fetus. In clinical practice the glucocorticoid dexamethasone is sometimes administered to mothers beginning premature labour to reduce the likelihood of respiratory problems due to deficiency of surfactant in the newborn infant.

During labour the surge of adrenaline, as well as initiating absorption of lung liquid, also leads to an increased secretion of surfactant into the lung lumen. Ventilation with air causes a further large increase in the release of surfactant.

Breathing movements

The fetus makes shallow breathing movements that occur in distinct episodes occupying about half the time. The movements are very rapid (often over 100/min) and shallow, only 1 or 2 ml of liquid being displaced by each 'breath'. These breathing movements are more frequent when the $P\text{CO}_2$ is high in the fetal range and less frequent when the $P\text{O}_2$ is very low (below 20 mmHg). In the case of $P\text{O}_2$ this is the opposite of the adult response and there is no evidence of the close link between $P\text{O}_2$ and $P\text{CO}_2$ levels and breathing, characteristic of postnatal respiratory control. Indeed, for much of the time the fetus is apnoeic despite arterial blood gas tensions that would provoke intense hyperventilation at any other stage of life. This observation led Barcroft to propose that the respiratory centre or some other component of the respiratory control mechanism is inhibited in the fetus and that the inhibition is released in some way after delivery; the nature of the inhibitory influence is not known.

Numerous factors other than sensitivity to $P\text{O}_2$ and $P\text{CO}_2$ affect fetal respiratory movements. In the fetal lamb, breathing movements can result fron tactile and thermal stimuli; reflexes such as the Hering–Breuer reflex (p. 155) arising in the lungs can also be demonstrated. It has been shown that fetal breathing movements occur only during periods when the electroencephalogram shows evidence of REM (rapid eye movement) sleep. This link between breathing and a cerebral event may be analogous to the disturbance of breathing in postnatal life at times of high emotion such as passion, anger and fear.

Integration of cardio-respiratory adaptations

The first breaths may be taken in response to cold or to tactile stimuli but very soon the inhibition of the responsiveness to chemical stimuli (Po_2 and Pco_2) must be released in some way; otherwise breathing would stop as soon as the infant became warm and comfortable. The breathing movements cause air to enter the lungs, which have been cleared, or are in the process of being cleared, of liquid following activation of the absorptive mechanism by a high level of circulating adrenaline. Surfactant, released into the alveolar spaces in the course of gestation and in response of adrenaline, is adsorbed to the newly created interface between air and liquid, which allows the retention of air in the small air spaces. The entry of air into the lungs causes relaxation of the smooth muscle of the pulmonary arterioles and the other cardiovascular changes described earlier.

Cardio-respiratory disorders in the newborn

Newborn infants, and particularly pre-term infants, may develop respiratory disorders because of inadequate adaptation to life outside the uterus. For example, depression of the respiratory centre by asphyxia or drugs may lead to failure to start breathing. In very pre-term infants in the two weeks after birth, immaturity of the respiratory control system may cause recurrent episodes of apnoea (failure to breathe). Lack of surfactant and immaturity of the mechanism for absorption of lung liquid causes various syndromes of respiratory difficulty, the best known of which is *hyaline membrane disease*. These respiratory disorders are the major causes of the perinatal deaths that occur in pre-term infants (Fig. 28.11). Failure of adequate ventilation can cause a return to the high pulmonary vascular resistance characteristic of the fetus and to right-to-left shunting of blood through the the foramen ovale and the ductus arteriosus.

Gastrointestinal adaptation

The infant takes milk from the breast within a few hours. The early milk, known as *colostrum*, is slightly viscous with a high protein content but little fat. On the second or third day, the milk becomes much more abundant and has its usual composition (Table 15.4, p. 221). The colostrum contains important antibodies of the IgA class, specific for the mother's own gastrointestinal bacteria. They are produced in the mammary gland by lymphocytes that have migrated from the submucosa of the gastrointestinal tract. They probably play an important role in preventing bacterial invasion of the newborn infant while allowing a gastrointestinal flora to develop in the lumen of the large intestine.

During intrauterine life the functions of the gastrointestinal tract are probably limited to the absorption of water and electrolytes from amniotic liquid and lung liquid. Morphological development of the small intestine, with the appearance of all the epithelial cell types seen in the adult, is completed by 17 weeks. Both the rate of structural development and the rate of appearance of particular enzyme systems can be accelerated by glucocorticoids and by thyroxine.

In the newborn period rapid development of the digestive enzymes takes place. For example, in rat jejunum, the quantity and activity of the brush-border enzyme sucrase-isomaltase (p. 267) increases more than five-fold in the first few weeks. Synthesis and secretion of bile acid increase gradually during the final three months of gestation but bile salt reabsorption does not develop until the first few days of postnatal life.

Relative immaturity of enzyme development and bile salt production explains one of the handicaps suffered by the pre-term infant — its limited capacity for intestinal absorption. When the intake of milk is adequate, the infant may pass large fatty stools, unless fed with special low-fat milks. The very pre-term infant, after an initial weight loss, only regains its birthweight in 2 or 3 weeks unless fed by the intravenous route, a procedure with appreciable difficulties and hazards.

Renal function

The fetal kidney develops from interactions between an upward growing ureteric bud, derived from the preceding mesonephros, and tissue referred to as metanephric blastema. The first nephrons appear at about 8 weeks and the next 26 weeks are characterised by vast increases in their number and in the complexity of the branching systems connecting them to the collecting ducts. After 34 weeks no new nephrons are formed but the glomeruli become increasingly complex structures

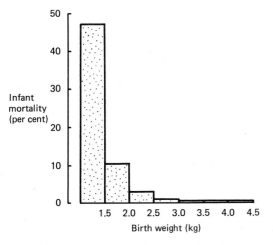

Fig. 28.11 Mortality rate in the first week of life for infants of different birth weights. (Data for England and Wales for 1978 In: Infant and perinatal mortality by birthweight: 1978 estimates. OPCS Monitor 1981: D H 3 81/2)

containing thinner, larger, more infolded glomerular membranes. At the same time, the tubular parts of the nephron, particularly the proximal convoluted tubule and loop of Henle, are lengthened. This growth continues into postnatal life; the average length of the proximal tubule is 2 mm in the newborn infant, 8 mm at 3 years and 20 mm in an adult.

During mid-fetal life the kidney produces large volumes of hypotonic urine. This is added to amniotic fluid, which is swallowed and reabsorbed, and probably contributes little to the overall economy of the fetus. It may, however, serve to regulate the distribution of salts and water between the fetus and its surrounding fluid.

In the mature infant during the month after birth, the glomerular filtration rate (GFR) increases three-fold from 20 up to 60 ml/min per 1.73 m^2 (the adult value for body surface area). Renal tubular functions, including sodium reabsorption, acidification and concentrating ability, are poorly developed at birth but increase two- or three-fold in the first month. Inability to conserve sodium leads to large losses in the urine of the normal infant and thus to a reduction in the volume of the extracellular fluid in the 2 days following birth. This is reflected in a 5 to 10 per cent fall in body weight that occurs in almost all infants in the first two days and is regarded as part of normal neonatal adjustment.

The pre-term infant has a lower GFR (about 16 ml/min per 1.73 m^2 at 32 weeks gestation) and the postnatal increase is smaller, to about 40 ml/min per 1.73 m^2 after a month. In the pre-term infant renal tubular functions are also incompletely developed. Amino aciduria and glycosuria due to inadequate tubular reabsorption are common up to 34 weeks. Neonatal sodium losses are greater and more prolonged in these infants, reflecting impaired sodium reabsorption. Their ability to concentrate and acidify the urine is usually very limited. It follows that in the medical care of the newborn infant, particularly when premature, the margin for error in fluid and electrolyte therapy is narrow. The small pre-term infant is susceptible to wide variations in plasma osmolality and is liable to develop a metabolic acidosis. In part this is due to the limited capacity for urinary excretion of the acids derived from intermediary metabolism.

LACTATION

Development of the breasts at puberty requires not only the rapidly rising levels of oestrogens and gonadotrophins but also normal levels of a wide range of other hormones including growth hormone, adrenal steroids and possibly prolactin. Further development of the breasts, including the formation of the secretory alveoli occurs during pregnancy under the influence of the high levels of oestrogen, progesterone, prolactin and placental lactogen (HPL; p. 339). At this stage some milk is secreted into the ducts and a few drops may be expelled from the nipples. Free flow of milk does not occur until the second or third day after delivery. These changes are summarised in Figure 28.12.

The factors that induce lactation after birth are not yet clear. It is possible that the sudden fall in oestrogen, progesterone and HPL levels removes an inhibitory influence on the action of prolactin. Prolactin specifically promotes the production of the enzymes required for the synthesis of the lactose and protein of milk. prolactin production is increased by suckling; average levels are related to the number of suckling episodes. Prolactin production is increased by suckling; average During lactation prolactin levels are higher in mothers whose food intake is limited, so that effective breast

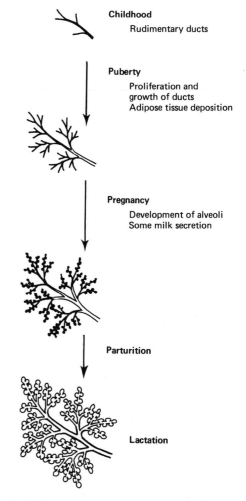

Childhood
Rudimentary ducts

Puberty
Proliferation and growth of ducts
Adipose tissue deposition

Pregnancy
Development of alveoli
Some milk secretion

Parturition

Lactation

Fig. 28.12 Stages in the development of a lobule of breast under the influence of hormones as described in the text.

feeding continues despite the marginal maternal malnutrition.

Prolactin secretion can be inhibited by the dopaminergic drug *bromocriptine*, which can be used to suppress lactation.

Milk ejection

While prolactin is responsible for the secretion of milk into the lumen of the alveoli, a second hormone, oxytocin (p. 307), is responsible for its ejection. In the breast the tubules all converge on the nipple and each, just before reaching it, has a dilated portion, the ampulla, which acts as a milk reservoir (Fig. 28.13). Smooth muscle lining the duct walls is particularly abundant in the ampulla and is stimulated by oxytocin.

The secretion of oxytocin is in part a response to the tactile stimulus of the baby suckling but also occurs in many mothers in anticipation of suckling in response to the baby crying or becoming restless (Fig. 28.14).

Lactation and birth interval

Regular suckling inhibits the production of gonadotrophins (p. 304) and therefore inhibits ovulation. If a mother does not breast feed, ovulation and menstruation return about six weeks after parturition. In many societies 50 per cent of non-lactating mothers are pregnant again within six months of delivery.

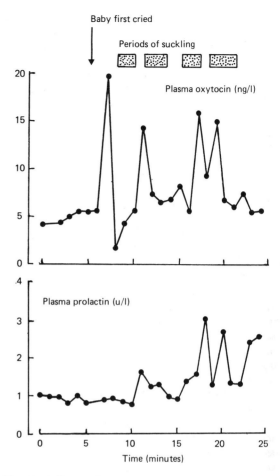

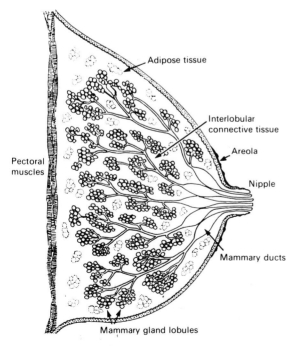

Fig. 28.13 Structure of lactating breast (From Gardner D L, Dodds T C 1976 Human histology, 3rd edn. Churchill Livingstone, Edinburgh)

Fig. 28.14 Changes in the concentrations of oxytocin and prolactin in the maternal plasma before and during suckling 28 days after delivery. (After McNeilly A S et al. 1983 British Medical Journal 286: 260)

On the other hand prolonged lactation causes prolonged amenorrhoea and a temporary infertility. Since maternal sub-nutrition in developing countries is associated with high prolactin levels this effect is marked in such countries; the provision of nutritional supplements for nursing mothers is associated with a reduction in the birth interval. In the world as a whole the contraceptive effect of lactation has a more significant effect on birth rate than all other contraceptive methods combined.

Milk

In recent years it has been increasingly recognised that breast milk has a composition best suited to the needs of a human infant and that cow's milk and formula feeds derived from it have many disadvantages. The trend away from breast feeding in the 1950s and 1960s in western countries has to a large extent been reversed.

Nutrition

Table 15.4 (p. 221) shows typical values for various constituents in human milk and in cow's milk. Many of the differences are of practical importance. For example the high sodium content of formula feeds sometimes causes sodium overload, dehydration and convulsions; the high phosphate content is associated with hypocalcaemia. Cow's milk has a low cystine content and cystine is an essential amino acid in infants. Many formula-fed infants gain excessive weight perhaps because the high sodium content induces thirst, which causes an excessive demand for milk.

Protective function

Breast milk contains a large number of anti-viral and anti-bacterial substances including immunoglobulins, particularly IgA, complement components and lysozyme, as well as defensive cells such as T- and B-lymphocytes, macrophages and polymorphonuclear leucocytes. Colostrum is particularly rich in IgA. Breast-fed infants have a much lower liability than bottle-fed infants to infective diseases, particularly diarrhoea. The difference is greater in conditions in which the clean preparation of a bottle-feed is difficult.

FURTHER READING

Canning J F, Boyd R D H 1984 Water and mineral exchange between mother and fetus. In: Beard R W, Nathanielsz P W (eds) Fetal physiology and medicine. 2nd edn. Dekker, New York, pp. 481–509

Chard T (ed) 1986 The human placenta. Clinics in obstetrics and gynaecology 13: 421–663

Cowie A T, Forsyth I A, Hart I C 1980 Hormonal control of lactation. Springer, Heidelberg

Dobbing J (ed) 1981 Maternal nutrition in pregnancy — eating for two? Academic Press, New York

Findlay A L R 1984 Reproduction and the fetus. Arnold, London

Howie P W, McNeilly A S 1982 Fertility after childbirth. In: Bonnar J (ed) Recent advances in obstetrics and gynaecology 14. Churchill Livingstone, Edinburgh, p. 181

Huszar G 1986 Physiology and biochemistry of the uterus in pregnancy and labour. CRC Press, Boca Raton

Hytten F E, Chamberlain G V P 1980 Clinical physiology in obstetrics. Blackwell Scientific, Oxford

Jelliffe D B, Jelliffe E F P 1981 Breast milk and infection. Lancet 2: 419

Johnson M, Everitt B 1984 Essential reproduction, 2nd edn. Blackwell Scientific, Oxford.

Jones C T, Nathanielsz P W (eds) 1985 The physiological development of the fetus and newborn. Academic Press, New York

Neville M C, Neifert M R 1983 Lactation: physiology, nutrition and breast feeding. Plenum, New York

Rivers R P A 1984 Adaptation of the new-born to extrauterine life. In: Beard R W, Nathanielsz P W (eds) Fetal physiology and medicine, 2nd edn. Dekker, New York, p. 779–804

Strang L B 1977 Neonatal respiration. Blackwell Scientific, Oxford

Whitehead R G 1983 Nutritional aspects of human lactation. Lancet 1: 167–169.

29

Bone and the metabolism of calcium and phosphorus

Bone is a living tissue with remarkable properties. It gives support and protection to the softer parts of the body; it is strong but light in weight and it can grow and remodel itself to withstand normal or new stresses. Bone is also a store for calcium and phosphorus, which are essential for the function of all tissues.

THE TISSUES OF THE SKELETON

Bone

The shafts of the long bones are made of hollow cylinders of compact bone containing marrow. The ends of the long bones and also the vertebrae and the flat bones are supported internally by a lattice-work of trabecular or spongy bone (Fig. 29.1). The trabeculae are arranged in a pattern that apparently reflects the load carried by the bone.

Dry bone contains about 25 per cent organic matter and about 75 per cent inorganic material. Collagen accounts for some 90 per cent of the organic matter (*matrix*), the remainder being glycosaminoglycans, glycoproteins, lipids and peptides. The mineral of

bone is *hydroxyapatite*, $Ca_{10}(PO_4)_6OH_2$. Various ions, notably sodium, magnesium, potassium, fluoride, chloride, bicarbonate and citrate are substituted into the hydroxyapatite crystal.

The bones contain 99 per cent of the body's calcium, 88 per cent of the phosphorus, 50 per cent of the magnesium, 35 of the sodium and 9 per cent of the water.

Bone strength

Bone owes its strength to its two main components. The hydroxyapatite gives rigidity and strength, particularly on compression; the matrix of collagen fibres gives resilience and elasticity. Compact bone is nearly as strong as cast iron but is much lighter and more flexible (Table 29.2).

A bone may be abnormally fragile if the amount of bone is abnormally low (*osteoporosis*), when the bone matrix is not fully calcified (*osteomalacia*, due to vitamin D deficiency), or when the collagen is abnormal (*osteogenesis imperfecta, the brittle bone syndrome*).

Table 29.2 Bone as a structural material. Comparison of bone with wood, cast iron and mild steel

Parameter	Bone	Wood	Cast iron	Mild steel
Breaking stress on bending (kg/mm²)	20	7	28	50
Breaking stress on twisting (kg/mm²)	6	0.7	14	25
Young's modulus (kg/mm²)	1100	1000	9000	20 000
Density (kg/m³)	2000	600	8000	8000

Data of Bell G H 1970 Advancement of Science 6:1

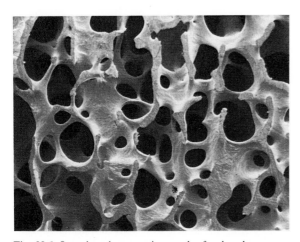

Fig. 29.1 Scanning electron micrograph of trabecular (cancellous) bone from the human sternum, × 20. (Courtesy of W J Whitehouse)

Bone cells

The four main types of cell associated with bone are: osteoblasts, osteocytes, osteoclasts and fibroblasts (Fig. 29.3)

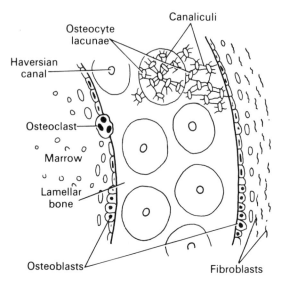

Fig. 29.3 Diagram of cross-section of adult cortical bone to indicate the arrangement of Haversian canals, the osteocytes with their canaliculi, and the cells lining the bone surfaces. The periosteal surface is on the right, the endosteal surface on the left. (After Vaughan J M 1975 Physiology of bone, 2nd edn. University Press, Oxford)

Osteoblasts line all bone surfaces except those undergoing active resorption by osteoclasts and a few bone surfaces in the skull sinuses that are lined with epithelium. Histologically some osteoblasts appear to be very thin with flattened nuclei ('lining cells') while others are larger and appear to be more active. All osteoblasts are able to respond to stimuli such as changes in the levels of parathyrin (parathyroid hormone) or calcitonin (p. 361). The osteoblasts, together, form a membrane (Fig. 29.4) that has some of the properties of an epithelial membrane. This is indicated by the difference in the composition of the extracellular fluid on either side of the membrane and by the secretion of collagen onto one side only.

Osteoclasts are responsible for bone resorption. They are large multinucleate cells having between 10 and 20 nuclei (Fig. 29.5).

Osteocytes are derived from osteoblasts that become enclosed by bone during bone formation. Each occupies a space within the bone known as a *lacuna* and gives out cytoplasmic processes about 100 μm in diameter that reach out to a bone territory and also communicate with similar processes from osteoblasts or from other osteocytes (Fig 29.6). The function of the osteocyte is not yet clear but it is certainly an active cell and is responsible for rapid exchanges of calcium between bone and the extracellular fluid, particularly in response to parathyrin (p. 360).

Fibroblasts are found on the surface of bone outside

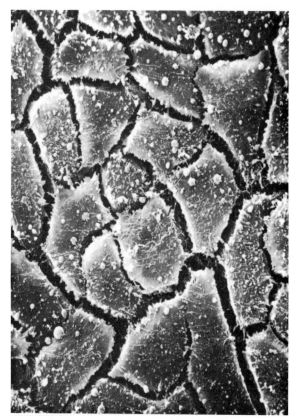

Fig. 29.4 Scanning electron micrograph of bone endosteum ($\times$ 1850). The osteoblasts are closely approximated and their surfaces show microvilli. (From Davis W L et al. 1975 The endosteum as a functional membrane. In: Talmage R V et al. (eds) Calcium-regulating hormones. Excerpta Medica, Amsterdam)

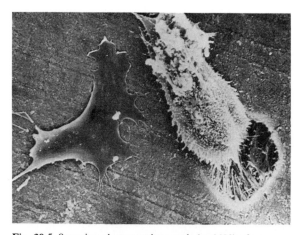

Fig. 29.5 Scanning electron micrograph ($\times$ 1400) of an osteoclast in culture causing excavation of a cut bone surface in vitro. The adjacent non-osteoclastic cell caused no change in the surface. (From Chambers T J et al. 1984 Journal of Cell Science 66:383)

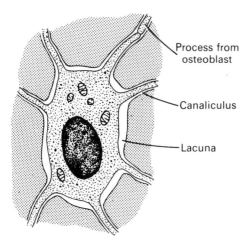

Fig. 29.6 Diagram of an osteocyte to illustrate the manner in which cytoplasmic processes communicate with similar processes from other osteocytes and from osteoblasts on the bone surface.

the layer of osteoblasts and pre-osteoblasts. They appear to be inactive except after fractures. There is no evidence that they turn into osteoblasts.

Bone growth

Bones develop in two different ways. Some, notably the long bones, appear in the fetus as cartilagenous models and are then replaced by bone (Fig. 29.7). Others, such as the flat bones of the skull, are formed directly within connective tissue membranes without an intermediate stage as cartilage.

A long bone grows in length by the growth of the epiphyseal cartilage. In this the cells are arranged in regular longitudinal columns produced by repeated cell division (Fig. 29.8). Each row of cells is enclosed in a tunnel of cartilage with thin partitions between adjacent tunnels. As the cells approach the diaphyseal (shaft) side of the plate they enlarge and the cartilage around them becomes calcified. The cells next to the marrow cavity die and the thin transverse partitions of cartilage disappear leaving tunnels that are invaded by capillaries and by osteoblasts.

The osteoblasts put down several layers of bone on the inner walls of the tunnels. In this way only a narrow channel containing a blood vessel and a few cells remains. This concentric arrangement of bone is called a *Haversian system*. Narrow canaliculae pass both radially and circumferentially in the Haversian system to convey nutrients to the enclosed osteocytes.

During the growing period, the growth of the epiphyseal cartilage keeps pace with its replacement by bone so that the epiphyseal plate of cartilage is always present as a thin and regular zone. It is important to recognise

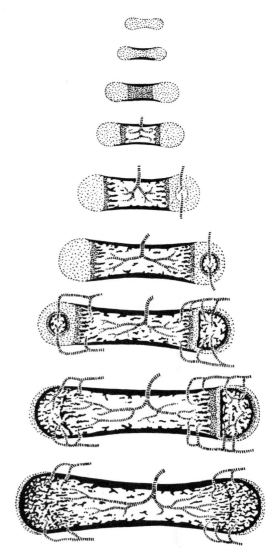

Fig. 29.7 The development of a long bone from a cartilage precursor as seen in longitudinal section. Light stipple, cartilage; heavy stipple, calcified cartilage; black, bone; cross-hatching, arteries. (After Bloom W, Fawcett D W 1968 Textbook of histology, 9th edn. Saunders, Philadelphia)

that calcification of cartilage is not ossification. Cartilage is not transformed into bone, it is replaced by it. Calcification of cartilage is defective in vitamin D deficiency and in this condition the epiphyseal cartilage is much wider than normal.

Bone remodelling

Because bone is rigid it cannot increase in size by interstitial growth. Growth in width by long bones and all growth by other bones is achieved by the deposition of new bone on the surface of existing bone. As a child

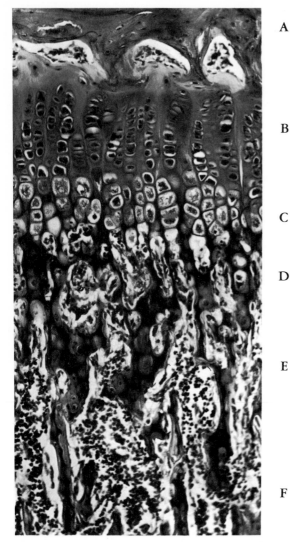

Fig. 29.8 A longitudinal section through the upper epiphyseal cartilage plate of the tibia in a normal young rat, showing the normal growth processes (× 140). A, Epiphyseal bone. B, Epiphyseal cartilage with regular columns of dividing cells. C, Enlarged dying or dead cells surrounded by calcified cartilage. D, Transverse cartilage partitions have disappeared. The tunnels are invaded by capillaries and osteoblasts. E, Bone is being laid down on cartilage and removed and bony trabeculae are laid down. F, Marrow cavity containing blood vessels and bone cells. (By courtesy of HA Sissons)

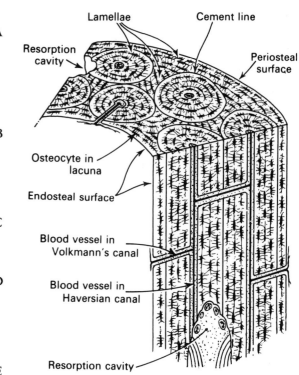

Fig. 29.9 The cortex of the shaft of a long bone to show osteoclastic resorption and the formation of a new Haversian system. (After Harris W H, Heaney R P 1970 Skeletal renewal and metabolic bone disease. Little Brown, Boston)

grows, not only must new bone be laid down on the surface of a bone but also bone must be removed from the centre by osteoclasts.

Even in an adult, bone is continually being remodelled. Both the laying down of new bone (*accretion*) and the removal of bone (*resorption*) occur simultaneously; each amounts to about 500 mg (12.5 mmol) of calcium daily. Figure 29.9 shows Haversian systems and resorption cavities, together with one new Haversian system being formed.

Studies with radioactive isotopes have also shown that part of the calcium within the bone is readily exchangable with the extracellular fluid. It is thought that this exchange takes place at bone crystal surfaces exposed to extracellular fluid on the walls of the lacunae, canaliculae and Haversian canals. The continual exchange of the mineral between bone and the extracellular fluid is illustrated by the use of radio-isotope bone scans. There is also increased turnover when there are healing fractures or at the growing ends of bone in normal children (Fig. 29.10).

Bone has a remarkable capacity for remodelling. For example, in a child with a fracture that has healed with deformity, the deformity gradually diminishes. Little is known about the control of this process but it seems likely that small electrical currents are involved. In the absence of stress on the skeleton, for example in immobilised patients, bone resorption is greatly increased, presumably as a result of a lack of these electrical stimuli. Conversely regular exercise increases the bone mass.

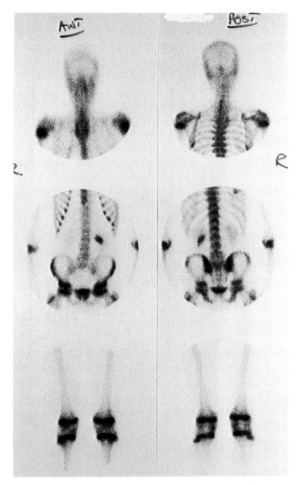

Fig. 29.10 Radio isotope bone scan in a normal 14-year-old boy. A dose of polyphosphate linked to ^{99}technetium is administered intravenously. Two hours later the patient is scanned with a gamma-detecting system. Much of the dose not taken up by the bones has been eliminated by the kidneys and the isotope can be seen in the residual urine in the bladder. (Courtesy of G. Neil)

Calcification

The process of calcification is still not fully understood. It is clear that collagen fibrils play an important part; the earliest deposits of calcium salts are seen by electron microscopy in or between the fibres.

The osteoblasts play an important role in mineralisation, possibly by increasing the local concentrations of calcium and phosphate ions immediately adjacent to the area of calcification or possibly by producing vesicles, derived from mitochondria, laden with calcium phosphate. It is thought that the first mineral formed is an amorphous calcium phosphate that is later converted into hydroxyapatite.

There are several known inhibitors of calcification.

The best known is pyrophosphate (H_2PO_3-O-H_2PO_3). This is present in many tissues including bone and probably prevents inappropriate calcification. It is broken down to two phosphate residues by alkaline phosphatases. In a rare inherited disorder known as hypophosphatasia, the alkaline phosphatase activity in the plasma is very low; pyrophosphate levels in plasma and urine are increased, and bone mineralisation is defective. As a result, the patients have bone changes not unlike those of vitamin D deficiency rickets. Analogues of pyrophosphate, particularly substances with a -P-C-P- core instead of -P-O-P- have proved useful in the treatment of patients with diseases characterised by excessive bone turnover such as Paget's disease.

Cartilage

Cartilage contains cells known as chondrocytes embedded in a matrix that consists mainly of collagen and a proteoglycan containing the glycosaminoglycans, chondroitin-4-sulphate, chondroitin-6-sulphate and keratan sulphate in varying proportions. Three types of cartilage are recognised. In *hyaline* cartilage about 75 per cent of the material is water; collagen forms 25 to 70 per cent and glycosaminoglycans 14 to 40 per cent of the dry weight. In *fibrocartilage* collagen fibres constitute the greatest proportion of the organic matter with only about 2 per cent of glycosaminoglycans. *Elastic cartilage* occurs in the external ear and in parts of the larynx; it contains about 20 per cent of elastin.

Mature hyaline cartilage is avascular and contains no nervous tissue or lymphatic vessels. The chondrocytes are metabolically active cells and their principal function appears to be the synthesis of matrix. They have several anaerobic metabolic pathways and nutrients reach the cells by diffusion through the matrix.

Cartilage grows in volume interstitially when the chondrocytes it contains multiply and produce more matrix. It also grows by apposition as a result of matrix synthesis by the cells on the surface, collectively known as the perichondrium.

Joints

Adjacent bones in the skeleton may be joined to one another simply by fibrous tissue (*fibrous joint*), as in the skull, or by cartilage (*cartilaginous joint*). But where an appreciable amount of movement between the bones is needed they articulate by a *synovial joint* at which the bone ends are coated by a thin layer of hyaline cartilage (*articular cartilage*) and joined by a fibrous tube (*fibrous capsule*), lined by a *synovial membrane*. The cavity of the joint is occupied by *synovial fluid*.

The scanning electron microscope has shown that the apparently smooth surface of articular cartilage is in fact

Fig. 29.11 Appearance of normal articular surface from the hamate bone, as seen by the scanning electron microscope (× 890). The 'chicken wire' appearance is due to a network of fine fibrils in the surface matrix. (Courtesy of I. Redler. From Clinical Orthopaedics 103:262)

gently undulating and is many times 'rougher' than engineering bearings (Fig. 29.11). The peak-to-peak distance of the undulations is about 5 μm and the depressions are about 2.5 μm deep. The superficial zone of the cartilage matrix contains tightly packed collagen fibres lying parallel to the surface forming a 'skin'. The deeper fibres form an open meshwork; the fibres next to the bone are disposed radially towards the joint surface. The glycosaminoglycan content varies inversely with that of collagen, being as low as 3 per cent of dry weight superficially and much higher towards the cartilage/bone interface.

Synovial membrane
The fibrous capsule of a joint passes from one bone to the other to form a closed cavity. It is lined internally by the synovial membrane, a connective tissue membrane two or three cells thick containing a rich capillary network.

Two types of cell can be identified by electron microscopy in synovial membranes. Type A cells appear to be phagocytic and can be shown to take up particulate matter that has been injected into joints. Type B cells are less numerous and probably synthesise hyaluronic acid.

Synovial fluid
The cavity of a joint contains straw-coloured viscous synovial fluid. Its viscosity is due to the presence of hyaluronic acid secreted by the B cells of the synovial membrane. In other respects the composition of synovial fluid resembles that of plasma except that the

protein concentration is 10 to 20 g/litre. The volume of synovial fluid in a normal joint is quite small: in the human knee, for instance, it is between 0.5 ml and 2.0 ml.

Mechanism of joint action
By sliding the femoral condyles of an amputated human knee joint against the corresponding articular surface of the tibia it has been found that the coefficient of friction is about 0.01, which is three times better than that of ice sliding on ice and more than 10 times better than the value found in a plain lubricated bearing.

A complete explanation of this very successful form of lubrication has not yet been found. Since the viscosity of the lubricating film is increased as the articulating surfaces approach under load it is likely that the liquid phase of the synovial fluid, trapped in the undulations of the cartilage, is squeezed away and a thickened gel remains.

CALCIUM METABOLISM

The skeleton contains at least 99 per cent of the total body calcium, which in a young adult is about 1.2 kg. After the third decade of life bone resorption exceeds bone accretion and there is a slow but progressive loss of bone, which is greater in women than in men.

Dietary calcium
In Europe and the USA the average daily calcium intake in adults is 800 to 1000 mg. In developing countries the intake is often considerably less (200 to 400 mg/day). The main sources of calcium are milk and cheese, green vegetables and, in Britain and the United States, artificially enriched bread.

It is not clear whether a minimum dietary requirement for calcium can be defined in man. Typical recommendations of official bodies have been about 400 mg/day for adults with greater amounts in childhood, pregnancy and lactation. However, there is little evidence that a low calcium intake does any harm in otherwise healthy people or that calcium supplements should be advised for people with a low intake. It is possible that a relative calcium lack may contribute to a very rare form of rickets seen in South Africa and that calcium lack due to impaired absorption may play a part in the loss of bone seen in older women. In general, however, populations in developing countries with a low calcium intake do not suffer from excessive bone loss or impaired dental development.

It seems clear that the intestine has a remarkable facility for adapting to a low calcium diet and calcium balance can be achieved with a level of dietary calcium as low as 150 mg daily. During starvation, however, a negative calcium balance occurs as calcium continues to be lost in the urine and in the intestinal secretions.

Intestinal absorption

In a healthy adult in calcium balance and on a western diet containing 25 mmol (1000 mg daily), the faeces contain about 20 mmol and the urine about 5 mmol daily. Figure 29.12 shows typical values for the exchanges between the plasma and the other tissues.

Calcium is absorbed from all parts of the small intestine by facilitated diffusion. In addition an active transport mechanism is present mainly in the duodenum and upper jejunum. A calcium-binding protein appears to be important for this active transport, which is controlled by the hormone calcitriol (p. 363).

Many factors affect calcium absorption in man. It is increased by parathyrin or by vitamin D in excess. It

diminishes with advancing age and is greatly reduced in vitamin D deficiency, in renal failure and in intestinal malabsorption.

Plasma calcium

Calcium is constantly entering the plasma from bone and gut and leaving it for bone, gut or urine. Nevertheless the plasma calcium is maintained within narrow limits, a constant concentration of ionised calcium being necessary for the normal function of muscles and nerves.

The normal range for total plasma calcium is 2.2 to 2.6 mmol/l. Just under half of this is bound to plasma proteins, particularly albumin, a small proportion is complexed with citrate and phosphate and the remainder circulates as ionised calcium. The complexed and ionised calcium are together known as the *ultrafil-*

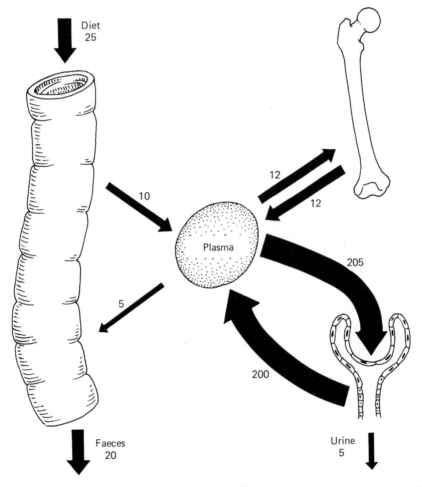

Fig. 29.12 Calcium exchanges in a healthy adult. The figures (in mmol/day) show that in health the urinary and faecal calcium excretion together equal the dietary calcium and that bone resorption and bone accretion are equal. In developing countries figures for dietary calcium and faecal calcium may be much lower (typically 12.5 mmol and 9.5 mmol respectively) but in other respects figures for developing countries are similar to those shown.

trable fraction or *diffusible fraction*. While it is the level of ionised calcium in the plasma that is physiologically important, the methods available for its measurement are not suitable for routine use. In clinical practice, the total plasma calcium is measured and appropriate allowances are made in patients with abnormalities of the plasma albumin.

The binding of calcium to protein is affected by pH; it is reduced in acidosis and increased in alkalosis. Because calcium is bound to protein, changes in the total plasma calcium, without any change in the level of ionised calcium, follow changes in the plasma proteins. Thus a low plasma calcium is found with a low plasma albumin in cirrhosis of the liver or in the nephrotic syndrome.

One consequence of the protein-binding of plasma calcium is of practical importance. If a tourniquet is applied to the arm in order to take a venous blood sample, the pressure within the vein rises and so does the pressure within the capillaries that supply it. Fluid is lost into the interstitial space but blood cells and large molecules, such as proteins, cannot escape and their concentration rises. Since calcium is partly bound to albumin its concentration also rises and misleading results may be obtained. This effect is minimised by taking a blood sample as quickly as possible after a tourniquet has been applied.

Urinary excretion of calcium

About 9 g of calcium pass daily into the glomerular filtrate from the diffusible fractions of the plasma calcium. Most of this is reabsorbed by the tubules (Chap. 12) and in normal people the urinary excretion is 2 to 10 mmol/day (80 to 400 mg/day). Calcium reabsorption is increased in hyperparathyroidism and decreased in hypoparathyroidism and in the presence of a sodium diuresis.

PHOSPHORUS METABOLISM

The phosphorus content of an adult man is about 800 g; four-fifths of this is in the bones, the remainder being in the cells as organic phosphates, phospholipids or nucleic acids. The inorganic phosphorus concentration in the plasma in fasting adults is between 0.8 and 1.4 mmol/l (2.5 to 4.5 mg/100 ml). Higher values are found in infants. Almost all the inorganic phosphate is diffusible, only 12 per cent being protein-bound.

Since phosphorus is present in all animal and plant cells dietary deficiency never occurs in man. Phosphate depletion may occur as a result of renal tubular disorders (Chap. 12) and, very rarely, in patients who consume excessive quantities of aluminium hydroxide, an antacid that binds phosphate in the gut.

Phosphate is excreted by the kidney, and in the steady state the amount excreted is equal to that which the gut absorbs. Ninety per cent of the phosphate filtered at the glomerulus is reabsorbed in the tubule; there is no good evidence for tubular secretion. Defects in phosphate reabsorption occur in patients with parathyroid overactivity and in patients with inherited disorders of the renal tubules. In these conditions the plasma phosphate level tends to be low. A high plasma phosphate is found in renal failure.

HOMEOSTASIS OF CALCIUM AND PHOSPHORUS

A constant and normal concentration of ionised calcium in the extracellular fluid is of great importance in, amongst other things, muscular contraction, neural and neuromuscular transmission and the activity of several enzymes. If the ionised calcium is low, tetanic spasms (p. 361) or convulsions may occur and may be fatal. If the plasma ionised calcium is high, cardiac function is disturbed and calcium may be deposited in the kidney or other tissues.

Three hormones play a part in the maintenance of a constant concentration of ionised calcium in the extracellular fluid: parathyrin (parathyroid hormone), calcitonin and calcitriol (1,25-dihydroxycholecalciferol).

Parathyrin

Human parathyrin is a single-chain polypeptide containing 84 amino acid residues (Fig. 29.13). It is

1
H₂N—Ser—Val—Ser—Glu—Ile—Gln—Leu—Met—

15
His—Asn—Leu—Gly—Lys—His—Leu—Asn—Ser—

Met—Glu—Arg—Val—Glu—Trp—Leu—Arg—Lys—Lys—

30
Leu—Gln—Asp—Val—His—Asn—Phe—Val—Ala—Leu—

45
Gly—Ala—Pro—Leu—Ala—Pro—Arg—Asp—Ala—Gly—

Ser—Gln—Arg—Pro—Arg—Lys—Lys—Glu—Asp—

60
Asn—Val—Leu—Val—Glu—Ser—His—Glu—Lys—Ser—

75
Leu—Gly—Glu—Ala—Asp—Lys—Ala—Asp—Val—

Asn—Val—Leu—Thr—Lys—Ala—Lys—Ser—Gln—COOH

Fig. 29.13 Sequence of amino acid residues of human parathyrin. The fragment 1 to 34 (heavy type) is biologically active.

produced in the parathyroid glands, which are usually four in number and are usually found in the neck adjacent to the posterior surface of the thyroid gland. The parathyroid glands are normally about 6 mm long and weigh between 20 and 50 mg. Accessory parathyroid tissue is not uncommon lower in the neck or in the thorax.

Two types of cell are found within normal parathyroid glands; the *chief cells*, with large nuclei nearly filling the cell, and *oxyntic cells*, with small nuclei and acidophil granules in the cytoplasm. The function of the oxyntic cells is not known. Normal glands also contain a substantial proportion of fat cells.

Secretion

Like other peptide hormones parathyrin is initially synthesised as a larger precursor molecule, pre-proparathyrin with 115 amino acid residues. The first 25 residues of this are the 'signal segment' and serve to direct the growing molecule into the lumen of the endoplasmic reticulum. This segment is split off before the complete molecule is formed. The resulting proparathyrin contains 90 residues and is in turn split in the Golgi complex to yield parathyrin itself.

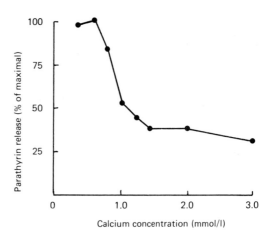

Fig. 29.15 Relation between the release of parathyrin (measured by radio-immunoassay) and calcium concentration in the medium in dispersed parathyroid cells from normal human parathyroid glands. (After Brown E M et al. 1979 American Journal of Medicine 66:923)

The major stimulus for the secretion of parathyrin is the plasma level of ionised calcium and it can be shown that parathyrin secretion increases when the extracellular fluid (ECF) calcium level falls (Fig. 29.14); but as the ECF calcium falls farther, parathyrin secretion reaches a maximum (Fig. 29.15). At high ECF calcium levels parathyrin secretion is not completely suppressed. Magnesium levels also influence parathyrin secretion but to a much smaller extent, high levels causing an inhibition of parathyrin secretion. This effect is probably not important at physiological levels. Parathyrin secretion is increased by catecholamines, notably beta-adrenergic agents. The human gland is innervated with noradrenergic nerve endings, which may play a part in modifying the sensitivity of the gland to levels of ionised calcium.

Metabolism

The half-life of parathyrin in the blood is about 20 minutes so changes in hormone secretion play an important part in the minute-to-minute regulation of the plasma calcium level. Parathyrin is broken down into smaller fragments by the Kuppfer cells of the liver, and fragments, particularly biologically inactive carboxy-terminal parathyrin fragments, are found in the circulation. These may make the interpretation of radio-immunoassays for plasma parathyrin difficult. Parathyrin is also removed from the circulation by the kidneys; patients with renal failure often have raised parathyrin levels, in part because of defective parathyrin metabolism.

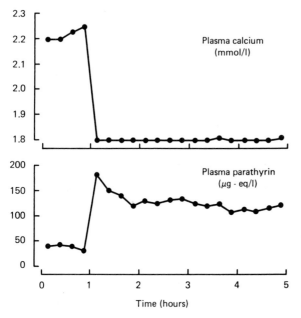

Fig. 29.14 Effect of an acutely produced and constantly maintained hypocalcaemia on plasma parathyrin levels. Mean values for six normal dogs. The hypocalcaemia was achieved with injection of EGTA (ethylene glycol-bis-(β-aminoethylether)-N,N' — tetraacetic acid), a calcium chelating agent; a bolus injection was followed by an infusion, the rate of which was regulated in such a way as to achieve a constant plasma calcium level. (Data of Fox J, Heath H 1982 American Journal of Physiology 242:E287)

Actions

The kidney and the skeleton are the main target organs for parathyrin. Actions on both tissues serve to raise the extracellular calcium concentration.

Parathyrin has several actions on cells of the renal tubules, all probably mediated by adenylate cylase (Chap. 23; Fig. 29.16). The best known are an increase in calcium reabsorption, a decrease in phosphate reabsorption and an increase in the rate at which calcidiol is converted to calcitriol (p. 363). In turn the increased calcitriol concentrations lead to an increase in active calcium absorption in the small intestine. Other renal tubular actions of parathyrin include a decrease in the reabsorption of bicarbonate by the proximal tubules, a decrease in proximal tubule reabsorption of sodium and possibly an increase in magnesium reabsorption.

The major effect of parathyrin on bone is an increase in bone resorption. It was at one time thought that this was mediated principally by the osteoclasts and osteocytes. It is now clear that the primary direct action of parathyrin is on osteoclastic cells to cause an increase in the transfer of calcium from the immediate vicinity of the bone to the general extracellular fluid. Prolonged stimulation of bone *in vitro* with parathyrin leads to an increase in the number and activity of osteoclasts but this is thought to be secondary to an action on osteoblasts.

An excess of parathyrin (*hyperparathyroidism*) results in hypercalcaemia because of increased calcium reabsorption in the renal tubule, increased calcium absorption in the intestine, and increased bone resorption. In a few cases the patient is severely ill with confusion, drowsiness and eventually coma with plasma calcium values as high as 5.0 mmol/l. More often the plasma calcium is lower; the condition may be diagnosed when the patient has developed urinary calculi, or be found 'by accident' in a screening procedure. A few patients complain of bone pains and fractures, the results of the bone demineralisation. Figure 29.17 shows the characteristic radiological abnormality seen in such patients.

Hyperparathyroidism is not the only cause of hypercalcaemia. Other frequent causes include neoplasms with secondary deposits in bone, neoplasms secreting a parathyrin-like substance and an excessive intake of

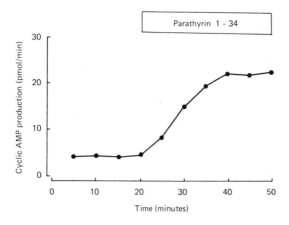

Fig. 29.16 Production of cyclic AMP by isolated perfused bone before and after the addition to the perfusing fluid of synthetic bovine parathyrin (residues 1–34) at a concentration of 3 ng/ml. In a similar study it was shown that a fragment containing residues 3–34 was inactive even at a much higher concentration. (Data of Martin K J et al. 1981 Endocrinology 109:956)

Disorders of parathyrin secretion

Excessive or deficient secretion of parathyrin causes well-recognised clinical disorders.

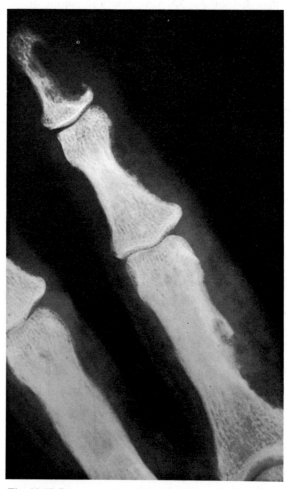

Fig. 29.17 Bone resorption (subperiosteal erosions) in the phalanges of the hand in a patient with severe hyperparathyroidism. (Courtesy of O.L.M. Bijvoet)

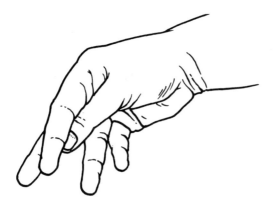

Fig. 29.18 Position of the hand in tetany.

vitamin D. Hypercalcaemia of any cause is characterised by thirst, tiredness, weakness and, if severe, coma and death. Untreated hypercalcaemia causes renal damage.

Deficient parathyroid activity (*hypoparathyroidism*) is uncommon. Most cases result from removal of the parathyroid glands or damage to their blood supply during surgical operations on the thyroid. Hypoparathyroidism is characterised by hypocalcaemia; some patients may have no symptoms, others may be depressed or may develop muscular spasms in the hands and feet known as *carpo-pedal spasm* or *tetany* (Fig. 29.18). A few patients, notably children, may have generalised convulsions, and occasionally infants with tetany get a spasm of the laryngeal muscles leading to difficulty in breathing (*laryngismus stridulus*). In the early stages of tetany sensory phenomena are present, such as widespread tingling feelings and sensations of heat and flushing (*paraesthesiae*). Two tests can be used to demonstrate the neuromuscular hyperexcitability before tetany occurs (*latent tetany*). In *Chvostek's test* tapping over the facial nerve in front of the ear produces twitching of the facial muscles. In *Trousseau's test* carpal spasm is induced by inflating a sphygmomanometer cuff round the upper arm to a pressure exceeding the systolic blood pressure and maintaining the occlusion for 2 minutes. Ischaemia of nerve trunks increases their excitability and reinforces the effect of a low concentration of calcium in the plasma.

The factor most closely related to the onset of tetany is a reduction in the plasma concentration of ionised calcium. This may be caused by a reduced total plasma calcium or by a reduced proportion of ionised calcium due to alkalaemia caused by vomiting or by overventilation.

Apart from hypoparathyroidism, hypocalcaemia may be caused by vitamin D deficiency (rickets in children and osteomalacia in adults), by renal failure or by a rare inherited disorder, *pseudohypoparathyroidism*, in which

there is a defect in the cyclic AMP-mediated response of the tissues to parathyrin.

Calcitonin

Calcitonin is a lipophilic single-chain peptide of 32 amino acid residues (Fig. 29.19). Unlike parathyrin the complete structure is required for biological activity but appreciable variations in amino acid sequence occur between different species.

Calcitonin is secreted by the parafollicular cells (C-cells) of the thyroid gland. These cells contain granules that increase in number during a period of prolonged hypercalcaemia and calcitonin has been identified within the granules by fluorescent antibody techniques. Calcitonin release is stimulated by high levels of ionised calcium in the plasma (Fig. 29.20).

Calcitonin has actions on bone and the kidney, both serving to lower plasma calcium levels. Calcitonin reduces bone resorption both when induced by parathyrin (Fig. 29.21) and also in the absence of para-

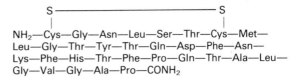

Fig. 29.19 Amino acid sequence of human calcitonin.

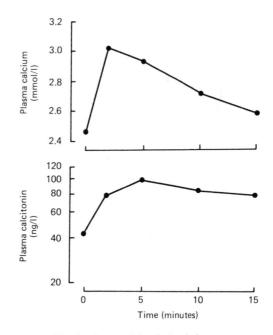

Fig. 29.20 Rise in plasma calcitonin levels in response to hypercalcaemia induced in five normal volunteers by a one-minute intravenous infusion of calcium (2 mg/kg body weight). (Data of Hillyard C J et al. 1983 Lancet 1:846)

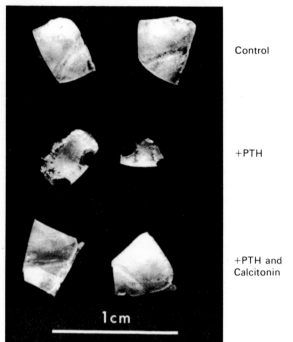

Control

+PTH

+PTH and
Calcitonin

1cm

Fig. 29.21 Mouse calvaria in tissue culture to show the effect of calcitonin on the bone resorption induced by parathyrin. (Courtesy of Jennifer Nisbet)

thyrin. In the kidney, calcitonin reduces calcium reabsorption (an effect opposite to that of parathyrin) but also decreases phosphate reabsorption (an effect similar to that of parathyrin). Calcitonin also increases transiently the urinary excretion of sodium.

Apart from hypercalcaemia, calcitonin secretion is also stimulated by gastrin, CCK-Pz and glucagon. Thus, as calcium is absorbed from a meal there is little or no rise in plasma calcium levels and it has been suggested that calcitonin provides a 'fine adjustment' to calcium homeostasis.

Calcitonin excess has been described in patients with medullary carcinomas of the thyroid. Surprisingly these patients seldom have hypocalcaemia probably because of compensatory action of the parathyroid glands. There is as yet no evidence of a syndrome due to calcitonin deficiency.

Calcitonin gene related peptide
It has recently been recognised that in addition to coding for the calcitonin precursor, the calcitonin gene also codes for a newly recognised peptide, calcitonin gene related peptide (CGRP). The physiological significance of this substance is still unclear. CGRP causes reduction of plasma calcium in the rat but an increase in the chick. Human CGRP stimulates adenylate cyclase

in cultures of human bone cells but the relevance of this fact is not known. CGRP is also found throughout the central nervous system in the rat and may be a neurotransmitter.

Vitamin D and calcitriol
The name vitamin D is applied to a number of fat-soluble compounds, the most important being vitamin D_2 (ergocalciferol) and vitamin D_3 (cholecalciferol). Ergocalciferol does not occur naturally but is produced artificially by the ultraviolet irradiation of a plant sterol, ergosterol. Cholecalciferol is the naturally occurring compound in animals and is produced in man by the irradiation of a precursor, 7-dehydrocholesterol, found in the skin (Fig. 29.22).

Vitamin D is found in a limited number of foodstuffs but fish livers are by far the richest source. Fatty fish such as salmon, herrings and sardines are good sources of vitamin D. The vitamin D content of eggs and butter is very variable and depends on the diet and exposure to sunlight of the hens and cows. Margarine and powdered milk for infants are usually fortified by the

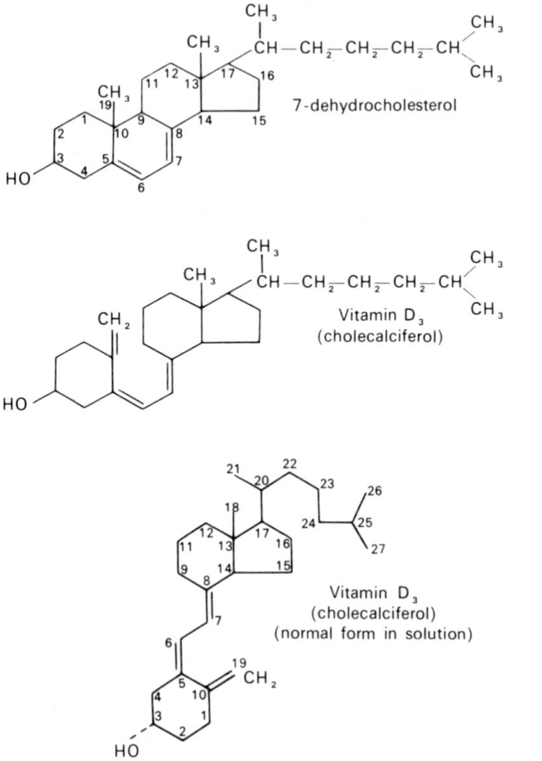

7-dehydrocholesterol

Vitamin D_3
(cholecalciferol)

Vitamin D_3
(cholecalciferol)
(normal form in solution)

Fig. 29.22 Structures of 7-dehydrocholesterol and vitamin D_3 (cholecalciferol). The lower structure represents the ('elongated') form that vitamin D takes in solution and in crystals. Vitamin D_2 (ergocalciferol) differs from vitamin D_3 only in the structure of the side chain: it has a double bond at C22–23 and an additional methyl group (C28) at C24.

addition of vitamin D_2. In the United States and some other countries vitamin D is added to all milk.

Infants and young children require some 10 to 18 μg of vitamin D per day. It is important to note that the toxic effects of hypercalcaemia may be produced by higher doses — as little as 50 μg per day in some infants. The vitamin D requirement for adults is about 2.5 μg daily.

Vitamin D is absorbed in the upper half of the small intestine in the presence of bile salts. Vitamin D and its metabolites circulate in the plasma bound to an α-globulin. Adipose tissue and muscle are the most important sites of storage. Vitamin D stores in man may be enough to postpone signs of vitamin D deficiency for several years.

Metabolism
Both vitamin D_2 and vitamin D_3 are hydroxylated in the liver to give 25-hydroxy derivatives, which represent the most important forms of vitamin D in plasma. A further hydroxylation takes place in the kidney to yield either the physiologically active 1,25-dihydroxychole-calciferol (calcitriol) or an alternative metabolite 24,25-dihydroxycholecalciferol, the physiological role of which is uncertain.

Calcitriol secretion
Production of calcitriol by the renal tubules is regulated mainly by plasma levels of parathyrin and thus by the plasma calcium. When the plasma calcium is low, parathyrin levels increase and calcitriol is the principal vitamin D metabolite produced. When the plasma

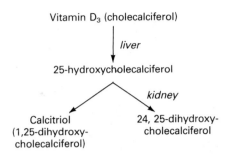

calcium is high the principal metabolite is 24,25-dihydroxycholecalciferol. Other factors promoting the production of calcitriol include low levels of phosphate in the plasma and increased levels of growth hormone or prolactin.

The relation between parathyrin and vitamin D metabolism is illustrated by the fact that in patients with parathyroid insufficiency large doses of vitamin D (1 to 3 mg daily) are needed to raise the plasma calcium but the same effect can be achieved with as little as 2 μg of calcitriol daily.

Actions of calcitriol
The best-known site of action of calcitriol is on the small intestine. It promotes the active absorption of calcium. In this way the substance appears to be responsible for the intestinal response to a low-calcium diet. The detailed mode of action of calcitriol in the mucosal cell is not yet clear; it enters the cell and binds to receptor proteins within the nucleus. There the synthesis of the calcium-binding protein is stimulated.

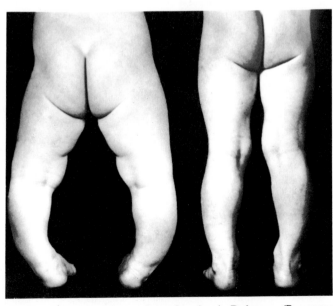

Fig. 29.23 Infantile rickets before treatment and 2 years later after vitamin D therapy. (By courtesy of Richards I D G et al. 1968 Lancet 1:803)

Calcitriol probably has actions on bone, to stimulate osteoclasts, on the proximal convoluted tubules of the kidney, on the parathyroid glands and on muscle cells. Until recently it was thought that all these actions, like that in the gut, involved the stimulation of the synthesis of specific proteins. Recently, however, evidence has been obtained that calcitriol has a rapid effect in modifying responsiveness to parathyrin in bone cells, increasing responsiveness; it is thought that this effect is a direct action on the plasma membrane.

Disorders

Vitamin D deficiency occurs in patients who lack the vitamin in the diet and also lack adequate exposure to ultraviolet radiation. This combination occurs particularly in North Africa, the Middle East and parts of the Indian subcontinent. In Britain vitamin D deficiency is found particularly in Asian immigrants and in housebound elderly women. Vitamin D deficiency also occurs in disorders that impair its absorption in coeliac disease, in obstructive jaundice and after partial gastrectomy.

In children lack of vitamin D causes *rickets*, with stunted growth and bowing of the limbs (Fig. 29.23). In adults the corresponding disease is known as *osteo-*

malacia; it causes bone pain and tenderness, and sometimes causes fractures.

In both rickets and osteomalacia there is inadequate deposition of calcium salts in newly formed bone matrix. In rickets ossification is retarded or ceases but the cartilage cells of the epiphyseal plate continue to grow, producing swellings adjacent to joints and to the costal cartilages ('rickety rosary'). Since cartilage is transparent to X-rays, radiographs of rickets are easily recognised (Fig. 29.24). The process of bone remodelling, which normally maintains the shape of the bones, is abnormal and the bones tend to bend. Deformities of the pelvis in girls may lead subsequently to difficulties in childbirth.

No disorder of the hepatic 25-hydroxylation step has been recognised but the renal 1-hydroxylation is impaired in renal failure and in a rare inherited disorder, vitamin-D-dependent rickets.

Other hormones

An adequate supply of growth hormone from the anterior pituitary is necessary for proliferation of the cells of the epiphyseal cartilage and therefore, for the growth in length of a long bone. In hypophysectomised animals epiphyseal activity is much reduced or even absent; it can be restored by administration of growth hormone. There is no evidence that this hormone influences the time of closure of the epiphyses.

Excessive activity of the thyroid gland is associated with loss of bone; the rate of bone formation is increased but the rate of bone resorption is increased to a greater extent. Increased loss of bone is a feature of mineralocorticoid excess whether due to excessive activity of the adrenal cortex or to steroid therapy.

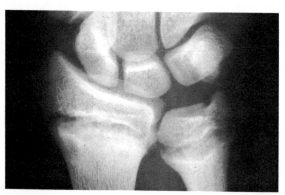

A

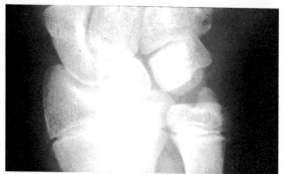

B

Fig. 29.24 A. Radiological appearance of the right wrist in an adolescent with rickets. Note the widened, irregular epiphyses. B. The same wrist after treatment; the epiphyses are now normal.

FURTHER READING

Brown E M 1982 PTH secretion in vivo and in vitro. Mineral and Electrolyte Metabolism 8: 130–150

Jaworski Z F G 1981 Physiology and pathology of bone remodeling. Orthopaedic Clinics of North America 12: 485–512

Klahr S, Hammerman M R, Martin K, Slatopolsky E 1983 Renal effects of parathyroid hormone and calcitonin. In: Dunn M J (ed) Renal endocrinology. Williams and Wilkins, Baltimore, pp. 259–322

MacLaughlin J A, Holick M F 1983 Photobiology of vitamin D₃ in the skin. In: Goldsmith L A (ed) Biochemistry and physiology of the skin. University Press, Oxford, pp. 734–754

Smith R 1985 Exercise and osteoporosis. British Medical Journal 290: 1163–1164

Spencer H, Kramer L, Lesniak M, De Bartolo M, Norris C, Osis D 1984 Calcium requirements in humans. Clinical Orthopaedics 184: 270–280

Spiegel A M, Marx S J 1983 Parathyroid hormone and vitamin D receptors. Clinics in Endocrinology and Metabolism 12: 221–241

Growth and development

Accurate knowledge of the normal growth and development of children is essential for the recognition of the deleterious effects of any form of chronic disease. Body growth in boys and girls is a continuing process throughout childhood and adolescence. It is exceedingly rapid in the first 2 years of life and less so during the middle years of childhood. Later there is a growth spurt over the period of puberty followed by cessation of growth when the adult height is reached.

Charts of height plotted against age, known as *height charts*, and of height increment per year plotted against age, known as *height velocity charts*, have been constructed for normal British boys and girls by Tanner and his colleagues. The height chart for boys is shown in Figure 30.1. The centre line, or 50th centile, represents the growth curve of the average boy; the 97th and 3rd centiles are ±1.881 standard deviations from the mean. A boy whose height lies above the 97th centile is taller than 97 per cent of the population whereas a boy whose height lies above the 3rd centile is taller than only 3 per cent of the normal population. Although 3 per cent of the heights fall above the 97th centile and 3 per cent below the 3rd centile, boys with heights outside these limits are potentially abnormal and may require investigation. The height velocity chart for boys, calculated over periods of 1 year, is shown in Figure 30.2. The height charts for girls are similar

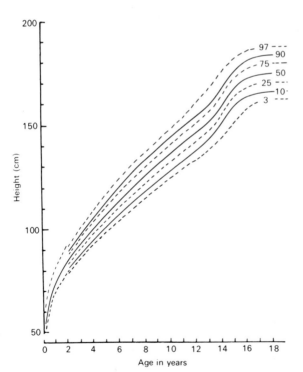

Fig. 30.1 Height chart for boys. The lines represent the centiles for children followed at successive ages. (After Tanner J M, Whitehouse R H 1976 Archives of Disease in Childhood 51:170)

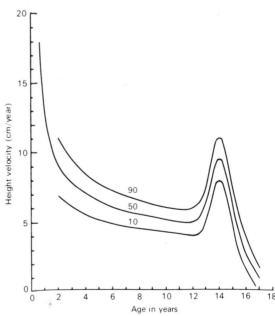

Fig. 30.2 Height velocity chart for boys. The centiles are appropriate to children who have their peak velocity at the average age. (After Tanner J M, Whitehouse R H 1976 Archives of Disease in Childhood 51:170)

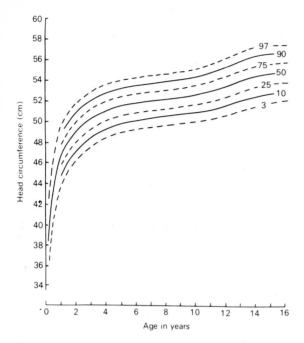

Fig. 30.3 Head circumference chart for boys. (After Tanner J M 1984 In: Forfar J O, Arneil G C (eds) Textbook of paediatrics. Churchill Livingstone, Edinburgh)

The growth in head circumference for boys is shown in Figure 30.3. Girls have slightly smaller heads than boys but the growth pattern is similar. A rapid increase in size occurs during the first year of life followed by a less rapid increase during the second year. Thereafter growth in head circumference is very gradual. The increase in head circumference during early life reflects the important postnatal growth spurt of the underlying brain (Fig. 30.4). The brain is particularly vulnerable during this period of rapid growth and adverse factors may damage the forebrain, brain stem or cerebellum and lead to mental subnormality, blindness, deafness or cerebral palsy. The cellularity of the cerebellum increases particularly rapidly during the first year of life and the cerebellum may suffer most from, for example, under-nutrition or deficiency of thyroid hormones at this time (Fig. 30.5).

The weight of newborn boys in relation to gestational age is shown in Figure 30.6. A similar chart for girls shows that they are slightly lighter than boys from 34 weeks gestation onwards. By definition, infants of 'low birth weight' (formerly called 'premature') have a birth weight of 2500 g or less. They are quite often of the expected weight for gestational age, for example, when born before term because of a sudden placental haemorrhage, the pregnancy having been clinically normal up to that point. Another group of infants is classified as 'light-for-dates' because their birth weights are below the normal standard for the gestational age. These infants have been subjected to adverse prenatal influences, such as inadequacy of maternal nutrition or of

except that they show an earlier growth spurt. *Weight charts* for both boys and girls are also available. These charts were prepared for British children but similar values are found in most developed countries. In developing countries charts based on the findings in well nourished local children should be used.

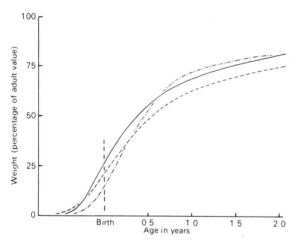

Fig. 30.4 Brain growth. Comparative fresh weights of three brain regions during growth. Weights for forebrain (———), brainstem (– – – –) and cerebellum (–·–·–) have been calculated as a percentage of the adult value. (After Dobbing J, Sands J C 1973 Archives of Disease in Childhood 48:757)

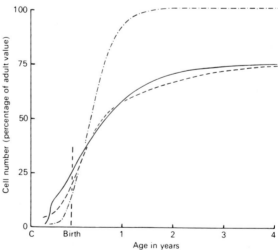

Fig. 30.5 Brain cellularity. Comparative values for cell number in three brain regions during growth. Values for forebrain (———), brainstem (– – – –) and cerebellum (–·–·–) have been calculated as a percentage of the adult value. (After Dobbing J, Sands J C 1973 Archives of Disease in Childhood 48:757)

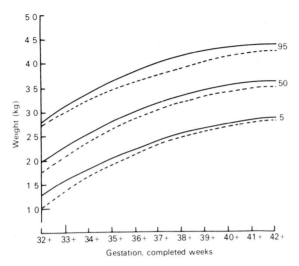

Fig. 30.6 Birth weight in relation to gestational age for boys. The channels marked by interrupted lines give the centiles of weight for first-born infants; the channels marked by continuous lines give the centiles for later born infants. First-born infants tend to have lower birth weights than their siblings. (After Tanner J M 1984 In: Forfar J O, Arneil G C (eds) Textbook of paediatrics. Churchill Livingstone, Edinburgh)

placental function, chronic intrauterine infection or genetically determined congenital malformation. Both 'pre-term' and 'light-for-dates' newborn infants, particularly the latter, are considered 'at risk' with regard to their future progress.

A further parameter of growth and development is the skeletal or bone age. Tanner and his colleagues have described a detailed method of assessment, based on an X-ray of the left wrist and hand, which may be used from the age of 1 year. Stages in the development of the lower end of the radius and ulna, the carpal bones and the metacarpal bones and phalanges of the first, third and fifth digits are used to compile a maturity score on which the bone age is based. In the United States, Greulich and Pyle have published an atlas of the stages of development seen in the X-ray of the left wrist and hand in boys and girls from which the bone age may be determined by visual comparison. Use of this atlas assesses the average normal British child's bone age as about 6 months retarded in comparison with the Tanner method. There is considerable normal variation in bone age at a given chronological age, particularly during adolescence.

Puberty

During puberty there is a spurt in growth and the body undergoes functional and structural changes making it capable of procreation; the sexual organs mature and the secondary sexual characteristics develop. In girls the pelvis grows rapidly in preparation for childbirth and the amount of fat increases over the shoulders, pelvis, buttocks and thighs. In boys there is an increase in muscle mass, the shoulders become broader and the voice breaks. Transient gynaecomastia is common. Psychological changes occur in both sexes.

Tanner has described stages of puberty numbered 1

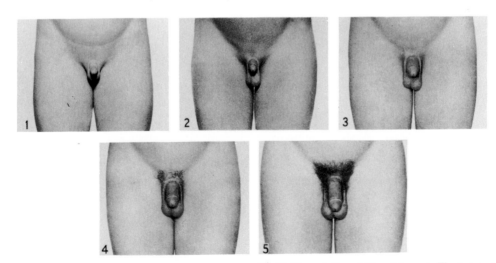

Fig. 30.7 Standards for genital maturity ratings. (By courtesy of J. M. Tanner) *Stage 1* Pre-adolescent. The testes, scrotum and penis are about the same size and shape as in early childhood. *Stage 2* The testes and scrotum are enlarged slightly. The skin of the scrotum is reddened and changed in texture. There is little or no enlargement of the penis at this stage. *Stage 3* The penis is enlarged slightly, mainly in length. There is further growth of the testes and scrotum. *Stage 4* The penis is enlarged further in length and breadth and there is development of the glands. The testes and scrotum are further increased in size and the scrotal skin is darker. *Stage 5* The genitalia are of adult size and shape.

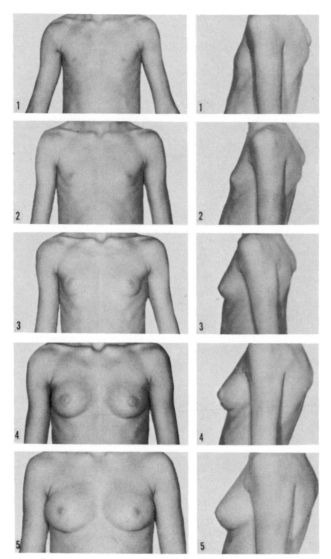

Fig. 30.8 Standards for breast development ratings. (By courtesy of J. M. Tanner) *Stage 1* Pre-adolescent. There is elevation of the papilla only. *Stage 2* Breast bud stage: elevation of the breast and papilla as a small mound. There is enlargement of the areolar diameter. *Stage 3* There is further enlargement and elevation of the breast and areola, with no separation of their contours. *Stage 4* The areola and papilla form a secondary mound projecting above the contour of the breast. *Stage 5* Mature stage: there is projection of the papilla only, due to recession of the areola to the general contour of the breast.

to 5, based on the growth of the genitalia and pubic hair in boys and the growth of the breasts and pubic hair in girls. Genital maturity ratings in boys are shown in Figure 30.7, breast development ratings in girls in Figure 30.8 and pubic hair ratings in boys and girls in Figure 30.9.

In both sexes the subcutaneous fat on the trunk and limbs increases in thickness rapidly during the first year of life and then decreases during the middle years of childhood. In girls an increase in trunk and limb fat begins from the age of about 8 years and continues during the years of puberty so that a girl who has tended to be obese during childhood may become more so as an adolescent. From the age of about 8 years trunk fat increases in boys but there is virtually no increase of fat in the limbs. Because of such variations in body fat distribution at different ages, weight charts give somewhat different information from that supplied by height charts.

In the average boy the penis begins to enlarge at the age of 12 years and pubic hair appears between the ages of 12 and 13 years. However, there is considerable

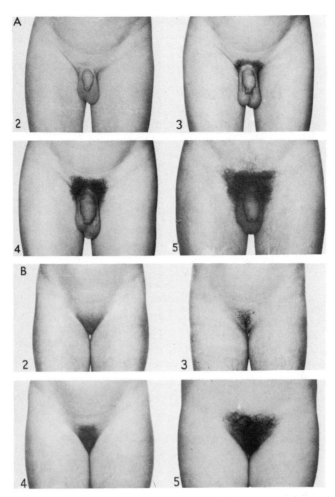

Fig. 30.9 Standards for pubic hair ratings in boys (A) and girls (B). (By courtesy of J. M. Tanner) *Stage 1* Pre-adolescent. No pubic hair is present. *Stage 2* There is a sparse growth of long, slightly pigmented, downy hair, straight or slightly curled, chiefly at the base of the penis or along the labia. *Stage 3* The hair is considerably darker, coarser and more curled. It spreads sparsely over the pubic symphysis. *Stage 4* The hair is now adult in type, but the area covered is still considerably smaller than in the adult. There is no spread to the medial surface of the thighs. *Stage 5* The hair is adult in quantity and type with a distribution of the horizontal (or classically 'feminine') pattern. Spread to the medial surface of the thighs is present. (In males, spread up the linea alba occurs late and is rated as stage 6)

normal variation in the time of onset of these pubertal signs and the penis may begin to enlarge at 10 years or as late as 14 years. If the scatter in 95 per cent of the normal British population is taken into account, a boy is showing precocious puberty if growth of the penis occurs before the age of 10 years or delayed puberty if growth of the penis does not begin until later than 14 years.

In the majority of girls breast enlargement begins at the age of 11 years and pubic hair appears between the ages of 11 and 12 years, the scatter for 95 per cent of the normal population being 9 years to 13 years for the commencement of breast development. The average age at the menarche is 13 years and 95 per cent of girls first

menstruate between their 11th and 15th birthdays. A girl is showing precocious puberty if the breasts enlarge before the age of 9 years and delayed puberty if they show no enlargement after the age of 13 years. In normal individuals, as well as individual differences in the age of onset of puberty, there is variation in the time taken to advance through the various stages. Although the first breast development in girls is usually only 6 months earlier than the first genital development in boys, the growth spurt occurs about 2 years earlier in girls so that the adult height is reached at a correspondingly younger age.

It is thought that puberty begins when the hypothalamus becomes less sensitive to feed-back inhibition by the small quantities of sex hormones produced during childhood by the gonads. Gonadotrophin releasing hormone (GnRH) therefore increases and the plasma levels of luteinising hormone (LH) and follicle stimulating hormone (FSH) rise.

In the male FSH stimulates the production of spermatozoa by the testes while LH stimulates Leydig cell function and the synthesis of testosterone. When testosterone reaches the target organs it is converted into dihydrotestosterone (DHT) by the enzyme 5α-reductase. DHT is metabolically more active than testosterone and its formation is essential for masculinisation to take place.

In the female, FSH stimulates follicular development in the ovary and oestrogen synthesis by the follicles. LH stimulates oestrogen synthesis, and induces ovulation and hence the formation of corpora lutea, which produce progesterone. The principal oestrogen is oestra-diol-17β (p. 329). A small quantity of testosterone is formed in the female by peripheral conversion from androstenedione.

In both sexes, the plasma levels of androgens of adrenal origin rise sharply before those of LH and FSH. Adrenal androgens stimulate the growth of pubic and axillary hair and may play a part in the anabolic processes associated with skeletal maturation and the growth spurt.

Disorders of growth

Short stature during childhood and adolescence has many causes and, since an individual's height is related to the average of the father's and mother's heights, parental height should always be taken into consideration. Racial differences also affect the rate of growth and the time of onset of puberty. Chromosomal defects of the autosomes or of the sex chromosomes may be associated with short stature. Hereditary defects of the skeleton lead to stunting; impaired growth results from lack of growth hormone (Fig. 30.10) or of thyroid hormones (Figs. 30.11, 30.12 and 30.13). Organic disorders of the central nervous system and the cardio-

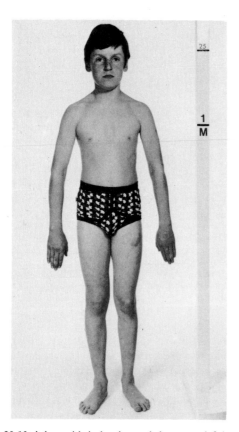

Fig. 30.10 A boy with isolated growth hormone deficiency diagnosed at the age of 14.1 years. His height was 134 cm, the average height of a boy of 9.5 years. His weight was 28 kg and his bone age was 10.7 years. There were no pubertal changes. He was of normal intelligence but his face resembled that of a boy several years younger. He was treated with growth hormone and his final height of 164 cm, reached at the age of 18.4 years, was between the 3rd and 10th centiles. (By courtesy of Constance C. Forsyth)

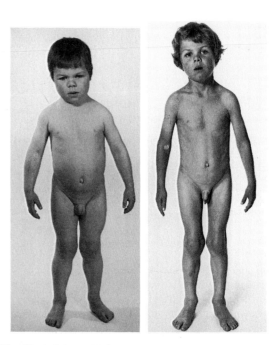

Fig. 30.11 A boy with hypothyroidism aged 8.7 years (left). His height was 104 cm, the average height of a boy of 4.4 years. His weight was 21 kg and his bone age was 1.8 years (Fig. 30.12). He was overweight for his height with a distended abdomen. His intelligence was normal. The photograph on the right shows the same boy after one year's treatment with thyroxine. His height had by then increased by 11 cm and his weight was unchanged. The bone age had advanced to 3.8 years. (By courtesy of Constance C. Forsyth)

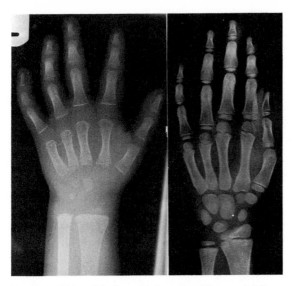

Fig. 30.12 Wrist of the boy with hypothyroidism aged 8.7 years shown in Figure 30.11. On the right is the wrist of a normal boy of the same age. (By courtesy of Constance C. Forsyth)

vascular, respiratory, renal, haemopoietic or alimentary systems may interfere with growth. In addition, adverse psychological factors due to an unhappy home life are very important in this respect. In the developing countries undernutrition is a well recognised cause of short stature and delayed puberty. In developed countries such undernutrition is rare but, in the condition known as coeliac disease (p. 222), in which the small intestinal absorption of food is inadequate, undernutrition leads to failure of growth. Children whose growth has been slowed by illness show a greater-than-normal rate of growth upon correction of the disorder. This rapid phase of growth continues until the child has reached his normal growth centile before the illness and has therefore been called 'catch-up' growth. The mechanisms that control the return to the normal pattern of growth have still to be elucidated. A child whose congenital heart lesion is corrected by surgery may, after the operation, show catch-up growth when he grows faster than a normal child of the same age. Successful treatment of chronic pulmonary or renal

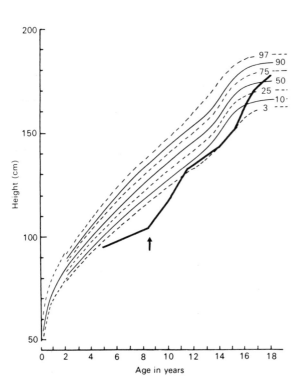

Fig. 30.13 Growth chart of the boy in Figure 30.11 to show 'catch up growth' due to treatment with thyroxine (started at the time indicated by the arrow). His final height of 178 cm was between the 50th and 75th centiles. (By courtesy of Constance C. Forsyth)

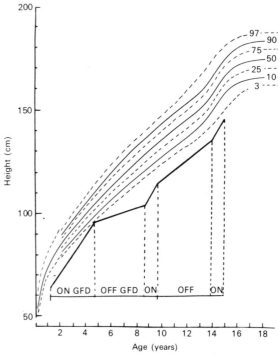

Fig. 30.14 Height chart of a boy with coeliac disease. His parents were illiterate and treatment with a gluten-free diet (GFD) could be maintained only under supervision in hospital. Catch-up growth is shown during periods on the gluten-free diet but his growth was abnormally slow when the diet was stopped at home. Eventually he learned to follow the diet himself and grew well without hospitalisation. He was lost to follow-up at the age of 15 years. (By courtesy of Constance C. Forsyth)

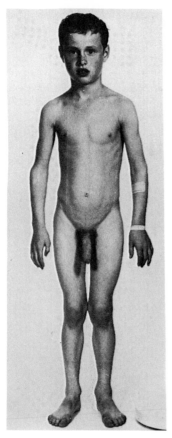

Fig. 30.15 A boy with precocious puberty aged 8 years. (By courtesy of Constance C. Forsyth)

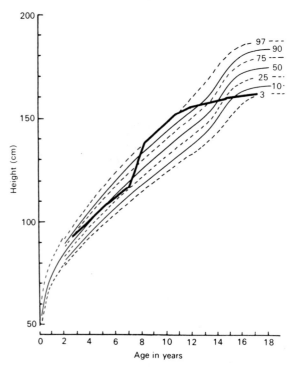

Fig. 30.16 Height chart of the boy in Figure 30.15. His height had been recorded for several years before the onset of precocious puberty and had shown a normal growth pattern along the 50th centile line. When first seen with precocious puberty at the age of 8 years his height was 136 cm, the average height of a boy of 10 years; his weight was 29.5 kg and his bone age was 11.8 years. The control of the onset of puberty had been disturbed by a brain tumour affecting hypothalamic function. Partial excision and radiotherapy controlled further growth of the tumour. The precocious puberty was treated with an anti-androgen drug. The height chart shows the rapid growth associated with the precocious onset of puberty, followed by a number of years of decreasing growth, leading to short stature as an adult. His final adult height of 160 cm was just below the 3rd centile. (By courtesy of Constance C. Forsyth)

disease leads to improved growth as does treatment of anaemia during childhood or the use of a gluten-free diet in coeliac disease (Fig. 30.14). Excessive growth during childhood and adolescence is a much rarer problem. It may be due to constitutional factors or to damage to the central nervous system and it is common in children who develop precocious puberty (Figs. 30.15 and 30.16).

Growth and development in childhood and adolescence show wide physiological variations and are affected by many pathological processes. As children who are too small or too tall or whose puberty is delayed or advanced may suffer from remediable disorders, accurate knowledge of the subject is of great clinical importance.

FURTHER READING

Brook C G D (ed) 1981 Clinical paediatric endocrinology. Blackwell Scientific, Oxford

Brook C G D (ed) 1982 Growth assessment in childhood and adolescence. Blackwell Scientific, Oxford

Dobbing J 1981 Later development of the brain and its vulnerability, In: Davis J A, Dobbing J (eds) Scientific Foundations of Paediatrics, 2nd edn. Heinemann, London, pp. 744–759

Greulich W W, Pyle S I 1959 Radiographic atlas of skeletal development of the hand and wrist, 2nd edn. University Press, Stanford

Marshall W A, Tanner J M 1981 Puberty. In: Davis J A,

Dobbing J (eds) Scientific Foundations of Paediatrics, 2nd edn. Heinemann, London, pp. 176–209

Savage D C L, Evans J 1984 Puberty and adolescence. In: Forfar J O, Arneil G C (eds) Textbook of Paediatrics, 3rd edn. Churchill Livingstone, Edinburgh, pp. 366–388

Sinclair D C 1985 Human growth after birth, 4th edn. University Press, Oxford

Smith D W 1977 Growth and its Disorders. Saunders, Philadelphia

Tanner J M 1978 Foetus into man: physical growth from conception to maturity. Open Books, London

Tanner J M, Whitehouse R H, Cameron N, Marshall W A, Healey M J R, Goldstein H 1983 Assessment of skeletal maturity and prediction of adult height, 2nd edn. Academic Press, London

Tanner J M 1984 Physical growth and development. In: Forfar J O, Arneil G C (eds) Textbook of paediatrics, 3rd edn. Churchill Livingstone, Edinburgh, pp. 278–330

Tanner J M 1986 Normal growth and techniques in growth assessment. Clinics in Endocrinology and Metabolism 15: 411–451

31

The nervous system

The nervous system can be divided into *central* and *peripheral* portions. The central nervous system consists of the brain and the spinal cord. The peripheral part has 43 pairs of nerves that leave the cerebrospinal axis and pass to the various organs of the body. The peripheral nerves contain fibres of two kinds, *afferent* or *sensory* fibres, carrying nerve impulses from the periphery to the central nervous system and *efferent* or *motor* fibres carrying impulses from the central nervous system to muscles and glands and other organs.

The nervous system is the main co-ordinator of the activities of the body. The afferent nerves bring to the central nervous system information about the external world from receptors that are sensitive to stimuli such as light, sound, temperature or pressure, and also information about the internal state of the body, for example tension in muscles or distension in viscera. As a consequence of the arrival of these impulses the central nervous system sends impulses along the efferent nerves to produce appropriate movements of muscles or secretion of glands. The pathways taken by impulses after they arrive at the central nervous system are very complex but the basic principle is that impulses are handed on from nerve cell to nerve cell until finally they emerge in an efferent nerve to produce a response in an effector organ such as a muscle or a gland. Sometimes this process rises to conscious levels but many of the activities of the body are regulated without our being aware of them. These activities controlled by the nervous system are called *reflex actions*, or simply *reflexes*, and the pathways followed in the nervous system along afferent, junctional and efferent neurones are called *reflex arcs*.

In man the central nervous system contains 10 000 million neurones, all formed by the sixth month of intra-uterine life; no mitotic figures can be found after birth. If tritiated thymidine, which is incorporated into the DNA of cells about to divide, is given intracerebrally to rats, a few neurones are labelled. But this small production of neurones — if it does occur in man as well as the rat — is too small to be of importance in recovery from cerebral injuries. Neurones are described further in Chapter 32.

The neuroglia

Each neurone of the central nervous system in man is surrounded by about ten glial cells, their delicately folded membranes covering the neurone except at the synaptic knobs. Neuroglial cells make up a quarter to one-half of the volume of brain tissue. When the adult number of neurones is reached the glial cells multiply rapidly especially in the last months of intra-uterine life and the first 18 months of extra-uterine life. If the diet of the infant rat is deficient during the period of glial multiplication its brain may be permanently damaged. In spite of much research it is not possible to state definitely that undernutrition of human infants results in low intelligence but some low-birth-weight babies have poor intelligence in later life. It is probable that substances are transferred from blood to neurone through the glial cells, particularly the astrocytes (Fig. 31.1). In tissue culture, only those neurones

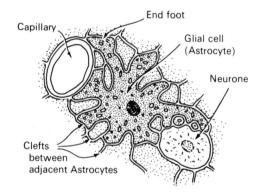

Fig. 31.1 Sketch of neurone–glial–capillary arrangement as shown by the electron microscope. An astrocyte is interposed between the endothelium of the capillary and the neurone. The cells, axons, dendrites and astrocytes are tightly packed, with narrow clefts (greatly exaggerated here) of about 15 nm between them. (From Kuffler S W 1967 Proceedings of the Royal Society Series B 168:8)

surrounded by glia survive for any length of time. Glial cells are rich in glycogen, contain only a tenth of the RNA of the neurones but havé more lipid and very much more carbonic anhydrase.

Glial cells, unlike neurones, can multiply throughout life. The oligodendrocytes form myelin like the Schwann cells in the peripheral nerves; the microglia phagocytose degenerating neurones. The membrane potential of glial cells, about 90 mV, is mainly due to the difference in potassium concentration between the interior of the cell and that in the narrow clefts between them. Depolarising currents passed through glial cells do not make them discharge.

Cerebral circulation

The importance of an adequate blood supply to the brain scarcely needs stressing. Arrest' of the cerebral circulation for more than about 5 seconds is followed by unconsciousness, and cerebral ischaemia of longer than 3 minutes causes irreparable damage to the grey matter of the cortex, the Purkinje cells of the cerebellum and the cells of the basal nuclei.

Since, in man, there are almost no anastomoses between the branches of the internal and external carotid arteries, the blood supply to the brain depends on the arterial circle at the base of the brain within the cranial cavity, into which blood is brought by the two internal carotid arteries and by the two vertebral arteries (Fig. 31.2). Studies in rabbits, in which the arrangement of these vessels resembles that in man, have shown that the internal carotid artery and the basilar artery share the blood supply to each cerebral hemisphere in such a way that there is normally, in a steady state, no interchange of blood between them.

The arterial circle clearly provides for continued perfusion of all parts of the brain even if a large vessel should become blocked. Further, the branches of the arterial circle, that is the anterior, middle and posterior cerebral arteries, intercommunicate through their small ramifications over the cortex. The cerebral vascular system can be outlined in man by injecting a radio-opaque solution into a carotid artery.

The cerebral vessels have a prominent internal elastic lamina but their muscle coat is less well developed than that of arteries of comparable size elsewhere in the body. The grey matter is richly supplied with capillaries but the white matter is less vascular. The venous sinuses of the dura carry away blood from the brain; in addition they also receive cerebrospinal fluid through the arachnoid villi (p. 380).

Cerebral blood flow

The rate of blood flow through the brain can be measured in man by causing the subject to breathe nitrous

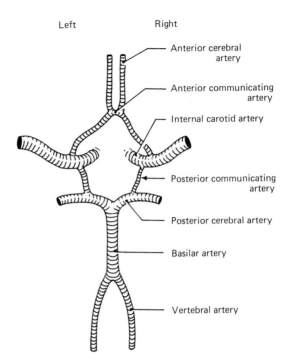

Fig. 31.2 The arterial circle (circle of Willis) at the base of the human brain. The internal carotid arteries, LIC and RIC, supply a larger volume of the brain than do the vertebral arteries. In normal persons the left vertebral artery is often larger than the right, which may be very small; one or other posterior communicating artery may be narrow or absent. In fact in only 50 per cent of normal persons is the arterial circle present as in the diagram. Movements of the head and neck cause considerable changes in blood flow in the vertebral arteries because they pass through the transverse processes of the atlas and because they are relatively fixed as they enter the foramen magnum. Since the lumen of the internal carotid artery can be constricted from 30 mm^2 to 5 mm^2 with little reduction in the flow, this important artery could be said to be much larger than is haemodynamically necessary.

oxide and measuring the concentration of the gas in samples of blood taken from the internal carotid artery and the jugular bulb over a period of 10 minutes. Application of Fick's principle (p. 87) shows that approximately 55 ml of blood flows through 100 g of brain per minute. If the weight of the adult brain is 1400 g the total flow is about 770 ml per min or 15 per cent of the cardiac output. The carotid–venous oxygen difference is about 6 ml per 100 ml of blood. The oxygen consumption is therefore (55/100) × 6 or 3.3 ml oxygen per 100 g per minute, which is not very different from the requirement of muscles during active work. The whole brain therefore consumes about 46 ml oxygen per minute, equivalent to an energy utilisation of about 20 W. The oxygen consumption varies relatively little over a wide range of arterial P_{CO_2} and P_{O_2}. Infants with their large brains require a relatively large proportion of the total oxygen consumption. Cerebral blood flow is reduced in the elderly.

It is, of course, likely that even if the total blood flow remains constant there may be considerable regional differences in blood flow through different parts of the brain. The blood flow through the baboon's cerebral cortex can be measured through the intact skull by injecting the γ-emitter ^{133}Xe in saline into the internal carotid artery and determining its clearance rate with scintillation counters placed over the skull. The decay curve shows a fast component and a slow component, representing, respectively, the flow through grey and white matter. When the P_{O_2} and arterial blood pressure are within the normal range the mean cerebral blood flow is 52 ml per 100 g per min; the flow in the grey matter is 72 ml per 100 g per min and in the white matter 19 ml per 100 g per min.

Mental activity does not increase the cerebral oxygen consumption or blood flow as estimated by the nitrous oxide method. This technique gives the sum of the flow in all regions of the brain. However if ^{133}Xe injected into the carotid artery is used local blood flow can be estimated by means of collimeters at different sites on the skull. In this way Ingvar and his colleagues have measured the flow in 32 regions of one human hemisphere. In normal subjects a verbal test gave an increase in blood flow up to 25 per cent in the frontal region; a visual task increased the blood flow in the occipital, frontal and parietal regions; reading caused an increase in blood flow in the post-central and other areas.

The skull of the human baby is not completely ossified and at each beat of the heart the pulsations of the brain are transmitted to the anterior fontanelle. When the baby cries the venous pressure rises and the increase of intracerebral pressure bulges the anterior fontanelle. In the adult, just as in the child, the intracranial pressure rises when violent expiratory efforts are made. It falls in the standing position because the pressure in the veins falls (to negative values) and venous drainage is facilitated. Blood entering the skull at each systole displaces a similar amount of blood from the veins, but if there is a prolonged increase of arterial pressure cerebrospinal fluid may also be forced out of the skull.

Control of cerebral blood flow

Cerebral blood flow remains remarkably constant even when the mean arterial pressure varies over the range 60 to 130 mmHg (Fig. 31.3). Only when the arterial or, more strictly, the difference between arterial and venous pressure (perfusion pressure) falls below 60 mmHg or when the cardiac output falls below 3 litres per minute does the cerebral circulation become insufficient. The

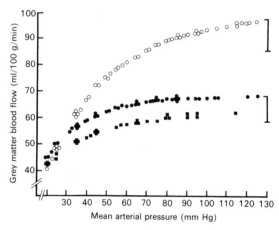

Fig. 31.3 The black circles show the relation in the baboon between mean arterial pressure and blood flow in the grey matter when the nerves are intact and when the P_{CO_2} and P_{O_2} are kept constant. The curve of flow is nearly flat between 60 and 130 mmHg — this is the range of autoregulation. The open circles show the effect of sympathectomy; there is no flat region of this curve. Stimulation of the sympathetic (black squares) brought the relation back to normal. (After James I M et al. 1969 Circulation Research 25:80)

process whereby a relatively high blood flow is maintained as pressure is reduced from physiological levels to about 60 mmHg is known as *autoregulation* and appears to depend upon two factors; one, an intrinsic factor that probably represents a response of vascular smooth muscle, is comparatively slow, being complete in 30 to 40 seconds. The other is neural and is mediated by the dilator pathway carried for part of its length by the VIIth cranial nerve. If this pathway is interrupted or if atropine is given, there is no longer vasodilatation and blood flow falls to low levels when the animal becomes hypotensive. The constancy of flow at high pressure (> 130 mmHg) appears to depend largely upon an intact sympathetic pathway (Fig. 31.3).

The cerebral vascular responses to hypoxia and hypercapnia also depend upon intrinsic and neural factors. If the constrictor fibres are cut, the flow response to both hypoxia and hypercapnia is enhanced. If the dilator pathway is cut, the response to hypercapnia is markedly reduced and the response to hypoxia is largely abolished. If both pathways are cut, or if all the peripheral arterial chemoreceptors are denervated, blood flow may actually fall in response to hypoxia but there is evidence of a slow residual intrinsic response to CO_2 (Fig. 31.4).

From this we may deduce that in the intact animal the vascular response to changes in arterial pressure and P_{CO_2} is determined by alterations in the balance of

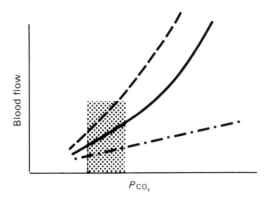

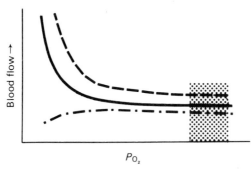

Fig. 31.4 Changes in the cerebral blood flow in response to changes in P_{CO_2} and P_{O_2}. The dotted area indicates the normal values in each case. The continuous line shows the responses with all nerves intact. Interrupted lines (———) indicate changes seen when the constrictor pathway is cut and —·—·— indicates the changes seen when the dilator fibres are cut. (By courtesy of M. J. Purves.)

constrictor and dilator neural activity superimposed upon an intrinsic smooth muscle response.

Metabolism of the nervous system

By comparing the arterio-venous differences in oxygen, carbon dioxide and glucose it has been found that the RQ of the brain is very nearly 1 and that the oxygen utilised is equivalent to the amount of glucose that disappears, that is 4.9 mg per 100 g per min. Brain tissue uses glucose almost exclusively as a source of energy, the glycogen content being too low, about 0.1 per cent, to make an important contribution. The brain also uses small quantities of two ketones, 3-hydroxy-butyrate and acetoacetate.

In some conditions in which consciousness is depressed the oxygen consumption of the brain is reduced; for example, hypoglycaemia reduces it by 20 per cent, diabetic coma by 50 per cent and surgical anaesthesia by 40 per cent. But sleep reduces consumption by only 3 per cent. Conversely, in experiments on cats it was found that oxygen consumption by the cerebral cortex increases by as much as 80 per cent when the cortex is stimulated electrically.

In the fetus and infant the synthesis of new proteins in the brain is quite rapid as might be expected from the rapid growth of the brain. Synthesis slows down gradually and in adult life it is much the same as in other tissues.

The water-soluble proteins of brain tissue are similar to those in other tissues and have a comparable turnover but the lipoproteins of the myelin sheath contain protein with a turnover rate so low that they can be regarded as almost metabolically inert.

Nervous tissue is peculiar in being relatively isolated from the rest of the body because of the difficulty with which many substances, including amino acids, pass into it from the blood, and in its very limited ability to store carbohydrate in the form of glycogen. The brain's dependence on glucose makes it very sensitive to hypoglycaemia. Utilisation of glucose for energy production in the brain follows the tricarboxylic acid cycle but only about 25 per cent of the glucose used by the brain is oxidised in this way. The remaining 75 per cent is used for the formation of amino acids, chiefly glutamic acid and aspartic acid, which are used partly for protein synthesis but mainly for oxidation by pathways that exist in the nerve cell for the production of energy.

CEREBROSPINAL FLUID

The central nervous system is covered by three membranes or meninges (Fig. 31.5). Beneath the tough *dura mater* is the narrow *subdural space*, containing a very small amount of tissue fluid. This space is bounded internally by the *arachnoid mater*, which is separated from the *pia mater* by the *subarachnoid space* containing cerebrospinal fluid (CSF). The subarachnoid space does not communicate with the subdural space but is continuous with the ventricular system of the brain through medial and lateral apertures in the roof of the fourth ventricle. The arachnoid and pia covering the brain and spinal cord are connected by strands of arachnoid tissue; the pia closely invests the surface of the brain and dips down into the fissures and sulci. At the base of the brain the two membranes are widely separated and form large spaces known as cisterns, the largest being the *cerebello-medullary cistern* or *cisterna magna* (Fig. 31.6).

The cerebral blood vessels passing through the subarachnoid space are invested with two layers of arachnoid. The branches that penetrate into the brain are accompanied by extensions of the subarachnoid space. There are similar extensions of the subarachnoid space along the cranial and spinal nerve roots.

A sample of CSF can be obtained in man by passing

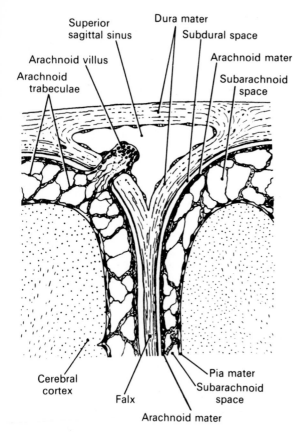

Fig. 31.5 Coronal section through the vertex to show the meninges. (After Weed L H 1923 American Journal of Anatomy 21:191)

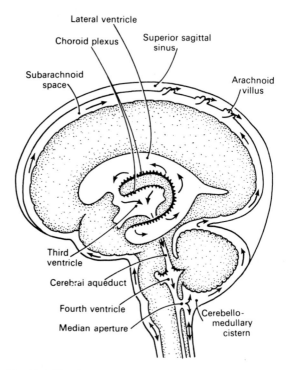

Fig. 31.6 The circulation of the cerebrospinal fluid. (After Gatz A J 1970 Manter's essentials of clinical neuroanatomy and neurophysiology. Davis, Philadelphia)

a long needle between the third and fourth lumbar spinous processes into the spinal subarachnoid space (*lumbar puncture*; Fig. 31.7). The subarachnoid space may also be entered by passing a needle through the atlanto-occipital membrane into the cisternal magna (*cisternal puncture*). This procedure is seldom used to obtain CSF because it is less safe than lumbar puncture.

Composition

Normal CSF is a clear colourless fluid, of specific gravity 1005, containing not more than 5 lymphocytes per mm^3. The pH, about 7.33, remains nearly constant in the presence of large changes of plasma pH. There is potential difference of about +5 mV between CSF and blood; the maintenance of this difference must involve an active transport mechanism. The chemical composition of CSF is shown in Table 31.8. The protein content in the lumbar region (400 mg/litre) is greater than in the ventricles (100 mg/litre) or in the cisterna magna (200 mg/litre).

Radioisotope investigations show that oxygen, carbon

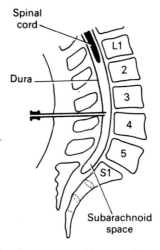

Fig. 31.7 Lumbar puncture. The space between lumbar vertebrae 3 and 4 is most commonly used but an alternative is the space between 4 and 5. The cord is out of danger but the nerves of the cauda equina are sometimes encountered.

dioxide, alcohol, barbiturates, glucose and lipophilic substances pass quickly into the brain from the blood. Inorganic ions and most highly dissociated compounds, amino acids and sucrose pass very slowly into the brain.

Table 31.8 Comparison of the chemical composition of blood plasma and cerebrospinal fluid.

Component	Blood plasma	Cerebrospinal fluid
Protein	60–80 g/l	200–400 mg/l
Urea	2.5–6.5 mmol/l	2.0–7.0 mmol/l
Glucose (fasting)	3.0–5.0 mmol/l	2.5–4.5 mmol/l
Sodium	136–148 mmol/l	144–152 mmol/l
Potassium	3.8–5.0 mmol/l	2.0–3.0 mmol/l
Calcium	2.2–2.6 mmol/l	1.1–1.3 mmol/l
Chloride	95–105 mmol/l	123–128 mmol/l
Bicarbonate	24–32 mmol/l	24–32 mmol/l

Note the higher chloride and lower glucose content of CSF as compared with blood plasma. CSF glucose levels vary with the plasma glucose and are about 70 per cent of the latter. The concentration of calcium in the CSF is similar to that of ionised calcium in plasma.

These facts have suggested that there is a barrier composed of a lipid membrane separating the blood from the CSF and the extracellular fluid of the brain. The anatomical basis of the *blood–brain barrier* is shown in Figure 31.9. In the brain the capillaries differ from those elsewhere in the body in that the endothelial cells are joined by tight junctions about the entire periphery of each cell. In other words they are bound together by a 'strip weld' unlike the 'spot welds' of the endothelia of other capillaries. This means that lipophobic substances that do not readily penetrate cell membranes are excluded from the brain unless actively transported through cells.

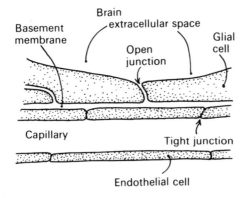

Fig. 31.9 The blood–brain barrier. There is a continuous band of tight junctions between the endothelial cells of the capillaries. The basement membrane does not seem to be a barrier. (After Rall D P 1971 in: La Du B N et al. (eds) Fundamentals of drug metabolism and drug disposition Williams & Wilkins, Baltimore, p. 76)

Formation

Most, but probably not all, of the cerebrospinal fluid is formed by the secretory activity of the cells of the choroid plexuses. These are rich networks of blood vessels projecting into the cavities of the lateral ventricles and third ventricle, which are covered only by the pia mater and ependyma. The choroid plexuses are supplied with blood by anterior and posterior choroidal arteries that arise from the internal carotid and posterior cerebral arteries. It is possible that a small quantity of CSF is normally formed by ultrafiltration from brain parenchyma.

The CSF formed in the lateral ventricles passes into the third ventricle by the inter-ventricular foramina and then by the cerebral aqueduct to the fourth ventricle, from which it escapes by three foramina into the subarachnoid space round the brain and spinal cord (Fig. 31.6). Blockage of any of the foramina causes the ventricles upstream to dilate. Blockage of the cerebral aqueduct, for example, causes distension of the third ventricle and the two lateral ventricles (*internal hydrocephalus*). Cerebrospinal fluid is produced continuously at a rate of 0.5 ml per minute (720 ml per 24 h). Since the total volume of CSF is 120 ml the whole of the CSF must be exchanged every four hours or so. Further, since the pressure of the CSF remains relatively constant the production must be balanced by an equal absorption of fluid. The movement of CSF from the lateral ventricles into the ventricular system and subarachnoid space is no doubt helped by the pulsations of the choroid plexuses and is maintained by its continuous absorption as it passes over the cortex and down the spinal cord.

Mechanism of formation of CSF

The primary process in the secretion of CSF is the active transport of sodium across the apical membranes of the epithelial cells of the choroid plexus by a Na^+/K^+–exchange pump. Sodium enters the cell across the basolateral membrane down its electrochemical gradient in exchange for H^+. The protons are obtained from the dissociation of carbonic acid derived from CO_2 under the influence of carbonic anhydrase, which is plentiful in the cells. How chloride and bicarbonate follow Na^+ into the CSF is not yet known but there is evidence that the Na^+/K^+–pump creates a potential difference between CSF and cell that would force the anions to move with the sodium. This solute movement creates an osmotic gradient across the plexus and water flows passively. The resulting CSF is slightly hyperosmotic to plasma. The choroid plexus belongs to a group of epithelia with 'leaky' (that is, low resistance) so-called tight junctions and has transport properties similar to gallbladder, renal proximal tubule and small intestine (Fig. 31.10).

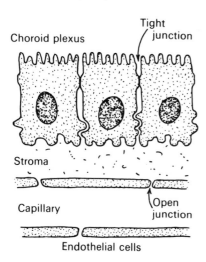

Fig. 31.10 The barrier between blood and cerebrospinal fluid. Drugs and other substances cannot enter the CSF without passing through the cells of the choroid plexus. (After Rall as in Fig. 31.9.)

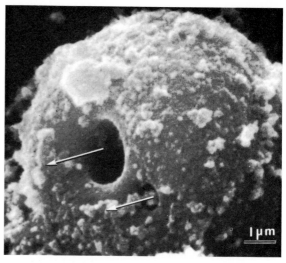

Fig. 31.11 Scanning electron micrograph of a giant vacuole in a mesothelial cell of an arachnoid villus. Two openings are seen through which tracer material (colloidally suspended Thorotrast) is passing. (From Tripathi R 1974 Brain Research 80:503)

There are homeostatic mechanisms that maintain the constant concentrations of K^+, Mg^{2+}, Ca^{2+}, hydrogen ions, amino acids, catecholamines and other constituents. The importance of these mechanisms is clearly illustrated when a pH fall of 0.05 units increases ventilation four-fold (Chap. 10) and an elevation of CSF glycine produces hypothermia, hypotension and motor inco-ordination.

Reabsorption

Cerebrospinal fluid is absorbed mainly into the venous system through the arachnoid villi, invaginations of the subarachnoid space into the large venous sinuses of the cranium (Fig. 31.5). The arachnoid villi contain a labyrinth of cells separating CSF and blood. The electron microscope has shown that these cells contain large vacuoles opening into the CSF (Fig. 31.11). When the pressure in the subarachnoid space is greater than the pressure in the superior sagittal sinus, the vacuoles open into the blood and CSF passes down the pressure gradient through the vacuoles into the blood. When the subarachnoid pressure is lower than that in the sinus, reflux of blood is prevented by collapse of the vacuoles. It is likely that a rise in CSF pressure sufficient to operate this mechanism occurs at each arterial pulse. The venous sinuses remain patent in spite of the low hydrostatic pressure within them because they are enclosed between layers of tough dural membrane.

Some CSF must be absorbed elsewhere because in chronic obstructive hydrocephalus the increase in brain size per day is only 2 per cent of the amount of fluid formed per day. CSF is probably absorbed into the venous system in the extensions of the subarachnoid space along the roots of the spinal nerves, into the spinal veins and through the ependymal linings of the ventricles. Absorption of CSF into the blood is favoured by the colloid osmotic pressure of the plasma protein, since CSF normally contains very little protein.

Pressure

If a vertical tube is attached to the lumbar puncture needle the CSF rises about 10 cm when the patient is lying on his side and about 30 cm when he is sitting. A rise of intracranial venous pressure produced by coughing or by digital compression of the internal jugular veins causes the CSF pressure to rise rapidly above these values and the pressure falls rapidly when the compression is removed. The pressure of the CSF in the ventricles may be measured by inserting a catheter attached to a transducer.

Functions

Cerebrospinal fluid acts as a cushion between the soft and delicate brain substance and the rigid cranium. It supports the weight of the brain and distributes the force of blows on the head. The volume of the brain and its blood vessels changes from time to time and such changes take place at the expense of the volume of CSF; when the volume of blood in the brain is increased the volume of CSF is diminished and when the brain degenerates or atrophies there is an increase in the volume of CSF.

Cerebrospinal fluid also acts as a 'sink' in that any solutes that are at a higher concentration in the extracellular fluid of the brain diffuse into the CSF and are carried into the blood at the arachnoid villi. Some substances are transported actively by the cells of the choroid plexus from CSF into the blood. These include 5-hydroxytryptamine, adrenaline and certain drugs such as penicillin.

FURTHER READING

Bito L Z, Davson H, Fenstermacher J D (eds) 1978 The ocular and cerebrospinal fluids. Academic Press, New York

Bradbury M 1979 The concept of a blood–brain barrier. Wiley, Chichester

Kuffler S W, Nichols J G, Martin A R 1984 From neurone to brain: a cellular approach to the function of the nervous system. Sinauer, Sunderland, Mass.

McIlwain H, Bachelard H S 1985 Biochemistry and the central nervous system. Churchill Livingstone, Edinburgh

Ottoson D 1983 Physiology of the nervous system. Macmillan, London

32

Neurones

The central nervous system (CNS) is a collection of some 10^{13} nerve cells bound together, not with connective tissue as in other organs, but by modified nerve cells called *neuroglia*. The glial cells are divided into the central *astrocytes* and *oligodendrocytes* and the peripheral *Schwann cells*. Glial cells outnumber nerve cells by about 10 to 1 and make up about half of the bulk brain. Schwann cells and oligodendrocytes form the myelin sheaths surrounding some nerve fibres. Glial cells also have an important role in the stabilisation of the ionic and chemical environments of nearby nerve cells but their function is not yet understood. Because the real function of the glial cells in the working of the CNS is not known, the CNS is generally examined as though the glial cells were absent.

The nervous system, both peripheral and central, has several functions. The terminals of sensory neurones transform energies to which they are subjected into a form that the CNS can use. Figure 32.1 shows that the signal from a nerve fibre attached to a single receptor in the eye of a crab (*Limulus*) is composed of a series of electrical pulses identical in size, shape and duration and that the properties of the input signal are transformed or transduced into a frequency code in proportion to the intensity of illumination. These all-or-none impulses are conducted into the nervous system for interpretation.

A number of specific pathways can be identified within the nervous system. One leads, for example, from the retina to the occipital cortex via the optic nerve and the lateral geniculate nuclei. The pathway is not a direct line from eye to brain but is interrupted at several stages by *synapses*, the small gaps between fibres terminating on the cell itself. Information from the *pre-synaptic* structure (nerve fibre) is then transmitted to the target or *post-synaptic* structure (nerve cell, gland cell or muscle cell).

Almost all the information coming into the nervous system has to be summed in terms of time and space (integrated): for example, how long a light source shines into the eye and how big an object is. Various input channels are also integrated before effective action can

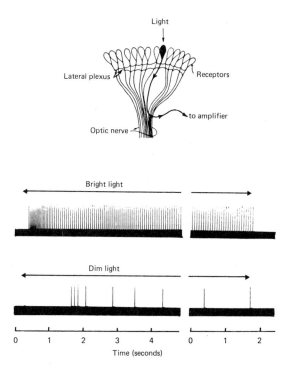

Fig. 32.1 Responses recorded from a single ommatidium from the eye of the shore crab (*Limulus*). The upper record shows the response to a bright light, the lower to a dim light. Note that the only difference is the frequency of the response, not the size of the recorded action potentials. (From Hartline H K et al. 1952 Cold Spring Harbor Symposla on Quantitative Biology 17:125)

be taken. A cup of tea is drunk because it looks like tea, smells like tea, tastes like tea and because a sensation of thirst is felt. The integrative action of the nervous system ensures that an appropriate output or *effector response* is derived. In the case of the cup of tea it is either drunk or poured away.

Nerve cells

The basic unit of the nervous system is the nerve cell and its associated processes. Each nerve cell (Fig. 32.2)

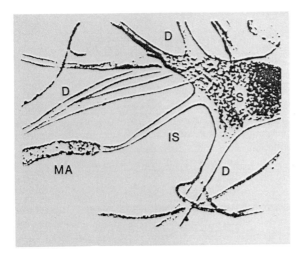

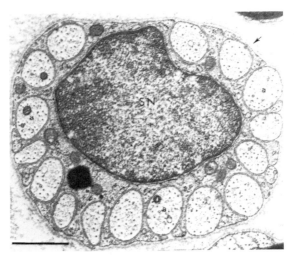

Fig. 32.2 Photomicrograph of part of a single human spinal motoneurone, unfixed and unstained. The cell body or soma (S) is seen together with the proximal parts of numerous dendrites (D). Note also that the initial segment (IS) of the axon is unmyelinated. MA: myelinated axon. Note also the numerous granules seen in the cell body extending into the proximal parts of the dendrites but not into the initial segment. (After Chang H T 1952 Cold Spring Harbor Symposia on Quantitative Biology 17:189)

Fig. 32.3 A transmission electron micrograph of a peripheral nerve of a rat. 16 unmyelinated axons (a) are seen within the cytoplasm of a single Schwann cell, the nucleus of which is shown (SN). Each axon lies within a separate pocket in the surface of the cell. The entire unit is surrounded by basal lamina (arrow). Horizontal calibration bar = 1 μm. (Courtesy of L. Duchen)

consists of a cell body, processes called *dendrites* and a specialised process that conducts information away from the cell body, the nerve *axon*. Cell bodies are either arranged in layers or in discrete collections as *nuclei* (grey matter). The axons are arranged centrally as the *tracts*, which connect the central nervous system both longitudinally and transversely (white matter), and form the peripheral nerves, which conduct information from the sensory endings into the nervous system (centripetally) and effector information away from the nervous system (centrifugally).

BEHAVIOUR OF RESTING NERVE TISSUE

The axons are collected into bundles bound together by connective tissue and the bundles are collected together to form the nerve trunks. Individual peripheral axons are surrounded by two structures. They are embedded in Schwann cells around which is a thin layer of connective tissue called the *neurilemma*. The Schwann cells are either wrapped around the axon, forming a bandage of a double layer of Schwann cell membrane to produce the *myelin sheath*, or the axon becomes almost completely engulfed by the Schwann cell (Figs. 32.3 and 32.4). This difference means that myelinated nerve axons are only in direct contact with extracellular fluid at the junctions (the nodes of Ranvier)

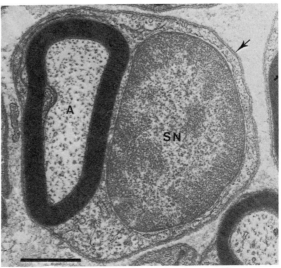

Fig. 32.4 Transverse section of a myelinated nerve fibre from the sciatic nerve of a rat. A single axon (A) containing microtubules and neurofilaments is associated with a Schwann cell. The basal lamina (arrow) lies outside the plasmalemma of the Schwann cell, the nucleus of which (SN) compresses the myelin and axon. (Courtesy of L. Duchen)

between two Schwann cells, whereas non-myelinated axons are exposed along their whole length. Myelinated axons are also larger (2–20 μm in diameter) than non-myelinated axons (0.3–1.2 μm in diameter).

Nerve fibres convey information as all-or-none voltage pulses (Fig. 32.1) and these voltage pulses are generated across the axonal membrane and not the Schwann cell membrane.

Nerve axons are filled with a conducting aqueous gel but do not conduct their brief voltage pulses passively like pieces of thin copper wire. They have a longitudinal resistance much higher than copper and if an electrical pulse is injected into one end of a nerve fibre it fades away within a millimetre. The all-or-none impulses are conducted over considerable distances without decrement because of an active process using energy.

The giant nerve fibre of the squid has been extensively used in the study of conduction.

Chemical composition

If the chemical composition of the intracellular and the extracellular compartments of the giant axons of the squid are compared it is clear that the compartments have different ionic compositions (Table 32.5). These chemical concentrations, however, do not necessarily reflect the actual free ionic concentrations; potassium ions are probably ionically free but other ions may not be. For example, using a marker molecule (*aequorin*), which emits light in the presence of Ca^{2+}, the intracellular concentration of free Ca^{2+} has been found to be around 40 nmol/l. Thus only 1/10 000th of the internal calcium concentration is free to take part in ionic interplay. This low concentration is maintained partly by the transport of Ca^{2+} out of the cell and partly by mitochondrial uptake but mainly by axoplasmic calcium buffers. Sodium ions may not all be free since their activity coefficient is some 30 per cent less than that in the extracellular fluid. The excess K^+ in the axoplasm is balanced electrically, mainly by the ionised proteins.

Table 32.5 Concentrations of major ions in axoplasm and extracellular fluid in the squid giant axon.

| Ion | Concentration (mmol/kg water) | | |
	Internal	External	Ratio inside:outside
Na+	49	440	1:9
K+	410	22	19:1
Cl-	123	560	1:6
Isethionate-	250	0	–
Aspartate-	75	0	–
Other organic anions	48	0	–
Ca2+	0.4	10	1:25
Mg2+	10	54	1:5.4
Water	865 g/kg	870 g/kg	

The conductivity of squid axoplasm is approxiamtely 50 to 80 per cent of that of the extracellular fluid. (After Hodgkin A L 1951 Biological Reviews 26:339, and Keynes R D 1964 Journal of Physiology 169:690)

Membrane permeability

That there is some barrier to the free movement of ions between the intracellular and extracellular compartments is apparent from the ionic concentration gradients that exist across the cell membrane and also from the observation that if radioactive K^+ is injected into tbe axoplasm it takes several hours for it to be transferred to the extracellular fluid. This barrier is the cell membrane, which has a high electrical resistance (700 ohm/cm²) and a high capacitance (1 $\mu F/cm^2$).

The importance of this membrane is shown by the fact that if the axoplasm is removed from a nerve and replaced with an isotonic solution of K_2SO_4 (the $SO_4{}^{2-}$ serving as a membrane-indiffusible anion to replace the organic anions) then the nerve still shows a resting membrane potential, retains its excitability (Fig. 32.6) and can conduct many thousands of nerve impulses. If the membrane is damaged the nerve fibre rapidly loses its membrane potential and the internal and external solutions come quickly into equilibrium.

As well as being able to maintain the ionic concentration gradients the membrane has also been shown to possess different permeabilities to the various ions present.

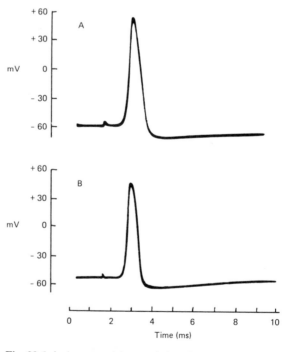

Fig. 32.6 Action potentials recorded under almost identical conditions from (A) an axon filled with K_2SO_4 and (B) an intact axon. The potential scale gives the recorded voltage relative to that of the bathing fluid, sea water in both cases. (From Baker P F et al. 1961 Nature 190:885)

Membrane potential and the Nernst equation

Because of the differential distribution of ions, the differing permeability of the membrane to the different ions, and the fact that the membrane is impermeable to the internal organic anions, a potential difference develops across the membrane between the intra- and extracellular fluids. To explain this potential difference we may, for the moment, ignore Ca^{2+} (which is either bound or transported out of the cell, and to which the membrane is very impermeable) and Na^+ (to which the membrane is also much less permeable than it is to K^+). This leaves K^+ as the only other ion present in high concentration to which the membrane is permeable and which is out of equilibrium.

Potassium ions would tend to diffuse out of the cell by flowing down their concentration gradient, but the negative charge left behind in the cell attracts them back into the interior of the cell. For the cell to be in equilibrium, with no net loss or gain of K^+, the forces acting upon the K^+ ions would be equal and opposite and the membrane potential would be equal to the Nernst potential for potassium (Chap. 2).

When tested for its ability to predict the resting membrane potential, the Nernst potential for potassium

gives a fair approximation to the measured potential. A closer approximation to the measured potential is obtained if the Goldman constant field equation (p. 13) is used. This equation takes into account all the ions present and weighs their contribution to the potential according to their membrane permeabilities. If, more simply, only Na^+ is considered in addition to K^+, its contribution to the membrane potential can be included. If, for example, the permeability to Na^+ is 1/75th of the permeability to K^+, the equation becomes

$$E = \frac{RT}{zF} \ \ln \ \frac{[K^+]_o + 1/75 \ [Na^+]_o}{[K^+]_i + 1/75 \ [Na^+]_i}$$

One consequence of having the ions behaving at equilibrium in the resting nerve in a Nernst-like distribution is that if the measured potential difference is plotted against the log of the external K^+ concentration a straight line relationship should be obtained, with a slope of 58 mV change in potential for a ten-fold change in external K^+ concentration. Figure 32.7 shows that this relationship does hold over a large part of the concentration range tested. However, the relationship begins to deviate from the theoretical at an external K^+ concentration of 10 mmol/l or less. This is because, as the external K^+ concentration decreases, the contribution of the external Na^+ to the equilibrium increases. Thus the experimental findings are predicted more accurately by the simple Goldman equation than by the Nernst equation. However, the ratio of the external and internal K^+ concentrations remains the most important single factor in governing resting membrane potential (Table 32.8).

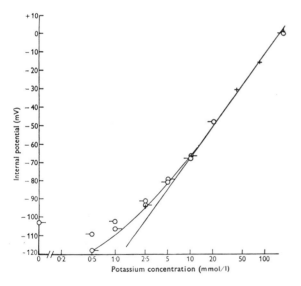

Table 32.8 Effect of altering the axoplasmic fluid. Composition on the membrane potential of the squid nerve fibre.

Internal solution	External solution	Potential(mV)
600 mmol/l KCl	Sea water	−60
600 mmol/l NaCl	Sea water	0
600 mmol/l NaCl	600 mmol/l KCl	+60

(After Hodgkin A L 1964 The conduction of the nervous impulse. University Press, Liverpool)

Fig. 32.7 Relation between resting potential of frog muscle fibres and the external K^+ concentration ($[K]_O$). Note the logarithmic scale. +, potentials measured after equilibration for 10–60 minutes; ○, potentials measured 20–60 seconds after a sudden change in concentration; –○, after an increase and ○–, after a decrease in $[K]_O$. For large values of external K^+ concentration the measured potentials agree well with the Nernst equation (if $[K]_i$ is taken as 140 mmol/l) and the deviation at low external K^+ concentrations can be partly explained by taking the contribution of the Na^+ concentration into account. (From Hodgkin A L, Horowicz P 1959 Journal of Physiology 148:127)

Membrane permeability to sodium ions

Both K^+ and Na^+ ions are continually moving down their electrochemical gradients and the ionic gradients are maintained by the operation of the sodium pump (Chap. 2). This is a Na^+/K^+ exchange system that uses energy in the form of ATP. Agents that uncouple oxidative phosphorylation, and thus the formation of ATP, such as cyanide or dinitrophenol, do not cause an im-

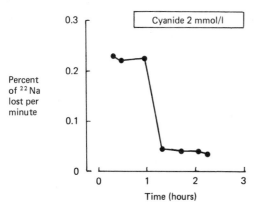

Fig. 32.9 Poisoning a squid axon with cyanide reduces the sodium efflux. (After Caldwell P C et al. 1960 Journal of Physiology 152:561)

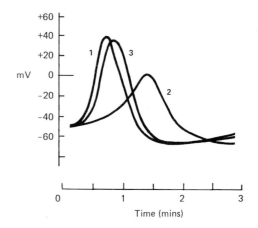

Fig. 32.10 The effect of reducing the external Na$^+$ concentration on the size of the action potential in a squid giant axon. Three responses are superimposed: 1 and 3 in sea water before and after changing the bathing solution to 33 per cent sea water (2). (After Hodgkin A L, Katz B 1949 Journal of Physiology 108: 37)

mediate marked change in the membrane potential even though the efflux of Na$^+$ is reduced to very low levels (Fig. 32.9). Subsequent injection of ATP restores the pump. If all the extracellular K$^+$ is replaced by another cation, the Na$^+$ efflux falls abruptly but reversibly to about one-third of its normal value. This observation is consistent with the view that sodium efflux is part of a Na$^+$/K$^+$ exchange system.

Thus the long-term steady-state equilibrium for nerve and muscle fibres is a dynamic equilibrium and not a simple passive electrochemical equilibrium. Moreover, this equilibrium itself provides a source of energy in the form of a potential difference.

BEHAVIOUR OF ACTIVE NERVE

The fact that an axon filled with K$_2$SO$_4$ can generate a resting potential and, if stimulated, an action potential, shows that the energy used in this process is probably derived from the dynamic equilibrium. Further evidence for this idea is seen if one examines the potential change that occurs upon activation of a nerve fibre. Figure 32.6 shows the potential change recorded from an isolated squid axon into which a recording electrode has been inserted to measure the voltage of the interior of the fibre relative to the bathing fluid. It can be seen that the potential starts at the resting level, which is negative, and goes towards a positive potential before returning once again to the resting negative level. Using the data presented in Table 32.5 for the squid axon, one can calculate that the equilibrium potential for the K$^+$ distribution is -75.5 mV whereas that for the Na$^+$ distribution is $+54.8$ mV. It is tempting to assume that activation of a nerve fibre causes a cyclic change in the permeability of the membrane to K$^+$ and Na$^+$. At rest

the nerve membrane is highly permeable to K$^+$ relative to Na$^+$; activation switches the relative permeabilities so that the membrane becomes more permeable to Na$^+$ than to K$^+$. The resting permeabilities are then restored. If this were so, then there would be a moment during the action potential at which the equilibrium is determined by the Na$^+$ distribution and the potential approaches $+54.8$ mV. This possibility can readily be tested. If the assumption is correct the peak potential during activation should be related to the external Na$^+$ concentration. Figure 32.10 shows that this is indeed found experimentally. It is therefore clear that the major source of energy for the action potential is the concentration gradient for Na$^+$.

This observation allows us to predict certain other consequences of a nerve fibre becoming active. If the membrane permeability to Na$^+$ does increase then the nerve fibre would have to gain Na$^+$ during each action potential. The membrane permeability to Na$^+$ would have to be abruptly increased and then restored to normal. To restore the fibre to its resting state the extra cations gained during the action potential would have to be removed. In terms of energy conservation this would be most easily accomplished if K$^+$ were to leave the cell down its concentration gradient. This would imply that the permeability of the membrane to K$^+$ is increased above its resting level for a short period after the Na$^+$ influx.

Changes in membrane permeability

It is fairly easy to measure experimentally the movement of ions from one compartment to another: one can

Table 32.11 Ionic exchange during the action potential at 20 °C.

Parameter	Squid axon	Frog nerve
Mean diameter (μm)	500	10
Na$^+$ gain per nerve impulse (pmol/cm^2)	3–4	5×10^{-5}
K$^+$ loss per nerve impulse (pmol/cm^2)	3–4	3–6×10^{-5}

(After Hodgkin A L 1964 The conduction of the nervous impulse. University Press, Liverpool)

either use radioactive Na$^+$ in the bathing solution to see if it enters the nerve fibre or one can inject a small quantity of radioactive K$^+$ into the nerve fibre to see if it leaves when the nerve becomes active. Table 32.11 shows the concentration changes found for Na$^+$ and K$^+$ in unmyelinated giant squid nerve fibres and for myelinated frog nerve fibres.

The quantity of ions exchanged in the myelinated nerves is much smaller than that in the giant axon mainly because the exchange is restricted to much smaller areas of active membrane, located at the nodes of Ranvier. To gain a better idea of the ionic exchange we can express the values as approximately 20 000 ions crossing each μm^2 of nerve per impulse in the squid nerve and 300 000 ions crossing each μm^2 of nodal

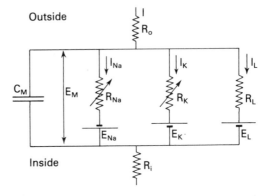

Fig. 32.12 Equivalent circuit for the nerve membrane. R_{Na} and R_K vary with membrane potential and time; the other components are constant. (After Hodgkin A L, Huxley H E 1952 Journal of Physiology 117: 501)

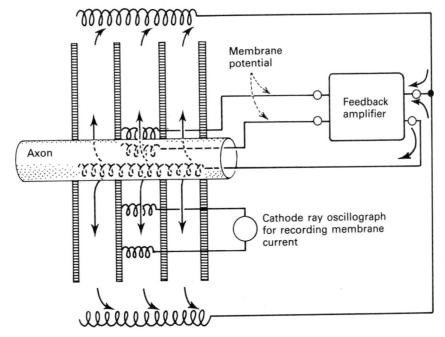

Fig. 32.13 Voltage clamp. A fine bare wire is passed along the centre of an axon to connect electrically a length of axon; a large area of axonal membrane thus becomes active at the same time. Partitions isolate a short length of the axon. The radially directed current generated by an action potential is measured by two wires in the external solution (one near the axon and the other parallel to it but further away). This current is measured and passed back across the membrane in the opposite direction and prevents a change in voltage across the membrane. The same current is injected through a further wire passed along the axis of the axon and insulated except in the partitioned portion of the axon. The wire that connects the length of the axon electrically is also used to measure the voltage inside the axon. This wire is connected to a variable voltage source that sets the voltage of the axon interior to any desired level. The current generated by the axon is measured and passed in the opposite direction to 'clamp' the axon voltage at any desired level.

membrane per impulse in the frog nerve. Two points need to be noted. First, the concentration change is minute but the number of cations flowing is enough to give the recorded change in the potential. Secondly, the action potential is derived from the electro-chemical concentration gradient for Na^+ and restored by the chemical concentration gradient for K^+. The Na^+/K^+ pump only plays a part in the much longer time-span needed to restore the resting concentrations; it plays no part in the millisecond or so that the action potential lasts.

It now remains to demonstrate the permeability changes associated with the nerve action potential. Figure 32.12 shows that the membrane can be considered as being built up of a large number of electrical units. The actual conducting channels for each ion can be represented by resistances in parallel across the membrane (R_K, R_{Na} and R_L). Each of these is connected to a battery (E_K, E_{Na} and E_L) the voltage of which is determined by the equilibrium potential for that ion. The internal and external solutions can be represented by two fixed resistances (R_i and R_o) and the capacitance of the membrane by (C_m). If the axon is considered as an infinite series of these elements we can try to define their function and, most importantly, the changes they show, by the changing conductances for each ion during the action potential. The membrane capacitance does not change during an action potential so we can exclude this part of the circuit from our consideration. Similarly we can exclude any change in the resistance of the internal and external solutions. As the values for the batteries can be considered as constant the changes occurring in the various membrane resistance channels during the action potential must be determined.

Hodgkin and Huxley devised a method for setting the voltage of the interior of an axon at any desired level (*voltage clamp*, Fig. 32.13). This apparatus could then be used to measure the current flow across the membrane. Figure 32.14 shows the current generated by the axon in one such experiment. It can be seen that the current record shows two phases: a brief inward current and an outward current that lasts for as long as the voltage clamp is applied. Choline ions are much larger than Na^+ and do not cross the membrane but they are osmotically equivalent. If approximately nine-tenths of the external sodium ions are replaced by choline ions to give equal activities of sodium ions on both sides of the membrane, the initial inward current is abolished. This implies that the inward current is carried by sodium ions. It is possible to calculate the current carried by Na^+ as the difference between the current when the Na^+ concentration is equal on both sides of the membrane and when the external solution has a normal Na^+ content.

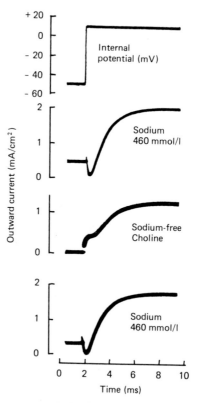

Fig. 32.14 An example of the membrane currents recorded from a squid giant axon clamped at +15 mV. The top trace represents the 'clamp' signal. The lower three traces show the resulting membrane currents in the presence and absence of external Na^+. (From Hodgkin A L, Huxley A F 1952 Journal of Physiology 116:449)

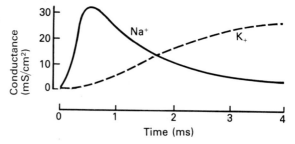

Fig. 32.15 Conductance changes in a squid giant axon after a change in membrane potential from −60 mV to 0 mV in a voltage clamp experiment. (After Hodgkin A L, A F Huxley 1952 Journal of Physiology 116:473)

The long-lasting outward current is due to the movement of K^+ out of the axon. If axons are pre-loaded with ^{42}K and clamped to give various outward currents, it can be shown that the current is related to K^+ efflux. The slope of this relation is equal to Faraday's constant (96 500 C/mol).

All of these conclusions have been supported by experiments with specific blockers of the Na^+ and K^+ channels (p. 11).

Using Ohm's law these currents can be investigated in terms of the conductance change occurring for each ion:

$$\frac{V}{I} = R \text{ or } I = \frac{1}{R} \times V$$

where V = v oltage, I = current, R = resistance and 1/R = conductance (usual symbol, g). Thus,

$$I_{Na} = g_{Na} (V - V_{Na})$$

and

$$I_K = g_K (V - V_K)$$

where V = applied voltage and V_{ion} = the equilibrium potential for that ion.

A graphical display of the sodium conductance versus time (Fig. 32.15) shows that it rises rapidly and then decays exponentially even though the axon is still clamped. This return of the sodium conductance to its normal level is called inactivation. The potassium conductance shows a small time lag then rises slowly and is maintained for as long as the clamp is applied. By applying voltage pulses to the axon it can be shown that the membrane must be returned to its resting voltage level before the sodium conductance can be increased again. This fact limits the frequency with which action potentials can occur; a nerve has a maximum frequency of firing that is roughly inversely proportional to the duration of the action potential.

All-or-none behaviour

When it was shown that the change in g_{Na} was proportional to the deviation from the resting voltage it was possible to explain why an action potential was all-or-none in nature. If an axon is depolarised the g_{Na} increases; this allows Na^+ to enter the axon and causes further depolarisation. This, in turn, leads to a further increase in g_{Na}, and so on (Fig. 32.16). This cycle continues until the g_{Na} is inactivated. The delay in the change in g_K allows the sodium ions to 'win in the equilibrium race' but because of the inactivation of g_{Na} it restores the axon to its resting level. In fact the increase in g_K above its resting level causes the axon to become more negative than normal for a few milliseconds (Fig. 32.17). This imposes another limitation on the ability of nerve axons to generate repetitive activity because the prolonged increase in g_K means that the nerve fibre is further away from its threshold level,

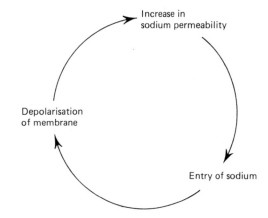

Fig. 32.16 The regenerative linkage between membrane potential and sodium permeability. (After Hodgkin A L 1951 Biological Reviews 26:384)

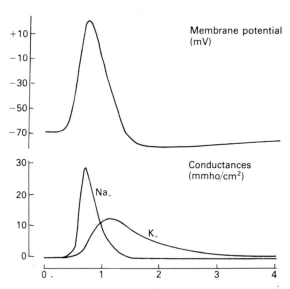

Fig. 32.17 Relation between the action potential and the changes in the conductances for Na^+ and K^+ (After Hodgkin A L, Huxley A F 1952 Journal of Physiology 117:500)

so that a stronger current is needed to generate an action potential until g_K is restored to normal.

In essence the generation of a nerve action potential is very simple. Once the membrane potential reaches a threshold level the self-generating increase in the ease with which Na^+ crosses the membrane causes a momentary state in which the permeability of the membrane to Na^+ is much greater than that to K^+. For a squid nerve fibre the potential across the membrane has to be reduced from its normal level of around -70 mV to -55 mV, at which level the inward permeability to sodium ions becomes slightly greater than the outward permeability to potassium ions. Consequently Na⁺ is driven into the axon along both a chemical concentration gradient and an electrical gradient. The system returns to its resting level by the inactivation of the increase in g_{Na} and the increase in g_K above its resting level.

Membrane channels

Inherent in this account is the assumption that the membrane has small holes or channels through which the ions pass and that these channels are different for sodium and for potassium ions. In an electrolyte ions move with differing velocities because of their differing ionic radii in aqueous solution. These differing mobilities are seen because ions do not move alone but with a shell of water molecules that they bind to themselves — a 'hydration shell'. Although Na⁺ is a smaller ion than K⁺ in the crystalline state it binds more water molecules and is a bigger ionic complex in solution. Estimates of the sizes of the Na⁺ and K⁺ channels, by using other ions to replace them in voltage clamp experiments and determining the largest ion that passes through them, show Na⁺ channels to have an ovoid cross-section of 0.3×0.5 nm and K⁺ channels to have a circular cross-section of 0.3×0.3 nm. The Na⁺ channel is permeable to K⁺ but twelve times more so to Na⁺. Further, the interior of the channel must bear a negative charge to exclude anions.

It would seem to be easier simply to open or close channels of varying size rather than to alter the cross-sectional area of one channel, so that specific channels for the different ions have been suggested. Evidence for the separate existence of channels for Na⁺ and K⁺ also comes from the observation that the movement of Na⁺ can be blocked by tetrodotoxin (TTX), a poison derived from puffer fish, and that the K⁺ channel can be blocked by tetraethyl ammonium (TEA). These blockers are specific; TTX does not affect the K⁺ current of active axons and TEA does not affect the Na⁺ current.

Since the activation of sodium and potassium channels depends on the voltage across the axon, it is possible that the opening of the channels is effected by an electric field acting either upon a charged molecule, moving it across the membrane, or on a molecule with a dipole and turning it around in the membrane. Such charged molecules act as 'gates' by opening and closing channels. The opening of a gate generates a small current (*gating current*) and the flow of ions through the channel generates a large *ionic current*. At rest the gates are considered to be closed, so hyperpolarisation does not affect the gate since something that is already closed cannot be further shut. No gating current can therefore be generated; only a capacitative current of equal and opposite magnitude to that produced by membrane depolarisation will be recorded. This capacitative current can then be subtracted from the current to a polarising pulse to reveal the gating current. In this way the properties of channels are beginning to be elucidated.

Conduction along active nerve

When a nerve is made active the polarity across the membrane is momentarily reversed. In the voltage clamp experiments a long length of nerve is made active instantaneously by a fine wire running inside the axon. In the normal functioning of the nervous system axons generate action potentials either because of the activity of the sensory terminations (receptors) to which they are connected or by the activity generated in the nerve cell body from which they arise. The action potential is then conducted as a wave along the length of the axon.

If a small part of the axonal membrane becomes active then the axonal interior at this site becomes momentarily positive with respect to the external solution. This is connected, albeit with a rather high resistance pathway, to an area of axoplasm that is negative with respect to the external solution. Opposite voltages are thus connected via a resistive pathway and current flows along the axon. However, the high resistance to the passage of such a current causes the current to flow along an easier path, which it finds by flowing outwards across the axonal membrane ahead of the active region. The circuit is then completed by the current flowing back into the axon at its active region (Fig. 32.18). This idea is the *local circuit* theory.

Knowledge of the resistances of the various paths in the axon support this theory. An axon of radius 25 μm has a membrane resistance of some 2000 ohms/cm². With an axoplasm resistivity of some 60 ohm/cm the internal longitudinal resistance is some 3 000 000 ohm/cm. The outward current, ahead of the

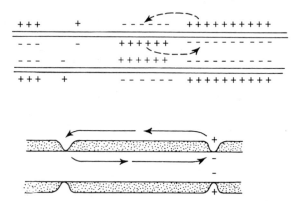

Fig. 32.18 The local circuit theory. Above: non-myelinated axon. Below: myelinated axon. (After Hodgkin A L 1975 Proceedings of the Royal Society Series B 148:1)

active region, reduces the potential across the membrane by drawing charge out of the membrane capacitance. If the membrane potential is reduced, the permeability to Na$^+$ increases. If this depolarisation is large enough, part of the membrane ahead of the active region reaches its threshold level and itself becomes active. This process is then repeated along the length of the axon. Not only does the sequential permeability change cause an 'explosive' all-or-none depolarisation-repolarisation sequence at the active region but it also ensures that the axon conducts an impulse at a fixed velocity along its length. Once it is active the axon becomes absolutely unable to conduct another impulse for 1–2 ms until it has repolarised to its resting level (the *absolute refractory period*); for several milliseconds afterwards its ability to conduct is limited because of the increase, above resting level, of the potassium permeability (the *relative refractory period*). The active region is therefore conducted away from the source of excitation. If the stimulus continues the nerve fibre fires repetitively at a rate determined both by the absolute refractory period and by the strength of the excitatory source; stronger stimuli are required to initiate an action potential during the relative refractory period.

If an axon is stimulated artificially anywhere along its length the active region is conducted away from the site of stimulation both in its normal direction (*orthodromic*) and in the abnormal direction (*antidromic*). Since the conduction is due to the circular flow of current the resistances encountered determine how far ahead of the active region the current density will be sufficiently strong to discharge the membrane capacitance so as to depolarise the nerve to threshold. They thus control the velocity with which the active region is propagated along the length of an axon. The longitudinal resistance of axons is proportional to their cross-sectional area and so to the square root of their diameter. Consequently conduction velocity increases as the square root of the diameter for a fixed membrane capacitance.

In myelinated nerve fibres the process of conduction is slightly different. The multi-layered wrapping of Schwann cell membrane, the myelin sheath, makes the transmembrane resistance to current flow very high and the nerve membrane is only in low-resistance contact with the extracellular fluid at the junctions between the adjacent Schwann cells at the nodes of Ranvier (Fig. 32.19). These are 0.1 to 10 mm apart; the separation being proportional to the diameter of the axon.

The effect of having a low-capacitance insulating layer around the nerve membrane is to increase the longitudinal spread of the currents generated between active

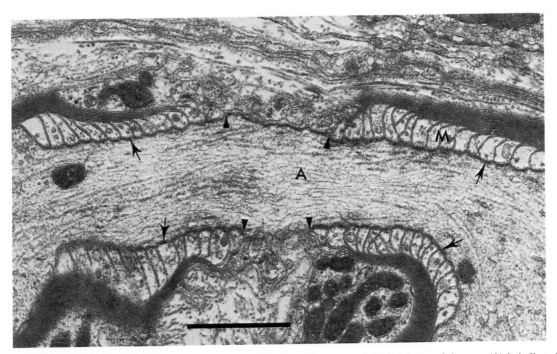

Fig. 32.19 Transmission electron micrograph of a node of Ranvier. The extent of the nodal part of the axon (A) is indicated by arrow-heads, the nodal axolemma having a dense lining. Externally the axolemma is separated from the extracellular space by gap substance and basal lamina. On either side of the node the lamellae of the myelin sheath (M) terminate in a series of expansions, each of which is adjacent to the axolemma and attached to it by dense granules (arrows). Mitochondria are seen in the cytoplasm of the Schwann cell. The horizontal calibration bar represents 1 μm. (Courtesy of L. Duchen)

and inactive regions; the effect of the low-resistance pathway at the nodes is to make the active region leap from node to node. This form of conduction is called saltatory conduction (Latin: saltare, to leap). This form of fast conduction has many advantages. High-speed conduction in unmyelinated axons is only seen in giant nerve fibres. These giant nerve fibres are usually involved in an animal's escape behaviour such as the jet propulsion seen when water is ejected from the syphon in squids and the rapid backward movement given by the tail flick in crayfish or the rapid contraction of the body wall of the earthworm that enables it to retract into ,its burrow. A myelinated axon conducts much faster than an unmyelinated one of comparable diameter (Table 32.20).

Another advantage of saltatory conduction is that the excitatory area of membrane is much smaller so that much less Na^+ enters with each impulse. This means that less metabolic energy is needed to pump the ions out once the impulse has passed.

Confirmation that the saltatory process does occur in myelinated nerve fibres comes from the demonstration that in isolated myelinated axons the inward flow of current occurs only at the nodes. Outward current would be expected in the inter-nodal portions of the nerve fibre if the capacitance of the inter-nodal region was discharging passively into the node.

The nodal membrane differs greatly from that found in unmyelinated axons. The potassium channels are absent at the nodes but present between the nodes. The repolarisation of the nodal membrane is accomplished by a very rapid reduction in sodium permeability accompanied by a high membrane leak current. Thus it is not surprising that extensive demyelination, for

Table 32.20 Comparison of conduction velocities in myelinated and unmyelinated nerve fibres.

Nerve	Diameter (μm)	Temp (°C)	Velocity (m/s)
Cat (myelinated)	2–20	38	10–100
Cat (unmyelinated)	0.3–1.3	38	0.7–2.3
Frog (myelinated)	3–16	24	6–32
Squid (unmyelinated)	500	20	25

(From Hodgkin A L 1964 The conduction of the nervous impulse. University Press, Liverpool)

example, in multiple sclerosis, leads to a conduction block of the axon. However, in mammalian axons chronically demyelinated with diphtheria toxin the sodium channels appear to spread from the nodal membrane into the previously internodal membrane; the axon behaves like an unmyelinated axon.

Recording the extracellular activity in nerves

It is possible to use the external current flow around an active bundle of nerve fibres to study the behaviour of nerve either isolated from the body or even in situ. One common experiment is to record the compound action potential from the isolated sciatic nerve of the frog. It is called compound because the frog sciatic nerve is composed of many thousands of individual nerve fibres.

The experimental arrangement is to have the nerve in contact with an array of five electrodes, two to stimulate the nerve, two to record the resulting activity and one between these two pairs to shunt the stimulating current to earth to prevent it reaching the recording electrodes (Fig. 32.21). If the piece of nerve between

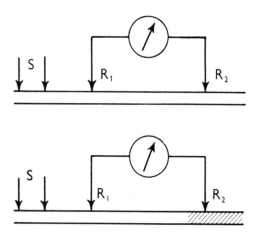
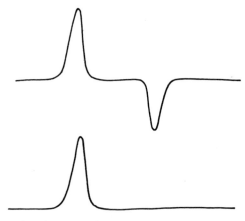

Fig. 32.21 The electrical changes accompanying the passage of a nerve impulse as seen by an oscilloscope connected to external recording electrodes R_1 and R_2. S = stimulating electrodes. An upward deflection is seen when R_1 is negative relative to R_2. A diphasic recording (upper trace) is obtained when R_1 and R_2 are both on an intact nerve fibre. A monophasic recording (lower trace) is obtained when the nerve under R_2 is cut or crushed.

the recording electrodes is undamaged then as the wave of activity approaches the first of the pair of electrodes this becomes negative relative to the second. As the wave of activity reaches the midpoint of the electrode pair the potential at the two electrodes becomes equal and the voltage returns to zero. As it passes the second electrode and goes away from it this becomes negative relative to the first electrode. Thus a biphasic action potential is recorded. If, however, the piece of nerve is damaged between the recording electrodes then only the first half is seen as a monophasic action potential.

The most accurate measurements of nerve activity can be made by this type of technique; if it is assumed that the distribution of nerve fibres in the nerve trunk is homogeneous, the recorded voltage is proportional to the number of active fibres. The relation between the stimulating voltage and the amplitude of the response is a sigmoid curve (Fig. 32.22), which indicates that the population of nerve fibres is composed of a few with a very low threshold to activation, a few with a high threshold and the majority with intermediate thresholds. Thus a very simple experiment can give information about the distribution of fibres in a nerve according to their threshold. If certain assumptions are made about the relation between threshold and conduction velocity, and between conduction velocity and fibre diameter, the distribution of fibre diameters in the nerve trunk can be derived. In general, fibres with the lowest threshold have the largest diameter and the fastest conduction velocity.

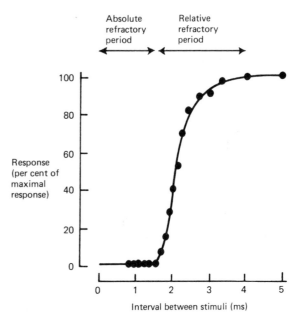

Fig. 32.23 The response to a second of a pair of supra-maximal stimuli applied to the nerve expressed as a percentage response to that of the first of the pair versus the stimulus separation. Each point represents the mean of 10 separate observations. The absolute refractory period of the nerve is indicated as is the duration of the relative refractory period. (Courtesy of A. Angel.)

Using this preparation it is easy to show the response of the nerve trunk to two closely spaced supramaximal stimuli (Fig. 32.23). At separations of around 1.0 to 1.5 ms no fibres are activated by the second stimulus of the pair because the nerve fibres are all in their absolute refractory states. With stimulus separations between 1.5 and 4.0 ms, more and more fibres are excited ·by the second stimulus since they are in their relative refractory period.

A compound action potential can readily be recorded in man from parts of the body where the nerve trunks lie near the surface and are thus electrically accessible. Useful records can for example be obtained from the digital nerves in response to stimulation of the nerves at the wrist, in the anti-cubital fossa or even in the axilla (Fig. 32.24). The major reason for recording from the fingers is that the muscles controlling their movement are mainly above the wrist and the large signals obtained from activation of the muscles are rapidly attenuated with distance. For example, stimulation of the radial nerves leads to muscle activity in the thenar eminence but not in the fingers themselves, where stimuli passing (antidromically) down sensory nerves can be recorded.

Such recordings have many uses. A subject can report any paraesthesiae associated with the nerve stimulation;

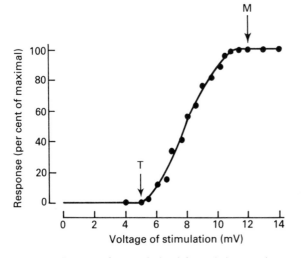

Fig. 32.22 Response from an isolated frog sciatic nerve in relation to the voltage of stimulation. Each point represents the mean of ten separate observations. T represents the threshold voltage below which no response was seen and M represents the maximal voltage above which the response did not increase in amplitude. (Courtesy of A. Angel.)

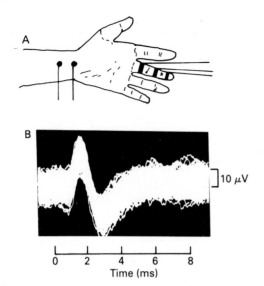

A

B

]10 μV

```
 L    L    L    L    L
 0    2    4    6    8
```
Time (ms)

Fig. 32.24 A, Experimental set-up to record the antidromic nerve action potential from digital nerves in response to nerve stimulation in man. B, A record obtained by superimposing 40 consecutive responses to electrical stimulation. (Courtesy of A. Angel.)

if the subject reports nothing, but action potentials are normal for voltage and velocity, then at least peripheral nerve damage below the stimulus site can be excluded as a cause of the sensory loss. To measure the conduction velocity one must compare the latency to activation from two stimulating sites along the nerve path. The separation of the two sites divided by the difference in the latency of the response gives a measure of the conduction velocity. The activity of the nerves before and after surgery to relieve the *carpal tunnel syndrome* (compression of the median nerve at the wrist) can be recorded. If a peripheral neuropathy, such as that associated with diabetes, is suspected then one can check the nerve function directly to see whether their nerve activity is within the normal limits established with normal subjects.

FURTHER READING

Carpenter R H S 1984 Neurophysiology. Arnold, London
Hodgkin A L 1965 The conduction of the nervous impulse. University Press, Liverpool
Kandel E R, Schwartz J H 1985 Principles of neural science, 2nd edn. Elsevier, Amsterdam
Katz B 1966 Nerve, muscle and synapse. McGraw Hill, New York
Ottoson D 1983 Physiology of the nervous system. Macmillan, London
Stein J F 1982 An introduction to neurophysiology. Blackwell Scientific, Oxford

33

Synapses

The meeting-place of two neurones is called a synapse; at this point their surface membranes are very close together, but there is no cytoplasmic continuity between them. The synapses between different types of excitable cell vary in their structure, but have some features in common. In general, the presynaptic fibre divides into numerous fine branches that then end in greatly expanded terminals, *presynaptic knobs*, which make intimate contact with part of the membrane of the cell

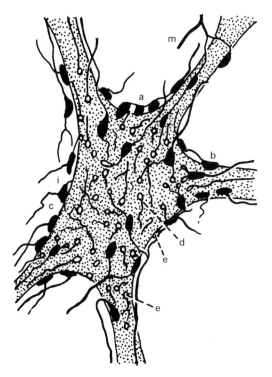

Fig. 33.1 This drawing of a motor cell of the spinal cord shows that it is invested by a large number of synaptic knobs from many neurones. The synaptic density is about 20 per 100 μ^2. The surface area of a motoneurone is on average 165 000 μ^2. This gives about 33 000 synapses. a, b, strong bulbs; c, i, terminal buttons; d, e, fine bulbs; m, terminal nerve fibre. (Cajal S R Y 1933 Histology. Baillière, Tindall & Cox, London).

body or dendrites of the *post-synaptic* cell. A single anterior horn cell may be invested by as many as 33 000 synaptic knobs (Fig. 33.1) derived from a large number of axons. In the part of the pre-synaptic knob closest to the post-synaptic cell there is always a dense assembly of spherical vesicles (synaptic vesicles) about 50 nm in diameter (Fig. 33.2). There are no vesicles in the post-synaptic cell. The width of the extracellular space separating the pre- and post-synaptic membranes, the *synaptic cleft*, is another rather constant feature; it is generally about 25 nm.

The electrical resistance of the synaptic cleft is low enough to prevent any appreciable spread through the post-synaptic membrane of the electric current that flows around the presynaptic terminal when an impulse arrives there. Another factor that militates against electric excitation of the post-synaptic membrane by presynaptic action currents is the relatively greater area of the post-synaptic membrane. Except in a few special situations the coupling between the pre- and post-synaptic membranes is chemical rather than electrical. It depends on the release of a chemical transmitter substance from the presynaptic terminal, which then diffuses across the synaptic cleft and interacts with receptor sites on the post-synaptic membrane so as to cause a specific change in its ionic permeability. At some synapses the nature of this change is such as to produce a depolarisation and hence an excitatory effect. At others the permeability change may tend to stabilise the membrane potential at its resting value or may even cause a hyperpolarisation; these synapses are inhibitory.

Some obvious distinctions between transmission of an impulse along a nerve fibre and transmission across a synapse follow directly from this description. First, although the impulse can travel equally well in either direction along a nerve fibre, its passage across a synapse is strictly unidirectional. No chemical transmitter is released when an antidromic impulse arrives at the post-synaptic membrane, so that such an impulse cannot travel backwards any further than the first synapse it reaches. Secondly, passage across a synapse involves a finite time delay because the release of the

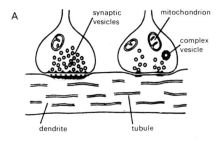

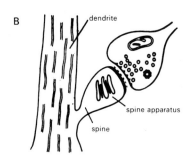

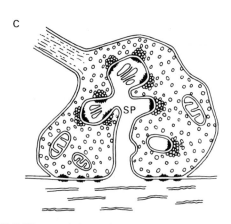

Fig. 33.2 The morphology of some synapses. A, Two types of synaptic knob found on the soma and dendrites of cortical neurones. B, A dendritic spine of a neocortical pyramidal cell with its synapse. C, A more complicated synapse found on the spine (sp) of a dendrite of a hippocampal pyramidal cell. (From Eccles J C 1964 The physiology of synapses. Springer, Berlin)

transmitter, its diffusion across the synaptic cleft and its action on the post-synaptic membrane are relatively slow processes. In a spinal motoneurone, delay from this source, to which has to be added a smaller contribution from the slowness of conduction in the very fine pre-synaptic nerve branches, is about 0.4 ms. In autonomic ganglia it may be somewhat longer. As will be

seen later (p. 424), a knowledge of the total delay in a complex reflex pathway is valuable in determining the number of synapses involved. Thirdly, the intervention of a chemical transmitter results in a susceptibility of synapses to blocking by a wide variety of drugs that have relatively little effect on conduction in nerve fibres. These may act either by interfering with the synthesis or release of the transmitter, or by changing the sensitivity of the post-synaptic membrane. The last distinction, and by no means the least important, is that although some synapses — in particular the neuromuscular junction (p. 489) — operate in such a way that there is a one-to-one correspondence between presynaptic and post-synaptic impulses, the majority do not. In most neurones, a spatial and temporal summation of the several excitatory and inhibitory post-synaptic potentials takes place, and the post-synaptic membrane is triggered only by an appropriate combination of the impulses arriving along the presynaptic pathways. In contrast, therefore, to the all-or-none behaviour of peripheral nerves, synapses operate in a graded fashion, enabling the neurone to carry out an integration and sifting of the incoming information.

Many of our ideas about the mechanism of transmission across excitatory synapses have originated from micro-electrode studies of the neuromuscular junction. It is important to note that there is no doubt as to the identity of the chemical transmitter at the motor end-plate, which is one of the places where acetylcholine exerts its 'nicotinic' effect, to use the term introduced by Dale, as opposed to its 'muscarinic' effect, when it acts as a peripheral parasympathetic humoral transmitter. The characteristic action of nicotine in this context is to cause rapid excitation, followed by block; this action is antagonised by substances like curare. Muscarine, on the other hand, has a slower and longer-lasting action, and is antagonised by atropine.

Another relatively simple type of synapse where acetylcholine is certainly the transmitter is found in the ganglia of the autonomic system. Sympathetic ganglia have provided particularly convenient material for studies on the chemistry of synaptic transmission, since it is not too difficult to perfuse their blood vessels and both to test the perfusate for the appearance of acetylcholine during electrical stimulation of the pre-synaptic nerve trunk and to see whether perfusion with acetylcholine sets up impulses in the post-synaptic fibres. These ganglia were also used in making some of the earlier electrical recordings of synaptic potentials, the superior cervical ganglion being conveniently accessible to electrodes without interruption of its blood supply. However, the potential changes observed with external electrodes were somewhat complex and as elsewhere internal microelectrodes were needed for a proper examination of the mechanism.

Synaptic transmission

Central excitatory synapses

When a microelectrode is inserted into a spinal moto-neurone, a resting membrane potential of about 70 mV is recorded, with the cell interior negative with respect to the outside. Afferent nerve fibres from muscle spindles enter the spinal cord by the dorsal root and make synaptic contact with the cell bodies of motoneurones in the anterior horn. If a volley is set up electrically in these afferent neurones, then the effect on the membrane potential of the cells with which they synapse depends upon the number of afferent fibres excited.

If a few afferent fibres are activated then a small depolarising potential is recorded rather like an end-plate potential. In this case it is called an *excitatory post-synaptic potential* or EPSP; it reaches a peak rapidly and then declines over about 15 ms (Fig. 33.3). Excitation of more afferent fibres increases the magnitude of these changes until the membrane potential falls to a critical value of about 60 mV, when the motoneurone fires and an action potential is superimposed on the EPSP (Fig. 33.4).

The membrane of the axon hillock, the region where the axon begins, has a lower threshold for triggering an action potential than that of the soma or dendrites. It is therefore likely that the conducted action potential originates from this point.

The EPSP is monophasic and non-propagating; it is not all-or-none like the action potential but spreads electrotonically across the soma of the neurone. EPSPs elicited simultaneously at different sites summate in amplitude. Summation occurs when the intensity of the input volley is increased, so that more synapses are activated and a greater area of membrane is depolarised.

The transmitter substance (which has not yet been

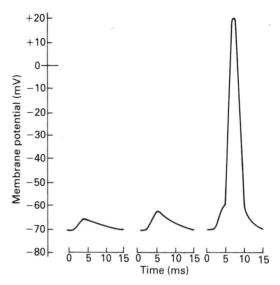

Fig. 33.4 The effect of increasing the stimulus intensity on membrane potential. When a threshold of about −60 mV is reached a conducted action potential ensues.

established) is released from the post-synaptic membrane, diffuses across the synaptic cleft, binds to and then interacts with specific receptors in the post-synaptic membrane. This causes an increase in permeability to cations and depolarisation results.

Central inhibitory synapses

Stimulation of a muscle spindle afferent fibre reflexly excites an agonist muscle and at the same time inhibits the antagonist motoneurone. When the membrane potentials are recorded in the inhibited neurone, a hyperpolarisation is observed, that is the membrane potential becomes more negative. This potential change is called an *inhibitory post-synaptic potential* or IPSP and takes the form of a mirror image of the EPSP (Fig. 33.5). Its effect is to take the membrane potential further away from the threshold for generating an action potential and also by increasing the permeability to K^+ and Cl^- it reduces the effects of permeability to other ions that would otherwise cause depolarisation. Thus any EPSP that occurs during an IPSP is less effective in exciting the cell. This change in permeability appears to allow smaller ions with a hydrated diameter, similar to that of potassium and chloride, to pass through inhibitory channels; that is, pores are opened up by the inhibitory transmitter substance and allow K^+ and Cl^- through, whereas passage of sodium, with a large hydrated diameter, is prevented. Consequently, during the IPSP, chloride is gained and potassium lost by the post-synaptic cell, making its interior more negative. This type of inhibition has received the name of direct

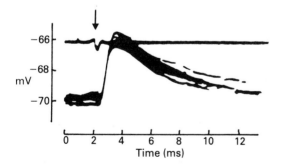

Fig. 33.3 Excitatory post-synaptic potentials recorded intracellularly from a biceps-semitendinosus motoneurone by means of a double-barrelled micropipette. The potential change in response to afferent volleys from the biceps-semitendinosus is recorded; the arrow indicates the action potential recorded from the afferent nerve as it enters the dorsal horn. Fifteen or more traces are superimposed. (From Coombs J S et al. 1955 Journal of Physiology 130:396).

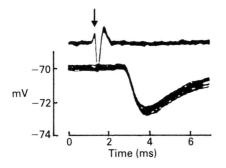

Fig. 33.5 Inhibitory post-synaptic potentials recorded as in
Figure 33.3 except that an afferent nerve from the
quadriceps, a muscle antagonistic to the biceps-
semitendinosus, was stimulated. The arrow indicates the
action potential in the afferent nerve. The extent of the
hyperpolarisation is related to the intensity of the stimulus.
(From Eccles J C 1957 Physiology of nerve cells. Johns
Hopkins Press, Baltimore)

inhibition. However, there is a second inhibitory
phenomenon known as *presynaptic inhibition*. When a
monosynaptic EPSP is elicited by the stimulation of an
afferent neurone from a muscle spindle, the amplitude
of the EPSP is reduced by stimulating certain other
fibres. When the latter were stimulated alone no IPSP
could be obtained. It is now known that the fibres from
a muscle spindle receive a synaptic input from smaller
fibres close to their terminals — an axo-axonal synapse
(Fig. 33.5). The function of these smaller fibres is to
reduce the amount of excitatory transmitter released.

Renshaw cell inhibition
A third type of inhibition that acts on the α-motoneu-
rone has been described. The axon that leaves the
anterior horn motoneurone sends off branches before
leaving the cord to make excitatory synapses with small
interneurones called Renshaw cells. The latter in their
turn make synaptic contact with the motoneurone that
is inhibitory (Fig. 33.6). This is a feed-back inhibition
that may serve to limit the frequency of impulses that
the motoneurone sends to the muscles.

Figure 33.6 summarises some of the main excitatory
and inhibitory connections to the α-motoneurones in the
spinal cord. The only type of synapse within the central
nervous system acetylcholine has been identified with
certainty as the transmitter is at the junctions between
the Renshaw cells and the recurrent collaterals, which
are of course branches from efferent axons that also
release acetylcholine at the motor end-plates. Interneurones intervene in the pathway between Ia afferents
from muscle spindles (Fig. 33.6) and the inhibitory
connections on the antagonist motoneurones. Moreover,
although the chemical identity of the transmitter
involved in direct inhibition is not yet certain, it seems

likely to be the same for all the direct inhibitory
terminals, since all of them are blocked in a similar
fashion by strychnine and tetanus toxin, whereas the
most active blocking agent for the presynaptic inhibitory synapses seems to be picrotoxin.

As far as synaptic transmission within the brain itself
is concerned, the picture is at present less clear.
However, evidence is steadily accumulating that the
mechanisms that have been demonstrated in the spinal
cord also operate in the brain.

Transmitters in the CNS
We come now to the difficult question of the chemical
identity of the transmitters in the central nervous
system. The criteria to be satisfied should ideally be as
follows: (1) the substance should be known to be
present in pre-synaptic terminals, along with the
enzymes necessary for its synthesis; (2) on stimulation
of the pre-synaptic nerves it should be released in
adequate quantities; (3) its action on the post-synaptic
structures, when applied directly, should be identical
with the normal transmitter action; (4) in some cases at
least, an inactivating enzyme should be present in the
synaptic cleft; (5) blocking and competitive agents
should affect its normal action and the action on direct
application in the same way.

However, although various substances satisfy one or
two of these criteria and are therefore suspected of being
transmitters, the only situation in which the evidence
is reasonably complete is at the excitatory terminals of
the recurrent collaterals on the Renshaw cells in the
spinal cord, where, as has already been mentioned,
acetylcholine seems definitely to be the transmitter. It
has long been known that acetylcholine and the enzyme
choline acetylase are present in the brain, that injection
of acetylcholine into cerebral arteries gives rise to excitatory effects, and that acetylcholine is released in the
cortex on stimulation of afferent tracts, but the
complexity of the central nervous system is such that
experiments of this type do not readily establish which
specific pathways are cholinergic. One technique that
has considerable resolving power is a histochemical
examination of brain slices for the presence of acetyl-
cholinesterase. Application of acetylcholine from multi-
barrelled micropipettes shows that some of the large
pyramidal cells in deeper layers of the motor cortex can
be activated by the local release of small quantities of
acetylcholine. However for technical reasons only some
of the cholinergic interconnections within the brain have
been identified with certainty.

There is also strong evidence that certain mono-
amines, in particular noradrenaline, dopamine and 5-
hydroxytryptamine, are central transmitters. The total
number of monoaminergic neurones is small, but histochemical studies have shown that those release

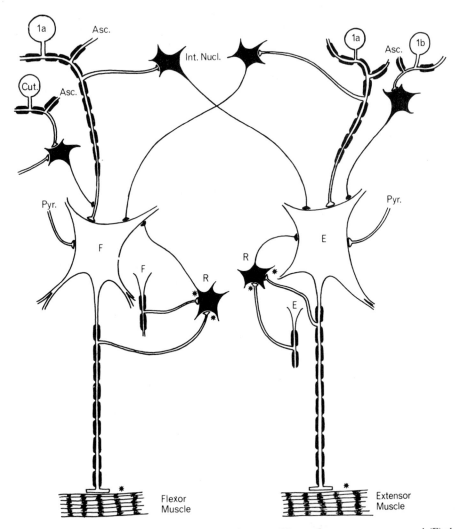

Fig. 33.6 A schematic diagram of some of the interconnections between (F) two flexor motoneurones and (E) the motoneurones of the antagonist extensor muscle. Inhibitory neurones and their synaptic terminals are shown in black. The recurrent collaterals make cholinergic connections (*) with Renshaw cells (R). 1a, cell bodies of afferent fibres from annulospiral endings on muscle spindles within the corresponding muscles. 1b, cell body of an afferent fibre from a Golgi organ in the tendon of the extensor muscle. Cut., cell body of a cutaneous afferent, which is connected to an inhibitory neurone having a presynaptic inhibitory terminal on one of the 1a excitory endings. Int. Nucl., inhibitory neurones in the intermediate nucleus. Pyr., excitatory terminals of the descending pyramidal tract. Asc., branches of the afferents joining the ascending sensory fibre tracts. (By courtesy of R. D. Keynes)

noradrenaline radiate widely to supply many areas of the brain. Glutamate and certain other amino acids may also act as central transmitters. They certainly stimulate a high proportion of neurones when applied by iontophoresis but they have yet to be shown to satisfy the criteria listed in the previous paragraph. As far as inhibitory transmitters are concerned, circumstantial evidence has long pointed to the amino acids glycine and γ-aminobutyric acid (GABA) as possible candidates but attempts to decide between them proved impossible. It appears that both play a part in central inhibitory

mechanisms, glycine being more important in the spinal cord and GABA in many areas of the brain. Hughes and Kosterlitz, in 1975, found two pentapeptides (enkephalins) in the brain with powerful opiate (morphine-like) properties. Larger peptides, endorphins, with similar properties have been found in the pituitary. They are probably neurotransmitters; usually they have a depressive effect.

One of earliest compounds found in the brain is *substance P* (a peptide with II residues), which also has vasodilator properties. It has been detected by immunological methods in many parts of the human nervous system, notably the dorsal horn of the spinal cord, where there are many thin unmyelinated C fibres. The physiological significance of these fibres is uncertain but substance P is likely to be a neurotransmitter on the sensory pathway.

A number of peptides has been found in nervous tissue and may play a role as transmitters or modulators of synaptic function. In addition to substance P they include neurotensin, endorphins, encephalins, thyrotropin releasing hormone, gonadotrophin releasing hormone, bradykinin, gastrin, CCK-Pz, bombesin, oxytocin, vasopressin, melanocyte stimulating hormone, melanocyte stimulating releasing-inhibitory factor, adrenocorticotrophic hormone and somatostatin. Other substances such as histmine, purines and prostaglandins have also been postulated as transmitters or modulators.

Proteins and other macromolecules found in nerve endings are not synthesised there but mainly in the cell body. They then pass down the axon, being guided along microtubules. Some substances move at a rate of only a few millimetres per day, not much faster than a peripheral nerve can grow during regeneration. Other substances move extremely fast. In a wide range of experiments on both peripheral and central neurones, a fast component of axonal flow is consistently found moving at a rate of about 400 mm/day in mammals. Still other substances are observed to move at an intermediate rate. In general, the substances involved in the synthesis and metabolism of the neurotransmitters move at either the fast or intermediate rate. The phenomenon is not restricted to individual macromolecules; microvesicles, mitochondria and other intracellular organelles are also involved. There is also evidence for a retrograde flow, molecules moving from the nerve endings up to the cell body. This seems to apply to endogenous substances but not to exogenous substances such as tetanus toxin. A considerable traffic of molecules is therefore occurring all the time within the axoplasm.

FURTHER READING

Carpenter R H S 1984 Neurophysiology. Arnold, London
Eccles J C 1964 The physiology of synapses. Springer, Berlin
Kandel E R, Schwartz J H 1985 Principles of neural
    science, 2nd edn. Elsevier, New York
Siegel G, Allers R W, Agranoff B W, Katzman R (eds) 1981
    Basic neurochemistry, 3rd edn. Little Brown, Boston
Stein J F 1982 An introduction to neurophysiology.
    Blackwell Scientific, Oxford

34

Sensation

The application of a stimulus to the skin can evoke a variety of sensations including touch, cold, warmth and pain. These different modalities of sensation depend on the activation of specific receptors and interactions among their central actions. Vision, hearing, taste and olfaction depend on the stimulation of highly specific sense receptor organs; these specialised forms of sensation, in contrast to the skin senses, are usually referred to as *special senses*.

The sensory processes of an animal may be investigated by training it to respond differentially to two stimuli and then testing the limits of this discrimination by behavioural trials, including the technique of conditioning. Similar methods may be used with human subjects but it is usually more convenient to rely upon previous learning by obtaining verbal reports, provided that suitable precautions are taken to avoid mistaken inferences. Thus a colour-blind person may have learned to call a leaf 'green' and blood 'red', but may fail to distinguish these hues when appropriately tested.

There is no direct or automatic relation between a stimulus and the sensory effect it produces but in ordinary usage the two are often taken to be the same. For instance, a sound may be described as loud, but the word 'loud' properly refers to the psychological effect and not to the stimulus, which is more correctly described as intense or powerful. Indeed, although loudness is determined mainly by the intensity of a sound, it is also a function of its frequency. There is no precise and immutable correspondence between physical and psychological dimensions.

Although end-organs are specialised to be sensitive to different forms of stimulus energy, the quality of a sensation does not depend upon the type of energy that arouses it. A vibrating tuning-fork placed on the lower end of the radius gives rise to a sensation of vibration, whereas the same fork placed on the head or near the ear arouses a sensation of sound. A variety of excitatory stimuli applied to a given end-organ evoke the same kind of sensation. An electric current, pressure and light applied to the eye all evoke sensations of light. This is so even though experiments with single nerve fibres show that all nerve impulses, however they are initiated, are the same. A similar stimulus applied to different end-organs evokes different sensations: different kinds of stimuli applied to one end-organ all cause the same sensation. The quality or modality of the sensation aroused by the stimulation of any end-organ or nerve depends on the central nervous system as well as the end-organ.

It may be asked whether there is any lower limit to the sensitivity of a sensory system. The classical view has been that the subject either experiences a sensation or does not, and that there is some minimal stimulus energy (the *absolute threshold*) below which a sensation cannot be evoked. The concept of a psychological threshold is clearly allied to that of a physiological threshold, such as the minimal energy required to excite a neurone. Such a threshold does not have a constant value, since if we repeatedly present a sound of a given low intensity, and ask the subject whether he can hear it, he will sometimes report that he can, and sometimes that he cannot. This variability means that the threshold can be defined only statistically, by stating the energy required to evoke a positive response with some arbitrary probability (usually 50 per cent).

In any threshold experiment, the experimenter includes blank stimuli, in order to check the reliability of the subject. If a subject reports a significant number of these as perceived, the experimenter may either reject him as unreliable, or inform him, so that he is trained to become reliable in the sense that he has to be reasonably sure before reporting a stimulus as perceived. It is possible to encourage a subject to be more adventurous, for example by giving a large penalty for missing a stimulus presented and only a small one for perceiving one not in fact presented. In this case his threshold is lower, but he is 'unreliable' in the sense that he reports stimuli that are not there. A complete and accurate definition of threshold should therefore include the proportion of blanks reported as perceived. In practice, such a threshold measurement is extremely laborious, needing to be repeated with different criteria, so that a curve may be drawn, relating threshold to the proportion of blanks perceived. As an example of the relationship, the absolute threshold for vision is about 4 to 6 photons absorbed when 2 per cent or less of blanks are seen, but can be reduced to 1 to 2 photons if 15 to 30 per cent of blanks are seen. In many experiments, such differences are not important.

A related problem is the measurement of differential sensitivity, for example the subject's ability to decide whether one sound is louder than another. The traditional procedure has been to determine a *difference threshold*, estimated as the difference in energy required to produce some arbitrary proportion (usually 75 per cent) ,of judgements that a variable stimulus is more intense than a standard. Many measures of sensory acuity take this form.

Weber found that as the intensity of the standard stimulus increases, the size of the difference threshold is a constant proportion of the intensity level at which it is measured. The law is valid at intermediate intensities but does not hold at very low intensities where it is difficult to detect the stimuli, and it may not hold at very high intensities. Thus although we may be able to distinguish between 20 and 21 g by the sense of touch, we cannot distinguish between 2.0 and 2.1 mg, nor between 200 and 210 kg. Over the major portion of the intensity range the Weber ratio is, however, approximately constant, typical values being for touch 1/10, for hearing 1/5, for olfaction 1/3, and for vision 1/100 of the magnitude of the stimuli being compared.

Fechner devised a scale of sensation and related it to the stimulus intensity. He assumed that all difference thresholds, since they rest upon an equal probability that two stimuli can be discriminated, are subjectively equal. Then by integration he obtained the formula:

$$R = a \log S$$

Sensation intensity (R) = constant (a) × logarithm of the stimulus intensity (log S). A constant ratio of stimulus energies is thus needed to produce a constant difference in sensory magnitude.

Such a relationship has been found useful especially in the measurement of sound intensity, where a logarithmic unit, the decibel (p. 483), is in everyday use. However, a decibel scale, though satisfactory for the measurement of sound transmission, is of more doubtful value in psycho-acoustics. A tone of 100 decibels, for example, sounds much more than twice as loud as a tone of 50 decibels. This observation implies that a subject can define sensory magnitude introspectively and can assign a numerical value to a given sensation. Extensive experiments involving 'magnitude-naming' have suggested a sensory scale in the form of a power function:

$$R = a.S^b$$

where R is sensation intensity, S is stimulus intensity and a and b are constants. The power function has two arbitrary constants (a and b), which can be selected to give a good fit, whereas the logarithmic function has only one. The former can therefore be more easily adapted to fit a given set of data. Both functions imply that the stimulus scale is compressed at its upper end in relation to the sensation scale. There is no reason why either should represent the truth about sensory magnitude; which gives the better fit may depend primarily on the definition adopted for sensory magnitude. Many sets of published data, from psychology or neurophysiology, fit either function with equal inaccuracy.

If we are concerned solely with the characteristics of a sense organ, we may correlate stimulus intensity with an electro-physiological measure. In general, while sensory quality is related to the place where afferent fibres terminate, intensity is coded in terms of their discharge frequency. Thus it is known that the rate of firing of receptors in the eye of *Limulus* (king crab) is logarithmically related to the intensity of light; and in the case of a muscle-spindle the frequency of impulses in the afferent nerve is roughly a logarithmic function of the load. However, in the cutaneous system the frequency of impulses in a single afferent nerve fibre approximates to a power function of the degree of indentation of the skin for some mechano-receptors and to logarithmic function for others.

CUTANEOUS SENSES

Stimulation of the skin gives rise to a sensation of touch, of warmth, of cold or of pain, and these are described as the four 'modalities' of cutaneous sensation. On the basis of these sensations we attribute properties to external objects.

The sense of touch

This sense allows us to distinguish between hard and soft bodies and to judge their shape. In practice, however, muscle-joint sense may also be used to estimate hardness and, although we judge the roughness of a surface by passing the tips of the fingers gently along it, our conclusion may also depend on the auditory stimuli produced at the same time. The threshold of the tactile sense is measured by von Frey's bristles, which consists of a series of fibres of different thicknesses mounted on match-sticks. Each is calibrated by pressing the end of the bristle on a balance until it just bends. This weight divided by the cross-sectional area of the bristle gives the pressure exerted on the skin. A newer method is to use electromechanical transducers that deliver adjustable mechanical indentation to the skin.

If the skin is explored with a bristle it is found that the tactile sense is distributed in a punctate fashion. The map of the distribution of the touch spots in any given area varies from day to day and this variability makes it difficult to believe that there is a fixed anatomical basis for the touch sense. By means of a large series of bristles von Frey found that the smallest pressure in g/mm^2 required to elicit a sensation of touch varied in different parts of the skin (Table 34.1). If these values are converted into lb/in^2 (second column) quite ridiculous values are obtained; the lips (fourth entry in the table) are certainly sensitive to much less than 3.5 lb on an area of 1 in^2, thus the adequate stimulus for eliciting a sensation of touch cannot be mere pressure. If a finger is inserted into a bowl of mercury contact is felt only at the air/mercury junction, where the skin is deformed by the abrupt change of pressure. Deeper in the mercury at the tip of the finger, although the pressure is actually much greater, there is no deformation. Thus deformation rather than pressure is the effective stimulus.

Touch spots are thickly distributed around hair follicles. The root of each living hair is surrounded by a network of nerve fibres; the nerve elements become very scanty when the hair is shed. Each hair pivoted at the skin surface acts as a lever to transmit deformation to the nerve-endings in the root round the shaft. When the hairs are removed the sensitivity to touch is greatly reduced.

Table 34.1 Threshold pressure in g/mm^2 required to elicit sensations of touch and of pain on various areas of the skin surface as measured by von Frey. In the second column the values have been converted into lb/in^2 to show that there is a fallacy in expressing the threshold in terms of pressure (see text).

Area	Touch g/mm^2	lb/in^2	Pain (g/mm^2)
Cornea			0.2
Conjunctiva			2
Tongue and nose	2	2.8	
Lips	2.5	3.5	
Finger-tip and forehead	3	4.3	300
Back of finger	5	7.1	
Palm, arm, thigh	7	10	
Forearm	8	11	20
Back of hand	12	17	100
Calf, shoulder	16	23	30
Abdomen	26	37	15
Outside of thigh	26	37	
Skin and sole	28	40	
Back of forearm	33	47	30
Loins	48	68	
Thick parts of sole	250	356	200

Afferent fibres that innervate the receptors in hair follicles have, characteristically, a large receptive field (perhaps several centimetres in diameter) but some tactile receptors with a field not more than 0.5 mm in diameter may be supplied by a single nerve fibre (Table 34.5).

The tactile sense can be sub-divided into the categories of touch, which is very short-lasting; flutter-vibration aroused by repetitive mechanical stimulus; and pressure, which is more persistent. Each sensation lasts only a little longer than the stimulus. The sensory mechanisms interact. If a finger is held lightly against a revolving cog wheel each stimulus gives rise to a separate sensation until the contacts follow one another at more than 500 or 600 per second. Above this frequency of stimulation the rotating cog wheel is described as smooth, the separate sensations having fused into a continuous sensation. If, nevertheless, the amplitude of vibration of an object applied to the skin is very high, a sensation of vibration may persist up to 8000 Hz and, with practice, amplified speech vibrations can be felt by the fingers and recognised.

The tactile sense shows adaptation during the continued application of stimuli; it is partly peripheral and partly central. We are aware of the contact of our clothes with the skin when they are first put on but this sensation quickly disappears. It can, however, be brought to consciousness by an act of the will or by a slight movement of the body. In the same way a new denture is very obvious at first but after a time the wearer becomes unconscious of its presence.

Localisation
When a blindfolded person is touched not only does he have an impression of the strength of the stimulus but also he can indicate the point touched with considerable accuracy. The power of localisation depends partly on the position at which the nerve fibres from the tactile end-organs enter the spinal cord and on their higher connections and partly on experience. A pencil laid between two crossed fingers of a blindfolded subject gives the sensation of contact by two pencils. Experience also plays a part in visual localisation. After removal of a congenital cataract a person blind from birth is not able at first to localise his visual impressions; the power to do so grows as experience of his new sense develops.

Discrimination
If two points on the skin are touched simultaneously and with identical stimuli by means of a pair of dividers, the subject reports that two separate points have been touched, provided that the distance exceeds a value depending on the area of skin under test (Table 34.2).

Table 34.2 The two-point discrimination threshold*

Area	Separation in mm
Tip of tongue	1
Anterior surface of finger-tip	2
Posterior surface of third phalanx	6
Palm of hand	11
Back of hand	32
Back of neck	54
Middle of back	67

* The distance at which two points on the skin touched simultaneously with approximately the same pressure must lie apart to be recognised as separate points of contact. From Weinstein S 1968 In: Kenshalo D R (ed) The skin senses Thomas Springfield

If the skin is carefully explored for touch spots it is found that in the area showing the lowest two-point threshold they are less than 1 mm apart but at no part of the body is the distance between these spots more than 6 mm. A low density of touch spots is not the explanation of poor discrimination.

This two-point threshold is usually three or four times the error of localisation in the same region. This apparent anomaly is partly due to the diffuse nature of the stimulus. The blunt point on the skin stretches the surrounding skin and localisation is probably determined by the centre of strongest stimulation; in the case of two-point stimulation the whole stretched area is effective in giving a broad impression and obscuring the presence of the two points. In other words, when the two points of contact are fairly close to one another the stimulus is not very different from that produced by one contact. Convergence of afferent fibres on to neurones in the tactile pathway in the central nervous system determines the size of the receptive fields of neurones in the sensory pathway and is another important factor influencing the accuracy of two-point discrimination.

Projection
This is most highly developed in vision but it occurs also with tactile sensation. If a pudding is stirred with a spoon, lumps may be detected and the bottom of the pan feels hard. The stimuli that originate these sensations are applied to the skin in contact with the upper end of the spoon but the sensations are projected to the lower end of the spoon.

Temperature sense
Although we are apt to think of the skin as being uniformly sensitive all over its surface, each modality has a punctate distribution. In the case of the temperature sense this can be shown by slowly passing a small warm metal rod over the skin. At some places no sensation of warmth is aroused, while at other places, called 'warm spots', a sensation of warmth is quite

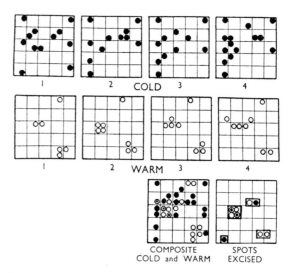

Fig. 34.3 Maps of cold and warm spots on an area of 1 cm² on the upper arm. The successive maps were made at intervals of two days. All the spots are combined in the diagram marked 'Composite Cold and Warm'. The spots in the last diagram were excised but no specialised nerve-endings were fond. (Dallenbach K M 1927 American Journal of Psychology 39: 416)

distinct. The 'cold spots' can be mapped out by passing a cold metal rod over the skin. The cold spots are more numerous and do not coincide with the warm spots. Furthermore, tests made from day to day show that the distribution of these spots continually alter (Fig. 34.3). The punctate distribution is lost if the skin becomes red, as in sunburn, in which all parts give rise to a sensation of warmth on being touched with a warm rod. A further observation suggesting that the two receptors are distinct is that a hot rod passed over a cold spot may give rise paradoxically to a sensation of cold.

A piece of cloth and a piece of metal at the same temperature, either high or low, arouse quite different sensations due to the differing thermal conductivities of the stimulus material. The thermal sensations depend in part on the rate of withdrawal or addition of heat. If a finger of one hand is placed in hot water and a finger of the other in cold and after 30 seconds both are placed in water at an intermediate temperature the water feels cold to the former and warm to the latter. It is reasonable to conclude that the cause of the sensation, in this experiment, is a fall or a rise in the temperature of the nerve-endings already adapted to different temperatures. This cannot, however, account for the sensation of cold in the following experiment. If a cold object such as a coin is pressed on the forehead and then removed the sensation of cold persists, although at this time the temperature of the end-organs must be rising.

The experiment with the hot and cold water shows a feature common to all sensations — adaptation. The finger kept in cold water for some time does not feel cold; it becomes adjusted to the new situation, which, since it arouses no sensation, becomes a new zero. The finger in the hot water also shows adaptation but in the opposite direction. This experiment also shows that the temperature sense is not to be regarded as a thermometer; with its shifting zero it cannot measure absolute temperature. It can, however, detect quite small temperature differences. The sensitivity of the exposed areas of the skin (face, hands and scalp) is less than that of areas normally covered, such as the arms and forearms. At ordinary skin temperatures differences as small as 0.2°C can be appreciated by the arms whereas differences of 0.5 to 1.0°C are required by the fingers. The mucous membrane of the mouth is relatively insensitive to heat; tea can be drunk at a temperature that is painful to the finger.

Electrophysiological studies can account for the above sensory results (Fig. 34.4). In the snout of the cat distinctive cold receptor terminals have been seen with the electron microscope. The nerve fibres supplying them are myelinated (Table 34.5).

Iggo has found that the 'cold' receptors of primates have a very restricted receptor field in both hairy and glabrous skin. The speed of conduction of nerve impulses in the nerve trunk remote from the receptors ranged from 0.6 to 15.3 m/s; the speed of the majority corresponds to myelinated axons 1 to 3 μm in diameter. The receptors discharged in bursts that showed adaptation but they continued to discharge at constant thermoneutral temperatures. Electrophysiological experiments on conscious human subjects are now providing confirmation of the results obtained from non-human primates that establish modality-mechanoreceptors. Peripheral thermoreceptors are discussed in Chapter 41.

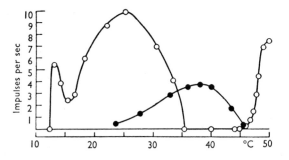

Fig. 34.4 Graph showing the frequency of the steady discharge of a single cold fibre (open circles) and of a single warm fibre (solid circles) when the receptors on the surface of the cat's tongue were exposed to constant temperatures within the range of 10° to 50°C. (Zotterman Y 1953 Annual Review of Physisology 15: 363)

The pain sense

In the following paragraphs we are concerned only with pain actually arising in the skin. Pain projected to the surface of the body when internal organs are diseased (referred pain) is discussed later (p. 411).

Pain elicited by stimulation of the skin has a pricking, burning or itching quality and is well localised. The pain threshold may be raised by one-third by distracting the subject's attention but in sunburnt skin it may be lowered by half. If the finger just proximal to the nail-bed is pressed against a hot electric bulb a double pain is produced. The first sensation arises abruptly and is pricking in quality; it is probably carried in moderately in moderately large fibres conducting impulses at about 10 m/s. The second sensation follows a second or more later, has a burning quality but is less abrupt in onset and disappearance; it is carried in non-myelinated fibres. If the circulation through the finger is obstructed by a bandage to produce asphyxia of the skin and nerves distal to the bandage the first pain is abolished more quickly than the second pain; the underlying mechanisms must therefore be different.

Quite gentle exploration of the skin surface with a needle produces a painful sensation at certain places. The pain end-organs are distributed in a punctate fashion, independently of the end-organs of touch or temperature. Any given area of skin may show ten times as many pain spots as touch spots. These pain endings have different characteristics from the tactile end-organs; the threshold stimulus is quite different and the order of increasing sensitivity is completely different from that given for touch (Table 34.1). The pain sense has a relatively slow rate of adaptation. Asphyxia reduces the response of the other senses but may increase the response to painful stimuli. In syringomyelia, a disease of the spinal cord in which the central canal is enlarged, pain may disappear while the other cutaneous senses remain. Pain is certainly a separate modality and is not due simply to excessive stimulation of nerve-endings.

Pain sensation may be tested by thermal radiation. The threshold temperature of the skin that gives rise to pain lies between 43° and 47°C with slow or no adaptation. Sudden application of water at 37°C to a large area of the skin may cause a sensation of pain that disappears in a few seconds. Pain sensation can also be tested by a pressure algometer, which consists of a calibrated spring-loaded metal cylinder 0.5 cm in diameter. It is applied perpendicularly with gradually increasing force to the body surface until the patient describes the pressure as painful. The threshold of complaint is normally about 2 kg. At the receptor a painful stimulus depolarises the nerve-endings and sets up impulses. Mechanical or chemical stimuli could produce the effect directly or indirectly by releasing a

Table 34.5 Cutaneous receptors (By courtesy of A. Iggo)

Name	Structure	Location	Receptive field	Effective stimulus	Sensory function
TACTILE RECEPTORS. Rapidly adapting					
Pacinian corpuscle PC		subcutaneous	100 mm²	vibration 40–600 Hz movement	vibration
Krause end bulb RA	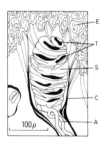	dermis of glabrous skin	2 mm²	vibration 10–200 Hz movement	touch, spatial analysis, intensity
Meissner corpuscle RA		dermis of glabrous skin	12 mm²	low frequency vibration 5–200 Hz movement	flutter, spatial analysis, intensity
Hair follicle receptors RA	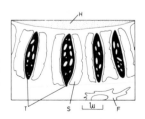	hair follicles	1.5 cm²	hair movement or vibration 5–40 Hz	flutter, spatial analysis, intensity

Table 34.5 (Cont'd)

Name	Structure	Location	Receptive field	Effective stimulus	Sensory function

TACTILE RECEPTORS. Slowly adapting

Name	Structure	Location	Receptive field	Effective stimulus	Sensory function
Merkel receptor SAI		base of epidermis	11 mm^2	indentation and pressure	spatial analysis, intensity
Ruffini ending SAII	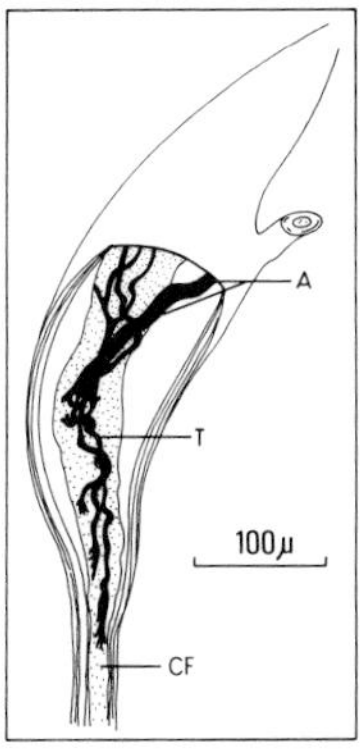	dermis	60 mm^2	stretch of skin, pressure	(pressure touch)
C-mechano-receptor	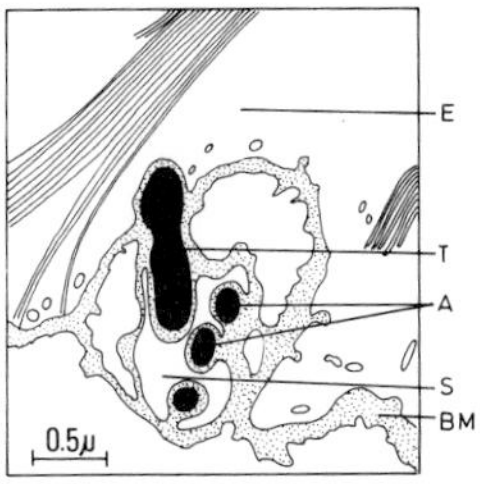	dermo-epidermal boundary	2 mm^2	indentation, slow movement	(itch)

THERMORECEPTORS

Name	Structure	Location	Receptive field	Effective stimulus	Sensory function
cold	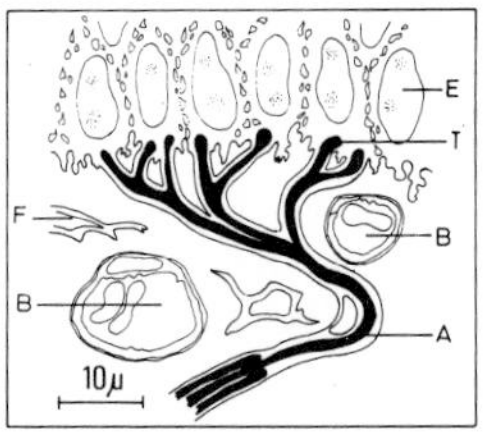	base of epidermis	1 mm^2	steady and falling temperatures 40°–10°C	cold
warm		base of epidermis	1 mm^2	steady and rising temperature 35°–50°C	warmth and heat

Table 34.5 (Cont'd)

Name	Structure	Location	Receptive field	Effective stimulus	Sensory function
NOCICEPTORS					
Mechanical	?	skin	3 mm²	pinprick squeezing	pain (sharp, first)
Thermomechanical	?	skin	3 mm²	> 42 °C severe mechanical, algogenic chemicals	pain (dull, second)

Key to diagrams: A, axon; B, capillary; BM, basement membrane; C, capsule; CF, collagen fibres; E, epidermis; F, fibroblast; H, hair shaft; L, laminae; M, Merkel cell; S, Schwann cell; T, nerve terminal. The abbreviations PC, RA, SAI and SAII are used in the text for these receptors.

chemical substance from damaged cells. Keele and his colleagues have investigated the second possibility by the simple expedient of raising a skin blister with cantharidin and then applying the substances to be tested to the exposed base of the blister. Blood, plasma or inflammatory exudate withdrawn into a siliconed syringe have very little pain-producing activity; on transfer to a glass vessel, pain-producing activity appears in a few minutes but declines and disappears in about an hour. The pain-producing substance (PPS) is a polypeptide with pharmacological properties resembling those of bradykinin. Pure bradykinin in a concentration of 0.1 μg/ml produces pain when applied to a blister base. The skin possesses many proteolytic enzymes that are known to be released when it is damaged. It is therefore reasonable to speculate that tissue injury sets free an enzyme capable of acting on some component of the plasma proteins to give PPS, which then produces pain. Haemolysis of red cells (and indeed damage to any cell) releases potassium ions and application of the haemolysate to the base of the blister produces pain. This is, however, somewhat greater than that produced by a solution of potassium chloride, containing the same amount of potassium as the haemolysate, and made isotonic with NaCl. Since 5-hydroxytryptamine (5HT) causes pain when it is placed on the base of a blister it may be that damage to blood platelets by releasing 5HT also gives rise to pain. 5HT potentiates the algogenic effect of bradykinin and of potassium. Acetylcholine even in high dilution gives rise to pain immediately. It is not likely that histamine is of any importance in this respect because pain is caused only when high concentrations, unlikely to be produced by injury, are applied. Recent experiments by Keele suggest that the algogenic effect is due mainly to AMP.

Prostaglandin E$_2$ is produced in inflamed tissue. It does not directly excite the pain-endings but it can potentiate the action of algogens such as 5HT and bradykinin. Pain can be relieved by non-steroidal anti-inflammatory agents, such as aspirin (acetyl salicylic acid) and indomethacin. Both chemicals block the formation of prostaglandins by inhibiting the enzyme, prostaglandin synthetase. Their analgesic action is probably indirect and due to a fall in tissue prostaglandin concentration, which in turn reduces the potency of the algogens formed during the general inflammatory action.

Pruritus or itching may be defined as 'an unpleasant cutaneous sensation that provokes the desire to scratch'. The sensation may be mild, in which case it is almost pleasurable, and this is quite common in elderly people; sometimes it may be so severe as to cause the sufferer to attempt suicide. Pruritus may be generalised, as in jaundice, or it may be confined to quite a small area of skin or to a particular part of the body such as the perineum or the nostrils. The sensation arises in nerve-endings in the epidermis since pruritus cannot be elicited in areas denuded of epidermis. It can be produced in a sensitive area by chemical, mechanical, thermal or electrical stimuli, and mild forms of such stimuli may elicit itching in a localised area of skin long after the initial pruritus has subsided. Thus, light stroking of an insect bite may produce itching weeks after the local reaction has subsided. In other words, the skin remains in a state of increased excitability. If the itching so produced leads to vigorous scratching, the area of excitable skin enlarges and the threshold is further reduced.

By inserting stinging hairs of a tropical plant *Mucana pruriens* into the skin, Shelley and Arthur showed that the most effective site for itch production was the dermo-epidermal junction; they believe that damage to the skin liberates endopeptidases that act on peripheral nerve filaments and produce the sensation of itch. An alternative explanation is that the endopeptides form polypeptides (PPS) and these in turn excite cutaneous receptors. This sensation is carried in the sensory spinal nerves to the spinothalamic tract and then to the thalamus and sensory cortex. Because no itching can be elicited in analgesic skin, itching has been thought to be a kind of pain sensation. In syphilitic disease of the posterior roots of the spinal cord (tabes dorsalis) the sense of touch may be lost without loss of the sense of pain; itching can be elicited in the affected areas of skin. On the other hand the fact that removal of the epidermis and the subepidermal nerve network abolishes itch but not pain suggests that itch is a distinct sensory experience. If this is accepted it is easy to understand how it is that itch and pain can be experienced simultaneously and that immersion of the skin in water at 40° to 41°C quickly abolishes itch but intensifies pain. The itch threshold may be affected by psychological factors. It is not clear why scratching relieves itching but it may do so by disturbing the rhythm of afferent impulses travelling towards the spinal cord, by local depletion of kinins or by afferent inhibition in the central system (central interaction).

Tickle can be demonstrated all over the body by light touch with a wisp of cotton wool. After a tickle stimulus, adjacent areas of skin are more sensitive with the result that a single light touch stimulus applied within them will arouse tickle. The stimulus for tickle is so slight that involvement of an end-organ deeper than the most superficial layer of the skin seems unlikely. It may arise in slowly adapting mechanoreceptors, particularly the SA II (Table 34.5), which may continue with a persistent discharge after a brief stimulus.

Physiological basis of cutaneous sensations

The experiments just described provide evidence for the hypothesis that there are four 'modalities' of cutaneous sensation, and indeed the punctate distribution of the sensitive areas makes it logical to search for special receptors. The older histologists found many elaborate endings in the skin and, rather rashly, labelled them 'pressure' endings, 'cold' endings and so on, simply on the basis of their morphology. Since then the simple correlation between cutaneous receptor morphology and sensation has been questioned.

Exact analysis requires a detailed study of the properties of component elements in the sensory pathways. Combined electrophysiological and morphological studies, principally in laboratory animals and monkeys, have established the existence of several well-defined kinds of afferent units (Table 34.5) with strict correlation of functional properties and morphology for the encapsulated receptors.

The names given to the sensory receptors in Tables 34.5 and 34.6 are derived from two sources — either based on the morphology of the receptors where this is known (and often) given the name of their discoverer) or based on their physiological properties and sensory functions. For these reasons there can be several alternative names in current use. An important difference in physiological properties is recognised among the cutaneous mechanoreceptors. Some of them are excited only briefly by steady mechanical stimulation of the skin, although they respond very well to an oscillating or repeated on/off indentation of the skin. Because of these properties they are called *rapidly adapting* (abbreviated to RA). Other tactile receptors continue to discharge impulses during steadily maintained indentation of the skin, as for example by constant pressure on the buttocks when sitting on a chair. For this reason they are called *slowly adapting* (abbreviated to SA). In Tables 34.5 and 34.6 the tactile receptors compose the rapidly adapting group as follows: Pacinian corpuscles (abbreviated PC); Krause end-bulbs; and Meissner corpuscles named after their discoverers. Together with the hair-follicle receptors they are put in the rapidly adapting category on the basis of their functional properties and given the abbreviation RA (for rapidly adapting). The Pacinian corpuscles are given a separate abbreviation because of their distinctive properties. In the slowly adapting group of tactile receptors we find *first* the Merkel receptor, which denotes the slowly adapting Type I cutaneous receptor and abbreviated SAI, *second* the Ruffini ending, denoting the slowly adapting Type II receptor and abbreviated SA II and *third*, tactile receptors with non-myelinated afferent axons and which are called C-mechanoreceptors. Although it has not been possible to make such exact studies, similar findings have been made in man (Table 34.6).

The cutaneous sensory pathways in the central nervous system to which the cutaneous afferent fibres

Table 34.6 Properties of cutaneous receptors in glabrous skin of the human hand. Based on single fibre electrophysiological recordings from the median nerve. (From Vallbo A B, Johansson R S 1978 In: Gordon G (ed.) Active touch. Pergamon, Oxford

project arise in either the dorsal horn of the spinal cord or in the dorsal column nuclei in the medulla oblongata. At each of these places the incoming afferent fibres make both specific and non-specific connections. That is, there are some neurones excited for example only by particular kinds of mechanoreceptors or thermoreceptors, and others which are excited by the convergence on to them of many kinds of cutaneous receptors. The former provide a specific, modality defined, sensory pathway, whereas the latter are not specified in the same way. Within each of the possible sensory pathways these afferent fibres may have inhibitory and/or excitatory actions and the interaction of excitation and inhibition decides the degree and kind of sensory pathway activity. For example, nociceptor-excited neurones in the dorsal horn can have their discharge abolished by concurrent excitation of cutaneous mechanoreceptors that excite interneurones that inhibit the nociceptor neurones and reduce their activity. This kind of action provides a satisfactory explanation of the efficacy of counter-irritation or rubbing the skin to relieve pain or itch, since impulses from the mechanoreceptors inhibit or block the excitatory effect of the nociceptors. In addition there are powerful and selective descending inhibitory mechanisms with an origin in the brain stem and cerebral cortex that shape the sensory inflow to the brain.

Although the idea of exclusive 'modality specific' pathways must be revised there is now evidence that in animals individual 'modality-specific' afferent fibres enter both 'relatively specific' as well as 'non-specific' centripetal pathways. The divergence and richness of pathways for afferent units excited by mechanical stimuli (that is within the touch/pressure modality) could provide for two kinds of pathway. Also certain cells in the trigeminal nucleus in monkeys are excited by impulses from thermoreceptors but not by impulses from mechanoreceptor units. Therefore some cells at several levels in the sensory pathway display an input specificity.

Within the 'tactile' modality several distinct sensations can be recognised in both sensory and behavioural tests. The mechanisms have been analysed to include; (a) specific cutaneous receptors, (b) specifically activated neurones in the dorsal horn and dorsal column nuclei, and (c) frequency dependent neurones in the somato-sensory cortex. Detailed frequency analysis (threshold analysis) studies of the elements in the pathway establish a strong correlation between the unit activity and the sensations of flutter (present at 6 to 40 Hz) and of vibration (40 to 500 Hz). The sense of vibration arises in Pacinian corpuscles, flutter is mediated by rapidly adapting receptors (Meissner's corpuscles in glabrous skin and hair follicle afferents in hairy skin) and the slowly adapting mechanoreceptors do not contribute to either sensation. Thus the sensory

pathways have the capacity to preserve an input from the 'sub-modality specific' cutaneous receptors.

AFFERENT IMPULSES FROM THE VISCERA

Afferent fibres from the viscera (stomach, intestine and other abdominal organs) are carried alongside the fibres of the sympathetic and parasympathetic systems. Fibres conveying visceral sensation are therefore sometimes spoken of as 'autonomic afferents' although the autonomic system is strictly speaking an efferent system. Many of these viscerosensory fibres form part of visceral reflex arcs. Some mediate the sensation of visceral pain; visceral pain can be relieved by sympathectomy, that is by cutting sympathetic nerves. After section of the splanchnic nerves Pacinian corpuscles in the mesentery degenerate just as those in the skin do when a cutaneous nerve is cut. There is apparently no essential difference except in size between viscerosensory fibres and afferent fibres from the skin. In the cat impulses in the splanchnic nerves have been traced into the cord, up the dorsal columns of white matter on the same side to the nucleus gracilis on the same side and then across the midline to the opposite thalamus; more slowly running impulses project via the spinothalamic tracts to the thalamus on both sides and also to the hypothalamus.

Records of activity in single fibres of the vagus and pelvic nerves show that there are several kinds of visceral receptors. Very slowly adapting mechanoreceptors are present in the stomach, intestine and urinary bladder. The rate of firing depends on the rate of distension of these viscera, being greater the more sudden the distension. The nerve endings are activated by passive distension and by active contraction. Impulses pass from the receptors along non-myelinated fibres with a conduction velocity of less than 2.5 m/s. Pacinian corpuscles that are in the mesentery adapt very quickly; they have large myelinated axons (conduction velocity 40 m/s). Their function is unknown. Other rapidly adapting receptors exist, for example the receptors in the urethra responding to the flow of urine. Chemoreceptors in the gastrointestinal mucosa are excited by a pH of less than 1.5.

In a conscious unanaesthetised person the abdominal viscera, provided that they are healthy, can be cut or burned without causing pain; that is clearly demonstrated when a knuckle of colon, brought through the abdominal wall by the surgeon, is opened painlessly some days later without any anaesthetic. Wolf and Wolff found that Tom's normal healthy gastric mucosa was not sensitive to pinching or electric stimulation but, if the mucosa became hyperaemic and oedematous, pain was readily evoked by these stimuli. The pain threshold of this viscus is normally high but it may be lowered by inflammatory changes. However, pain arises in the absence of inflammation if the appropriate kind of stimulation is applied. For example, pain is produced if the mesentery is pulled upon or injected with irritant material; since all the nerve fibres from the five metres of gut are crowded into the 15 cm long mesentery, traction on this structure must necessarily stimulate a much larger number of nerve fibres than does cutting or pinching of an equal length of the gut. Thus the production of pain by stimulation of visceral nerves depends on (a) the strength of the stimulus, (b) the number of nerve fibres stimulated, and (c) the pain threshold at the moment of stimulation.

Pain impulses from the abdominal viscera are conveyed almost entirely in afferents passing in the sympathetic nerves, especially the splanchnic nerves. If a balloon passed into the small intestine is inflated the subject feels pain in the centre of the abdomen but after bilateral section of the splanchnic nerves inflation of the balloon does not cause pain. Vagotomy has no effect on pain produced by distension of the small intestine. Further, patients with a complete transection of the spinal cord at about L1, which renders the abdominal wall anaesthetic, can not only experience intestinal colic but localise the pain in the centre of the abdomen. Learmonth reported that a patient who had been given a spinal anaesthetic to anaesthetise the lower part of the body experienced pain he accurately localised to the bladder when the superior hypogastric plexus was crushed; the afferent fibres must of course have entered the cord above the level of the anaesthetised part of the cord. Pain from pelvic viscera is also mediated by afferent fibres in the pelvic (parasympathetic) nerves.

It is well known that pain arising from a diseased organ may be projected to a definite position on the surface of the body (*referred pain*). A knowledge of the areas of localisation of pain is, however, of great service in diagnosis and has been summarised in Table 34.7. The position at which a patient feels pain may coincide with the position of the tissue in which it is produced, or the pain may be felt at a distance from the place of its production. The pain due to pinching the skin on the surface of the body is felt by the subject at the point of stimulation. However, when a transposed pedicle skin graft with intact innervation is pinched, the blindfolded patient experiences the pain in the position from which the graft was taken and not in its new site. Moreover, pain due to heart disease (angina pectoris) may be projected to the left arm even when this has been amputated. Pain is, therefore, projected to a position in the body image and not to any particular tissue. This phenomenon is further illustrated by the fact that pain produced in organs such as the diaphragm and the testis, which have migrated during development, is projected to the primary or embryonic site of the organ.

Rubbing the diaphragm at operation, or electrical stimulation of the phrenic nerve, produces pain that is felt at the root of the neck; the diaphragm develops in the neck and acquires its nerve supply there. The testis develops near the kidney but low in the abdomen; testicular pain is felt in the lower abdomen and not in the testis itself. In other words the sensorium seems to make contact with, and to become aware of the position of, the organs in embryonic life and it continues to use the same reference map. The alimentary tract is embryologically a midline organ and pain arising in it or in any other midline organ should, according to this interpretation, be projected to various levels of the midline no matter whether the part concerned had migrated right or left. This is what is actually found. Thus in colic due to violent peristalsis of the intestine, pain is felt in the midline. In disorders of the stomach pain is felt in the midline high up in the abdomen; small-intestine pain is felt in the umbilical region; colon pain is situated in the midline in the lower part of the abdomen. The gall-bladder is embryologically a midline organ and true gall-bladder pain is felt in the epigastrium but, if the inflamed viscus irritates the diaphragm, pain is felt in the neck and right shoulder. It is unlikely that any nerve fibres from the gall-bladder or its peritoneal covering reach the spinal cord by the phrenic nerve, since the gall-bladder can be painlessly removed under spinal anaesthesia in which the phrenic nerves and the diaphragm are functioning normally. Distension of the bile duct usually gives pain in the midline of the abdomen but sometimes in the back. Pain arising in the body and cervix of the uterus is felt in the midline about 4 cm above the symphysis pubis.

When the parietal peritoneum is irritated as a consequence of visceral disease, pain is sharply localised to the site of irritation and is associated with tenderness and often with spasm (rigidity) of the adjacent skeletal muscles. Thus the pain of early appendicitis is felt in the midline near the umbilicus. Not until the parietal peritoneum, supplied by the somatic nerves, is irritated is the pain felt at the situation of the inflamed appendix, that is, generally, in the right iliac fossa. Similarly, although distension of the gall-bladder produces pain in the centre of the epigastrium, inflammation of the fundus of the gall-bladder is associated with pain in the right hypochondrium in an area overlying the diseased organ.

Visceral pain can be modified by anaesthetisation or irritation of the skin area in which the pain is felt. The pain of gastric ulcer is reduced by anaesthetising the abdominal wall. The pain of angina pectoris can be relieved by anaesthetising the painful area of the left arm and angina pectoris projected into an amputated limb is relieved by anaesthetising the brachial plexus. Moreover, if, in a patient in whom angina pectoris is

Table 34.7 The segmental sensory innervation of the viscera

Organ	Superficial areas to which pain is referred	Thoracic 1	2	3	4	5	6	7	8	9	10	11	12	Lumbar 1	2	Parasympathetic sacral 2	3	4	Afferent pathway from viscus
Heart	Precordium and inner arm	+	+	+	+	?													Middle and inferior cervical and thoracic cardiac nerves
Lung	No referred pain*		+	+	+	+	+	+											Inferior cervical and thoracic nerves (convey reflex impulses)
Liver and gall-bladder	Right upper quadrant and right scapula							+	+	+									Greater splanchnic nerve
Stomach	Epigastrium						+	+	+	+									Greater splanchnic nerve
Small intestine	Umbilicus									+	+	?							Greater splanchnic nerve
Colon { ascending	Suprapubic, deep pelvic and anus											+	+	+					Lumbar chains and preaortic plexus
sigmoid and rectum }																+	+	+	Pelvic nerves and plexuses
Kidney	Loin and groin										+	+	+	+					Renal plexus via lowest splanchnic nerve and upper lumbar rami
Ureter	Loin and groin											+	+	+	+				Renal plexus and upper lumbar rami
Bladder { fundus	Suprapubic, perineum and penis											+	+						Hypogastric plexuses
bladder, neck }																+	+	+	Pelvis nerves and plexuses
Uterus { fundus	Suprapubic region and lower back, perineum										+	+	+	?					Hypogastric plexuses
cervix }																+	+	+	Hypogastric plexuses
Testes, vas deferens, seminal vesicles, prostate	Pelvis, perineum										+	+	+	+					Hypogastric plexuses

* Lung parenchyma is insensitive. Pain from larger bronchi is transmitted over somatic vagal axons. When disease spreads to parietal pleura pain is transmitted over intercostal nerves.

(Derived from: White J C et al. 1952 The autonomic nervous system, 3rd edn, Kimpton, London; Bonica J J 1968. Anesthesiology 29: 793)

elicited by exercise, an area of skin is blistered by cantharidin, the pain induced by the exercise may be felt in the blistered area. Even after complete cutaneous anaesthesia intended to relieve abdominal pain the patient may complain of a dull, aching, deep form of pain that is usually localised in or near to the diseased organ itself. This pain is similar to that produced by stimulation of the coeliac ganglion and is relieved only by section of sympathetic nerves.

The probable 'explanation' of the results of experiments on diaphragmatic pain is as follows. Nerve impulses from the diaphragm and from the skin of the shoulder reach and synapse with common neurones in the same segment of the spinal cord (Fig. 34.8). These neurones are normally associated in sensation with impulses coming from the cutaneous sensory field. The impulses from the viscera increase the excitability of the neurones, which then become more readily excited by the cutaneous input. Figure 34.8 illustrates the mode of action. The normal threshold for pain is at the level

represented at (a) in Figure 34.8. Anaesthetising the shoulder area reduces the number of impulses reaching the cord from the shoulder and so raises the threshold as shown at (b) and (c). Irritation of the diaphragm to a degree represented by the height of the triangle at (a) normally produces a shower of impulses that reach the threshold and pain is felt. After anaesthetising the shoulder, however, a similar degree of irritation of the diaphragm represented by (b) now falls short of the threshold and there is no pain. A larger stimulus (large triangle at (c)) such as could be produced by a phrenic nerve crush can, however, reach the threshold and cause pain. The observations on angina pectoris already mentioned may also be explained on this theory, if we postulate that blistering increases the number of afferent impulses arriving at the central nervous system and so lowers the threshold for pain.

SENSORY PATHWAYS IN THE CENTRAL NERVOUS SYSTEM

The nerve impulses that enter the central nervous system in cutaneous afferent fibres all make synaptic connections in the spinal cord (for dorsal root afferents) or the brain stem (for cranial nerve afferents). Onward transmission of the information is from the neurons with which the afferents make synaptic contact. Several major pathways exist (Fig. 34.9). They are:

1. The dorsal column — dorsal column nuclei — lemnisco-thalamo cortical system (dorsal column system).

2. The spinocervico-lemnisco-thalamic sytem (spinocervical system, SCT).

3. The spinothalamic system (STT).

Each of these pathways occupies a different region of the spinal cord, but they all eventually enter the thalamus and go from there to the somato-sensory cortex. The dorsal column system occupies the ipsilateral dorsal column and is a pathway from the large cutaneous tactile receptors (Meissner (RA), Pacinian (PC) and hair follicle (RA) receptors). The spinocervical tract, which has an ipsilateral dorsolateral location in the spinal cord, is also a tactile pathway, particularly from hair follicle receptors. The slow-adapting receptors (SAI and SAII) also project through the dorsal column system but the spinal pathways may be less direct than for the PC and RA receptors. The spinothalamic tract has a crossed anterolateral position, and is a pathway for thermal and for noxious sensations, as well as for tactile inputs. It is sectioned in the surgical operation of anterolateral cordotomy to relieve chronic pain.

Although these pathways are well-defined none of them provides an exclusive route for any sensation. Thus surgical interruption of any single path, although

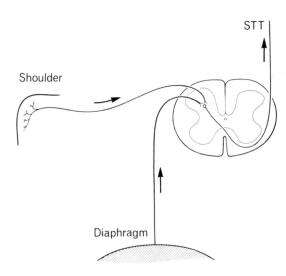

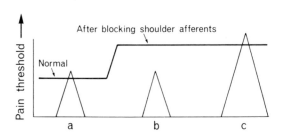

Fig. 34.8 Visceral pain. (a) When the diaphragm is rubbed pain is felt in the shoulder. (b) When the diaphragm is rubbed after anaesthetisation of the shoulder no pain is felt. (c) Crushing the phrenic nerve after anaesthetisation of the shoulder is painful. STT: spinothalamic tract (After Brown F R 1948 Lancet: 386)

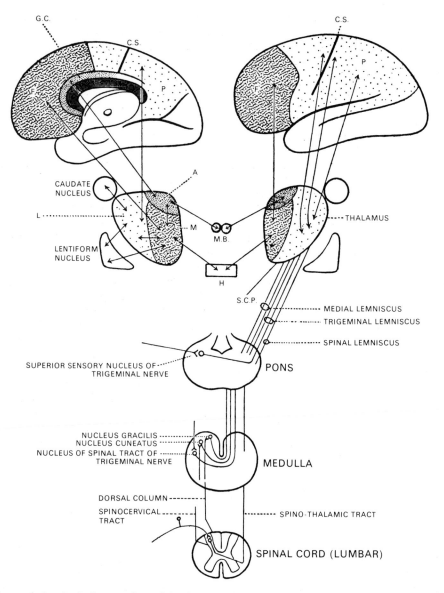

Fig. 34.9 Major cortical and spinal connections of the thalamus. G.C. = gyrus cinguli; C.S. = central sulcus with motor and somaesthetic areas on each side; F = frontal area; P = parietal area; A = anterior group of thalamic nuclei; M = medial group of thalamic nuclei; L = lateral group of thalamic nuclei; M.B. = mamillary bodies; H = hypothalamus; S.C.P. = superior cerebellar peduncle. On the upper right of the diagram the projections are to the lateral surface of the cerebral hemisphere: on the upper left the projections to the medial surface of the cerebral hemisphere are given. Internuclear connections of the thalamus are shown only on the left. The lines joining the various parts of the thalamus and cortex have in most cases been given arrows to indicate that impulses pass in either direction. (By courtesy of G. W. Pearce.)

it may yield temporary relief or interference with a sensation, does not cause permanent sensory impairment.

Descending control of sensory pathways

The cutaneous sensory pathways are not one-way channels, conducting sensory impulses to the brain in an automatic and uncontrolled manner. Instead, the brain imposes a variable degree of control over the conductivity of the various ascending pathways. This central modulation is produced by efferent nerves acting at the various synaptic junctions of the relay nuclei of the ascending pathways. Sites of these synaptic interactions are the dorsal horn of the spinal cord, dorsal column nuclei and thalamic nuclei. The actions can be both facilitatory, enhancing transmission at a synapse, and inhibitory, by depressing synaptic transmission. Often these two effects are balanced, and inhibition of one sensory channel may be simultaneously accompanied by facilitation of another.

These descending control mechanisms have taken on a renewed importance with the recent discovery of brain-stimulated analgesia (BSA; or stimulation-produced analgesia, SPA) and of the endorphins and enkephalins. Brain-stimulated analgesia can be induced in both man and animals by electrical stimulation of the median raphe nuclei and the peri-aqueductal grey matter in the brain stem through implanted electrodes. During and after stimulation the subject develops an indifference to noxious stimuli that had previously caused severe pain or behavioural activity consistent with a painful state.

Beta-endorphin is a 31 amino acid peptide molecule, produced in the brain and the pituitary gland. The concentration of beta-endorphin in cerebrospinal fluid has been found to increase during brain-stimulated analgesia. Part of the molecule consists of enkephalin, a pentapeptide, which occurs in two forms as leu-enkephalin (tyrosine-glycine-phenyalanine-leucine) and met-enkephalin (Tyr-Gly-Gly-Phe-methionine). These enkephalins are naturally occurring and can bind to the same receptor sites in the body with which opiates react. Their actions can be blocked by naloxone, which is a morphine antagonist. It is therefore probable that they have the same pain-reducing properties as morphine. Since brain-stimulated analgesia can also be prevented by naloxone it is likely that it may work through the release of an enkephalin. These peptides thus become links at one stage in the descending control mechanisms that can cause analgesia, but the exact sites of action are still under investigation.

The thalamus

The thalami are two large masses of grey matter about 4 cm long placed on either side of the third ventricle and extending posteriorly, as the pulvinar, to overhang the superior colliculi. Each thalamus possesses three main nuclei; the anterior and medial form the *palaeothalamus*, while the lateral nucleus, which occupies the greater portion of the thalamus including the pulvinar, constitutes the *neothalamus*. The geniculate bodies (the *metathalamus*) lie near the pulvinar, superolateral to the colliculi.

The thalamus can be regarded as a relay station on the ascending sensory pathways (Fig. 34.9). The anterior nucleus receives impulses from the mamillothalamic tract and transmits impulses to the gyrus cinguli. The medial nucleus receives some impulses via the hypothalamus from the viscera; most visceral afferent fibres, however, relay in the lateral nucleus of the thalamus whence fibres pass to the somato-sensory area

of the cerebral cortex. Impulses can also pass from the frontal cortex to the medial nucleus and from there to the hypothalamus. The ventral portion of the lateral nucleus receives afferents from the medial, spinal and trigeminal lemnisci, which carry impulses subserving proprioceptive, tactile, pain and temperature senses, and sends out efferents through the posterior limb of the internal capsule to the postcentral gyrus of the cerebral cortex (C.S. in Fig. 34.9).

Thus the somatic sensory impulses originating in, say, the right side of the body, cross over to the left thalamus, which transmits them to the cerebral cortex on the left side only. The lateral nucleus of the thalamus also receives fibres from the dentate nucleus of the cerebellum of the opposite side and relays impulses to the motor cortex. Impulses from the cochlea pass through several synapses before reaching the medial geniculate nucleus from which fresh impulses pass to the auditory cortex in the superior temporal gyrus (474). The lateral geniculate nucleus relays visual impulses from the retinae to the occipital cortex on the same side (p. 461). These *cortical relay nuclei* do not act in a random way but relay impulses from points on a limb, for example, to specific areas on the cortex; similarly every point on the retina has a corresponding point in each part of the occipital cortex in spite of the intervention of the relay in the lateral geniculate nucleus.

In addition to these cortical relay nuclei there are *association nuclei* in the neothalamus that receive impulses from the relay nuclei and project to the association areas of the cerebral cortex, namely the prefrontal, parietal and occipital cortex. The dorsomedial nucleus is the largest of those; it receives fibres from the lateral nucleus of the thalamus and from the hypothalamus and projects largely to the cortex of the frontal lobe. The thalamus also sends impulses to the caudate and lentiform nuclei, and the hypothalamus.

When the thalamogeniculate artery is blocked in man, the caudal portions of the thalamus are destroyed and there is a temporary loss of cutaneous sensation on the contralateral side of the body (a crossed hemianesthesia) with permanent loss of sense of position of the limbs resulting in ataxia. After the lapse of a few weeks the patient may complain of insufferable pain on the affected side. Stimuli, such as a pinprick, which do not on the normal side give rise to anything more than discomfort, may cause quite severe pain The threshold for pain is actually raised but the reaction to pain is exaggerated. There are no motor disturbances. This is described as the *thalamic syndrome*. The reason for these overactions is unknown; they do not occur when the sensory cortex alone is removed and cannot be due solely to a release from cortical control.

When the cerebral cortex is removed on one side

(hemi-decortication) in man there is, for a few days, anaesthesia in the opposite side, then painful stimuli are appreciated but only poorly localised. Tactile sensation may eventually return but not the position sense. The return of crude sensation is possibly partly due to the ability of the thalamus on the decorticate side to subserve crude sensation and partly to bilateral representation of touch and pain as mentioned above. Position sense is not bilaterally represented in the thalamus.

SENSORY AREAS OF THE CEREBRAL CORTEX

Since little information about sensation can be gained from animal experiments, except perhaps by the study of conditioned reflexes or by behavioural studies and then only by inference, most of our knowledge must come from clinical investigation. For example, a conscious patient may describe his sensations when areas of the cortex exposed at operation are stimulated electrically. Data have also been obtained from the investigation of patients with traumatic or pathological lesions, although in such cases we are dependent on the co-operation of a patient who has a lesion the extent of which may be difficult to judge even at later post-mortem examination. Information obtained in this way is not always entirely satisfactory.

The sensory areas of the cortex are the highest points in the brain reached by the impulses concerned in sensation. Although they are undoubtedly important as relay or junctional areas in the complicated pattern of the cerebral neurones, we are not justified in claiming that these areas are the seat of sensations and consciousness. The cortical representation of pain is less well documented but it can be argued that the cerebral cortex is necessary for the full appreciation of pain; after bilateral frontal leucotomy the pain is still felt but the emotional reaction is no longer present.

Cortical injury seldom causes pain but in a few patients pain arising from damage to the temporal cortex has been relieved by electrical stimulation of an area in or near the posterior limb of the internal capsule.

The most important part of the brain in relation to tactile and bodily sensation is the parietal lobe and an account of this is given in the following section. The occipital and temporal lobes, which are concerned with the central representation of vision and hearing, are discussed in Chapters 37 and 38.

The parietal lobes

When the region of the postcentral gyrus in man is stimulated electrically, sensations of touch and pressure are aroused. This is the primary somato-sensory area (SI) of the cerebral cortex. Occasionally feelings of

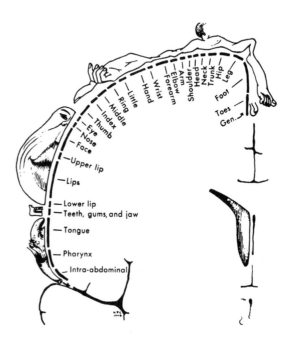

Fig. 34.10 Sensory homunculus. The right side of the figurine is laid upon a cross-section of the hemisphere, drawn somewhat in proportion to the extent of sensory cortex devoted to it. The length of the underlying black lines indicates more accurately the comparative extent of each representation (W Penfield & T Rasmussen 1950 The Cerebral Cortex of Man, Macmillan, New York)

warmth are elicited but only rarely is a painful sensation reported, and no muscular movements occur if stimulation of the precentral gyrus is avoided. Sensation of the leg, trunk, arm and face on the opposite side of the body is represented in that order from above downwards (Fig. 34.10) and area representation in the sensory cortex (*somaesthetic area*) is, therefore, very similar to that of the motor cortex (p. 438) lying immediately in front of it. The postcentral convoluton receives impulses via the thalamus from the medial lemnisci and spinothalamic tracts. Stimulation of the posterior lip of the precentral gyrus, which is usually regarded as part of the motor area, also gives rise to sensations similar to those arising on stimulation of the postcentral gyrus.

The sensory areas in animals have been mapped out in conscious animals by inserting recording micro-electrodes into the cortex, connecting them to an amplifier and thence to an oscillograph or a loudspeaker. The experimenter, by touching various parts of the animal's body in turn, finds the area of skin giving a discharge of impulses. In this way the representation of the body surface — leg, arm and one side of the face from above downwards — on the contralateral postcentral gyrus has been confirmed. A small *secondary sensory area* (SII) has been found at the lower end of the postcentral gyrus. There is a bilateral representation of the body. Pain can be elicited by electrical stimulation of SII.

Removal of the postcentral gyrus leads to impairment but not complete abolition of the ability to detect differences in weight and texture and of stereognosis — the ability to recognise objects through touch. The latter implies more than superficial touch perception since temperature and deep pressure sensibilities as well as appreciation of weight (from joint receptors) are all involved. *Tactile agnosia* is the inability to recognise objects through touch when all relevant sensory pathways are intact. It occurs in lesions of the posterior parietal lobe and lesions of this part of the brain on the left side may produce bilateral tactile agnosia. This capacity to recognise, the failure of which gives rise to the different varieties of agnosia, is essentially a function of the cerebral cortex and depends on the ability of sensory perceptions to evoke the neuronal responses necessary to identify the object perceived.

A lesion of the left angular gyrus in a right-handed person may result in inability to write (*agraphia*). This deficit is sometimes accompanied by inability to distinguish right from left, inability to recognise individual fingers and inability to calculate. Lesions in the parietal area in man may produce a loss of the ability to find the way even in the patient's own house together with the loss of the ability to conceive space even in two dimensions. When we are aware of the position of our body relative to other objects around us the position of its various parts, head, trunk and limbs, to one another, we are also aware of changes in all these relationships. To this sort of awareness the term *body image* has been assigned. Disturbances of the body image are particularly liable to occur when disease affects the parietal lobe of the right or non-dominant cerebral hemisphere. If this region is damaged there may be total neglect of one half of the body and the patient may have difficulty in carrying out such everyday acts as dressing and sitting down in a chair. Damage to the parietal lobe of the dominant hemisphere may sometimes make it impossible to carry out actions to command or even

perform complex actions at all. This inability to perform organised movements in the absence of paralysis is termed *apraxia*.

Taste has been localised in the lowest part of the postcentral gyrus. Lesions in this area cause disturbances of taste on the opposite side of the tongue as well as cutaneous sensory impairment on the face on the opposite side. Electrical stimulation gives rise to taste sensations. Impulses from each side of the tongue cross over almost completely to the opposite side in the medial lemniscus to the thalamus and so on to the cortex.

After removal or destruction of the postcentral gyrus there is a considerable recovery of sensation, a fact that may be explained by ipsilateral representation of sensation or by supposing that representation is not confined to the post-central gyrus as is usually assumed. It is now thought that the sensory paths from the limbs and trunk are bilateral. The second somatic area (SII) containing ipsilateral representation is intermingled with the classical contralateral representation. The lemniscal pathway goes almost exclusively to the contralateral side of the hemisphere; the anterolateral system (spinothalamic system) is probably the main source of ipsilateral representation. Damage to the sensorimotor cortex on one side impairs the touch and pressure sense of the hand on the same side in both man and monkeys and it is no longer realistic to regard the sensory and motor cortical mechanisms as being independent.

FURTHER READING

Gordon G (ed) 1977 Somatic and visceral sensory mechanisms. British Medical Bulletin 33: No 2
Gordon G 1978 Active touch. Pergamon, Oxford
Iggo A, Iverson L L, Cervero F (eds) 1986 Nociception and pain. Cambridge University Press
Kerr F W L, Wilson P R 1978 Pain. Annual Review of Neuroscience 1: 83–102
Zotterman Y 1976 Sensory functions of the skin in primates. Pergamon, Oxford

35

Spinal reflex mechanisms

The spinal cord

No trace of segmentation can be seen on the surface of the spinal cord but it is convenient to describe it as if it were divided up into 31 segments from each of which arises a pair of *spinal nerves* (Fig. 35.1). The *dorsal roots* leave the cord in the dorso-lateral position as a number of rootlets that fuse to form a single trunk. This has an expansion, the *dorsal root ganglion*, which contains the cell bodies for the dorsal root axons. Nearly all the dorsal root axons have a cell body in the ganglion. The *ventral root* arises from a series of rootlets leaving the ventro-lateral aspect of the cord, which fuse first with each other and then with the dorsal root beyond the ganglion to form the spinal nerve (Fig. 35.1).

The cord can be divided into an H-shaped central zone surrounding the spinal canal composed mainly of nerve cells (the *grey matter*) contained within a periph-

eral part (the *white matter*) composed almost entirely of myelinated nerve fibres together with processes of the neuroglial cells. The grey matter is divided anatomically into three columns or horns of cells on each side — the dorsal horn, the ventral horn and, between them, the lateral horn. In general the dorsal horn is concerned with sensation, the ventral horn with movement, and the lateral horn, which is only present in the thoracic and upper lumbar regions, with the sympathetic part of the autonomic nervous system. The dorsal horn contains two areas in which small nerve cells predominate, the *thoracic nucleus* at its base near the midline and the *substantia gelatinosa*, which forms its dorsal cap.

Two techniques have been used after destruction of nervous tissue to determine the site of origin of nerve fibres and their route and destination. After a nerve fibre is severed from its cell a series of degenerative changes occur both in the fibre and in the detached cell body. Nerve fibres undergo a process called *Wallerian degeneration*. A few days after the section the degenerating myelin sheath in the severed part begins to break up, its unsaturated fats becoming stainable with osmic acid. Subsequently the degenerating mass is engulfed and removed by macrophages. The nerve cell body undergoes a process called *chromatolysis*. Within 4 days the RNA-containing *Nissl granules*, stainable with basic stains, are lost from basal parts of the dendrites and after 13 days the Nissl granules disappear from the cell entirely and the nucleus takes up an eccentric position. Thus, staining damaged tissue with osmic acid reveals where nerve fibres go, and looking for the chromatolytic changes in nerve cells shows where the degenerating fibres arise. It is therefore possible to build up maps of pathways within the CNS of experimental animals or of human patients with acquired nervous injuries by postmortem histological examination of nervous tissue.

The main ascending and descending nervous pathways in the spinal cord can be identified and are illustrated in Figure 35.2. By cutting peripheral nerves it can be shown that the skeleto-motor nerve cells are in the antero-lateral part of the grey matter. By cutting nerves to particular muscles the cells of origin of these

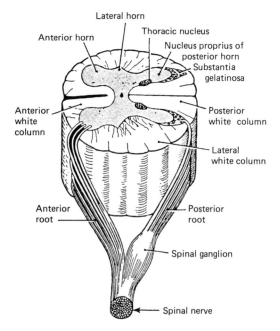

Fig. 35.1 A spinal segment from the thoracic region viewed from the left side.

Descending tracts

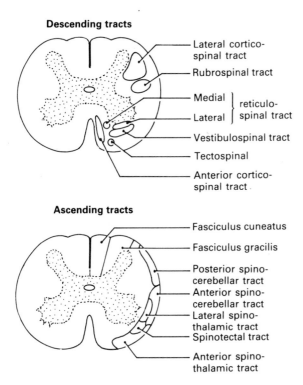

- Lateral cortico-spinal tract
- Rubrospinal tract
- Medial ⎫ reticulo-
- Lateral ⎬ spinal tract
- Vestibulospinal tract
- Tectospinal
- Anterior cortico-spinal tract

Ascending tracts

- Fasciculus cuneatus
- Fasciculus gracilis
- Posterior spino-cerebellar tract
- Anterior spino-cerebellar tract
- Lateral spino-thalamic tract
- Spinotectal tract
- Anterior spino-thalamic tract

Fig. 35.2 Transverse sections of human spinal cord to show (A) the positions of the descending tracts and (B) those of the ascending tracts. Intersegmental tracts lie between the grey matter and the descending tracts.

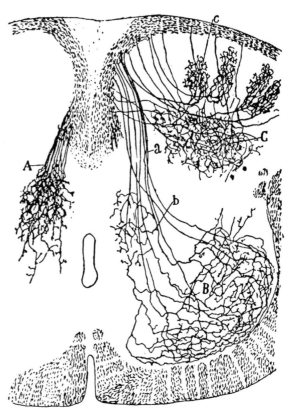

Fig. 35.3 Distribution of primary afferent fibre terminations in a cross-section of the spinal cord from the newborn rat. C, fibres to dorsal horn and possibly the substantia gelatinosa. a, fibres to ventral horn B with collaterals (b) to the intermediate nucleus of Cajal. A, dense termination of fibres to the intermediate nucleus. Golgi method. (From Cajal S R 1920 Histologie du systeme nerveux de l'homme et des vertebres. Maloine, Paris).

nerves can be identified. In most cases the nerve cells supplying one muscle are intermingled with the cells supplying other muscles so that the cell groups or *motoneurone pools* do not form discrete nuclei; however, they are functionally inter-related. For example, the flexor muscles have cells in the same part of the cord; motoneurone pools concerned with muscles having the same function, for example flexion at a particular joint, tend to be together while motoneurone pools having an opposite function at that joint tend to lie adjacent in the same horizontal plane. This anatomical distribution of nerve cell bodies can be studied more exactly by using the observation that if the cut ends of nerve fibres are dipped in a solution of horseradish peroxidase (HRP), or if the HRP is injected into a muscle then HRP is taken up by the nerve fibres and conveyed back to the nerve cell body, where it can be identified by appropriate stains.

The staining technique devised by Golgi makes use of the reaction of nervous tissue with ammoniacal silver solutions. If suitably pre-treated, about 0.1 pre cent of the cell population in the tissue takes up the silver solution, which is reduced to metallic silver and appears as a brown stain. If a cell does stain it stains in its

entirety. This allows the determination of where an incoming axon terminates and allows a three-dimensional reconstruction of the terminal zone. Examination of the cells shows not only the cell body but also the three-dimensional spatial distribution of the dendrites. In this way it was possible to determine the regions in which large axons entering the spinal cord terminate (Fig. 35.3). Similar conclusions have been reached more recently by using techniques involving the insertion of micro-electrodes filled with a solution of HRP into functionally identified axons or nerve cells.

Figure 35.3 also shows that each incoming axon branches repeatedly to give fine unmyelinated terminal branches that synapse (Chap. 33) on the cell bodies or dendrites of cells in a large area at the same level in the cord. Conversely each cell body has synapses from a large number of afferents. Indeed it has been estimated that some 50 per cent of the surface of the cell body and dendrites is covered with synaptic knobs.

Spinal reflexes

The nerve fibres entering the spinal cord not only provide information to be passed to higher centres about the external world near, or on, the skin surface and about the activity and position of the limbs but also participate in reflex actions of muscles. A *reflex action* may be defined as the activation of muscles in an involuntary, automatic and stereotyped manner. The patterns of reflex actions indicate that there may be either a fixed 'wiring pattern' in the spinal cord or a fixed programme of activity that can be thrown into action by certain stimuli. For example if the skin of a paraplegic man is pinched, the leg is withdrawn by a *flexion reflex*. The energy with which this reflex occurs depends on the strength of the applied stimulus. Similar reflex actions can be seen in a decerebrate frog, in which the co-ordination of the action may be very precise; if a small piece of paper soaked in acid is applied to its flank, the frog moves one of its legs to flick off the irritating stimulus.

Reflex activity may be measured in a number of ways. First, the tension produced by a single muscle can be used as a measure of the output of its motoneurones. Secondly the discharge in a single fibre, or in a whole nerve, may be recorded (Chap. 32). Thirdly, recordings may be made with a micro-electrode from the interior of a motoneurone or extracellularly from nearby.

The integrated muscle responses were used by Sherrington to explore reflex activity in the spinal cord. He used an animal preparation that was anaesthetic and had no emotive response to pain. This was achieved by the process of decerebration in which, under anaesthesia, the entire brain rostral to the junction between the inferior and superior colliculi (part of the mid-brain and all of the thalamus and cortex) had been removed. On recovery from the anaesthesia such a preparation shows *decerebrate rigidity*, in which the anti-gravity muscles are tonically contracted and the animal has a position of 'exaggerated standing' with the limbs, neck and tail extended and the back arched. Such a preparation breathes spontaneously and maintains a near normal blood pressure.

Four reflexes can be studied in such a preparation. The *myotatic or stretch reflex* is the automatic contraction a muscle gives when it is stretched. It is used clinically as the automatic 'jerk' response a muscle shows to tapping its tendon and is used to determine the integrity of the spinal cord at various levels. The *flexor reflex* is the contraction of flexor muscles in response to an overtly or potentially injurious stimulus. In the *crossed extensor* reflex the leg opposite to that giving a flexion response becomes extended to compensate, ordinarily, for the shift in the load when the opposite leg is flexed. When the flank is irritated by an 'electric flea', rhythmic

co-ordinated movement of a limb results, the *scratch reflex*.

Sherrington showed that reflexes were usually produced in response to an iterative input to the spinal cord, either with an artificial electrical activation of the peripheral nerves or because the experimental stimulus is maintained, causing an iterative activation of the peripheral nerves. With the exception of muscle 'jerks' all reflexes are the result of a train of nervous activity that has to be summed in time (*temporal summation*) to produce motoneuronal activation. Figure 35.4 shows the response from a muscle to an electric flea. When the

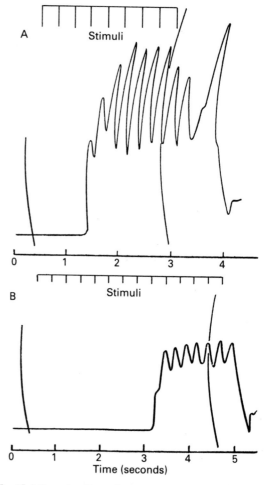

Fig. 35.4 Scratch reflexes from a spinal dog to show temporal summation. The records show the deflection of a spring attached to the hindleg muscle involved in the reflex. The stimulus, an electric shock or 'flea', is greater in A than in B. Note the more rapid appearance of the reflex, the greater amplitude of response and the longer lasting after effect in A compared with B. (After Sherrington C S 1947 The integrative Action of the nervous system, University Press, Cambridge).

'flea' was made more intense not only was the reflex more intense but it was still not seen until after the 'flea' had been applied three times. With the less intense 'flea' nothing appeared until the ninth application. Figure 35.4 also illustrates another phenomenon: the reflex does not stop immediately the stimulus is removed. The muscle activity continues after the removal of the stimulus, the so-called 'after discharge'. This figure also shows that the after-discharge lasts longer with the stronger stimulus. Another property of reflex activation is that the motoneuronal output is also determined by the addition of information coming into the spinal cord from different sources, *spatial summation*. Thus Figure 35.5 shows the responses obtained to two 'fleas' at different positions on the animal's flank. The experimenter has arranged the intensity of the two 'fleas' such that either applied alone gives no response but when

both are applied together a scratch response develops quickly.

Sometimes the reflex activation can be shown to produce not a positive response but an *inhibition* of a reflex. If the left hindleg of a cat were pinched, the left leg would flex and the right leg would extend. Suppose the animal were presented with two conflicting stimuli by pinching both hindlegs at the same time. Normally the animal has to decide which was the more intense pinch and ignore one of them, otherwise the animal would drop its hindquarters to the ground, or else extend both hindlegs to escape the stimulus. In fact it can be shown that the animal resolves the conflict by partly or totally inhibiting the crossed extensor reflex. It is clear that reflexes can, under certain circumstances, be automatically turned off, so that a 'programme' for deactivating the motoneurone pools is present in the

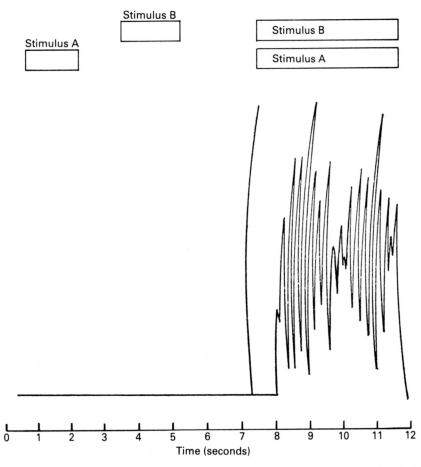

Fig. 35.5 Scratch reflex from a spinal dog to show spatial summation. Experimental arrangement as in Fig. 35.4. Two stimuli at different sites were each insufficient to elicit a reflex when applied separately. Note the vigorous response when both 'fleas' were applied simultaneously. (From Sherrington C S 1947 The integrative action of the nervous system, University Press, Cambridge)

spinal cord. These simple experiments show that nerve volleys or a sustained nerve discharge can have effects that excite motoneurones sufficiently intensely to cause them to fire (*excitation*), to cause an increase in excitability without discharge (*subliminal excitation*) or to cause a decrease in the total motoneuronal output (*inhibition*).

One other aspect of diminished output must be considered. Let us suppose that two inputs to the cord are activated so that both alone produce a subliminal effect on two separate but overlapping groups of motoneurones. If the stimuli are applied together the region of overlap could give sufficient excitation to discharge those motoneurones receiving an input from both stimuli. This would give a bigger output than would be predicted from the effect of either input alone; this phenomenon is called *facilitation*. Suppose, now, that either input alone is increased in size to discharge all the motoneurones under their influence. Both inputs together now have an overlapping pool of motoneurones that receive signals to discharge. Thus the output from the simultaneous activation of both inputs would be less than the sum of the outputs to each stimulus applied separately. This phenomenon is called *occlusion* to distinguish it from inhibition.

Ventral root responses
Early workers stimulated the spinal cord with fine needle electrodes and recorded the response evoked in the ventral root. They showed that the conduction from

an afferent fibre to a motoneurone involved a delay at the single synapse of 0.8 to 1.0 ms. They also showed that the ventral root response to a brief stretch applied to a muscle had a similar central delay and concluded that such reflex actions involved only a single synapse.

Some information about the 'wiring diagram' within the spinal cord has been obtained from studies of the responses to the stimulation of afferent fibres from muscle spindles (type Ia fibres) and Golgi tendon organs (type Ib fibres; Fig. 35.6). In general an afferent volley in Ia fibres subliminally excites motoneurones supplying the same muscle and or muscles with synergistic actions. It inhibits motoneurones with antagonistic actions on the same limb. Group Ia afferent volleys also have weak effects on the motoneurones for the opposite limb, inhibiting the synergists and exciting the antagonists. The excitatory transmitter released at group Ia nerve endings is thought to be glutamate or aspartate.

Afferent volleys in group Ib fibres usually inhibit the motoneurones supplying the muscle from which the volley originates and they excite the motoneurones for antagonistic muscles. The role of muscle spindles and other muscle receptors is described later. The inhibitory transmitter in the spinal cord is thought to be γ-aminobutyric acid (GABA).

The control of motoneurone excitability
Motoneurones impaled with fine glass micro-electrodes show a resting potential that varies between -60 and -80 mV. The action potentials recorded are similar to

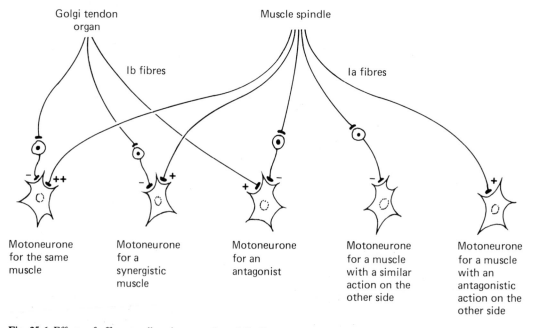

Fig. 35.6 Effects of afferent volleys in group Ia and Ib fibres on spinal motoneurones: +, subliminal excitation; −, inhibition; ++, excitation sufficiently intense to cause a motoneurone to discharge.

those seen in squid nerve fibres (Chap. 32). It seems that nerve cells function in the same way but the resting potential is further away from the equilibrium potential for potassium ions. This difference may be related to the continuous bombardment of the cell with afferent impulses.

If low voltage stimuli are applied to a muscle nerve to activate only the Group Ia afferent nerve fibres, and the ventral roots are cut to prevent antidromic impulses, the response of a motoneurone to a particular afferent input can be examined. If recordings are made from motoneurones innervating muscles synergistic to those whose nerves are stimulated, the cell shows a transient depolarisation about 0.5 ms after a single afferent nerve volley. The depolarisation is not all-or-none, but

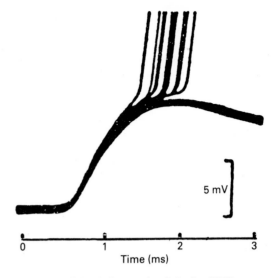

Fig. 35.8 A sufficiently intense depolarisation EPSP causes the motoneurone to fire an all-or-none impulse. (From Coombs J S et al. 1955 Journal of Physiology 130: 374)

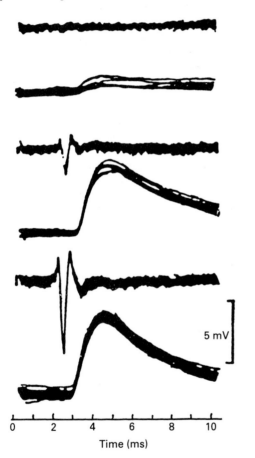

Fig. 35.7 Three pairs of records consisting of about 25 consecutive responses from the inside of a gastrocnemius motoneurone (lower traces) to stimulation of gastrocnemius afferents at increasing stimulus strengths shown by the cord dorsum responses (upper traces). The intracellular records show that the cellular response is a monosynaptically generated depolarisation taking the membrane potential towards the firing level (excitatory post-synaptic potential, EPSP). (After Eccles J C 1964 The physiology of Synapses. Springer, Berlin).

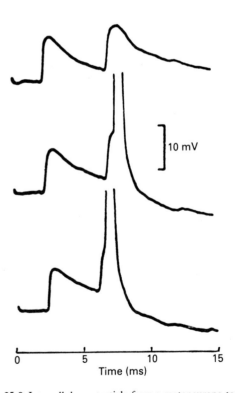

Fig. 35.9 Intracellular potentials from a motoneurone to show summation in time (temporal summation). Note that in all cases the EPSP sum fire the motoneurones in the 2nd and 3rd records. (From Eccles J C 1957 The physiology of nerve cells. John Hopkins Press, Baltimore)

proportional to the size of the incoming nerve volley (Fig. 35.7); if it is large enough the nerve cell generates an all-or-none action potential (Fig. 35.8). The depolarisation is called the *excitatory post-synaptic potential* or EPSP and may be increased by afferent impulses from different muscle nerves (spatial summation) and when one nerve volley follows closely after another (temporal summation) (Fig. 35.9). The spatial summation is not always algebraic (Fig. 35.10). Since synapses are scattered over the dendritic and somatic membranes, that is, on and remote from the cell body, it is not surprising that the EPSP from synaptic activity at a site remote from the cell body should be smaller and rise more slowly than that from activity on or near the cell body. In frog spinal motoneurones, fibres in the lateral columns of the spinal cord synapse on the cell body and those of the dorsal roots on the dendrites; stimulation of fibres at these different sites produces the EPSP depolarisation that would be predicted.

In similar experiments it has been shown that the effect of afferent volleys in Group Ia fibres from muscles antagonistic to the impaled motoneurone produces a hyperpolarisation; that is, the cell membrane potential becomes more negative. This is called the *inhibitory post-synaptic potential* (IPSP). The IPSP, like the EPSP, is

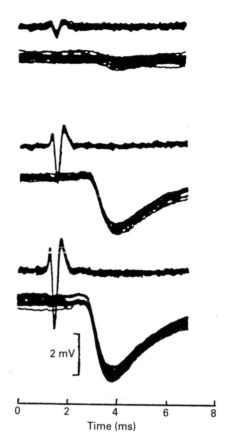

Fig. 35.11 Three pairs of records consisting of about 25 consecutive responses from the inside of a biceps semi-tendinosus motoneurone (lower traces) to stimulation of quadriceps afferents at increasing stimulus strengths shown by the cord dorsum responses (upper traces). The intracellular records show that the cellular response is a hyperpolarisation taking the membrane potential away from its firing level, hence inhibitory post-synaptic potential. (After Curtis D R, Eccles J C 1959 Journal of Physiology 145: 529)

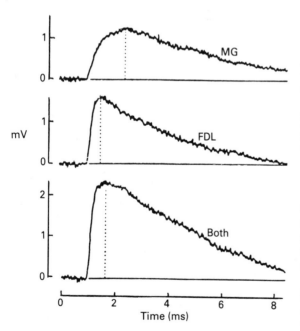

Fig. 35.10 Non-algebraic spatial summation. Responses in a flexor digitorum longus motoneurone to stimulation of its own nerve (FDL), to that of the medial gastrocnemius (MG) and both at once. Note that the response to both gives only some 83 per cent of the expected algebraic summation. Each trace is the averaged response to 25 successive stimuli. (From Burke 1967 Journal of Neurophysiology 30: 1114)

a graded response (Fig. 35.11) and shows both spatial and temporal summation. However the IPSP is only seen after a latency of 1.3 ms (compared to 0.5 ms for the EPSP). This difference results from the interpolation of a second synapse with a delay of 0.8 ms.

In summary a motoneurone is subject to both inhibitory and excitatory stimuli each mediated by different chemical transmitters. Its potential at any time, and therefore the likelihood of an all-or-none depolarisation, reflects the sum of all the inhibitory and excitatory effects.

Control of firing rate of motoneurones

Immediately after a motoneurone has discharged there is a period, lasting between 60 and 180 ms, of hyper-

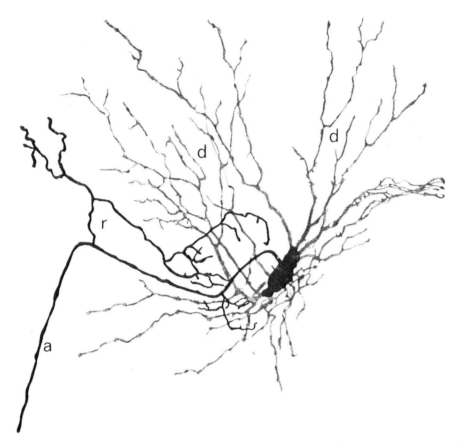

Fig. 35.12 Motoneurone from the spinal cord of a fetal cat stained with the Golgi silver stain. r, recurrent collateral; d, dendrites; a, axon. (From Cajal S R 1911 Histologie du système nerveux. Maloine, Paris).

polarisation. This causes a reduction in the excitability of the cells for a similar period.

Some 70 to 80 per cent of spinal motoneurones give off branches from their axons whilst still in the spinal cord; these turn back and terminate within the moto-neurone pools and are known as *recurrent collaterals* (Fig. 35.12). They terminate on an interneurone called a *Renshaw cell*, the function of which is to generate the after-hyperpolarisation in the motoneurones. Like other interneurones the Renshaw cell is subjected to a variety of inputs and not just that from the recurrent collaterals. To be effective in feedback inhibition it seems to be important that the Renshaw cells are in close proximity to the motoneurones. The recurrent collaterals also terminate in motoneurone pools of unrelated muscles, for example, with the ankle extensor motoneurones it has been shown that the amount of inhibition exerted is proportional to the frequency at which the motoneurones are firing. The percentage reduction in firing rate is therefore greater for moto-neurones with low rates of firing. In this way moto-neurones firing at high rates suppress the discharge of

motoneurones firing at low rates so that a particular reflex discharge consists of a core of steadily discharging motoneurones surrounded by a fringe of inhibited motoneurones. A well-defined motor output is therefore obtained.

Two groups of motoneurones are recognised. Large motoneurones give a phasic discharge (that is, it quickly fades away even though the stimulus is maintained); small motoneurones give a tonic discharge (that is, one maintained throughout the period of stimulation). The Renshaw feedback system ensures that a muscle produces a graded smooth contraction rather than a jerky series of contractions.

Presynaptic inhibition

One further type of inhibitory control should be mentioned. This is the ability of axon terminations to alter the release of transmitter from other axon terminals by means of synapses between axons. Some stimuli alter the membrane polarisation of nerve fibres to give a long-lasting (200 to 300 ms) depolarisation. Since the amount of transmitter liberated from a nerve terminal depends on the total excursion of the membrane potential, the amount of transmitter can be markedly reduced by quite small depolarisations of the terminals. Terminals that give an EPSP in motoneurones give a smaller EPSP if depolarised; this effect is known as *pre-synaptic inhibition*.

MUSCLE RECEPTOR AFFERENTS

The principal receptors found in muscle and tendons are described in Chapter 38. Table 35.13 lists the afferent nerves associated with each and indicates their function. Figure 35.14 indicates the major differences between muscle spindles and Golgi tendon organs. The

Table 35.13 Afferent nerves from receptors in skeletal muscle

Receptors	Afferent nerve type	Typical velocity (m/s)
Muscle spindle	Ia	102
	II	50
Golgi tendon organs	Ib	86
Pacciniform corpuscles	III	10
Free nerve endings	III	10
	IV (unmyelinated)	2

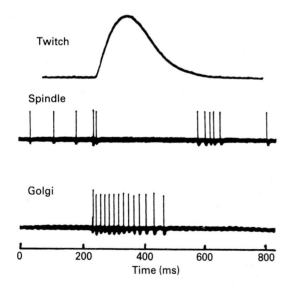

Fig. 35.14 Recordings from afferent fibres from muscle spindles and Golgi tendon organs to show their different discharge properties during a muscle contraction. (From Matthews P B C 1972 Mammalian muscle receptors and their central actions, Arnold, London)

spindles signal a decrease in length by reducing the number of impulses while the Golgi tendon organs respond to an increase in tension with an increase in impulses.

Muscle spindle afferents
Muscle spindles (p. 507) are found in almost all muscles and are most plentiful in muscles concerned with fine movement. The type Ia fibres (primary afferents) innervate the helical structures in the middle of the spindles (equatorial zone). The type II fibres (secondary afferents) innervate the adjacent parts of the spindle (juxta-equatorial zone; Fig. 40.16, p. 506).

In general, muscle spindle afferents signal a change in length but the two groups of receptors have different functions. The equatorial receptors with Ia afferents signal both spindle length and the rate of change of length. In contrast the juxta-equatorial receptors with type II afferents signal only length (Fig. 35.15). These fibres have a smaller response in terms of impulses per second for each mm/s stretch.

As described in Chapter 38, the responsiveness of the muscle spindle receptors is modified by the action of γ-efferents. Two types of γ-efferents are recognised but these are not anatomically separable. About 25 per cent of the γ-efferents are known as γD efferents and modify the dynamic sensitivity (response to change in length) while the remaining 75 per cent are γS efferent and modify the static sensitivity (response to length).

Muscle spindles take part in the control of movement in two ways . First, passive stretching of muscle causes an increased afferent discharge and consequently increased motoneurone output down α-efferents. Secondly, activation of the γ-efferent fibre makes the poles of the spindle contract and stretch the non-contractile central portion of the spindle. In turn this leads to an increase in afferent impulses and so an increase in motoneurone output.

Golgi tendon organ afferents
Tendon organs (p. 506) signal an increase in the tension in a tendon and are mainly found at muscle–tendon junctions. Tendon organs have a high threshold when a muscle is stretched passively but a low threshold when the tension is generated actively by muscle contraction.

Other receptor afferents
Free nerve endings with unmyelinated (type IV) nerve fibres discharge in response to noxious stimuli applied to the muscle, such as ischaemia, squeezing or injections. The small-diameter myelinated nerves (type III) convey the effects of mechanical stimulation applied to the surface of a muscle.

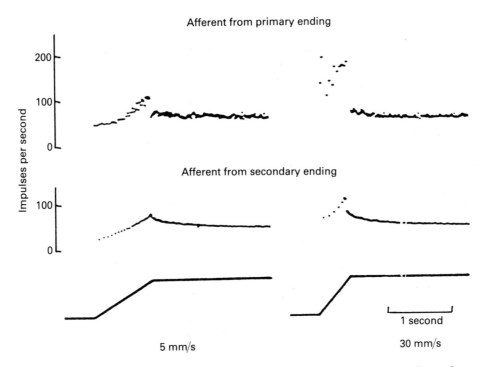

Fig. 35.15 Comparison of the responses of primary and secondary afferents in a de-efferented muscle to a 3-mm stretch applied at two velocities, 5 mm/s (left) and 30 mm/s (right). The response of the afferents is expressed as the instantaneous frequencies. (This is accomplished by measuring the intervals between successive impulses, electronically deriving a signal proportional to the reciprocal of this interval and plotting it as a dot at the time of the second impulse of the pairs.) The time scale of 1 second only applies to the constant muscle length states; during the stretches the record has been expanded somewhat (600 ms for slow and 100 ms for fast stretches). (From Brown M C et al. 1965 Journal of Physiology 177: 140)

Role of muscle afferents in the control of muscle

The simplest example of the role of the muscle spindles relates to the maintenance of a steady position or posture. If, for example, an extensor muscle is exerting a constant force at a fixed length then a small stretch applied to the muscle automatically makes it contract harder by activation of the monosynaptic path from the spindle afferent to the spinal motoneurone until the stretch has been removed and the spindle discharge is restored to its starting level. Conversely, a small decrease in length causes it to contract less by decreasing the excitation of the spinal motoneurone by the spindle afferents until the muscle is pulled out once again to its starting length. This sort of control acts to fix a muscle length around a set level.

It is more difficult to understand the place of this system in allowing a limb to take up a new position, since the length is changing. It was suggested at one time that the γ-efferent fibres initiated a change in muscle length by modifying the signals coming from the spindles, so that the movement of the muscle as a whole

was a reflex result. It is clear, howeve, that for normal movements the α-afferents and the γ-efferents are activated simultaneously. The γ-efferents may regulate the initial force and the velocity of the movement to relate to the load, as anticipated by the higher centres in the CNS. The system may be 'cheated', for example when one picks up an empty suitcase expecting it to be full.

FURTHER READING

Lenman J A R 1975 Clinical neurophysiology. Blackwell Scientific, Oxford.

Ottoson D 1983 Physiology of the nervous system. Macmillan, London.

Matthews P B C 1981 Evolving views on the internal operation and functional role of the muscle spindle. Journal of Physiology 320: 1–30

Sherrington C S 1947 The integrative action of the nervous system. University Press, Cambridge

Taylor A, Prochazka A (eds) 1981 Muscle receptors and movement. Macmillan, London.

36

Supraspinal control of movement

In the last chapter we saw that several motor programmes were present in the spinal cord which are able to produce stereotyped but fairly complex co-ordinated movements, for example, the scratch reflex, by producing a sequential activation of various moto-neurone and interneurone pools. In this chapter we consider how these basic programmes are modified to maintain the body's position and posture and to allow purposive movements.

The brain stem

The brain stem forms the upward continuation of the spinal cord and is composed of three parts (Fig. 36.1).

The *medulla oblongata* contains groups of cells concerned with the regulation of the cardiovascular and respiratory systems, and also the cranial nerve nuclei. In addition there are the long ascending and descending tracts including those from and to the cortex and cerebellum, as well as two prominent fibre decussations, the output from the dorsal column nuclei, which crosses to the opposite side of the brain to continue upwards in the medial lemniscus, and, at a slightly lower level, the decussation of the pyramidal tract, the fibres of which originate in the cerebral cortex.

The *pons* can be divided into two parts. A basilar portion contains the pontine nuclei and the pyramidal

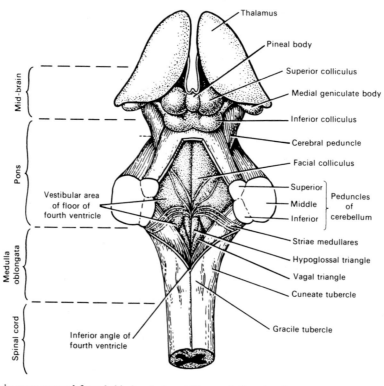

Fig. 36.1 The brain stem exposed from behind and above. The cerebellum has been removed by section through the peduncles.

Table 36.2 The effects of section of the brain stem at various levels on motor behaviour

	Spine	Medulla	Pons (decerebrate)	Midbrain
			Section at upper level of:	
Spontaneous respiration	No	Yes	Yes	Yes
Muscle tone: extensor	None	Small	Very high	Normal
flexor	Small	Small	Little	Normal
Support body weight	No	No	Yes Until disturbed	Yes Maintained
Tonic labyrinthine reflex	No	No	Yes	Yes
Tonic neck reflex	No	No	Yes	Yes
Righting reflex	No	No	No	Yes
Spontaneous movement	No	No	No	No

with their nuclei; the anterior portion or base, which forms the cerebral peduncles with the pyramidal and cortico-pontine fibres; between these is the tegmentum, which contains most of the other tracts present in the hindbrain and also the oculomotor, trochlear and red nuclei. In the middle of the tegmentum the aqueduct is surrounded by the central grey matter. Lying between the tegmentum and the cerebral peduncles is a layer of heavily pigmented cells called the *substantia nigra*.

An indication of the functions of the various parts of the brain stem can be obtained from the effects of section at various levels in experimental animals (Table 36.2).

Normally man maintains his correct posture by integrating the information coming from the eyes, the vestibular apparatus and the neck muscles. In the animal with a midbrain section the visual reflexes for maintaining an upright posture are not operating so the animal must rely on its neck muscle receptors and labyrinths to maintain its posture.

and cortico-ponto-cerebellar fibres; this serves as a site for the interconnection of the cerebral cortex with the cerebellum. The tegmental part of the pons forms the upward continuation of the medulla.

The *midbrain* consists of three parts. The posterior portion, the tectum or roof, which forms the colliculi

Neck reflexes

The tonic neck reflexes can be seen in the pontine (decerebrate) animal in which the labyrinths have been destroyed. In the cat these are logical contractions of the body musculature to attain a set posture. Thus if the head of a cat is bent upwards, the forelegs extend and the hindlegs flex; if the head is bent down the forelegs

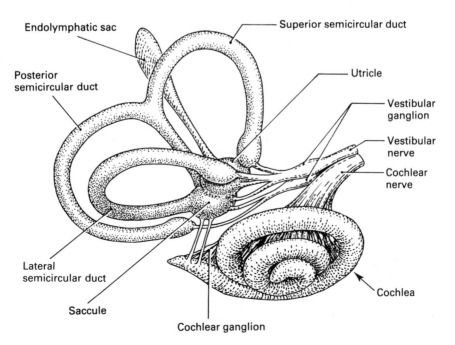

Fig. 36.3 The membranous labyrinth.

flex and the hindlegs extend with the animal assuming a posture as though it were either looking up or down. If the head is turned to the right, and thus the body weight is shifted to the right, the animal extends the two right limbs and flexes the two left ones. In all three examples the body posture remains fixed until the head is moved. Since they are maintained they are called tonic neck reflexes. The importance of these reflexes in maintaining a normal posture can be shown by the observation that monkeys whose first three cervical dorsal roots have been anaesthetised lose their balance almost as badly as they do after labyrinthectomy.

The vestibular apparatus and labyrinthine reflexes

The *bony labyrinth* consists of three communicating cavities filled with perilymph; the *vestibule*, the *semicircular canals* and the *cochlea*. The bony labyrinth contains *membranous labyrinth*, which consists of the *duct of the cochlea*, the *utricle* and *saccule* (two small sacs lying in the vestibule) and the three *semicircular ducts* (Fig. 36.3). These form a closed system filled with endolymph. The superior and posterior semicircular canals lie in vertical planes at right angles to one another while the lateral or horizontal canal is in a plane that is horizontal when the animal assumes its normal position. In man this corresponds to the attitude used to look at the ground two or three paces ahead, that is with the head bent forward at an angle of approximately 30°. All three canals are thus orientated in planes at right angles to one another. Each duct has a wider

portion or *ampulla* at its base containing the *ampullary crests* or *cristae*, which possess hair cells, the cilia of which are embedded in a mass of gelatinous material, the *cupula* (Fig. 36.4).

The semicircular canals

The canals are filled with endolymph, so, if the head is rotated, the inertia of the fluid causes it to lag behind the movement. The ampulla moves while the endolymph remains stationary. This movement deflects the cupula, distorts the cilia and excites the hair cells (Fig. 36.5). Thus head movement is resolved by the characteristic movements of the cupulae in the six canals into two directions in each of the three planes at right angles to each other. Since the relative movements of the cupulae on the two sides of the head are opposite, one set of nerves is excited and the other inhibited. This is because the deviations of the cilia in one direction excite hair cells and in the other direction inhibit them.

The inertia imposed upon the system by the endolymph means that the cupulae should be affected by the angular acceleration of the head rather than by its absolute position or its velocity. The cupula behaves as a damped pendulum and the actual pattern of discharge signals the velocity of head movement. This gives the vestibular apparatus a nasty trick to play. Since the endolymph-cupula coupling is damped there is a frequency of head movement that it cannot interpret, around 3–5 cycles per minute. The slow movements of the whole body such as occur in a car or in a ship at sea thus produce confusion since the vestibular apparatus cannot interpret them either as a velocity or acceleration of the head. This confusion about what is happening and what is being signalled is possibly a basis for motion sickness.

One aspect of the inertia of the system is that the canals emit no signal when the head is stationary or has been moving at a uniform velocity for about 15 seconds.

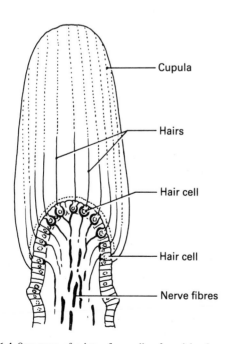

Fig. 36.4 Structure of crista of ampulla of semicircular canal.

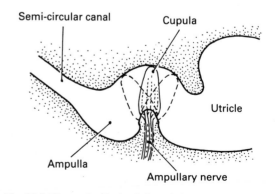

Fig. 36.5 The mode of stimulation of the semicircular canals. The cupula, situated on top of the crista, completely blocks the ampulla of the membranous canal. Movements of the endolymph make the cupula swing.

On stopping after such a movement it takes the cupulae about 15 seconds to recover their initial positions and so, when the movement is stopped, the subject experiences the sensation of a rotation in the opposite direction. This sensation also lasts for about 15 seconds. One way to demonstrate this phenomenon objectively is to observe eye movements. Rotation of the body gives conjugate movements of the eyes in the direction opposite to the movement, enabling the eyes to be fixed on a point in space. Consequently if one rotates the head to and fro while looking at a finger the finger appears stationary. On the other hand if the finger is moved to and fro at the same rate, with the head stationary, it cannot be seen clearly because of the inability of the visual system to interpret the signals quickly. If a subject is rotated in a chair (Bárány chair) the slow phase of the eye movements (*nystagmus*) is in the opposite direction to the rotation, enabling the eyes to be fixed on a stable point in space. When the chair is suddenly halted these phases reverse and the post-rotational nystagmus again lasts for about 15 seconds.

The movement of the eyeballs in the orbit can be recorded electrically by placing recording electrodes on the skin at the outer canthi of the eyes. Records of the nystagmus obtained can be used in clinical diagnosis.

Another way of producing nystagmus is the *caloric test*. The horizontal canal lies close to the tympanic membrane so when warm or cold water is placed in the ear it sets up thermal currents in its endolymph that disturb the cupula. Because only one canal is affected the resulting nystagmus is easy to interpret. The test is, however, unpleasant for subjects with normal canal function as the imbalance from the signals from both sides of the head can cause nausea and vertigo.

The adaptation of the canals with a period of about 15 seconds is not the only form of adaptation shown; they can also show a long-term adaptation leading to phenomena such as the apparent 'heaving' of dry land after a day at sea, the complete compensation for unilateral destruction of a labyrinth as can occur in Ménière's disease, and the ability of ballet dancers and ice skaters to spin at high speed and suddenly stop with no apparent ill effects.

The saccule and utricle

The saccule and utricle each consist of a rounded membranous bag containing a patch of hair cells approximately 2 mm in diameter called the *macula*. At the base of these are found two types of hair cells, either bottle shaped (Type 1) or cylindrical (Type 2; Fig. 36.6). These cells possess both afferent and inhibitory efferent nerve endings. Both types of hair cell have a tuft of cilia emerging from their top surface, which is embedded in a gelatinous substance lying above them. The cilia on one side of the cell are shorter and thinner than those on the other. Projecting from one edge is the thickest cilium, the kinocilium. This arrangement of cilia may confer on the cell its directional sensitivity. The cells are excited when the cilia are bent in one direction and inhibited when they are bent in the opposite direction. The gelatinous material (*otolith membrane*) is loaded with crystals of calcium carbonate, the *otoliths*. Therefore bending the head in any direction bends the cilia because of the weight of the otoliths and the directionally sensitive hair cells signal the head deviation. The utricle appears to signal mediolateral movements and the saccule superio-inferior movements; both signal antero-posterior movements.

Labyrinthine function

While the semicircular canals detect movement of the head, the utricle and saccule record the static position of the head with respect to the vertical.

Postural reflexes involving the labyrinth can be studied in animals with the first three cervical dorsal roots either severed or anaesthetised to eliminate neck reflexes. In both decerebrate and midbrain animals the labyrinthine reflexes involve activation of the extensor muscles of all four limbs in the same sense, that is, extension when the animal is lowered, but flexion when the animal is moved bodily upwards.

The interplay of neck, labyrinthine and eye reflexes is illustrated by the ability of a cat, when thrown upwards with its back initially parallel to the ground, to land perfectly. It ascends with all four limbs flexed (labyrinthine reflex), turns its head to the proper horizontal position (labyrinthine reflex), then turns its body to lie in correct relation to its head (neck reflex), extend its four limbs (labyrinthine reflex) and finally lands safely upon the ground (under visual control).

Decerebrate rigidity

Decerebrate rigidity throws light upon the various mechanisms involved in the control of the *lower* motoneurones in the spine. In most animals decerebration results in a posture aptly described as one of exaggerated standing. A similar condition is seen in man after lesions of the midbrain. The legs and arms become hyper-extended and the back arched (*opisthotonus*) so that the lying body is supported on the head and heels. That it is due to over-activity in the anti-gravity muscles is indicated by the observation that animals which normally hang upside down, such as the sloth, go into flexor spasm when decerebrate. If the section to produce a decerebration is made on one side, then only the ipsilateral muscles become rigid. This result demonstrates that the pyramidal tract and motor cortex are not directly involved in the production of rigidity since this tract crosses over to the other side of the body below the level of the section.

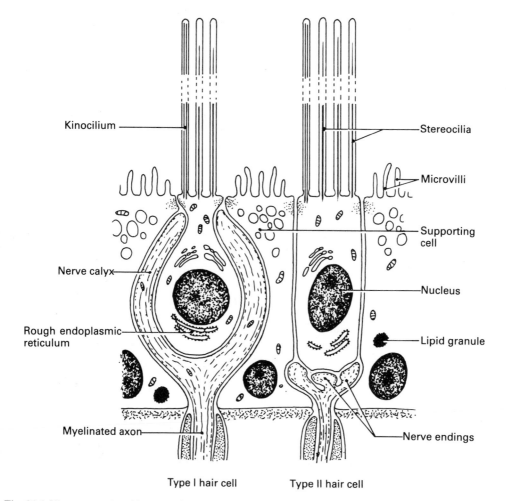

Kinocilium

Stereocilia

Microvilli

Supporting cell

Nerve calyx

Nucleus

Rough endoplasmic reticulum

Lipid granule

Myelinated axon

Nerve endings

Type I hair cell   Type II hair cell

Fig. 36.6 Ultrastructural architecture of the hair cells and nerve endings in the sensory epithelium of the crista. (After Wersäll J 1956 Acta Otolaryngol: Suppl 126)

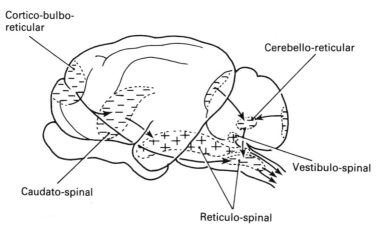

Cortico-bulbo-reticular

Cerebello-reticular

Caudato-spinal

Vestibulo-spinal

Reticulo-spinal

Fig. 36.7 Cat's brain to show the position of structures giving inhibition (−) and facilitation (+) of spinal motoneurones controlling hindlimb extensor muscles. (After Lindsley et al. 1949 Journal of Neurophysiology 12:197)

If the dorsal roots of a decerebrate animal are cut, the rigidity vanishes from the muscles whose afferent innervation is through these dorsal roots. If only one muscle is left innervated, its rigidity persists until the appropriate dorsal root is cut. This fact indicates that the rigidity is caused by a process of autogenic excitation, possibly from the stretch receptors in the muscles. It is likely that this excitation involves increased activity of both the alpha and the gamma motoneurones.

Special areas within the brain have been described, at least in experimental animals, where electrical stimulation leads to stimulation of spinal motoneurones and exaggeration of extensor reflexes (Fig. 36.7). Other areas were identified in which stimulation leads to inhibition of extensor reflexes. These effects were mediated by the gamma motoneurones of extensor muscles. It was suggested that the hyperactivity of these muscles resulting from decerebration was caused by removal of some of the inhibitory areas.

This explanation can be only partly true. It has also been shown that decerebrate rigidity can be abolished by destruction of the vestibular nuclei. It is clear therefore that the alpha motoneurones sum at least two excitatory inputs, one from the reticular facilitatory area and the other from the vestibular nuclei, to give a maintained discharge. Both of these inputs appear to exert both a direct monosynaptic activation and an indirect activation via the gamma loop of alpha spinal motoneurones.

THE CEREBELLUM

The cerebellum is connected to brain stem structures by three distinct tracts of axons called the cerebellar peduncles. The connection to the midbrain is by the superior cerebellar peduncles, to the pons by the middle cerebellar peduncles and to the medulla by the inferior cerebellar peduncles.

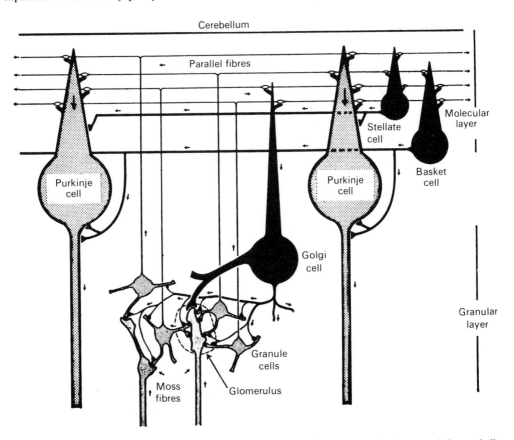

Fig. 36.8 Diagram showing the principal features that have been postulated for the moss-fibre input and the cerebellar glomerulus. The Golgi, stellate and basket cells, shown in black, are all inhibitory in action. The broken line represents the glial lamella that ensheathes a glomerulus. The diagram is drawn as for a section along the folium and the main distribution of the basket and stellate cells would be perpendicular to the plane of the diagram, but they are also distributed as shown to a band of several Purkinje cells along the folium. The arrows indicate the direction of impulse propagation. (Eccles J C 1969 The Inhibitory Pathways of the Central Nervous System. Liverpool, University Press)

Microscopic anatomy

The grey matter on the surface of the cerebellum has a characteristic histological appearance owing to the presence of the large Purkinje cells, but there are no local differences that distinguish one part of the cerebellar cortex from another. Three layers can be seen on section, an outer molecular layer, a Purkinje cell layer and a granular layer (Fig. 36.8). Deep in the cerebellum is a mass of white matter containing the cerebellar nuclei, four on each side, the medial fastigial nucleus, the lateral dentate nucleus and, between these, the globus and embelliform nuclei. The most prominent feature is the presence of the large Purkinje cells in the middle layer, which have branched dendritic trees spreading in a plane transverse to the long axis of the cerebellar folium. These dendrites form synaptic connections with fibres that run longitudinally down the folium. The latter are axons that arise from cells in the granular layer, which pass outwards and divide in a sans serif-shaped manner and run parallel with each other down the folium. It has been estimated that each Purkinje cell makes about 100,000 to 200,000 synaptic connections with parallel fibres. The axon of the Purkinje cell forms the efferent output from the cerebellum, relaying in the deep cerebellar nuclei and vestibular nuclei.

The input to the cerebellum is through two types of afferent neurones, the climbing fibre and the mossy fibre. The climbing fibre after branching to send a collateral to the deep nuclei, climbs up the efferent axon of its associated Purkinje cell and clings close to its dendrites forming strong excitatory synaptic connections. The mossy fibres synapse (in structures called glomeruli) with the dendrites of glomerular cells. The climbing fibres come from the inferior olive, which receives an input from cerebral cortex, spinal cord and the special senses. The mossy fibres come from the spinal cord (particularly carrying information from muscle spindles), visual, auditory, vestibular, reticular and pontine (relaying cortical information) neurones. The mossy fibres thus excite the granular cells, which in turn excite the Purkinje cell through their parallel fibres. Besides the granular cell there are three other interneurones in the cerebellar cortex, the Golgi cell, the basket cell and the stellate cell. The latter three cells act by 'sharpening up' spatial patterns of excitation by a process of lateral inhibition. The Golgi cells are excited by the parallel fibres and their short axons form inhibitory synapses with the granular cell and therefore exert their effect on the cerebellar input. Basket cells, on the other hand, are also excited by the parallel fibres but exert an inhibitory effect on the Purkinje cell and therefore exert their effect on cerebellar output (Fig. 36.8).

Cerebellar connections

These are frequently described on a phylogenetic basis, which corresponds roughly to a subdivision in terms of afferent input. The archicerebellum (flocculonodular node), the oldest part, is referred to as the vestibulo-cerebellum, the paleocerebellum as the spinal cerebellum and the neocerebellum, as the pontocerebellum. From a functional point of view a more useful classification is based on the projections from the cerebellar cortex. The flocculo-nodular node sends an output that by-passes the cerebellar nuclei and terminates in the lateral part of the vestibular nucleus (Deiter's nucleus), which in turn projects via the lateral vestibulo-spinal tract to spinal motor neurones of the axial body musculature. It also receives a projection from the vestibular nucleus.

The vermis, on the other hand, also receives an input from the vestibular nucleus and in addition a small input from the axial (trunk) body surface via the spino-cerebellar tracts, but projects to the fastigial nucleus and from here via the medial vestibular spinal tract to the spinal motor neurones controlling the axial body musculature.

The paravermal cerebellar cortex receives an input mainly from the spinocerebullar tracts. These convey information of cutaneous and proprioceptive origin from receptive fields on the hind and forelimbs. These inputs are projected topographically (Fig. 36.9), as a distorted body map with axial structures represented in the vermis and limbs on the paravermal cortex. The afferent projection from this part of the cortex is to nucleus interpositus (globose and embelliform nuclei) and from there to the red nucleus and parts of the reticular formation. These in turn project to the spinal motor neurones controlling the proximal limb muscles through the rubro-spinal and lateral reticulo-spinal tracts. The input and output from the flocculonodular node, vermal and paravermal regions is strictly ipsilateral. Finally, the

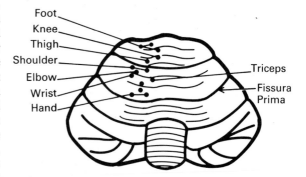

Fig. 36.9 Localisation of discharges in the dorsal surface of the cerebellum from different parts of the fore- and hind-limb in a monkey. (Adrian E D 1943 Brain 66:298)

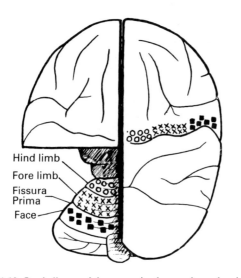

Hind limb
Fore limb
Fissura
Prima
Face

Fig. 36.10 Cerebellar receiving areas in the monkey, showing their connection with different parts of the motor cortex. Stimulation of the area of the motor cortex marked ○ (leg area) produced potentials in the cerebellum in the area marked ○; a similar relationship held for the areas marked × and ■. (Adrian E D 1943 Brain 66:301)

lateral hemispheres of the cerebellum (neocerebellum) receive their input from and project back to the contralateral cerebral hemispheres. The cortical efferent axons relay in cells of the pontine nuclei and the inferior olive and project to the contralateral cerebellar hemisphere. The projection is somatotopically arranged and is partially superimposed on the sensory topographical map on the vermal and paravermal parts of the cerebellum (Fig. 36.10). The efferent projection is to the dentate nucleus, which sends its axons to terminate in the ventrolateral thalamic nucleus, which in its turn projects to the cortex.

Cerebellar function

The functional connections of the input to and the output from the cerebellar cortex are very simple. The action of the Purkinje cell efferents upon the deep cerebellar nuclei and Deiter's nucleus is solely inhibitory. There is good evidence that GABA is the transmitter released by the Purkinje cell efferents.

The climbing fibres excite the deep nuclear cells and the Purkinje cells. The mossy fibres that form the major part of the input to the cerebellum excite the granule cells, which in turn excite the Purkinje cells via the parallel fibre system. Excitation of a single parallel fibre has little effect on Purkinje cell discharge compared with the powerful excitation given by a single climbing fibre. The other cell types in the cerebellar cortex act as inhibitory interneurones. The Golgi cells are excited

by the parallel fibre system and inhibit the granule cells. The basket and stellate cells are also excited via the parallel fibre system and inhibit Purkinje cells.

Thus the final output from the cerebellum is an integral of the excitation exerted upon the deep cerebellar nuclei by the incoming fibres and the inhibition exerted upon them from the Purkinje cells. Each Purkinje cell receives a direct input from one climbing fibre and indirect inputs from a variety of sources indirectly via the mossy fibres. Since the climbing fibres originate input from the cerebral cortex it has been suggested that the cerebellum sharpens the effects of the motor commands from the cerebral cortex much as the Renshaw cell does in the spinal cord. The cerebellum, however, integrates a far wider array of sensory inputs (cutaneous, proprioceptive, auditory, vestibular and visual) and co-ordinates muscle groups rather than a single muscle. The cerebellum is also involved in the timing of activation of functionally separate muscle groups in order not only to produce the movement but also to stop or adjust it.

Effects of cerebellar damage

Removal of parts of the nervous system, although a useful method for investigating function, gives results that need to be interpreted cautiously. In the case of the cerebellum this is especially so since it is very difficult to make lesions in it or remove parts of it without also damaging the brain stem. Since the cerebellum has no role in the initiation of movements but rather with their modification, its removal does not destroy any reflexes but does alter their character (Fig. 36.11).

Removal of the cerebellum in dogs is followed by *asthenia* (weakness), *hypotonia* (reduction of the tone of the muscles) and irregular contractions of muscles with *tremor* instead of the normal smooth regulated contraction. The staggering gait is known too as *cerebellar ataxia*. After a prolonged period of recovery there is a certain amount of compensation in which standing and walking are much improved, but recovery is never complete. The improvement is largely due to a switch to ocular control, since if the recovered animal is blindfolded the gait immediately deteriorates.

Since the cerebellar cortex shows localisation of function, removal of different parts gives different effects. If only one side of the cerebellum is removed, the effects are confined to the same side of the body. If only the flocculonodular lobe is removed, in monkeys there is an oscillation of the head, a tendency to fall and the animal walks with a staggering gait with the limbs abducted. There is, however, no tremor and no change in reflexes. This syndrome is due to overactivity in the vestibular system since it is not seen if the labyrinths

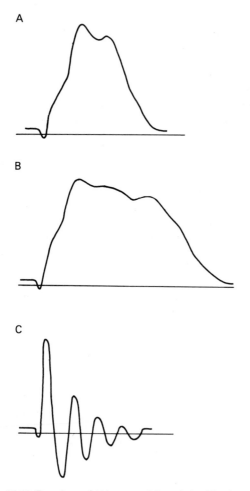

Fig. 36.11 Drawings of (A) a normal knee jerk, (B) a knee jerk in a spastic limb, and (C) a pendular knee jerk from a patient with an acute cerebellar lesion. (Holmes G 1968 Introduction to Clinical Neurology, 3rd edn. Livingstone, Edinburgh)

Ataxia

This term descibes the unsteadiness, clumsiness and bad co-ordination of movements. Balance is disturbed by lesions of the flocculonodular lobe, unregulated contractions of the axial musculature occur after lesions of the vermis, unco-ordinated contractions of the ipsilateral limb muscles occur after lesions of the paravermal cerebellum and damage to the lateral lobes leads to an inability to make smooth, timed, skilled movements, particularly those under visual control. For example, on attempting to touch the nose with the finger the face may be struck violently since not only is the force of the movement inappropriate but there is

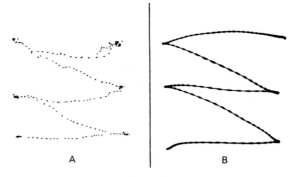

Fig. 36.12 Records obtained by photographing points of light attached to the tips of the forefingers as a patient with a lesion of the right side of the cerebellum attempted to move each finger slowly and accurately between series of luminous red points (not visible in the photographs) in a dark room. Each flash of light corresponds to 40 ms. The range of each movement was about 75 cm. B is the record obtained from the left hand, A, that from the right. The irregularity in the rate and in the directions of movements of the affected hand, and the failure to arrest this finger accurately at the points, are well shown in A. (Holmes G 1939 Brain 62:12)

have been previously destroyed. If the inferior peduncles are cut the results are similar. Lesions of the posterior lobe resulting from midline cerebellar tumours occur particularly in children, and lead to difficulty in maintaining balance (although there is no tremor); the feet are placed wide apart and there is a tendency to fall backward.

The cerebellar cortex is the part most often damaged in man and more is known of the effect of lesions here than in the deeper parts. The observations stem from the clinical correlation study made by Gordon Holmes on soldiers in the 1914–18 war who sustained injuries to the cerebellum. He described the symptoms that have since been associated with cerebellar disease: hypotonia, ataxia and intention tremor.

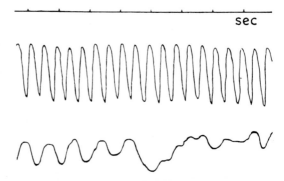

Fig. 36.13 Tracings of rapid pronation-supination. The movements of the affected arm (below) were for a time regular though slower and of smaller amplitude than the normal, but later they became irregular and the arm became more less fixed in supination. (Holmes G 1939 Brain 62:22)

also a tendency to overshoot the target, *dysmetria* (Fig. 36.12). The patient is also unable to make rapid alternating movements such as rotation of the wrist between pronation and supination (Fig. 36.13). Loss of co-ordination also occurs; movements are broken down into components and executed slowly, a phenomenon particularly marked in speech, which in patients with cerebellar lesions is slow and 'scanning', each syllable in a word being pronounced individually as though it were a separate word.

Hypotonia

This is seen as a reduced activity of muscles, shown by the knee jerk, the flaccid feel of the muscles on examination and their rapid fatiguability.

Intention tremor

This is perhaps the most prominent feature of cerebellar malfunction and is characteristic of cerebellar disease. Any voluntary movement is accompanied by a tremor, which may be very severe.

One way to illustrate the disabilities found in cerebellar disease is to draw a square on a sheet of paper viewed in a mirror; symptoms similar to both dysmetria and intention tremor are noted.

THE BASAL GANGLIA

The basal ganglia or basal nuclei (Fig. 36.14) found adjacent to the thalamus, consist of three cellular groups, the *caudate nucleus*, the *putamen* and *globus pallidus*. Two further cell groups are often included: the *subthalamic nucleus* and the *substantia nigra*, some of whose cells contain the dark pigment melanin.

The corpus striatum receives two excitatory inputs: a projection from the cerebral cortex that is topographically arranged and employs glutamate as the excitatory neurotransmitter, and a diffuse projection from the intralaminar thalamic nuclei. The axons of the striatal cells project to the globus pallidus where their predominant effect is one of inhibition, employing *gamma amino-butyric acid (GABA)* as the transmitter. Excitatory effects are also seen in which case acetylcholine is the transmitter. The axons of the globus pallidus cells project to both the nucleus ventralis anterior and nucleus ventralis lateralis of the thalamus, the same thalamic nuclei to which the cerebellum projects; these thalamic nuclei in turn project to the cerebral cortex. Thus the major flow of information is in the form of a feedback loop: cortex–corpus striatum–globus pallidus–thalamus–cortex. The structure forms an important sub-cortical link between the motor cortex, to which the thalamic nuclei project, and the association cortex (those parts of the cortex that have no known sensory or motor function); its axons also project into the corpus striatum. The *pars compacta* of the substantia nigra receives an inhibitory input, with GABA as transmitter, from the putamen and projects back to both parts of the corpus striatum where they exert their action using dopamine as transmitter. Whether this neurotransmitter exerts an inhibitory or excitatory action is still uncertain. The cells of the pars compacta also project on the other part of the substantia nigra, the pars reticulata, which forms another important output from the basal ganglia to the brain stem reticular formation.

Despite the wealth of detail of the anatomy, physiology and pharmacology of the basal ganglia, little is known of the precise function of these structures in the control of movement. As is the case with the cerebellum, their function has been broadly categorised

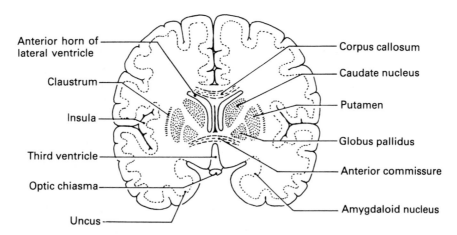

Fig. 36.14 Coronal section through the adult human brain just behind the optic chiasma. The caudate nucleus, the putamen and the globus pallidus together form the corpus striatum.

by careful correlation of damage with motor dysfunction. In animal experiments destruction of the caudate nucleus causes hyperactivity and its electrical stimulation causes inactivity. Destruction of the putamen leads to a loss of postural reflexes. Lesions of the subthalamus produce ballistic movements of the contralateral limbs. In man, disease of the basal ganglia produces states either of poverty of movement or of unwanted spontaneous movement. The basal ganglia can be affected by many disease processes, including genetically predetermined degeneration (such as Huntington's disease), the deposition of metals such as copper (Wilson's disease) or mercury, and the loss of cells in the substantia nigra (Parkinson's disease).

Two main types of disturbance are seen in disease of the basal ganglia in man: motor inactivity manifested as *bradykinesia* (the slowing down of voluntary movements) and *akinesia* (a general poverty of movement), and motor hyperactivity shown as *hypertonia*, in which both flexor and extensor muscles of the limbs become rigid. *Tremor*, seen at rest, takes the form of 'pill rolling' movements of the hand, and disappears during an intentional movement (unlike the movements in cerebellar disease). Various involuntary movements also occur. These appear as *chorea*, a series of rapid, uncontrolled shaking or twitching movements involving the whole body as seen in Sydenham's chorea and Huntington's chorea. These two types of chorea may be the result of damage to the caudate nucleus. *Athetosis*, the slow writhing movements of one or more limbs, particularly the hands, is possibly due to damage of the globus pallidus and adjacent parts of the striatum, and *hemiballismus* ('throwing half the body'), in which an arm or a leg is suddenly thrown violently outwards or the body twists explosively sideways, is associated with damage to the subthalamus.

The best known disorder of the basal ganglia is *Parkinson's disease*. The patient displays *akinesia*, seen as a mask-like or expressionless face, and *tremor*, which is seen as an alternating contraction of agonist and antagonist muscles at a rate of around five per second at rest and which usually disappears during movement. There is in addition *rigidity*, seen as a resistance to passive movement, often felt as 'cogwheel' rigidity when the limbs are flexed passively, due to the superimposition of the tremor on the rigidity, and *bradykinesia*, which is seen as a slowness in initiating and executing voluntary movements and in some cases as an inability to make a movement such as smiling. The tremor vanishes if a patient develops a hemiplegia or if the motor cortex is destroyed; both intention tremor and Parkinsonian tremor can be abolished if lesions are made in the thalamic nucleus ventralis lateralis to which both the globus pallidus and the dentate nucleus project. Tremor is also abolished by severing the superior cerebellar peduncle, which contains only fibres coming from the cerebellum. The tremor thus seems to result from an imbalance of cerebellar and basal ganglia actions.

The finding that, in Parkinson's disease, the substantia nigra is de-pigmented and that the dopamine content of the substantia nigra and the corpus striatum is reduced has led to the treatment of the disease by oral administration of the dopamine precursor L-hydroxyphenylalanine. Most of this chemical is enzymatically converted to dopamine both outside and inside the brain. Many patients show clinical improvement particularly of the bradykinesia and both tremor and rigidity may be improved.

THE SENSORI-MOTOR CORTEX

The surface of the cortex is marked by furrows called sulci, the areas between sulci being called *gyri* or *convolutions* (Figs. 36.15 and 36.16). The cortex can be divided into various major parts or *lobes*; the frontal lobe comprises that area in front of the central sulcus, the parietal lobe that area behind the central sulcus. The posterior part of the cerebral hemisphere is the occipital lobe and the area below the posterior ramus of the lateral sulcus is the temporal lobe. The term limbic lobe is applied to the region of the cerebral cortex that lies on the medial side of the hemisphere adjacent to the corpus callosum and the attachment of the brain stem. Each lobe is subdivided into numerous gyri by smaller sulci.

Structure of the cortex

The cerebral cortex varies in thickness from 4 mm in the anterior central gyrus to 1.25 mm near the occipital pole. On the basis of cellular and fibre distribution it can be divided into six layers (Fig. 36.17) Essentially there are only two types of cell. The *pyramidal cell* possesses dendrites with spinous processes and a dendritic arborisation that occupies a vertically aligned cylinder approximately 500–600 μm in diameter which may extend up to the cortical surface. Their axons either leave the cortex or form recurrent collaterals. The *stellate cell* has smooth dendrites and a dendritic arborisation contained within a cylinder (500 μm–600 μm diam) confined to layer IV. These cells have an axon that projects either horizontally or to other layers of the cortex (mainly I, V and VI). Some stellate cells have an axon that divides to give two vertical branches, one projecting to superficial layers the other to deeper layers.

The cortex receives afferent information from the thalamus, the fibres from which terminate mainly in

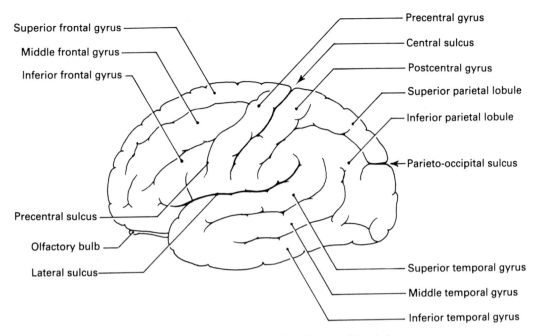

Fig. 36.15 The lateral aspect of the left cerebral hemisphere.

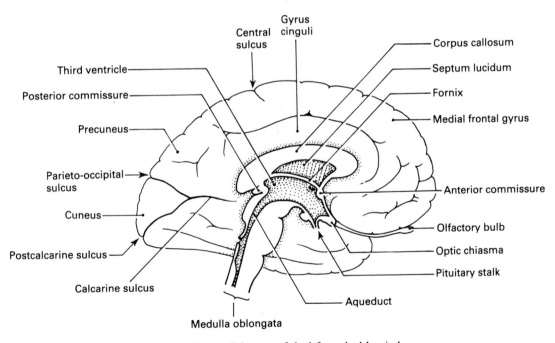

Fig. 36.16 The medial aspect of the left cerebral hemisphere.

layer IV, forming synapses on the spines of pyramidal cell dendrites, and to a smaller extent in layers I and VI. Cells with axons leaving the cortex are found mainly in layers III and V but also in layers I and VI. The axons that leave the cortex may make connections within the cortex by way of branches; many of the axons of cells in lower layers have collaterals that run vertically to terminate in layers II and III. The stellate cells of layer IV can influence the cells in lower layers by their horizontal projections ending on the dendrites of

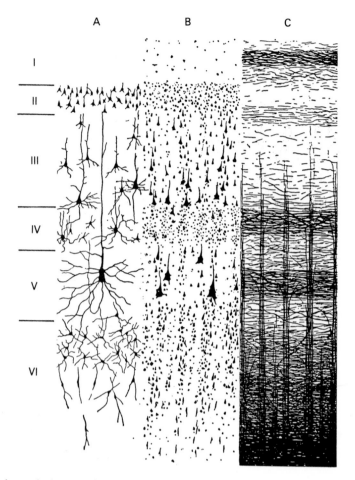

Fig. 36.17 Structure of the cerebral cortex. A, stained with the Golgi method to show the orientation of cell bodies, axons and dendrites. B, stained by the Nissl method to show the granules contained in cell bodies and the basal parts of dendrites. C, nerve fibres shown by the Weigert method. (After Brodmann 1909 Vergleichende Lokalisationslehre der Grosshirnhinde. Leipzig)

pyramidal cells passing through this layer; they can also influence the pyramidal cells of more superficial layers via vertical axons, which ascend to ramify and terminate on the terminal arborisations in layer I.

The cortex has two overall features. First, there is the 'vertical' arrangement of the cylinders in which the terminal dendritic arborisations and afferent terminal arborisations are restricted, at right angles to the cortical surface. Secondly, bands of fibres run 'horizontally', tangentially to the surface. This structural arrangement has suggested that the motor cortex consists of radially oriented groups of cells, each with a distinct input and output, and interacting with other groups via horizontal axons and intercortical fibres. It is interesting to note that after complete denervation of the cortex only a small proportion of the synapses degenerate, suggesting that most synapses are intrinsic.

Localisation of function within the cortex

In 1861 Broca correlated post mortem findings with losses of function in life and showed that there was an area in the cortex specifically related to speech. Similar studies by Hughlings Jackson in 1868 correlated areas of cortical damage with types of paralysis after a stroke and with patterns of the start and spread of motor activity in focal epilepsy. He demonstrated that there was a specific motor area and that this had various sub-areas for different parts of the body. Later it was shown that electrical stimulation of the pre-central gyrus caused movements of the opposite side of the body. Ultimately it proved possible to build up a detailed map of the parts of the body in relation to different parts of the motor area. (Fig. 36.18). It is important to note that the body surface is greatly distorted with large areas of the cortex used for parts requiring skilled use such as

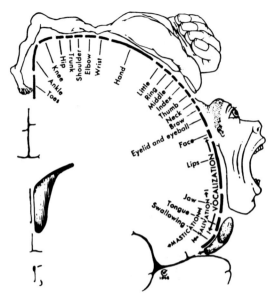

Fig. 36.18 Motor homunculus. The right side of the figurine is laid upon a cross-section of the hemisphere. This diagram gives the results of many experiments carried out at operation under local anaesthesia of the scalp. The exposed cerebral cortex was stimulated directly, usually by laying bipolar electrodes on it, the points of the electrodes being 3 mm apart. The stimulator provided 60 pulses of current per second. Sitmulation of the cortex over the areas marked in thick lines produced movements of the muscles in the parts labelled. (Penfield W, Rasmussen T 1950 The Cerebral Cortex of Man. Macmillan, New York)

the hands and the lips. In addition to this 'primary' motor cortex, with its strictly contralateral influence, there is another, the second motor area, located on the medial surface of the cortex. This area has more bilateral influence than the primary motor cortex.

Efferent pathways

The efferent fibres from the cortex, which outnumber afferent fibres by approximately 3 to 1, can be separated into three types: short or long intracortical fibres, inter-cortical fibres connecting one hemisphere with the other through the corpus callosum, and fibres leaving the cortex (corticofugal fibres). Of the corticofugal fibres only some 20 per cent pass below the level of the medulla to form the cortico-spinal tract; the remainder pass to the basal ganglia, thalamic motor relay nuclei, pontine nuclei, red nucleus, cranial nerve motor nuclei and parts of the pontine and medullary reticular formation and also to the somatic sensory nuclei in the medulla (Chap. 34). Most of the nuclei are topographically arranged (that is, a distorted figurine can also be superimposed upon them according to which parts of the body they project). Thus the cortex is linked to the spinal cord directly by the *pyramidal tract*

(cortico-spinal tract), and indirectly by *extrapyramidal pathways* through the various subcortical structures. The final destination of the pyramidal and extrapyramidal projections is often the same.

Of the pyramidal tract fibres only 40 per cent originate in the motor cortex proper. The remainder come from areas immediately anterior (20 per cent) and from the postcentral gyrus (sensory cortex) and nearby parts of the parietal cortex (40 per cent). Only some 3 per cent of the fibres are derived from the large Betz cells and only about 10 per cent of the fibres have diameters greater than 3 μm and conduction velocities in excess of 15 m/s. The remainder are small myelinated and unmyelinated fibres with conduction velocities as low as 0.1 m/s. Because of the disparity in the speeds at which the small and large fibres can influence the spinal cord cells it is attractive to assume that the fibres with small diameters exert a *tonic* influence and those with large diameters a *phasic* influence on motoneurones, the former via interneurones and the latter perhaps directly on motoneurones. However, only a few corticospinal fibres, particularly those innervating the distal musculature, exert a monosynaptic influence upon α and γ motoneurones; the major effect of the pyramidal tract is actually through spinal interneurones.

Function of the motor cortex

Much of the earlier work on cortical function was carried out by Sherrington and his colleagues who studied the responses to repeated electrical stimulation of points on the cortical surface. Table 36.19 shows the main findings.

The various maps of the cortex in relation to parts of the body should not be interpreted as giving evidence

Table 36.19 Summary of findings in experiments in which the motor cortex is subjected to repeated stimulation

1. Motor response is always on the side opposite to that stimulated.

2. Stimulation at one point may give reciprocal effects on antagonists (for example activation of flexors with inhibition of extensors).

3. Flexors easier to stimulate than extensors.

4. The latency of the response varied.

5. At the end of stimulation, an 'after-discharge' causes first a sustained contraction and later phasic contractions (clonus)

6. Stimulation of one site could facilitate or inhibit the response to simultaneous stimulation at another.

7. Responses to stimulation at one site could be diminished or absent after earlier stimulation at the same site.

8. Stimulation usually produces an apparently purposeful movement.

of a point-to-point projection from the cortex to the body's musculature. They are, in fact, areas of maximal influence on particular muscle groups but these areas are surrounded by larger areas in which the responsiveness declines gradually. The map shown, for example, in Figure 36.18 ignores this blurring of the body image in the interests of clarity. If, for example, the muscles acting around the ankle of a cat are separated, and the tension in each in response to cortical stimulation is measured, it can be demonstrated that each muscle can be activated from a large part of the area of the cortex associated with the hind leg. Stimulation of the centre of an area gives a high tension with a short latency. As the stimulating electrode is moved away from the central spot, tension decreases and the latency of the response increases. This effect is illustrated in Figure 36.20.

One correlation can be made from the various cortical maps. It is that the size of the representation on the cortex reflects the need for skilled movements. One corollary of this is that the effect of pyramidal tract fibres on the spinal motoneurones, as measured by the EPSPs, is greater for motoneurones serving the forearm and hand than for those of more proximal muscle groups.

The major sensory inflow to the motor cortex is from the skin and from deep receptors in the opposite side of the body; cortical cells concerned with a particular movement receive a short latency input from the joints and muscles involved and from areas of skin affected by the movement. Some of this sensory input is direct from the thalamus but most is indirect through cortical connections from the adjacent sensory cortex or from the cerebellum and the basal ganglia via the thalamus.

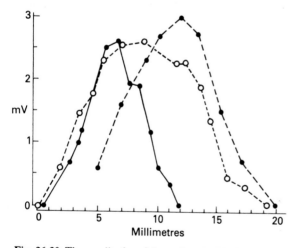

Fig. 36.20 The amplitudes of the excitatory post-synaptic potentials evoked by cortical stimulations along a line passing through the maximal point for three spinal motoneurones. (Philips C G 1967 Archives of Neurology 17:188)

Motor defects after cortical damage

Section of the pyramidal tract in a monkey is followed by a transient paralysis. Its duration is so short that it is uncertain whether it is due to the post-operative trauma or to a loss of motor cortical influence. The only permanent loss is the inability of the animal to make skilled movements with its digits. The effect of damage restricted to the pyramidal tract in humans is difficult to assess since such lesions are rare; the major loss is in the ability to make certain skilled movements.

After cortical damage, there is a decrease in muscle tone (*hypotonia*), weakness (*paresis*), unwillingness to use the affected limb, some paralysis, resistance to passive movements of the joints (*spasticity*), a decrease in reflex threshold, some reflex responses becoming chronic, and the inability to make skilled movements.

Lesions in the motor area itself have severe effects, giving first a flaccid paralysis with the later development of spasticity. Spasticity is seen earlier when the damage extends to include other parts of the precentral gyrus. Classically, the late effect of damage to the motor cortex is a spastic paralysis without muscle wasting, but the effect of particular lesions may depend on a number of factors including the age of the patient. The extent of subsequent recovery also varies greatly. In many patients the loss of skilled movements is the major permanent difficulty since the loss of postural and ordinary locomotor skills may be compensated for to a great extent by the cortex on the opposite side.

THE EXTRAPYRAMIDAL SYSTEM

The output from the motor cortex is usually divided into the pyramidal tract for those fibres passing directly to the spinal cord and the extrapyramidal system for the fibres leading, in the first instance, to other parts of the brain, particularly the red nucleus, the vestibular nuclei and the reticular formation. Each of these structures has in turn tracts leading from them to the spinal cord and at each site their activity is influenced by the basal ganglia and cerebellum.

Red nucleus

The red nuclei are distinct masses of tissue located in the mid-brain just above the pons (Fig. 36.1). Each nucleus has a dorso-medial part related to the arm and a ventro-lateral part relating to the leg.

The efferent fibres from the red nucleus cross to the opposite side and travel beside the pyramidal tract fibres to terminate either in the lateral reticular nucleus or onto interneurones in the spinal cord, in positions similar to those of the pyramidal tract fibres. The function of the rubro-spinal tract fibres appears to be to excite flexor and inhibit extensor α- and γ-motoneurones.

The red nuclei receive inputs from the cerebral cortex, from the cerebellum, from the dentate nuclei, from the globus pallidus, from the reticular formation (see below) and an afferent projection from the spinal cord.

Destruction of the red nuclei causes disturbances similar to those seen with damage to the pyramidal tract except that skilled movements of the digits recover. Simultaneous damage to the cortex and the red nuclei lead to an inability to make voluntary movements but postural control is little affected.

Vestibulo-spinal system

There are two vestibulo-spinal tracts, both of which are concerned with the maintenance of posture and the provision of support against gravitational forces. The *lateral vestibulo-spinal tract* rises from Deiter's nucleus, a group of neurones found over a considerable length of the pons and the medulla (Fig. 36.1). This nucleus receives fibres from the utricle of the vestibular apparatus, from the spinal cord, from the cerebellum and from the fastigial nucleus. Its major projection is to the same side of the spinal cord where fibres supply a monosynaptic excitation to extensor motoneurones of the trunk and proximal limb girdle muscles. Other fibres end on the mid-line inhibitory interneurones and so give inhibition of antagonistic flexor muscles. Other efferent fibres from Deiter's nuclei go to other parts of the vestibular nuclei, to the lateral reticular nuclei and to cervical somatic motor nuclei.

The *medial vestibulo-spinal tract* originates from the medial vestibular nucleus, which receives its main input from the semicircular canals. The tract leads to the cervical part of the spinal cord and influences the motoneurones on both sides that supply the neck muscles.

Reticulo-spinal system

The reticular formation is a diffuse collection of cells and fibres that extends from the spinal cord up to the thalamic intralaminar and thalamic reticular nuclei. However, it is possible to distinguish anatomically and histochemically various groupings of cells that are effectively and functionally separate nuclei. There are two major groups of cells, one in the pons the other in the medulla, which send important tracts to the spinal cord.

The *medial reticulo-spinal tract* arises in the pontine part of the reticular formation including both inhibitory and facilitatory areas. The fibres of this tract mainly terminate in the ventro-medial part of the spinal cord. Most terminate on interneurones but a few of those from facilitatory areas make direct monosynaptic connection with motoneurones.

The lateral reticulo-spinal tract arises mainly from cells in the inhibitory areas of the medulla. Its spinal projection is mainly on the same side and the tract terminates on interneurones with the effect of inhibiting α- and γ-motoneurones mainly to extensor muscles.

Tecto-spinal fibres

These fibres arise in the tectum of the mid-brain and project to interneurones in the opposite side of the cervical spinal cord. They are concerned with the functional ability of a person to direct his gaze or turn the head accurately towards a sound or a light source.

FURTHER READING

Carpenter R H S 1984 Neurophysiology. Arnold, London.
Ottoson D 1983 Physiology of the nervous system. Macmillan, London.
Stein J F 1982 An introduction to neurophysiology. Arnold, London.

37

Vision

A horizontal cross-section of the eye is shown in Figure 37.1. The eyeball, which is approximately spherical and about 24 mm in diameter, has a tough fibrous coat, the opaque posterior part of which, the sclera, becomes continuous at the limbus with the more strongly curved transparent cornea.

Light entering the eye through the cornea passes through the aqueous humour in the anterior chamber, the pupillary aperture of the iris, the lens and the vitreous body before striking the photosensitive retina that lines the posterior two-thirds of the eyeball. The retina is separated from the sclera by a vascular pigmented layer, the choroid, which is continued forward into the ciliary body and the iris.

The eye is normally directed so that the image of an object being focused falls upon the fovea, the central portion of the macula, a depression in the retina situated a short distance to the lateral side of the posterior pole

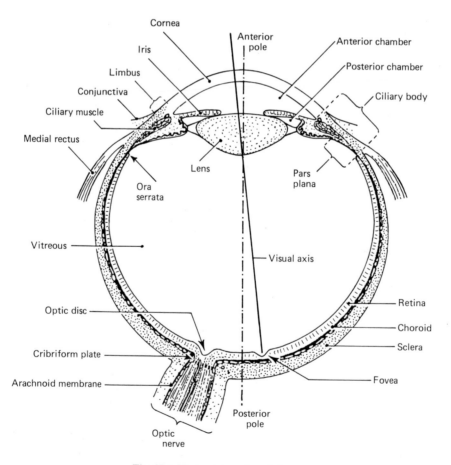

Fig. 37.1 Horizontal section of the eye

of the eye. Nerve fibres arising in the retina run across the retinal surface to pass out of the eyeball through perforations in the sclera (lamina cribrosa) a short distance to the medial side of the posterior pole. The point of exit of the nerve fibres is seen as the *optic disc*.

Eyelids

The human eye is protected by the strong bony orbit and by the eyelids, which are lined by conjunctiva on their inner surfaces. A number of sensitive hairs (eyelashes) project from the margins of the lids. In addition to the sweat and sebaceous glands associated with the hair follicles, the lids contain tarsal glands secreting an oily fluid that covers the edge of the lids and prevents tear fluid from flowing over.

The eyelids are closed by the orbicularis oculi innervated by the seventh (facial) nerve. The upper lid is raised by the levator palpebrae superioris supplied by a branch of the third (oculomotor) nerve. Deep within this muscle are some smooth muscle fibres supplied by nerve fibres from the sympathetic plexus on the carotid artery.

The lids close reflexly when the cornea, conjunctiva or eye-lashes are touched, when a very bright light is shone into the eye or when an object suddenly approaches close to the eye. Blinking also occurs spontaneously about 20 times a minute and serves to renew the fluid film over the cornea. Since a blink lasts about 300 ms we are normally blacked out for about one-tenth of our waking time, but we are quite unaware of it. The eyelids can of course be closed voluntarily although many people have difficulty in closing just one eye. The eyelids are normally closed during sneezing and sleep.

Tears

The fluid that moistens the conjunctiva and cornea is secreted partly by the lacrimal glands, which lie in the upper and outer part of the orbit, and partly by accessory lacrimal glands on the inner surfaces of the lids. Since tear fluid does not normally accumulate, its rate of secretion is presumably adjusted to compensate exactly for the rate of loss by evaporation. When foreign bodies or other irritants get into the eye, the discharge of tear fluid from the lacrimal glands into the upper conjunctival sac is greatly accelerated by reflex activation of the parasympathetically innervated glands. Adrenergic fibres innervate the blood vessels and may innervate the secreting cells. If the rate of discharge is so great that drainage of the fluid into the nasolacrimal duct through the small orifices, puncta lacrimalia, at the medial margin of each lid cannot remove the fluid fast enough, then tears spill over on to the cheek (lacrimation). Weeping may also occur in emotional circumstances.

The tear fluid produced during lacrimation is an isotonic solution of sodium chloride and bicarbonate with a pH of about 7.4 and a low protein content. The fluid, which contains a bactericidal enzyme, lysozyme, serves to wash foreign bodies or irritant materials out of the conjunctival sac. The fluid that normally fills the conjunctival sac and is spread by blinking to form a film over the cornea is rather more viscous, because of evaporation, and has an oily surface layer.

Cornea

The cornea is composed mainly of collagen fibrils with the same refractive index as that of the mucopolysaccharide matrix in which they lie. The fibrils are arranged in lamellae between which lie the fixed cells. Anteriorly the cornea is bounded by a condensed stromal layer, which is covered by a stratified epithelium of remarkable regularity. The cornea obtains nearly all the oxygen required for its metabolism directly from the atmosphere through its anterior epithelium. The anterior surface of the cornea forms the major optical focusing component of the eye; its good optical properties rapidly disappear if it is not continuously moistened with tear fluid. At the edge of the cornea the epithelium continues as the conjunctiva; this covers the anterior part of the sclera and is reflected forwards to line the eyelids. Posteriorly the cornea is bounded by an elastic membrane and an endothelium. The transparency of the cornea depends critically on its state of hydration, which appears to be regulated by the stratified corneal epithelium that actively transports sodium from the tear fluid to the stroma and chloride in the opposite direction. The cornea is richly supplied with free nerve endings; even slight damage to the corneal epithelium is intensely painful.

The aqueous humour

The aqueous is a clear protein-free fluid isosmotic with plasma; its function is to maintain the shape of the eyeball and thereby the refracting surfaces and to provide nutrition for the lens and posterior surface of the cornea.

Formation

The aqueous humour is formed continuously by the ciliary epithelium at a rate of 2 to 3 μl/min and passes forwards over the anterior surface of the lens, through the pupil and drains from the eye at the iridocorneal angle into the sinus venosus sclerae (SVS; canal of Schlemm). Although plasma-like (minus protein) in composition, it is a secretion, bicarbonate being one of the anions. As the lens obtains its energy from glucose by anaerobic metabolism, bicarbonate is important in buffering the lactic acid produced. Glucose and urea are present in concentrations lower than in plasma, whilst vitamin C is at a higher concentration.

The fate of the aqueous humour

The aqueous recirculates from the ciliary epithelium and is filtered from the anterior chamber at the irido-corneal angle into the SVS. The latter is a thin-walled vein that extends circumferentially round the sclera. It is so highly permeable that molecules as big as large proteins are able to penetrate its wall. Between the wall of the SVS and the anterior chamber are numbers of trabeculae or laminar plates, which are perforated with small holes. As the trabeculae lie in parallel, the holes become partly occluded as the plates come together, thus increasing the resistance of flow of the aqueous through them. It is suggested that an increase in pressure of the aqueous distends the space between the plates, thereby lowering the resistance to drainage, a fall in pressure having the reverse effect. Such a mechanism could act as an autoregulatory process to keep the intra-ocular pressure constant.

The intra-ocular pressure

The mechanism described above provides resistance to flow and therefore creates a pressure within the eyeball that serves to maintain its shape. The pressure is constant throughout life at 16 mmHg (range 10 to 20 mmHg or 1.3 to 2.6 kPa).

Glaucoma

This is a disease of the eye in which the intra-ocular pressure is abnormally high. Any rise in pressure is transmitted through the vitreous humour and impedes the retinal circulation with a risk of atrophy of the retina and consequent blindness.

Glaucoma is one of the commonest causes of blindness so its early diagnosis is important. A moderate increase in intra-oculular pressure maintained over a

number of years will gradually induce blindness. An acute rise in pressure to about 60 to 70 mmHg causes considerable pain and may result in blindness in a few days. The major cause of glaucoma is an increased resistance to filtration and treatment is directed at relieving this. The secretion of aqueous may be temporarily reduced by drugs such as acetazolamide (Diamox), which is a carbonic anhydrase inhibitor and interferes with the production of bicarbonate and hence reduces the rate of fluid formation. The causes of increased resistance are not always known but increased pressure occurs after intra-ocular haemorrhage or infection. There are protective mechanisms for removing debris produced by such events. Large numbers of phagocytes are to be found on the trabecular surfaces and in the interstitial spaces near the SVS: these phagocytes ingest debris and reduce it to smaller molecules, which pass easily into the SVS.

The lens

The lens is composed of ribbon-like fibres arranged in concentric laminae. The cortex of the lens is softer than the central nucleus. The substance of the lens has a very high protein content (about 35 per cent) and is enclosed by a strong, elastic, membranous capsule that is attached to the ciliary body by suspensory ligaments (Fig. 37.2). The thickness of the lens capsule is not uniform; the part covering the posterior surface of the lens is uniformly thin, while the part covering the anterior surface is mostly thicker with a thin central portion. The anterior surface of the lens is much less curved than the posterior surface.

The suspensory ligaments of the lens are kept tense by the intra-ocular pressure, which tends to increase the diameter of the annular ciliary body. When the tension

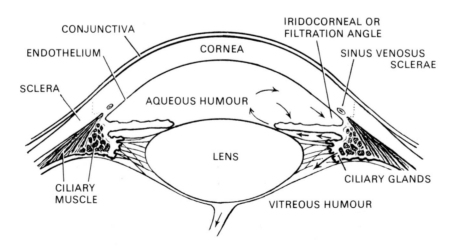

Fig. 37.2 The probable source of the aqueous humour in the ciliary glands and the routes of absorption into the circulation. The ciliary glands lie in the ciliary body, which is a ring-like structure. The suspensory ligaments of the lens are shown.

is released by contraction of the ciliary muscle, the anterior surface of the lens bulges forward. The increased convexity of the central portion of the anterior surface increases the optical power of the lens. The change in shape of the lens is restricted to its anterior surface by the non-uniform thickness of its capsule.

The ciliary muscle is responsible for the accommodative changes (alterations in optical power) of the lens. It has several different groups of fibres, circular and longitudinal, which form a meshwork so that it may be regarded as a single muscle. The main nerve supply to the ciliary muscle is by parasympathetic fibres that run from a mid-brain nucleus together with the third nerve to the ciliary ganglion where they relay to pass in the short ciliary nerves to the eye. Parasympathetic stimulation causes the ciliary muscle to contract so that the eye is accommodated for near vision. There is probably also antagonistic sympathetic control of accommodation although the mechanism of this action is not clear (Fig. 37.22).

Although the lens has no blood supply it is a metabolically active tissue that continues to grow throughout life. The lens uses glucose as its source of energy but since the Po_2 of aqueous humour is low most of its metabolism is by anaerobic glycolysis. Oxygen is relatively unimportant in lens metabolism; a lens can be kept anaerobically without affecting its transparency provided that the medium contains glucose. The interior of the lens is 75 m V negative to the aqueous humour.

It has long been assumed that the chief cause of presbyopia was increasing hardening of the lens associated with dehydration. However, the water content of both the nucleus (63 per cent) and the cortex (67 per cent) does not change significantly as age increases. The hardening is best explained by an increased adhesion of the fibres (cells) of the nucleus. The ciliary muscle does not become weaker as age advances but because of the increasing stiffness of the lens it is unable to produce so much accommodation. In children the lens is pale yellow because of a pigment that absorbs strongly in the near ultraviolet; the senile lens is even more yellow and may be somewhat cloudy. The senile lens is very liable to become opaque (cataract).

The vitreous body is a transparent jelly-like substance that fills the posterior cavity of the eye. In fact the vitreous body is not simply a structureless protein gel but a tissue with an extensive, though delicate, skeleton of collagen-like fibres.

The iris

The iris is a heavily pigmented screen containing muscle fibres lying in front of the lens. The outer edge of the iris is hidden behind the corneoscleral junction while the inner edge forms the margin of the normally circular pupil. The iris has a well-differentiated sphincter muscle, which can constrict the pupil to as little as 1 mm in diameter. The iris also contains some radially arranged myoepithelial cells that lie posterior to the sphincter muscle and help to dilate the pupil.

The sphincter muscle of the iris is innervated by parasympathetic nerves and the dilator muscle by sympathetic fibres. Variations in the tonic level of activity in the parasympathetic system provide the major control of pupil diameter. The origin and pathway of these fibres is illustrated in Figure 37.22.

Although the dilator muscle normally plays only a small part in controlling pupil diameter, injuries of the cervical cord that interrupt the sympathetic pathway give rise to an obviously small pupil (miosis). Such a lesion, which also paralyses the smooth muscle of the levator palpebrae superioris, causes the upper eyelid to droop (ptosis) and the eyeball to retract (enophthalmos). These signs constitute Horner's syndrome.

Effect of drugs on the intra-ocular muscles

Accommodation of the lens and constriction of the pupil can be produced by placing parasympathomimetic substances such as eserine into the conjunctival sac from which they reach the intra-ocular muscles by diffusion. Conversely parasympatholytic substances such as atropine cause accommodation to be relaxed and the pupil to dilate. Pupillary dilatation can also be produced by activating the sympathetic system or simulating its action with drugs such as amphetamine or phenylephrine. Morphine causes intense pupillary constriction while intoxication by alcohol causes dilatation.

IMAGE FORMATION IN THE EYE

In a lens system, light is refracted or bent out of its original direction when it passes from one medium into another with a different refractive index. The refractive indices of the cornea, aqueous humour and vitreous body are all very nearly the same as water (1.33) while

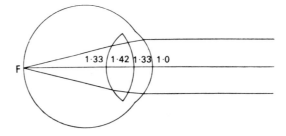

Fig. 37.3 The normal (emmetropic) eye. This diagram shows how the rays of light are refracted when there is a difference of refractive index between any two media. The figures give the approximate refractive indices of the media.

the material of the lens has an effective refractive index of 1.42. Thus light is refracted when it passes into the eye through the air–cornea interface and again on entering and leaving the lens (Fig. 37.3).

The power of the whole eye when unaccommodated for near vision is about 60 dioptres (the power of a lens in dioptres is the reciprocal of its focal length in metres). Some 20 dioptres of this power are contributed by the lens and 40 dioptres by the anterior corneal surface. If refraction at the corneal surface is eliminated, as when swimming under water, the eye becomes very long-sighted and clear vision is impossible. Normal vision can, of course, be achieved underwater by wearing goggles that exclude water and allow the refractive power of the air–cornea surface to remain intact. If the lens of the eye has to be removed because it becomes opaque a spectacle lens of approximately 10 dioptres must be supplied. The power of the spectacle lens that is needed is less than that of the lens that has been removed because it is placed further away from the retina.

Accommodation

Accommodation consists of three associated events — the convergence of the optical axes, an increase in the power of the lens and constriction of the pupils. When the gaze is suddenly transferred from a distant object to one nearer at hand the retinal images in the two eyes are at first both blurred and also disparate, that is they do not fall on corresponding points of the two retinae.

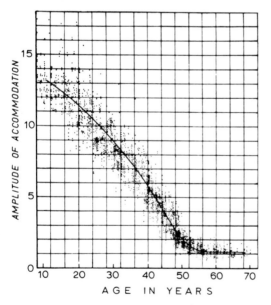

Fig. 37.4 One thousand and fifty observations on the amplitude of accommodation to show how it varies with age. The amplitude is expressed on the ordinate in dioptres. (After Duane A 1912. Ophthalmoscope 10:489)

After a latent period of about 160 ms, however, the axes of the eyes begin to converge so as to move the images of the nearer object on to corresponding parts of the two retinae. After a longer latent period (about 360 ms) the power of the lenses starts to increase to bring the images of the nearer object into focus. Although these corrections may take about a second to complete, the subject is usually unaware of their occurrence.

An object that is as close to the eye as it can be without appearing blurred is said to be at the near point. The near point is normally about 7 cm from the eye at 10 years of age. By the age of 40 the near point has receded to about 20 cm and tasks such as threading a needle may become difficult. When presbyopia is fully established the near point may be 40 cm from the eye and reading fine print without spectacles becomes difficult.

The range of accommodation can be simply measured by finding the range of convex and concave (plus and minus) lenses that can be placed in front of the eye without causing a distant object to appear blurred. The range of accommodation diminishes steadily throughout life (Fig. 37.4) until the condition of presbyopia is fully established at the age of 50 or 60 years.

Errors of refraction

If a subject has normal vision parallel rays of light entering the eye are brought to a focus on the retina when his accommodation is relaxed naturally or when his ciliary muscle is paralysed with atropine. Such a subject is said to be an emmetrope. On the other hand, if the subject is myopic (short-sighted) parallel rays are brought to a focus in front of the retina, while if he is hypermetropic (long-sighted or, in USA, hyperopic) parallel rays are focused behind the retina (Fig. 37.5).

The refractive error of a myope can be corrected if he wears a minus (or diverging) lens in front of the eyes (Fig. 37.5E) of the appropriate power to bring distant objects to a sharp focus. About 6 per cent of school children aged 15 in the UK are found to be short-sighted. A short-sighted child is not likely to be good at games because he cannot see well at a distance but often his intelligence is slightly better than average. The middle-aged myope at the onset of presbyopia has the advantage that he can read if he removes his glasses.

The refractive error of a hypermetrope can be corrected by placing converging lenses in front of the eyes (Fig. 37.5B, C), but he can see distant objects clearly without spectacles by using his accommodation and he may for this reason be less hampered than his short-sighted neighbour. However, uncorrected hypermetropia may lead to fatigue and headaches from the continuous effort of accommodation and a convergent squint may develop because of the close link between accommodation and convergence.

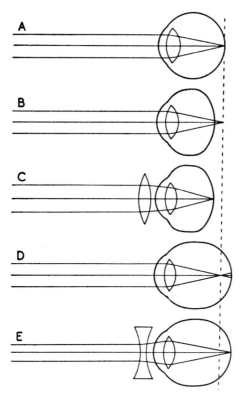

Fig. 37.5 Diagram illustrating the common refractive errors of the eye and the methods of correction. A, emmetropic eye. B and C, hypermetropic eye. D and E, myopic eye.

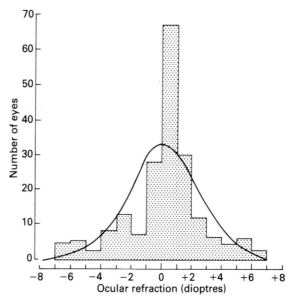

Fig. 37.6 The curve of distribution for ocular refraction in 194 eyes. The continuous lines indicate the actual observations while the dotted lines indicate the fitted normal curve. The fact that the former is more peaked than the latter suggests that, while the optical components vary over a wide range, in an individual eye these components are usually so correlated as to produce emmetropia. (Sorsby A et al. 1957 Special Report Series. Medical Research Council. No. 293)

A refractive error arises when the refractive power of the eye is not well matched to its axial length. Although the powers of the cornea and lens, as well as the length of the eye, show quite wide variations from person to person, a surprisingly large proportion of the population have an insignificantly small overall refractive error (Fig. 37.6). This suggests that the three variables are not randomly associated but must be partially correlated.

Another type of defect, known as *astigmatism*, occurs when the curvatures of the refracting surfaces of the eye are different along different meridians. This results in the focal length of the eye being different in different meridional planes (that is in different planes passing through the visual axis of the eye). If the shortest and longest focal lengths occur in meridional planes at right angles to each other and if the focal length changes smoothly between these values, the subject is said to have a regular astigmatism. When a subject with a regular astigmatism views a fan of radiating lines some appear sharply focused while those at right angles are blurred. The error can be corrected by providing a cylindrical spectacle lens of the correct power with its axis set at such an angle as to equalise the focal lengths in the different meridional planes. If a spherical correction is also required it is usually formed on one side of the spectacle lens while the cylindrical surface is formed on the other.

If the corneal surface becomes irregularly distorted, due for example to healed ulceration, irregular astigmatism is present. In this case the only means of correction is a 'contact lens' that effectively replaces the irregular corneal surface by an optically regular one.

The magnitude of a subject's refractive error can be measured by placing lenses of different power in front of his eyes until the best visual acuity is obtained. When difficulties of age or language prevent the co-operation of the patient, the refractive error can be estimated by retinoscopy. In this technique the examiner shines a light into the subject's eye and then checks whether the light reflected back from the fundus leaves the eye in a parallel beam.

The pupil

If the image produced by an optical system is not correctly focused it is blurred. The extent of the blurring depends upon the magnitude of the focusing error and the diameter of the entrance pupil. As the pupil becomes smaller the effect of defocusing becomes less, the optical system having a greater depth of focus. However, even when it is in best focus, the image formed by any optical system is usually somewhat degraded by spherical and chromatic aberrations and the effects of diffraction at the pupil.

Spherical aberration is due to the central and peripheral parts of the lens system having different focal lengths while chromatic aberration arises because the focal length is different for light of different wavelengths. The amount of blurring produced by these defects can be reduced by having a small pupil so that only the central portion of the lens is used. Reducing the pupil size, however, reduces the amount of light reaching the retina and increases the blurring caused by diffraction. Since the resolving power of the nervous part of the visual system diminishes as the retinal light intensity is reduced there is, for every external light intensity, an optimum pupil size at which these various factors most nearly balance each other. It is found that over a wide range of light levels the natural diameter of the pupil of the eye corresponds closely to the optimum size.

The diameters of both pupils are normally the same and depend upon the amount of light falling on both retinae. Thus shining a light into one eye not only causes contraction of the pupil in the eye (direct light reflex) but also an equal contraction of the pupil of the other eye (consensual reflex). The pupillary light reflex has a latent period of about 250 ms and the contraction may not be complete for several seconds. Dilatation of the pupil in response to reduction of the light entering the eye may be even slower. The pathways of these reflexes are described on page 463.

Contraction of the pupils also occurs when a subject looks at a near object (the near reflex). The increase in the depth of focus produced in this way probably helps to minimise the blurring resulting from the slight under-accommodation usual in near vision.

The pupils contract during sleep, although they normally dilate if the eyes are closed. Dilatation of the pupils occurs in conditions such as fear, pain or asphyxia, presumably as part of the generalised sympathetic response.

Visual acuity

Visual acuity is measured by the appreciation of fine detail in a visual image. If a subject with normal vision looks at a well-lit pattern of parallel light and dark bars of equal width he can distinguish the individual bars only if they subtend an angle at his eye of at least half a minute of arc. A visual acuity as high as this is achieved only over a small region of the subject's visual field around his fixation point and only when the level of illumination is high. Only a short way from the fixation point the acuity is very much less, and even in

the centre of the visual field visual acuity is reduced if the light is dimmed. Visual acuity is also much reduced if the contrast of the pattern is reduced, that is if the luminances of the light and dark regions of the pattern are made more nearly equal.

It is not surprising that the ultimate limit of 'grating' acuity should be reached with bars about half a minute of arc wide because this is approximately the angle subtended by the central foveal cones, which are 2 μm in diameter. However, the effect of diffraction and aberrations in the lens system is to reduce the contrast of the detail of the retinal image below that of the object and it has been shown that this reduction in image contrast plays some part in determining the ultimate acuity. Optical factors (and these include the size of the elements of the receptor mosaic) are not alone in determining visual acuity. The reduction in acuity associated with lower contrast and lower levels of illumination, as well as that associated with peripheral vision, depend upon the nervous mechanisms involved.

Resolution of the separate elements of a pattern is not the only kind of task that taxes to the limit the ability of the visual system to detect spatial differences. The ability of a subject to detect the lateral displacement of one half of a line with respect to the other half (Vernier acuity) has been much studied. The minimum displacement, rather less than 10 seconds of arc, that can be detected when the lines are long presumably depends upon the organisation of the visual nervous system at quite a high level.

For clinical purposes a subject's visual acuity is usually measured by asking him to read a specially constructed chart of test types (Snellens' types, Fig. 37.7). Each line of letters is marked with the distance in metres at which the small squares subtend one minute of arc. A normal subject standing 6 metres from a well-lit chart should easily be able to distinguish the letters of the 6-metre line. If this is so his acuity is reported as 6/6. A subject with defective vision might only be able to read the 60 metre line; his acuity would be reported as 6/60. If the low acuity is due to a refrac-

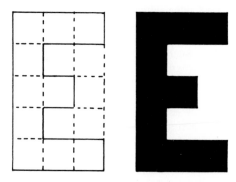

Fig. 37.7 The method of construction of Snellen's types.

tive error it will be raised by making the subject look through a small aperture that increases the depth of focus and reduces the amount of blurring produced by any error in focusing or by aberrations.

The visual fields

The visual field is that area of the inner surface of a sphere around the subject within which a luminous object can be seen. The extent of the field of vision is measured with a perimeter. The subject covers one eye and looks with the other at a fixation point at the centre of the apparatus. A small white disc is brought from the periphery towards the fixation point until the subject indicates that he can see it. The angular distance of the disc from the visual axis is recorded and the measurement is repeated for another meridian. The shape of the field is dependent to some extent upon the shape of the face since it is restricted on the medial side by the nose and above by the supra-orbital margin (Fig. 37.8). Laterally there is no obstruction; with the eyes looking straight ahead objects can be seen up to about 100° away from the visual axis on each side. If the eyes are moved left and right the total field of vision around the head becomes quite considerable with a blind zone behind the head of as little as 130°.

Although an object may be detected when it is far from the centre of the visual field, especially if it is moving or flashing, visual acuity and colour recognition may be so poor that the object cannot be recognised. A subject's inability to recognise an object, although he is aware of its position, is in normal circumstances overcome by turning the eyes so that the image of the object falls upon the fovea. Flashing lights or moving objects appearing in the periphery of the visual field have a strong tendency to cause the appropriate involuntary changes of fixation. In retinitis pigmentosa central vision may remain but peripheral vision is lost. The patient is greatly handicapped because he has difficulty in finding objects in his environment.

The blind spot

If a small object is moved within the visual field until its image falls upon the optic nerve head, where there are no photo-receptors, it is no longer visible. Thus the normal visual field of each eye has a 'blind spot' or scotoma about 5 or 6° in diameter situated some 15° lateral to the fixation point. We are usually quite unaware of the existence of this blind area as we may also be unaware of other scotomata resulting, for example, from local retinal damage.

THE RETINA

The retina is formed from the optic vesicle, which grows out from the fore-brain of the embryo and is thus a part of the central nervous system. The outer wall to the optic vesicle forms the pigmented layer of the retina while the photoreceptors and nervous layers of the retina are formed from the inner wall. In the adult eye (Fig. 37.1) the retina lines the posterior part of the eyeball extending as far forward as the ora serrata, about 5 mm in front of the equator of the eyeball. Near the centre of the retina, a millimetre or so from the posterior pole of the eye, there is a depression in the retina, the fovea centralis, formed by lateral displacement of the cells of the inner retinal layers. About 3 mm to the nasal side of the fovea the sclera is pierced by the optic nerve.

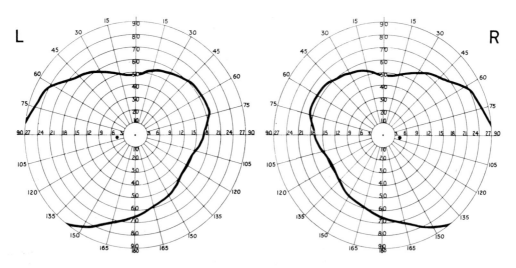

Fig. 37.8 The fields of vision. The black spot 15° lateral to the centre of the field is the blind spot.

The retinal blood supply

The retina has two blood supplies. The central retinal artery enters the eye with the optic nerve and spreads its branches out over the inner surface of the retina to nourish its inner layers. The tributaries of the retinal vein run alongside the arteries, the retinal vein passing out of the eye in the optic nerve. A separate choroidal system of vessels lies between the pigment epithelium and the sclera and supplies the outer layers of the retina. Damage to either vascular system can cause blindness.

The retinal circulation does not appear to be under nervous control. High arterial CO_2 concentrations and low oxygen concentrations produce some degree of vasodilatation. High arterial oxygen tension causes vasoconstriction. Light pressure on the globe of the eye increases the intra-ocular pressure and decreases the pressure gradient across the walls of the retinal arteries, which dilate in a minute or so. This is presumably a local myogenic response responsible for autoregulation of blood flow.

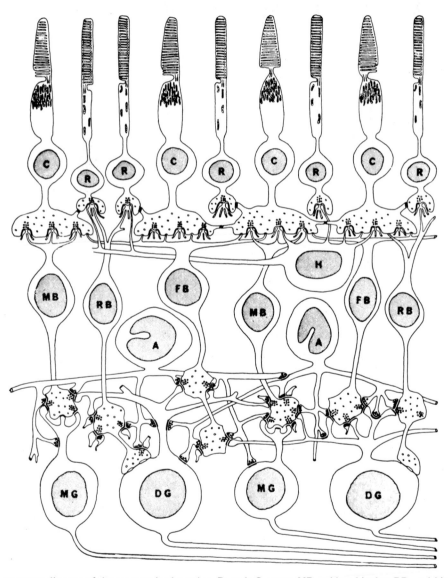

Fig. 37.9 A summary diagram of the contacts in the retina. R, rod; C, cone; MB, midget bipolar; RB, rod bipolar; FB, flat bipolar; H, horizontal cell; A, amacrine cell; MG, midget ganglion; DG, diffuse ganglion. (Dowling J E, Boycott B B 1966 Proceedings of the Royal Society Series B 166:80). The outer segments of the rods cones have closely packed lamellae in which the visual pigment is located. The inner segments contain large mitochondria. Light passes upwards in the figure and traverses the nervous elements before reaching the rods and cones.

Ophthalmoscopy

The structures inside the eye can be examined by the use of an ophthalmoscope. A beam of light is directed through the subject's pupil to illuminate the back of the eye (fundus oculi). The examiner looks along the beam of light into the subject's eye and if both his eye and the subject's eye are focused for infinity the retinal vessels and optic nerve head (optic disc) can be clearly seen but the retina itself, being nearly transparent, is not visible. The pigment layer of the retina hides the choroidal vessels so that the background of the fundus is a fairly uniform orange colour. The yellow colour of the macula lutea cannot usually be distinguished although its position, about two disc diameters to the temporal side of the optic disc, can be inferred from the absence of large blood vessels. The nerve fibres leaving the eye become myelinated, and therefore visible, only as they reach the optic disc.

Fine structure of the retina

The photosensitive cells, the rods and cones (Fig. 37.9) lie in the outermost layer of the retina next to the pigment epithelium Except in the foveal region, light reaching the photoreceptors must first pass through the other layers of the retina. Over most of the retina, rods and cones are found side by side, but in the central fovea only very closely packed (rod-shaped) cones are found. The most peripheral parts of the retina, where the receptors are widely separated, have very few cones.

The rods and cones make synaptic connections with bipolar cells and these in turn connect with the ganglion cells. The ganglion cells give rise to the optic nerve fibres, which run towards the optic nerve head as the innermost layer of the retina. Ganglion cells, and to a lesser extent bipolar cells, can have quite extensively spreading dendrites so that each ganglion cell may be influenced by the activity of a large number of rods and cones. Further lateral interactions are mediated by the horizontal and amacrine cells (Fig. 37.9). In all regions of the retina, except the central fovea, the ganglion cells can be seen to be connected, through intermediate bipolar cells, to rods as well as cones. Over most of the retina there are many more photoreceptors than ganglion cells although in the fovea the ratio of ganglion cells to cones may be more nearly one; however, this does not necessarily mean that even in the fovea each nerve fibre is connected to only a single cone.

Photopigments and vision

Rhodopsin and scotopic vision

In order that light falling upon the retina should generate signals that can be transmitted to the nervous system, the light must first be absorbed by the photosensitive pigments of the rods and cones. The first

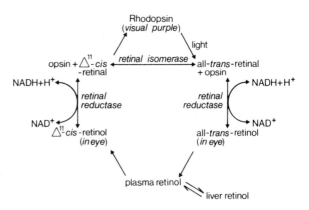

Fig. 37.10 The visual cycle. The *trans*-from of vitamin A (retinol), which predominates in the liver reserves and the blood, is the most active isomer in all physiological roles of the vitamin other than that of vision. For vitamin A to give rise to a visual pigment, it must be converted in the eye to a *cis*-isomer of retinal by the enzymes retinal reductase and retinal isomerase. The *cis*-retinal combines with the protein opsin to form rhodopsin. Light falling on the retina splits retinal from the protein opsin by isomerising it to the *trans*-configuration. The liberated *trans*-retinal may then be either changed back to the *cis*-form by retinal isomerase to regenerate rhodopsin, completing an isomerisation cycle in the eye, or reduced to vitamin A by retinal reductase.

photopigment to be isolated from the retina was rhodopsin, which was extracted from the outer segments of the rods.

Rhodopsin (called visual purple, although its colour is mauve) is a conjugated protein that has as its prosthetic group a molecule of retinal (vitamin A aldehyde) present in the form of its 11-*cis* stereo-isomer. It has been found that when a molecule of rhodopsin absorbs a quantum of light the retinal moiety undergoes a stereo-isomeric change to the all-*trans* form (Fig. 37.10). It is believed that it is this change that somehow results in the generation of a nervous signal. Subsequently the retinal splits from the opsin; the free retinal and opsin no longer absorb visible light and the rhodopsin is said to be bleached. In the presence of the appropriate enzyme systems the retinal and opsin are reconjugated to regenerate rhodopsin. In cases of chronic vitamin A deficiency rhodopsin synthesis is impaired, dark-adaptation (p. 457) may be slow and incomplete, and in extreme cases overt retinal degeneration may occur.

The relative ease with which solutions of extracted rhodopsin can be bleached by light of different wavelengths can easily be measured to provide the 'action spectrum' of rhodopsin. It is important to distinguish this 'action spectrum', which relates to the effect of light upon the pigment, from the 'absorption spectrum,' which simply relates to the amount of light absorbed without consideration of any change that it produces.

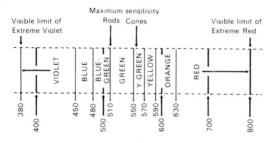

Fig. 37.11 The colour names given to the various parts of the spectrum. Wavelengths are in nm.

Although the absorption and action spectra of rhodopsin come from quite different kinds of measurement, they are, in fact, very similar in shape because each quantum of light that is absorbed has the same chance of causing a pigment molecule to be bleached.

Rhodopsin in solution is bleached by lights with a range of wavelengths (λ) corresponding to the orange-to-violet part of the visible spectrum (Fig. 37.11) with an optimum in the green ($\lambda = 502$ nm). Rhodopsin also absorbs and can be bleached by ultraviolet radiation.

The bleaching of photopigments in the living eye can be demonstrated by an ophthalmoscopic technique. A weak monochromatic light is shone on the retina through one half of the pupil. A fraction of this light, after passing through the retina, is reflected back from the pigment epithelium and choroid, passes back through the retina and leaves the eye through the other half of the pupil. The emerging light is allowed to fall on a sensitive photocell so that its intensity can be measured. If measurements of the intensity of the reflected light are made before and after the retinal photopigments are bleached by exposing them to a very bright light, then the fraction of the weak measuring light that returns through the pupil is found to be greater after bleaching, since less is absorbed. This technique shows that the absorption spectrum of the photopigment in the peripheral retina is the same as that of rhodopsin in solution.

When measurements are made of the relative abilities of low-intensity lights of different wavelengths to produce visual sensation, it is found that the curve obtained (the equal energy scotopic luminosity curve, Figure 37.12a) is very similar to the action spectrum of rhodopsin. This, and the fact that those parts of the retina in which the rhodopsin-filled rods are most closely packed function best at low light levels, has led to the conclusion that rhodopsin is the photosensitive pigment responsible for vision at low luminance levels (scotopic vision).

Photopic vision
When a subject views a scene illuminated by white light of low intensity his visual acuity is low and he is unaware of any sensation of colour. However, when the illumination level is sufficiently raised objects can be seen in much greater detail and in their natural colours

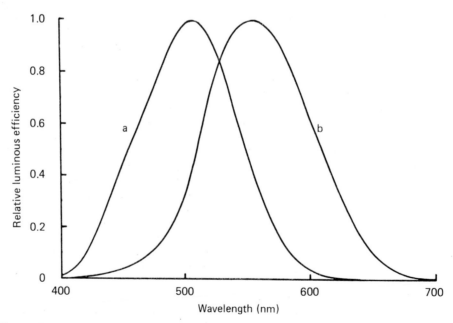

Fig. 37.12 The equal energy luminosity curve (a) for rod vision, as measured at low intensities in the extrafoveal area of the retina; (b) for cone vision, as measured at high intensities at the fovea.

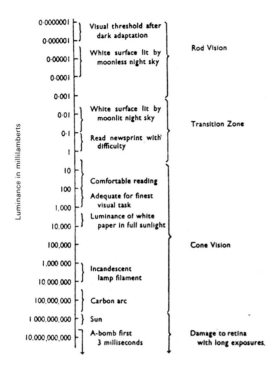

Luminance in milliamberts

0·0000001	Visual threshold after dark adaptation	
0·000001		Rod Vision
0·00001	White surface lit by moonless night sky	
0·0001		
0·001		
0·01	White surface lit by moonlit night sky	Transition Zone
0·1		
1	Read newsprint with difficulty	
10		
100	Comfortable reading	
1,000	Adequate for finest visual task	
10,000	Luminance of white paper in full sunlight	
100,000		Cone Vision
1,000 000	Incandescent lamp filament	
10 000,000		
100,000,000	Carbon arc	
1 000,000,000	Sun	
10,000,000,000	A-bomb first 3 milliseconds	Damage to retina with long exposures.

Fig. 37.13 Range of luminance to which the eye may be subjected with indications of the receptive mechanisms involved. (By courtesy of F. W. Campbell.)

(Fig. 37.13). Vision at high luminance levels (photo-topic vision) appears to be mediated by retinal cones (high acuity being achieved by using the densely packed mosaic of cones in the fovea) while scotopic vision is mediated by peripherally sited rods.

Measurements of the absorption spectra of the outer segments of cones from primate and human retinae show that cones do not all contain the same pigment. The measured absorption spectra fall into three separate groups probably corresponding to the presence of three different photopigments. None of the cones has an absorption spectrum like that of the rod pigment rhodopsin (with maximum absorption at about 500 nm)

The absorption spectra of two photopigments present in the human foveal cones have been measured in the living eye by the ophthalmoscopic technique described earlier (p. 454). The two foveal cone pigments detected in this way by Rushton have been called 'erythrolabe' (the more red-sensitive pigment) and 'chlorolabe' (the more green-sensitive one). The absorption spectra of these two pigments correspond to the two commoner types found in isolated cones. Cones containing the blue-sensitive 'cyanolabe' seem to be relatively scarce and probably completely absent from the central fovea. The chemical nature of these pigments is unknown but

it is probable that, like rhodopsin, the cone pigments are conjugated proteins.

When the relative energies of high-intensity lights of different wavelengths needed to give a particular sensation of brightness are measured (Fig. 37.12b), it is found that a yellow–green light of wavelength 560 nm is the most effective. This wavelength lies between the absorption maxima of the cone pigments erythrolabe and chlorolabe (540 and 570 nm), which are probably largely responsible for determining the bright-ness of lights at the photopic level. If the equal energy luminosity curves of photopic and scotopic vision are compared (Fig. 37.12) it is evident that the whole scotopic sensitivity curve is displaced towards shorter wavelengths. The displacement of the peak scotopic sensitivity towards the blue is known as the 'Purkinje shift'.

Ultraviolet (UV) radiation is normally invisible not because the retinal photopigments are insensitive to UV but because the lens contains a yellow pigment that prevents the UV from reaching the retina. People who have had their lenses removed (because they have become opaque) can see UV quite well. Normal people may be aware of ultraviolet radiation as a vague haze because the lens pigment fluoresces strongly.

Colour vision

Trichromacy

The quality of the sensation produced by a light to moderate or high intensity depends upon its spectral composition. However, the spectral composition does not uniquely determine the sensation because different mixtures of monochromatic lights may appear identical. For two light stimuli to be indistinguishable it is only necessary for them to be alike in the values of three suitably chosen independent quantities. This three-fold nature of colour vision is known as trichromacy.

The trichromacy of colour vision may be illustrated by the familiar fact that the stage lighting engineer, provided with red, green and blue lights, can, by mixing them in suitable proportions, reproduce almost any other colour. In fact, although any pale or unsaturated colour can be reproduced exactly, it is only possible to match approximately some pure spectral, that is 'saturated', colours. ('Saturation' is the technical term for freedom of a colour from admixed white.) An exact match can always be obtained, however, if one of the three primary colours is added not to the other two, but to the test colour that it is required to match. For example, spectral yellow can nearly be matched with a mixture of red and green but, to perfect the match, a little blue must be added to the yellow to make it slightly paler. If the addition of a light to one of the two fields on which the matching is being carried out is by

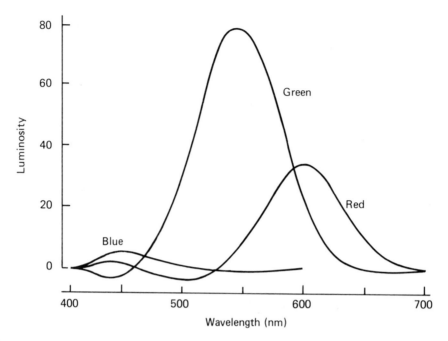

Fig. 37.14 The amounts of red (wavelength 650 nm), green (530 nm) and blue (460 nm) primaries required to match a constant quantity of a test light of variable wavelength. When the ordinate of any curve is negative, this means that the corresponding primary must be added to the test light in order to match a mixture of the other two primaries. (After Wright W D 1928 Transactions of the Optical Society 30:141)

convention represented as equivalent to its subtraction from the other, then the amounts, positive or negative, of three specified primaries required to match a given light provide a set of three quantities that define uniquely the sensation that it produces. Figure 37.14 shows the result of measuring these quantities for monochromatic lights of all spectral wavelengths, when red, green and blue primaries are used. The primaries need not necessarily be red, green and blue, but these have the advantage as primaries that the quantities of them required to match other colours are mostly positive, and when negative, are small.

Basis of trichromatic vision
It is now accepted that the trichromatic nature of normal colour vision is determined by the existence in the retina of three kinds of photosensitive pigment molecules segregated in three different groups of cones. If there are just three different pigments, and if the nature of the effect on pigment molecule of absorbing a quantum of light is independent of its wavelength, which it is, then the trichromacy of normal colour vision is an inevitable consequence. Since the degrees of excitation of the three kinds of cone are the only independent variables, the sensation produced by a visual stimulus must be capable of description in terms of three quantities.

This is not to say that the perceived colour of a visual stimulus is entirely determined by its spectral composition. It is well known that the appearance of a coloured object is dependent upon the visual environment in which it is seen and the recent visual experience of the subject. If a subject places a coloured filter in front of one eye for a few minutes and then, after removing it, looks around first through one eye and then the other, he will see that the apparent colours of things around him are very different according to which eye he uses. Again, the colour of a small object may appear quite markedly different if viewed against different, large, strongly coloured backgrounds. These effects do not disturb colour matches however much they change the subjective appearance.

It should be noted that objects which seem to have the same colour when lit by one source of light may well not match when lit by a light of different spectral composition. The spectral composition of the light reflected from an object depends, of course, upon both the illumination and the spectral variation in reflectivity of the object.

Colour-blindness
Abnormalities of colour vision known as colour-blindness are common in men (about 8 per cent) but much less common in women (0.4 per cent). The

common abnormalities are inherited as X-linked recessive characters.

Colour-blind subjects fall into a number of fairly sharply defined categories. Monochromats are quite unable to distinguish colours at all: a monochromat can match any two lights simply by adjusting their intensities. Monochromats are of two kinds. Rod monochromats have a luminosity curve like that of normal dark-adapted subjects; they see very poorly in bright surroundings and are presumed to lack functional cone mechanisms. Cone monochromats, on the other hand, appear to lack the rod mechanism: although their vision is more or less normal in bright surroundings, they see very badly when the illumination is reduced to scotopic levels. Monochromatism is rare, cone monochromatism exceptionally so.

Dichromats, who can match all colours with suitable mixtures of two primaries, are of three kinds. Protanopes and deuteranopes (each about 1 per cent of males) are often grouped together with the anomalous trichromats as 'red-green' blind. They have very little ability to discriminate colours at the red end of the spectrum, and thus confused red, brown and green objects, though they can usually distinguish yellow objects by their higher reflecting power. Protanopes and deuteranopes differ from each other in the form of their photopic luminosity curves. Protanopes are relatively insensitive to red light and appear to lack the more red-sensitive pigment erythrolabe. Deuteranopes have luminosity curves similar to normal subjects and appear to have none of the green-sensitive pigment. The third kind of dichromatic vision is tritanopia. Tritanopes, who are as often female as male, are rare. They have normal colour discrimination at the red end of the spectrum, but they have little ability to distinguish blue from green. Tritanopes, sometimes called 'blue-blind', appear to lack the blue-sensitive pigment cyanolable.

Anomalous trichromats, comprising nearly 6 per cent of the male population, resemble normal subjects in that they require three primaries to match all colours by colour mixture, but they require them in abnormal proportions. The cause of anomalous trichromacy is unknown: anomalous trichromats may have abnormal pigments.

Colour-blind subjects, even when their colour-discrimination is very poor, are often unaware of their defect. In familiar situations they compensate for their defective colour-discrimination by an increased use of alternative clues based upon prior knowledge of the usual colours of objects that they recognise by their shape. It may only be on rare occasions, when these clues are absent, that the defect becomes apparent.

The detection of colour-blindness is important in selecting people for jobs in which it is necessary to be able to distinguish coloured markings or coloured light signals. A convenient quick test consists of a set of 'pseudo-isochromatic plates', of which Ishihara's are probably most widely used. Each plate has an array of multi-coloured dots so that a letter or figure is formed by dots of one colour, other colours forming the background. Some plates are designed to be read easily by the normal, but not by the colour-blind subject, which others can be read only by the colour-blind subject; some plates are interpreted differently by normal and colour-blind. This test is very efficient at separating the normal from the abnormal, but it does not distinguish well between different types of abnormality. To decide whether a subject with a mild abnormality can safely be employed in a particular occupation, a special test designed to imitate the task that has to be performed is often used.

Though hereditary colour-blindness is very much commoner, defects of colour vision can also be acquired as a result of diabetes mellitus or disease of the retina, optic nerve or visual cortex. These acquired defects are usually accompanied by severe defects of visual acuity or of visual fields.

Dark-adaptation

It is a familiar fact that on leaving a brightly lit house on a dark night one sees badly but, after some time in darkness, one can see many objects that were at first invisible. The increase in visual sensitivity (fall in threshold) that occurs while the eyes are in darkness or near-darkness is called dark-adaptation, and the decrease in sensitivity caused by exposure to bright light is called light-adaptation. In subjects with vitamin A deficiency dark-adaptation occurs more slowly and the ultimate sensitivity is less.

The course of dark-adaptation after the eye has been adapted to a bright white light is shown in Figure 37.15. Thresholds were tested with 1° circular fields of various colours placed 5° away from the fixation point. It is clear that the curve for orange test stimuli falls into two phases separated by a sudden change in gradient. With slightly different conditions of preadaptation a similar two-phase dark-adaptation curve can be obtained with white, yellow, green or blue test stimuli but, if the test stimulus is either deep red (to which the rods are very insensitive), or falls upon the fovea (where there are no rods), the second phase is absent. Orange, yellow, green or blue test stimuli look coloured, however dim they seem, during the first phase but look white at threshold during the second phase. Deep red and foveal stimuli always appear coloured if they are visible at all. Vision during the first phase of dark-adaptation is attributed to cones and during the second phase to rods.

It appears, then, that both the rod and cone mechanisms are rendered less sensitive by light-adaptation, but that the sensitivity of the red mechanism is lowered

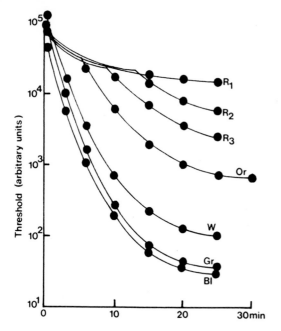

Fig. 37.15 Course of dark-adaptation for 1° circular fields of various colours, places 5° from the fixation point. Wavebands were isolated by means of filters. Bl = blue, Gr = green, W = white, Or = orange; R_3, R_2 and R_1 are reds of successively longer wavelength. (From Brindley G S 1970 Physiology of the retina and visual pathway. Arnold London)

by a much larger factor, so that for the first few minutes of dark-adaptation the threshold is determined by cones. At the end of this time the sensitivity of the cone mechanism is increasing only slowly but the sensitivity of the rod mechanism (which is inherently greater) is increasing rapidly. Thus, when the rods overtake the cones, there is a sudden increase in the rate at which the threshold falls.

When dark-adaptation is complete, the sensitivity of the retina is such that a flash of blue-green light from a field whose diameter subtends 10 seconds of arc at the eye may be seen if as few as 50 quanta of light enter the eye. Probably no more than 5 of these quanta are absorbed by rhodopsin molecules, and these absorptions must in general occur in different photoreceptors, since a 10 seconds of arc field illuminates about 350 rods. Thus each rod must be capable of being stimulated by a single quantum, though only if several such stimulations occur whithin a small time and area is any sensation produced.

There is strong circumstantial evidence that the decrease in sensitivity that accompanies light-adaptation depends upon the bleaching of the retinal photopigments and that dark-adaptation depends upon their regeneration. During dark-adaptation the logarithm of the threshold of both the cone and rod mechanisms can

be shown to be inversely related to the concentration of the appropriate photopigment present. This relation rules out the simple idea that the sensitivity at any time is determined by the amount of photopigment available for catching quanta. The mechanism by which sensitivity and photopigment concentration are related is still unknown.

THE NEUROPHYSIOLOGY OF VISION

Electrical activity of the retina

When the retina is exposed to light a characteristic change in potential difference occurs between an electrode placed on the cornea and one on an indifferent site. This is the electroretinogram or ERG (Fig. 37.16). The electrical activity recorded in this way has not been very useful in unravelling the processes by which images can be turned into electrical activity and transmitted to the cortex as action potentials. It has proved to be of diagnostic aid in the hereditary disease of retinitis pigmentosa. In this condition, the ERG disappears before there is much visual impairment. A more direct approach of intracellular recording has been more fruitful.

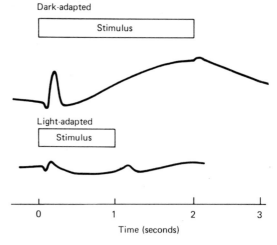

Fig. 37.16 Electroretinograms of the human retina. (After Hanitzsch et al. 1966 Vision Research 6:245)

Intracellular recording from retinal elements

The photoreceptors respond to illumination by hyperpolarising, the magnitude of which is proportional to the intensity of the light stimulus. In the absence of light a current flows through the plasma membrane of the outer segment (the so-called dark current) due to a flux of sodium ions. When the receptor is exposed to a light stimulus, a decrease in the permeability to

Central illumination

R

H

B

A

G

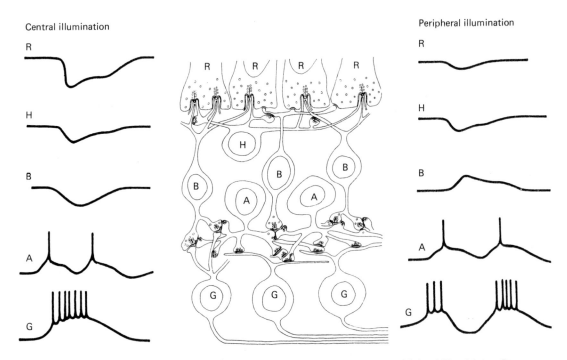

Peripheral illumination

R

H

B

A

G

Fig. 37.17 Recordings from the retinal cells in response to central illumination and to peripheral illumination. R = receptors, H = horizontal cell, B = bipolar cell, A = amacrine cell, G = ganglion cell. Central illumination leads to hyperpolarisation of receptors, horizontal cells and bipolar cells. Spike-like discharges are seen in the amacrine and ganglion cells. Peripheral illumination leads to hyperpolarisation of the receptors and horizontal cells but depolarisation of the bipolar cells. Spike discharges are seen in the amacrine and ganglion cells at the beginning and end of illumination. (After Dowling J E 1970 Investigative Ophthalmology 9:655)

sodium occurs as a consequence of which the cell interior becomes more negative. This electrical change is the beginning of a series of effects that are conveyed through the retinal neurones electrotonically to synapses on both bipolar and horizontal cells (Fig. 37.17). The bipolar cells then transmit a graded electrical signal to the ganglion and amacrine cells with which they are in contact. Receptor cells are also able to influence one another and this is brought about by the horizontal cells, the latter receiving an input from a large area of the retina. The horizontal cell also responds by a hyperpolarisation. The retinal region from which the bipolar cells receive input is approximately circular and consists of a central zone and a surrounding area, which are antagonistic; if the central zone responds to a small spot of light, stimulation of the surround has the opposite effect. The bipolar cells are relatively insensitive to diffuse illumination and, therefore, even at this level, processing has taken place with the cell responding to contrasts rather than brightness of light. The amacrine and ganglion cells respond differently from the other retinal elements in that they not only have slow potential changes but they also respond to light with repetitive spike discharges. The amacrine and the bipolar cells

feed into the ganglion cells in which the final integration of the retinal response occurs. A characteristic of the ganglion cells is that they fire at a low rate even in the absence of illumination. Retinal ganglion cells have roughly circular receptive fields with the cell at the geometrical centre (Fig. 37.18). They are functionally divided into 'on-centre' and 'off-centre' fields. In the case of the on-centre fields, a spot of light directed at the centre excited the ganglion cell, whereas when it shone on to the periphery, activity was suppressed. In the off-centre field, the opposite effects occurred. If the whole field was illuminated, the action of the centre and the periphery cancelled each other out, with just a weak on-and-off effect as the light is turned on and off. It must be remembered that even a very small spot of light covers the receptive fields of many ganglion cells, some of which are excited and some inhibited, also the fields differ widely in size, being larger in the periphery of the retina than at the fovea. The fields also overlap and may also change depending upon the level of illumination. A ganglion cell that at high levels of light has a spectral sensitivity typical for cones, may, at low levels of light change to having one typical of rods. This is not surprising since ganglion cells are connected to both

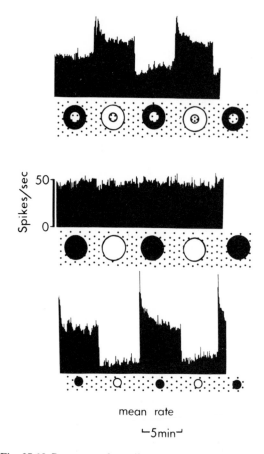

Spikes/sec 50 — 0 —

mean rate

⌐5min⌐

Fig. 37.18 Responses of an off-centre ganglion cell in a cat retina to switching off and on either an annulus (top record), a large spot (middle record) or a small spot (bottom record). The small spot illuminated only the centre of the receptive field, the annulus only the surround, while the large spot stimulated both centre and surround. (Bishop P O, Rodieck R W 1965 Symposium on information processing in sight sensory systems. California Institute of Technology,)

rods and cones. It is concluded that their function is not to convey information about absolute levels of illumination but rather to detect contrasts.

Lateral geniculate nucleus

Retinal ganglion cells send their axons to both the lateral geniculate nucleus and the superior colliculus (Fig. 37.19). Simultaneous records from single cells in the retina and lateral geniculate nucleus have shown that although the cells of the nucleus are influenced by the impulses in many optic tract fibres, they are often very strongly influenced by the discharges from one particular ganglion cell. It is thus not surprising that the behaviour of cells of the lateral geniculate nucleus is similar to that of the retinal ganglion cells that drive them, though they usually adapt more rapidly and completely. Like ganglion cells they have concentrically organised receptive fields of various sizes, many of which have colour-specific centre and surround regions. The antagonistic surround regions of the receptive fields of geniculate neurones are rather more diffuse than those of retinal ganglion cells, though the significance of this difference is obscure. Cells in the primate lateral geniculate nucleus respond briskly to moving visual stimuli but they do not show any directional effects nor indeed any specific response to moving, as compared with flashing, stimuli.

The lateral geniculate nucleus receives afferent fibres from both eyes but individual cells can usually only be excited by stimulation of one eye. Most cells can be inhibited by stimuli falling on corresponding regions of the retina of the other eye. It has also been found that the activity of cells in the geniculate nucleus can be influenced by stimulation of the vestibular and other sensory systems. The functional significance of these influences is not yet known.

Occipital cortex

Removal of the cerebral cortex produces blindness without interfering with the reaction of the pupils to light. The area of the human occipital cortex involved in vision lies on the walls of the postcalcarine sulcus on the medial surface of the occipital lobe (Brodmann's area 17), occasionally extending a short distance on to its lateral surface.

The path of the fibres in the optic nerve has been found by studying the degeneration that occurs after removal of different parts of the retina. The fibres from the nasal half of each retina in man cross over at the optic chiasma (Figs. 37.19 and 37.20) so that the fibres from the right halves of the two retinae pass into the right optic tract to the right lateral geniculate body from which new fibres go as the *optic radiations* to the calcarine cortex. The macular fibres concerned in central vision lie nearly centrally in the optic tracts and end to the posterior part of the lateral geniculate body, the macular relay fibres then going to the tip of the occipital lobe. Removal of the occipital cortex in man has often left some macular vision but this is likely to depend on incomplete removal of the area of cortex concerned rather than on bilateral cortical representation of the macula for which there is no anatomical basis. After damage to the visual cortex a patient may be able to localise large objects in his blind field even though he has no awareness of 'seeing' them. It may be that the residual ability depends on the superior colliculus or other structures in the visual pathway.

The results of correlation of the position of lesions with the shape of the visual field obtained by perimetry

VISUAL
FIELD
DEFECTS

VISUAL
FIELDS

L.   R.

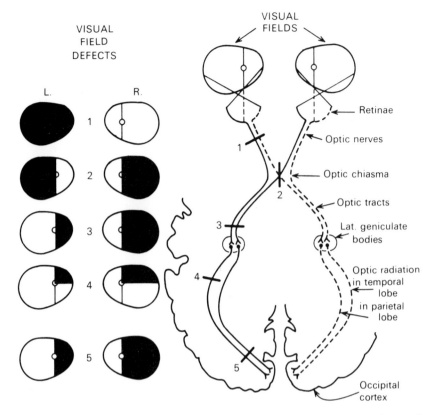

Retinae

Optic nerves

Optic chiasma

Optic tracts

Lat. geniculate
bodies

Optic radiation
in temporal
lobe
in parietal
lobe

Occipital
cortex

Fig. 37.19 The course of the fibres involved in vision from the right and left halves of the two retinae to the occipital cortex. The small diagrams on the left indicate the blind parts of the field of vision (in black) produced by the lesions 1 to 5 described below. There is a relay in the lateral geniculate body. A lesion at 1 cutting through the left optic nerve results in complete blindness of the left eye with loss of light reflexes. A lesion at 2 involving the central part of the optic chiasma interrupts the fibres from the nasal halves of the retinae and produces bitemporal hemianopia. A lesion at 3 divides the optic tract containing fibres from the left halves of both retinae and produces blindness in the right halves of the visual fields (homonymous hemianopia); the pupil does not contract when a light is thrown on the left halves of the retinae. A lesion at 4 cutting through the optic radiations also produces blindness in the left halves of the retinae (homonymous defect), but the light reflex is normal. A lesion at 5 at the posterior pole of the occipital cortex causes blindness in the right side of the macular field of vision. (Macleod J (ed.) 1974 Davidson's principles and practice of medicine, 11th ed. Churchill Livingstone Edinburgh)

show that the centre of the field is represented in the tip of the occipital lobe at the posterior end of the postcalcarine sulcus, and that the upper half of each retina (lower half of the field of vision) is represented on the upper part of the visual area of the cortex. Conversely the lower half of the retina is represented on the lower half. The area of the cortex connected with the macula and devoted to central vision is, as might be expected from the power of the macula to appreciate colour and fine detail, large compared with that subserving peripheral vision (Fig. 37.21).

The pathway from retina to cortex can be thought of in simple terms as six nerve cells, three in the retina, one in the lateral geniculate body and two in the cortex.

The areas adjacent to the occipital cortex, Brodmann's areas 18 and 19, are association areas in which co-ordi-

nation of eye reflexes with other reflexes occurs. The interpretation of what is seen, for example a printed word, requires the presence of these association regions; their destruction causes visual agnosia.

Cortical processing of visual information

Information processing in the visual cortex follows a hierarchically arranged order of cells with an increasingly complex function. Neurones are only activated when the applied stimulus had a certain shape and occupies a certain position in the visual field. On the basis of the response of the cells to certain stimuli, neurones are grouped into a number of classes that function with increasing complexity: circularly symmetric simple, complex and hypercomplex cells.

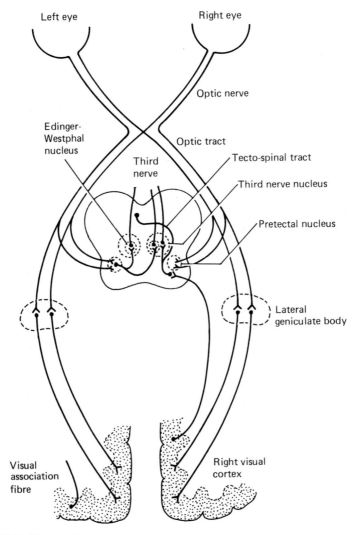

Fig. 37.20 The visual pathways to show the connections with the nuclei of the midbrain.

The circularly symmetrical simple cells are present in the highest proportion in layer 4 of the cortex and behave rather like the ganglion cells from which they receive their input by having receptive fields of antagonistic off-and-on regions. They respond maximally to a line and edge or a slit and have been called feature detectors. The receptive fields tend to be elongated rather than truly circular and the stimulus must be orientated on the retina so that its long axis coincides with that of the receptive field to have a maximum effect. Orientations at right angles become ineffective and intermediate positions have weaker effects. As each simple cell has an input from a ganglion cell, it receives information from only a limited part of the retina and responds to the image's special pattern. Complex cells

have larger receptive fields than the simple cells just described and they also differ in the fact that they have no on or off areas. They respond to slits, lines and edges of a given orientation when they fall in the receptive field and response is enhanced if the stimulus moves. In summary, they provide information about the orientation of a stimulus, are involved in movement perception but provide little information about its position in the receptive field. They are to be found in layers 2, 3, 5 and 6 in area 17 of the cortex.

The hypercomplex cells, as their name implies, are even more fussy. Their receptive fields are divided into activating and antagonistic, rather like those described for the simple cells, but not only has the orientation of the stimulus to be correct but in order to obtain a

Left hemisphere

Right visual field

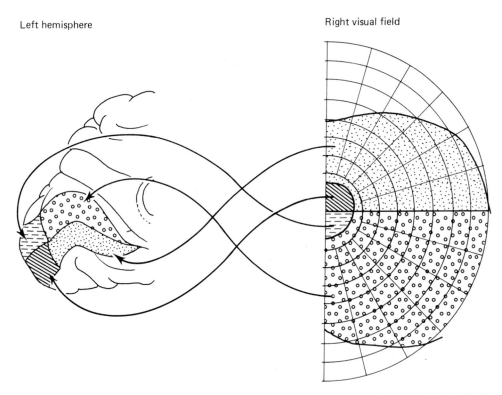

Fig. 37.21 Projections of the different parts of the retina on the cerebral cortex. (After Holmes G 1918 British Journal of Ophthalmology 2:383)

response the length of the stimulus must be within certain limits.

In summary, the information sent from the retina to the occipital cortex is not simply from point to point. The information transmitted undergoes transformation first in the retina and then in the cortex. The ganglion cells pass information from larger fields on the periphery of the retina and small ones from the region of the fovea; they provide for the resolution of fine detail and information about contrast. The shape of the receptive field changes in the cortex to one that is rectangular and this change helps in the analysis of the image. Further analysis is carried out by the complex and hypercomplex cells. It has been suggested that there are higher order neurones involved, probably in areas 18 and 19, which may be able to synthesise the details described into a whole picture and they have been given the name 'pontifical cells'.

Visual reflexes

When the superior colliculi are stimulated electrically dilatation of the pupil occurs along with conjugate movements of the eyes towards the opposite side, that is lateral movements of both eyes simultaneously through equal angles. It is possible, however, that these results are simply due to spread of current to neighbouring structures. When the superior colliculi are destroyed the pupillary contraction on exposure to light remains, but if the pretectal area just rostral to them is destroyed at the same time, the light reflex can no longer be obtained. This is explained in Figure 37.20; some fibres from the retina travel in the optic nerve and optic tract but pass medial to the lateral geniculate bodies to end in the pretectal area, where the first synapse occurs. Second-order relay neurones cross in the posterior commissure and reach the Edinger–Westphal part of the third nerve nucleus on both sides from which nerve fibres pass via the ciliary ganglion to the sphincter pupillae. The phenomenon of contraction of the pupil on accommodation but not on exposure to light, a common finding in certain diseases of the nervous system, is probably due to interruption of the pathways in the pretectal region. The light reflexes remain after cortical ablation since they do not require a cortical pathway. The very much longer sympathetic pathway to the eye is illustrated in Figure 37.22.

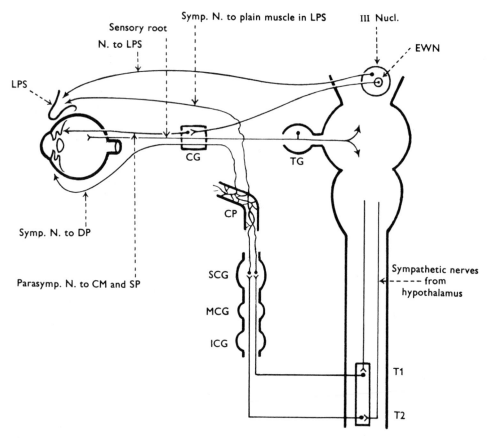

Fig. 37.22 Diagram of the course of the autonomic fibres to the eye. III Nucl. = oculomotor nucleus. EWN = Edinger–Westphal nucleus. LPS = levator palpebrae superioris. CG = ciliary ganglion. T1, T2 = first and second thoracic segments of spinal cord. SCG, MCG and ICG = superior, middle and inferior cervical sympathetic ganglia. TG = trigeminal ganglion. DP = dilatator pupillae. SP = sphincter pupillae. CM = ciliaris muscle. CP = plexus on internal carotid artery (By courtesy of G. W. Pearce)

MOVEMENTS OF THE EYES

The eyeball is supported by the fatty tissues of the orbit, which form a socket for it. Within this socket the eyeball is free to rotate and also, since the socket is not rigid, to move a little from side to side and up and down. The eyeball is made to rotate by the action of three pairs of muscles. The lateral and medial recti rotate the eyeballs outwards or inwards about a vertical axis, but the other four muscles cause rotation around oblique axes so that they produce movements with both vertical and horizontal components. The extra-ocular muscles are supplied by the cranial nerves III, IV (superior oblique) and VI (lateral rectus), which originate from nuclei in the midbrain. The actions of the extra-ocular and intra-ocular muscles (which are controlled from associated midbrain nuclei) are very closely linked, so that both eyes act together and conjugate movements, convergence and accommodation

all occur together in a harmonious fashion. This prevents double vision (diplopia) by ensuring that the two retinal images always fall on corresponding points on the retinae in the two eyes. Corresponding points are distributed around the two foveae so that those in the right half of one retina correspond with those in the right half of the other; those in the upper half of one retina with those in the upper half of the other, and so on.

If the two eyes do not move sufficiently precisely together double vision may occur. However, when the two retinal images do not correspond with each other there may be a tendency for one of the retinal images to be suppressed so that it gives rise to no conscious perception. In children with refractive errors who squint, the image from the squinting eye is often suppressed to such an extent that vision in that eye progressively deteriorates unless use of the squinting eye is deliberately forced by frequent occlusion (that is

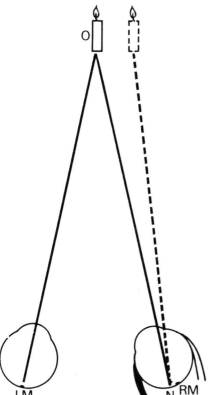

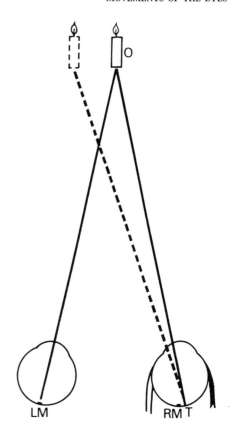

Fig. 37.23 Paralysis of the right lateral rectus. Rays reach both eyes from an object O the image of which falls on the left macula LM. The right eye is deviated inwards by the unopposed medial rectus, the image of O falling on an area N to the nasal side of the retina. This area possesses innate directional value (local sign) to the right. Since the eccentric area is less sensitive than the macula the image belonging to it is less clear (the false or 'ghost' image). The false image is to the same side as the paretic eye — homonymous diplopia. (By courtesy of A. A. Douglas)

Fig. 37.24 Paralysis of the right medial rectus. Rays reach both eyes from an object O the image of which falls on the left macula. The right eye is deviated outwards by the unopposed lateral rectus the image of O falling on an area T to the temporal side of the retina. This area possesses innate directional value (local sign) to the left. Since the eccentric area is less sensitive than the macula the image belonging to it is less clear (the false or 'ghost' image). The false image is to the side opposite the paretic eye — crossed diplopia. (By courtesy of A. A. Douglas)

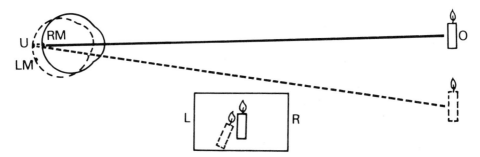

Fig. 37.25 Paralysis of the left superior oblique. The action of the superior oblique comprises depression, abduction and intorsion. In paralysis the eye is elevated and extorted by the inferior oblique and deviated inwards (adducted) by the superior and inferior recti. The image of O will fall on the macula of the right eye but, in the left eye, on the area U above and to the nasal side of the macula. The false image is therefore below and homonymous. It is the vertical element of the diplopia that is noticed by the patient. The inset shows the position of the images in detail. RM, righ macula; LM, left macula. (By courtesy of A. A. Douglas)

covering up) of the other eye. When paralytic squint occurs diplopia is quite obvious to the patient. The false image seen by the squinting eye is projected as indicated in Figures 37.23, 37.24 and 37.25.

Fixation movements

When a subject looks around him his gaze is continually being shifted from one point to another in discrete jumps called 'saccades'. The nature of saccadic eye movements can readily be seen if the eyes of a subject are observed while he is reading. A normal subject makes four or five separate saccadic fixation movements in scanning along each line of text (Fig. 37.26a). Saccadic movements may involve rotation of the eyeballs through many degrees or through only a few minutes of arc. The saccadic rotation always occurs very quickly, its time course not being under voluntary control.

Even if a subject attempts to fixate a target as steadily as he can, his eyes do not stay perfectly still but continue to make small drifting and saccadic movements of which he is unaware (Fig. 37.26b). This micro-tremor, about 100 Hz, is so small that to an unaided observer the eyes appear to be quite still. In the absence of such small movements of the eyes, and hence of the image on the retina, vision of the outside world rapidly fades. A simple way of experiencing this fading can be achieved by looking at a large, uniformly illuminated field (such as the blue sky) through a small pin-hole in a piece of card held very close to the eye. If the pin-hole is moved from side to side about two or three times a second, then a fine network of lines will be seen super-imposed upon the uniform background. These lines are the shadows of the small blood vessels that lie in front of the receptor layer of the retina. As soon as the movement of the pin-hole is stopped the shadows disappear. Experiments in which the retinal images of objects in the outside world are stabilised instrumentally have shown that the fading is most rapid and complete if the objects are small, but that it always occurs to an appreciable extent. It has been suggested that the fading is a result of sensory adaptation in the retina, but in view of the fact that many retinal ganglion cells have very well maintained discharges (p. 459), while adaptation is much more rapid and complete at higher levels in the visual pathway, it seems more likely that the fading is a result of adaptation at these higher levels.

If the object being fixated is moving, the subject's eyes make the appropriate smooth following movements (Fig. 37.26c) upon which saccadic fixation movements may be superimposed. Smooth following movements of the eyes are produced reflexly whenever the gaze is transferred to a moving target; they cannot be produced voluntarily in the absence of such a target. The only kind of eye movement that can be made voluntarily is

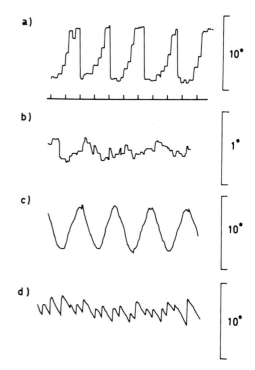

Fig. 37.26 Horizontal eye movements of a subject (a) reading, (b) steadily fixating a small object (note different vertical scale), (c) looking at a pendulum bob, (d) looking at a rotating drum. The time scale below record (a) shows seconds. (By courtesy of J. G. Robson)

the saccade. If a subject in a moving vehicle looks out at the passing landscape then his eyes alternately make smooth following movements and saccadic jumps in the opposite direction (Fig. 37.26d). The resulting oscillation is known as 'optico-kinetic nystagmus'. During the slow phase of the nystagmus the image of the passing scene remains more or less stationary on the retina, while in the fast phase the eyes are restored towards their undeviated position.

Smooth eye movements are also produced when a subject's head is rotated. If the head rotates through a small angle then an approximately compensating rotation of the eyes in the opposite direction is brought about by vestibular reflexes. A larger or more prolonged rotation of the head results in a nystagmoid movement. These movements occur even if the eyes are closed and may persist for some time after cessation of a prolonged rotation.

At birth the fixation reflex is present but weak, and eye movements are rather independent and unco-ordinated. By 5 to 6 weeks of age both eyes can simultaneously fixate an object, that is the conjugate fixation reflex is established, and a child can follow a moving target over a short range. By about 3 months objects of interest are voluntarily fixated and the beginning of co-ordinated eye and hand movements is seen. Fully co-ordinated movements of convergence and divergence do not usually appear before 6 months.

Although it has been found possible to elicit eye movements by electrical stimulation of many different nervous structures, the central mechanisms involved in the control of eye movements are not well understood.

Perception of depth and distance

A subject with one eye covered can still estimate, with a fair degree of accuracy, the relative distances from him of objects in his field of vision, as well as the actual distance from him of objects of known size. The relative distances of objects can be judged from such clues as the relative sizes of their retinal images (if the objects are of similar actual size), the occlusion of part of a distant object by a nearer one, the greater amount of detail visible in nearer objects and, if there is relative movement between the objects in the field and the subject, the paralactic changes that result. If the subject can use both eyes a further clue to the absolute distance of an object from him is given by the degree of convergence of his eyes necessary to make the two retinal images of the object fall on corresponding retinal areas.

As well as these effects, a subject who examines a near object with both eyes can make use of the fact that he gets somewhat different (that is disparate) views of the object with each eye. If the disparity of the retinal images is not too great the subject is unaware of it although he perceives the object extending in depth in a way that never occurs if he uses one eye only. Binocular vision of this kind is called stereoscopic vision. The existence of stereoscopic vision is believed to depend upon the presence in the visual cortex of cells that respond specifically to retinal images with particular degrees of disparity. In man the nasotemporal division at the decussation of the optic chiasma is complete. The cortical visual cells for central vision seem to be connected by fibres going across the corpus callosum from one hemisphere to the other. These interhemispheric fibres seem to be necessary for midline stereopsis. If kittens are brought up in such a way that they are not allowed to use both eyes at the same time during a short critical period of their development, they do not establish the required neural connections and do not achieve stereoscopic vision.

FURTHER READING

Fatt I 1978 Physiology of the eye. Butterworth, Boston

Kandel E R, Schwartz J H (eds) 1985 Principles of neural science, 2nd edn. Elsevier, New York

Ottoson D 1983 Physiology of the nervous system. Macmillan, London

Perkins E S, Hill D W 1977 Scientific foundations of ophthalmology. Heinemann, London

Pettigrew J D, Sanderson K, Levick W R (eds) 1986 Visual neuroscience. Cambridge University Press

Rose F C 1983 The eye in general medicine. Chapman & Hall, London

38

Hearing and speech

Hearing is one of the perceptual processes by which animals are continually being informed about their environment. In man the general information from the ears, such as the proximity of a source of sound, is augmented by the more specific information contained in speech. Speech and hearing must be regarded as two complementary activities that subserve the function of communication. If complete deafness is congenital or occurs in infancy before vocalisation has reached the stage of speech the child fails to develop the ability to speak, although he may be taught to speak intelligibly by special methods.

The external ear and middle ear

The external acoustic meatus, about 2.5 cm long in the adult, passes from the auricle to the tympanic membrane. The skin of the outer one-third of the meatus possesses numerous ceruminous or wax-secreting glands that are modified sweat glands; numerous sebaceous glands open into the hair follicles. Wax, a mixture of the two kinds of secretion, contains lysozyme and immunoglobulins. Accumulation of wax in the external meatus is a common cause of impaired hearing.

The tympanic membrane, about 1 cm in diameter, is composed of radial and circular collagenous fibres

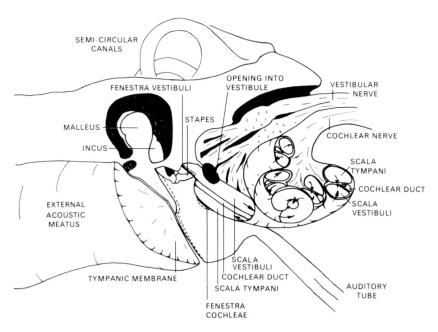

Fig. 38.1 A three-dimensional view of the ear. When the tympanic membrane is pushed inwards to the position indicated by the dotted lines the ossicles move to the positions shown by dotted lines. The stapes attached by the annular ligament to the margin of the fenestra vestibuli (oval window) is pushed into the scala vestibuli and the secondary tympanic membrane, which closes the fenestra cochleae (round window), bulges. The arrows indicate the flow of lymph. It should be noted that the diagram has been slightly distorted to show the actions of the oval and round windows, which do not as a result occupy their true anatomical relation. (By courtesy of I. C. Whitfield)

covered externally by stratified squamous epithelium continuous with the skin and internally by a mucous membrane of ciliated columnar epithelium. The outer surface of the membrane is concave; the inner convex surface, as seen from the middle ear or tympanic cavity, has the manubrium of the malleus (handle of the hammer) attached to it. The malleus articulates with the incus (anvil) and the incus with the stapes (stirrup), the base of which is attached by fibrous tissue to the margins of the fenestra vestibuli (oval window). These very light ossicles in the air-filled tympanic cavity link the ear drum to the inner ear (Fig. 38.1). The tensor tympani muscle, by its attachment to the root of the manubrium of the malleus, draws the tympanic membrane in, and at the same time, through the articulations between the three ossicles, pushes the stapes into the internal ear. The small stapedius muscle tends to have the opposite effect, namely to pull the stapes out of the internal ear. In response to sound, or to mechanical stimulation of the external acoustic meatus, auricle or surrounding skin, these muscles contract reflexly, pulling in the tympanic membrane and tightening it and pushing the footplate of the stapes inwards, presumably because the tensor tympani is more powerful than the stapedius. The result is that sound transmission across the middle ear is impaired for tones of low frequency and the ear is partially protected from damage by loud sounds.

The ear drum and the ossicles act as a kind of transformer to convey vibrations of the light medium, air, to the denser, watery media in the internal ear. The area of the ear drum is about 90 mm^2, whereas the area of the base of the stapes in only 3.2 mm^2. The pressure on the fluid under the stapes is thus many times greater than the air pressure that makes the ear drum move. In the absence of this impedance-matching function only a very small proportion of the energy of the sound would reach the inner ear, as happens if the conducting function of the middle ear is abolished and the sound reaches the internal ear fluids directly. In the course of the condition called otosclerosis, a familial and progressive deafness beginning in young people, the base of the stapes becomes joined by bone to the margins of the fenestra vestibuli. This condition causes severe deafness (Fig. 38.10C).

The auditory tube leads from the anterior part of the middle ear to the nasal part of the pharynx. The pharyngeal end is normally closed but during swallowing it opens and allows the air pressure in the middle ear to be equalised with the atmospheric. If the pressure is not equal on the two sides the drum is pushed in (as in the case of the descent of a diver) or drawn out (as on ascending in an aeroplane). Such abnormal displacement may produce pain and impaired hearing and damage to the ear drum but this discomfort can be avoided by frequent swallowing while the air pressure is altering. Reduced acuity of hearing may also result when the tube is blocked by the swelling of the mucous membrane that accompanies a 'cold'; in this case the oxygen in the middle ear is absorbed and the ear drum is pushed in by the external atmospheric pressure.

The internal ear
This section deals with cochlear function only. Other parts of the internal ear, the semi-circular canals and otolith organs, are concerned with the maintenance of balance and play no part in hearing; they are discussed in Chapter 36. The basic structure of the cochlea is given in Figure 38.2. If the three canals are wrapped two and three-quarter times round the modiolus (the central pillar of the cochlea) and a cross-section made, the appearance seen in Figure 38.1 can be accounted for. More details can be seen in Figure 38.3. The *basilar membrane*, about 31 mm long, is composed of fibres that run radially from the osseous spiral lamina of the modiolus to the spiral ligament, or crista basilaris, which binds the basilar membrane to the external bony

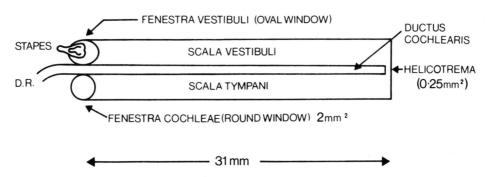

Fig. 38.2 Basic structure of the inner ear. If this system of three tubes (scala vestibuli, ductus cochlearis and scala tympani) could be wrapped two and three-quarter times round the modiolus (central pillar of the inner ear) the actual anatomical relationships would be reached. D.R. = ductus reuniens, which communicates with the saccule.

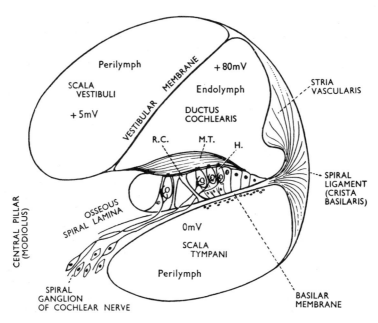

Fig. 38.3 A cross-section through the three canals of the cochlea to show the structures on the basilar membrane. H., hair cells; M.T., membrana tectoria; R.C., rods of Corti. The reticular lamina is a net-like membrane holding in its apertures the hairs of the hair cells (Fig. 27.28). The cochlear partition comprises the basilar membrane, the vestibular membrane (Reissner's membrane) and the structures contained in the ductus cochlearis. The endolymph in the ductus cochlearis (scala media) is 80 mV positive with respect to the perilymph in the scala tympani. The perilymph in the scala vestibuli is 5 mV positive to the perilymph in the scala tympani. The naked nerve fibres are about 0.15 μm in diameter as they arise from the hair cells. As they pass centrally they become myelinated (2 to 5 μm). The fine nerve fibres passing through the organ of Corti must be bathed in perilymph or fluid resembling it. All the sensory hair cells are richly innervated; the nerve endings are of two kinds, sparsely granular afferent and richly granular efferent.

wall of the cochlea. The fibres are short (0.04 mm) near the foramen vestibuli and increase gradually to the apex of the cochlea at the helicotrema, where they are about 0.5 mm long. The spiral organ of Corti is formed of about 4000 rods of Corti, which make a spiral tunnel on top of the basilar membrane. On either side of this tunnel are hair cells the bristle-like processes of which are attached to the underside of the tectorial membrane (Fig. 38.4). Filaments of the cochlear nerve lie on the

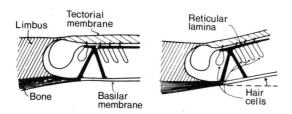

Fig. 38.4 The shearing action between the hair cells and the tectorial membrane, when the cochlear partition is deflected. This shearing action results in bending or deflection of the hairs relative to the reticular lamina. (From Davis H 1960 In: Rasmussen G L, Windle W F (eds) Neural mechanisms of the auditory and vestibular systems. Thomas, Springfield, Illinois)

exterior of the hair cells and pass to the spiral ganglion lying nearer the modiolus. The fluid in the scala vestibuli and the scala tympani (the perilymph) is very like cerebrospinal fluid in chemical composition except for a somewhat higher protein content; the perilymph, however, may not be continuous with the cerebrospinal fluid. The endolymph in the ductus cochlearis has a composition more like that of intracellular fluid, with high potassium and low sodium concentrations; however, the main anion is chloride as in extracellular fluid. It is probably secreted by the cells of the stria vascularis (Fig. 38.3).

Mechanical aspects of cochlear function
If the air pressure in the external auditory meatus is suddenly increased the tympanic membrane is pushed inwards and this movement is transferred by the chain of ossicles to the footplate of the stapes, which also moves inwards, increasing the pressure in the scala vestibuli. This increased pressure causes the cochlear partition to be displaced towards the scala tympani, raising in turn the pressure in the latter and causing the secondary tympanic membrane (the membrane of the round window) to bulge outwards into the middle ear.

This displacement of the cochlear partition is not maintained because the partition is elastic and the scalae communicate via the helicotrema. The pressure difference between the scala vestibuli and scala tympani is soon equalised by fluid transfer via the helicotrema and the partition returns to its rest position. However, if the tympanic membrane is being moved in and out fairly rapidly, as by the vibrations of a sound wave, there is not sufficient time for the fluid to move back and forth through the helicotrema and the cochlear partition accordingly vibrates in sympathy with the sound waves. The ability of perilymph to move through the helicotrema instead of displacing the cochlear partition is one of the factors that limit the low frequency range of hearing to about 30 Hz.

The characteristics of the vibration of the cochlear partition have been observed under microscope with stroboscopic illumination. The response to a tonal stimulus is a travelling wave moving from base to apex (Fig. 38.5). An example of a travelling wave is that produced by moving one end of a slack horizontal rope rhythmically up and down. The waves in the rope appear to progress along it, whereas plucking a stretched string produces standing waves and the nodes and antinodes remain in the same positions. However, there are important differences between the travelling waves in a rope and those in the basilar membrane. Whereas the rope is uniform along its length, the membrane is certainly not so. Not only does it increase some twelve-fold in width between the base and the apex but it is very much stiffer at the basal than at the apical end. An important result of this gradation of properties is that the wave grows progressively in amplitude as it travels away from the base and then it rather suddenly dies out. Further, the point of maximum amplitude varies with the sound frequency,

being in the basal turn for the highest frequencies and moving further and further towards the apex as the sound frequency is decreased.

Recently the use of coherent light has enabled the patterns in the 10 to 20 kHz region to be observed directly by a form of laser interferometry. Further confirmation has come by placing a very small (80 μm) radioactive source on the membrane. As the membrane vibrates the velocity of the source produces a corresponding change in the frequency of the emitted radiation that can be measured by suitable techniques.

The direction of movement of the travelling wave (base to apex) is entirely determined by the intrinsic properties of the basilar membrane and is in no way dependent on the vibration being 'introduced' into the cochlea at the basal end. If an artificial stapes is constructed near the apex it is found that the wave still travels from the (stiffer) basal region of the membrane to the less stiff apical end. Indeed our ability to hear by bone conduction depends on this property, since in this case the vibration is introduced into the cochlea rather diffusely via the bony wall itself.

The mechanics of the basilar membrane thus provide some separation of the frequency components of a sound but this separation is clearly quite insufficient to account for the observed pitch discrimination of the auditory system. It has indeed become obvious that neurological mechanisms must play a major role. It must be remembered that pitch discrimination is not the only, or even perhaps from an evolutionary point of view the most important, role of the cochlea. In the localisation of sound, transients like those produced by snapping twigs are far more important than tones, and a good transient response is not readily compatible with a sharply tuned filter system. Some compromise has therefore been inevitable.

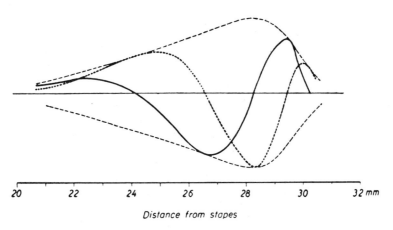

Fig. 38.5 The measured longitudinal bending of the cochlear partition for a tone of 200 Hz for two moments separated by a quarter period. (von Békésy G 1947 Journal of the Acoustic Society of America 19:455)

Endocochlear potential

By inserting microelectrodes into guinea-pig cochlea, Békésy found that the endolymph in the ductus cochlearis (scala media), even in the absence of any acoustic stimulation of the ear, was electrically positive by some 80 mV to the perilymph in the scala tympani and the scala vestibuli. This is called the endocochlear potential. When a microelectrode penetrated into the cellular structures on the basilar membrane (hair cells and supporting cells) negative potentials were found; such internal negativity in cells is to be expected and is, of course, well known in nerve and muscle cells. The total potential difference between the endolymph in the cochlear duct and the interior of the cells is about 140 mV.

Although the fluid in the cochlear duct has a high potassium content and the scala tympani contains perilymph with a sodium/potassium ratio akin to extracellular fluid, it does not seem that the differences in ion concentrations are responsible for the endocochlear potential. However, the potential falls rapidly when the oxygen supply is cut off and is abolished when cyanide is injected into the endolymphatic space. The dependence of the potential on metabolism suggests that the stria vascularis is closely implicated in its production. It is to be noted that the large potential difference (80 mV) between endolymph and perilymph is found only in the mammalian cochlea; the endocochlear potential in birds is very small. In spite of the anatomical continuity of the membranous labyrinth, the potential difference in the semicircular canals, utricle and saccule, is nearly zero (less than 2 mV).

The main barrier between the cochlear duct and the scala tympani appears to be the reticular lamina, the stiff membrane covering the hair-bearing ends of the hair cells. Thus the structures of the organ of Corti and indeed the basilar membrane itself lie within the perilymphatic space. There may be, nevertheless, slight local differences in the lymph in the vicinity of these structures. For example, the composition of the fluid in the space between the reticular lamina and the tectorial membrane probably differs from that in the rest of the cochlear duct, being rich in mucopolysaccharides.

Cochlear microphonic

The steady potential difference between the cochlear duct and the scala tympani is reduced by a displacement of the basilar membrane towards the scala vestibuli and increased by a displacement of the basilar membrane in the opposite direction, that is, towards the scala tympani. These alterations in potential are maintained so long as the deformation of the basilar membrane is maintained. Such displacements have been made experimentally by applying pressure to the fluids in the scalae or by gently touching the membrane itself with a needle. These potential changes are associated with the shearing forces between the tectorial membrane and the hair cells held in the reticular lamina (Fig. 38.4). The mechanism can be visualised by flexing a book and observing the relative motion between the two covers. The alternating potential produced in this way when the basilar membrane is set into vibration by a sound is known as the cochlear microphonic. It was first recorded from the fenestra cochleae and an 'indifferent' electrode in the neck, but with suitable filtering techniques it is possible to record it in man from more accessible points, for example the tympanic membrane.

The cochlear microphonic corresponds closely to the characteristics of the applied sound stimulus; it is virtually an electrical equivalent of the applied acoustic stimulus and is quite different from the action potentials in the auditory nerve. The potential changes of the microphonic follow the frequency of the applied sound stimulus at all audible frequencies; they resemble quite closely the waveform of the stimulus. They have virtually no latent period or threshold and increase progressively in amplitude with increase in sound energy up to quite high sound pressure levels (100 decibels (pp. 478 and 483). The fact that the potentials decline and eventually disappear when oxygen is cut off shows that they depend on the metabolism of the cells of this region.

Because of the conductivity of the fluids, recording from the electrode on the fenestra cochleae, as described above, reproduces the recombined microphonics from all points of the cochlea, albeit predominantly those from the basal turn. However, if a pair of electrodes is inserted through the cochlear wall so that they lie opposite to one another across the basilar membrane/hair cell complex, one in the cochlear duct and the other in the scala tympani, a record of cochlear microphonics from a much more localised region can be made. Such studies demonstrate that tones of low frequency produced microphonics with amplitude's greatest at the apical parts of the cochlea while microphonics from tones of high frequency could be recorded only near the base. By studying the phase relations of the microphonics at different distances from the stapes they were also able to confirm the existence of travelling waves.

In addition to the pure alternating component of the cochlear microphonic, which reproduces the sound stimulus frequency, there is often observed, at high stimulus intensities, a steady displacement of the baseline lasting as long as the stimulus. This so-called 'summating potential' may be ascribed to non-linear vibration of the basilar membrane/hair cell complex at large displacements.

Action potential of cochlear nerve fibres

The estimate of the threshold sensitivity of the ear given on page 482 shows that the amount of mechanical energy available for stimulating the nerve endings in the cochlea is, even for the every-day range of sounds, very small indeed. The tiny mechanical movements of the hair cells produced by such sounds must release a store of energy many times that of the original sound. Just how the nerve impulses are initiated is not understood. There has been much discussion about whether the cochlear microphonic corresponds to a receptor generator potential. It seems on the whole unlikely that the microphonic potential stimulates the nerve endings directly; electron microscope studies have revealed what appears to be a synaptic junction between the base of the hair cell and the afferent nerve fibre, but so far no transmitter has been identified.

The responses of individual fibres in the auditory nerve have been investigated by a number of workers. All these studies show that there is for each fibre some characteristic sound frequency for which it is most sensitive (Fig. 38.6). As the stimulus intensity is raised, the fibre responds over a wider and wider frequency range, which may reach as much as two or even three octaves at high intensities. It will be noted that the response curves are asymmetric triangles which qualitatively mirror the mechanical disturbance of the basilar membrane. The nerves fibres arise from the basilar membrane in an orderly manner, those with high characteristic frequencies arising from the basal end and those with lower characteristic frequencies arising progressively farther towards the apical end. Just as any single sound frequency sets in motion a considerable length of the basilar membrane, so too does the membrane in turn excite a large number of auditory

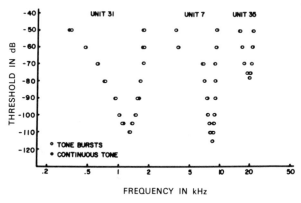

Fig. 38.6 Threshold response curves for three cat auditory nerve fibres. Each fibre responds best to some particular frequency, the 'characteristic frequency', but responds over a progressively wider band of frequencies as the sound intensity is raised. The response areas are similar whether the stimulus tone is short lasting (50 ms) or continues indefinitely. (From Kiang N 1965 Discharge patterns of single fibers in the cat's auditory nerve. M.I.T. Press, Cambridge, Mass)

nerve fibres. It can be inferred from curves like those of Figure 38.6 that a single tone at a moderate intensity (say 40 dB SPL) may cause some 20 per cent of all the fibres in the auditory nerve to discharge. There is thus no question of discrimination being carried out in terms of excitation of specific auditory nerve fibres by specific frequencies. It can also be seen that increasing the stimulus intensity increases the number of excited fibres, as well as increasing the rate of discharge in individual fibres.

Many, if not all, auditory nerve fibres show some 'spontaneous' activity in the absence of a sound stimulus — the mere presence of nerve impulses is not of itself capable of eliciting a sensation of sound. It appears to be the juxtaposition of groups of active fibres and groups of relatively inactive fibres that is necessary for this. It has been suggested that localised neural damage, by giving rise to spurious patterns of activity and inactivity, may be one basis of the distressing condition of tinnitus, in which persistent noises are heard in the head without any external stimulus. There is a tendency for nerve impulses to be discharged preferentially for one direction of shear of the hair cells rather than the other, as the basilar membrane moves back and forth. This means that at low frequencies (say up to 1000 Hz) the impulses in the auditory nerve tend to be synchronised with the waves of the stimulating tone. However, the nerve fibres are unable to 'follow' at very high rates, and for tones above 1000 Hz this synchrony is progressively lost.

There has been much argument as to whether or not the periodicity of the impulses in the auditory nerve is capable of providing information about the pitch of the note at low frequencies. At the present time there is little evidence in support of this hypothesis and a good deal against it. It is not possible to review this evidence here; suffice it to say that it has been shown that there is not a one-to-one correspondence between perceived pitch and nerve impulse periodicity.

Central connections of the cochlear nerve

The fibres of the auditory nerve leave the cochlea in an orderly manner so that they are arranged in order of their frequency sensitivity. As the nerve enters the brain stem this orderliness is preserved and the individual fibres terminate in the cochlear nucleus in the same way. Second-order fibres arising in the cochlear nucleus synapse in olivary and lemniscal nuclei and eventually reach the inferior colliculus. Throughout this pathway the same anatomical orderliness is preserved, so that the spatial relation of two given groups of active fibres remains the same in the colliculus as it was at the cochlea. However, owing to crossing over of some fibres in the medulla, inputs from both ears reach each colliculus. There is no sharpening of the response as we

Fig. 38.7 Response of a neurone in the auditory cortex of the cat to a rising frequency. The signal bar represents a steady tone that rose in pitch at the point shown by about 10 per cent ($1\frac{1}{2}$ semi-tones) to a new steady value. The time taken to make the change was 50 ms. The neurone responded to the change but not to either of the steady tones. Note that it did *not* respond when the frequency *fell* through the same range. (After Whitfield I C, Evans E F 1965 Journal of Neurophysiology 28:655)

ascend the system, so that a single tone activates just as high a proportion of neurones at the collicular level as it did at the auditory nerve level. The identification of a musical note appears to depend on the pattern of distribution of activity in the total array of nerve fibres rather than the activation of some specific neurone. Indeed the patterns of distribution of activity in the auditory pathway seem to mimic closely the corresponding acoustic spectra (Fig. 38.17) and this may indeed be how we 'recognise' a particular sound such as a vowel or a note produced on a musical instrument.

Bilateral removal of the auditory cortex does not seriously interfere with the ability to discriminate the pitch and intensity of sounds. However, it does interfere with the ability to recognise temporal sound patterns. A cat without its auditory cortex can, for example, still distinguish tone A from tone B, but cannot distinguish the sequence ABA from the sequence BAB. Neurones have been found in the auditory cortex that respond to a rising frequency but not to a frequency falling through the same range (Fig. 38.7), while others respond only to falling and not to rising frequencies. Presumably such neurones play an important role in the discrimination of the patterns just referred to, and perhaps in responding to the complex frequency changes involved in speech.

The classical auditory pathway, as just described, from the ear to the cortex, is not the only one, since cats in which this pathway had been cut in the mid-brain could readily be aroused from sleep by loud sounds. The nerve impulses must be presumed to pass in a parallel pathway in the mid-brain reticular formation. There are also ascending pathways, which can be shown electrically, from the cochlea to the vermis of the cerebellum and from there to the cerebrum.

Descending paths
The ascending pathway is paralleled throughout its length by a system of descending fibres terminating in the various nuclei and even, in the form of the olivo-cochlear bundle, reaching the hair cells in the cochlea itself. It has been shown electrophysiologically that the olivo-cochlear bundle is capable of inhibiting auditory nerve activity, while the brain stem centrifugal pathway can alter the acoustic thresholds of the ascending neurones in which they terminate. Behaviourally, in cats, blocking of descending pathways has been shown to impair the resolving power of the ear — that is to say the ease with which two or more simultaneous sounds such as a set of harmonics can be separately heard, or the ease with which a signal may be detected against a noisy background. These pathways are quite as complex as the ascending ones and may well have a whole range of other functions not yet understood.

The right ear predominates in hearing; this is evidence for dominance in the brain's left hemisphere. If different sounds are presented in each ear at the same time the tendency is to hear only one sound — that fed to the right ear.

Localisation of the apparent source of a sound
The position of the source of a sound may be detected in either of two ways. If the head is kept still the observer can point to the source of the sound right or left of the saggital plane. Alternatively the head may be turned from side to side until the sound seems to be directly ahead. The second is the more accurate method. In practice the eyes as well as the ears are used in localisation. If the source cannot be seen, for example, a bird singing in a tree, localisation by hearing alone is sometimes quite difficult.

The ability to localise the source of a sound depends partly on the difference in loudness at the two ears and partly on the difference in time of arrival at the two ears. If the wavelength much exceeds the width of the head the sound waves readily pass round the head and reach the further ear with only a small and undetectable reduction in intensity; with such tones the difference in time of arrival is the clue to localisation. (Fig. 38.8A). Some subjects can detect time differences as small as 0.01 ms, which corresponds to a path difference in air of 3.5 mm. When the frequency is such that the wavelength is nearly the same as the width of the head (about 1500 Hz) the phase difference gives ambiguous clues

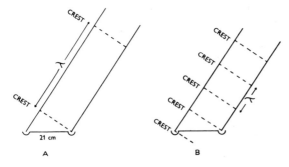

Fig. 38.8 (A) shows how a sound source is located by the crest of a wave (or some other distinctive part) reaching one ear before the other. The semicircles at the ends of the 21-cm horizontal line represent the ears. (B) shows how this method breaks down when the wavelength is short compared with the distance between the ears, that is 21 cm. In this case one crest arrives at the left ear as the following crest reaches the right ear. The velocity of sound in air is approximately 330 m/s at 0 °C and varies directly as the square root of the absolute temperature of the air.

about localisation as shown in Figure 38.8B. Above 1500 Hz the head casts a 'sound shadow'; these short waves cannot get round the head, just as the waves of the sea cannot get round a long breakwater. Consequently if the source of a high-frequency note is to one side of the median plane the difference of intensity at the two ears allows of localisation. The superior olive is the first level at which binaural interaction occurs, and the lateral division of this nucleus is thought to play a role in localisation. It has been shown that the probability of firing of a neurone in this nucleus depends on the relative time of arrival of a click stimulus at the two ears (Fig. 38.9).

These two clues, difference in time of arrival and difference in intensity, are not enough to decide whether the source is in front of or behind the observer.

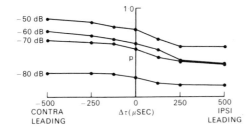

Fig. 38.9 The relative probability of firing (p) of cells in the lateral nucleus of the cat's superior olive as a function of the time difference ($\Delta\tau$) between the arrival of a click at the two ears. Curves are given for various intensity levels of the stimulus. (Note: sound travels about 15 cm in 500 μs) (From Hall J L 1965 Journal of the Acoustical Society of America 37: 814–823)

Small rotational movements of the head may enable more information to be obtained. A familiar sound, such as the human voice, may be easily recognised as coming from behind the observer because the auricle shades the ear from high frequencies and so alters slightly the quality of the voice. This differential filtering effect of the auricle indeed varies continuously as the position of the sound source changes in azimuth and elevation. The resultant change of timbre is probably one factor that enables persons totally deaf in one ear to locate the source of a sound.

Inside a room, reflections cause the sound to arrive from many directions. However, if the reflected sound is delayed by not more than a few milliseconds, we hear only the primary source, without any echoes (the 'precedence effect'). Although the secondary sources are not heard as such, they are not entirely suppressed, since they reinforce the apparent loudness of the direct sound. If two sound sources in a room are quite different, as for example two different speakers at a cocktail party, then it is usually possible by switching attention to suppress either source at will.

The temporal lobes

The route taken by impulses from the cochlea to the medial geniculate body and to a relatively small area of auditory cortex in the superior temporal convolution has already been described. The cortex does not appear to be essential for pitch discrimination, but is concerned with the processing of more elaborate sound patterns and the way they change with time. It thus plays an essential role in the recognition of such things as speech and music.

Although destruction of both temporal lobes in the cat does not render the animal deaf and does not deprive it of the ability to discriminate pitch and intensity, nevertheless there is some effect on the appreciation of tones. Removal of one temporal lobe results in a hearing loss of up to 5 decibels. Destruction of either the ipsilateral or contralateral cochlea in addition to removal of one temporal lobe increases the loss to some 15 dB, an increase greater than the sum of the losses produced by destruction of the cochlea or the cortex alone.

However, ablation of both temporal lobes has a very severe effect on the localisation of a single sound source, although as long as one lobe remains intact localisation of such sources is virtually unimpaired. In the presence of more than one sound, source localisation is affected even when only one lobe is destroyed. Thus, for example, the 'precedence effect' (above) is disrupted for sounds originating on the side opposite to the lesion. Thus we may expect that with damage to a single temporal lobe localisation will be more difficult in a room than in the open air, because of the presence of reflected sound in the room.

Electrical stimulation of the superior temporal convolution in man gives subjective buzzing, clicking or booming sounds but it has not so far been possible to produce any 'organised' response by such stimulation.

The effect of lesions in the temporal lobes in man is extremely variable. A circumscribed lesion of the superior temporal gyrus on the left side may give rise to pure word deafness in which the subject is unable to understand spoken words with no deficit in reading or verbal expression. Aphasia in one or other form is a common result of damage to the temporal cortex.

The temporal lobe has a function in relation to memory and recall for, although damage to one temporal lobe has little effect on the memory, removal of both lobes may reduce the memory span to a few minutes.

Measurement of acuity of hearing

Quantitative measurements of hearing are made with a *pure-tone audiometer*. The test must be made in a sufficiently quiet room since extraneous sounds cause masking (p. 479), which raises the threshold of hearing. The pure-tone audiometer consists of an oscillator producing pure sine waves that are fed to a telephone earpiece through an attenuator network to control the intensity of the sound. When the intensity of a given note is made very small it is inaudible but if the intensity increased slowly then at a certain value the note is heard. This is the *threshold of audibility*. If the test is performed separately for each ear at a selected number of frequencies the threshold can be established and specified in terms of a standard set of values corresponding to the hearing of normal young persons. There are national and international standards for the normal threshold of hearing for pure tones.

The threshold of audibility is lowest, that is the auditory acuity is greatest, in the region 1000 to 4000 Hz; at lower and higher frequencies the sound intensity must be greater to produce an auditory sensation. The lowest and highest audible frequencies thus depend on the intensity of the tone used, but the average limits are 30 and 20 000 Hz in young persons. In old people the threshold in the higher frequencies is raised so that in practice their upper limit may be much lower, say 5000 Hz (Fig. 38.10B).

By varying the intensity of the note produced by a pure-tone audiometer in a rhythmic fashion the minimum perceptible difference in intensity can be measured. Except near the threshold of audibility it is of the order of 1 dB. By varying the frequency of a note rhythmically the minimum fractional difference in frequency that is perceptible can be found; in the range 500 to 4000 Hz it is 0.3 per cent, but outside this range it is greater. A tone must persist for 10 to 15 ms before a pitch can be assigned to it but most people require the tone, especially if it is of low frequency, to last upwards of 100 ms before it supplies an experience of pitch.

The method of measuring intelligibility, first used by telephone engineers, is also useful for investigating deafness and the efficiency of deaf aids. A list of disconnected words containing a wide variety of speech sounds but without context is read out to a listener who writes down what he hears. The script is then checked with the original list and the percentage of sounds heard correctly — spelling errors are of course neglected — is usually referred to as the 'intelligibility'.

When this test is made in the simplest possible conditions — that is, with the reader speaking directly to the listener in the same room — the intelligibility is high, but the vowel *e* as in 'ten' and the consonants *th*, *f* and *v* often give rise to errors. If now the listener hears the voice of the reader through a loudspeaker system that transmits all the speech frequencies up to 1000 Hz but cuts out all the higher frequencies the intelligibility may be only 40 per cent although almost all the energy (85 per cent) of the original speech sounds is present. Sounds like *s*, *th* and *f* are particularly difficult to distinguish. This is an artificial *high-frequency deafness*. If, on the other hand, the loudspeaker transmits only the speech frequencies above 1000 Hz the intelligibility is now 86 per cent although only a small fraction of the original speech energy (17 per cent) is transmitted. In spite of this severe frequency distortion, ordinary speech with its context is easily understood but it does not, of course, sound natural.

The pure-tone audiometer can be used to investigate the hearing of persons with impaired hearing. Useful diagnostic information is obtained by measuring the amount by which the threshold is raised over the range of frequencies. Audiometers intended for clinical use are calibrated so that zero mark on the intensity control at each frequency corresponds to the average threshold found in young people with normal hearing. This statistical concept of normal hearing is shown on the graph paper used to record the results as a straight line marked 0 dB hearing level (Fig. 38.10). If a person has impaired hearing of a particular tone its intensity must be increased x db above the average threshold before it is heard; this is plotted as a point *below* the normal threshold in Figure 38.10, and is known as a hearing loss of x dB at the frequency tested. If a number of tones is used the results fall into a curve called the *audiogram*.

Important prognostic information can be gained from the audiogram since a definite relation has been found between the degree of deafness in the important speech frequencies, say 500 to 2500 Hz, and the quality of speech. Deaf children learn to speak normally provided the loss is less than 30 dB; a greater degree of impair-

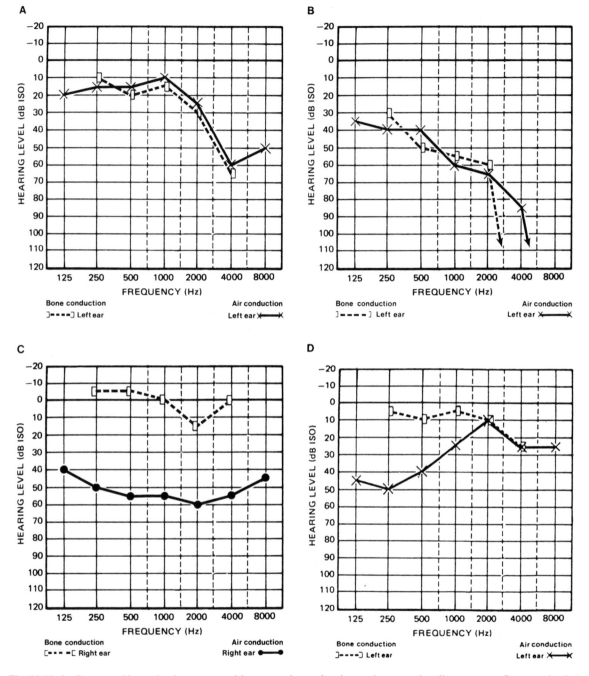

Fig. 38.10 Audiograms. Air conduction was tested by an earphone placed over the external auditory meatus. Bone conduction was tested by a vibrator on the mastoid process. The hearing level in dB is shown on the ordinate, zero indicating the threshold of hearing in young healthy people. The abscissa is scaled (in octaves) in Hz. A, industrial deafness of moderate degree at age 59; B, well marked presbycusis; C, otosclerosis at age 36; D, perforation of tympanic membrane. (Courtesy of A. G. Gibb)

ment prevents an infant from learning to speak naturally but may permit him to acquire speech with careful training. In the presence of a loss of 90 dB, however, even acquired speech is poor. Good hearing in the lower frequencies (up to 500 Hz, say) does not compensate for deafness in the high frequencies, since it is the latter that allows us to distinguish the different speech sounds.

Deafness due to middle-ear disease is so common that it is important to be able to test many people quickly. The pure-tone audiometer is not suitable because it is a rather uninteresting artificial test requiring a special room and considerable time; it can be applied only to one person at a time. The gramophone audiometer provides a somewhat empirical but yet practical test that can quickly pick out persons with defective hearing. Specially made records are played with an electrical pick-up that is connected to 20 or more single earphones to allow a whole class of children to be tested simultaneously. The children apply the earpiece to one ear at a time and hear a voice calling out numbers, which they copy down. As the record proceeds the voice becomes fainter and fainter in steps of 3 dB. When the speech is too faint to be understood the children either make mistakes or stop writing. When the performance of normal children has been found with this apparatus, it is easy to detect children who have even minor defects of hearing.

Von Békésy test

A useful modification of the pure-tone test has been described by von Békésy. As before, the patient listens to a tone in an earphone. A low tone just below threshold is gradually increased in intensity until the sound becomes audible; at this point the patient presses a switch, which results in a gradual reduction in intensity; when the tone becomes inaudible the patient releases the switch. The process is repeated throughout the complete frequency range. The tone is presented initially as a continuous tone and then as an interrupted note every 2.5 s to give a series of short 'beeps'.

Rinne's and Weber's tests

Sound vibrations can be conducted to the inner ear through the bones of the skull, but normally air conduction is much more effective. This can be shown by applying a vibrating tuning-fork (500 Hz) firmly to the mastoid process just behind the ear. When the sound dies away the prongs of the fork are brought near the external auditory meatus and the sound is heard once more, provided that the meatus is not blocked and that the ear drum and ossicles are intact. Rinne's test is then said to be positive.

Weber's test is carried out by placing a vibrating 500 Hz fork on the mid-sagittal line of the head (the vertex). If one ear is plugged by the finger to exclude room noise the sound produced by the fork appears to be louder in that ear. Thus in unilateral disease affecting the conducting system (middle-ear disease) Weber's test is referred to the diseased ear. When the organ of Corti

or the cochlear nerve is damaged unilaterally Weber's test is referred to the normal ear.

Rinne's and Weber's tests are used in clinical practice to distinguish middle-ear (conduction) deafness from inner-ear (perceptive) deafness. In conduction deafness Rinne's test is usually negative and Weber's test indicates the diseased ear. In perceptive deafness Rinne's test is positive and Weber's test indicates the normal ear.

Noise

Noise is not only to be defined in physical terms but also in psychological terms such as a sound that is disturbing or annoying. The loudness of sounds can be measured either subjectively or objectively. In the subjective method the loudness of a sound is compared with the loudness of a note of 1000 Hz that can be adjusted until the listener judges that it has the same loudness as the sound being investigated. When this equality has been achieved the intensity of the 1000 Hz note can be read from the instrument in dB above an arbitrary zero, which has been internationally agreed as $20 \ \mu\text{N/m}^2$. If the reading is n dB the sound is said to have an intensity of n phons. It is more usual to employ objective sound level meters that have a microphone and a calibrated amplifier with a number of alternative frequency response characteristics based on those of the ear at different sound levels. Such instruments give a reading of the sound level in dB above the same refer-

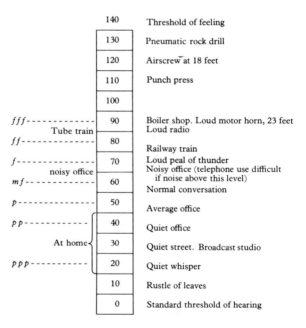

Fig. 38.11 A range of phon values. The phon is defined on this page. On the left are given the values of the musical *p* (piano) and *f* (forte) markings as used by the orchestral conductor Leopold Stokowski.

ence level. This objective method does not necessarily give a true index of loudness. A range of phon values is given in Figure 38.11.

Masking

Whenever there is a noise (as in a railway train) conversation becomes difficult and the speech power must be raised. This effect begins when the noise level reaches 20 phons and the loudness of speech is increased up to noise levels of 90 phons, beyond which the intensity of the speech cannot compete with the noise. The increase in the loudness of the voice is often revealed if the noise suddenly ceases. The nature of this masking effect has been investigated with the pure-tone audiometer. First, in a quiet room the threshold of audibility is measured, then a masking tone is continuously sounded and the threshold is measured again. Masking tones of moderate intensity make it difficult to hear notes of neighbouring frequency but if the masking tone is very loud there is masking not only of neighbouring tones but also of all tones of higher frequency. For this reason loud tones of low frequency impair the intelligibility of speech.

SPEECH

The importance of the left cerebral hemisphere for speech was demonstrated by Broca in 1861 when he showed that in adults loss of speech could be associated with disease of the left frontal lobe. In children cerebral dominance is less well established so that before the age of four unilateral injury to the brain may result in little impairment of speech and in later childhood speech disorders due to localised brain damage may recover relatively well. The non-dominant cerebral hemisphere in adults may aid comprehension of words but it is not clear if it contributes to the production of speech. Although Broca's area on the third frontal convolution is particularly important for the expressive side of speech, the temporal lobe and particularly Wernicke's area on the first temporal gyrus and the adjacent portion of the parietal lobe are the main regions concerned with the understanding of speech and the process of word-finding.

Children vary greatly in the rate and manner of acquiring speech. The baby's first cries usually express hunger or discomfort, but if they always have the effect of attracting attention he may learn to cry for this reason alone. By three months he has acquired several vowels and has learned to smile. By six months he can vocalise consonants and he is learning how to laugh. By nine to ten months he speaks his first word, usually Dada or Mama and by one year of age he has acquired another word, for example Ta. The time at which this is accomplished depends on many factors, such as the state of health and level of intelligence, and it may be accelerated or delayed by learning to walk. At 18 months the vocabulary is about 12 words. In the second year the child may have a vocabulary of 80 words and he often uses one-word sentences, such as 'Up', meaning 'Lift me up'. At the end of the second year two-word phrases are uttered and by the age of five years sentences of five words are being used. From two years onwards the vocabulary increases rapidly.

Disorders of language function

The importance of Broca's area (areas 44 and 45) for the expression of speech and the temporal lobe for comprehension and word finding has been referred to above. Hughlings Jackson, in his analysis of expressive aphasia, drew attention to the fact that although propositional speech is lost when this area is damaged simple emotional utterance may be preserved. At the same time as the ability to talk out loud is lost, there is also loss of internal speech, so that the patient cannot put his thoughts into words. In *jargon aphasia*, which occurs in disease affecting the temporal lobe, there is failure to understand both written and spoken language but speech remains fluent; however because the patient can no longer adequately monitor his own speech he makes many errors and the speech may amount to jargon. If the pathway between Wernicke's and Broca's areas is interrupted the patient is able to understand spoken and written speech but talks fluently with many errors — *conduction aphasia*. In extensive lesions of the dominant hemisphere involving both frontal and temporal lobes both language production and comprehension are lost — *global aphasia*. In *nominal aphasia* there is inability to name objects; this may be due to impairment of the connections between Wernicke's area and the surrounding brain and is often the earliest manifestation of dysphasia.

The organs of speech

The lungs and chest wall act as bellows that drive air through the larynx between the two sharp folds, the *vocal folds* or vocal cords, and set them into vibration, much in the way that air blown through the lips makes them vibrate. Normally speech is produced on expiration but an abnormal type of speech can be produced on inspiration. The vocal folds stretch from the thyroid cartilage in front to the mobile arytenoid cartilages at the back of the larynx; the triangular space between them is called the *glottis* or *rima glottidis*. The muscles controlling the arytenoids (Fig. 38.12) open or close the glottis, while the tension of the folds is regulated by the vocalis muscle lying in each fold and by the cricothyroid muscle, which tilts the thyroid cartilage and so elongates the vocal folds (Fig. 38.13). When the interior of a normal larynx is inspected through a mirror placed

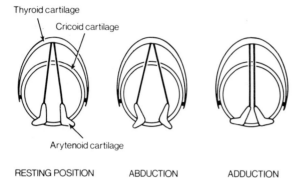

Thyroid cartilage

Cricoid cartilage

Arytenoid cartilage

RESTING POSITION   ABDUCTION   ADDUCTION

Fig. 38.12 A diagrammatic cross-section of the larynx to show the movement of the arytenoid cartrilage and the vocal folds.

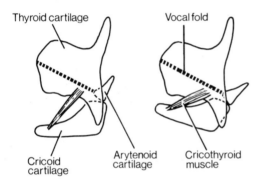

Thyroid cartilage   Vocal fold

Cricoid
cartilage   Arytenoid   Cricothyroid
                   cartilage   muscle

Fig. 38.13 A side view of the cartilages of the larynx to show the manner in which the cricothyroid muscle approximates the cricoid and thyroid cartilages and so stretches the vocal folds.

obliquely against the soft palate, the vocal folds are midway between full adduction and full abduction in quiet breathing. During vigorous breathing the folds open farther in inspiration. When the subject is asked to say 'ah' or 'ee' (that is, to phonate) the folds approximate. The frequency of a note can be regulated by the tension in the vocal folds. If the tension increases, the frequency rises and there may be considerable increase, up to 50 per cent, in the length of the folds. The vocal folds are lubricated by thin mucus secreted mainly in the ventricles, which are spaces formed by folds of the laryngeal mucosa immediately above the vocal folds. In whispering the anterior two-thirds of the vocal folds are approximated, free escape of air occurring in the space between the two arytenoid cartilages posteriorly.

Small needle electrodes have been placed in the intrinsic laryngeal muscles in man to record action potentials. Even in quiet respiration there is some electrical activity, which increases on inspiration in the adductors (vocalis and cricothyroid mainly) whereas it is diminished in the abductor (the posterior crico-arytenoid). The process of phonation begins with an increase in the electrical activity in the adductor muscles, which reaches a maximum just before the onset of the sound (Fig. 38.14). The time between the beginning of the electrical activity and the onset of the sound — 0.35 to 0.55 s — is necessary to allow the pressure to build up to the value needed to produce the sound. On the other hand the activity of the posterior crico-arytenoid muscle is inhibited just before sound is produced. An increase in the volume of the sound causes no change in electrical activity in the adductors but with a rise in pitch there is an increase in activity

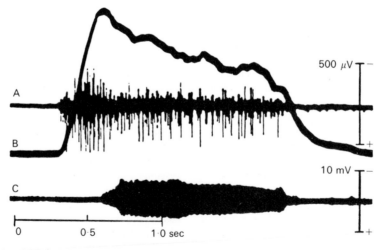

500 μV

A

B

10 mV

C

0   0·5   1·0 sec

Fig. 38.14 Electrical activity in the left vocalis muscle during phonation. *A*. The action potential pattern. *B*. A trace electronically derived from *A* that gives the mean action potential amplitude. *C*. Microphone recording of sound ee, frequency 285 Hz. The subject was a 64-year-old women with the right vocal cord immovable but with the left vocal cord moving normally. (Faaborg-Anderson K 1957 Acta Physiologica Scandinavica 41 (Suppl. 140):54)

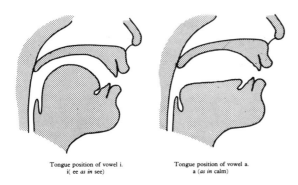

Tongue position of vowel i.
i(ee *as in* see)

Tongue position of vowel a.
a (*as in* calm)

Fig. 38.15 The positions of the tongue used in the formation of two vowels to show how the shape of the cavity of the mouth is altered. In this way the resonant properties of the cavity can be made to vary over a wide range. (After Ward I C 1948 The phonetics of English. Heffer, Cambridge)

that indicates that the tension in the vocal folds is adjusted to a given pitch before the sound is actually produced. No change in the pattern of electrical activity is seen when different vowels are produced. When the subject is asked to think about production of a vowel without actually emitting any audible sound, the electrical activity of the adductor muscles increases.

The sound produced in the larynx is greatly modified by the acoustic properties of the mouth, throat and nasal cavities. The tongue, by alterations in its shape and position, has the main control over the resonant characteristics of the oral cavity (Fig. 38.15) but the positions of the lips and jaws are also of importance in the production of speech sounds. The vowel sounds are produced by vibrations of the vocal folds (that is, are voiced), the air stream passing freely through the mouth. In the production of a consonant the air stream is either partially or completely obstructed so that it cannot issue freely from the mouth. Some of the consonants are very short, for example *t* and *p* and *k*, and may be regarded as particular ways of beginning or ending vowel sounds, but some consonants, such as *m*, can be spoken without a vowel. The larynx does not appear to be involved in the production of many consonants, that is the majority are unvoiced. A laryngeal component can, however, be added to some consonants to make them voiced; in this way *f* becomes *v*, and *s* becomes *z*.

The vagus nerve carries motor and sensory fibres to and from the larynx. The superior laryngeal branch, after receiving a twig from the sympathetic, divides into the internal laryngeal nerve, which is sensory to the upper larynx, and the external laryngeal nerve, whichs supplies the cricothyroid muscle. All the other intrinsic muscles are supplied by the recurrent laryngeal nerve, which also gives sensory fibres to the larynx below the vocal folds. After section of the recurrent nerve the

vocal fold on the denervated side lies in or close to the midline. The cricothyroid muscle (which is, of course, unaffected) stretches the paralysed vocal fold by tilting the thyroid cartilage. Full adduction or overadduction of the opposite vocal fold brings the folds together and in many cases speech is normal. In bilateral recurrent nerve paralysis the folds lie motionless near the midline, producing hoarseness. If the superior laryngeal nerves are cut, the upper part of the larynx is anaesthetic and voice is hoarse because the vocal folds cannot be made tense.

There are good reasons for regarding the upper resonators (mouth, throat and nose) and not the larynx as the main organs of speech, but the most dramatic evidence is furnished by the phenomenon of oesophageal speech. After complete surgical removal of the larynx the trachea is made to open on the surface of the neck while the oesophagus retains its relation with the mouth. If the patient acquires the trick of swallowing air he can bring it up in a belch that sets the lower edge of the inferior constrictor of the pharynx (cricopharyngeus muscle) into irregular vibrations, which are conveyed to the mouth cavity. The patient uses the same mouth positions as he did before his operation to modify this oesophageal sound and although the vibrations of this pseudolarynx are extremely irregular compared with those of the true larynx, yet he can with practice produce oesophageal speech, which, although rather hoarse, is readily intelligible. For natural and normal speech the larynx of course produces the sound and determines the fundamental pitch of the voice. But the variable resonances of the mouth and throat determine the quality of the sound that conveys the information from speaker to listener; this is also shown by the fact that the intelligibility of words is only slightly affected by singing them at different pitches. The mouth and throat are put into the proper position for the formation of speeeh with the help of the kinaesthetic sense, which gives information to the brain of the position of the tongue, lips and jaws. In addition the ear, in both normal and oesophageal speech, is used to monitor the muscular adjustments so that the desired speech sounds are produced. We hear our own words by air conduction about 1 ms after they are spoken; if this auditory feed-back is delayed by electro-mechanical methods for say 200 ms the subject is apt to stutter and his speech is slowed. If a speaker is deaf the ear cannot function as a proprioceptor and his speech is defective; if a normal subject is asked to sing a simple musical scale when a strong masking noise smothers the sound of his own voice he sings badly out of tune. When a steady note is sung there is a periodic fluctuation in frequency of 5 or 6 Hz. These fluctuations are produced by the auditory feed-back mechanism because, if the sound of the voice is delayed electrically before reaching the subject's ears, the fluctuations are larger and occur more slowly.

Analysis of speech sounds

The energy involved in speech is very small (10 to 25 microwatts in ordinary conversation) but the complexities of speech and musical sounds can be easily shown by using a microphone and amplifier connected to a cathode-ray oscillograph (Fig. 38.16). The vowels have waveforms that recur regularly throughout their duration at the frequency of vibration of the vocal folds. The pattern is usually very complicated showing, in addition to the fundamental laryngeal tone, a considerable number of harmonics of much higher frequency, some of which may even be of greater amplitude than the fundamental. Consonants like *p*, *b*, *t*, *d* are so short — electrical engineers refer to them as 'transients' — that no sensation of pitch is given by them; sibilants, *s* and *z*, may last as long as vowels and are characterised by small waves of very high frequency. Transitional consonants like *m*, *n*, *ng* also last for some time. Voiced consonants such as *z* and *v* have a waveform that recurs at the fundamental laryngeal frequency. A study of oscillograms of vowels suggests that each puff of air that

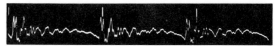

A.   Male voice. Laryngeal frequency 110 Hz

B.   Female voice. Laryngeal frequency 229 Hz

Fig. 38.16 Oscillograms of the vowel sound 'ah' as in 'father'. (A) Spoken by a man and (B) spoken by a woman. The vertical white lines are 0.01 s apart. The ordinate gives a measure of air pressure at the speaker's mouth. (Fletcher H 1929 Speech and hearing. Macmillan, London)

comes up from the larynx sets the cavities of the mouth and throat into vibration. This vibration gradually diminishes until the next puff of air comes up from the larynx. This is well illustrated by the oscillogram of the vowel 'ah' as in 'father', when spoken by a man (Fig. 38.16A). When the same vowel is spoken by a woman (Fig. 38.16B) the time between the laryngeal puffs is reduced to about half, with the result that the

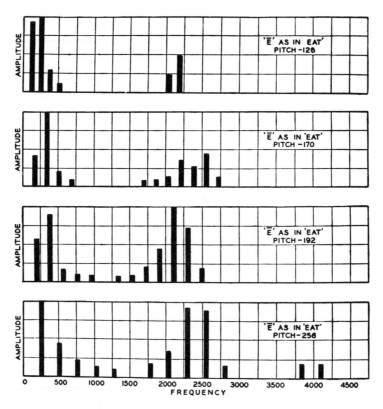

Fig. 38.17 Acoustic spectra of vowel sound 'ee' at different frequencies of the fundamental laryngeal tone (128, 170, 192 and 256 Hz) to show the general similarity of the spectra. (Fletcher H 1929 Speech and hearing. Macmillan, London)

vibrations of the air in the mouth diminish very little before the next puff comes along. Although the two waveforms of 'ah' in Figure 38.16 are quite different, the listener has no difficulty in recognising that both speakers are pronouncing the same vowel. It is thus unlikely that the ear recognises vowels by their waveforms and this is confirmed by the following considerations. When one listens to speech in a room, part of the sound arrives directly from the speaker to the ear and part indirectly after reflection from the walls; the reflected waves are out of phase with the direct wave. In many gramophone or microphone amplifiers the higher frequencies are not emitted from the loudspeaker in their original phase relationship to the low frequencies. In both examples, although the original waveform is considerably changed, the sound does not appear to be altered.

An acoustic spectrum is obtained by analysing a speech waveform to obtain the amplitude and frequency of its various components and some examples are given in Figure 38.17. If spectra of the same vowel spoken at different pitches (or, to express it objectively, at different laryngeal frequencies) are compared it is found that, in spite of the alteration in the frequency of the fundamental as the pitch of the voice is raised, the overtones are relatively unchanged and a characteristic grouping of the higher frequency components can be recognised in all the spectra. Presumably it is this grouping that is recognised by the ear; the higher frequencies produced in the mouth and throat must be important for differentiating and recognising the vowels.

The rate of vibration of the vocal folds, which can be easily found from oscillograms, gives a clue to the sex of the speaker. A deep-voiced man may have a laryngeal tone of 90 Hz, but in the average man it is usually between 125 and 145 Hz. The average woman's laryngeal tone is from 230 to 256 Hz, but in a shrill-voiced woman it may be as high as 300 Hz. The deepest bass note that can be sung is about 66 Hz, while the highest soprano note is about 1056 Hz. This is a range of 2^4 or four octaves.

The decibel notation

The energy involved in speech ranges from 0.0001 μW in a very soft whisper up to 1000 μW in very loud talking. The ear, like the other sense organs, follows approximately the Weber–Fechner law, which implies that equal steps on a logarithmic scale of intensity are equal steps on a loudness scale, and it has been found convenient to describe differences in power-level in the decibel notation:

Difference in power-level in decibels =

$$10 \log_{10} \text{ (ratio of the two powers)}$$

For example, if we use the figures quoted above the difference in power-level between a soft whisper and loud talking is

$$10 \log_{10} \frac{1000}{0.001} = 10 \log_{10} \frac{10^3}{10^{-3}}$$
$$= 10 \log_{10} 10^6 = 10 \times 6$$
$$= 60 \text{ decibels, or } 60 \text{ dB.}$$

This formula shows that 1 dB is equivalent to a 26 per cent increase in power; 10 dB to a ten times increase in power; 20 dB to one hundred times increase in power.

FURTHER READING

Ballantyne J, Martin J A M 1984 Deafness, 4th edn. Churchill Livingstone, Edinburgh

Espir M L E, Rose F C 1983 The basic neurology of speech and language, 3rd edn. Blackwell Scientific, Oxford

Proctor D F 1980 Breathing, speech and song. Springer, Berlin

Rosenberg M E 1982 Sound and hearing. Arnold, London

Singh R P 1980 Anatomy of hearing and speech. University Press, Oxford

Yost W A, Neilson D W 1977 Fundamentals of hearing. Holt, Rinehart & Winston, New York

39

The chemical senses

Taste and smell are referred to as the chemical senses because the receptor organs are remarkably sensitive to a wide variety of chemical substances. However the nose, the mouth and the genital apertures, and many mucous membranes are sensitive to irritants such as ammonia. This third form of chemical sense is referred to as 'common chemical sensibility'. A sensation described as a taste may in fact arise from the simultaneous stimulation of the taste and smell receptors; this is the case with onions and with wine. The close association between the two senses is shown by the lack of flavour of many food substances when the sense of smell is lost during a cold in the head. It is convenient to use the word flavour for the sensation aroused by the simultaneous stimulation of these receptors.

The senses of taste and smell are not as well developed in man as they are in other mammals. Man can detect quite minute amounts of certain substances but he has come to depend so much on his visual equipment that it is not surprising that the olfactory part of his brain is relatively small. The sense of smell is, like the sense of vision, normally projected on to the environment but the sense of taste is not so projected. Although an odorous substance stimulates end-organs in the nose, the sensation is referred to or projected on to the source of the odour. Thus we say that the rose has a sweet perfume, not 'there is a sweet perfume in the nose'.

SENSE OF SMELL (OLFACTION)

The greater part (or respiratory region) of the nasal cavities is lined by columnar ciliated epithelium interspersed with goblet cells which are capable of producing large quantities of mucus. In man the olfactory area, about 3 cm² in area on each side, is situated in a narrow cleft in the highest part of each nasal cavity above the superior concha. Each area possesses 50 million of olfactory cells, which lie among supporting cells (Fig. 39.1). Non-medullated nerve fibres arise from the olfactory cells and form a plexus in the deeper parts of the mucosa and then pass through the cribriform plate of

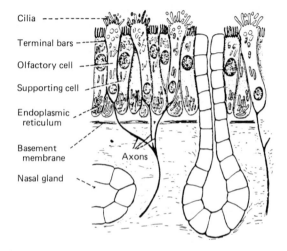

Cilia
Terminal bars
Olfactory cell
Supporting cell
Endoplasmic reticulum
Basement membrane
Axons
Nasal gland

Fig. 39.1 Olfactory epithelium and component cells. The nasal glands keep the epithelium moist. Each olfactory cell has about a dozen cilia each up to 200 μm long on its free surface. The microvilli of the supporting cells project into the layer of mucus that covers the olfactory epithelium (After Garven H S D, de Lorenzo A J D)

the ethmoid bone to the olfactory bulb where contact is made with second-order neurones in complicated synapses (glomeruli). These second-order neurones are mainly mitral cells going to the pre-piriform cortex and tufted cells sending axons to the opposite bulb. To establish conditioned reflexes to odours, the olfactory receptors, the olfactory bulbs and tracts and the piriform cortex are necessary but no other parts of the rhinencephalon.

Direct inspection of the nasal cavities after inhalation of light magnesia powder shows that the air-stream does not rise above the superior concha on inspiration and is at an even lower level on expiration. Thus in ordinary quiet breathing the air does not impinge on the olfactory area directly but only as eddies coming off the main stream. When we attempt to smell a substance by sniffing, the air-stream reaches the olfactory area directly either because it is travelling more rapidly or because it is directed there by a change in the shape of the nostrils. If air cannot reach the olfactory areas, for example because of swelling of the mucosa during a cold in the head, the sense of smell is lost. To give rise to a sensation of smell an odorous substance must be soluble in the mucus covering the olfactory area. Odorous substances must of course be volatile and must be soluble in lipids.

Many substances lose their odour within a few minutes of presentation. This may be a result of either a rapid adaptation of the end-organs or a washing away of the odoriferous molecules by mucus. Adaptation is at least part of the explanation since loss of odour tends to be specific, that is, any other odour, if quite different from the first, is easily perceived. The term adaptation seems appropriate in the case when the occupants of a stuffy room are quite unaware of their odour whereas a newcomer is at once unpleasantly conscious of it. Neutralisation of one odour by another occurs to some extent but usually disagreeable odours, for example that of faeces, are disguised by overwhelming them with powerful, but more pleasant, odorous substances.

There is much speculation about the physical or chemical nature of the stimulus that gives rise to an olfactory sensation. The old classification of odours into four main groups, (1) fragrant, (2) acid or sour, (3) burnt and (4) caprylic (disagreeable or putrid) is not satisfactory. There is no simple relation between chemical constitution and odour. Atomic bromine and chlorine have no odour but Br_2 and Cl_2 have. Similar odours may be given by substances with very different chemical constitution, for example hydrocyanic acid and nitrobenzene both smell of bitter almonds. Some sulphur-containing compounds have a smell like bad eggs. If, however, the sulphur is replaced by oxygen the compound is odourless. In the case of optically active substances it frequently happens that one stereo-isomer has a more intense smell than its mirror image.

Substances with similar odours are adsorbed to a similar extent on adsorbents such as active carbon even if they have quite different chemical constitutions; conversely substances with different odours behave differently towards the adsorbents used. Some sort of selective adsorption may occur in the nose. Molecules with a similar odour have a similar shape and size even if they differ considerably in chemical formula. The odour of substances may depend on their molecules fitting into specifically shaped receptor sites.

The minimum stimulus required to arouse a sensation of smell varies with different substances. Some substances, like mercaptan, chlorophenol and skatole, can be detected in the air at very high dilutions. The nose is a very sensitive chemical detector. It is possible to detect 0.01 mg of mercaption in a room of 230 cubic metres (say 28 ft by 22 ft by 13 ft high). Since 0.01 mg

of mercaptan contains 1×10^{17} molecules, each sniff of 20 ml contains 1×10^{10} molecules, about enough to cover the receptive area with a layer one molecule thick. However, in the absence of some selective action by the olfactory epithelium it is difficult to understand how one molecule of mercaptan in 50 thousand molecules of air can produce an olfactory sensation or indeed how the adsorption of a small number of molecules can set up a nerve impulse. A clue to the olfactory code may be furnished by cases of specific anosmia, just as clues to the mechanism of colour vision are supplied by cases of colour-blindness. Examples of specific anosmia are: 10 per cent of people cannot detect the odour of HCN; 3 per cent cannot detect isobutyric acid; 0.01 per cent cannot detect butyl mercaptan.

Records of the electrical activity of the mitral cells in the olfactory bulb of the rabbit when air containing an odoriferous substances is drawn through its nose show that the anterior part of the olfactory area is easily excited by esters (fruity smell), which are slightly soluble in water. Oil-soluble substances, on the other hand, excite the posterior area more easily.

Potentials have been recorded from microelectrodes placed in the olfactory epithelium of both man and animals. The frequency response is different for different odours but similar for similar odours. In animals experiments with micro-electrodes have shown that an individual olfactory cell (primary receptor) responds to some odours and not to others. The possession of a relatively small number of primary receptors of this yes-or-no character could account for the ability to detect a very large number of odours. For example, if an animal possessed only one such receptor it would be able to detect two classes of substances, odorous and non-odorous; if it possessed two different types of receptors it could discriminate four classes; if it possessed 20 different receptors, over a million different patterns are possible.

The perception of nearly all odours depends on simultaneous stimulation of the olfactory end-organs and the nerve endings of the trigeminal nerve in the nasal cavity. The proportion of the trigeminal element varies from odour to odour. Pinching recommends, that instead of the traditional camphor and peppermint, which have large trigeminal components, musks and floral odours, which are relatively 'pure' olfactory stimulants, should be used clinically to test the olfactory apparatus.

Many mammals react to odours (pheromones) emitted by members of the same or other species. For example the introduction of a strange male into a group of female rats may cause fetal resorption. The steroid hormones have an odour like that of musk and women but not men are said to be able to detect steroid odours. It is difficult to assess the influence of pheromones in man because of the complexity of his behaviour but these external chemical messengers may act at the subconscious level.

SENSE OF TASTE (GUSTATION)

The taste receptors or *taste buds*, about 9000 in the adult, are placed mainly on the peripheral parts of the dorsum of the tongue, being most easily found in the groove surrounding the vallate papillae: some buds occur on the soft palate and a few on the epiglottis. In children they are much more numerous and much more widely distributed over the tongue and on the insides of the cheeks. The oval taste buds embedded in the stratified epithelium covering the tongue are usually described as containing thin fusiform taste cells surrounded by supporting cells like the staves of a barrel. Electron microscope pictures suggest that the different appearances of the cells in the taste bud are due to their being at different stages of development. The taste cells have microvilli on their free surfaces. Experiments with tritiated thymidine have shown that taste cells are produced by mitotic division of cells at the edge of the bud, which migrate to the centre of the bud where they disintegrate and disappear after a week. Since the afferent nerve fibres do not degenerate, the nature of the receptor-nerve contact is rather difficult

to imagine. Radiotherapy of the mouth region may damage the taste buds; all foods then may taste alike (mouth blindness).

The *main nerves of taste* (Fig. 39.2) are the lingual branch of the glossopharyngeal (IX) for the posterior third of the tongue, including the vallate papillae, while the anterior two-thirds are served by the chorda tympani branch of the facial (VII). All the nerve fibres pass centrally to the tractus solitarius, a long column of grey matter in the medulla oblongata. From here fibres cross the midline and pass to the posterior ventral nucleus of the thalamus and then on to the lower part of the postcentral gyrus and probably other areas nearby. After destruction of the postero-medial ventral nucleus, goats drink strong solutions of quinine, acid or salt, which they had repeatedly refused before the operation. Stimulation of this area of the thalamus in intact unanaesthetised animals produces 'rejecting' movements of the jaw and tongue exactly as seen when a solution of quinine is squirted into the mouth. The lingual branch of the fifth nerve is the nerve of common sensibility for the anterior two-thirds of the tongue; the lingual branch of the glossopharyngeal (IX) carries both taste and common sensibility fibres for the posterior third.

Probably no true taste fibres pass into the brain stem by the fifth nerve, but tactile, pain and thermal sensations conveyed by this nerve play an important

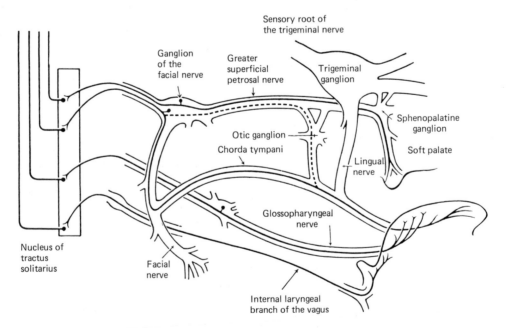

Fig. 39.2 Pathways of the tastes fibres are given by bold lines. The interrupted line is an alternative route for taste from the anterior two-thirds of the tongue that appears to be present in some persons. Although these pathways are accepted by most neurologists there is still some doubt as to details. (After Brodal A 1948 Neurological anatomy in relation to clinical medicine. Clarendon Press Oxford)

part in the recognition of taste sensations. When the fifth nerve in man is cut or destroyed the sense of taste is immediately lost in the front of the tongue but it returns in some cases after a few hours, in others after years. If the facial nerve is divided above its ganglion the sensation of taste is lost permanently on both the palate and the anterior part of the tongue; although the fifth nerve is intact, it is unable to provide a sensation of taste.

The sensibility of the tongue can be investigated by placing small drops of the test substances in solution in water on the protruded tongue while the subject holds his nose. Such experiments show that there are four basic tastes, namely *sweet*, *sour*, *salt* and *bitter*. It is, however, difficult to get good evidence to support this simple classical description. For example many people confuse sourness and bitterness and most people say that the sweetness of lactose differs from that of glucose. Further it has been shown that individual receptor cells are sensitive to many stimuli, that is they are not rigidly specific but an individual cell may be more sensitive to one kind of chemical stimulus than another. Sweet tastes are most easily perceived at the tip of the tongue, bitter at the back, sour at the edge and salt both on the tip and the edge (Fig. 17.1, p. 234). Sour and bitter tastes can also be appreciated at the posterior margin of the hard palate. The speed of recognition of the particular variety of taste, especially when the tongue is protruded, is relatively slow. The full sensation that allows the taste to be correctly recognised may not appear for several seconds. Tastes in everyday life, that is apart from laboratory experiments, are a mixture of gustatory, olfactory, tactile, thermal, and kinaesthetic sensations. By kinaesthetic sensation is meant the notion of hardness or toughness or elasticity obtained from the impulses arising in the end-organs of the muscles and joints used in chewing. If the nose is held and chewing is forbidden it is exceedingly difficult to distinguish between turnips, apples and onions.

A microelectrode placed in a taste cell of the rat usually detects a depolarisation in response to a taste stimulus. Electrodes have been placed on the exposed chorda tympani of man during operations on the middle ear. Action potentials were recorded when salt, sweet and bitter substances were placed on the tongue but the application of water reduced the spontaneous activity in the nerve. It thus appears that man, unlike the cat, dog and rhesus monkey, does not possess a specific water taste.

Sour-tasting materials all contain acids — vinegar contains acetic acid, citrus fruit citric acid, sour milk lactic acid. Whereas very weak acids do not have a sour taste, strong acids like hydrochloric acid, which dissociates almost completely in aqueous solution, have a sour taste at very high dilution. The sour taste of hydrochloric acid must be due to H^+ ions and not to Cl^- ions because 0.00125 N NaCl is tasteless whereas 0.00125 N HCl is sour. Organic acids like citric acid are, however, sourer than would be expected if hydrogen-ion concentration were the only factor determining sourness. It seems reasonable therefore to assume that both the anion and the undissociated molecule as well as the hydrogen ion play a part in determining the degree of sourness of an acid.

The typical salt substance is sodium chloride; calcium chloride and potassium chloride also have a salt taste but, since all chlorides do not have exactly the same taste, the cations must have a modifying influence. The salt taste is not, however, a specific property of the chloride ion since sodium bromide, sodium iodide, sodium sulphate and sodium nitrate all have salt tastes.

The factors determining sweetness are more puzzling and are not clearly related to chemical constitution. A number of organic substances, certain proteins, sucrose, glycerine, sodium cyclamate and saccharine, and a few inorganic substances, such as the salts of lead and beryllium, all have a sweet taste. The α-amino acids are sweet but polypeptides are often bitter. L-Tryptophan is bitter, D-tryptophan is sweet and the racemic mixture is bitter-sweet. The sweetest sugar is fructose, then come sucrose and glucose, with lactose a long way behind. If a 2 per cent solution of sucrose is used as the standard of comparison then saccharine is apparently 350 times sweeter than sucrose. Numerous other sweetening agents, some many thousand times sweeter than sucrose, have recently been prepared and are of great interest to food manufacturers and to diabetics whose sugar intake must be small.

A bitter taste is given by a variety of substances, for example caesium chloride, potassium iodide, magnesium sulphate, picric acid, and alkaloids such as quinine, strychnine and aloin.

Some·tastes are not easily included in the above four-fold classification, for example alkaline and metallic tastes. It may be that in these cases the common chemical sensibility is stimulated. Freshly distilled water has an alkaline taste owing to the absence of carbon dioxide. Electrical stimulation of certain parts of the tongue with a.c. or d.c. gives rise to an 'electric taste'. Anodal stimulation of the tip of the tongue gives a sour or metallic taste, which is at least partly dependent on an intact chorda tympani. Some substances give rise to a persistent taste sensation, for example, saccharine and iodides. This is presumably due to their excretion in the saliva.

No instance has been reported in which one of the four taste sensations has been absent or impaired by disease. It has, however, been found that phenylthio-carbamide and allied substances are bitter to about 60 per cent of persons and tasteless (unless very high concentrations are used) to 40 per cent, and that the ability to taste these substances is inherited according to Mendelian laws. Most people cannot taste sodium benzoate; a few describe it as either sweet or bitter.

The threshold concentration needed to arouse a sensation of taste varies widely with different individuals and depends somewhat on the method of testing but the following are average values: sour, 0.0045 per cent HCl; salt, 0.055 per cent NaCl; sweet, 0.45 per cent fructose, 0.7 per cent sucrose, 0.01 per cent cyclamate, 0.001 per cent saccharine; bitter, 0.001 per cent brucine. The smallest difference in the strength of a test solution that can be distinguished is about 30 per cent.

McCance lowered the salt content of the blood of a number of subjects on a low-salt diet by making them sweat in a radiant heat bath. The subjects found that nearly all food stuffs had lost their flavour but the sense of taste returned within half an hour of taking salt by mouth.

Patients with adrenal cortical insufficiency have a very much lower threshold for the four modalities of taste. Treatment with mineralcorticoids does not alter the threshold but treatment with glucocorticoids brings it back to the normal level. D-Penicillamine used in the treatment of a number of conditions lowers the serum caeruloplasmin and serum copper and decreases the taste-sensitivity in all four modalities. Administration of copper by mouth restores taste-sensitivity. Diabetics have a slight hyposensitivity to glucose not correlated with the level of blood glucose. In old age the taste threshold is raised partly because of a reduction in the number of taste buds and possibly because of a loss of cerebral neurones.

The sense of taste shows adaptation. After cane sugar has been held in the mouth for 2 minutes the threshold for cane sugar may be raised 10 times. At the same time the threshold for salt may be lowered a little. It is a matter of ordinary experience that successive draughts of a sweet drink become noticeably less sweet. After a sour stimulus, distilled water may arouse a sweet sensation. Many examples of interaction between

substances with easily recognised tastes could be given. Caffeine increases the sourness of citric acid and, as every coffee drinker knows, sucrose reduces the bitterness of caffeine. The temperature of the food affects gustation. Food has often more flavour when it is hot; iced food needs much more flavouring. Such a loss of flavour on cooling is not, however, universal; for example, the threshold for quinine is lower when the temperature of the solution is low. The flavour of food can be accentuated by adding flavour potentiators such as monosodium glutamate and certain 5'-nucleotides (disodium inosinate and disodium guanylate). These substances are effective in concentrations of the order of 100 parts per million but how they enhance flavour is quite unknown.

Symmetrical gustatory sweating is the name given to the sweating occurring on the head and face when irritants, such as chillies, are chewed; in a few persons it is aroused by eating chocolate. It is seldom felt in a cool climate or when the body is cooled but is experienced by nearly everyone in a tropical climate. This form of sweating has usually been described as a reflex phenomenon initiated by excitation of pain receptors in the mouth but recent experiments indicate that the response is not related to the spicy nature or temperature of the food. The physical or mental effort associated with eating may be enough to account for the phenomenon.

FURTHER READING

McBurney D H 1984 Taste and olfaction. In: Darien-Smith I (ed) Handbook of physiology, Vol III: Sensory processes. American Physiological Society, Bethesda, pp. 1067–1068

Mozell M M, Hornung D E, Leopold D A, Youngentob S L 1983 Initial mechanisms basic to olfactory perception. American Journal of Otolaryngology 4: 238–245

Norgren R 1984 Central neural mechanisms in taste. In: Darien-Smith I (ed) Handbook of physiology, Vol III: Sensory processes. American Physiological Society, Bethesda, pp. 1087–1127

Schiffman S S 1983 Taste and smell in disease. New England Journal of Medicine 308: 1275–1279, 1337–1343

40

Skeletal muscle

Muscles consist of large numbers of elongated cells, usually referred to as muscle fibres. When these fibres are suitably activated they develop tension and shorten. Skeletal muscle fibres contract only in response to activity in their motor nerve fibres. Action potentials in these motor neurones are conducted to their terminals, the motor end-plates, where the process of *neuromuscular transmission* leads to a similar action potential in the corresponding muscle fibre; this then spreads in both directions along the muscle fibre initiating a mechanical contraction in the underlying myofibrils.

Nerve action potential
    ↓   (Neuromuscular transmission)
Muscle action potential
    ↓   (Contraction coupling)
Muscle contraction

Motor nerve fibres usually branch as they approach their termination so that a single nerve fibre supplies a number of muscle fibres, all of which contract simultaneously in response to each nerve impulse. The group of muscle fibres along with the nerve fibre that supplies them is known as a *motor unit*.

NEUROMUSCULAR TRANSMISSION

Each adult muscle fibre is innervated by a terminal branch of one motor nerve. At the region of apposition both the nerve and muscle are specialised and form the motor end-plate (Fig. 40.1). The membranes of the nerve and muscle fibres are separated by a cleft 50 to 100 nm wide and the folding of the two membranes is such that this close apposition occurs over about 2000 μm^2 of membrane. This structure is analogous to that of a synapse in which two neurones come into close apposition. The motor end-plate, however, differs from synapses elsewhere in that each action potential in the nerve fibres gives rise to a single action potential in the muscle fibre.

When an action potential reaches the terminal part of the nerve fibres, *acetylcholine* (ACh) is released from the nerve terminals. This then diffuses in the cleft that separates the nerve and muscle membranes and acts on the muscle membrane in a way that leads to depolarisation and the generation of an action potential in the muscle fibre.

Acetylcholine is formed in the nerve terminal by a process involving the enzyme *choline acetyl transferase*, which, like all neuronal proteins, is synthesised in the cell body and actively transported along the axon at a rate of about 400 mm/day. In the resting fibre ACh remains stored within the nerve terminals in synaptic vesicles. When the fibre is depolarised by an action potential, some acetylcholine is released from the vesicles into the synaptic cleft. This release occurs only if there is an adequate concentration of Ca^{2+} in the extracellular fluid and entry of Ca^{2+} into the nerve terminal during the action potential plays an important part in the releasing mechanism. If the extracellular Ca^{2+} concentration in the end-plate region is reduced the amount of ACh released during each action potential is also reduced. An excess of extracellular Mg^{2+} has a similar effect because it blocks the entry of Ca^{2+}. The intensely poisonous bacterial toxin from *Clostridium botulinum* inhibits the release of ACh from the nerve endings. It has been used experimentally to block neuromuscular transmission and in man causes the disease 'botulism'.

After its release into the synaptic cleft ACh is rapidly broken down and rendered inactive by the enzyme *acetylcholine esterase*; under normal conditions, however, the local concentration of ACh persists for long enough to depolarise the muscle membrane and to initiate one action potential. The ACh that is released on nerve stimulation cannot normally be detected in the fluid that has perfused the muscle but, if the acetylcholine esterase is inhibited by *eserine* (*physostigmine*), *prostigmine* or *edrophonium*, then ACh can be identified and measured in the perfusate. In the presence of these drugs the concentration of ACh in the end-plate region remains high for some time after each action potential and a single nerve impulse may then give rise to more

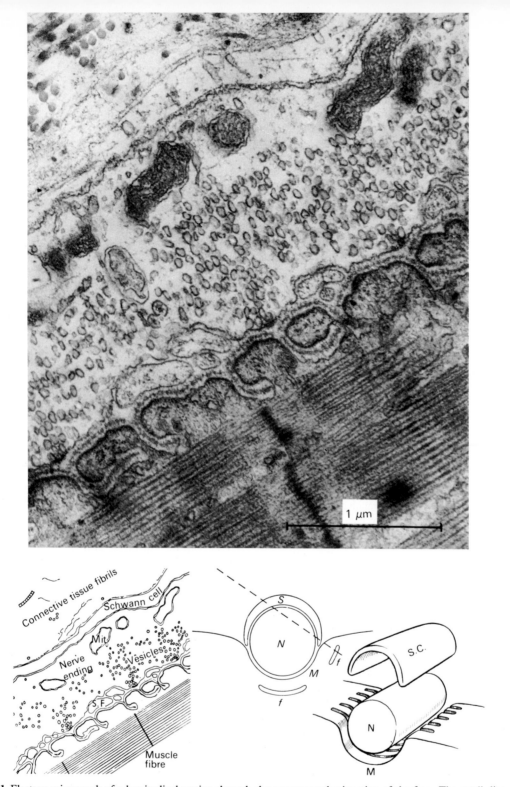

Fig. 40.1 Electron micrograph of a longitudinal section through the neuromuscular junction of the frog. The small diagram on the left below is a reduced tracing of the electron micrograph. Mit., mitochondria. S. F. Schwann finger, which extends a little way into the cleft between the nerve terminal and the muscle fibre. The 'exploded' diagram on the right shows the Schwann cell, S.C. lifted off the terminal branch of the motor nerve N which lies in a shallow gutter on the surface of the muscle fibre M. The gutter has semi-circular junctional folds. The small diagram in the centre is a transverse section through the nerve terminal N with the Schwann cell covering it, except for the part in contact with the muscle fibre, M; the junctional folds are cut through at f and f. The plane of the electron micrograph is shown by the dashed line; note that the section passes through the Schwann cell at two places. (Birks R et al. 1960. The fine structure of the neuromuscular junction of the frog. Journal of Physiology 150: 134)

than one action potential in the muscle fibres. Acetylcholine injected experimentally into the blood supply of a muscle is also destroyed by a choline esterase and it is only by injecting it in very large quantities that a muscle contraction can be provoked in this way. Other choline esters such as *suxamethonium* are not so rapidly inactivated and they produce a prolonged depolarisation of the muscle fibre membrane, associated with a brief contraction followed by paralysis as long as the drug is present.

Acetylcholine reacts with 'receptor sites' on the end-plate region of the muscle fibre membrane to cause an increase in the permeability of the membrane to sodium and potassium ions. Sodiums ions then enter the cell under the influence of the concentration gradient and electrical gradient and the membrane potential is consequently reduced. The quantity of ACh released during normal neuromuscular transmission increases the membrane permeability to such an extent that the membrane is rapidly depolarised to a level at which an action potential is generated.

The situation described above is the normal one in which each nerve action potential gives rise to a corresponding muscle action potential. Normally an end-plate has a large surplus of receptors; in the cat some end-plates must have 92 per cent of their receptors blocked before neuromuscular conduction fails. The function of the neuromuscular junction may be modified in a number of abnormal and experimental conditions. For example, if the amount of ACh released from the nerve terminals is reduced by immersing the end-plate region in a solution containing too few Ca^{2+} ions, then the smaller amounts of ACh released by each nerve impulse may reduce the membrane potential of the muscle fibre by an amount that is insufficient to initiate a muscle action potential; the threshold for stimulation of the muscle fibre is not reached and the only electrical change in the muscle fibre is the local *end-plate potential*, which is the direct result of the increase in permeability of the muscle to sodium and potassium ions.

Although the permeability changes are strictly confined to the end-plate region, the current flow in this region causes some depolarisation of the immediately adjacent parts of the fibre, and this may be recorded a millimetre or two on either side of the end-plate. The increase in the local concentration of ACh that gives rise to the end-plate potential lasts for a few milliseconds, so that each ACh molecule reacts only once with the membrane receptors, but the end-plate potential itself decays much more slowly (Fig. 40.2) and may still be of significant size after 5 ms. If a second nerve action potential arrives during this time the further release of ACh that follows causes a further depolarisation, which may exceed the response to the first nerve impulse, and

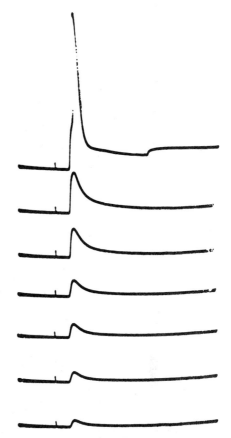

Fig. 40.2 Muscle fibres were immersed in Ringer's solution containing d-tubocurarine. They were then perfused with Ringer's solution to remove the tubocurarine. The effect of nerve stimulation was recorded at 3-second intervals beginning at the lowest trace. The amplitude of the end-plate potential increased, as this tubocurarine was worked out, until it reached the critical membrane potential when a propagated action potential is generated. (From Nastuk W L 1955 American Journal of Medicine 19: 663)

may perhaps exceed the threshold of the muscle fibre. The amplitude of the end- plate potential varies in a train of stimuli according to the frequency and duration of stimulation.

It is clear that the end-plate potential differs from the action potential in a number of ways: its time course is longer, it may be graded in its amplitude (though it is always much smaller), it does not leave the membrane in a refractory state, it is a local response that is not conducted along the length of the fibre, and it is associated with a simultaneous increase in permeability to sodium and potassium ions. Although end-plate potentials of this type are not normally seen, they are closely analogous to the *excitatory postsynaptic potentials* that occur in synapses between neurones and in tonus fibres (p. 397).

The drugs *tubocurarine* (*curare*) and *gallamine* compete with ACh for the receptor sites on the muscle membrane and thus render the muscle fibres less sensitive to ACh released during nerve activity. An appropriate amount of one of these drugs can reduce the depolarising action of ACh to a level at which sub-threshold end-plate potentials may be demonstrated. Some snake venoms contain components that combine irreversibly with the receptors and produce prolonged block. If the animal survives, new receptor molecules are synthesised and neuromuscular transmission is re-established within a week. An example is α-bungaro-toxin, which may be labelled with a fluorescent dye or with radioactive iodine, and can then be used to examine the ACh receptor site microscopically or to count the number of receptors.

The use of glass capillary micro-electrodes for recording the muscle fibre membrane potentials has revealed that in addition to the end-plate potentials already described there occur also spontaneous minia-ture end-plate potentials; these have the same form as the end-plate potentials that follow activity in the motor nerve fibre, but they occur quite spontaneously at random intervals, and they have a very much smaller amplitude (perhaps 0.5 mV). These spontaneous miniature end-plate potentials are caused by the release of ACh from the nerve terminals. The nerve terminal in fact 'leaks' small amounts of ACh when it is apparently at rest, and this 'leakage' of ACh is in the form of discrete 'quanta'. The amount of transmitter leaking out in this way is normally much too small (about 10^4 molecules) to have any important effect on the muscle fibre, but when an action potential invades the nerve terminal it accelerates the release of these quanta of ACh. The large quantity released by an action potential is merely a much more rapid form of the same process. Recently it has been shown that one molecule of ACh opens a 'gate' in the membrane for a few milliseconds; during this time a current of less than 5pA flows, depolarising the membrane by about 1 μV.

In the disease *myasthenia gravis* the skeletal muscles are easily fatigued. In the most severely affected fibres neuromuscular transmission is blocked and in others failure may develop during repetitive stimulation. Labelling with α-bungarotoxin has shown that the end-plates are abnormally large, but contain only 50 per cent to 10 per cent of the normal number of receptors. The loss of receptors may be due to a circulating antibody to the receptor molecules, which is found in nearly 90 per cent of the patients. The presynaptic release of ACh is normal. The symptoms of the disease may be alleviated by anticholinesterase drugs, although these can cause depolarising block due to persistance of ACh.

THE CONTRACTILE MECHANISM

Most of the space within each muscle fibre is occupied by *myofibrils*, longitudinal filaments approximately 1 μm in diameter. When examined by light microscopy, the fibres appear to be transversely striated; these striations are due to alternating zones of different refractive index within the myofibrils. The A (anisotropic) bands are birefringent, having a high refractive index, whereas the I (isotropic) bands have a lower refractive index. In most stained preparations of striated muscle tissue the A bands are more deeply coloured. In the centre of each I band is a Z line (Fig. 40.3), which is a disc of material running across the whole muscle fibre and joining the myofibrils to each other. The central region of the A band is paler and is known as the H (Hensen's) band. The region between one Z line and the next is known as a *sarcomere*. It is the fundamental unit of muscular

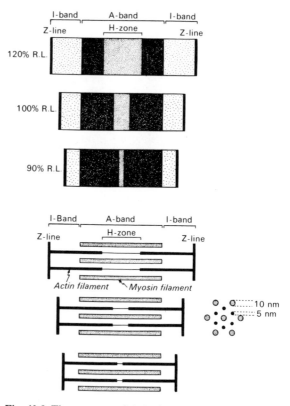

Fig. 40.3 The structure of skeletal muscle. The three diagrams at the top show the appearances as seen with the phase contrast or with the interference microscope at various percentages of the resting length, R.L. Note that the A band remains constant in length, about 1.5 μm in the rabbit psoas. The diagrams at the bottom show the arrangement of the filaments in muscle in both longitudinal and transverse section: the latter should be compared with the middle portion of Figure 40.4A. (After Huxley H E 1956 Endeavour 15: 177)

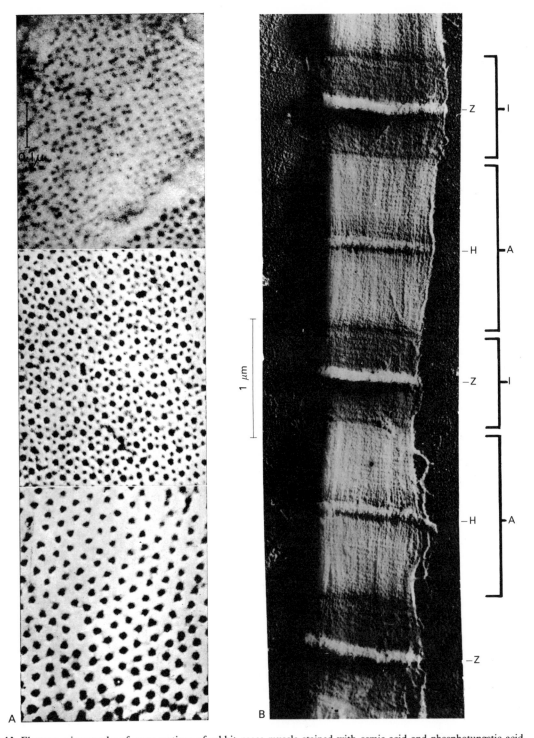

Fig. 40.4A Electron micrographs of cross-sections of rabbit psoas muscle stained with osmic acid and phosphotungstic acid. Top, thin actin filaments in the I band. Middle, double hexagonal array of filaments in the A band. Bottom, simple hexagonal array of myosin filaments in the H zone. (By courtesy of H. E. Huxley.) **B** Electron micrograph of toad muscle, platinum shadowed. I, isotropic band. A, anisotropic band. Z, Dobie's line. H, Hensen's band. (By courtesy of M. H. Draper and A J Hodge.)

contraction. The length of a sarcomere varies between 1.5 and 3.0 μm depending on the state of extension of the muscle fibres.

Contractile proteins

Electron microscope photographs (Fig. 40.4) give more information about the structure of myofibrils. Each myofibril contains a system of longitudinal filaments arranged in a regular pattern (Fig. 40.4A). In the I bands there are thin filaments consisting mainly of the protein *actin* arranged spirally along the filamentous protein *tropomyosin*. At regular intervals of nearly 40 nm there is a regulatory protein complex consisting of *troponins-C,-I* and *-T* (Fig. 40.5). The thin filaments are attached to the Z line or Z disc. The thin filaments

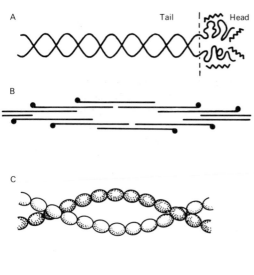

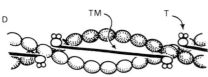

Fig. 40.5 A, myosin molecule. The 'tail', consisting of two coiled peptide chains (light meromyosin), gives rigidity to the thick filament. The 'head' contains two units of heavy meromyosin and two pairs of light peptide chains. The important cross-linking activity of myosin is related to the head; the light chains are related to ATPase activity. B, in the thick filaments the myosin molecules are arranged with their heads away from the middle of the filament. The heads project out toward the adjacent thin filaments. C, the backbone of the thin filament is a double stranded helix of actin; the two polypeptide chains are joined by disulphide bonds. D, tropomyosin molecules (TM), with double helical structure, lie as discrete filaments in each of the two grooves between the strands of actin. Troponin (T) molecules are bound to TM at intervals; each molecule contains three components, one of which (troponin-C) is a binding site for Ca^{2+}. (After Katz A M 1977 Physiology of the heart. Raven Press, New York

extend into the A band where they interdigitate with a system of thicker filaments. The thick filaments consist mainly of the protein *myosin*; these too are arranged in a regular manner; they lie approximately 45 nm apart, each being surrounded by six thin filaments (Figs 40.3 and 40.4A).

As the muscle changes in length, the thick and thin filaments slide over each other; during shortening the thin filaments move progressively further in between the thick filaments, and the I band becomes correspondingly narrower, though the width of the A band remains the same. At all but the shortest muscle lengths there is a region in the centre of the A band into which the thin filaments do not extend; this is the paler H zone, which becomes wider as the muscle fibre length increases.

The myosin molecules that form the thick filaments are arranged as shown in Figure 40.5; the head of each myosin molecule projects out from the thick filament toward an adjacent thin filament. Six such side-chains occur in a helical arrangement over a distance of 43 nm. These side-chains play an important part in the mechanism of muscle contraction; the central part of the thick filament, the H zone, does not have them.

Amongst the myofibrils is a system of fine tubules, the *sarcoplasmic reticulum*, which is important in activating the process of contraction. Transverse tubules extend inward from the surface of the muscle fibre; these are, in fact, inward extensions of the extracellular space within the substance of the fibre. The transverse or T-tubules are situated close to the end of the A bands in mammals. A second system of tubules extends longitudinally through the sarcoplasm amongst and around the myofibrils. This longitudinal component of the sarcoplasmic reticulum comes into close contact with the transverse tubules; the junction region is called a *triad* (see also Fig. 6.1).

The forceful contraction of muscle fibre is the result of a sequence of chemical reactions between the actin molecules and the myosin heads; in the course of this reaction the thin filament is drawn along the thick one.

It is suggested that in the presence of calcium ions a chemical bond forms between the thin filament and the myosin head (Fig. 40.6,1) and a cross-bridge is created. At low Ca^{2+} concentrations (less than 0.1 μmol/l) the troponin–tropomyosin complex prevents actin–myosin interaction. At higher concentrations Ca^{2+} binds to troponin-C and causes a change of shape in tropomyosin that uncovers active sites on actin at which cross-bridges are formed. Once the first link has been formed there is a strong tendency for a second form of linkage to follow (Fig. 40.6,2), and then a third (Fig. 40.6,3). The changes illustrated in Figure 40.6 can, however, only occur if there is movement of the thick filament by about 12 nm to the right in relation

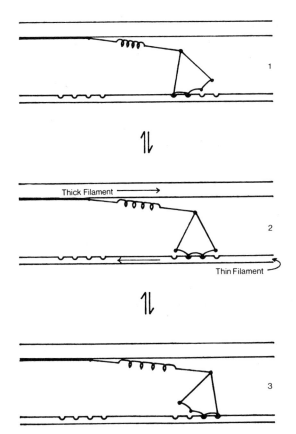

Fig. 40.6 Diagram of a possible mode of interaction between a thin (actin) filament and the side-chain of a thick (myosin) filament. The head of the myosin molecule links on to the actin in position 1, but once this linkage has formed there is a strong tendency for it to move into position 2 and then to position 3. Once this third position is reached the linkage may be broken down. (From Huxley A F 1974 Journal of Physiology 243: 30)

the myofibrils. Contraction occurs when ATP is added to glycerinated muscle fibres in the presence of free calcium and magnesium ions. During the course of this contraction ATP is converted to ADP and this conversion provides the energy necessary for the mechanical work done during shortening. If in such a preparation the supply of ATP becomes exhausted, the reaction ceases but the fibres remain stiff, a state that is analogous to the 'rigor mortis' that occurs when ATP disappears after death. This stiffness in the absence of ATP implies that the reaction has ceased with the filaments linked together. ATP is used for uncoupling the thin filaments from the myosin side-chains. The fact that energy is injected into the system by breakdown of ATP when cross-links are broken down suggests that at the onset of activity cross-links can be formed rapidly and the contraction begun before any ATP is required. In this sense resting muscle is ready for immediate activity.

Contraction coupling

Contraction of myofibrils is initiated by a release of calcium within the fibre. In the resting muscle calcium is actively pumped into the sarcoplasmic reticulum surrounding the myofibrils so that although the overall calcium content of the fibre is high the concentration of Ca^{2+} ions in the fluid that surrounds the actin and myosin filaments is less than 0.1 μmol/l. As the action

to the thin one, though some movement can occur if the side-chain of the myosin molecules becomes extended (as shown in Fig. 40.6) with a consequent increase in the muscle tension. Once the attachment of the myosin head has moved through this sequence of positions (and there may be more than the three shown in Fig. 40.6), it comes under the influence of an enzyme system that de-couples the actin–myosin complex and leaves the side-chain free to reattach to some other site on the thin filament. To break the cross-bridge a small amount of ATP must be split to ADP. Actomyosin is an ATPase that requires Mg^{2+} for activation; myosin alone has some ATPase activity but some 10^3 times lower.

The behaviour of contracting myofibrils can be examined after destruction of the muscle fibre membranes by immersion in glycerol at low temperatures. In such a preparation chemical agents can be applied directly to

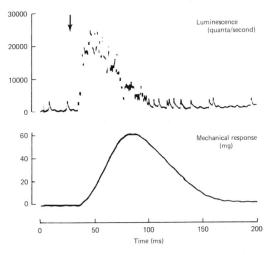

Fig. 40.7 Mechanical response and change in intracellular calcium concentration during a single isometric twitch in a muscle fibre dissected from tibialis anterior of a frog. The calcium concentration is shown by the luminescence (upper tracing) from the protein aequorin, which emits blue light when activated by calcium. It had been injected into the cytoplasm of the muscle fibre. The lower tracing shows the force developed. The moment of stimulation is shown by the arrow. (After Taylor S R et al 1975 Federation Proceedings 34: 1380)

potential travels along the surface sarcolemma (at 2 to 6 m/s) it initiates an action potential in the T-tubules. The *T-tubule potentials* are probably sodium spikes similar to those at the surface and are responsible for the transfer of activation from the surface towards the centre of a fibre. The T-tubules are about 50 nm in diameter, so inward spread of activation takes several ms but this is much less than the time that would be needed for diffusion of Ca^{2+} from the surface membrane. In mammalian muscle it is possible that the T-tubule activity does not propagate to the centre of the fibre following a single stimulus, so that only the more peripheral myofibrils are activated in a twitch. At the triads the terminal elements of the sarcoplasmic reticulum are stimulated by T-tubule depolarisation and release Ca^{2+} into the fluid near the myofibrils. The Ca^{2+} concentration rises to about 5 μmol/l, necessary for full activation of cross-bridge formation. The contraction is ended by Ca^{2+} being pumped back into the sarcoplasmic reticulum. The changes in intracellular Ca^{2+} concentration are illustrated in Figure 40.7.

MECHANICAL PROPERTIES OF MUSCLES

When a muscle is activated its fibres shorten or, if they are restrained from doing so, they exert tension on the tendons to which they are attached. The force that a muscle is able to exert is by no means constant and depends on the degree of activation, the muscle length and the rate at which it is shortening (or being length-ened). In the body muscle activity often involves an initial phase without movement during which an opposing force is overcome, followed by a period of acceleration up to a reasonably constant velocity, and ends in controlled deceleration. Lengthening, too, is complex, and may be brought about by the action of antagonists, sometimes against continuing agonist activity. Experimentally *isometric* and *isotonic* contractions have received most attention. The maximum isometric tension developed by mammalian skeletal muscle is about 35 mN/mm².

If a muscle is activated while its ends are rigidly fixed, so that no shortening can occur, it is said to contract isometrically. This is the simplest situation and it will be described first.

The isometric twitch

If a muscle fibre is stimulated by a single electrical pulse of adequate amplitude, an action potential passes along it, followed by a brief contraction, a muscle twitch. A similar, though much more forcible, muscle twitch may be obtained from the whole muscle after stimulation of its motor nerve; all the fibres in the muscle then contract simultaneously. Figure 40.8 shows the tension record during such an isometric twitch contraction. The muscle action potential is over in a few milliseconds but the mechanical contraction lasts much longer. The contraction also depends on the type of muscle stimulated (Fig. 40.8a, b) because muscles are composed of different types of motor unit (Fig. 40.8c–f) in various proportions.

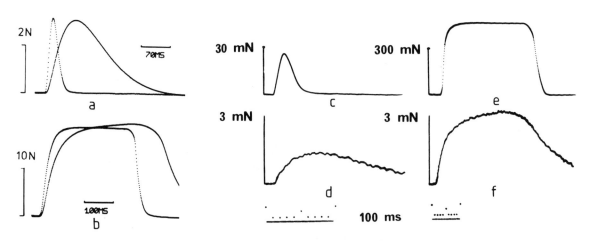

Fig. 40.8 The variety of muscle isometric contractions in the cat. *a* and *b* are whole muscles: flexor digitorum longus (fast) and soleus (slow). In *a* the twitches clearly show the differences between the contraction and relaxation times of the two types of muscle. The fully fused tetani in *b* are also different — soleus tension not only rises more slowly in the initial phase but also shows a second slowly rising phase in contrast to the flat or falling plateau produced by fast muscle. (By courtesy of A. J. Buller) The contractions in *c–f* of motor units stimulated in isolation in flexor digitorum longus muscle: *c* and *d* are twitches, *e* and *f* fully fused tetani. The motor unit of *c* and *e* is fast twitch, whilst *d* and *f* are from a slow-twitch unit: note that the tension of the slow unit is much less than that of the fast. (Bagust J et al 1973 Journal of Physiology 231:87. By courtesy of D. M. Lewis)

The twitch of a whole muscle is due to the summed activity of many muscle fibres, and its amplitude therefore varies with the number of fibres stimulated. By varying the strength of an electrical stimulus applied to the motor nerve it is possible to excite different numbers of nerve fibres and therefore different numbers of muscle fibres with corresponding differences in twitch tension, but once the stimulating pulse is made

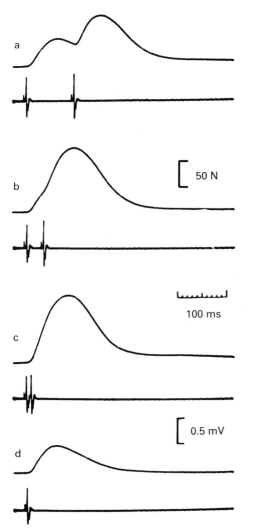

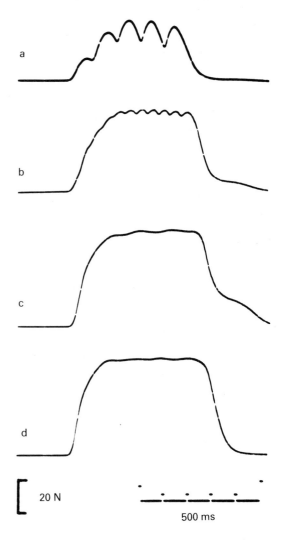

Fig. 40.9 The fusion of the mechanical response in human skeletal muscle when the interval between stimuli to the nerve is reduced. Isometric tension is shown in the upper trace of each pair and the surface electromyogram in the lower trace. Stimuli were applied to the ulnar nerve at the wrist, and the tension developed by the first dorsal interosseous muscle was recorded by holding a force transducer against the index finger level with the distal end of the first phalanx into which the muscle is inserted. A single stimulus was applied in *d*, and a twitch was recorded. In c, b and a pairs of stimuli were applied with intervals of 10, 35 and 100 ms, respectively. The pairs of stimuli evoke electromyograms that are distinct at all intervals, but the tension responses are fused. Fusion is complete and smooth at 10 ms. At longer intervals two components are seen, and maximum tension is lower. (By courtesy of K. W. Ranatunga.)

Fig. 40.10 The effect of frequency of nerve stimulation on the mechanical response of human skeletal muscle. The nerve to biceps was stimulated at its motor point at a strength near maximal for biceps tension without much recruitment of adjacent muscles. Tension was recorded by a transducer applied to the distal forearm. Because of the lever ratio in the forearm, the tension at the biceps tendon was about six times greater. In each case a train of stimuli lasting 500 ms was applied at the following frequencies per second: *a* 10, *b* 22, *c* 100 and *d* 200. In *a* individual contractions are seen (compare Fig. 40.9a). In *b* the contraction is almost fused and tension is greater. At a higher frequency in *c* complete fusion occurs without much increase in tension. When the frequency was increased further, *d*, the plateau tension was very similar to that in *c* but the rising phase was faster. The irregular fall of tension in *b* and *c* was probably due to reflex contraction. (By courtesy of K. W. Ranatunga.)

large enough to excite all the nerve fibres a further increase does not lead to a further increase in tension.

If instead of a single pulse, pairs of stimuli are delivered to the motor nerve and these are so timed that the second stimulus falls during the twitch contraction that followed the first, a second twitch grows out of the first one (Fig. 40.9), the tension rising to a higher level than in a single twitch. The closer together the two stimuli the higher is the tension so long as the second pulse is outside the refractory period of the nerve and muscle that follows the first pulse. This higher tension may result from the double action potential propagating further along the T-tubule with consequent activation of central myofibrils. Pairs of short interval action potentials occur in natural human contractions.

Tetanus

If a motor nerve is stimulated by a train of pulses the tension in the muscle rises progressively higher with each of the first few pulses until a plateau is reached (Fig. 40.10). If a high rate of stimulation is used the contraction is then continuous and a smooth tension record is obtained; when the stimulus rate is low the tension is not smoothly maintained but fluctuates at the frequency of the stimulating pulses. The tension generated during the smooth 'fused' tetanus (or 'complete'

tetanus) that accompanies stimulation at a high rate is considerably larger than the twitch tension of that muscle.

In a living animal muscle fibres are seldom activated at the high rates necessary for a smooth tetanic contraction, but since impulses are normally delivered to different motor units at different times, the whole muscle contracts smoothly, although the rate of stimulation for each muscle fibre may be quite slow. This situation may be reproduced experimentally by subdividing the nerve supplying a muscle and stimulating different groups of fibres asynchronously. Figure 40.11 shows how the force increased with increasing stimulus rate. At frequencies higher than those necessary to produce maximal tension, the tetanus still changes in that the tension rises more quickly (compared with c in Fig. 40.10). Maximum rate of rise of tension is elicited by frequencies some three times higher than those necessary for maximum tension: these frequencies do not occur naturally except possibly in the extra-ocular muscles or, briefly, as close pairs of action potentials.

The effect of muscle length on tension

There is a characteristic relationship between muscle length and the tension that develops in an isometric tetanus (Fig. 40.12). The maximum tension develops

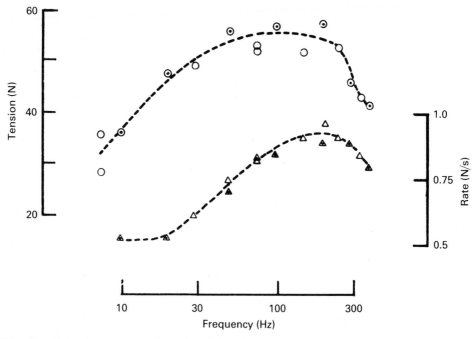

Fig. 40.11 The effect of stimulus rate on muscle tension, derived from the experiment on human biceps illustrated by Figure 40.10. The plateau tensions elicited by repetitive stimulation at different frequencies (abscissa) are plotted as circles on a scale shown by the left-hand ordinate. The maximum rate of development of tension during the rising phase of the tetanus was also measured and has been plotted as triangles using the right-hand ordinate. Note that the abscissa has a logarithmic scale. Maximum tension was achieved at about 50 stimuli per second, but a frequency of nearly 200 was needed to elicit maximum rate of rise of tension. This second frequency rarely occurs physiologically. (By courtesy of H. M. Ismail)

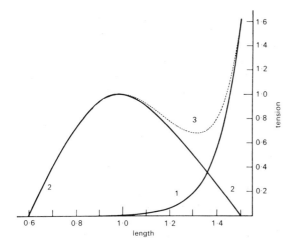

Fig. 40.12 Diagram of tension-length relations of sartorius muscle of frog or toad. (1) At rest passively stretched; (2) extra force developed during maximal tetanus; (3) dotted line, total force in maximal tetanus, sum of (1) and (2). The length is given as a fraction, or multiple, of the standard length in the body: the tension of the maximum force developed. (From Hill A V 1953 Proceeding of the Royal Society Series B 141: 113.)

when the muscle is at a length usually approaching the maximum that it takes up in the intact animal; at lengths shorter than this the tension is smaller, and if the muscle is stretched beyond this optimum length the active tension also declines, though at extreme lengths the connective tissue in and around the muscle resists extension with a considerable force and dominates the situation. Figure 40.12 shows the effect of length on one muscle. In other muscles the relative contributions of passive (1) and active (2) tension may be different. Mammalian muscles have more connective tissue, which increases the passive tension element, and as a result the total tension (3) does not always show a region of negative slope. Another factor is the extent of activation. Active twitch and tetanic tension are both maximal near the resting length of the muscle in the body. However an unfused (physiological) tetanus is greatest at significantly longer muscle lengths because twitches are prolonged at long muscle lengths and therefore summate more effectively.

A. F. Huxley and his colleagues have shown that the form of the isometric *length-tension curve* can be explained in terms of the sliding filament theory of muscle contraction. The maximum active tension develops when the sarcomere lengths are such that there is sufficient overlap between thick and thin filaments in the myofibrils for all the side-chains of each thick filament to have access to the thin filament so that a maximum number of cross-links can form. When,

however, the muscle is extended beyond this optimum length, the thin filaments are pulled out from among the thick ones, the overlap is less, and there are correspondingly fewer possible sites for cross-link formation; the greater the extension, the smaller is the overlap and the lower the tension.

When the muscle shortens from the optimal length each thin filament moves further in between the corresponding thick filaments, but this movement is impeded when, at a sarcomere length of 2.2 μm, each filament meets another one moving in the opposite direction. Some part of the contractile force is then taken up in compressing these filaments against or past each other so that the external force generated by the muscle is correspondingly less at the shorter length. If shortening proceeds further, a point will be reached, at a sarcomere length of 1.5 μm, at which the ends of the thick filaments become compressed against the Z line; further shortening is impeded and the tension falls.

The effect of speed of shortening on muscle tension

Muscle develops less tension during shortening than in an isometric contraction at the same length, and the more rapid the shortening the lower is the muscle tension. Conversely, the muscle cannot shorten so quickly against a large force as against a small one. The *force-velocity* relationship can also be explained by the sliding filament theory.

A. F. Huxley has pointed out that the sliding filament theory of muscle contraction offers an explanation for the *force- velocity relationship* in active muscle. Cross-links form between thick and thin filaments in the myofibrils exerting a force that tends to draw the thin filaments along the thick ones. The formation of these links is a chemical process, the rate of which is limited and depends among other things on the availability of calcium ions; once formed, however, the links are broken down at a rate that depends to a large extent on how fast the filaments move and allow rotation of the myosin heads.

When the filaments are stationary or movement is slow, the formation of cross-links can proceed at a normal rate, and each link may have a long life since the myosin head is unlikely to rotate into the position where enzymatic breakdown can occur. A large number of cross-links are therefore present and tension is high. When, however, shortening occurs and the filaments move over each other, the actin–myosin linkages can move into the configuration in which enzymatic breakdown may occur; each link has therefore a shorter life, and at any time there are fewer of them with a correspondingly smaller total tension. Men pulling in a rope provide a useful analogy; if the rope is stationary, or moving only slowly, all their hands are on it and the force is maximal. When, however, the rope is being pulled in more quickly there are always a number of hands off the rope preparing to take a new hold, and the force is correspondingly smaller. Velocity of shortening is maximal with zero load and tension is maximal with no shortening. Maximal power is available when the load and the shortening velocity are both at about one-third of their maximal values. Efficiency of work (external work/energy used) is highest in this region of the force-velocity relationship.

The force developed by a muscle depends on the number of fibres arranged in parallel to pull on the tendon. For maximal tension within a given volume of muscle the fibres are short and numerous; such muscles are often multipennate, with a central tendon into which fibres are inserted obliquely. In contrast the shortening velocity of a muscle is proportional to the number of sacomeres in series. Muscles capable of rapid shortening therefore consist of long fibres.

The stiffness of muscle

The length:tension diagram (Fig. 40.12) illustrates a form of negative feedback within muscle. If an extra load is imposed on a steadily contracting muscle, the muscle extends and, according to the slope of the total tension/length curve, it develops more tension and resists excessive extension. Muscle stiffness may be calculated as change of tension/change of length. This stiffness has an effect similar to that of the stretch reflex (p. 420) but with two differences. First the muscle response is immediate; indeed, if rapid stretches are imposed on active muscle, the tension increase is maximal at the end of the change in length. Secondly the muscle stiffness appears to be small if judged from the slope of Figure 40.12. However if the tension is measured immediately at the end of a stretch, much higher values are obtained for stiffness. Stiffness is also higher for small than for large stretches. Maximal muscle stiffness is some ten times greater than the steady-state measurements of Figure 40.12. In some muscle contractions it has been demonstrated that the resistance to an unexpected load is due more to muscle stiffness than to the stretch reflex. A further property of the muscle stiffness is that it is directly proportional to the active tension in the muscle, so that stiffness is related to the task being performed. This is a consequence of the fact that much of the stiffness is located in cross-bridges; both tension and stiffness are proportional to the number of cross-bridges formed at any time. The tension excess during stretch is proportional to the velocity of stretch, another point of resemblance to the stretch reflex. However, if velocity is too high the force collapses, possibly providing a protective mechanism.

Fast and slow muscle

The preceding description takes little account of differences between muscles. In almost all mammals two types of twitch muscle have been described, fast and slow. Most experiments have been done on muscles of quadrupeds in which some extensors are active in posture to support the weight of the body and in these mammals the difference between slow postural muscles and fast phasic muscles is clearly seen (Fig. 40.8a,b). In man normal posture depends on continuous but minimal activity of extensors and flexors to maintain the centre of gravity over the joints (the paravertebral muscles and those supporting the head are exceptional). Correspondingly, in man there is not such a clear division into fast and slow muscles. However, large differences do exist between muscles in man. The speed of contraction may be characterised by measuring the contraction time of an isometric twitch (time from onset to peak of tension). The extra-ocular muscles are the fastest in the body, followed by the muscles of the jaw (40 ms) and those of the hand and foot (50 to 60 ms). The biceps brachii (70 ms) is faster than the muscles of the calf and the gastrocnemius (100 ms) is faster than the soleus (120 ms). Possibly the differences between human muscles are adaptations to the mass of the structure which they have to move.

There are a number of other differences between fast and slow muscle. Fast muscle relaxes faster, needs a higher stimulation frequency for tetanic fusion and has a higher rate of rise of tension and a greater velocity of isotonic shortening. Slow muscle is more efficient for a given work load. The contractile differences are reflections of biochemical differences. The actomyosin ATPase of fast muscle splits ATP more rapidly, the myosin heads contain different amino acid sequences and, together with other contractile proteins, are different electrophoretically. There is relatively more sarcoplasmic reticulum in fast muscle and it sequesters Ca^{2+} more rapidly. Electrically the fast muscle action potential is briefer and propagates faster, and the resting potential is slightly higher. End-plates are not identical and differ in their sensitivity to neuromuscular blocking agents; fast muscle is more sensitive to tubocurarine and similar competitive inhibitors, but less sensitive to depolarising agents such as decamethonium. This is particularly important in anaesthesia because the muscles of respiration may not have the same sensitivity as those of the limbs.

The twitches of fast and slow muscle differ in the way they are affected by a number of factors: three will be considered. Preceding activity, such as a tetanus, increases the twitch of fast muscle without any effect on its time course, possibly by increasing the central propagation into the T-tubules; in contrast a slow muscle twitch becomes smaller and briefer. Adrenaline,

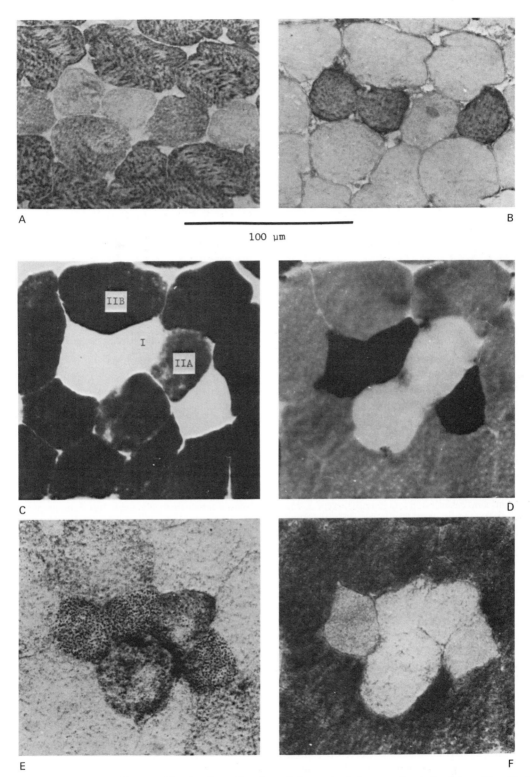

100 µm

Fig. 40.13 Histochemistry and immuno-histochemistry of cat fast twitch muscle. A, immuno-chemical staining with antibodies against fast myosin (mainly in Type IIB fibres). B, immuno-chemical staining with antibodies against slow myosin to stain mainly the Type I fibres. C and D, histochemical staining to show myofibrillar ATPase activity. In C the section was pre-incubated in an alkaline medium to inhibit the ATPase of slow twitch fibre while in D acid pre-incubation inhibits the ATPase of type II fibres and type I fibres are therefore predominantly stained. E shows the distribution of succinic dehydrogenase particularly in mitochondria. F shows phosphorylase involved in glycogen breakdown. (By courtesy of A. Rowlerson).

but not noradrenaline, also potentiates fast and depresses slow muscle. Physiological levels of adrenaline produce significant effects only in slow muscle because the threshold of fast muscle is five times higher. An increase of temperature increases the speed of contraction of isotonic and isometric tetani and twitches of both types of muscle, whilst the twitch tension of fast muscle decreases and that of slow muscle increases. These changes are physiologically important since muscle temperature is a few degrees above 30°C when at rest in a cool environment and rises to above 40°C during exercise, higher than the elevated core temperature.

Differences in contractile properties are accompanied by differences in muscle metabolism. Slow muscle has a greater density of capillaries and a high resting blood flow, similar to that reached in fast muscle in maximal activity. Slow muscle is red because of a high myoglobin content, but also has more lipid and oxidative enzymes, such as succinic dehydrogenase (SDH). As a result slow muscle is more resistant to fatigue during repetitive stimulation. In the past all fast muscle was considered to be pale, but some fast muscles are red and have the metabolic properties of slow muscle. The commoner white form of fast muscle has low concentrations of myoglobin and oxidative enzymes but large amounts of glycogen and enzymes concerned with glycolysis and anaerobic metabolism such as phosphorylase. Such muscle is capable of short periods of intense activity but fatigues rapidly with depletion of glycogen stores.

The microscopic structure of muscles may be examined by histochemistry and by reaction with antibodies to specific proteins. Figure 40.13 illustrates these techniques in detail. Fast muscle contains a majority of type II fibres and slow muscle consists mainly of type I. Most muscles, however, including those of man, are a mixture of all types. The proportions vary between individuals in a way that is related to muscle performance. Greyhounds, for example, have a higher proportion of type II fibres than do mongrel dogs. There are probably similar correlations with human athletic performance. Pathological conditions often affect one type of fibre in preference to the others, and biopsy specimens are useful in differential diagnosis.

Motor units

A motoneurone axon, all its branches and the muscle fibres innervated by it are called a motor unit. A motor unit is the quantum of motor response: once the motoneurone is excited all the fibres of the motor unit respond in an all-or-none manner in normal muscle. In man the motor unit contains from some 2000 muscle fibres (in calf muscle) to little more than 100 (lumbrical muscles). Extra-ocular muscle motor units may be even smaller (about 10 fibres suggested) but the presence of tonic muscle (below) makes calculations difficult. The

fibres of a motor unit are restricted to a limited region of the large muscles, but within their territory they are completely mixed with fibres of other units. In reinnervated muscle the fibres of one unit are often grouped together and give characteristic electrical responses (compare Fig. 40.14C). Motor units can be classified as slow-contracting, with great resistance to fatigue, or as fast-contracting, easily fatigued, or as fast-contracting with high fatigue resistance (labelled as S, FF and FR, respectively). Within each group there is variation of twitch contraction times, so a continuous spectrum exists from the fastest to slowest. A wide range exists in each muscle: Twitch contraction times of motor units have been found in human dorsal interosseous muscle from 30 to 100 ms (mean 55 ms) and in the gastrocnemius between 40 and 110 ms. Motor unit tensions also vary widely. In the interosseous muscle twitch tension of units range from 1 mN to 100 mN; in gastrocnemius the relative range is slightly higher (10 mN to 2 N), but it is clear that the units are large in the larger muscle. The larger muscles would also contain a greater number of units but fast units tend to be larger than slow ones (Fig. 40.8, c–f). The motoneurones of motor units also differ. Fast-contracting units have large, fast-conducting axons originating from large motoneurones. Slow motor unit neurones and axons are smaller, although still within the α range. Large motoneurones discharge at higher frequencies than the small ones.

After mechanical recording from a motor unit it is possible to fatigue it by repeated tetanisation. If the muscle is frozen for histochemistry and sections stained for glycogen, the fibres of the motor unit stand out white because their glycogen has been depleted. It is found that motor units are histochemically uniform and S, FR and FF units consist of type I, IIa and IIb fibres, respectively.

Voluntary control of muscle contraction

The force of muscle contraction may be modified by alteration of the number of motor units employed or by alteration of their rate of activation (Fig. 40.11). The nervous system makes use of both methods. When the force to be exerted is small, only a few of the motor units are active, and these are usually the smaller ones; the activity in the different units is, however, asynchronous, so that a smooth contraction of the whole muscle is obtained. For a more powerful contraction larger motor units are also brought into action, and to obtain very large forces all the motor units are activated at higher rates. The use of a number of small motor units for the less forcible movements gives an accuracy of control that is no doubt desirable for the fine movements, and could hardly be achieved by larger motor

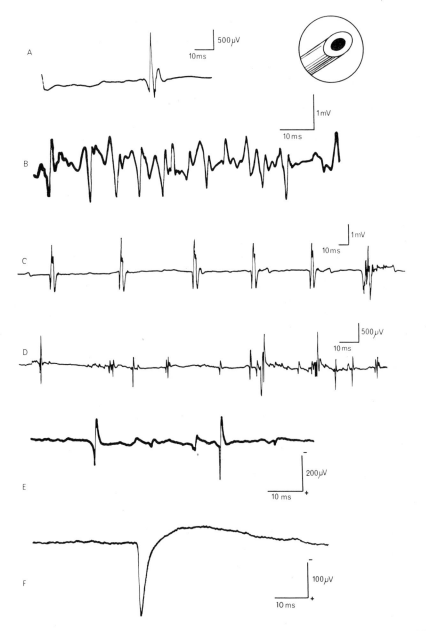

Fig. 40.14 Human electromyogram recorded with a concentric electrode (inset). A, Motor unit action potential from healthy subject during weak voluntary contraction. B, Interference pattern recorded from healthy muscle during prolonged contraction. C, High amplitude long duration action potentials recorded from muscle of patient with disease affecting anterior horn cells. D, Short duration polyphasic potentials recorded from muscle of patient with muscular dystrophy. E, Fibrillation potentials recorded from denervated muscle. F, Positive sharp wave recorded from denervated muscle. (By courtesy of J. A. R. Lenman.)

units. The organisation of motor units in size and speed is related to their use in natural contractions. For example, in stereotyped voluntary contractions small motoneurones have lower thresholds than large ones, so small slow motor units are recruited before large fast ones. This regular recruitment order persists in other types of contractions such as very rapid transient (ballistic) ones.

Trophic effects of nerve

Although there are clear differences between the fast and slow fibres, either type can be changed into the other experimentally. If a fast muscle is subjected to the pattern of activation that would be usual for a slow one, it gradually changes its characteristics. Such a change may be brought about by implanting the nerve of the (slow) cat soleus muscle into a denervated (fast) flexor hallucis longus; when this re-innervation has occurred, the flexor hallucis is found to have a slower twitch than previously, its enzyme systems, both those concerned directly with contraction and those regulating fibre metabolism, have changed toward the pattern seen in slow muscles, and a number of new capillaries have been generated together with an increase in resting blood flow. The opposite transformation from slow to fast can also be produced by the appropriate nerve transposition. A similar change from fast to slow follows repeated stimulation of the nerve to the (fast) flexor hallucis longus at rates that are normal for the (slow) soleus.

Denervated muscle

Intermittent high frequency stimulation of denervated muscle changes some of the properties of slow muscle. Therefore the pattern of activity of the muscle modifies somewhat the type of proteins that are synthesised.

Activity patterns may not be the only way in which nerves influence muscle. It is suggested that a chemical is released from the nerve that affects gene expression in the muscle. A denervated muscle undergoes a number of changes. The most obvious of these is atrophy of the fibre, which, if not re-innervated within a few months, involves degeneration and irreversible loss of fibres. The muscle fibres show spontaneous activity known as *fibrillation*; this is a useful diagnostic finding (Fig. 40.14E). Fibrillation arises from generator sites in individual fibres that wax and wane over a three-day cycle. The action potentials become smaller and prolonged and are resistant to tetrodotoxin unlike normal muscle spikes. The twitch is potentiated and prolonged possibly as a result of changes in the sarcoplasmic reticulum. Finally the whole of the muscle membrane becomes hypersensitive to ACh.

Many of these changes are a consequence of the loss of natural activity in the paralysed muscle and can be reproduced by procedures that block neuromuscular transmission but leave the nerve histologically intact. Crush injuries to a peripheral nerve in man that block conduction without nerve degeneration produce changes in the muscle. These changes are partly due to the reduction in muscle activity but they are quantitatively smaller than those following nerve section; these differences suggest that a chemical trophic factor is released from the intact nerve. It is known that the transport of materials along the axon from the cell body of the motoneurone may persist after nerve impulse block.

The nature of the supposed trophic factor is unknown

but the effects of activity are clear and the consequences may be of use therapeutically.

The increased activity of physical training causes hypertrophy of muscle fibres by the addition of myofibrils, an increase of metabolic enzymes and the addition of new capillaries. Natural activity, in contrast to artificial stimulation, does not seem to influence the contractile proteins. Greyhounds have a larger proportion of Type IIb fibres than do other dogs, and they maintain this proportion even after a year of sedentary existence.

Muscle has a limited capacity for repair. After damage it is replaced by fibrous tissue. If cut across, the degenerated fibres induce sprouting of axons nearby and re-innervation occurs; the two halves will be joined by a scar. Axon sprouting and re-innervation also occur if part of a muscle is denervated by motor neurone disease. Experimentally only 20 per cent of the neurones need to survive for full recovery of tension. After extensive muscle damage some recovery can occur by neighbouring fibres extending into the gap but regeneration is probably small.

If a muscle is abnormally stretched new sarcomeres are laid down at the ends of the fibres. This is part of the normal process of growth and occurs even in denervated muscle.

Tonic muscle

Some skeletal muscle is different from the twitch fibres. It is called *tonic* or slow muscle. Each fibre in tonic muscle is innervated by a number of nerves, so the fibre is covered by many end-plates over its whole length. The fibres cannot generate action potentials but are activated by end-plate potentials that spread only passively and locally. Such fibres do not respond mechanically to a single stimulus. Repetitive stimulation generates a slow-rising smooth tetanus, the tension of which increases with stimulation frequency: several hundred pulses per second are necessary for full activation. Tonic muscles respond to depolarising neuromuscular blocking agents with a prolonged contracture.

Tonic fibres occur in large proportions in the extraocular muscles, but also are found in the muscles of the middle ear and possibly the larynx; all are innervated by cranial nerves of α-diameter. Muscles innervated by spinal nerves have no tonic fibres, but many intrafusal fibres (p. 507) have similar properties.

ELECTROMYOGRAPHY

When a motor unit is activated, all its constituent muscle fibres carry action potentials at almost the same time. The resulting electrical field is much larger than that generated by a single nerve fibre, and it can be recorded relatively easily in a human subject with fine wires or needle electrodes introduced into muscles. Conduction in muscle fibres is 10–20 times slower than that in the motor nerve.

In healthy muscle no electrical activity is seen when the muscle is relaxed, but during a weak voluntary contraction motor unit action potentials can be recorded; during maximal effort these can no longer be distinguished from one another and appear as an 'interference pattern'. In disease affecting the lower motor neurones a reduced number of motor unit potentials may be recorded so that individual units can be recognised even during a strong contraction. When motor neurones are lost, as in poliomyelitis and motor neurone disease, surviving axons send out sprouts to re-innervate denervated muscle fibres and these enlarged units give rise to potentials of high amplitude and long duration. In muscle disease, on the other hand, when few motor units are lost but some of the muscle fibres in the units may have degenerated, the number of motor unit potentials is not reduced but individual potentials are of short duration and polyphasic. In denervated muscle apparently spontaneous contraction of muscle fibres takes place which appears as fibrillation potentials. These are short-duration low-amplitude potentials, which have an initial positive phase unless recorded from the end-plate zone. Positive sharp waves are also recorded from denervated muscle particularly following electrode movement (Fig. 40.14).

Measurement of nerve conduction velocity (Fig. 40.15) has been found to be clinically useful. Nerve conduction may be slowed if there is demyelination along the course of a peripheral nerve, as may be the case in certain forms of peripheral neuropathy. In 'entrapment neuropathies' where there is local compression of a peripheral nerve, as for example where the median nerve is compressed in the carpal tunnel, there may be slowing of conduction along the affected segment of nerve.

MUSCLE METABOLISM

Muscle obtains the energy for mechanical work from chemicals with an efficiency of about 0.25. The principal fuels used by muscle tissue are carbohydrates and fats. The relative amounts used may be approximately determined from the respiratory quotient (RQ), which is obtained from measurements of inspired and expired gases. The relation between RQ and metabolic fuels is explained on page 161. At rest the RQ is usually about 0.85. The changes of metabolism during muscular exercise are described in Chapter 11.

MUSCULAR FATIGUE

The loss of muscular power that occurs during fatigue may be due to failure at a number of different places including central synapses, the motor end-plates and the contractile machinery. Merton has suggested that in a simple human limb movement it is probably the muscle fibres themselves that become fatigued. If a muscular movement of the hand is carried on to complete fatigue and at this moment the circulation in the arm is arrested by inflating a sphygmomanometer cuff there is no recovery of strength until the cuff is released and the blood flow restored, although muscle action potentials can still be recorded in response to nerve stimulation. Since occlusion of the circulation in the arm does not affect the central nervous system and yet delays recovery, the site of fatigue must be in the muscle fibres themselves. However, Stephens and Taylor have found that when a muscle contracts maximally fatigue may occur at the neuromuscular junction before contractile failure of the muscle fibres develops. The site of fatigue may depend on the nature and severity of the muscle activity. Even when the site is muscular one can speculate that it is conduction within the T-tubules that is blocked rather than depletion of metabolites or other factors directly affecting contractile proteins. The effect

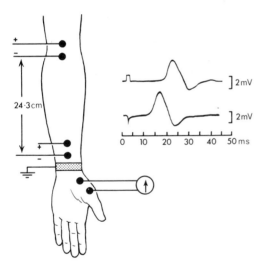

Fig. 40.15 Motor conduction measurement in the median nerve of a diabetic patient with the carpal tunnel syndrome. The latency, 10.0 ms between the stimulus at the wrist and the evoked potential, is greatly increased. Since the latency after stimulation at the elbow is 16.0 ms and the distance between the stimulating cathodes 24.3 cm the conduction velocity elbow to wrist is

$$\frac{24.3}{16 - 10} = 40 \text{ m/s (normal, above 47 m/s)}$$

(Lenman J A R, Ritchie A E 1976 Clinical electromyography, 2nd edn. Pitman, London)

would be due to K⁺ accumulation and Na⁺ depletion within the extracellular space of the T-tubules. Conduction failure at such sites might be regarded as a mechanism protecting the contractile machinery from irreversible damage.

The general fatigue experienced after severe exercise is probably due to events at the synapses in the central nervous system. This may be regarded as a protective mechanism since central fatigue is manifest before there is any block at the neuromuscular junction and long before the muscle itself is incapable of contraction. It should be kept in mind that the word fatigue has also a psychological meaning; fatigue may, for example, arise through lack of interest in a routine and boring task. This is very different from the physiological meaning of fatigue.

Normal active muscle exhibits a slight tremor with a dominant frequency near 10 Hz. The tremor increases in some pathological states and also after strong exercise; this physiological increase may persist for a day or more.

SENSORY INNERVATION OF SKELETAL MUSCLE

Skeletal muscle contains many sense endings. Some of these give rise to sensations of discomfort or pain when the muscles is fatigued; these can be regarded as protective, preventing the individual from overworking his muscles. The remaining sense endings pass information to the central nervous system about the mechanical events in the muscle. This information is supplied to the motoneurones that control the motor units in the muscle and is used to make adjustments to the discharge of motor impulses. Branches of the afferent fibres carry duplicate information to higher levels of the nervous system, such as the cerebellum. For many years it was thought that limb position sense was derived only from joint receptors. There is recent evidence, however, that muscle receptors project to the cerebral cortex and are essential to conscious perception of position. Thus, despite local anaesthesia of the hand and fingers (where the joint receptors exist), pulling on a muscle still creates a quantitative sensation of movement. Moreover the vibration of a muscle, which stimulates muscle spindles (below), confuses a subject's sense of limb position.

Two types of sensory nerve ending are present, tension receptors called *Golgi tendon organs* and length receptors called *muscle spindles*.

Golgi tendon organs

The Golgi tendon organs (Fig. 40.16) are mounted on connective tissue lying in series with the muscle fibres. They issue signals when the connective tissue is

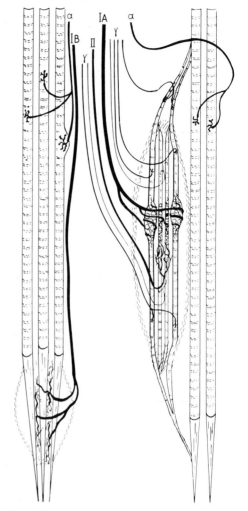

Fig. 40.16 Diagrammatic drawings of a muscle spindle and a tendon organ. The muscle spindle on the right is attached to extrafusal muscle fibres and tendon. It consists of small diameter intrafusal muscle fibres that are largely enclosed in a connective tissue capsule. Longitudinally the drawing is not to scale (the length of a spindle may be fifty times its width). Transversely in the drawing the width of the extrafusal muscle fibres represents a diameter of 40 μm; the intrafusal fibres are drawn to the same scale and represent diameters of about 20 μm for the two long fibres with nuclear bags at the equator of the spindle and about 10 μm for the two short fibres with nuclear chains at the equator. The group of nerve fibres shows the relative diameters of these fibres to each other. The largest nerve fibre, marked IA, supplies the main primary afferent ending lying over the nuclear bags and chains. Fibre II goes to a secondary afferent ending on the nuclear chain fibres adjacent to the primary ending. Six small γ fibres ('γ efferents', 'fusimotor fibres') of varying sizes supply motor endings on the intrafusal muscle fibres. The motor end-plates on the extrafusal muscle fibres are supplied by larger α nerve fibres. The remaining IB nerve fibre goes to the encapsulated tendon organ on the left; the branches of the afferent nerve ending lie between the tendons of a group of extrafusal muscle fibres. (By courtesy of Sybil Cooper)

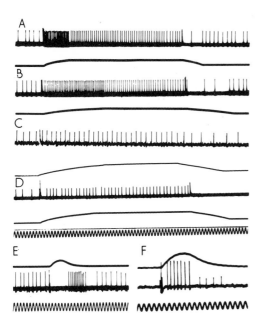

Fig. 40.17 Impulses originating in receptor organs in the soleus muscle of a decerebrate cat and recorded by cathode ray oscilloscope in single nerve fibres in the dorsal spinal roots. The ventral spinal roots were intact so that motor impulses may be travelling in both α and γ motor nerve fibres to the muscle to maintain tone in the extrafusal muscle fibres and to activate the intrafusal muscle fibres. All the other muscles in the limb were denervated. In A to D the second trace records the application and release of a 4 mm stretch to the muscle. The time signal of 50 Hz is shown below D.

A and B, Responses from the primary ending of a muscle spindle. In A the stretch is applied at 25 mm/s, and in B at 10 mm/s. In both cases the discharge rate rises rapidly during the dynamic part of each stretch, reaching 200 /s in A and 150 /s in B. The discharge is steady during maintained stretch and slows during release of stretch, after which it returns quickly to the resting rate.

C, Response from a secondary ending of a muscle spindle to a muscle stretch at 10 mm/s. The increase in discharge rate during the dynamic period is much less marked than in B. The rate is steady during maintained stretch and shows some slowing on release of stretch.

D, Response from a tendon organ to a muscle stretch at 10 mm/s. Owing to the high threshold of the organ the increase in discharge is slow to start. The discharge continues during the maintained stretch but stops at once when the stretch is released and does not start again.

E and F, Responses of the three kinds of ending to a maximal shock to the muscle nerve. Tension is recorded in the upper traces and 50 Hz is shown below. E, Primary ending. The discharge stops during the contraction but comes in at an increased rate during relaxation. F, Secondary ending (small deflections) and tendon ending (large deflections). The secondary ending shows no response during contraction but give a discharge during relaxation. The tendon organ discharges during contraction but stops during relaxation. (By courtesy of Sybil Cooper.)

stretched by forces produced by the contraction of the muscle. The Golgi tendon organ is, therefore, mainly activated by active contraction of the muscle fibres. The tendinous structure of the Golgi organ has inserted into it 10 to 15 muscle fibres belonging to about the same number of motor units. Activation of any one motor unit of this set will stimulate the afferent nerve fibre. The discharge frequency depends on the rate of rise and on the steady tension. Each Golgi tendon organ, therefore, signals the summed tension of a limited number of motor units. The total number of Golgi organs in many muscles is approximately equal to the number of motor units, so their total sensory input could theoretically be decoded by the central nervous system to give information about the contraction of individual motor units.

Inactive muscle can be extended within physiological limits with very little rise of tension, so the extension of an inactive muscle by a joint movement has little effect on Golgi organs. However, many movements, for example, walking down a flight of stairs, involve elongation of an active muscle; in this example the activity of the thigh extensors acts as a brake opposing the descent. The discharge of a Golgi tendon organ is shown in Figure 40.17F. It can be seen that the ending discharges only during the phase of tension produced by the muscle contraction.

Muscle spindles

The spindle is much more complicated than the tendon organ; the basic element is a small bundle of skeletal muscle fibres a few millimetres long that lies within a fluid-filled capsule (Fig. 40.16). The fibres are unusual because they are much smaller in diameter than the other fibres; they are called *intrafusal fibres* to distinguish them from the large extrafusal fibres that make up the bulk of the muscle. The ends of the intrafusal fibres, which may protrude some distance beyond the poles of the spindle-shaped capsule, are attached to the connective tissue structure of the muscle. Two main types of intrafusal muscle fibres have been identified by differences in the arrangement of the cell nuclei. If these are closely packed in a group, they are called *nuclear bag fibres*. If they are arranged in a line they are called *nuclear chain fibres*. More recently the nuclear bag fibres have been divided on histochemical and electromicroscopic grounds into bag_1 and bag_2 fibres.

The bundle of intrafusal fibres is often innervated by branches of the α motoneurones supplying extrafusal fibres but has a more numerous, specific supply. These latter motor nerves are small, and called either γ efferents or fusimotor fibres (Fig. 40.16). The motoneurones that give rise to these fibres lie scattered in the motoneurone pool supplying the extrafusal fibres but their activity is controlled differently.

The motoneurones that branch to innervate muscle spindles have been called β although they are anatomically indistinguishable from the general population of α motoneurones. The β fibres innervate all intrafusal fibre types with simplified end-plates. Two types of γ innervation occur. One type ends in very simple plates on bag₁ fibres; the other forms 'trails' over nuclear chain and bag₂ fibres, with intermittent simple junction regions similar to those on tonic extrafusal fibres described on page 504. These two types have different functions described below.

Intrafusal motor units are numerically small and endings from more than one motoneurone make contact with an individual intrafusal muscle fibre; this is called polyneural innervation of the muscle fibre.

The main sensory nerve ending of the intrafusal muscle is found on the mid-capsular region called the equatorial zone. The contractile apparatus of the intrafusal muscle fibre is weakened at the equator, the cross-striation being very faint. The main sensory ending, the primary ending, consists of unmyelinated nerve terminals with many small swellings wrapped around the equatorial zone. It is sometimes called an annulo-spiral ending and is the terminal of a large myelinated afferent fibre. In some spindles there are in addition sensory endings called secondary endings, which lie a small distance away from the primary ending mainly on the chain intrafusal muscle fibres. There is a great range of complexity in muscle spindles both in the number of intrafusal muscle fibres and the number of sensory endings.

The sensory nerves that form the primary endings are of large diameter, usually the largest in the muscle nerve, slightly larger than the fibres serving the Golgi tendon organs and about twice as large as the fibres serving the secondary endings. The nerves of primary endings and tendon organs are of the same size as α motoneurones. It is not possible to generalise about the sizes of these nerves since the spectrum of fibre sizes varies with different muscles and with different animals but the spindle primary afferents are described as group IA, the Golgi tendon organ afferents as group IB and the secondary ending afferents as group II (see Fig. 40.16). The fastest fibres have conduction velocities up to 70 m/s in man but may be as high as 110 m/s in some species such as the cat.

If an isolated spindle is held in a slightly stretched position the sensory endings discharge nerve impulses steadily; if the length of the spindle is increased the frequency rises during the time of stretching and declines to a steady value that may be only slightly different from the initial frequency. The period during which the increase in length occurs is called the dynamic phase, and the increase in frequency during this phase is called the dynamic response. There is a marked difference in the behaviour of the primary and secondary endings during the dynamic phase. The primary endings have a noticeable dynamic response, the secondaries have little or none. This difference is illustrated in Figure 40.17A, B and C. Thus a nerve centre supplied with the output of both primaries and secondaries from a spindle could calculate the instantaneous length from the secondary discharge and the rate of change of length from the dynamic response of the primary ending.

The response of muscle spindles to stretch is non-linear. This characteristic is especially true of primary endings, which are not very sensitive to large-amplitude movements. Disturbances of a few micrometres, however, can produce marked changes in discharge rate, so that the sensitivity may be as much as a hundred-fold greater than for large movements. Vibrations of this small amplitude applied to muscle or tendon therefore drives the discharge of a IA afferent at the frequency of the vibrator.

The spindle intrafusal muscle lies in parallel with the extrafusal muscle, so that changes in length imposed on the muscle when the joints are moved are also equally imposed on the muscle spindles within the muscle. In a passively extended muscle the spindles signal stretch. The situation becomes more complicated when the muscle contracts. If the extrafusal muscle is made to contract but the intrafusal muscle is inactive the spindle shortens passively and the sensory discharge declines or stops. If the intrafusal muscle contracts in isolation it cannot, since it is very feeble, move the joints to which the muscle is attached; contraction of the muscular poles of the spindle stretches the equatorial zone of the spindle and leads to a vigorous discharge.

The two types of fusimotor fibres described above modify the discharge of muscle spindles differently. One type, known as static fusimotor (or γ_s), produces fast, twitch-like contractions of both chain and bag₂ fibres, which increase the discharge of both secondary and primary endings to steady stretch. The dynamic response of primary endings, measured as the increase in discharge rate during extension, is reduced. The dynamic fusimotor fibres (γ_D) act on bag₁ fibres causing slow localised contractions. This only influences the responses of primary endings causing increases in their static and dynamic responses. Thus the central nervous system is able to control independently the sensitivity to muscle length and velocity of movement. There is evidence of such independent activation of γ_D and γ_s motoneurones. The β fibres may be similarly divided. Small α motoneurones innervating slow motor units have dynamic action when they innervate spindles (β_D). Larger α motoneurones that innervate fast-twitch fatigue-resistant (FR) motor units have static fusimotor action when they branch to innervate intrafusal fibres

(β_s). In muscles where β action has been looked for carefully it has been found in association with nearly a third of the α motoneurones.

If the intrafusal and extrafusal muscles are stimulated simultaneously the discharge from the spindle varies according to the resistance to shortening experienced by the extrafusal fibres. If the muscle meets little resistance to shortening and so makes an isotonic contraction, it brings together the points of attachment of the two ends of the spindle and thus the tension applied to the equatorial zone is slight and there is little afferent discharge. If the extrafusal contraction is isometric, or nearly so, the intrafusal contraction is concentrated on the equatorial zone and so a vigorous stimulation of the sensory endings occurs. Thus if the motor centres send simultaneous messages to the intra- and extrafusal muscle, the reply from the sense endings will indicate how much muscle shortening has occurred. The spindle discharge is relayed back to the motoneurones of the extrafusal muscle, where by excitatory synaptic action the discharge of the motoneurone tends to increase. Thus if the muscle meets resistance during shortening extra contractile force is called in by way of the spindles. However, this is a simplification because other influences act on the extrafusal motoneurone that can control it independently of its spindle feed-back. Movements are possible even after section of all sensory afferent feed-back from the muscle.

The impulses from the spindle play a part in the nervous control, at the subconscious level, of muscular activity both during movement and during sustained contractions and contribute to position sense as well.

When the skeletal muscles are examined histologically great variation is found in the density of muscle spindles and tendon organs. A few muscles, for example the cricothyroid and the extra-ocular muscles in many animals, have no spindles at all; some muscles have spindles and no tendon organs; others, like the diaphragm, have few spindles or tendon organs. The highest densities are found in the small muscles of the limbs such as the lumbricals and interosseous muscles. It seems reasonable to suggest that those muscles which take part in delicate movements need a more extensive sensory equipment.

FURTHER READING

Bagust J, Knott S, Lewis D M, Luck J C, Westerman R A 1973 Isometric contractions of motor units in a fast twitch muscle of the cat. Journal of Physiology 231: 87–104

Carlson F D, Wilkie D R 1974 Muscle physiology. Prentice Hall, London

Huxley A F 1974 Muscular contraction. Journal of Physiology 243: 1–43

Katz B 1966 Nerve, muscle and synapse. McGraw Hill, New York

Matthews P B C 1981 Evolving views on the internal operation and functional role of the muscle spindle. Journal of Physiology 320: 1–30

Thesleff S (ed) 1977 Motor innervation of muscle. Academic Press, London

Vrbova G et al 1978 Nerve/muscle interaction. Chapman and Hall, London

41

Thermoregulation

In 1775, Blagden described how a man in a small room heated by a red-hot stove remained well while a piece of steak beside him cooked. Thus was thermoregulation in man demonstrated. Animal species are often described as 'cold-blooded' or 'warm-blooded'. Fish, amphibia, reptiles and invertebrates are *poikilotherms* or temperature conformers: their internal temperatures depend on the environment. The rates at which biochemical reactions proceed reflect the activities of enzymes, which increase with temperature up to the point at which denaturation starts, and so the activities of poikilotherms depend on environmental temperature and thus on weather, season and time of day. Poikilo-thermic species do defend body temperature, but mainly through behavioural responses that cause them to move from less favourable to more favourable environments; even unicellular organisms do this. If escape is not possible they are vulnerable. The reptiles that dominated the earth for 300 million years probably became extinct because the climate became cold and unsettled. The birds and mammals that succeeded them are *homeotherms* or temperature regulators: they evolved means of maintaining stable body temperatures over a range of environments (Fig. 41.1).

The advantages of constant readiness for activity to predators or potential prey are obvious. Constant internal temperature may also have allowed more complex structure and function to evolve. Thermo-regulation is, however, costly of energy. Benedict observed that the daily energy expenditure of a snake, a marmot and a rabbit of about equal weight – respect-ively, a poikilotherm, a hibernator and a homeotherm — was about 30, 120 and 190 kJ/kg. Hibernators evolved a compromise: they are homeotherms in summer, and conceal themselves and become torpid in winter.

Although homeotherms vary widely in size and belong to diverse families they all maintain internal temperatures within or close to the narrow range 37–39 °C. This may simply reflect the highest tempera-ture that does not damage enzymes. Burton and Edholm, however, have pointed out that, if rates of heat

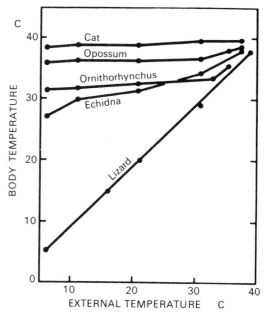

Fig. 41.1 Variation of body temperature of different species of animals after 2 hours in environmental temperatures of from 5°C to 35°C. This figure shows that there is a difference between the behaviour of homeothermic animals (like the cat), which can maintain a constant body temperature in spite of large changes in the external (ambient) temperature, and poikilothermic animals (like the lizard) in which body temperature varies with that of the environment. Ornithorhynchus (platypus) and echidna are Australian monotremes, phylogenetically primitive mammals. (Martin C J 1930 Lancet 2:565)

loss and heat production are plotted against the internal temperature of an animal living in an 'average' terres-trial environment, the straight line and rising curve that describe these relations run nearly parallel only when the internal temperature is near to 37 °C; fluctuations in body temperature then alter heat production and loss about equally, and are easily corrected. Outside this range the lines diverge and control would be unstable. Clinical experience does indeed show that variations in body temperature in the range 33–41 °C are usually corrected spontaneously, whereas wider deviations become self-perpetuating and intervention is needed to save life.

BODY TEMPERATURE

In health body temperature measured under standard conditions shows little variation among individuals (Fig. 41.2). The temperature of the body is not, however, constant in space or time. The distinction between core and shell is of fundamental importance (Fig. 41.3). The body is considered to consist of a core, in which heat is produced and stirring and control mechanisms maintain a uniform temperature, surrounded by an insulating shell through which there is a temperature gradient. This is a simplification; the temperature of the core is not uniform, the boundary between core and shell not sharp or fixed and the tissues of the shell are not inert. But mathematical representations of such a 'model' reproduce the thermal behaviour of the real body. The temperature gradient through the shell is normally continued by gradients through clothing and the surface layer of air.

Core temperature

It is not easy to measure human core temperature accurately. When the body is warm temperatures taken in mouth, axilla and rectum may agree within 1°C. The temperature in the rectum is usually the highest and is often regarded as the best index, but it may be 0.3°C above the temperature of blood in the aorta, perhaps because of bacterial metabolism. When the legs are

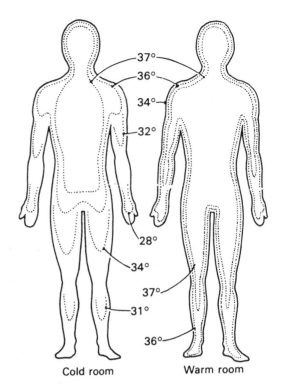

Cold room   Warm room

Fig. 41.3 The temperature gradients (°C) forming a 'core' and a 'shell' in a man in a warm and a cold environment (After Aschoff J, Wever R 1958 Naturwissenschaften 20:477)

cold, blood returning in the iliac veins can lower rectal temperature. Mouth temperature is affected by mouth breathing, eating or drinking (Fig. 41.4). The temperature in the axilla is on average 0.6°C lower than in the

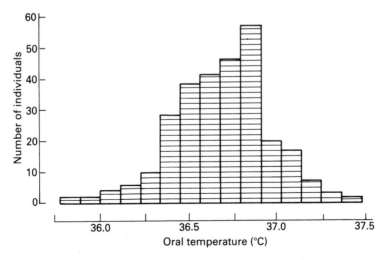

Fig. 41.2 The frequency distribution of oral temperature in 276 medical students. All temperatures were taken between 8 a.m. and 9 a.m. with the subjects seated in a warm classroom. (After Ivy A C 1944 Quarterly Bulletin of the Northwest University Medical School 18:22)

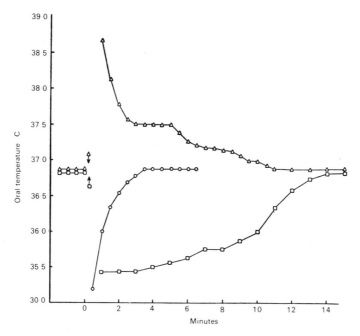

Fig. 41.4 Oral temperatures of the same subject taken with a standard 'half minute' mercury-in-glass clinical thermometer every 30 seconds in 'normal' conditions (○), showing that 3 to 4 minutes are required to obtain an accurate reading. Also shown are the effects on oral temperature of drinking 350 ml of hot tea (△) at 50°C and 350 ml cool water (□) at 10°C; in both cases oral temperature took at least 10 minutes to approach the original level. (Leithead C S, Lind A R 1964 Heat stress and heat disorders. Cassells, London)

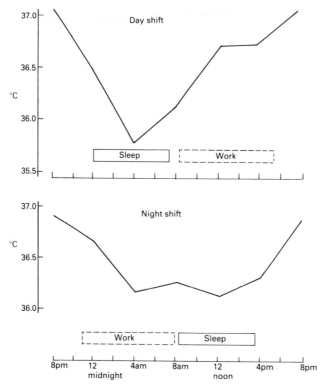

Fig. 41.5 Average body temperature curves on day shifts and on night shifts. (After van Loon J H 1963 Ergonomics 6:267) The flattening of the circadian rhythm during night shifts tends to increase over successive nights.

mouth and is difficult to measure accurately. Benzinger's claim that the tympanic membrane temperature reflects that of the hypothalamus because both are supplied by branches of the internal carotid artery is unreliable in cold subjects. A 'pill' that transmits a temperature-modulated radio signal from the stomach is useful for research. The most informative site may be the oesophagus behind the heart but a probe here is uncomfortable.

Core temperature is in general higher in children and lower in neonates and the elderly. It shows diurnal variation, which is an example of a circadian rhythm (Fig. 41.5). In exercise oral temperature rises by 1 or 2°C. In women body temperature rises after ovulation and remains high during the luteal phase of the menstrual cycle (p. 332); this is an action of the compounds to which, in humans, progesterone breaks down. At rest the most active tissues are the liver, followed by the heart and secreting glands; in dogs the surface of the liver may be 1.0°C warmer than arterial blood, and blood in the right heart 0.2 °C warmer than in the left. During activity skeletal muscle has the highest temperature.

Shell temperature

On the trunk the shell comprises skin and superficial layers of fat and muscle and its effective thickness depends largely upon fat content. On the head and neck the shell is relatively thin. In comfortable conditions the surface temperature in these areas is commonly 33–34°C. In the limbs the effective thickness of the shell is variable: when the body is warm the core extends into the limbs and there is a gradient through their surface layers; when it is cold the core does not extend into the limbs and the temperature gradient is developed over their whole length. Thermoregulatory responses vary blood flow to the surface and so raise or lower surface temperature. This inevitably has most effect at the periphery. Figure 41.6 shows how the gradient through the shell in the forearm varies with outside temperature. Figure 41.7 shows the gradient on the surface of the arms. In man vasomotor control is confined to the limbs and has most effect at the extremities.

Shell insulation varies among individuals. Young women typically contain 25 per cent body fat and young men 16 per cent; female clothing provides correspondingly less insulation, and reports of accidents suggest that women are more likely to survive cold exposure. Long-distance swimmers are commonly 'well covered'. Most mammals are fur-covered and show less vasomotor control than man but some vary heat exchange through appendages: for example, the rabbit and the elephant in the ears, and the rat in the tail. Aquatic mammals are insulated by thick layers of fat, and their arteries are

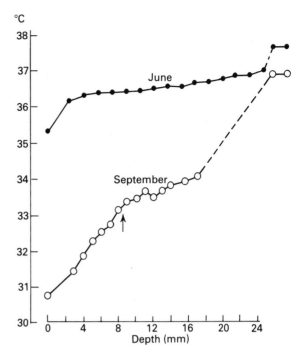

Fig. 41.6 Thermal gradients through the thickness of superficial tissues in the forearm. The upper line shows the gradient on a hot day in summer, the lower line the gradient on a cool day in autumn. The arrow shows the depth of the fascia. (Bazett H C, McGlone B 1927 American Journal of Physiology 82:415)

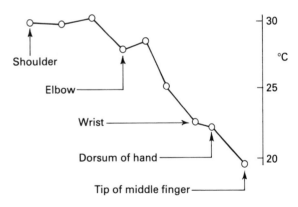

Fig. 41.7 Gradient down the length of a limb. Temperatures on the surface of the left arm of a healthy subject, 30 minutes after it had been exposed to an ambient temperature of 18°C.

surrounded by venous plexuses, which allow outgoing blood to pass its heat to blood returning from the surface — an example of insulation by counter-current exchange. This mechanism enables birds' feet to be poikilothermic. It is seen in vestigial form in man in the association of venae comitantes with deep arteries.

Another feature of human vascular anatomy, the traversing of the cavernous sinus by the internal carotid artery, is a vestige of a heat-exchange mechanism that, in species in which it is better developed, protects the brain from excessive rises in temperature during exertion.

HEAT BALANCE

It is often helpful to study physiological regulations by drawing up a 'balance sheet'. Body temperature rises if the total of heat gains exceeds total losses and vice versa; constant temperature requires that the totals be equal. Table 41.8 lists routes by which heat is gained and lost. A simple equation relates them:

$$\text{Heat balance} = S = M \pm (R + C + K) - E$$

Where S is the rate of storage of heat, M is heat production by metabolism, R, C and K are exchanges with the environment by radiation, conduction and convection, respectively, and E is heat loss as latent heat of evaporation. M is always positive and E always negative. The '$\pm$' sign attached to the sum of R, C and K indicates that this sign depends on circumstances: usually the environment is cooler than the body and so this sign is negative. S may be positive or negative in the short term but if it does not approach zero survival time is limited. The standard unit is now the watt or joule per second. Kilojoules per minute, hour or day are in common use. The superseded kilocalorie (kcal) is met in the literature and is the basis of useful practical units for heat production and insulation, the 'met' and the 'clo'. 1 kcal is equal to 4.2 kJ. The terms are commonly expressed per square metre of body surface, with some

justification since heat is exchanged through the surface, but 'surface area' is estimated empirically from height and weight.

Radiation, conduction and convection can be calculated individually from appropriate physical laws but it is easier to consider them together by using Newton's Law of Cooling. This states that heat flow per unit of surface area is proportional to the difference in temperature. If the proportionality constant, thermal conductance, is replaced by its reciprocal, insulation, the heat balance equation takes the form:

$$\text{Heat balance} = M - E \pm \frac{T_b - T_e}{I_t + I_c + I_a}$$

where T_b and T_e are the temperature of the body and its environment and I_t, I_c and I_a are the insulations due to the tissues of the body shell, clothing and air on the surface. Approximate values for all terms can be found or predicted by methods described by Burton and Edholm. The equation can be used to predict environmental temperatures within which heat balance can be maintained, and to measure insulation. The *met* (50 kcal/m²/h) and *clo* (0.18°C/(kcal/m²/h)) are useful units because they have practical, easily visualised magnitudes: 1 met is the heat production of a resting man and 1 clo the insulation of typical clothing of a western man.

Heat gains
These are *obligatory* — occurring without reference to temperature regulation and imposing demands on it — and *facultative* — available to physiological regulation as means of restoring heat balance. Among the former, in the physiological rather than clinical context, *basal metabolic rate* (BMR) is the minimum cost of remaining alive and well: that is, the total energy cost of maintaining the structure and composition of the body. Biochemical processes such as membrane transport and synthesis are more efficient than those which, like respiration and circulation, involve mechanical work, but all the energy expended in internal processes ultimately leaves the body as heat. In physiological contexts BMR is usually taken to be 40 kcal/m²/h, equivalent to 170 kJ/m²/h, 290 kJ/h or about 7 MJ/d. For clinical purposes BMR means metabolic rate measured in defined circumstances and expressed relative to values listed by pioneers of calorimetry. BMR varies relatively little among individuals: the 95 per cent confidence limits are ± 30 per cent of the mean. Women appear to have a lower BMR than men but the difference disappears if BMR is expressed relative to the weight of the body without its fat. BMR declines gradually with age. It is reduced in undernutrition, possibly as a compensatory mechanism.

Table 41.8 Heat balance in man

Heat gains	Heat losses
Metabolic	Convection
Basal metabolism	Ambient temperature
Heat increment of feeding	Air currents
Synthesis	Conduction
Physical exercise	Immersion in water
Shivering	Radiation (long wave)
Brown adipose tissue	to surroundings and sky
(infants)	Skin vasodilatation
Radiation	Evaporation:
Short-wave from sun	Insensible perspiration
Long-wave from	Thermoregulatory
surroundings	sweating
Convection	Ventilation (panting)
hot climates	
Ingestion	
hot foods (trivial)	

Resting heat production is generally taken to be 25 per cent higher than BMR, that is 50 kcal/m²/h (1 met), 210 kJ/m²/h or 9 MJ/d. The increase over BMR reflects postural muscular contraction and the cost of maintaining the circulation against gravity. Feeding is followed by increased heat production, which lasts for several hours and reflects costs of eating, digestion, absorption and early metabolism; it typically dissipates about 8 per cent of the energy ingested. Storage and growth cause further feeding-related increases in heat production. Synthesising fat consumes 20 per cent of the available energy; growth is more costly.

Physical *exercise* is the major variable in heat production. Some of the energy expended may appear as external mechanical work, but at its best the human body achieves a mechanical efficiency of around 20 per cent (so falling between steam and diesel engines): 80 to 100 per cent of the energy appears as heat. The inefficiency is due to thermodynamic limitations and to friction in muscles and joints. The energy costs of a wide range of activities have been tabulated. In summary, light exercise such as walking increases heat production to three to five times resting level; maximum effort increases it to ten to twenty times, depending on fitness.

Shivering is the principal source of facultative heat production available to man. It builds up gradually: at first motor units contract irregularly and out of phase, increasing muscle tone, and later regular synchronised contractions develop. Maximum shivering increases heat production to four to six times resting level. It warms the body more effectively than equivalent exercise because exercise brings blood into the limbs and increases convective heat loss; about 80 per cent of the heat produced by shivering is retained, compared with 50 per cent of the heat produced in exercise.

Non-shivering thermogenesis

'Thermogenesis' simply means 'heat production'. The term is best avoided, for it has no agreed definition. Non-shivering thermogenesis can reasonably be used to mean facultative, thermoregulatory heat production from sources other than shivering. Infants possess such a source in brown adipose tissue (see below). It is doubtful whether adults possess any such source. Humans over a year old probably do not possess significant amounts of functioning brown adipose tissue, and there is no evidence that they develop it (as rodents do) if exposed to prolonged severe cold.

No other significant sources of non-shivering thermogenesis have been identified. Evidence claimed to suggest that exposure to cold produces a substantial increase in metabolism not attributable to shivering is open to criticism. It is generally accepted that the injection of noradrenaline increases metabolism, but the increase, of the order of 10 to 30 per cent, is trivial in comparison with that produced by shivering and may only reflect tensing of muscles in response to injections. Increases of this order in response to cold are probably due to pre-shivering muscle tension. Increased thyroid activity occurs in rodents exposed to cold, and may contribute to raising metabolism. This does not seem to happen in man.

Other heat gains

Heat acquired by ingestion of hot food or liquids is usually negligible. People exposed to the sun or hot machinery gain heat by radiation even if the air is cold. 'Black' skin absorbs twice as much radiant energy from sunlight as 'white' skin — about 90 per cent versus 45 per cent. This may seem inappropriate, but it is usually explained on the basis that the pigment in skin, melanin, protects chromosomes by absorbing ultraviolet energy: skin cancer is common in white people who sunbathe excessively. At the infra-red wavelengths at which hot objects and living bodies radiate all skin is an almost perfectly 'black' radiator.

Heat loss

At rest 75 per cent of the heat produced by the body is lost by *conduction*, *convection* and *radiation* from its surface. Transfer by pure conduction is unimportant in air. Convection is usually the largest component. In apparently still air the warmth of the body's surface creates convective air movement equivalent to a velocity of about 15 cm/s. This limits the depth of the layer of air trapped on the surface to about 1 cm. A breeze of 4 km/h (2.5 mph) doubles heat loss from the surface and a 30 km/h (20 mph) wind increases it fivefold. Little trapped air is then left so further increase in air movement has little further effect on exposed surfaces.

Exchange of heat by radiation depends on the difference in temperature between the outer surface of the body or clothes and surrounding surfaces, on the emissivity of the surfaces and on the transparency of the interposed medium. Emissivity and transparency depend on wavelength and may differ for incoming and outgoing radiation. Special account has to be taken of radiation when the body is exposed to surfaces at a very different temperature from the ambient air: for example, the sun, the night sky, hot machinery and heaters. This can often be done satisfactorily by substituting a globe thermometer reading (see below) for air temperature.

In many circumstances all routes of heat transfer can be considered together by using Newton's Law. This makes the *insulation* separating the body core from the outside world a key quantity. The insulation of the body shell is best measured with the subject immersed in stirred water at a constant temperature, which fixes surface temperature and removes external insulation.

The water temperature chosen determines vasomotor state. Insulation is found by dividing temperature difference by heat flow. The heat flow through the shell comes from two sources: heat produced in the body and heat withdrawn from it (an immersed body is not generally in heat balance). Heat produced is found from oxygen consumption (with a deduction for heat lost via the head and in respiration, which does not traverse the shell). Heat withdrawn from the body is found from the rate of change of core temperature (which becomes nearly constant soon after immersion) and the mass and specific heat of the core.

The formula, which involves assumptions but is useful in practice, is:

$$\text{Insulation (clo)} = \frac{21.2 \times (T_c - T_w)}{M + (2.3 \times \dot{T}_c \times W/A) - 50}$$

The terms and units are: T_c, body core temperature, and T_w, water temperature (°C); M, metabolic rate $(kJ/m^2/h)$; $\dot{T}_c$, rate of fall of core temperature (°C/h); W, body weight (kg); A, body surface area (from Dubois' formula, m^2). The constant 21.2 combines 23.3, to convert $°C/(kJ/m^2/h)$ to clo, and 0.91, the fraction of the body surface immersed; 2.3 combines the specific heat of the body, 3.48 kJ/kg/°C, and the fraction of body weight assumed to be the core, 0.67; 50 is an estimate of heat loss $(kJ/m^2/h)$ from the head and respiratory tract.

Dubois found that *evaporation* dissipates 25 per cent of resting heat production; this relation is accurate enough to have been used to measure energy expenditure at rest. Evaporation at rest, often called *insensible perspiration* or *insensible loss of water*, is obligatory. Respiration involves ventilating 70 m^2 of warm moist alveolar epithelium and this causes evaporation of about 0.4 litre of water a day; the loss would be much greater if it were not for the counter-current exchange of moisture in the upper respiratory tract. Evaporation occurs through the skin because it is not impermeable: about 0.5 l/d evaporates — 10 per cent of what would be lost from an exposed wet surface of equal area. The total of 0.9 l/d accounts for 2.2 MJ/d of heat. Losses from the respiratory tract can be much greater in some circumstances: for example climbers at high altitude breathe dry air at extreme ventilation rates and lose several litres a day.

Sweating
Sweating consists of the active secretion of water on to the skin. It provides a means of dissipating heat, the effectiveness of which distinguishes man from all other species. The maximum rate of sweating is of the order of 2 l/h, or 5 litres in a day. If all of this evaporates it dissipates up to 3 $MJ/m^2/h$. This figure, approaching 20 times basal metabolic rate, is similar to the maximum rate at which a man can produce heat. Ability to sweat varies among individuals and improves with experience of hot climates. Sweating is, however, subject to fatigue. Whether sweat evaporates depends on humidity and air movement. Since sweating is the only way in which the heat produced in the body can be lost in environments above body temperature, heat balance cannot be maintained in such environments if humidity is high, if ventilation is poor or if clothing impedes evaporation. Sweating is extravagant of water and continues even if the water is not replaced; dehydration then ensues.

Sweat glands are distributed uniformly over the body in man. Although it had been believed that emotional sweating is confined to the hands and feet, Roddie and his colleagues, provoking it by mental arithmetic, showed that it has the same distribution as thermal sweating.

Sweating is an active process, not a simple filtration. If the circulation to a limb is cut off by a tourniquet sweating is unaffected for several minutes and then gradually falls to zero. In contrast to vasomotor control, the sympathetic nerves that control sweating do not show resting activity. In man they are unusual in that the transmitter at the postganglionic endings is acetylcholine. Adrenaline has no effect on sweating in man (unless given intra-arterially in high dose, when some stimulation, blocked by phentolamine, occurs). Atropine reduces sweating (its use preoperatively to reduce bronchial secretion can add to thermoregulatory difficulties in hot operating theatres). Vasodilatation accompanies sweating: as in the salivary glands, it is probably caused indirectly by release of bradykinin.

Heat storage
The body is not in heat balance at every moment but gains and loses heat: for example heat is stored during exercise. Large animals can store substantial amounts of heat. (The camel exploits this to avoid using water in thermoregulation: its temperature oscillates by several degrees over the day.) Heat is not distributed uniformly in the body but in principle:

Heat stored = change in mean body temperature
        × body mass × body specific heat

In man mean body temperature $(\bar{T}_b)$ is found from a weighted average of rectal temperature (T_{re}) and mean skin temperature $(\bar{T}_{sk})$:

$$\bar{T}_b = 0.67 \times T_{re} + 0.33 \times \bar{T}_{sk}$$

where mean skin temperature is a weighted average of skin temperatures on the head (T_{he}), the arms (T_a), the hands (T_{ha}), the foot (T_f), the legs (T_l), the thighs (T_{th}) and the trunk (T_t):

$$\bar{T}_{sk} = 0.07 \times T_{he} + 0.14 \times T_a + 0.05 \times T_{ha}$$
$$+ 0.07 \times T_f + 0.13 \times T_l + 0.19 \times T_{th}$$
$$+ 0.35 \times T_t$$

THERMOREGULATION

Thermoregulation is a good example of homoeostasis maintained by a feedback control system. Any control system must include effectors to alter the quantity controlled, a controlling centre to 'tell' the effectors what to do and a sensor to 'feedback' the current state of the controlled quantity to the controller. Since the output of a sensor is governed by the quantity it senses there is a closed loop of causation round the system. There must also be pathways from the sensor to the controlling centre and from the centre to each effector: thus the simplest system has five components (Fig. 41.9).

Temperature receptors

Central thermoreceptors

There is much evidence that the hypothalamus is sensitive to temperature. Its temperature must be very close to that of its large, direct supply of blood. Hypothalamic sensitivity to temperature thus completes the

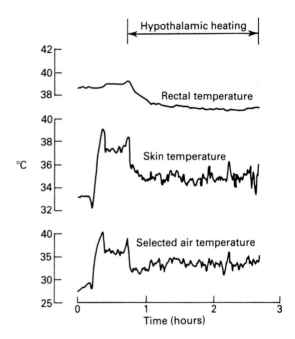

Fig. 41.10 Study of behavioural temperature regulation in the squirrel monkey (*Saimiri sciureus*) during prolonged hypothalamic heating, showing rectal, mean skin, and air temperatures selected by the animal. (After Adair E R et al. 1970 Journal of Comparative Physiology and Psychology 72:17)

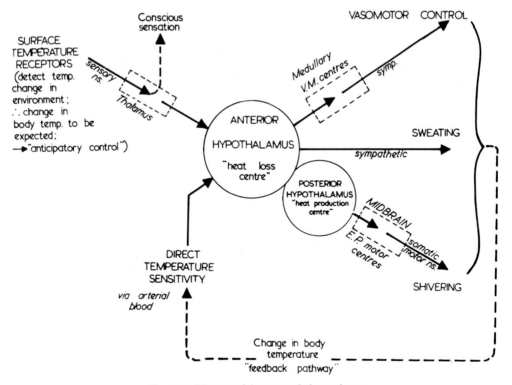

Fig. 41.9 Diagram of thermoregulation pathways.

closed loop in the control system. Figure 41.10 demonstrates this sensitivity: an animal's thermoregulatory responses, including behavioural ones, can be driven by varying the hypothalamic temperature, and they continue to reflect hypothalamic temperature although they are inappropriate to body temperature.

The neurones responsible have not been identified. They appear to be located in the anterior rather than the posterior hypothalamus, to be a small minority of the cell population, to be distributed throughout this area and not localised to particular regions, and to include more cells responsive to warming than to cooling. It is not known whether there are separate ther-

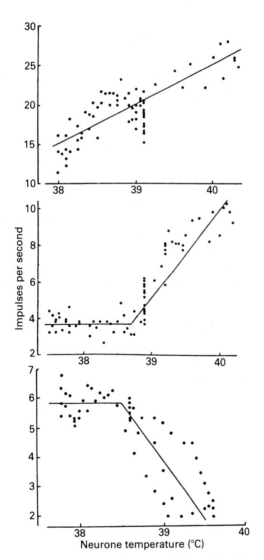

Fig. 41.11 Firing rates of three cells, in the pre-optic area of the hypothalamus in a rabbit, related to hypothalamic temperature. (Hellon R F 1967 Journal of Physiology 193:381)

moreceptor cells that, together with inputs from the periphery, synapse upon controlling cells, or whether the cells that constitute the central controller are themselves thermosensitive. The firing rates of single units show a variety of stimulus/response patterns (Fig. 41.11).

Peripheral thermoreceptors

The sensitivity of the skin to temperature is familiar to everyone and responses to forced changes of skin temperature are the aspect of thermoregulation most often demonstrated in class experiments. Nevertheless the receptors responsible cannot be confidently identified. An early belief that Krause's endings provide sensitivity to cold and Ruffini's to warmth has been abandoned, and it is doubtful whether thermal sensitivity is localised to fixed 'spots'. All forms of cutaneous sensation probably involve a complex process of interpretation of information from many receptors and from past experience. The adaptations that make cells thermosensitive may not be recognisable histologically.

Recordings from afferent nerves show clearly that 'warm' and 'cold' receptors exist. When impulse frequencies are recorded over a wide range of temperatures two groups of fibres show peaked relationships to temperature, with maxima above and below normal skin temperature (Fig. 41.12). There appear to be about ten times as many warm as cold receptors. When skin temperature moves outside the range spanned by the two peaks the conscious sensation becomes less specific, and painful.

Sensing of environmental temperature is 'open-loop'; the response cannot alter the environment, but awareness of environmental temperature gives advance warning of an impending disturbance of body temperature and enables responses to be initiated before there has been actual disturbance. Responses to open-loop sensors cannot, however, be quantitatively accurate and feedback, or closed-loop, information is still essential. Heating systems in buildings often have outdoor as well as indoor sensors. The thermoreceptors in the skin may similarly improve performance in the physiological system.

Like many other sense organs, cutaneous thermoreceptors show accommodation; their output in response to a constant stimulus declines with time (Fig. 41.13). This means that it reflects rate of change of skin temperature rather than actual temperature. Simple subjective experiments in which the hands are immersed in water first at one temperature and then at another illustrate this. This property in effect provides second-order rate information for thermoregulation, and it may be valuable because of the large thermal mass of the body. It has also been suggested that surface receptors respond to the temperature gradient through the skin rather than to a single temperature; this would

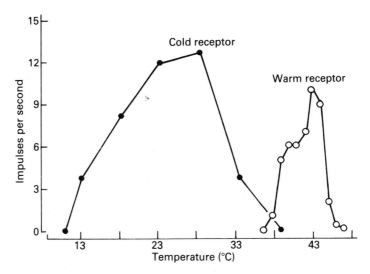

Fig. 41.12 Rat scrotal thermoreceptors. Static sensitivity curves for two receptors, one cold and one warm. The cold receptor had a maximal static sensitivity at 28°C and was silent at 38°C. The warm unit became active at or just below 38°C and so there was no simultaneous activity in these 2 classes of receptor. (After Iggo A 1969 Journal of Physiology 200:403)

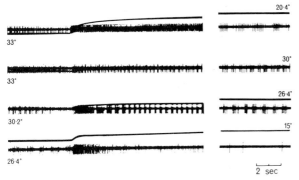

Fig. 41.13 Recordings from a monkey cold receptor in hairy skin (myelinated axon). In each record one trace shows the action potentials in the cold unit and a few smaller action potentials in unrelated units; the other trace shows temperature at the thermode/skin interface recorded with a thermistor. Each record was begun after the skin had been at the initial temperature for at least 5 minutes. The right hand column of records shows the adapted discharge. (After Iggo A 1969 Journal of Physiology 200:403)

have similar consequences, but the evidence is not conclusive.

Internal surfaces in the respiratory and gastro-intestinal tracts also possess thermoreceptors. Inhaling cold air can cause shivering during inspiration. Hot food and drink cause vasodilatation and sweating: hot tea is therefore more cooling than cold water. Curry and chillies are 'hot' because they stimulate thermoreceptors; they also induce vasodilatation and sweating. There is

strong evidence for temperature sensitivity in the spinal cord but the receptors have not been identified.

Afferent pathways

The afferent pathway from central thermoreceptors must be short or non-existent. Afferent fibres from receptors in the skin travel in cutaneous nerves and relay in the dorsal horn of the spinal cord. Secondary neurones cross a few segments higher and ascend in anterolateral tracts on the opposite side. The route into the hypothalamus is unknown.

Central control

This is principally located in the *anterior hypothalamus*. Animals with brain-stems sectioned below the hypothalamus are not completely poikilothermic; spinal animals make thermoregulatory responses as do patients with spinal cord transection. The extra-hypothalamic mechanisms are relatively ineffective and probably unimportant in intact animals. In contrast to many hypothalamic functions, thermoregulation cannot be assigned to particular areas or nuclei. It is only abolished by lesions that destroy most of the anterior hypothalamus. It used to be taught that lesions in the anterior hypothalamus impair vasodilatation and sweating and that lesions in the posterior hypothalamus impair shivering, with the implication that the anterior hypothalamus contains a heat-loss centre and the posterior hypothalamus a heat-production centre. Some dissociation of the effects of lesions is seen (Fig. 41.14), but it is likely that thermoregulation is primarily a function of the anterior hypothalamus, and lesions in the

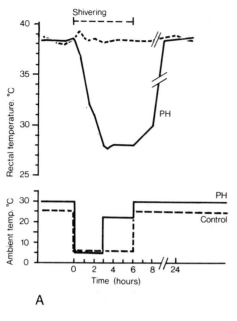

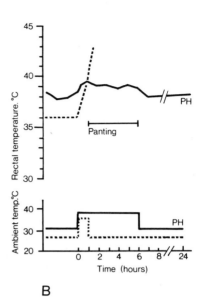

A   B

Fig. 41.14 The effect of experimentally induced lesions of the hypothalamus on three dogs, whose rectal temperatures and corresponding ambient temperatures are represented by solid, dashed and dotted lines. A shows the response of a normal control dog (dashed line) and an experimental dog (solid line) to a cold environment: by shivering the normal dog maintained his rectal temperature, but the dog with the hypothalamic lesion (PH) became hypothermic. B shows that the same dog (PH) could maintain a normal temperature by panting when exposed to a hot environment, while another dog with a different hypothalamic lesion (dotted line) rapidly became hyperpyrexic. (After Keller A D 1950 Physical Therapy Review 30:511)

posterior hypothalamus interrupt descending pathways to effectors.

Chemical transmission

The hypothalamus contains 5-hydroxytryptamine and noradrenaline. In the cat injection of 5-hydroxytryptamine into the anterior hypothalamus leads to shivering and a rise in body temperature; injection of noradrenaline causes a fall in temperature. Cross-circulation experiments showed that transferring CSF or hypothalamic perfusate between rhesus monkeys caused a recipient to shiver when a donor was cooled, but the substance responsible was not identified. Different transmitters are effective in different species.

There is evidence that prostaglandin E1 plays a part in thermoregulation. When 100 ng or less is injected into the lateral ventricles in cats and rabbits the body temperature rises; when fever is induced by pyrogens its concentration in CSF increases. There is also evidence that the concentrations of sodium and calcium in the hypothalamus are important in thermoregulation.

Integration of incoming stimuli

Much effort has been devoted to studying the relative contributions of the two principal inputs — blood

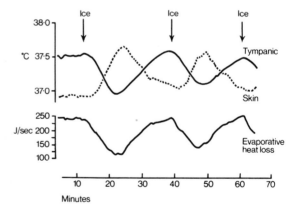

Fig. 41.15 Records of the evaporative heat loss and the temperatures of the skin (dotted line) and the tympanic membrane (solid line) of a human subject in an ambient temperature of 45°C. Three times, on the ingestion of 450 g of iced sherbet ('Ice'), the tympanic temperature (equivalent to the intracranial temperature) and the heat loss from sweating declined in parallel, while the consequent reduction in sweating allowed the skin temperature to rise. The rate of sweating follows the intracranial, not the skin, temperature. (After Benzinger T H 1959 Proceedings of the National Academy of Sciences U.S.A. 45:645)

temperature and surface temperature — to the control of thermoregulation. Experience broadly shows that warming or cooling the skin readily elicits vasomotor responses, whereas change in deep body temperature is needed to activate sweating and shivering. It is, however, difficult to demonstrate vasomotor responses unless the subject is initially thermoneutral, and surface stimuli influence and can elicit sweating and shivering.

Figure 41.15 shows how central and peripheral inputs can exert control in turn: when a subject in a hot room swallowed ice this lowered internal temperature and inhibited sweating. Skin temperature rose, and this re-established sweating. In Figure 41.16 the core temperature of a subject with a warm skin was gradually increased and sweating began at a particular tympanic temperature; when skin temperature was lowered the tympanic temperature at which sweating began became higher. Conversely in Figure 41.17 the temperature of a subject with cool skin was lowered and shivering began at a particular tympanic temperature; when skin temperature was raised this temperature became lower.

There has been a rather sterile debate over the existence and nature of a 'set point' in physiological thermoregulation. It reflects a concept that a control system compares the state of the quantity it controls with a

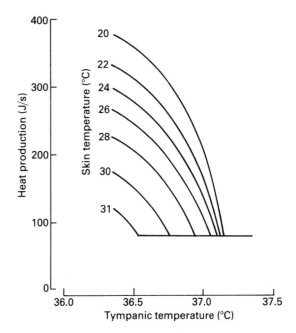

Fig. 41.17 Heat production (measured by oxygen consumption) of a healthy man at various tympanic membrane and (whole-body) skin temperatures. When the skin temperature was 20°C, lowering internal temperature below about 37.2°C caused heat production to rise (due to initiation of shivering). When skin temperature was fixed at progressively lower temperatures, a greater fall in internal temperature was needed to evoke shivering. (After Benzinger T H 1959 Physiological Reviews 49:671)

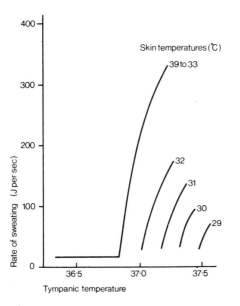

Fig. 41.16 Rates of evaporative heat loss (sweating) from a healthy naked man at varying tympanic membrane temperatures. At skin temperatures between 39° and 33°C sweating began at a sharply defined 'internal' temperature (about 36.9°C). At any given 'internal' temperature evaporative heat loss diminished progressively with skin temperatures falling below 33°C. The experiment demonstrates the interaction of central and cutaneous receptors in the control of sweating. (After Benzinger T H 1959 Physiological Reviews 49:671)

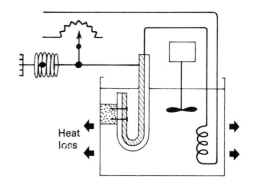

Fig. 41.18 A proportional thermostat that uses a bimetal strip as sensor, and controls the temperature of a water bath. (After Hardy J D 1961 Physiological Reviews 41:521)

'reference input' and responds to the difference. Artificial controllers often do work in this way but consideration of the model in Figure 41.18 shows that they need not. In this model the linkage between the bimetal strip and the variable resistor could be made adjustable: this would allow a human to 'set' bath temperature, but would not alter the effectiveness of control of temperature.

The model shown in Figure 41.18 illustrates one further important property of control systems, *load error*. If the outside temperature falls the temperature of the bath falls at first. The bi-metal strip bends, increasing the heater power so that the increased heat

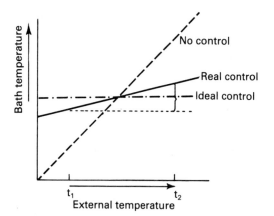

Fig. 41.19 Control characteristic of the thermostat shown in Figure 41.18. Ideal control is unobtainable; the real control (solid line) differs and the difference (bracket) is the load error.

loss is eventually balanced. In the new steady state the bath temperature must remain marginally lower than before so that the additional power is maintained. Plotting the bath temperature against outside temperature (Fig. 41.19) gives a line intermediate between the line of equality (no thermostat) and the horizontal (an ideal controller). The slope of the line might be decreased by increasing the 'gain' of the controller but a horizontal line cannot be achieved. Load error can be demonstrated in physiological experiments (Fig. 41.20).

The relation shown in Fig. 41.19 is a regression line whose position and slope could reflect not only external temperature but any factor that can alter bath temperature (including the setting of an adjusting knob). The real relation is thus a multiple regression. The interaction of the inputs from central and peripheral receptors may be best understood on the basis that both contribute input variables to such a regression.

Efferent pathways

The major output pathway for thermoregulation is the sympathetic nervous system. It supplies arterioles, sweat glands and brown adipose tissue. The peculiarity in chemical transmission to the sweat glands in man has been noted. Shivering is controlled by an outflow of fibres from the posterior hypothalamus to motor centres in the tegmentum of the mid-brain and pons, where

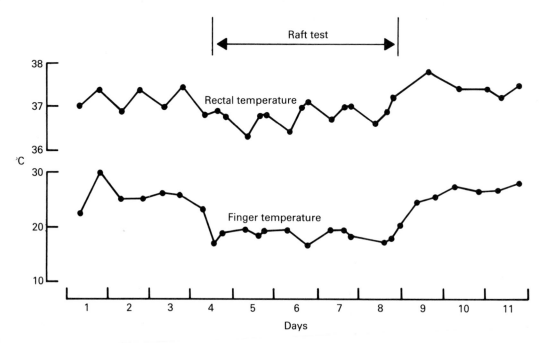

Fig. 41.20 Load error in an actual experiment. The upper line shows mean rectal temperatures of eight subjects, who lived in a tented, inflatable life-raft on Tromsø Fjord in the Norwegian Arctic for the period shown. Although rectal temperature was maintained during the test, it was significantly lower. The lower line, showing finger-tip temperature, shows that the subjects were vasoconstricted during the test, but not maximally. They shivered for about 10 per cent of the time.

they 'tap into' the extrapyramidal motor system and where the oscillatory pattern seems to be added. Impulses descend in the tectospinal and rubrospinal tracts to anterior horn motoneurones.

Vasomotor control

Flow of blood from core to surface by-passes the insulation provided by fat and other tissues and brings shell insulation under physiological control. Measurement by plethysmography shows that the blood flow through the hand, most of which supplies skin, can change by a factor of 30 to 100 times in response to thermal stimuli (Fig. 41.21). Insulation changes locally in proportion (Fig. 41.22) and this is reflected in skin temperature (Fig. 41.23). In the vasoconstricted state the blood supply to the skin of the extremities is largely shut down (Fig. 41.24) and blood returns via deep rather than superficial veins, so that the arterial supply is precooled (Fig. 41.25). In the vasodilated state arteriovenous anastomoses in the finger-tips open and allow a rapid flow of arterial blood close to the surface (Fig. 41.26).

Although these responses are dramatic, vasomotor control only operates over a small part of the body surface. In an average person the insulation of the shell as a whole changes from about 0.15 clo in the fully vasodilated state to 0.75 clo in full vasoconstriction. Variations among individuals, mainly reflecting body fat, can halve or double these values. A fivefold change still appears substantial, but the effect of insulation on heat balance depends on how much heat is being produced. This interplay will be considered later. The other principal effectors, sweating and shivering, have already been discussed.

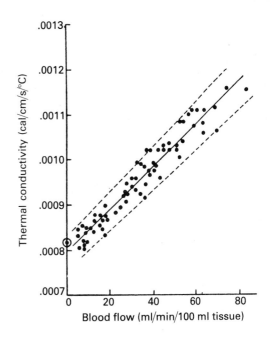

Fig. 41.22 The relation between effective thermal conductivity of the skin and blood flow in a finger. The point for zero flow, circled by a ring, was obtained by occlusion of the flow by a cuff on the proximal phalanx, while the other data for low flows were obtained by vasoconstriction to cold. (Burton A C, Edholm O G 1955 Man in a cold environment. Arnold, London)

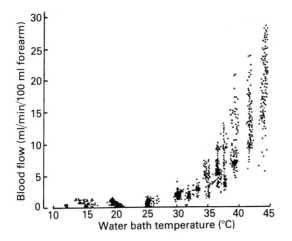

Fig. 41.21 Forearm blood flow plotted against water bath temperature. The forearm and hand were kept in water at a particular temperature for two hours. The blood flow declines with decrease of temperature. (After Barcroft and Edholm 1943 Journal of Physiology 102:5)

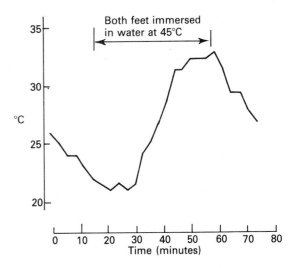

Fig. 41.23 Reflex vasodilatation in the normal human upper limb. The procedure followed is a standard clinical test. The delay followed by a rapid, full response is characteristic of the procedure, but difficult to explain. (Richards R L 1946 The peripheral circulation in health and disease. Livingstone, Edinburgh)

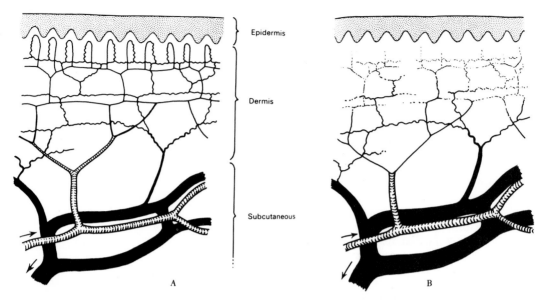

Fig. 41.24 Diagram to show the increased thickness of the insulating layer of skin that results from acute immersion in cold water. A, normal vascular arrangements; B, during immersion in cold water, showing also the possibility of counter-current heat exchange. (Maclean D, Emslie Smith D 1977 Accidental hypothermia. Blackwell, Oxford)

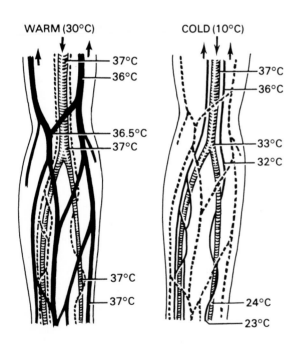

Fig. 41.25 Diagram of vasculature in the human forearm showing how constriction and dilatation of the superficial veins and the deep venae comitantes could provide a countercurrent heat exchange mechanism. (After Krog J 1974 In: Borg A, Veghte J H (eds) The physiology of cold weather survival NATO: AGARD Report no. 620)

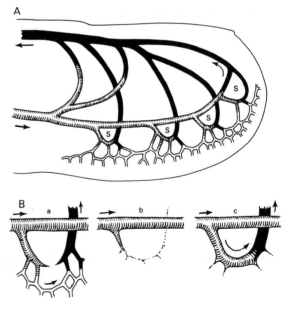

Fig. 41.26 A, Diagram of the vasculature in the human finger pulp showing arteriovenous anastomoses (shunts) (S). B, The sequence of changes in the shunting mechanism in response to cold: a) normal temperature: arterio-venous shunt closed, capillaries perfused; b) cold vasoconstriction; c) cold vasodilatation first affects the arteriovenous shunt. (After Hale A R, Burch G E 1960 Medicine (Baltimore) 39:191)

THERMONEUTRALITY AND THERMAL COMFORT

Man's three thermoregulatory effectors are brought into play in succession. In a comfortable environment heat balance is maintained without sweating or shivering and with peripheral vasoconstriction near mid-range. If the environment becomes colder vasoconstriction increases to a maximum, and then shivering comes into play progressively. If the environment becomes warmer or exertion increases heat production vasodilatation occurs, and then sweating. Thus thermoregulation can be divided into zones according to the effectors in use (Figs. 41.27 and 41.28).

The narrow range C–D in Figure 41.26 is the *thermoneutral zone*. Within it heat balance is maintained without increased heat production or evaporation: thermoregulation is achieved with the least expenditure of energy.

It must be emphasised that this account applies only to man: the pattern of thermoregulation is quite different in other species. Most mammals are better insulated, by fur or fat, than man. This makes variation

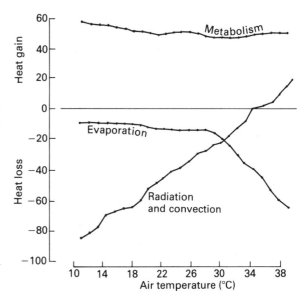

Fig. 41.28 Components of heat balance over a wide range of air temperatures in a clothed man. At low temperatures heat loss is mainly by radiation and convection, at high temperatures by evaporation. Between about 25°C and 29°C ambient temperature heat regulation is largely by vasomotor changes. The corresponding range for an unclothed man is 29°C to 31°C. (After Gagge A P et al 1938 American Journal of Physiology 124:30)

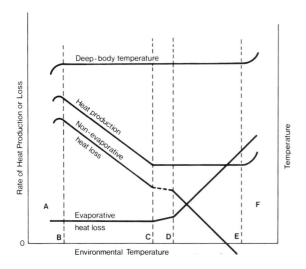

Fig. 41.27 Diagrammatic representation of the relationships between heat production, evaporative and non-evaporative heat loss and deep-body temperature in a homeothermic animal resting but free to move in a metabolic chamber. A, zone of hypothermia; B, temperature of peak metabolism and incipient hypothermia; C, critical temperature; D, temperature of marked increase in evaporative loss; E, temperature of incipient hyperthermal rise; F, zone of hyperthermia; CD, zone of least thermoregulatory effort; CE, zone of minimal metabolism; BE, thermoregulatory range. 'Environmental temperature' assumes air and mean radiant temperatures equal to one another, free convection and relative humidity 50 per cent. (Mount L E 1974 In: Monteith J L, Mount L E (eds) Heat loss from animals and man, p. 425. Butterworth, London)

of heat production a more effective regulatory mechanism; in rats, for example, it is the most important effector and operates over the whole range of environmental temperatures the rat can tolerate. Thus rats do not have a thermoneutral zone. No other species sweats as much as man does. The panting of animals is a fairly effective way of increasing evaporation, especially when combined with vascular arrangements that cause blood cooled in the respiratory tract to cool blood supplying the brain preferentially. Rats threatened with hyperpyrexia spread saliva over their bodies, where it may evaporate.

Thermal comfort in man does not correspond with body temperature or the state of heat balance. One can be intensely uncomfortable while maintaining body temperature by shivering; Barcroft described a state of comfort that he called 'basking in the cold' when he had made himself severely hypothermic. Thermal comfort seems to be associated with absence of sweating, shivering, or either extreme of vasomotor tone — that is, with being in the thermoneutral zone. In this state the mean skin temperature is typically around 33°C. The fact that significant use of physiological effectors causes discomfort is an important feature of thermoregulation in man.

The effectiveness of the human thermoregulatory effectors

Taking average values, shivering generates up to 1.5 MJ of heat per hour; vasomotor control varies shell insulation from 0.15 to 0.75 clo; sweating dissipates up to 5 MJ of heat per hour. We can calculate the ranges of control adult man's three effectors provide by means of the heat balance equation.

If a man wearing ordinary clothes is at rest in thermal comfort (i.e. not sweating or shivering), in addition to his variable shell insulation his clothes contribute 1 clo and the surface layer of air 0.8 clo, giving a total insulation· of 1.95–2.55 clo. Resting metabolism is 1 met; evaporation dissipates 25 per cent of this. Core temperature must be 37°C and heat balance must be zero. Solving for environmental temperature gives, according to the state of vasomotor control, 18–22°C. This reasonable result at least provides a check on the method. If we consider the case of an unclothed man the range becomes 26–30°C. Table 41.29 shows the results of further calculations.

Although the results are only representative they have important implications. The environmental temperature at which a nude person maintains heat balance with minimum thermoregulatory effort is approximately 28°C. Shivering is barely able to maintain heat balance in an unclothed man in the British climate. If the ambient temperature rises above 30°C sweating is the only means by which heat balance can be maintained. Provided the sweat can evaporate, sweating is very effective: in a natural environment it would hardly ever be inadequate.

These results justify describing man as, unusually for a mammal, a tropical animal. This is not the same thing as a desert animal: man's physiology is based on free availability of water. Palaeontological evidence suggests that man did evolve in the tropics.

The range of control from varying tissue insulation is only 4°C. Evidently vasomotor control is a fine adjustment. This at first seems contrary to experience, for we move in environments with a wider range of temperatures than 4°C without sweating or shivering. The explanation is that civilised man makes little use of physiological thermoregulation. Sweating or shivering or even substantial vasoconstriction or dilatation cause discomfort. This provides a drive for behavioural responses, which are the predominant effectors in man. In the short run, we put on or take off clothing, open or close windows, turn heaters on or off. On a longer time-scale we pursue the technologies of clothing, building and air-conditioning. By these means we maintain a microclimate, at an almost constant — tropical — temperature around most of the body surface.

It has been suggested that the development of behavioural thermoregulation was a significant factor in cultural evolution: as man spread from the tropics the challenge of living at the current furthest point provided a stimulus for the achievements of the age. However, appreciation that even in temperate latitudes man is living outside his biological habitat should convey a warning that he depends on his behaviour and technology. Excursions on moors and hills where there is no shelter, with inadequate clothing and emergency resources, can prove fatal.

Clothing

Clothing provides insulation that man needs to survive in comfort and safety outside the tropics. Clothes insu-

Table 41.29 Ranges of physiological temperature regulation available from sweating, from vasomotor control and from shivering

	Air temperature at which nude man would be in heat balance °C	Temperature at which normally clothed man would be in heat balance °C	Effect on heat balance of nude man at 28°C air temperature kJ/h	Resulting rate of change of body temperature °C/h
Max. sweating	150°	(Clothes would interfere with sweating)	−5000	−19°
Sweating				
Max. vasodilatation	30°	22°	−90	−0.3°
Vasomotor range	28°	20°	0	0
Max. vasoconstriction	26°	18°	+55	+0.2°
Shivering				
Max. shivering	−10°	−40°	+960	+4°

All figures are the results of calculations for an assumed average individual. The figures for extreme temperatures should not be taken as practical ones, but as indicating the relative ranges of control available. In practice air movement and humidity usually make the effective temperature of an environment more unfavourable than the air temperature alone would indicate. Also, tolerance may be limited by local injury to the body surface and not by ability to maintain heat balance. Sweating and shivering at high rates can only be sustained for a limited time.

0.5 clo   1 clo   2 clo   3 clo   6 clo

Fig. 41.30 Typical clothing with insulations corresponding to about 0.5, 1, 2, 3 and 6 clo. (After Auliciems A, Hare A F 1973 Weather 28:478).

late by trapping air among the fibres of the material and between layers. Air has a low thermal conductivity and heat capacity, but if free to move it allows heat transfer by convection. Thus the best clothing traps the most air in the least mass of fibres. A heavy garment is often inefficient because its fibres conduct heat. Irrespective of the nature of the trapping material, perfectly trapped air gives an insulation of 1.8 clo per cm thickness. This is approached by wool, kapok and expanded synthetic materials. The fur of furry animals provides almost the theoretical value of insulation. Piloerection, which

occurs vestigially in man, varies the vertical thickness of the coat and so contributes to thermoregulation.

Figure 41.30 depicts the insulations of different clothing assemblies. Arctic clothing can approach an insulation of 12 clo over the trunk but the maximum averaged over the body is about 6 clo. Repeating the calculation for the resting man with 6 clo of clothing (vasoconstricted, and with only 0.5 clo from surface air since we are out of doors), predicts that he can be in heat balance in an environment at $-10°C$. If we increase heat production to 3.5 mets, typical of hard

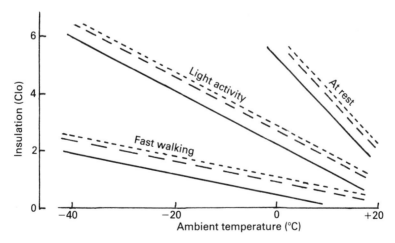

Fig. 41.31 Insulation required from clothing (including surface-trapped air) to maintain heat balance at different ambient temperatures, wind velocities and work rates. The three lines within each set correspond, from below upwards, to still air (———), a light breeze (— — —) and a moderate wind (------). Note that at complete rest the insulation required becomes more than the maximum obtainable from clothing (about 6 clo) at about freezing point. In contrast a man doing moderate work requires much less than the maximum attainable clothing insulation at the lowest temperatures at which the inevitable exposure of face, hands, etc. is tolerable. (After Newburgh L H 1949 Physiology of heat regulation and the science of clothing. Saunders, Philadelphia)

shivering or fast walking, the calculation gives the apparently absurd result, $-170\,°C$.

Both calculations are correct in principle. Even the best clothing is not adequate to maintain heat balance in a man at rest in an arctic climate. Therefore at night or when men are immobilised by fatigue or injury additional shelter is essential. A sleeping bag gives 8–11 clo of insulation, and although a tent has a lower clo value it makes the heat produced by all the occupants available to all — equivalent to increasing heat production. The second calculation demonstrates that the benefits of heat production and insulation are multiplicative. Either alone is relatively ineffective, but in combination they may exceed any requirements. Two further conclusions follow. Since arctic clothing is inadequate at rest but excessive at work it should be adjustable, and it should allow for some sweating. Secondly, as long as a man is active, tolerance of an arctic environment is more likely to be limited by local effects of cold on the more exposed parts of the body — the face, hands and feet — than by considerations of heat balance. Figure 41.31 shows insulations needed by men at rest and working in the cold, and demonstrates the interplay between heat production and insulation.

Clothing for exposed conditions must protect from water and wind. If water penetrates and displaces trapped air, insulation is lost and subsequent evaporation takes up much heat. However, water vapour diffuses through the skin and sweating may occur during work; it is important that moisture can escape. If wind penetrates, it displaces air and increases convective heat loss; even if it does not penetrate, wind pressure can reduce the layers of air within clothing. The ideal clothing assembly, which has not yet been achieved, would resist entry of liquid water but allow vapour to diffuse out, and would retain its thickness in high winds.

Assessing environments

The demand an environment places upon physiological thermoregulation depends upon air temperature, humidity and velocity, radiation, clothing and level of activity.

Air temperature and *humidity* are commonly measured with some form of 'wet and dry bulb' thermometer. The temperature of the wetted bulb is lowered by an amount that depends on humidity. Air movement must be standardised, usually at a high value by whirling the thermometers or mounting them in a sleeve with a fan. Random convective *air movement* is measured by a katathermometer, which has a large silvered bulb and is warmed to a specified temperature: the time taken to cool over a specified range is measured. Directional air movement is measured by an anemometer, which counts the revolutions of a light fan. *Radiation* can be

measured by a globe thermometer: the rise above air temperature of a thermometer enclosed in a blackened globe gives a measure of radiation.

It is often useful to be able to express the thermal effect of a situation by a single number. No scale is suitable for all environments but scales are available for each thermoregulatory zone.

In near-thermoneutral environments, in which subjects do not sweat or shiver, Bedford's effective temperature scale is appropriate. The inputs are dry bulb temperature, or globe temperature if higher, wet-bulb temperature and air velocity. Rest is assumed, and there are alternative graphs for clothed and unclothed subjects. The result is the temperature of still, saturated air with no radiative heat gain, which subjects had matched to the actual conditions. It is thus a subjective comfort scale.

In hot environments clothing and work rate are as important as the measurements of the environment itself. Among several scales Holling and McArdle's *predicted 4-hour sweat rate* is interesting. A nomogram expresses average measured rates of sweating in subjects exposed to combinations of the six variables. Since this measures the body's thermoregulatory response, it reflects demand on thermoregulation.

In cold environments humidity is unimportant and heat gain from radiation often so. The most urgent threat to subjects working outdoors is cold injury of exposed parts of the body, rather than general hypothermia. Siple's *wind chill* scale predicts, from air temperature and air velocity, the rate of removal of heat from an exposed surface such as the skin. The result can be expressed in heat units or on a graph with areas labelled from 'comfortable indefinitely' to 'exposed flesh freezes in one minute'. Air velocity determines the result more than temperature.

Immersion in water

Immersion is a special situation that defeats thermoregulation. A nude person in stirred water has effectively no external insulation. Still water and water trapped in clothing provide a little insulation. Calculation of the external temperature for heat balance in a resting man with no insulation other than vasodilated tissues gives $36\,°C$. Vasoconstriction would reduce this to $31\,°C$ but does not occur when the skin is at this temperature. Calculation for maximum shivering predicts that balance can just be maintained in water at $20\,°C$.

The implication, that survival time is limited in water below $20\,°C$, is important in the context of immersion accidents and shipwreck, and is confirmed by experience (Fig. 41.32). There are, however, individual exceptions. Swimming is known to entail about twice the heat production of shivering and so it might be

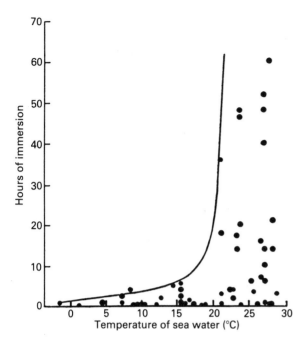

Fig. 41.32 Times for which survivors had been immersed in the sea before successful rescue plotted against water temperature. Each point represents an incident, involving a variable number of men. The curve was drawn arbitrarily. The distribution of the points shows that at sea temperatures above 20 °C the duration of survival is not limited by sea temperature, but at lower sea temperatures maximum time of survival is inversely related to water temperature. Occasional individuals survived exceptionally long immersions. (Molnar G W 1946 JAMA 131:1046)

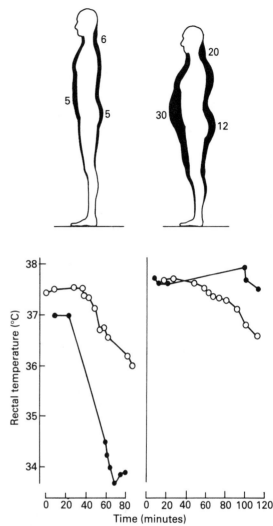

Fig. 41.33 Two men of contrasted build, G.P., an athlete (and physiologist) and J.Z., a professional long-distance swimmer, on one occasion remained at rest in water at a temperature of 16°C (open circles), and on another swam at their normal pace (closed circles). Their subcutaneous fat thicknesses (in mm) are also shown. (After Pugh L G C, Edholm O G 1955 Lancet 2:761).

expected that people who could continue swimming would be better able to maintain body temperature. The situation is more complicated. Figure 41.33 shows an experiment that compared a fit physiologist with a Channel swimmer. At rest they had tissue insulations of 0.44 clo and 0.94 clo respectively (below and above average). Swimming reduced these to 0.23 clo and 0.42 clo. The professional swimmer's insulation was still sufficient to retain enough heat to maintain balance in water at 16°C; the physiologist's was not and his core temperature fell precipitously. The swimmer's additional insulation came from fat; the existence of relatively lean long-distance swimmers, however, suggests that tissue insulation can be increased in other ways. The physiologist's experience was the typical one; after the sinking of the Lakonia in the Mediterranean in 1963, Keatinge pointed out that well-meaning advice to the victims to keep active in the water had been tragically wrong.

Attempting to swim in very cold water presents other hazards beside hypothermia. Initial contact of cold water with skin causes increases in respiration, pulse and arterial and venous blood pressures: the former can cause tetany and drowning and the latter sudden death in older subjects. Good swimmers who are not used to cold water may only be able to swim for a few minutes, and then stop and drown. This may be due to the 'diving response' — a combination of apnoea, bradycardia and muscular hypotonia provoked by contact of cold water with the face. A significant proportion of people rescued after immersion in cold water die shortly afterwards. A possible explanation is circulatory collapse leading to failure of coronary perfusion, and caused by the combination of hypothermia, upright posture, physical effort and loss of hydrostatic support of the circulation. Immersion in water above body temperature necessarily raises body temperature, and is sometimes used to achieve rapid re-warming.

THERMOREGULATION AT THE EXTREMES OF LIFE

The newborn

The temperature of the fetus has been reported to be 37.6–37.8°C, slightly above that of the mother, and clearly the fetus cannot control this. He or she is born, wet, into an environment 10°C or more below the critical temperature — estimated to be 32–34°C — for maintaining body temperature without increased heat production. The small body size implies small heat capacity and large surface, facilitating heat exchange and temperature change. Heat production by the newborn human in ideal thermal conditions has been estimated to be about 0.1 kJ/kg/min, rather more than a resting adult's on a 'per kg' basis. Tissue insulation is less than the adult's — 0.05 clo has been suggested — and insulation from air on the surface is less because of the small body radius. Measurements of newborn pigs suggest that unclothed human infants may lose 0.5 kJ/kg/min by convection, radiation and evaporation. Thus initial negative heat balance is inevitable. Measurements of the rate of fall of temperature in newborn babies suggest the negative balance may be as much as 0.8 kJ/kg/min.

The behavioural thermoregulatory responses so important in adult man are not available to the newborn except vicariously. Physiological thermoregulation is present from birth but the responses are less sensitive and the effectors less powerful than in the adult. Vaso-constriction is even less effective than in the adult and shivering is initially negligible.

The principal defence against cold is increased heat production in *brown adipose tissue*. This is present in the newborn of many mammals, including man, as light brown subcutaneous pads over the neck and upper part of the back, and deeper accumulations around thoracic and posterior abdominal viscera (Fig. 41.34). Its cells differ from white adipose cells in that they contain many small vacuoles of fat rather than few large ones, and numerous mitochondria (Fig. 41.35). The numbers of brown adipose cells decline rapidly with age in most species (though the macroscopic pads persist) and become negligible in man by one year. Adult rodents exposed to prolonged cold regenerate brown adipose tissue and hibernants possess it throughout life.

The original studies showed that exposure to cold or infusion of noradrenaline caused brown fat in newborn rabbits to increase its oxygen consumption from 0.1 to

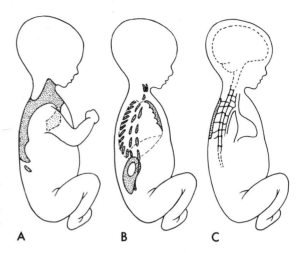

Fig. 41.34 A and B, distribution of brown adipose tissue in the baby. C, diagrammatic representation of the venous drainage from the interscapular pad. (From Aherne W, Hull D 1964 Proceedings of the Royal Society of Medicine 57:1172

6 ml O$_2$ per gram of tissue, accounting for between two-thirds and all of the increase in total metabolism; blood flow to brown fat increased three to four times and accounted for a quarter of the cardiac output. In the newborn human activation of brown fat increases metabolic rate two or three times.

Hypoxia or propranolol abolish the responses to cold and noradrenaline. Evidently brown fat is controlled by sympathetic nerves acting on noradrenergic β-receptors.

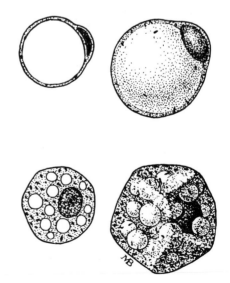

Fig. 41.35 Comparison between cells of white adipose tissue (top) and brown adipose tissue (bottom). On the left each cell is seen in section.

These activate adenylate cyclase, releasing cyclic-AMP, which activates a lipase. Some of the fatty acid formed is re-esterified and hydrolysis and resynthesis account for part of the energy dissipated. The rest of the fatty acid is oxidised in the mitochondria but instead of generating ATP oxidation is 'uncoupled' and produces only heat. The biochemical mechanism and its control are not fully understood. There may be a specific protein in the inner mitochondrial membrane that provides a 'proton conductance pathway' that allows protons to escape; alternatively or additionally cell membrane permeability may change so that the sodium/potassium pump performs more work.

Minimum metabolic rate per unit of body weight rises during the first 36 hours of life to about 1.5 times the level at birth; this is distinct from activation of brown fat and part of normal development. Thus a maximum heat production of 0.3–0.5 kJ/kg/min is achievable within a day or so. Over the next two weeks metabolism per unit weight rises to twice the initial level, after which it falls very gradually to the adult level.

A neonate relying on physiological responses would be hard put to it to maintain body temperature in a 'temperate' climate and close contact with the mother or external insulation is clearly necessary. Insulation does not simply establish heat balance at a lower ambient temperature: it also widens the range of environments over which a given capacity to produce heat can maintain body temperature. As in adult environments air temperature does not fully specify thermal environment: humidity and air movement are important, and the transparency or opacity of incubators to infra-red radiation is particularly important.

Newborn infants can sweat but do so less effectively than adults. It has been reported that in response to heat they increase evaporative heat loss two to four times (compared with the 50-fold increase available to adults). Hyperthermia may be one cause of cot deaths; some victims have infections and pyrexia, and this in combination with over-generous bedclothes and room heating may create a situation in which body temperature cannot be controlled.

The elderly

In old age subjective perception of ambient temperature is blunted, central control is less responsive, and resting metabolism and physical activity are reduced.

DISORDERS OF THERMOREGULATION

Fever (pyrexia)

Fever has been familiar as a feature of illness since ancient times. It is an internally originated increase in

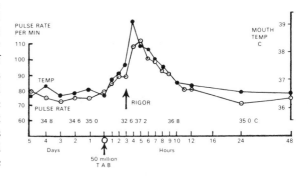

Fig. 41.36 Chart of mouth temperature and pulse rate in a male patient aged 37 who received an intravenous injection of typhoid vaccine (T.A.B.) containing 50 million organisms. An acute febrile reaction developed three hours later. The figures in the lower part of the chart indicate the temperature of the skin of the forearm measured electrically. At three hours after the injection the patient vomited and complained of pain in the back and legs and headache. He was pale and cold (skin temperature 32.6°C). Fifteen minutes later he developed a rigor. His mouth temperature increased rapidly and his skin became flushed and hot (37.2°C). Nine hours after the injection the patient felt much better. He was sweating profusely, his mouth temperature had fallen, but his skin temperature remained high.

core temperature in response to bacterial, protozoal and some viral infections and other disease processes, particularly those involving tissue breakdown. While the temperature is rising the patient feels cold and shows responses to cold — vasoconstriction, pilo-erection and shivering, which may be severe (*rigors*). What had been a normal temperature is evidently interpreted as low. The reverse happens when fever abates. The rates of change of temperature seen in malaria agree with the calculations of maximum effector capabilities shown in the Table on p. 526. The changes of temperature may be interpreted as due to changes in the 'set-point' of regulation.

The mechanism of fever involves two stages. Bacteria produce endotoxins, large heat-stable polysaccharides, which act as *exogenous pyrogens*. The action of leucocytes on these produces *endogenous pyrogen* polypeptide, the process taking an hour or more. Endogenous pyrogen acts rapidly, perhaps by affecting the synthesis or breakdown of prostaglandin E or some other transmitter (Fig. 41.36). Whereas illness can be seen to have a biological value — it takes the animal out of the competition when its performance is impaired — it is not clear whether fever is useful. Lowering a febrile temperature is generally harmless, and is essential if thermal runaway is imminent.

Malignant hyperpyrexia

This rare condition affects members of certain families. If a sensitive individual is anaesthetised, particularly with halothane, core temperature may rise at up to 6°C per hour and drastic attempts at cooling may not prevent death. The cause is a congenital abnormality of muscle. It is obviously important to identify susceptible subjects. If the condition does nevertheless occur, physiology suggests that immersion in cold water would reduce body temperature more effectively than packing the patient with ice (because it traps air and minimises convection crushed ice is a good insulator).

Heat stroke

Collapse may occur when the body temperature rises above about 41°C, through failure of thermoregulation to cope with an environment. This seldom happens outdoors because sweating is so effective, but in enclosed spaces humidity may prevent sweat from evaporating. Unacclimatised men who work hard in a hot climate may not sweat enough. If water lost in sweating is not replaced, sweating eventually ceases, but only after dehydration has led to circulatory failure.

Heat exhaustion

This is due to failure to replace water and salt lost in sweat. Acute dehydration occurs if water is not replaced. Since sweat is hypotonic the body fluids become hypertonic. Replacement of the water is the first essential; salt at this stage would make matters worse. More chronic heat exhaustion occurs after days or weeks of exposure to heat; it is due to hypovolaemia caused by the cumulative deficit of salt, the water having been replaced. The remedy is sufficient intake of salt (calculable from an estimate of sweating and the 0.1–0.25 per cent salt content of sweat).

Heat cramps (miners' cramps)

Heat cramps are due to acute hypotonicity in people sweating at high rates and replacing the sweat by drinking water.

Accidental hypothermia

Accidental hypothermia occurs when heat is lost to the environment faster than it is being produced. The interplay of environment, insulation and metabolism in determining heat balance has been discussed above, and the vulnerability of man to cold emphasised. Infants are at risk because of their small size and ineffective control mechanisms. Because their energy stores are quickly exhausted malnutrition is an important predisposing factor, as well as low ambient temperature and inadequate clothing. Children, although still at a size disadvantage, are remarkably resistant to hypothermia, in the

sense that they hold the records for survival of low core temperatures (9°C in one instance).

The elderly suffer from the same physiological handicaps as infants and hypothermia, often of insidious onset, is a well recognised hazard of old age, especially during illness. Social factors are equally important and a vicious circle is readily set up in which poverty, inadequate heating, inadequate clothing, under-nutrition (which further lowers BMR and reduces body fat), isolation and passivity are mutually reinforcing.

Active adults at risk of hypothermia include walkers and mountaineers, and victims of immersion. Precipitating factors on land are bad weather, inadequate clothing, fatigue and injury. The individual most at risk seems to be the lean, fit enthusiast who sets off at speed, perhaps without stopping to eat or pack extra clothing, and later tires. The nervous system is affected first: a climber becomes silent, withdrawn and unresponsive, slows down and may stumble. Wrong decisions and route-finding errors may lead to disaster, and bizarre behaviour has included shedding clothes. As core temperature falls below 33–35°C thermoregulation becomes ineffective, the rate of fall of temperature increases and consciousness and memory are progressively impaired; consciousness is lost below 30°C. The mean lethal core temperature is about 25°C, but 18°C has been survived. The immediate cause of death is ventricular fibrillation, probably due to changes in the balance between excitability, conduction and refractory period in heart muscle. In *immersion hypothermia* the same sequence occurs more rapidly, complicated by cardiorespiratory problems and the likelihood of drowning.

Cold injury

Cold injury of parts of the body exposed to cold may be *freezing* or *non-freezing*. Brief freezing does not necessarily damage tissues but frozen tissues are vulnerable. Necrosis when it occurs is dry and considerable regeneration is possible, so surgery should be late and conservative. Non-freezing cold injury ranges from chilblains through mild-to-moderate cold injury to 'immersion foot' or 'trench foot'. The pathology is not fully known but involves small blood vessels and terminal nerve filaments. Immobility is an important cause and if prolonged leads to injury even though skin temperature is relatively high. Cold injury has been a conspicuous feature of most wars. Recovery is slow and peripheral circulatory control may not recover fully, leaving the patient more susceptible in the future.

Artificial hypothermia

Anaesthesia depresses thermoregulation and muscle relaxants prevent shivering, so surgical patients are often mildly hypothermic. The lack of defences makes it easy to reduce body temperature. At 27°C the brain can tolerate hypoxia for 10–15 minutes. Core temperature can be reduced further, typically to 15°C, if an extracorporeal pump and heat exchanger are used.

The physiology of artificial, or induced, hypothermia has been better studied than that of accidental hypothermia. Pulse, respiration and blood pressure are depressed. The ECG shows a characteristic sequence of changes and ventricular fibrillation usually occurs, but is of no consequence in the operating theatre. Oxygen consumption falls, the haemoglobin dissociation curve shifts to the left and the plasma dissolves more oxygen. In consequence less haemoglobin is in the reduced form, and this impairs carbon dioxide carriage. Hypoxic metabolism occurs in superficial tissues. Thus several factors promote metabolic acidosis, which it is important to treat.

Defective thermoregulation

Rare cases of 'sick thermostat' syndrome present with generally low and unstable body temperature, much affected by the environment. Presumably the hypothalamus is at fault. Haemorrhage into the mid-brain or pons is a commoner cause of defective thermo-

regulation; in these cases core temperature is often high, but again abnormally dependent on the environment (Fig. 41.37). Descending pathways have presumably been damaged.

FURTHER READING

Adolph E F 1947 Physiology of man in the desert. Interscience, New York

Benzinger T H 1969 Heat regulation: homeostasis of central temperature in man. Physiological Reviews 49: 671–759

Bligh J 1973 Temperature regulation in mammals and other vertebrates. North-Holland, Amsterdam

Burton A C, Edholm O G 1955 Man in a cold environment. Monographs of the Physiological Society No. 2. Arnold, London

Dawes C S 1968 Foetal and neonatal physiology. Year Book, Chicago

Dill D B (ed) 1964 Adaptation to the environment. Handbook of Physiology, Section 4. American Physiological Society, Washington

Hardy J D 1961 Physiology of temperature regulation. Physiological Reviews 41: 521–606

Hardy J D, Gagge A P, Stolwijk J A J (eds) 1970 Physiological and behavioral temperature regulation. Thomas, Springfield, Ill.

Hellon R F 1967 Thermal stimulation of hypothalamic neurones in unanaesthetized rabbits. Journal of Physiology 193: 381–395

Lipton J M L (ed) 1980 Fever. Raven Press, New York

McArdle et al 1947 The prediction of the physiological effects of warm and hot environments. RNPRC Report RNP 47/391. Medical Research Council, London

Maclean D, Emslie-Smith D 1977 Accidental hypothermia. Blackwell Scientific, Oxford

Newburgh L H 1949 Physiology of heat regulation and the science of clothing. Saunders, Philadelphia (reprinted 1968 by Hafner, New York)

Pugh L G C 1955 The physiology of Channel swimmers. Lancet 2: 761–8

Pugh L G C 1966 Clothing insulation and accidental hypothermia in youth. Nature 209: 1281–6

Robertshaw D (ed) 1974, 1977, 1979 Environmental physiology. International Review of Physiology 7, 15, 20. University Park Press, Baltimore

Wessells N K (ed) 1974 Vertebrate structures and functions. Section V, Temperature adaptations. Freeman, San Francisco

Whittow G C (ed) 1970, 1971, 1973. Comparative physiology of thermoregulation. Volumes I, II, III. Academic Press, New York

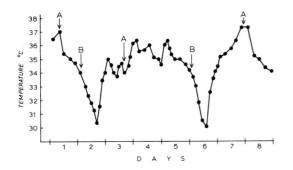

Fig. 41.37 Record of axillary temperatures from a female patient aged 68 unconscious for 3 months as the result of thrombosis of blood vessels at the base of the brain. At the arrows marked B extra blankets were applied; at A they were removed. The body temperature depended on external influences because the central thermo-regulatory mechanism had been destroyed.

Index